Steam /its generation and use

Babcock & Wilcox

161 East 42nd Street, New York, N.Y. 10017

Foreword

In 1867 George H. Babcock and Stephen Wilcox formed a partnership. The present company succeeded it in 1881.

This 39th edition of "Steam"—the first appeared in 1875—marks further advances in the production of steam and in the utilization of fuels.

A significant change in this new edition is the increased coverage of nuclear steam generating equipment in recognition of the increased importance of nuclear fuels as a source of energy for the production of steam.

This edition also reflects the augmented emphasis on quality assurance, which has effected important improvements in product quality during the last twenty-five years concurrently with large increases in the capacity of individual steam generating units.

The Company gratefully acknowledges the support, cooperation and loyalty of its patrons and employees, which have made possible its contributions in the field of steam generation. It expresses the hope that this volume may help to stimulate further advances in the art.

Table of contents

			Pages	
Introduction to steam			1 to 14	
Section I		**Fundamentals of steam generation and use**		
Chapter	1	Boiling and steam separation	1-1 to	1-9
	2	Thermodynamics of steam	2-1	2-20
	3	Fluid dynamics	3-1	3-17
	4	Heat transfer	4-1	4-20
Section II		**Steam generation from chemical energy**		
Chapter	5	Sources of chemical energy	5-1 to	5-22
	6	Principles of combustion	6-1	6-22
	7	Utilization of oil and gas	7-1	7-10
	8	Coal processing and handling	8-1	8-16
	9	Preparation and utilization of pulverized coal	9-1	9-16
	10	Cyclone Furnaces	10-1	10-8
	11	Stokers	11-1	11-6
	12	Boilers, superheaters and reheaters	12-1	12-20
	13	Economizers and air heaters	13-1	13-8
	14	Temperature, surface and pressure drop calculations	14-1	14-10
	15	Fuel-ash effects on boiler design and operation	15-1	15-26
	16	Boiler enclosures, insulation and casing	16-1	16-9
	17	Stacks, fans and draft	17-1	17-18
	18	Combustion by-products	18-1	18-6
Section III		**Steam generation from nuclear energy**		
Chapter	19	Nuclear fuels	19-1 to	19-12
	20	Principles of nuclear fission	20-1	20-15
	21	Nuclear steam supply systems	21-1	21-18

Pages

Section IV   Applications of steam

Chapter 22   Fossil-fuel boilers for electric utilities .... 22-1 to 22-15
        23   Nuclear installations for electric utilities .... 23-1 | 23-20
        24   Marine installations .... 24-1 | 24-19
        25   Industrial installations .... 25-1 | 25-10
        26   Chemical and heat recovery in the paper industry .... 26-1 | 26-14
        27   Industrial by-products utilization .... 27-1 | 27-10

Section V   Metallurgy and structural design

Chapter 28   Metallurgy of iron and steel .... 28-1 to 28-16
        29   Properties of structural materials .... 29-1 | 29-17
        30   Stress analysis and structural design .... 30-1 | 30-10

Section VI   Manufacturing and construction

Chapter 31   Manufacturing .... 31-1 to 31-26
        32   Construction .... 32-1 | 32-12

Section VII   Operation and maintenance

Chapter 33   Pressure, temperature, quality and flow measurement .... 33-1 to 33-28
        34   Operation of steam generating equipment .... 34-1 | 34-25
        35   Controls for steam power plants .... 35-1 | 35-26
        36   Maintenance .... 36-1 | 36-22

Tables of measurement .... T-1 to T-3

Glossary/symbols and abbreviations .... G-1 | G-7

Index .... I-1 | I-13

In this nuclear steam plant, shown during construction, heat will be released by nuclear fission in the reactor and transferred from the reactor coolant to generate steam in two nuclear steam generators. This photograph, taken inside the reactor building, shows the reactor vessel in position in the center and the two nuclear steam generators at the sides.

Introduction to steam

Steam is one of man's dependable servants. More and more in the background, steam is doing more and more work for man. In an electrically heated home steam may be seen only at the teakettle, but the chances are that the electricity used is generated by burning coal or gas and producing steam to turn the generator rotors in the electric power generating station. Even if the fuel is uranium and the heat supplied by nuclear fission, the generation of electricity is still accomplished by first generating steam.

In the U.S.A. the demand for electricity doubles every ten years. For the most part water resources suitable for power generation are already in service. Except for standby and peak-load units, approximately 90% of the new electric capacity being installed utilizes steam. The use of steam for electric power generation is expanding in most countries of the world, the principal exceptions being countries where available water power resources are greater than power needs.

Steam propels most of the world's naval vessels, and a high percentage of its water-borne commerce. It is used on a large scale in many industrial processes and is still much used for space heating.

Steam boilers today range in size from those required to heat a small-sized home to the very large ones used in electric power generating stations. Some single boilers recently or soon to be operating deliver approximately ten million pounds of steam and consume more than 500 tons of coal per hr. In these large units pressures range from 2500 to about 4000 psi and the steam is usually superheated to a temperature of 1000F or higher. Modern steam boilers operate safely and dependably and remain in service for many years with cleaning and repairs usually required only at scheduled outage periods.

Today's boilers owe their dependability and safety to more than a hundred years of experience in the design, fabrication and operation of water-tube boilers. During this period the properties of steam and water have been accurately determined and tabulated for use by the designer. A new understanding of heat transfer, fluid flow and boiler circulation has been developed. Means have been devised for burning large quantities of fuel economically and safely and for disposing of the products and by-products of combustion. Steels and alloy materials now available are stronger and more consistent in their properties, and advanced methods are used for their fabrication and inspection. Finally, industry-wide codes and standards have been adopted to regulate the design, fabrication and inspection of pressure parts.

The nuclear steam supply system is a relatively recent development, representing a union of nuclear physics and the steam boiler industry. During the last twenty years a large number of nuclear steam supply systems have been placed in operation for naval propulsion and for the generation of electricity. Some of these units for the electric power industry are comparable in capacity to the largest fossil-fueled boilers.

History of steam generation and use

The most common source of steam at the beginning of the 18th century was the "shell" boiler, little more than a kettle filled with water and heated on the bottom, Figs. 1

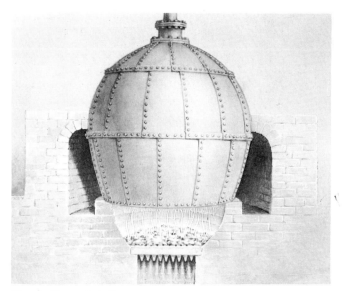

Fig. 1 Haycock boiler, 1720.

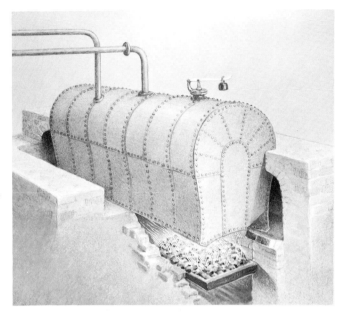

Fig. 2 Waggon boiler, 1769.

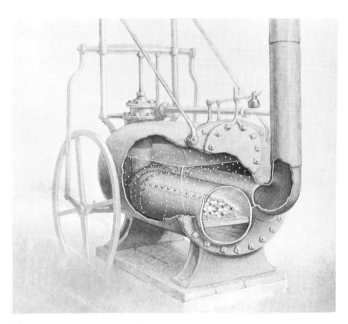

Fig. 3 Trevithick boiler, 1804.

and 2. This, in turn, was followed by early versions of the fire-tube boiler, Fig. 3. Both types were subject to disastrous explosions because of the direct heating of the pressure shell containing a large volume of water at saturated steam temperature.

The question of boiler capacity and safety was of primary importance, and it is no exaggeration to say that, for a time, failure to build adequate boilers threatened to halt industrial progress. In the meantime, some inventors recognized that one way to overcome deficiencies of the fire-tube boiler was to develop a satisfactory water-tube design which would have most of the heating surfaces formed of tubes, thus limiting the consequences of a pressure part rupture. However, this type did not

Fig. 4 Hero's engine.

enjoy much success until Stephen Wilcox introduced his improved version of the water-tube boiler in 1856. The basic features of his new invention permitted better water circulation and increased heating surface per unit. Of greater significance, the boiler was inherently safe.

Manufacture of this first "safe" boiler culminated many centuries of trial and error experimentation. Hero of Alexandria, probably in the first century A.D., had described a boiler and reaction turbine similar to the artist's concept shown in Fig. 4 but he made no suggestions for the useful application of the device. In fact, there is no record of steam's practical usage until the 17th century although there was descriptive publication in the late 16th century.

Beginning with the 17th century, many conditions existed which stimulated the rapid development of steam usage in a power cycle. Mining for ores and minerals had expanded greatly and large quantities of fuel were needed for smelting. Considerable fuel was needed for space heating and cooking. Industrial and military growth, especially in England, also demanded greater amounts of fuel. By the middle of the 1600's forests were being rapidly denuded and it became increasingly necessary to find some other basic source of energy. Thus, despite the fact that at one time people were executed in England for burning coal because it produced highly noxious and dangerous fumes, the dynamics of historical growth made it essential to remove these restrictions with the result that coal mining increased.

As large scale coal mining developed, mines became deeper and deeper, and often were flooded with water. The English, in particular, were faced with a very serious curtailment of their growing industrial, military and political might if they could not find some economical way to pump water from the mines. The importance attached to the problem can be seen from the great number of men working on it and by the many patents issued on machines to pump water using "the expansive power of steam."

The early machines used wood and charcoal for fuel. Many years elapsed before the applications of machine power to fuel procurement could bring the production of coal to a high enough point to displace wood.

Not all early developments in steam use were directed toward engines and pumps. In 1680 Dr. Denis Papin, a Frenchman, invented a steam digester for culinary purposes, using "a boiler under heavy pressure." To avoid an explosion, Papin added a contrivance which is the first safety valve of record.

First successful steam engines

The first commercially successful steam engine was patented by Thomas Savery in 1698, and is shown in Fig. 5. The following year he exhibited a model of this engine, including the boiler, before the Royal Society of England. Developed for pumping water by direct displacement, this engine was handicapped by the limited pumping height set by the pressure the boiler and vessels could withstand. Before its eventual displacement by Thomas Newcomen's engine, Desaguliers improved the Savery engine, applying the Papin safety valve to the boiler and using an internal jet for the condensing part of the cycle.

The earliest cylinder-and-piston steam engine was based on Papin's suggestion in 1690 that the condensation of steam should be used to make a vacuum beneath a piston after it had been raised by expanding steam. Newcomen's atmospheric engine was a practical application of this principle.

Among the several inventions attributed to Papin was a boiler with an internal firebox, the earliest record of such construction.

While Papin neglected his own ideas of a steam engine to develop Savery's invention, Newcomen, with his assistant, John Cawley, adapted Papin's suggestion of 1690 in a practical engine. Steam admitted from the boiler to a cylinder raised a piston by expansion and assistance from a counterweight on the other end of a beam actuated by the piston, Fig. 6. The steam valve was then closed and the steam in the cylinder condensed by a jet of cold water. The vacuum formed caused the piston to be forced downward by atmospheric pressure doing work on a pump. Condensed water in the cylinder was expelled through an escapement valve by the next entry of steam which was at a pressure slightly above atmospheric. The boiler used by Newcomen, nothing more than a plain copper brewer's kettle, was known as the Haycock type because of its shape, Fig. 1.

In 1711, Newcomen's engine was introduced into mines for pumping water. Whether its action was originally automatic or dependent upon hand operation of the valves is unknown. The story commonly believed is that in 1713 a boy named Humphrey Potter, whose duty was to open and shut valves of an engine he attended, caused the engine to manipulate these valves automatically by suitable cords and catches attached to the beam.

It was about this time that developers of the steam engine began to think in terms of fuel economy. Noting that nearly half the heat from the fire was lost because of short contact time between the hot gases and the boiler heating surface, Dr. John Allen (1730) may have made the first boiler efficiency determination. To reduce

Fig. 6 Newcomen's engine.

this loss, Allen developed an internal furnace with a smoke flue winding through the water like a coil in a still. Then, to prevent a deficiency of combustion air, he suggested the use of bellows to force the gases through the flue. This, probably, represents the first application of forced draft.

During the last half of this 18th century period, the great inventor James Watt made many significant improvements to the early steam engine which by now was completely separate from the boiler. While little is said in biographies of Watt about improvements of steam boilers, the evidence indicates that Boulton and Watt

Fig. 5 Savery's engine, 1700.

introduced the first "waggon boiler," so named because of appearance, Fig. 2. This was nothing more than a closed vessel for water and steam shaped like a covered wagon set over a fire pit. In 1785 Watt took out a number of patents for variations in furnace construction.

The next outstanding inventor and builder was Richard Trevithick, who as a boy of eight went to work in one of his father's mines in an English mining district. There he received as much engineering training as was available in those days. Since his father was manager of several mines, Richard was permitted to travel from engine house to engine house and observe the pumping engines, principally of Newcomen design.

Fire-tube boilers

Trevithick realized the major problem of these steam systems was the manufacture of the boiler. Whereas copper was the only material heretofore available, hammered wrought-iron plates could now be used although the maximum length was 2 feet. Rolled-iron plates became available in about 5/16-in. thickness in 1795.

In 1800 Trevithick made an engine for 65 psi pressure, having a 25-inch cylinder and a 10-ft stroke. The engine's high working pressure was possible only because of the successful construction of a high pressure boiler. Built in 1804, the boiler (Fig. 3) had a cast-iron cylindrical shell and dished end. The boiler and engine were mounted together.

As the demand increased for greater amounts of power, it was necessary to build larger and larger boilers, or to put up with the inconvenience of a multiplicity of small units. Later developments saw the single pipe flue replaced by many gas tubes, which increased heating surface. This was essentially the design in widespread use up to about 1870. However, fire-tube boilers, being limited in capacity and pressure, were not destined to fulfill the requirements which developed later for higher pressures and larger unit sizes. Also, there was the ominous record of many explosions.

Early water-tube boilers

A patent granted to William Blakey in 1766, covering an improvement in Savery's engine, includes a form of steam generator, Fig. 7. This probably was the first step in the development of the water-tube boiler. However, the first successful user of the water-tube boiler was James Rumsey, an American inventor best known for his early experiments in steam navigation. In 1788 Rumsey patented (in England) several types of boilers, some of which were water-tube designs.

About this time John Stevens, also an American, invented a water-tube boiler consisting of a group of small tubes closed at one end and connected at the other to a central reservoir, Fig. 8. Patented in 1803 in the United States, this boiler was actually used to supply steam for the engine of a Hudson River steamboat. As a boiler, the design was short-lived due to basic engineering problems in construction and operation. However, it is significant that Stevens, a lawyer, had petitioned Congress for a patent law to protect his invention. Such a law was enacted in 1790 and it may be said that the basis of our present patent laws grew out of this idea for a water-tube boiler.

Fig. 9 shows another form of water-tube boiler, this one patented in 1805 by John Cox Stevens. A boiler of this type can now be seen at the Smithsonian Institution, Washington, D.C.

In 1822, Jacob Perkins built a water-tube boiler which is the predecessor of the once-through steam generator. A number of cast-iron bars with 1¼-inch longitudinal holes were arranged over the fire in three tiers by connecting the ends outside of the furnace with a series of bent pipes. Water was fed to the top tier by a feed pump and superheated steam discharged from the lower tier to a collecting chamber.

Early developments of the B&W boiler

Stephen Wilcox proposed in 1856 what was to be a significant "break-through" for water-tube boilers. The

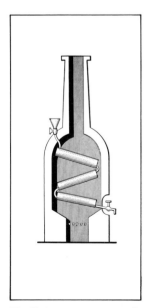
Fig. 7 First water-tube boiler. Built and patented by William Blakey in 1766.

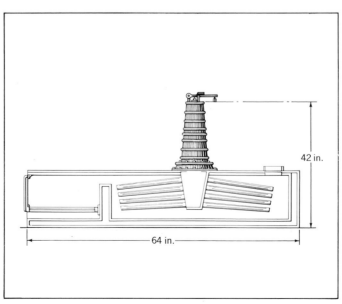
Fig. 8 Water-tube boiler of small tubes connected at one end to a reservoir. John Stevens, 1803.

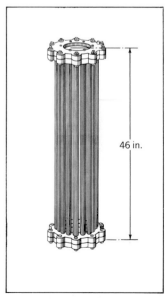
Fig. 9 Water-tube boiler with tubes connecting water chamber below and steam chamber above. John Cox Stevens, 1805.

design incorporated inclined water tubes connecting water spaces at the front and rear, with a steam space above, allowing better water circulation and more heating surface, Fig. 10. An added advantage was the reduced explosion hazard that was inherent in the water-tube design.

In 1866, George Herman Babcock became associated with Stephen Wilcox and the first Babcock and Wilcox boiler, Fig. 11, was patented a year later. By 1877, the B&W boiler had been modified as shown in Fig. 12.

Bent-tube boilers

The success and widespread acceptance of the inclined straight-tube boiler during an unprecedented period of rapid industrial growth stimulated other inventors to explore new ideas in boiler design. In 1880, Allan Stirling developed a design connecting the steam generating tubes directly to a steam separating drum and featuring low head room above the furnace. The Stirling Boiler Company was subsequently formed to manufacture and market an improved Stirling design, essentially the same as that shown in Fig. 13. These boilers featured bent tubes as contrasted to the B&W straight tubes.

Merits of bent-tube boilers for special applications were soon recognized by Babcock & Wilcox, and what had become the Stirling Consolidated Boiler Company was purchased by B&W in 1906. After the problems of internal tube cleaning were solved, the bent-tube boiler replaced the straight-tube B&W boiler.

Electric utilities

Steam was used originally to provide heat and power for local industrial use. With the advent of practical electric power generation and distribution, utility companies were formed to serve industrial and residential users over wide areas.

The plant of the Brush Electric Light Company, in Philadelphia, was the first such electric generating station in America. Four B&W boilers rated at 73 hp each were installed in this plant in 1881. The Fisk Street Station of the Commonwealth Edison Company, in service in 1903, was the first utility plant to use steam turbines exclusively for electric power generation. Ninety-six B&W boilers rated at 508 hp each were installed in this plant with turbine steam conditions of 170 psi pressure and 70F superheat.

During the first two decades of this century, there was an increase in steam pressures and temperatures to 275 psi and 560F (146F superheat) respectively. In 1921 the North Tees Station of the Newcastle Electric Supply Company (northern England) went into operation with steam at a pressure of 450 psi and a temperature of 650F. The steam was reheated to 500F and regenerative feedwater heating was used to attain a boiler feedwater temperature of 300F. Three years later (1924), the Crawford Avenue Station of the Commonwealth Edison Company, and the Philo and Twin Branch stations of the present American Electric Power system were placed in service for operation with steam at 550 psi and 725F at the turbine throttle. The steam was reheated to 700F.

A station designed for much higher steam pressure—the Weymouth (later named Edgar) Station of the

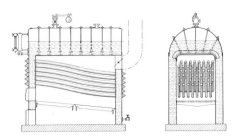

Fig. 10 Inclined water tubes connecting front and rear water spaces complete circuit with steam space above. Stephen Wilcox, 1856.

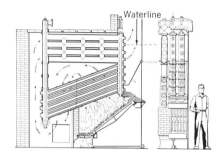

Fig. 11 First Babcock & Wilcox boiler, patented in 1867.

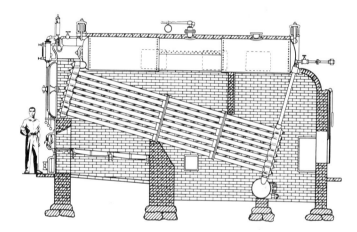

Fig. 12 Babcock & Wilcox boiler developed in 1877.

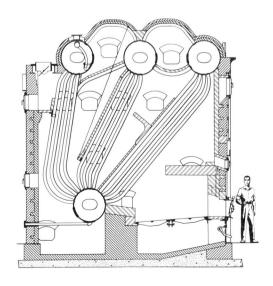

Fig. 13 Early Stirling boiler arranged for hand firing.

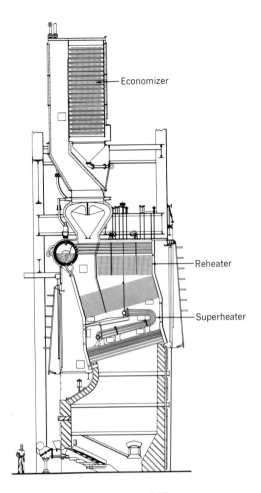

Fig. 14 High pressure reheat boiler, 1925.

Boston Edison Company—started up in 1925. The 3150 kw high pressure topping unit used steam at 1200 psi and 700F and the steam was reheated to 700F for the main turbines, Fig. 14.

Pulverized coal and water-cooled furnaces

Other major changes in boiler design and construction occurred in the twenties. Previously, as individual electric generating stations increased in capacity, the practice was merely to increase the number of boilers. This procedure eventually proved to be uneconomical and, instead, the individual boilers were built larger and larger. Soon, however, the size became such that existing furnace designs and methods of coal burning, such as stokers, were no longer adequate.

Insofar as fuel burning was concerned, the development of pulverized-coal firing provided the answer. The higher volumetric combustion rates and unit sizes made possible by burning pulverized coal could not have been fully exploited without the use of water-cooled furnaces, which not only eliminated the problem of rapid deterioration of the refractory walls due to slag, but also reduced fouling of convection heating surfaces to manageable proportions by lowering the temperature of the gases leaving the furnace.

Integral-Furnace boilers

At first furnace water-cooling was applied to existing boiler designs, with its circulatory system essentially independent of the boiler circulation. In the early thirties a new concept was born in which the furnace water-cooled surface and the boiler surface were arranged together so that each was an integral part of a boiler unit. Fig. 15 shows an early design of the Integral-Furnace boiler.

Package boilers

The increasing need for industrial and heating boilers combined with increasing costs of field assembled equipment led to the development in the late 1940's of the shop-assembled package boiler. Completely shop-assembled units are fabricated in capacities up to 350,000 lb of steam per hr at pressures up to 1300 psi and temperatures up to 900F.

Later boiler developments

In addition to reducing furnace maintenance and the fouling of convection heating surfaces, water-cooling also helped to generate more steam. Consequently, the boiler surface was reduced, since additional steam generating surface was available in the water-cooled furnace. Increased feed and steam temperatures and increased steam pressures, for greater cycle efficiency, still further reduced boiler tube bank surface, to be replaced by additional superheater surface.

As a result of these advances, boiler units for steam pressures above 1200 psi consist essentially of furnace water-wall tubes, superheaters and such heat recovery accessories as economizers and air heaters, Fig. 16. Boiler units for lower pressures, however, have considerable steam generating surface in tube banks in addition to the water-cooled surface in the furnace, Fig. 17.

Universal-Pressure boilers

An important milestone in the progress toward the production of electricity at the lowest possible cost was

Fig. 15 Integral-Furnace boiler, 1933.

the successful operation in 1957 of the first commercial unit for operation at a steam pressure above the critical value (3208 psia) at the Philo Plant of the Ohio Power Company (Fig. 18). This B&W Universal-Pressure steam generator for the 120-Mw unit delivers 675,000 lb of steam per hr at 4500 psi and superheated to 1150F with two reheats to 1050 and 1000F.

The Universal-Pressure boiler, so named because it can be designed for subcritical or supercritical operation, is capable of rapid load pick-up. Increase in load at rates up to 5% per minute, insofar as the boiler is concerned, is easily attained. In an emergency, the Universal-Pressure boiler is capable of increasing load from 25 to 90% of full load in four minutes, and from 90 to 100% of full load in another four minutes. The Universal-Pressure boiler, with its start-up system, enables close matching of steam and turbine metal temperatures and, thereby, reduces thermal stresses to a minimum during either a cold start or a hot re-start.

Fig. 19 shows one of two Universal-Pressure boilers of recent design, each of which will furnish the steam for a 1300-Mw-capacity generating unit in a large utility plant. Each boiler will supply 9,775,000 lb/hr of steam at 3845 psi and 1010F with reheat to 1000F.

Modified steam cycles

The continual quest for lower heat rates and, thus, higher cycle efficiency, has involved modifications of the conventional steam cycle. One of these, using high-temperature low-pressure mercury vapor to top a conventional steam cycle, dates back to the binary fluid mercury-steam unit placed in service in 1928 at a New England utility. Binary fluid "topping" cycles are so named because the rejected heat of one fluid cycle is used to supply heat to another fluid operating in a lower temperature range. In the mercury-steam cycle, the mercury condenser also acts as the steam boiler.

Other high efficiency cycles involve combinations of gas turbines and steam power, and direct thermal-to-electrical energy conversion. Direct-conversion systems under study for large power sizes include a magneto-hydrodynamic (MHD) unit topping the conventional steam cycle and using conventional fuel or a char by-product from coal gasification or liquefaction.

In spite of the many complex cycles devised to increase overall plant efficiency, the conventional steam cycle has, to date, proven to be the most economical.

The increasing use of high steam pressures and temperatures, reheaters, regenerative feedwater heaters, economizers, and air heaters have all led to improved efficiency in the modern steam power cycle.

Marine boilers

The water-tube boiler was successfully applied to the propulsion of naval and merchant vessels in the 1890's. An improved design, installed in 1899 in the United States cruiser *Alert* established the superiority of the water-tube boiler for marine propulsion. Subsequently the development of marine boilers for naval and merchant ship propulsion has paralleled that for stationary use. Throughout the 20th century, dependable water-tube marine boilers have contributed greatly to the excellent performance of U.S. naval and merchant fleets.

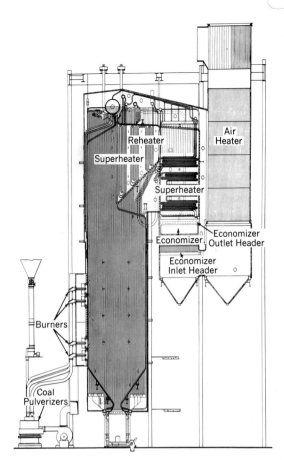

Fig. 16 Radiant boiler for 1650 psi and 1000F initial and reheat temperatures.

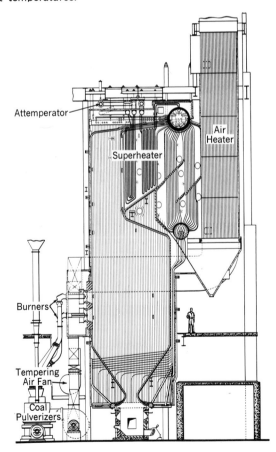

Fig. 17 Stirling boiler for 925 psi and 900F steam temperature.

Nuclear steam supply systems

From 1942, when Enrico Fermi demonstrated a controlled self-sustained fission reaction, nuclear energy has been recognized as an important source of heat for power generation. The first significant application of this new source for the generation of steam was the U.S.S. *Nautilus* prototype, which was operated at the National Reactor Testing Station in Idaho in the early fifties. This has been followed by a number of installations for the propulsion of naval vessels.

The first electric utility installation was the 90-Mw unit (net capacity) at the Shippingport Atomic Power Station of the Duquesne Light Co. This plant, owned partly by Duquesne Light Co. and partly by the U.S. Atomic Energy Commission, went into operation in 1957.

Construction permits were issued in 1955 and 1956 to three electric utilities for nuclear units approximately twice this size. These units—for Commonwealth Edison Company's Dresden Nuclear Power Station, Yankee Atomic Electric Company's Rowe Plant, and Consolidated Edison Company's Indian Point Station—went into commercial operation in the early 1960's.

Spurred by the trend to larger units, developments in the utilization of nuclear energy for electric power reached a milestone in 1963 when economics favored installation of nuclear steam supply systems rather than fossil-fuel-fired units in some geographical areas. Another milestone was reached in 1967 when nuclear units constituted 48% of the 54,000 Mw total of new steam-electric generating capacity ordered. In 1968 and 1969 orders for nuclear units continued as a smaller but substantial percentage of new capacity. The design shown in Fig. 21 illustrates a current nuclear unit for the 850 Mw power range.

Materials and fabrication

Pressure parts for water-tube boilers were originally made of iron and later of steel. More recently boiler drums and nuclear reactor vessels are fabricated from heavy steel plates and steel forgings joined by welding, with careful supervision and inspection. The development of the steam boiler has been necessarily concurrent with advances in metallurgy and progressive improvements in the fabrication of steel.

The cast iron generating tubes used in the first B&W boilers were later superseded by steel tubes. Shortly after 1900 B&W developed a commercial process for the manufacture of hot-finished seamless steel boiler tubes, combining strength and reliability with reasonable cost. In the midst of World War II, a mill was completed for the manufacture of tubes by the electric-resistance-welding process, and tubing produced by this method has been used subsequently in thousands of boilers.

The cast iron tubes used for steam and water storage in the original B&W boiler (Fig. 11) were soon followed by drums (Fig. 12) and, about 1888, drum construction was improved by changing from wrought iron to steel plates.

Prior to 1930, the standard method of joining boiler drum plates was by riveting. This construction limited the thickness of drum plates to about 2¾ in. because no satisfactory method was known to secure a tight joint with rivets in thicker plates. The only available alternative was to forge and machine a solid ingot into a drum, which was extremely costly. Boilers built prior to 1930 with pressures over 700 psi used the forged and machined drum.

The story behind the development of fusion welding was one of intensive search beginning in 1926. Welding techniques had to be improved in many respects. Equally, if not more important, an acceptable test procedure had to be found and instituted that would guarantee the drum without destroying it in the test. After extensive investigation of various methods of testing, it was decided in 1929 to adapt the medical X-ray machine to production examination of welds. By X-ray examination, together with physical tests of samples of the weld material, the soundness of the weld could be proved.

The United States Navy, during 1930, adopted a specification for construction of welded boiler drums for naval vessels and, in that same year, the first welded drums ever accepted by an engineering authority were a part of the B&W boilers installed in several cruisers. The Boiler

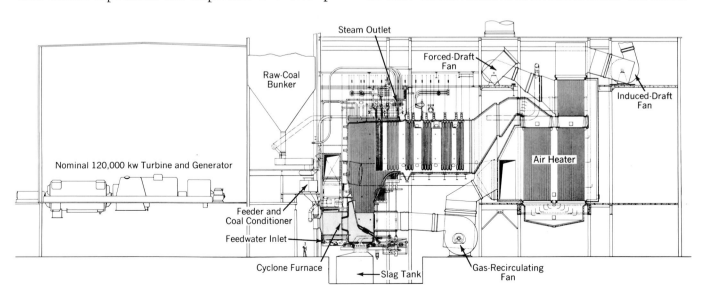

Fig. 18 Elevation view of a 120-Mw generating unit served by a B&W Universal-Pressure (UP) boiler operating at 5500-4500 psi, 1150F, with reheats to 1050F and 1000F.

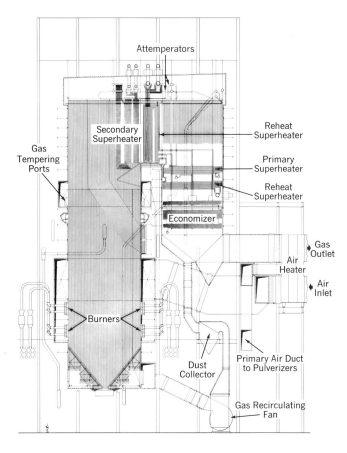

Fig. 19 Universal-Pressure boiler for 9,775,000 lb steam per hr.

Code Committee of the American Society of Mechanical Engineers issued, during 1930, complete rules and specifications for the fusion welding of drums for power boilers, and the following year B&W shipped the first welded power boiler drum built under this code.

The X-ray examination of welded drums and the rules promulgated for the qualification of welders and the control of welding operations were major first steps in the development of modern methods of quality control in the boiler industry. Quality assurance has received additional stimulus from the naval nuclear propulsion program, and more recently from the Nuclear Regulatory Commission in connection with the licensing of nuclear plants for power production. Quality control is discussed in Chapter 31.

Other important materials developments include improved firebrick to withstand higher temperatures in boiler furnaces, alloy steels for superheaters and nuclear steam supply systems, special materials including the metal zirconium for nuclear fuel cladding tubes, and alloys for control rods in nuclear reactors.

Summary

The history of the boiler industry is the story of the search for more efficient and dependable steam generators. Built into this history are fundamental concepts and basic inventions proved by experience to be sound. More recently introduced are the successful results of programmed research and development. This is the foundation on which today's research and development

is building tomorrow's improved and larger fossil-fueled boilers and nuclear steam supply systems.

Research and development

The research and development accomplished by Babcock & Wilcox requires the expenditure of many millions of dollars each year. The Alliance (Ohio) Research Center is staffed and equipped to investigate most of the problems in the broad spectrum of the company's technical interests. These include heat transfer, fluid mechanics, applied mechanics, and many other fields. The Lynchburg (Virginia) Research Center is devoted primarily to the nuclear and radioactive aspects of research for nuclear power. These include nuclear physics experiments using critical assemblies or a "swimming pool" research reactor, examination of radioactive material in hot cells, radiochemistry, and the development of uranium, thorium, and plutonium fuels.

Heat transfer

In the design of equipment for the production of steam, heat transfer is an extremely important technology. For many years B&W has been conducting heat transfer research from hot gases to the walls of tubes forming furnace enclosures or tube banks, and from tube walls to enclosed water, steam and air. Early in the 1950's research in heat transfer and fluid mechanics was initiated in the supercritical pressure region above 3208 psia where the properties of water and steam change continuously, rather than discontinuously, from what is clearly a liquid at low temperature to what is clearly a vapor at

Fig. 20 Radiant Boiler Flow Model—One-sixteenth scale model of 650 megawatt boiler used at B&W Research Center to confirm optimum air and gas flow distribution for maximum combustion efficiency.

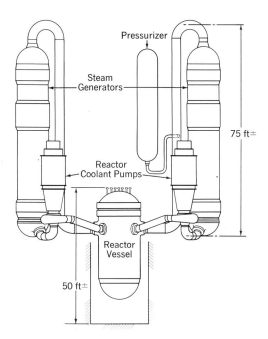

Fig. 21 Nuclear steam supply system for approximately 850 Mw. Two once-through steam generators are supplied by reactor coolant heated in a pressurized water reactor.

high temperature (Fig. 22). This pioneering work provided the technical foundation for the large number of supercritical-pressure once-through steam generators now in service in the electric power industry. Research on "departure from nucleate boiling," or "critical heat flux" (the limiting heat flux above which tube burnout is imminent), has permitted the design of fossil-fueled boilers and nuclear reactors with adequate, but not excessive, safety margins over the full range of operating conditions expected in the field (Chapter 1). Successful research has demonstrated that internal ribs in tubing provide important benefits, because nucleate boiling continues under conditions where it cannot be maintained in a smooth tube.

B&W designed and constructed a large scale apparatus in which electrical resistance heating of tubes is used to simulate heat generation by fission in a nuclear reactor core. This has permitted the investigation of critical heat flux in nuclear reactor fuel elements at the same water temperatures, pressures, flows and purities as exist in full scale cores under actual operating conditions (Chapter 4). These investigations have provided increased confidence in engineering calculations, and brought about major cost reductions in core design.

Fluid mechanics

Closely related to heat transfer, and of equal importance in steam generating equipment, is fluid mechanics. Both low pressure fluids (air and gas in ducts and flues) and high pressure fluids (water, steam and water mixtures, steam, fuel oil) must be investigated. The theories and mathematics of single-phase fluid flow are well understood, but the application of theory to the complex, irregular, and multiple parallel path geometry of practical situations is often difficult and sometimes impossible. In these cases analytical procedures must be supplemented or replaced by experimental methods. If reliable extra-

polations are possible, economical modeling techniques can be used (Fig. 23). Where extrapolation is not feasible, expensive large scale testing at full pressure, temperature, and flow rate must be undertaken.

The simplest and least costly experiments are those involving a single-phase fluid in which pressure differential and inertial forces are important, and fluid property changes (such as density or viscosity resulting from temperature change) are relatively unimportant. In these situations modeling techniques may be used reliably to determine flow patterns, mixing, and pressure drop, and the results extrapolated over a wide range of scale factors. On the other hand, situations involving large changes in physical properties of the fluids, phase change (boiling) and chemical interactions cannot be satisfactorily simulated by bench scale models, and require construction and operation of partial or full scale prototype equipment. As a last resort, experimental work may be performed on full scale operating equipment in a customer's plant, with the accompanying disadvantages of inconvenience to the customer, subordination of the desired testing conditions to operating requirements, poorly controlled conditions, and high costs.

Metallurgy

Since the manufacture of steam generating equipment, nuclear components, tubular products, and auxiliary equipment involves the fabrication of a wide variety of carbon, alloy, and stainless steels, as well as nonferrous metals, a highly competent metallurgical research staff equipped with the finest investigative tools is essential (Fig. 24). Areas of primary interest in the metallurgical field are steel melting practices, alloy developments, fabrication processes including welding, room temperature and high temperature properties, resistance to corrosion, wear resistance, and changes in material properties under nuclear irradiation. The metallurgical staff constitutes one of the largest research groups, and provides essential support to a wide range of activities throughout the company. Development of oxidation-resistant alloys which retain strength at high temperature, and determination of short-term and long-term high temperature properties permitted the increase in steam temperature which has been of critical importance in increasing power plant efficiency and reducing the cost of electricity. (*See also Chapter 29.*)

To assist in translating physical metallurgy information into optimized metalworking processes and products, a group of highly trained mechanical engineers works closely with the metallurgists in conducting complex experiments to determine the suitability of particular alloys for different applications. For example, the zirconium alloy used for nuclear fuel cladding in pressurized water reactors was subjected to water purity and heat transfer conditions simulating those of a reactor core to determine the extent and effect of the formation of zirconium hydride in the alloy. Complete control-rod-drive assemblies furnished by Diamond Power Specialty Corporation, as well as subcomponent assemblies of these drives, have been subjected to exhaustive tests under a wide variety of operating conditions to assure and demonstrate proper operation, reliability, and long life of these important products.

Fig. 22 Supercritical Heat Transfer Test Apparatus—A water treatment facility (left) supplies feedwater to a gas-fired furnace located behind the instrument panel (center). An electrically heated superheater section is enclosed in the nonmagnetic enclosure (top right). Power to heat the tube is fed through the heavy copper bus bar which enters the top of the wooden box.

Applied mechanics

The complex geometries and high stresses under which metals must serve in many products require careful study to permit prediction of stress distribution and intensity. Applied mechanics, a discipline with highly sophisticated analytical and experimental techniques, can provide designers with calculation methods and other information to assure the safety of structures and minimization of costs by eliminating unnecessarily conservative design practices. The analytical techniques involve advanced mathematical procedures and the use of large capacity digital computers. Despite the availability of these powerful tools, many practical problems cannot be solved by analytical methods, and must be attacked by experimental methods. Both steel and plastic models are utilized with strain gages, brittle lacquers, two-dimensional and three-dimensional photoelasticity, X-ray diffraction, vibration measurements, and other techniques. This branch of technology has contributed importantly to the feasibility and safety of advanced designs in many types of equipment (Fig. 25).

Chemical engineering

The chemical engineer plays an important role in research and development activities. Chemical engineering processes are fundamental to the combustion of natural fuels such as coal, oil, and natural gas, and by-product fuels such as blast furnace gas or bagasse. Process design is also important in establishing feasible and economical steps in the production of nuclear fuels and nuclear waste disposal. Chemical engineering plays a central role in the important and growing field of environmental control through reduction of air pollution, prevention of water pollution, water purification, and disposal of industrial and radioactive wastes. B&W has for many years been heavily involved in the combustion of by-product fuels, the reclamation of chemicals, and

Fig. 23 Reactor Vessel Hydraulic Flow Model—A one-sixth scale model reactor vessel is shown on the right. The pressure taps from individual venturis on 177 model fuel bundles are sequentially read by the device to the left of the control panel. The readings are converted to computer tape by the automatic data acquisition system for plotting and analysis.

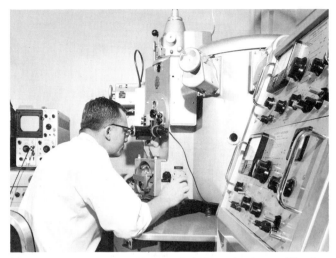

Fig. 24 Electron Beam Microprobe X-ray Analyzer—The impingement of a magnetically focused electron beam on a specimen results in the generation of characteristic X rays of the elements present. Elemental analyses can be performed on areas 1 micron (0.000039 in.) in diameter. The instrument is used for nondestructive chemical analysis of metallurgical materials.

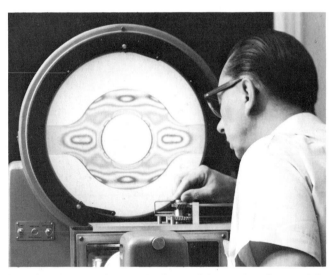

Fig. 25 Photoelasticity—Plastic models made of materials which exhibit birefringent light patterns under polarized light are used to provide visual and analytical stress patterns. Shown above is an enlarged cross section of a one-inch diameter tube from a membrane wall.

the minimization of environmental pollution in the pulp and paper industry. The company is currently investigating methods for removal of particulates as well as sulfur oxides and other pollutants from flue gases. (*See Chapter 18*).

Chemistry

The science of chemistry is involved throughout the production and utilization of materials. Therefore, a strong and diversified chemistry group is essential to provide support to research, development, engineering, and utilization of the entire spectrum of company products. The design and operation of fuel burning equipment must be supported by capabilities in the analysis of a wide variety of solid, liquid, and gaseous fuels and their products of combustion, and characterization of their behav-

ior under various conditions. Metallurgical research requires accurate quantitative determination of elemental major components and trace elements. Chemical reactions control high temperature oxidation and corrosion of steels, low temperature corrosion of air heaters, alloying and fluxing in steelmaking, formulation of refractory materials, and the complex processing, fabrication, and reprocessing procedures for uranium and plutonium fuels. The interactions of fission products inside nuclear fuel elements, and their radioactive decay, lie at the interface between chemistry and physics.

The requirements for chemical treatment of water in high-pressure steam generators for the prevention of deposits and corrosion extend quantitative analytical chemistry to its farthest limits. For example, in a large supercritical-pressure steam generating unit having a steam flow of 5,000,000 lb/hr, a non-volatile contaminant in the feedwater with a concentration of 2 parts per million would deposit solids inside the steam generating tubes at the rate of 10 lb/hr, or nearly one ton per week. This rate of deposition is not tolerable; therefore, water chemists must work with parts per billion, or fractions even smaller.

In pressurized-water nuclear reactors, the water-coolant system must be designed for boric acid addition and withdrawal for control purposes, and consideration must be given to radiolysis of water and solutes and to possible contamination by material released from a leaking fuel pin. The large national effort to develop liquid-metal-cooled fast breeder reactors is fostering research in the chemistry of sodium and the quantitative determination of trace quantities of solutes in the sodium.

Increasingly, chemical research and chemical analysis are extending beyond the traditional wet chemistry of test tubes, beakers, and titrations into electronic instrumentation, physical optics, electrochemistry, and particle physics for the refinement and precision required by the complex problems of the present and the future.

Physics

Physics provides the basis for most mechanical engineering, and finds direct application in the fields of nuclear engineering, electronic circuitry, and instrumentation. The complex calculations associated with the steady state, transient, and long-term characteristics of nuclear reactor cores (Chapter 21) depend primarily on the behavior of neutrons, their interactions with the nuclei of various natural and transuranic elements, and the decay and transmutation of various isotopes produced. The determination of physical constants for analytical equations and the verification of physics calculations require a wide range of nuclear physics experimentation, using exponential assemblies, zero power experiments (Fig. 26), or research reactors. Behavior of nuclear fuels and other materials under intense irradiation can be studied in test reactors, or in the cores of power reactors.

Materials irradiated by neutrons usually become radioactive, and require special precautions for handling, depending on whether the material is emitting alpha particles, gamma rays, or both, and on the intensity of these radiations. Materials that emit alpha particles, but not gamma rays (e.g., plutonium-239) can be handled in ventilated glove boxes (Fig. 27). If high-energy gamma

rays are emitted, the material must be handled remotely in thick-walled hot cells (Fig. 28). Strong emitters of gamma rays are often stored under water, and for this reason many hot cells have "storage pools" associated with them.

The physical interaction of materials with each other and with electromagnetic waves are phenomena which provide the basis of many primary sensors used in instrumentation. For example, temperature-measuring devices may depend on such phenomena as thermal expansion, change in electrical resistivity with temperature, thermoelectric effect, or electromagnetic radiation at high temperature. Remote detection of inhomogeneities in materials is possible using X-irradiation, gamma irradia-

tion, ultrasonics, eddy current distortions, or magnetic particle techniques.

The conversion of primary sensor output into useful information is performed by electrical circuitry, dependent on the physics of electron flow in wires, vacuum tubes, transistors, and other devices. Rapid advances are being made in applying the principles of solid state physics to thin films, integrated circuits, and semiconductor devices for use in instrumentation and control circuits. Laser beams show promise of a broad range of practical uses, and are undergoing intensive development. A laser holography technique for quality control inspection has already been put in use, and laser telemetry is being actively studied.

Fig. 26 Arrangement of equipment for zero power experiment to verify physics calculations for the Advanced Test Reactor (ATR). The ATR is now in operation at the Atomic Energy Commission's National Reactor Testing Station in Idaho.

Fig. 27 Pilot line for uranium-plutonium oxide pellet fabrication. Five separate glove boxes (from right to left) contain equipment to perform five successive steps in the process—granulating uranium-plutonium oxide powders, pressing the granules into oxide pellets, sintering the pellets at temperatures up to 1800C in a controlled-atmosphere furnace, checking dimensions of finished pellets, and grinding oversized pellets with a centerless grinder.

Fig. 28 Hot cells used for examination of irradiated materials. At the right, the operator of the remote, mechanical manipulator is performing operations inside the cell, which he observes through a leaded glass observation port. The man at the left is conducting metallographic examinations of irradiated material.

Nonmetallic materials

Many important materials of engineering are oxides or other compounds of metals collectively referred to as nonmetallic materials. Firebrick and insulating firebrick, ceramic oxide refractories, glasses, refractory cement and concrete, and insulating materials such as block, fibrous blanket, and bulk fiber materials fall into this category. The variety of applications ranges from cryogenic insulation to linings for many types of furnaces, each with its special requirements for temperature, corrosion, erosion, and thermal shock. To keep abreast of progress in this field requires extensive research in the formulation and processing of the complex mixtures and chemical compounds involved. While many scientific disciplines contribute to the solution of ceramic problems, empirical know-how and experience make major contributions.

Nuclear fuels

A special subdivision of nonmetallic materials is nuclear fuels. Although research is being conducted on carbides and nitrides of fissionable elements, all practical commercial nuclear fuels at the present time are oxides of uranium or plutonium. The chemistry of these materials is complex, particularly in the case of plutonium which has a variety of allotropic forms and valence states. Additional difficult problems arise from toxicity (especially plutonium), radioactivity under some circumstances, danger of accumulating a critical mass of fissionable material, extremely high specific value (dollars per gram), and from controls necessary to prevent the diversion of fissionable material to unauthorized persons. The handling of these materials therefore involves advanced techniques of chemistry and chemical engineering, often under conditions of remote control, as well as special handling and administrative precautions associated with these highly valuable, potentially dangerous, and politically sensitive materials.

At its Lynchburg Research Center, B&W has a fully equipped laboratory for research and pilot-scale production of uranium and uranium-plutonium oxide fuels in various forms for use in pressurized water and liquid-metal fast-breeder reactors (Fig. 27). This research and development capability provides support to two manufacturing facilities at the same location, one supplying naval nuclear fuel and the other fuel for commercial power reactors.

Mathematics

Modern research depends heavily on competent mathematics departments equipped with advanced computational devices. Experiments must be designed on the basis of statistical techniques to assure proper sampling and to obtain the maximum in results with the minimum of experimentation. Automatic data collection and reduction increases the speed and reliability, and reduces the cost, of experimental work. Data must be statistically analyzed to extract the greatest amount of usable information. Proper mathematical treatment can be provided only by the wide scale use of a digital computer. Some types of experimentation require the support of analog computational equipment, and in some instances a combination of analog and digital (hybrid) computer must be used. Mathematicians, statisticians, and computer programmers provide essential services to research scientists and engineers.

Advanced mathematical techniques are applied to management problems through the methods of operation research in a wide variety of areas, such as inventory control, production scheduling, process optimization, PERT (program evaluation and review technique) project control, and management information systems. Operations research does not substitute for managerial judgment, but it does provide managers with quantified information upon which sound decisions may be based.

Recapitulation

Steam is produced and used today at many different pressures and temperatures, in units of many different sizes, with heat from several different types of fuels. The knowledge and experience which are required to accomplish this cover a broad spectrum of technical disciplines.

Continuing advancement in the production and use of steam requires research and development laboratories with trained specialists backed by expensive equipment and supporting facilities. In design, production, construction, and service organizations it requires increasing skills of mind and hand, faster and more sophisticated computers, and a large investment in tools and handling equipment.

A search for excellence was begun more than a hundred years ago by George Babcock and Stephen Wilcox. Almost certainly the accomplishments of the past hundred years have exceeded their vision. But the search continues—for better materials, for ever higher standards of workmanship, for improved efficiency of design, and for reduced cost of fabrication and operation.

Fundamentals of steam generation and use

Section I

Steam is uniquely adapted, by its availability and advantageous properties, for use in industrial and heating processes and in power cycles. The properties of steam are described and tabulated in this section. The basic energy equations covering the generation and use of steam are presented together with steam cycles that are applicable in modern steam electric plants for fossil and nuclear fuels. The principles of fluid dynamics and heat transfer are discussed, and methods are presented for applying these principles to the design of steam generating equipment.

The nature of the boiling process is examined in Chapter 1. This includes investigations made to determine the maximum transfer of heat that is practicable under various conditions of pressure, temperature and fluid flow. The need for eliminating moisture and solids from the steam entering superheaters and steam turbines, and the means used for accomplishing this in a drum-type boiler are also presented.

Chapter 2 summarizes the basic concepts of thermodynamics, with particular reference to steam cycles. The properties of steam and water, as presented in the 1967 *ASME Steam Tables*, are discussed, and selected data from this publication are listed in Tables 1, 2 and 3. The energy equations for several thermodynamic processes, and the first and second laws of thermodynamics are presented. The concept of entropy is discussed. This is followed by reversible and irreversible processes and cycles for the conversion of heat to work, including temperature-entropy, enthalpy-entropy (Mollier), and power cycle diagrams for fossil and nuclear fuels. The chapter concludes with brief discussions of work functions and combustion equilibrium.

The economical design of steam generating units demands the maximum utilization of heat transfer surfaces within the limitation that fluid-flow requirements must be met without excessive power consumption by pumps or fans. It is fundamental to know the heat transfer rates obtainable with given fluid flow and tempera-ture conditions, and the corresponding fluid friction losses (pressure drops) for use in determining fan and pumping power.

Chapter 3 begins with the basic principles of fluid dynamics and develops formulas, based on theory and experimental data, for calculating the pressure loss from fluid friction for fluids flowing in channels of constant cross section. Losses in valves and fittings, enlargements, contractions and bends are included. Methods are given for calculating friction losses for flow through coils and rectangular ducts, and for the flow of gases over tube banks. Fluid flow and pressure drop in the two-phase flow region are discussed.

Boiler circulation and the means for obtaining it are examined, including consideration of the principles and application of natural and forced circulation. Circulation design criteria are discussed, and formulas are given for use in natural circulation calculations.

The three modes of heat transfer—conduction, radiation and convection—are described in Chapter 4, and formulas are presented for the calculation of heat transfer by each mode. Dimensionless numbers used in the calculation of convection are introduced and charts are provided for obtaining convection heat transfer data.

The concepts of conductance and resistance are presented and their use is illustrated in calculating heat transfer when different modes occur in parallel and in series. The determination and use of mean temperature difference for various flow arrangements is explained.

The application of the theoretical heat transfer relationships to the design of steam generators includes convection heat transfer from flue gases to tube banks, heat transfer to water and steam, the calculation of radiation heat transfer in boiler furnaces and cavities between convection banks, and heat transfer through the insulating materials of the boiler setting.

The application of experimental data in the nucleate boiling range to the design of the core of a water-cooled nuclear reactor is also treated in this chapter.

Radiant boiler fired by natural gas in a Southwestern central station.

Chapter 1

Boiling and steam separation

The process of boiling water to make steam is a familiar phenomenon. Thermodynamically, boiling is the result of a special case of heat addition to the working substance, water, in a constant-pressure constant-temperature process. The heat which must be supplied to change water into steam without raising its temperature is called the heat of evaporation or vaporization.

Boiling point

The boiling point of a liquid may be defined as the temperature at which its vapor pressure is equal to the total pressure above its free surface. This temperature is also known as the saturation temperature.

The term "boiling point" is most frequently used to identify conditions at standard atmospheric pressure, e.g., water boils at 212F, ammonia boils at −28F, and sodium boils at 1638F. However, boiling point or saturation temperature is actually a function of pressure and rises when pressure is increased.

Generation of steam in a closed vessel results in an increase in pressure due to a large increase in volume following a liquid-to-gas phase change. At the same time the temperature of both the water and the generated steam also increases. In boilers operating at pressures below the critical point, pressure is normally held at the desired value by maintaining a water level with a steam space above it, and regulating steam generation to balance steam flow delivered by the boiler.

Steam or water vapor are always present above a free surface of water, even in the presence of air or other noncondensible gases.

Mixtures of steam and water in the absence of a local free surface are also common where the two phases are flowing together in a tube or other flow channel. The weight fraction or percentage of steam in such a mixture is known as the quality. If a free surface does exist under flow conditions, such as separated or ring flow in a tube, the term quality is still used to describe the resulting steam fraction.

Properties of steam

Steam at saturation temperature is known as saturated steam. When heat is added to saturated steam out of contact with liquid, its temperature is increased and the steam is said to be superheated. The temperature of superheated steam, expressed as degrees above saturation, is called the degrees of superheat.

The properties of steam needed for the design of steam generating equipment are given in the ASME Steam Tables (see also Chapter 2). These properties include saturation temperatures corresponding to various pressures, the enthalpies (formerly called heat content) of water (h_f), evaporation (h_{fg}) and steam (h_g), and the specific volumes of water and steam, all at various pressures and temperatures.

Steam at supercritical pressures

When steam is compressed to and above the critical value of 3208.2 psia, some of the above terms no longer have their former significance. As the pressure and temperature of water approach the critical point (3208.2 psia and 705.5F), the enthalpy of evaporation (h_{fg} of the steam tables) rapidly decreases to zero. At and above 3208.2 psia the term "heat of evaporation" is meaningless (Fig. 1, Chapter 2).

Heat added to the working substance above its critical point produces a continuous increase in temperature. As a result there are changes in temperature-dependent properties, such as specific heat, viscosity, thermal conductivity, diffusion, and specific volume. With the exception of the last, values of these properties do not increase continuously with increasing temperature.

Operating pressures of boilers in the heat-power field have gradually increased over the years (see Introduction to Steam). Since 1945 many experimental operations have been conducted in the supercritical region, and today supercritical pressures are common in large-scale commercial practice. In these supercritical-pressure "boilers," there is no true boiling process and no latent

heat effect. The temperature rises as heat is added, and the change of state occurs gradually over a range of temperature.

The boiling process

The majority of fossil-fuel steam generators and all commercial nuclear steam supply systems operate at subcritical pressures. A comprehension of the boiling process is essential in the design of these units.

In today's boilers as much as 1 to 3 cu ft of steam per minute may be formed in a 5-ft length of 2½-in. tubing in the furnace area. Water must be continuously supplied for this steam generation and, in many designs, excess water is provided to protect the tubes from overheating. The movement of water and steam (within the boiler) which provides this water supply and removes the steam generated is known as "circulation." In some boiler designs, circulation is accomplished by a pump. In all supercritical-pressure boilers a pump must be provided to maintain circulation. However, at pressures below the critical, "natural" circulation occurs inherently in a water-tube boiler if the heating surface is disposed so that the steam is free to rise in inclined or vertical tubes as it forms (see Chapter 3).

One of the important criteria in the design of a boiler or nuclear reactor is the ability to remove the maximum amount of heat from a tube or flow channel at a rate equal to the maximum supplied by the source.

In order to obtain information on the nature of boiling, a number of investigators have experimented with electrically heated wires in a pool of water. Other investigators have performed the experiment of heating a tube or other type of flow channel cooled by a flow of water at a pressure below critical, and subjecting the tube to various levels of heat input.

Fig. 1 is a generalized curve summarizing the results of these investigations. This curve can be regarded as a general correlation of test results at a number of different heat inputs to heated wires in a pool of water or to heated tubes or flow channels. It can also be regarded as a series of different heat inputs to a single flow channel. In this case, the points on the curve represent a series of temperature differences (surface temperature minus bulk water or steam temperature) corresponding to the water and steam conditions existing at a single location on the flow channel for different levels of heat flux or heat input. If the channel is evenly heated along its length, the location represented is the outlet end of the heated section of the channel. Absolute values on the curve are dependent on many factors including pressure, flow-channel geometry, mass velocity, flux patterns and degree of water subcooling.

For all heat input conditions (points on Fig. 1), water pressure and temperature at the inlet to the channel remain constant. Hence, the amount of subcooling (saturation temperature minus water temperature) at the inlet also remains constant. Ideally, water flow through the tube is maintained at a fixed rate.

The initial heat flux at point A is shown increasing on a logarithmic scale for points to the right of A. Until point B is reached, the heat input is not sufficient to produce boiling.

At B the local heat flux is sufficient to raise the water temperature adjacent to the heated surface to saturation temperature, or slightly above, and a change from the liquid to the vapor state occurs locally. This change is characterized by the coexistence of both phases at essentially the same temperature locally, differing only in a few degrees of liquid superheat necessary for heat transfer, and by heat absorption required to overcome the molecular binding forces of the liquid phase. Here the change of state is accompanied by ebullition of the vapor as opposed to evaporation at a free surface and the term boiling is used to describe the process. Also the ebullition takes place at an interface other than that of the liquid and its vapor, actually at a solid-liquid interface; hence this boiling is described as "nucleate boiling."

Nucleate boiling

The bulk of the water does not reach saturation temperature until the heat flux of point S is reached. Between B and S the steam bubbles formed at the heated surface condense quickly in the main stream, giving up their latent heat to raise the temperature of the water. This condition is known as subcooled-nucleate or local boiling. Nucleate boiling occurs at all points up to C; beyond S the bubbles do not collapse, since this part of the curve represents boiling with the water bulk temperature at saturation.

Both nucleate-boiling regimes, subcooled and saturated, are characterized by very high heat transfer coefficients. These are ascribed to the high secondary velocities of water caused by the liberation of surface tension energies available in the liquid-vapor-solid interfaces at the instant of bubble release from the heating surface. This is a convection-type transfer coefficient based on bubble kinetics and is also affected to some extent by bulk mass velocity, depending on the velocity

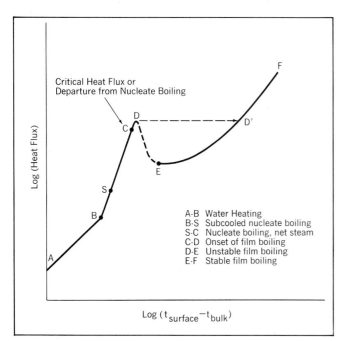

Fig. 1 Heat transfer to water and steam in a heated flow channel—relation of heat flux to temperature difference between channel-wall and bulk-water or steam temperature.

range. As the result of these high heat transfer co-efficients, tube- or flow-channel surface temperatures do not greatly exceed the saturation temperature.

Film boiling

Beyond the nucleate boiling region (*B-C* in Fig. 1) the bubbles of steam forming on the hot tube surface begin to interfere with the flow of water to the surface and eventually coalesce to form a film of superheated steam over part or all of the heating surface. This condition is known as "film boiling." From *D* to *E* film boiling is unstable; beyond point *E* film boiling becomes stable.

In a fossil-fuel-fired boiler or in a nuclear reactor, when the local heat flux exceeds that corresponding to point *D*, the surface temperature may rise very quickly, along the horizontal dotted line in Fig. 1, to point *D'*. If the temperature at *D'* is sufficiently high, heating surface burns out or melts. Hence, *D* is known as the burnout point and *C*, which may be very close to it, as the point of departure from nucleate boiling (DNB), or the critical heat flux.

Stable and even unstable film boiling is acceptable in certain types of heat transfer equipment where the temperature of the heat source is within the safe operating range of the equipment, or where the boiling film heat transfer coefficient is the controlling resistance to heat flux. Steam generators for pressurized-water reactor systems, which are actually water-to-boiling-water heat exchangers, and certain types of process heat exchange equipment are in this category. Film boiling conditions are also encountered in once-through boilers (*see Evaporation or Boiling, Chapter 4*).

Factors affecting DNB

The point of departure from nucleate boiling (DNB point) is defined in the preceding section and illustrated in Fig. 1. The effect of steam quality and heat flux on the location of the DNB point are demonstrated by Fig. 2. This figure illustrates the various heat transfer regimes taking place along the length of a uniformly heated vertical tube cooled by water flowing upward. On this figure the inner wall temperatures are plotted as functions of enthalpy and steam quality, starting with hot water, passing through the region where steam is being generated (0 to 100% quality), and finally into the superheated region.

By following the line for moderate heat flux it is seen that the metal temperature in the subcooled region is parallel to the water temperature, and only slightly above it. When boiling starts, the heat transfer coefficient increases and the metal temperature remains just above saturation temperature. Finally, at high steam quality, the DNB point is reached where the nucleate boiling process breaks down. The metal temperature increases at this point but decreases again as steam quality approaches 100%. In the superheat region the wall temperature again increases with, and approximately parallel to, the superheated steam temperature.

For the curve marked "high heat flux," the DNB point is reached at a lower steam quality, and the peak metal temperature is higher. At very high heat fluxes the DNB occurs at low steam quality and the metal temperature would be high enough to melt the tube if it were able to withstand the internal pressure without first plastically deforming and rupturing. At extremely high heat fluxes,

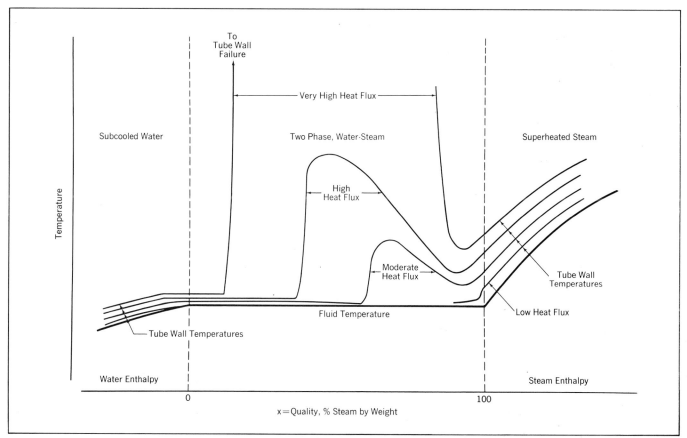

Fig. 2 Fluid and tube wall temperatures under conditions of water heating, nucleate boiling, film boiling and superheating steam.

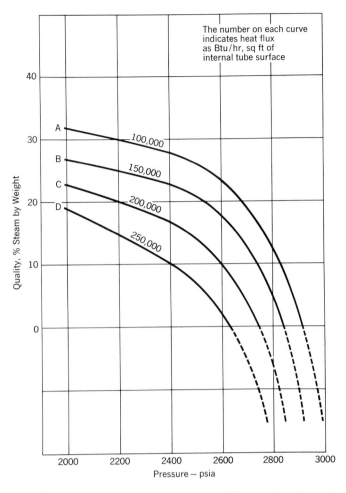

Fig. 3 Steam quality limit for nucleate boiling as a function of pressure.

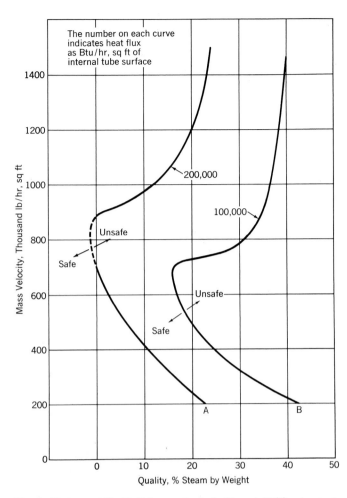

Fig. 4 Steam quality limit for nucleate boiling at 2700 psia, as a function of mass velocity.

DNB can occur in subcooled water. Avoidance of this last type of DNB is an important criterion in the design of nuclear reactors of the pressurized-water type.

Figs. 1 and 2 present the DNB phenomenon from the standpoint of a heated flow channel in which flow, pressure, and inlet temperature (inlet subcooling) remain constant. DNB is also affected by variations in mass velocity, pressure, subcooling and channel dimensions. (*See Heat Transfer in Pressurized-Water Nuclear Reactors, Chapter 4.*)

Many fossil-fuel boilers are designed to operate in the range between 2000 psi and the critical pressure. In this range, pressure has an important effect, shown in Fig. 3, in that the steam quality limit for nucleate boiling falls rapidly near the critical pressure, i.e., at constant heat flux the DNB point occurs at a decreasingly low steam quality as pressure rises. Many correlations of critical heat flux or DNB have been proposed, and are satisfactory within certain limits of pressure, mass velocity and heat flux. Fig. 4 is an example of a correlation which is useful in the design of fossil-fuel natural-circulation boilers. This correlation defines safe and unsafe regimes for two heat flux levels at a given pressure in terms of steam quality and mass velocity. Additional factors must be introduced when tubes are used in membrane or tangent walls or in any position other than vertical. Such factors include inside diameter of tubes and surface condition. The last of these, where the character of the

inside tube surface is purposely altered, will be discussed further in the section on "Ribbed tubes."

The preceding discussion applies only to subcritical pressures. As the operating pressure is increased the various flow and boiling regimes gradually disappear. However, there are tube metal temperature excursions in low-velocity supercritical-pressure operation similar to those found in subcritical boiling. This phenomenon, known as pseudo-film boiling, is currently under intensive experimental investigation.

Ribbed tubes

Since the 1930's Babcock & Wilcox has tried and tested a large number of devices, including internal twisters, springs, and various grooved, ribbed, and corrugated tubes, to inhibit or delay the onset of DNB. The most satisfactory overall performance was obtained with tubes having helical ribs on the inside surface.

Two types of rib configuration were developed:

1. Single-lead ribbed tube (Fig. 5a) for small internal diameters used in once-through subcritical-pressure boilers.
2. Multiple-lead ribbed tubes (Fig. 5b) for larger internal diameters used in natural-circulation boilers.

Both of these tubes have shown a remarkable ability to delay the breakdown of nucleate boiling. Fig. 6 is a comparison of the effectiveness of a ribbed tube to that

of a smooth tube in a membrane wall configuration. This plot is different from Fig. 4 in that heat flux is given as an average over the flat projected surface. This is more meaningful in discussing membrane wall absorption.

Since the ribbed tube is more expensive than a smooth-bore tube, its utilization in design involves an economic balance of several design factors. In most instances, there is no incentive to use ribbed tubes below 2200 psi.

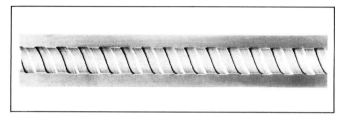

Fig. 5a Single-lead ribbed tube.

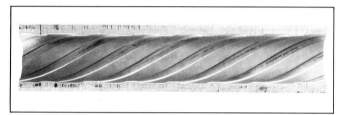

Fig. 5b Multiple-lead ribbed tube.

Steam separation and purity

Boilers operating below the critical point, except for once-through types, are customarily provided with a steam drum in which saturated steam is separated from the steam-water mixture discharged by the boiler tubes. The remaining water is then recirculated together with feedwater to the heat absorbing surfaces (*see Boiler Circulation, Chapter 3*). Saturated steam leaves, and feedwater enters this drum through their respective nozzles (with some exceptions in multidrum boilers). Also, the steam drum may serve as a vessel for boiler water treatment by chemicals and any necessary blow-down for reduction of solids concentration in the boiler water. However, the primary functions of this drum are to provide a free controllable surface for separation of saturated steam from water and a housing for any mechanical separating devices.

Above critical pressure there is no steam-separation function, since no interface can be formed between the steam and water phases. A once-through boiler, operating below critical pressure, evaporates water to dryness and superheats steam in one continuous passage through the tubes. A steam drum is not required in either case.

Size of the steam drum

The steam drum must be large enough to contain the necessary separating equipment and accommodate the changes in water level that occur with change in load.

A rapid increase in steam demand is usually accompanied by a temporary drop in steam pressure until the firing rate can be increased sufficiently to restore the pressure. During this interval the volume of steam throughout the boiler is increased, and the resulting "swell" raises the water level in the drum. The rise in water level depends on the rate and magnitude of the load change and the rate at which the heat and feed inputs can be changed to meet the load demand (*see Chapter 35*). Steam drums are designed to provide the volume necessary, in combination with the controls and firing equipment, to prevent excessive rise of water into the steam separators, resulting in carry-over of water with the steam.

Solids in boiler water

Boiler water contains solid materials, principally in solution. Steam contamination (solid particles in the superheated steam) comes from the boiler water, largely in the carry-over of water droplets. Therefore, in general, as boiler-water concentration increases, steam contamination may be expected to increase. The tendency to form foam also increases with boiler water high in dissolved solids, but a strict correlation of this tendency with boiler-water analyses is not yet available despite extensive research. Historically the carry-over of water into superheater tubes resulted in deposit of entrained solids in the superheater tubes. This caused increased tube temperatures and distortion and burnout of tubes (*see Fig. 13, Chapter 24*). Therefore, it was necessary to develop devices to remove water from the steam.

Turbine deposits

The need for extreme purity of steam for use in modern high-pressure turbines has provided additional incentive for reducing the carry-over of solids in steam. Troublesome deposits on turbine blades may occur with surprisingly low (0.6 ppm) total solids contamination in steam.

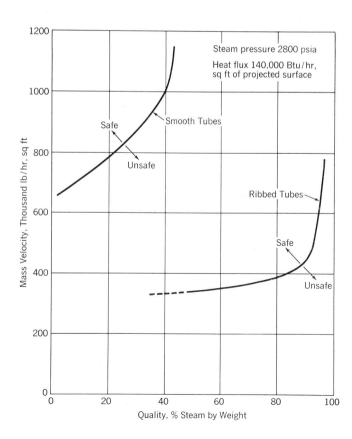

Fig. 6 Steam quality limit for nucleate boiling in smooth and ribbed tubes as a function of mass velocity.

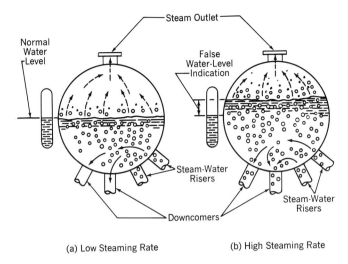

Fig. 7 Effect of rate of steam generation on steam separation in a boiler drum without separation devices.

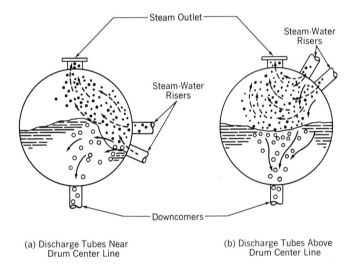

Fig. 8 Effect of location of discharge from risers on steam separation in a boiler drum without separation devices.

In the 500 to 900 psi range these deposits are usually water soluble and can be removed by periodic washing. In the 1000 to 1500 psi range, however, silica deposits predominate, and these deposits are not easily removed by water-washing. With operating pressures of 2000 psi and above, insoluble deposits appear to diminish. In some instances soluble deposits do occur, and may be controlled by water-washing at intervals.

Separation and solids removal

In a modern drum boiler, the separation of steam from the mixture delivered by the steam-water risers (Fig. 7) usually takes place in two steps. The primary separation removes nearly all the water from the mixture, so that, in effect, no steam is recirculated to the heating tubes. However, the steam may still contain solid contaminants which must be removed or reduced in amount before the steam is sufficiently pure for use in high-pressure turbines. This step is called secondary separation or "steam scrubbing." Both steps are usually accomplished in one steam drum.

Part of the contamination of the steam is caused by dissolved solids contained in tiny water droplets that may remain after primary separation. The rest of the contamination appears to be silica, either in solution in steam or in vaporized form. This type of contaminant cannot be mechanically removed by primary separation. Washing or scrubbing is necessary for its dilution or removal.

Gross impurities in the steam may be caused by periods of abnormally high water level from operational upsets, during which the separating equipment is submerged, allowing the water to be carried over in gulps. This action is called "priming." Another type of gross carry-over can occur if the boiler water produces excessive foam in the drum. With high concentration of solids in the boiler water, this "foaming" may be severe enough to render the separating devices ineffective. Foaming and priming are comparatively rare occurrences in the modern boiler with proper water-level regulation and control of boiler-water quality by chemical methods.

Factors affecting steam separation

Separation of steam from the mixture discharged into the drum from steam-water risers is related to both design and operating factors, which may be listed as follows:

Design factors

1. Design pressure
2. Drum size, length and diameter
3. Rate of steam generation
4. Circulation ratio—water circulated to heated tubes divided by steam generated
5. Type and arrangement of mechanical separators
6. Feedwater supply and steam discharge equipment and arrangement
7. Arrangement of downcomer and riser circuits in the steam drum

Operating factors

1. Operating pressure
2. Boiler load (steam flow)
3. Type of steam load
4. Chemical analysis of boiler water
5. Water level carried

In steam drums without separation devices, where separation is by gravity only, the manner in which some of the above items affect separation is indicated in simplified form in Figs. 7 and 8.

For a low rate of steam generation (up to about 3 ft/sec velocity of steam leaving the water surface) there is sufficient time for the steam bubbles to separate from the mixture by gravity without being drawn into the downcomers and without carrying entrained water droplets into the steam outlet (*see Fig. 7a*). However, for this same arrangement at a higher rate of steam generation (Fig. 7b) the time is insufficient to attain either of these desirable results. Moreover, the dense upward traffic of steam bubbles in the mixture may cause a false water level, as indicated.

The effect of the location of the riser circuits in relation to the water level is illustrated in diagrams a and b, Fig. 8. Neither arrangement is likely to yield desirable results in a drum where gravity alone is used for separation.

Separation by the action of gravity alone is possible if the velocity of either the mixture or the steam bubbles within the mixture is sufficiently low, but the arrangement will probably be uneconomical. For gravity separation in a single drum, the steam generated per sq ft of disengaging surface must be kept extremely low. A single drum under these conditions is generally uneconomical except for small low-duty boilers. By using multiple drums of reasonable size in series, as in Fig. 9a, somewhat higher steam outputs per ft length of drum are possible with gravity separation.

Operating pressure has an effect on the natural tendency of steam and water to separate. The relationship between pressure and the differential in the densities of water and steam (Fig. 16, Chapter 3) is indicative of this effect. In the separation of steam from water, the limiting velocity of a water particle conveyed in steam and the force of gravity both vary directly with the differential in the densities of the water and the steam. Hence, as the density differential diminishes with increase in operating pressure, so does the force of gravity available for separation. The effect of increasing operating pressure (above 300 psi for comparison) on steam flow per unit of flow area, on steam velocity above the drum water level, and on the force of gravity for separation is shown in Fig. 10. It will be noted that the percentage drop in gravity-separating force closely follows the drop in limiting velocity.

As steam pressure increases, the density of steam increases, and the size of steam bubbles in the mixture decreases. Consequently, the velocity of the mixture leaving the riser circuits is reduced. This permits a higher capacity per ft length of a given diameter drum, or the use of a smaller drum.

Mechanical steam separators for drums

As noted above, gravity steam separation alone is generally unsatisfactory for boilers of the usual sizes and operating requirements. Most steam drums, therefore, are fitted with some form of primary separator. Simple types of primary separators are illustrated in Fig. 9. These fa-

cilitate or supplement gravity separation. The extent and arrangement of the various baffles and deflectors should always allow for access to the drums.

In the B&W cyclone steam separator, shown in Fig. 11, centrifugal force many times the force of gravity is used to separate the steam from the water. Cyclones, essentially cylindrical in form, and corrugated scrubbers are the basic components of this type of separator.

The cyclones are arranged internally along the length of the drum, and the steam-water mixture is admitted

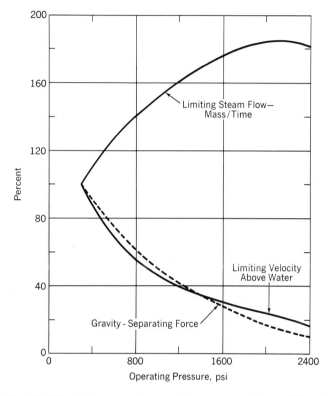

Fig. 10 Effect of increase in operating pressure (above 300 psi for comparison) on 1) limiting steam flow per unit of flow area, 2) limiting velocity above water, and 3) gravity-separating force —steam and water.

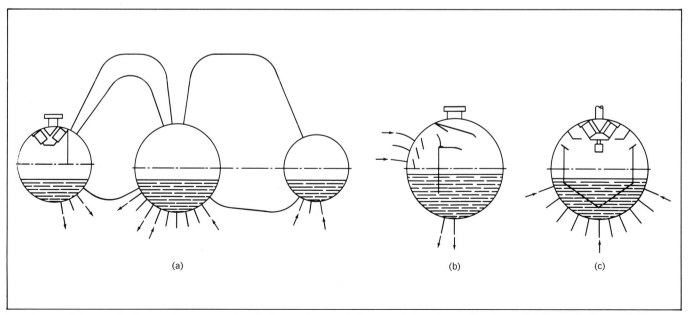

Fig. 9 Simple types of primary steam separators in boiler drums: a) deflector baffle, b) another type of deflector baffle, and c) compartment baffle.

tangentially. The water forms a layer against the cylinder walls, and the steam (of less density) moves to the core of the cylinder and then upward. The water flows downward in the cylinder and is discharged through an annulus at the bottom, below the drum water level. Thus, with the water returning from drum storage to the downcomers virtually free of steam bubbles, maximum net head is available for producing flow in the circuits, which is the important factor in the successful use of natural circulation (*see Chapter 3*). The steam moving upward from the cylinder passes through a small primary corrugated scrubber at the top of the cyclone (*see Fig. 11*) for additional separation. Under many conditions of operation no further refinement in separation is required, although the cyclone separator is considered only as a primary separator.

When wide load fluctuations and variations in water analyses are expected, large corrugated secondary scrubbers may be installed at the top of the drum (also shown in Fig. 11) to provide nearly perfect steam separation. These scrubbers may be termed secondary separators. They provide a large surface which intercepts water particles as the steam flows sinuously between closely fitted plates. Steam velocity through the corrugated-plate assembly is very low, so that re-entrainment of water is avoided. The collected water is drained from the bottom of the scrubber assembly to the water below.

Single, double and even triple rows of cyclone separators are installed in boiler drums, with ample room for access. For smaller boilers at lower pressures (100 psi), the separation of clean steam by single and double rows of cyclone separators is approximately 4000 and 6000 lb, respectively, per hr per ft of drum length. At pressures around 1050 psi, these values increase to 9000 and 15,000, respectively.

For large utility boilers—e.g., a Radiant boiler (Chapter 22) operating at a pressure of 2800 psi—separation

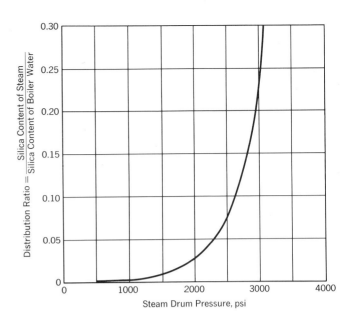

Fig. 12 Effect of pressure on silica distribution ratio.

per ft of drum length can be as high as 50,000 lb of steam per hour with three rows of cyclone separators. Actual limits can be established only by a complete analysis of the numerous design factors, both physical and functional, which influence the performance of these separating devices.

The combination of cyclone separators and scrubbers described above provides the means for obtaining steam purity corresponding to less than 1.0 ppm solids content under a wide variation of operating conditions. This purity is generally adequate in commercial practice. However, further refinement in steam purification is required where it is necessary to remove boiler-water salts, such as silica, which are entrained in the steam by vaporization or solution mechanism. Washing the steam with condensate or feedwater of acceptable purity may be used for this purpose.

Steam-washing

For any given operating condition, silica is distributed between boiler water and steam in a definite ratio, commonly referred to as the distribution ratio. As illustrated in Fig. 12, the value of the distribution ratio increases rapidly with increasing pressure. For example, if operating pressure is doubled from 1300 to 2600 psi, the distribution ratio increases tenfold. Experience has indicated that troublesome silica deposits will not form in condensing turbines if the silica concentration in the steam does not exceed about 0.025 ppm. By assuming an allowable silica concentration of 0.025 ppm in the steam and using the distribution ratios of Fig. 12, it can be deduced that above 2000 psi the silica content in the boiler water must be kept well below 1 ppm if turbine fouling is to be avoided. Actually it is often impractical to maintain boiler-water concentrations of silica sufficiently low to prevent turbine fouling, and other measures, such as steam-washing, are used to control this type of steam contamination.

Steam-washing is an absorption process by which silica vapor is absorbed from steam by wash water. A net trans-

Fig. 11 Double-row arrangement of cyclone-type primary steam separators, with scrubber elements at top of drum for secondary separation.

fer of silica takes place when the ratio of silica concentration in steam to that in the wash water differs from the distribution ratio. For example, if pure steam is in contact with water of high silica content, silica will transfer from the water to the steam. This action will continue until the distribution ratio has been established. In steam-washing, silica-laden steam is brought into intimate contact with relatively pure wash water, such as condensate or feedwater, and silica is absorbed from the steam by the wash water. The actual amount of silica transferred, and therefore the final silica concentrations

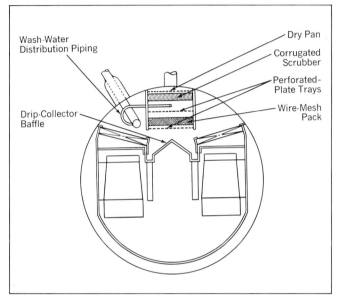

Fig. 13 Arrangement of steam-drum internals for washing silica-laden steam.

of the steam and wash water, will depend on the relative amounts of steam and water present, the degree of mixing, and the time of contact. In practice, neither the contact area between the steam and the water nor the contact time is sufficiently great to permit a complete interchange of silica from steam to water. As a result, the ratio of the silica concentration of the washed steam to that of the wash water does not quite reach theoretical equilibrium.

A steam-drum arrangement employing steam-washing is shown in Fig. 13. The drum is equipped with primary mechanical separators of the centrifugal type and corrugated scrubbers. Steam leaving the primary separators flows to a steam washer arranged in the top of the steam drum. The washer consists of a rectangular column approximately the length of the steam drum. Steam passes vertically upward through a perforated plate, a pack of stainless steel wire mesh, a second perforated plate, and finally a corrugated scrubber element. Wash water enters the drum through a nozzle and flows downward through the washer, counterflow to the steam. The steam velocity through the tray perforations maintains, above each tray, a layer of wash water which is kept in violent agitation by the steam. The wire mesh provides a large surface area for achieving intimate contact between the steam and the wash water.

In many installations where it is impractical to maintain the silica content of the boiler water low enough to prevent turbine deposits, the use of steam washers eliminates these deposits. In other cases where it is possible to prevent turbine deposits by large blowdown rates with resultant low silica content in the boiler water, the use of steam washers will permit operation with lower blowdown rates and higher boiler-water silica content.

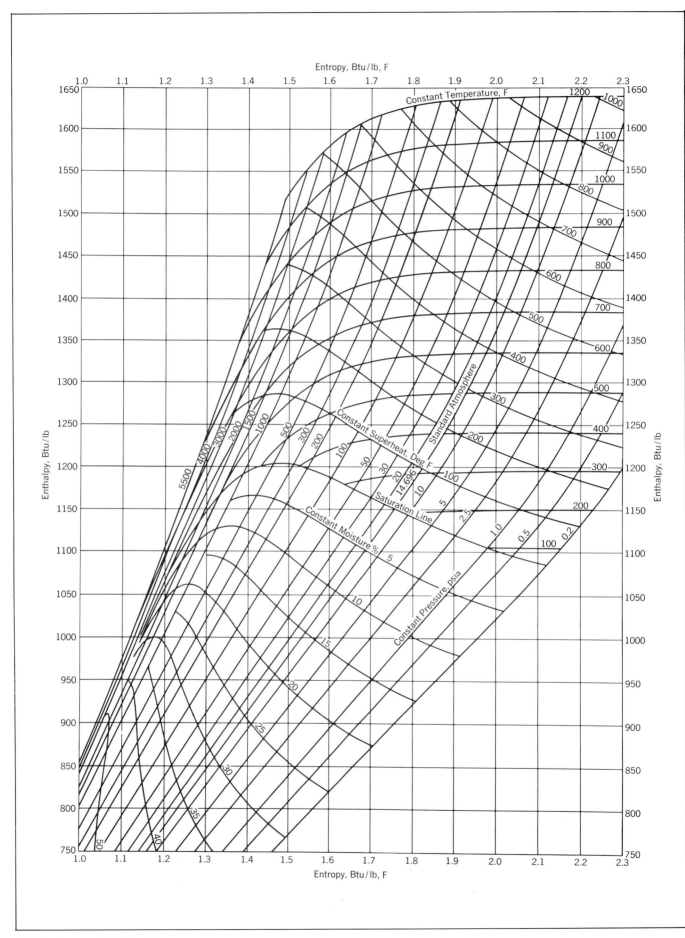

Mollier diagram (*h-s*) for steam.

Chapter 2

Thermodynamics of steam

Thermodynamics is the science concerned with conservation of energy and the rules governing energy changes into transient forms; namely, heat and work. Applications of this science are governed by two basic principles firmly established in the engineering field as the first and second laws. Although much broader in their applicability, these laws originally evolved from the development of the steam engine and its demonstration of the conversion of heat to mechanical work. Although this chapter deals mainly with heat and expansion work plus associated systems or working fluids, the principles involved have long been recognized as applying to all forms of work.

Regardless of the type of work or form of energy under consideration, the terms heat, work and energy have little practical significance unless the concepts of surroundings, systems, processes and cycles are included. In the case of expansion work the system under consideration is a fluid capable of expansion or contraction under the influence of pressure changes, temperature changes, chemical reactions or all three. The processes define just how these changes are constrained to take place. Cycles are sequential arrangements of processes capable of producing net heat flow and work when interposed between an energy source and an energy "sink." It is the cycle that is all important in power production. The surroundings represent sources and sinks devised to accommodate any interchange of mass, heat or work to or from the system. What happens to the surroundings when a cycle of processes is carried out by the system is of particular significance in the second law.

Steam, then, may be considered a thermodynamic system and, because of its availability and advantageous characteristics, it was inevitable that it should become a favored system in power generation and heat transfer. A unique combination of high thermal capacity (specific heat) on a volumetric or molar basis plus a high critical temperature have served to maintain this dominant position. High volumetric thermal capacity of a working fluid generally results in smaller equipment for any required maximum power output or heat transfer. A high critical temperature relative to the working temperature range dictated by material limitations permits the use of a vapor-power cycle with low compressor or pump work. Also, many heat transfer processes require the constant temperature possible in the vapor cycle through latent heats of vaporization or condensation. The subcritical temperature range of water matches well with temperature requirements of a large number of processes.

Properties of steam

The first step in design of steam generating equipment and cycle application, either for power or heat transfer or both is to establish reliable information on steam properties. Fortunately there is good world-wide agreement on this subject through the "International Conferences on Properties of Steam." The disagreements that do exist are not crucial and are rapidly being resolved. Steam tables currently in use in the United States are the "1967 ASME Steam Tables" based on agreements reached at the "Sixth International Conference on the Properties of Steam."

Data selected from the 1967 ASME Steam Tables are tabulated in Tables 1, 2 and 3. The first two columns of Tables 1 and 2 define the pressure-temperature correspondence for equilibrium between the liquid and vapor phases referred to as saturation. Steam heated beyond saturation to higher temperatures is superheated steam. Water heated to temperatures below saturation (subcooled water) is referred to as compressed water in the steam tables. Properties for the superheated steam and compressed water ranges are given in Table 3. Fig. 1, reproduced from the 1967 ASME Steam Tables, shows on a single plot the values of enthalpy and specific volume for steam and compressed water over a wide range of pressures and temperatures.

The steam tables also include the intensive properties of specific volume, specific enthalpy, and specific entropy for specified temperatures, pressures and states (liquid or gas). Intensive properties are those which are independent of mass; they are also independent of the type of process or any past history. These are the state and thermodynamic properties required for numerical solutions to design and performance problems involving steam for heat transfer and power. The special significance of the important properties of enthalpy and entropy is a consequence of the laws of thermodynamics.

Fortunately, engineering problems deal mainly with changes or differences in enthalpy and entropy and it is

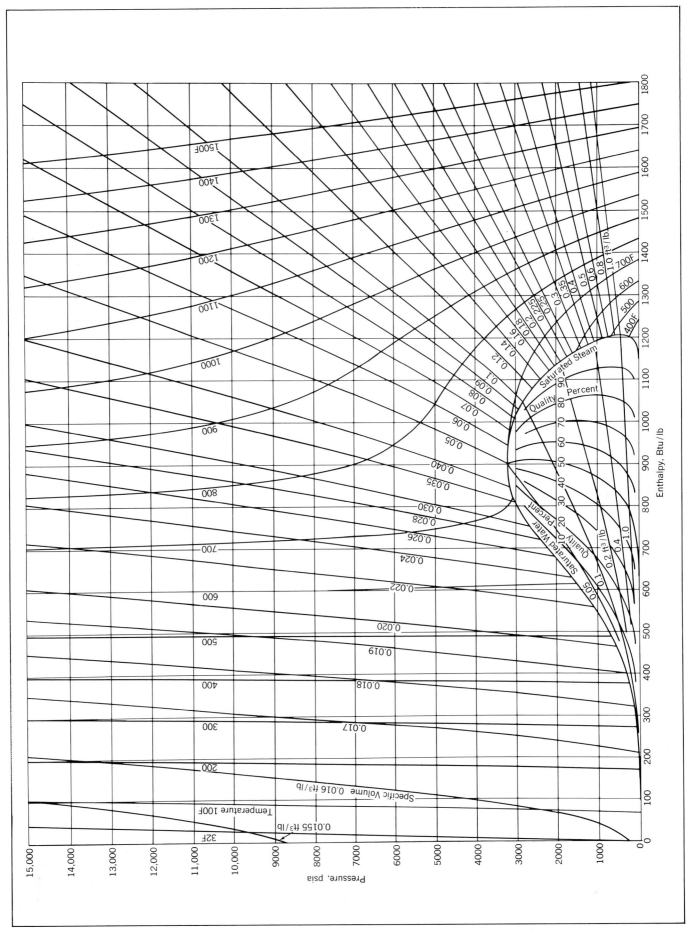

Fig. 1 Pressure-enthalpy chart.

Note: The following steam tables and Fig. 1 have been abstracted from *Thermodynamic and Transport Properties of Steam* (Copyright, 1967, by The American Society of Mechanical Engineers.)

Table 1
Properties of saturated steam and saturated water (temperature)

Temp F	Press. psia	Volume, ft³/lb			Enthalpy, Btu/lb			Entropy, Btu/lb, F			Temp F
		Water v_f	Evap v_{fg}	Steam v_g	Water h_f	Evap h_{fg}	Steam h_g	Water s_f	Evap s_{fg}	Steam s_g	
32	0.08859	0.01602	3305	3305	−0.02	1075.5	1075.5	0.0000	2.1873	2.1873	32
35	0.09991	0.01602	2948	2948	3.00	1073.8	1076.8	0.0061	2.1706	2.1767	35
40	0.12163	0.01602	2446	2446	8.03	1071.0	1079.0	0.0162	2.1432	2.1594	40
45	0.14744	0.01602	2037.7	2037.8	13.04	1068.1	1081.2	0.0262	2.1164	2.1426	45
50	0.17796	0.01602	1704.8	1704.8	18.05	1065.3	1083.4	0.0361	2.0901	2.1262	50
60	0.2561	0.01603	1207.6	1207.6	28.06	1059.7	1087.7	0.0555	2.0391	2.0946	60
70	0.3629	0.01605	868.3	868.4	38.05	1054.0	1092.1	0.0745	1.9900	2.0645	70
80	0.5068	0.01607	633.3	633.3	48.04	1048.4	1096.4	0.0932	1.9426	2.0359	80
90	0.6981	0.01610	468.1	468.1	58.02	1042.7	1100.8	0.1115	1.8970	2.0086	90
100	0.9492	0.01613	350.4	350.4	68.00	1037.1	1105.1	0.1295	1.8530	1.9825	100
110	1.2750	0.01617	265.4	265.4	77.98	1031.4	1109.3	0.1472	1.8105	1.9577	110
120	1.6927	0.01620	203.25	203.26	87.97	1025.6	1113.6	0.1646	1.7693	1.9339	120
130	2.2230	0.01625	157.32	157.33	97.96	1019.8	1117.8	0.1817	1.7295	1.9112	130
140	2.8892	0.01629	122.98	123.00	107.95	1014.0	1122.0	0.1985	1.6910	1.8895	140
150	3.718	0.01634	97.05	97.07	117.95	1008.2	1126.1	0.2150	1.6536	1.8686	150
160	4.741	0.01640	77.27	77.29	127.96	1002.2	1130.2	0.2313	1.6174	1.8487	160
170	5.993	0.01645	62.04	62.06	137.97	996.2	1134.2	0.2473	1.5822	1.8295	170
180	7.511	0.01651	50.21	50.22	148.00	990.2	1138.2	0.2631	1.5480	1.8111	180
190	9.340	0.01657	40.94	40.96	158.04	984.1	1142.1	0.2787	1.5148	1.7934	190
200	11.526	0.01664	33.62	33.64	168.09	977.9	1146.0	0.2940	1.4824	1.7764	200
210	14.123	0.01671	27.80	27.82	178.15	971.6	1149.7	0.3091	1.4509	1.7600	210
212	14.696	0.01672	26.78	26.80	180.17	970.3	1150.5	0.3121	1.4447	1.7568	212
220	17.186	0.01678	23.13	23.15	188.23	965.2	1153.4	0.3241	1.4201	1.7442	220
230	20.779	0.01685	19.364	19.381	198.33	958.7	1157.1	0.3388	1.3902	1.7290	230
240	24.968	0.01693	16.304	16.321	208.45	952.1	1160.6	0.3533	1.3609	1.7142	240
250	29.825	0.01701	13.802	13.819	218.59	945.4	1164.0	0.3677	1.3323	1.7000	250
260	35.427	0.01709	11.745	11.762	228.76	938.6	1167.4	0.3819	1.3043	1.6862	260
270	41.856	0.01718	10.042	10.060	238.95	931.7	1170.6	0.3960	1.2769	1.6729	270
280	49.200	0.01726	8.627	8.644	249.17	924.6	1173.8	0.4098	1.2501	1.6599	280
290	57.550	0.01736	7.443	7.460	259.4	917.4	1176.8	0.4236	1.2238	1.6473	290
300	67.005	0.01745	6.448	6.466	269.7	910.0	1179.7	0.4372	1.1979	1.6351	300
310	77.67	0.01755	5.609	5.626	280.0	902.5	1182.5	0.4506	1.1726	1.6232	310
320	89.64	0.01766	4.896	4.914	290.4	894.8	1185.2	0.4640	1.1477	1.6116	320
340	117.99	0.01787	3.770	3.788	311.3	878.8	1190.1	0.4902	1.0990	1.5892	340
360	153.01	0.01811	2.939	2.957	332.3	862.1	1194.4	0.5161	1.0517	1.5678	360
380	195.73	0.01836	2.317	2.335	353.6	844.5	1198.0	0.5416	1.0057	1.5473	380
400	247.26	0.01864	1.8444	1.8630	375.1	825.9	1201.0	0.5667	0.9607	1.5274	400
420	308.78	0.01894	1.4808	1.4997	396.9	806.2	1203.1	0.5915	0.9165	1.5080	420
440	381.54	0.01926	1.1976	1.2169	419.0	785.4	1204.4	0.6161	0.8729	1.4890	440
460	466.9	0.0196	0.9746	0.9942	441.5	763.2	1204.8	0.6405	0.8299	1.4704	460
480	566.2	0.0200	0.7972	0.8172	464.5	739.6	1204.1	0.6648	0.7871	1.4518	480
500	680.9	0.0204	0.6545	0.6749	487.9	714.3	1202.2	0.6890	0.7443	1.4333	500
520	812.5	0.0209	0.5386	0.5596	512.0	687.0	1199.0	0.7133	0.7013	1.4146	520
540	962.8	0.0215	0.4437	0.4651	536.8	657.5	1194.3	0.7378	0.6577	1.3954	540
560	1133.4	0.0221	0.3651	0.3871	562.4	625.3	1187.7	0.7625	0.6132	1.3757	560
580	1326.2	0.0228	0.2994	0.3222	589.1	589.9	1179.0	0.7876	0.5673	1.3550	580
600	1543.2	0.0236	0.2438	0.2675	617.1	550.6	1167.7	0.8134	0.5196	1.3330	600
620	1786.9	0.0247	0.1962	0.2208	646.9	506.3	1153.2	0.8403	0.4689	1.3092	620
640	2059.9	0.0260	0.1543	0.1802	679.1	454.6	1133.7	0.8686	0.4134	1.2821	640
660	2365.7	0.0277	0.1166	0.1443	714.9	392.1	1107.0	0.8995	0.3502	1.2498	660
680	2708.6	0.0304	0.0808	0.1112	758.5	310.1	1068.5	0.9365	0.2720	1.2086	680
700	3094.3	0.0366	0.0386	0.0752	822.4	172.7	995.2	0.9901	0.1490	1.1390	700
705.5	3208.2	0.0508	0	0.0508	906.0	0	906.0	1.0612	0	1.0612	705.5

Table 2
Properties of saturated steam and saturated water (pressure)

Press. psia	Temp F	Volume, ft³/lb			Enthalpy, Btu/lb			Entropy, Btu/lb, F			Energy, Btu/lb		Press. psia
		Water	Evap	Steam	Water	Evap	Steam	Water	Evap	Steam	Water	Steam	
		v_f	v_{fg}	v_g	h_f	h_{fg}	h_g	s_f	s_{fg}	s_g	u_f	u_g	
0.0886	32.018	0.01602	3302.4	3302.4	0.00	1075.5	1075.5	0	2.1872	2.1872	0	1021.3	0.0886
0.10	35.023	0.01602	2945.5	2945.5	3.03	1073.8	1076.8	0.0061	2.1705	2.1766	3.03	1022.3	0.10
0.15	45.453	0.01602	2004.7	2004.7	13.50	1067.9	1081.4	0.0271	2.1140	2.1411	13.50	1025.7	0.15
0.20	53.160	0.01603	1526.3	1526.3	21.22	1063.5	1084.7	0.0422	2.0738	2.1160	21.22	1028.3	0.20
0.30	64.484	0.01604	1039.7	1039.7	32.54	1057.1	1089.7	0.0641	2.0168	2.0809	32.54	1032.0	0.30
0.40	72.869	0.01606	792.0	792.1	40.92	1052.4	1093.3	0.0799	1.9762	2.0562	40.92	1034.7	0.40
0.5	79.586	0.01607	641.5	641.5	47.62	1048.6	1096.3	0.0925	1.9446	2.0370	47.62	1036.9	0.5
0.6	85.218	0.01609	540.0	540.1	53.25	1045.5	1098.7	0.1028	1.9186	2.0215	53.24	1038.7	0.6
0.7	90.09	0.01610	466.93	466.94	58.10	1042.7	1100.8	0.3	1.8966	2.0083	58.10	1040.3	0.7
0.8	94.38	0.01611	411.67	411.69	62.39	1040.3	1102.6	0.1117	1.8775	1.9970	62.39	1041.7	0.8
0.9	98.24	0.01612	368.41	368.43	66.24	1038.1	1104.3	0.1264	1.8606	1.9870	66.24	1042.9	0.9
1.0	101.74	0.01614	333.59	333.60	69.73	1036.1	1105.8	0.1326	1.8455	1.9781	69.73	1044.1	1.0
2.0	126.07	0.01623	173.74	173.76	94.03	1022.1	1116.2	0.1750	1.7450	1.9200	94.03	1051.8	2.0
3.0	141.47	0.01630	118.71	118.73	109.42	1013.2	1122.6	0.2009	1.6854	1.8864	109.41	1056.7	3.0
4.0	152.96	0.01636	90.63	90.64	120.92	1006.4	1127.3	0.2199	1.6428	1.8626	120.90	1060.2	4.0
5.0	162.24	0.01641	73.515	73.53	130.20	1000.9	1131.1	0.2349	1.6094	1.8443	130.18	1063.1	5.0
6.0	170.05	0.01645	61.967	61.98	138.03	996.2	1134.2	0.2474	1.5820	1.8294	138.01	1065.4	6.0
7.0	176.84	0.01649	53.634	53.65	144.83	992.1	1136.9	0.2581	1.5587	1.8168	144.81	1067.4	7.0
8.0	182.86	0.01653	47.328	47.35	150.87	988.5	1139.3	0.2676	1.5384	1.8060	150.84	1069.2	8.0
9.0	188.27	0.01656	42.385	42.40	156.30	985.1	1141.4	0.2760	1.5204	1.7964	156.28	1070.8	9.0
10	193.21	0.01659	38.404	38.42	161.26	982.1	1143.3	0.2836	1.5043	1.7879	161.23	1072.3	10
14.696	212.00	0.01672	26.782	26.80	180.17	970.3	1150.5	0.3121	1.4447	1.7568	180.12	1077.6	14.696
15	213.03	0.01673	26.274	26.29	181.21	969.7	1150.9	0.3137	1.4415	1.7552	181.16	1077.9	15
20	227.96	0.01683	20.070	20.087	196.27	960.1	1156.3	0.3358	1.3962	1.7320	196.21	1082.0	20
30	250.34	0.01701	13.7266	13.744	218.9	945.2	1164.1	0.3682	1.3313	1.6995	218.8	1087.9	30
40	267.25	0.01715	10.4794	10.497	236.1	933.6	1169.8	0.3921	1.2844	1.6765	236.0	1092.1	40
50	281.02	0.01727	8.4967	8.514	250.2	923.9	1174.1	0.4112	1.2474	1.6586	250.1	1095.3	50
60	292.71	0.01738	7.1562	7.174	262.2	915.4	1177.6	0.4273	1.2167	1.6440	262.0	1098.0	60
70	302.93	0.01748	6.1875	6.205	272.7	907.8	1180.6	0.4411	1.1905	1.6316	272.5	1100.2	70
80	312.04	0.01757	5.4536	5.471	282.1	900.9	1183.1	0.4534	1.1675	1.6208	281.9	1102.1	80
90	320.28	0.01766	4.8777	4.895	290.7	894.6	1185.3	0.4643	1.1470	1.6113	290.4	1103.7	90
100	327.82	0.01774	4.4133	4.431	298.5	888.6	1187.2	0.4743	1.1284	1.6027	298.2	1105.2	100
120	341.27	0.01789	3.7097	3.728	312.6	877.8	1190.4	0.4919	1.0960	1.5879	312.2	1107.6	120
140	353.04	0.01803	3.2010	3.219	325.0	868.0	1193.0	0.5071	1.0681	1.5752	324.5	1109.6	140
160	363.55	0.01815	2.8155	2.834	336.1	859.0	1195.1	0.5206	1.0435	1.5641	335.5	1111.2	160
180	373.08	0.01827	2.5129	2.531	346.2	850.7	1196.9	0.5328	1.0215	1.5543	345.6	1112.5	180
200	381.80	0.01839	2.2689	2.287	355.5	842.8	1198.3	0.5438	1.0016	1.5454	354.8	1113.7	200
250	400.97	0.01865	1.8245	1.8432	376.1	825.0	1201.1	0.5679	0.9585	1.5264	375.3	1115.8	250
300	417.35	0.01889	1.5238	1.5427	394.0	808.9	1202.9	0.5882	0.9223	1.5105	392.9	1117.2	300
350	431.73	0.01913	1.3064	1.3255	409.8	794.2	1204.0	0.6059	0.8909	1.4968	408.6	1118.1	350
400	444.60	0.0193	1.14162	1.1610	424.2	780.4	1204.6	0.6217	0.8630	1.4847	422.7	1118.7	400
450	456.28	0.0195	1.01224	1.0318	437.3	767.5	1204.8	0.6360	0.8378	1.4738	435.7	1118.9	450
500	467.01	0.0198	0.90787	0.9276	449.5	755.1	1204.7	0.6490	0.8148	1.4639	447.7	1118.8	500
550	476.94	0.0199	0.82183	0.8418	460.9	743.3	1204.3	0.6611	0.7936	1.4547	458.9	1118.6	550
600	486.20	0.0201	0.74962	0.7698	471.7	732.0	1203.7	0.6723	0.7738	1.4461	469.5	1118.2	600
700	503.08	0.0205	0.63505	0.6556	491.6	710.2	1201.8	0.6928	0.7377	1.4304	488.9	1116.9	700
800	518.21	0.0209	0.54809	0.5690	509.8	689.6	1199.4	0.7111	0.7051	1.4163	506.7	1115.2	800
900	531.95	0.0212	0.47968	0.5009	526.7	669.7	1196.4	0.7279	0.6753	1.4032	523.2	1113.0	900
1000	544.58	0.0216	0.42436	0.4460	542.6	650.4	1192.9	0.7434	0.6476	1.3910	538.6	1110.4	1000
1100	556.28	0.0220	0.37863	0.4006	557.5	631.5	1189.1	0.7578	0.6216	1.3794	553.1	1107.5	1100
1200	567.19	0.0223	0.34013	0.3625	571.9	613.0	1184.8	0.7714	0.5969	1.3683	566.9	1104.3	1200
1300	577.42	0.0227	0.30722	0.3299	585.6	594.6	1180.2	0.7843	0.5733	1.3577	580.1	1100.9	1300
1400	587.07	0.0231	0.27871	0.3018	598.8	576.5	1175.3	0.7966	0.5507	1.3474	592.9	1097.1	1400
1500	596.20	0.0235	0.25372	0.2772	611.7	558.4	1170.1	0.8085	0.5288	1.3373	605.2	1093.1	1500
2000	635.80	0.0257	0.16266	0.1883	672.1	466.2	1138.3	0.8625	0.4256	1.2881	662.6	1068.6	2000
2500	668.11	0.0286	0.10209	0.1307	731.7	361.6	1093.3	0.9139	0.3206	1.2345	718.5	1032.9	2500
3000	695.33	0.0343	0.05073	0.0850	801.8	218.4	1020.3	0.9728	0.1891	1.1619	782.8	973.1	3000
3208.2	705.47	0.0508	0	0.0508	906.0	0	906.0	1.0612	0	1.0612	875.9	875.9	3208.2

not necessary to establish an absolute zero for these properties even though this may be done in the case of entropy. The steam tables set an arbitrary zero internal energy and entropy for the liquid state of water at the triple point* corresponding to 32.018F and a vapor pressure of 0.08865 psia. The enthalpy of water under these conditions has a slight positive value as is evident later when the terms "internal energy" and "enthalpy" are explained.

Customarily, the boiler industry uses 80F and 14.7 psia as the zero enthalpy of air and combustion products, although this practice is not widespread in other related engineering fields. A more general reference is one atmosphere pressure (14.696 psia) and 77F (298.16K). This is referred to as the standard reference point for listing heats of formation of compounds from their elements in their standard states, latent heats of phase changes and free energy changes, all important thermodynamic quantities. Because of these different conventions associated with various branches of engineering, considerable care must be exercised in the interpretation of any tabulated set of properties.

Energy equations

Thermodynamic processes follow the conservation laws as applied to energy and mass exclusive of mass-energy exchanges. The latter, although important in nuclear reactions, are insignificant in combustion and heat engines. Based on this restricted mass-energy relation of the system and associated processes a balance prevails between energy, work and heat quantities entering and leaving the system except for short time intervals in which energy is being added or withdrawn under unsteady state (time-dependent) conditions. Because the terms heat and work refer to energy in transit they are recognized as characteristics or properties of the process, not the system. All other energy terms represent stored energy and are the properties used in describing a particular system and its potentials for change. Expressed as an equation the restricted energy conservation law is:

$$(1) \qquad E_2 - E_1 + E(t) = Q - W_k$$

$E_2 - E_1 = \Delta E$ is the change in stored energy at the boundary states 1 and 2 of the system, and $E(t)$ accounts for energy changes due to unsteady state performance [for steady state systems $E(t) = 0$]. Q is heat added to, and W_k is the work done by the system. If the system is open in the sense that mass enters and leaves, the term ΔE reflects stored energy entering and leaving with the mass.

Problems in the power field are generally concerned with open systems (Fig. 2) for which an alternate form of equation (1) lists a breakdown of the ΔE terms into internally and externally stored energy entering and leaving the process on a unit mass basis. This alternate of (1), sometimes called the general energy equation, for a flowing fluid is:

$$(2) \qquad \Delta u + \Delta(pv) + \Delta \frac{V^2}{2g_c} + \Delta Z = Q - W_k$$

* The triple point defines a unique pressure and temperature value where the three states of solid, liquid and gas coexist in equilibrium.

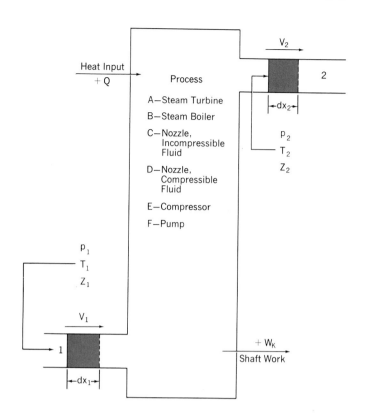

Fig. 2 Diagram illustrating thermodynamic processes.

Each term on the left in equation (2) is in its integrated form. This equation is represented diagramatically in Fig. 2 where the enclosure represents any one or some combination of devices. Δu represents the difference in internally stored energy associated with molecular and atomic motions and forces. Internally stored energy or simply internal energy, as used, is somewhat of a catchall to account for all forms of energy other than the kinetic and potential energies of the collective masses of the molecules. Except as otherwise noted, Δu is used in this chapter to refer to a nonreacting system in a chemical sense excluding the very important stored energy associated with heats of formation as well as some other forms identified solely with the structure of matter. Such restricted use is possible since no attempt is made to define this u in an absolute sense.

$\Delta(pv)$ is externally stored energy in that it reflects the difference in work required to move a unit mass into and out of the system. Both $\Delta(pv)$ and Δu as used here differ from the other forms of stored energy in that they are dependent only on the state variables of p, v and T through an equation of state.

The remaining terms of externally stored energy, $\Delta V^2/2g_c$ and ΔZ, depend on other physical aspects of the system. $\Delta V^2/2g_c$ represents a difference in the total kinetic energy of the fluid between two reference points. ΔZ represents any differences in energy as a result of changes in elevation in a gravitational force field. Strictly speaking, ΔZ should be shown as $g\Delta Z/g_c$, where g is the gravitational constant, 32.17 ft/sec^2.

The symbol g_c in the kinetic energy term is a conversion constant for units in a four-dimensional system of mass, length, time and force where both force and mass are measured in the same units such as pounds.

Table 3
Properties of superheated steam and compressed water (temperature and pressure)

Abs press. lb/sq in. (sat. temp)		100	200	300	400	500	600	700	800	900	1000	1100	1200	1300	1400	1500
								Temperature, F								
1 (101.74)	v	0.0161	392.5	452.3	511.9	571.5	631.1	690.7								
	h	68.00	1150.2	1195.7	1241.8	1288.6	1336.1	1384.5								
	s	0.1295	2.0509	2.1152	2.1722	2.2237	2.2708	2.3144								
5 (162.24)	v	0.0161	78.14	90.24	102.24	114.21	126.15	138.08	150.01	161.94	173.86	185.78	197.70	209.62	221.53	233.45
	h	68.01	1148.6	1194.8	1241.3	1288.2	1335.9	1384.3	1433.6	1483.7	1534.7	1586.7	1639.6	1693.3	1748.0	1803.5
	s	0.1295	1.8716	1.9369	1.9943	2.0460	2.0932	2.1369	2.1776	2.2159	2.2521	2.2866	2.3194	2.3509	2.3811	2.4101
10 (193.21)	v	0.0161	38.84	44.98	51.03	57.04	63.03	69.00	74.98	80.94	86.91	92.87	98.84	104.80	110.76	116.72
	h	68.02	1146.6	1193.7	1240.6	1287.8	1335.5	1384.0	1433.4	1483.5	1534.6	1586.6	1639.5	1693.3	1747.9	1803.4
	s	0.1295	1.7928	1.8593	1.9173	1.9692	2.0166	2.0603	2.1011	2.1394	2.1757	2.2101	2.2430	2.2744	2.3046	2.3337
15 (213.03)	v	0.0161	0.0166	29.899	33.963	37.985	41.986	45.978	49.964	53.946	57.926	61.905	65.882	69.858	73.833	77.807
	h	68.04	168.09	1192.5	1239.9	1287.3	1335.2	1383.8	1433.2	1483.4	1534.5	1586.5	1639.4	1693.2	1747.8	1803.4
	s	0.1295	0.2940	1.8134	1.8720	1.9242	1.9717	2.0155	2.0563	2.0946	2.1309	2.1653	2.1982	2.2297	2.2599	2.2890
20 (227.96)	v	0.0161	0.0166	22.356	25.428	28.457	31.466	34.465	37.458	40.447	43.435	46.420	49.405	52.388	55.370	58.352
	h	68.05	168.11	1191.4	1239.2	1286.9	1334.9	1383.5	1432.9	1483.2	1534.3	1586.3	1639.3	1693.1	1747.8	1803.3
	s	0.1295	0.2940	1.7805	1.8397	1.8921	1.9397	1.9836	2.0244	2.0628	2.0991	2.1336	2.1665	2.1979	2.2282	2.2572
40 (267.25)	v	0.0161	0.0166	11.036	12.624	14.165	15.685	17.195	18.699	20.199	21.697	23.194	24.689	26.183	27.676	29.168
	h	68.10	168.15	1186.6	1236.4	1285.0	1333.6	1382.5	1432.1	1482.5	1533.7	1585.8	1638.8	1992.7	1747.5	1803.0
	s	0.1295	0.2940	1.6992	1.7608	1.8143	1.8624	1.9065	1.9476	1.9860	2.0224	2.0569	2.0899	2.1224	2.1516	2.1807
60 (292.71)	v	0.0161	0.0166	7.257	8.354	9.400	10.425	11.438	12.446	13.450	14.452	15.452	16.450	17.448	18.445	19.441
	h	68.15	168.20	1181.6	1233.5	1283.2	1332.3	1381.5	1431.3	1481.8	1533.2	1585.3	1638.4	1692.4	1747.1	1802.8
	s	0.1295	0.2939	1.6492	1.7134	1.7681	1.8168	1.8612	1.9024	1.9410	1.9774	2.0120	2.0450	2.0765	2.1068	2.1359
80 (312.04)	v	0.0161	0.0166	0.0175	6.218	7.018	7.794	8.560	9.319	10.075	10.829	11.581	12.331	13.081	13.829	14.577
	h	68.21	168.24	269.74	1230.5	1281.3	1330.9	1380.5	1430.5	1481.1	1532.6	1584.9	1638.0	1692.0	1746.8	1802.5
	s	0.1295	0.2939	0.4371	1.6790	1.7349	1.7842	1.8289	1.8702	1.9089	1.9454	1.9800	2.0131	2.0446	2.0750	2.1041
100 (327.82)	v	0.0161	0.0166	0.0175	4.935	5.588	6.216	6.833	7.443	8.050	8.655	9.258	9.860	10.460	11.060	11.659
	h	68.26	168.29	269.77	1227.4	1279.3	1329.6	1379.5	1429.7	1480.4	1532.0	1584.4	1637.6	1691.6	1746.5	1802.2
	s	0.1295	0.2939	0.4371	1.6516	1.7088	1.7586	1.8036	1.8451	1.8839	1.9205	1.9552	1.9883	2.0199	2.0502	2.0794
120 (341.27)	v	0.0161	0.0166	0.0175	4.0786	4.6341	5.1637	5.6831	6.1928	6.7006	7.2060	7.7096	8.2119	8.7130	9.2134	9.7130
	h	68.31	168.33	269.81	1224.1	1277.4	1328.1	1378.4	1428.8	1479.8	1531.4	1583.9	1637.1	1691.3	1746.2	1802.0
	s	0.1295	0.2939	0.4371	1.6286	1.6872	1.7376	1.7829	1.8246	1.8635	1.9001	1.9349	1.9680	1.9996	2.0300	2.0592
140 (353.04)	v	0.0161	0.0166	0.0175	3.4661	3.9526	4.4119	4.8585	5.2995	5.7364	6.1709	6.6036	7.0349	7.4652	7.8946	8.3233
	h	68.37	168.38	269.85	1220.8	1275.3	1326.8	1377.4	1428.0	1479.1	1530.8	1583.4	1636.7	1690.9	1745.9	1801.7
	s	0.1295	0.2939	0.4370	1.6085	1.6686	1.7196	1.7652	1.8071	1.8461	1.8828	1.9176	1.9508	1.9825	2.0129	2.0421
160 (363.55)	v	0.0161	0.0166	0.0175	3.0060	3.4413	3.8480	4.2420	4.6295	5.0132	5.3945	5.7741	6.1522	6.5293	6.9055	7.2811
	h	68.42	168.42	269.89	1217.4	1273.3	1325.4	1376.4	1427.2	1478.4	1530.3	1582.9	1636.3	1690.5	1745.6	1801.4
	s	0.1294	0.2938	0.4370	1.5906	1.6522	1.7039	1.7499	1.7919	1.8310	1.8678	1.9027	1.9359	1.9676	1.9980	2.0273
180 (373.08)	v	0.0161	0.0166	0.0174	2.6474	3.0433	3.4093	3.7621	4.1084	4.4505	4.7907	5.1289	5.4657	5.8014	6.1363	6.4704
	h	68.47	168.47	269.92	1213.8	1271.2	1324.0	1375.3	1426.3	1477.7	1529.7	1582.4	1635.9	1690.2	1745.3	1801.2
	s	0.1294	0.2938	0.4370	1.5743	1.6376	1.6900	1.7362	1.7784	1.8176	1.8545	1.8894	1.9227	1.9545	1.9849	2.0142
200 (381.80)	v	0.0161	0.0166	0.0174	2.3598	2.7247	3.0583	3.3783	3.6915	4.0008	4.3077	4.6128	4.9165	5.2191	5.5209	5.8219
	h	68.52	168.51	269.96	1210.1	1269.0	1322.6	1374.3	1425.5	1477.0	1529.1	1581.9	1635.4	1689.8	1745.0	1800.9
	s	0.1294	0.2938	0.4369	1.5593	1.6242	1.6776	1.7239	1.7663	1.8057	1.8426	1.8776	1.9109	1.9427	1.9732	2.0025
250 (400.97)	v	0.0161	0.0166	0.0174	0.0186	2.1504	2.4662	2.6872	2.9410	3.1909	3.4382	3.6837	3.9278	4.1709	4.4131	4.6546
	h	68.66	168.63	270.05	375.10	1263.5	1319.0	1371.6	1423.4	1475.3	1527.6	1580.6	1634.4	1688.9	1744.2	1800.2
	s	0.1294	0.2937	0.4368	0.5667	1.5951	1.6502	1.6976	1.7405	1.7801	1.8173	1.8524	1.8858	1.9177	1.9482	1.9776
300 (417.35)	v	0.0161	0.0166	0.0174	0.0186	1.7665	2.0044	2.2263	2.4407	2.6509	2.8585	3.0643	3.2688	3.4721	3.6746	3.8764
	h	68.79	168.74	270.14	375.15	1257.7	1315.2	1368.9	1421.3	1473.6	1526.2	1579.4	1633.3	1688.0	1743.4	1799.6
	s	0.1294	0.2937	0.4307	0.5665	1.5703	1.6274	1.6758	1.7192	1.7591	1.7964	1.8317	1.8652	1.8972	1.9278	1.9572
350 (431.73)	v	0.0161	0.0166	0.0174	0.0186	1.4913	1.7028	1.8970	2.0832	2.2652	2.4445	2.6219	2.7980	2.9730	3.1471	3.3205
	h	68.92	168.85	270.24	375.21	1251.5	1311.4	1366.2	1419.2	1471.8	1524.7	1578.2	1632.3	1687.1	1742.6	1798.9
	s	0.1293	0.2936	0.4367	0.5664	1.5483	1.6077	1.6571	1.7009	1.7411	1.7787	1.8141	1.8477	1.8798	1.9105	1.9400
400 (444.60)	v	0.0161	0.0166	0.0174	0.0162	1.2841	1.4763	1.6499	1.8151	1.9759	2.1339	2.2901	2.4450	2.5987	2.7515	2.9037
	h	69.05	168.97	270.33	375.27	1245.1	1307.4	1363.4	1417.0	1470.1	1523.3	1576.9	1631.2	1686.2	1741.9	1798.2
	s	0.1293	0.2935	0.4366	0.5663	1.5282	1.5901	1.6406	1.6850	1.7255	1.7632	1.7988	1.8325	1.8647	1.8955	1.9250
500 (467.01)	v	0.0161	0.0166	0.0174	0.0186	0.9919	1.1584	1.3037	1.4397	1.5708	1.6992	1.8256	1.9507	2.0746	2.1977	2.3200
	h	69.32	169.19	270.51	375.38	1231.2	1299.1	1357.7	1412.7	1466.6	1520.3	1574.4	1629.1	1684.4	1740.3	1796.9
	s	0.1292	0.2934	0.4364	0.5660	1.4921	1.5595	1.6123	1.6578	1.6990	1.7371	1.7730	1.8069	1.8393	1.8702	1.8998

Table 3
Properties of superheated steam and compressed water (temperature and pressure)

Abs press. lb/sq in. (sat. temp)		Temperature, F														
		100	200	300	400	500	600	700	800	900	1000	1100	1200	1300	1400	1500
600 (486.20)	v	0.0161	0.0166	0.0174	0.0186	0.7944	0.9456	1.0726	1.1892	1.3008	1.4093	1.5160	1.6211	1.7252	1.8284	1.9309
	h	69.58	169.42	270.70	375.49	1215.9	1290.3	1351.8	1408.3	1463.0	1517.4	1571.9	1627.0	1682.6	1738.8	1795.6
	s	0.1292	0.2933	0.4362	0.5657	1.4590	1.5329	1.5844	1.6351	1.6769	1.7155	1.7517	1.7859	1.8184	1.8494	1.8792
700 (503.08)	v	0.0161	0.0166	0.0174	0.0186	0.0204	0.7928	0.9072	1.0102	1.1078	1.2023	1.2948	1.3858	1.4757	1.5647	1.6530
	h	69.84	169.65	270.89	375.61	487.93	1281.0	1345.6	1403.7	1459.4	1514.4	1569.4	1624.8	1680.7	1737.2	1794.3
	s	0.1291	0.2932	0.4360	0.5655	0.6889	1.5090	1.5673	1.6154	1.6580	1.6970	1.7335	1.7679	1.8006	1.8318	1.8617
800 (518.21)	v	0.0161	0.0166	0.0174	0.0186	0.0204	0.6774	0.7828	0.8759	0.9631	1.0470	1.1289	1.2093	1.2885	1.3669	1.4446
	h	70.11	169.88	271.07	375.73	487.88	1271.1	1339.2	1399.1	1455.8	1511.4	1566.9	1622.7	1678.9	1735.0	1792.9
	s	0.1290	0.2930	0.4358	0.5652	0.6885	1.4869	1.5484	1.5980	1.6413	1.6807	1.7175	1.7522	1.7851	1.8164	1.8464
900 (531.95)	v	0.0161	0.0166	0.0174	0.0186	0.0204	0.5869	0.6858	0.7713	0.8504	0.9262	0.9998	1.0720	1.1430	1.2131	1.2825
	h	70.37	170.10	271.26	375.84	487.83	1260.6	1332.7	1394.4	1452.2	1508.5	1564.4	1620.6	1677.1	1734.1	1791.6
	s	0.1290	0.2929	0.4357	0.5649	0.6881	1.4659	1.5311	1.5822	1.6263	1.6662	1.7033	1.7382	1.7713	1.8028	1.8329
1000 (544.58)	v	0.0161	0.0166	0.0174	0.0186	0.0204	0.5137	0.6080	0.6875	0.7603	0.8295	0.8966	0.9622	1.0266	1.0901	1.1529
	h	70.63	170.33	271.44	375.96	487.79	1249.3	1325.9	1389.6	1448.5	1504.4	1561.9	1618.4	1675.3	1732.5	1790.3
	s	0.1289	0.2928	0.4355	0.5647	0.6876	1.4457	1.5149	1.5677	1.6126	1.6530	1.6905	1.7256	1.7589	1.7905	1.8207
1100 (556.28)	v	0.0161	0.0166	0.0174	0.0185	0.0203	0.4531	0.5440	0.6188	0.6865	0.7505	0.8121	0.8723	0.9313	0.9894	1.0468
	h	70.90	170.56	271.63	376.08	487.75	1237.3	1318.8	1384.7	1444.7	1502.4	1559.4	1616.3	1673.5	1731.0	1789.0
	s	0.1289	0.2927	0.4353	0.5644	0.6872	1.4259	1.4996	1.5542	1.6000	1.6410	1.6787	1.7141	1.7475	1.7793	1.8097
1200 (567.19)	v	0.0161	0.0166	0.0174	0.0185	0.0203	0.4016	0.4905	0.5615	0.6250	0.6845	0.7418	0.7974	0.8519	0.9055	0.9584
	h	71.16	170.78	271.82	376.20	487.72	1224.2	1311.5	1379.7	1440.9	1499.4	1556.9	1614.2	1671.6	1729.4	1787.6
	s	0.1288	0.2926	0.4351	0.5642	0.6868	1.4061	1.4851	1.5415	1.5883	1.6298	1.6679	1.7035	1.7371	1.7691	1.7996
1400 (587.07)	v	0.0161	0.0166	0.0174	0.0185	0.0203	0.3176	0.4059	0.4712	0.5282	0.5809	0.6311	0.6798	0.7272	0.7737	0.8195
	h	71.68	171.24	272.19	376.44	487.65	1194.1	1296.1	1369.3	1433.2	1493.2	1551.8	1609.9	1668.0	1726.3	1785.0
	s	0.1287	0.2923	0.4348	0.5636	0.6859	1.3652	1.4575	1.5182	1.5670	1.6096	1.6484	1.6845	1.7185	1.7508	1.7815
1600 (604.87)	v	0.0161	0.0166	0.0173	0.0185	0.0202	0.0236	0.3415	0.4032	0.4555	0.5031	0.5482	0.5915	0.6336	0.6748	0.7153
	h	72.21	171.69	272.57	376.69	487.60	616.77	1279.4	1358.5	1425.2	1486.9	1546.6	1605.6	1664.3	1723.2	1782.3
	s	0.1286	0.2921	0.4344	0.5631	0.6851	0.8129	1.4312	1.4968	1.5478	1.5916	1.6312	1.6678	1.7022	1.7344	1.7657
1800 (621.02)	v	0.0160	0.0165	0.0173	0.0185	0.0202	0.0235	0.2906	0.3500	0.3988	0.4426	0.4836	0.5229	0.5609	0.5980	0.6343
	h	72.73	172.15	272.95	376.93	487.56	615.58	1261.1	1347.2	1417.1	1480.6	1541.1	1601.2	1660.7	1720.1	1779.7
	s	0.1284	0.2918	0.4341	0.5626	0.6843	0.8109	1.4054	1.4768	1.5302	1.5753	1.6156	1.6528	1.6876	1.7204	1.7516
2000 (635.80)	v	0.0160	0.0165	0.0173	0.0184	0.0201	0.0233	0.2488	0.3072	0.3534	0.3942	0.4320	0.4680	0.5027	0.5365	0.5695
	h	73.26	172.60	273.32	377.19	487.53	614.48	1240.9	1353.4	1408.7	1474.1	1536.2	1596.9	1657.0	1717.0	1777.1
	s	0.1283	0.2916	0.4337	0.5621	0.6834	0.8091	1.3794	1.4578	1.5138	1.5603	1.6014	1.6391	1.6743	1.7075	1.7389
2500 (668.11)	v	0.0160	0.0165	0.0173	0.0184	0.0200	0.0230	0.1681	0.2293	0.2712	0.3068	0.3390	0.3692	0.3980	0.4259	0.4529
	h	74.57	173.74	274.27	377.82	487.50	612.08	1176.7	1303.4	1386.7	1457.5	1522.9	1585.9	1647.8	1709.2	1770.4
	s	0.1280	0.2910	0.4329	0.5609	0.6815	0.8048	1.3076	1.4129	1.4766	1.5269	1.5703	1.6094	1.6456	1.6796	1.7116
3000 (695.33)	v	0.0160	0.0165	0.0172	0.0183	0.0200	0.0228	0.0982	0.1759	0.2161	0.2484	0.2770	0.3033	0.3282	0.3522	0.3753
	h	75.88	174.88	275.22	378.47	487.52	610.08	1060.5	1267.0	1363.2	1440.2	1509.4	1574.8	1638.5	1701.4	1761.8
	s	0.1277	0.2904	0.4320	0.5597	0.6796	0.8009	1.1966	1.3692	1.4429	1.4976	1.5434	1.5841	1.6214	1.6561	1.6888
3200 (705.08)	v	0.0160	0.0165	0.0172	0.0183	0.0199	0.0227	0.0335	0.1588	0.1987	0.2301	0.2576	0.2827	0.3065	0.3291	0.3510
	h	76.4	175.3	275.6	378.7	487.5	609.4	800.8	1250.9	1353.4	1433.1	1503.8	1570.3	1634.8	1698.3	1761.2
	s	0.1276	0.2902	0.4317	0.5592	0.6788	0.7994	0.9708	1.3515	1.4300	1.4866	1.5335	1.5749	1.6126	1.6477	1.6806
3500	v	0.0160	0.0164	0.0172	0.0183	0.0199	0.0225	0.0307	0.1364	0.1764	0.2066	0.2326	0.2563	0.2784	0.2995	0.3198
	h	77.2	176.0	276.2	379.1	487.6	608.4	779.4	1224.6	1338.2	1422.2	1495.5	1563.3	1629.2	1693.6	1757.2
	s	0.1274	0.2899	0.4312	0.5585	0.6777	0.7973	0.9508	1.3242	1.4112	1.4709	1.5194	1.5618	1.6002	1.6358	1.6691
4000	v	0.0159	0.0164	0.0172	0.0182	0.0198	0.0223	0.0287	0.1052	0.1463	0.1752	0.1994	0.2210	0.2411	0.2601	0.2783
	h	78.5	177.2	277.1	379.8	487.7	606.9	763.0	1174.3	1311.6	1403.6	1481.3	1552.2	1619.8	1685.7	1750.6
	s	0.1271	0.2893	0.4304	0.5573	0.6760	0.7940	0.9343	1.2754	1.3807	1.4461	1.4976	1.5417	1.5812	1.6177	1.6516
5000	v	0.0159	0.0164	0.0171	0.0181	0.0196	0.0219	0.0268	0.0591	0.1038	0.1312	0.1529	0.1718	0.1890	0.2050	0.2203
	h	81.1	179.5	279.1	381.2	488.1	604.6	746.0	1042.9	1252.9	1364.6	1452.1	1529.1	1600.9	1670.0	1737.4
	s	0.1265	0.2881	0.4287	0.5550	0.6726	0.7880	0.9153	1.1593	1.3207	1.4001	1.4582	1.5061	1.5481	1.5863	1.6216
6000	v	0.0159	0.0163	0.0170	0.0180	0.0195	0.0216	0.0256	0.0397	0.0757	0.1020	0.1221	0.1391	0.1544	0.1684	0.1817
	h	83.7	181.7	281.0	382.7	488.6	602.9	736.1	945.1	1188.8	1323.6	1422.3	1505.9	1582.0	1654.2	1724.2
	s	0.1258	0.2870	0.4271	0.5528	0.6693	0.7826	0.9026	1.0176	1.2615	1.3574	1.4229	1.4748	1.5194	1.5593	1.5962
7000	v	0.0158	0.0163	0.0170	0.0180	0.0193	0.0213	0.0248	0.0334	0.0573	0.0816	0.1004	0.1160	0.1298	0.1424	0.1542
	h	86.2	184.4	283.0	384.2	489.3	601.7	729.3	901.8	1124.9	1281.7	1392.2	1482.6	1563.1	1638.6	1711.1
	s	0.1252	0.2859	0.4256	0.5507	0.6663	0.7777	0.8926	1.0350	1.2055	1.3171	1.3904	1.4466	1.4938	1.5355	1.5735

(3)
$$\text{Force} = \frac{\text{mass} \times \text{acceleration}}{g_c}$$

When a one-lb force is exerted on a one-lb mass in the earth's gravitational field with acceleration of 32.17, we can write

$$1 \text{ lb force} = \frac{1 \text{ lb mass} \times 32.17 \text{ ft/sec}^2}{g_c}$$

and $\qquad g_c = 32.17$ ft lb mass/lb force, sec^2

Many current texts use the expressions lbf to designate lb force and lbm to designate lb mass. This is not done in this text because it is believed that the meaning is generally clear simply by using lb. As examples, the expression Btu/lb always means Btu/lb mass, and the expression ft lb/lb always means ft lb force/lb mass.

Application of the energy equation (1) or (2) requires dimensional consistency of all terms, and proper dimensional conversion constants are inserted as coefficients where required. For example, the terms u and Q, usually expressed in Btu/lb, may be converted to the equivalent ft lb/lb when multiplied by J, the mechanical equivalent of heat. Joule's experiments between 1843 and 1878, based on the conservation of energy, actually measured this conversion constant. Today, the international Btu/lb mass is defined as 2.326 Joules/g. Using this number, together with $g_c = 980.665$ cm/sec^2 (adopted 1901) or 32.17 ft/sec^2, results in:

(4) $\qquad 1 \text{ Btu} = 778.17$ ft lb force

Particular attention is called to the sign convention applied to heat and work quantities. In keeping with the concept that changes in stored energy are the manifestation of differences in heat and work effects (equation 1), heat quantities are positive when entering the system and shaft work is positive when leaving the system. Neither heat nor work are properties of the fluid or working medium but properties of the process as previously noted and are dependent on the process or path of integration. This integration in turn will determine whether the exchange is into or out of the system.

Since both u and pv of equation (2) are stored energy, they are system properties and their sum is also a property. Moreover they are both functions of the state variables and cannot be changed independently like the other two terms of stored energy. For this reason it is customary and convenient to consider the sum $(u + pv)$ as a single property h, called enthalpy.

(5) $\qquad h = u + pv$

In the application of steam, h is usually expressed in Btu/lb although other consistent units may be used. The following examples illustrate the application of the steady-state open-system energy equation (2) and the usefulness of enthalpy in the energy balance of specific equipment.

A) Steam turbine

In most practical cases ΔZ, ΔV and Q from throttle, 1, to exhaust, 2, (Fig. 2) are small compared to $h_1 - h_2$. This reduces energy equation (2) to:

$$u_2 + p_2 v_2/J - u_1 - p_1 v_1/J = -W_k/J$$

or (6) $\quad h_1 - h_2 = W_k/J$, Btu/lb

From (6) it is evident that the work done, W_k/J, for the steam turbine is equal to the differences between enthalpy, h_1, of the steam entering and enthalpy, h_2, of the steam leaving. However, it is seldom that both h_1 and h_2 are known, and further description of the process is required for a numerical solution of most problems.

B) Steam boiler

Since the boiler does no work, $W_k = 0$; and since ΔZ and ΔV from feedwater inlet, 1, to steam outlet, 2, are small compared to $h_1 - h_2$, (2) becomes:

$$u_2 + p_2 v_2/J - u_1 - p_1 v_1/J = Q$$

or (7) $\qquad Q = h_2 - h_1$, Btu/lb

Based on (7) the heat added, Q (positive), in the boiler per lb of feed is equal to the difference between h_2 of the steam leaving and h_1 of the feedwater entering. In this case the qualifying condition is a constant pressure process at the drum pressure. Equation (7) can then be solved knowing either of the two state variables (T or V) for points 1 and 2.

C) Water flow through a nozzle

For water flowing through a nozzle, the change in specific volume, Δv, is negligible. If also the change in elevation head, ΔZ, the change in internal energy, Δu, the work done, W_k, and the heat added, Q, are all negligible, equation (2) reduces to:

$$p_2 v_1 - p_1 v_1 + V_2^2/2g_c - V_1^2/2g_c = 0$$

or (8) $\quad V_2^2/2g_c - V_1^2/2g_c = (p_1 - p_2)v$, ft lb/lb

The increase in kinetic energy of the water is given in equation (8) for the pressure drop, $p_1 - p_2$. If the velocity of approach, V_1, is zero, equation (8) becomes:

$$V_2^2/2g_c = (p_1 - p_2)v, \text{ ft lb/lb}$$

or (9) $\qquad V_2 = \sqrt{2g_c(p_1 - p_2)v}$, ft/sec

The quantity $(p_1 - p_2)v$ is often referred to as the static head, H:

(10) $\qquad (p_1 - p_2)v = H$, ft lb/lb

By substituting H in equation (9) for its equivalent value $(p_1 - p_2)v$ from equation (10), the velocity of the jet becomes:

(11) $\qquad V_2 = \sqrt{2g_cH} = 8.02\sqrt{H}$, ft/sec

D) Flow of a compressible fluid through a nozzle

When steam, air or any other compressible fluid flows through a nozzle, the changes in the specific volume, Δv, and internal energy, Δu, are not negligible. If there is no change in elevation head, ΔZ, equation (2) becomes:

$$u_2 + p_2 v_2/J - u_1 - p_1 v_1/J + V_2^2/2g_cJ - V_1^2/2g_cJ = 0$$

or (12) $\quad V_2^2/2g_cJ - V_1^2/2g_cJ = h_1 - h_2$, Btu/lb

If the velocity of approach, V_1, is zero,

$$V_2^2/2g_cJ = h_1 - h_2$$

or (13) $\qquad V_2 = \sqrt{2g_cJ(h_1 - h_2)}$, ft/sec

From equation (13) it is evident that the jet velocity of a compressible fluid, such as steam or air, is a function of the enthalpies (h_1 and h_2) of the fluid entering and leaving the nozzle. This equation may be reduced to:

(14) $\qquad V_2 = 223.9\sqrt{h_1 - h_2}$, ft/sec

The same qualifying statements used under (A) also apply to this case.

E) Compressor

If a compressible fluid moves through an adiabatic compressor ($Q = 0$) and the change in elevational head, ΔZ, and the change in velocity, ΔV, are small compared to $h_2 - h_1$, equation (2) reduces to:

$$u_2 + p_2v_2/J - u_1 - p_1v_1/J = -W_k/J$$

or (15) $-W_k/J = h_2 - h_1$, Btu/lb

Note that W_k is negative, in keeping with the sign convention. Application of (15) is also subject to the same restriction as (6) and (14).

F) Pump

When an incompressible fluid, such as water, is substituted in (E), the change in specific volume, ΔV, is zero and internal energy changes, Δu, are zero for zero fluid friction, the energy equation (2) reduces to:

$$p_2v - p_1v = -W_k$$

or (16) $\qquad -W_k = (p_2 - p_1)v$, ft lb/lb

Since $(p_2 - p_1)\,v = H$, the pressure difference in ft of fluid flowing, equation (16) becomes:

(17) $\qquad -W_k = H$, ft lb/lb or ft

Because all real fluids are in fact compressible, it is important to know what is implied by the term incompressible. The meaning here is that the isothermal compressibility given by:

(18) $\qquad k_T = -\dfrac{1}{v}\left(\dfrac{\partial v}{\partial p}\right)_T$

may be assumed arbitrarily small approaching zero. This in turn implies that since neither v nor p are zero, ∂v must be zero and v a constant. Also, for isothermal conditions (by definition) there can be no change in u due to pressure changes only.

Laws of thermodynamics

Examples (A) through (F) in the foregoing illustrate applications of the energy balance in problems utilizing a fluid for heat transfer and shaft work. They also demonstrate the usefulness and convenience of the property of enthalpy. However, as pointed out in case (A) it is seldom that both h_1 and h_2 are known. Generally p_1, T_1 and p_2 are specified and h_1 can be found from the steam tables knowing p_1 and T_1. On the other hand, more information is required to establish h_2. If T_2 were an independent variable and its selection arbitrary, there would be an infinite number of solutions. This is contrary to experience. The answer lies in the combined principles of the first and second laws of thermodynamics and their consequences.

First law

The first law of thermodynamics is based on the conservation law expressed in equation (1) and, by convention, relates the heat and work quantities of this equation to internally stored energy, u. Only internal energy, u, and externally stored energy, pv, of equation (1) are directly affected by heat flow. Heat added to a system will not change the potential energy of its mass in a gravitational field nor will it affect the kinetic energy of this mass as a whole unless it is first converted to work. It is convenient to express the first law in the following form:

(19) $\qquad \Delta u = Q - W_k$

Second law

Although the first law treats heat and work as interchangeable, it is also a matter of experience that certain qualifications apply. Briefly, all forms of energy including the transient form, work, can be wholly converted to heat, but the converse is not generally true. Given a source of heat coupled with a heat-work cycle, such as heat released by high-temperature combustion in a steam power plant, only a portion of this heat can be converted to work. The rest must be rejected as heat to the stored energy of a sink at lower temperature, such as the atmosphere. This is in essence the Kelvin statement of the second law of thermodynamics. It can also be shown that it is equivalent to the Clausius statement that heat, in the absence of some form of external assistance, can only flow from a hotter to a colder body.

Entropy

Heat flow, like work, being energy in transit, is a function of a potential difference. The potential is easily recognized as temperature. If a quantity of heat is divided by its absolute temperature, the quotient can be considered a type of distribution property or factor complementing the intensity factor of temperature. Such a property, proposed and named entropy by Clausius, is widely used in all branches of thermodynamics because of its close relationship to the second law.

Rather than attempt to define entropy (Symbol S) in an absolute sense, which is the problem of the third law of thermodynamics, it will suffice to explain the significance of differences in this property given by:

(20) $\qquad S_2 - S_1 = \Delta S = \displaystyle\int_1^2 \frac{\delta(Q_{\mathrm{rev}})}{T} \times \left(\begin{array}{c}\text{total}\\\text{system}\\\text{mass}\end{array}\right)$

where:

ΔS = change in entropy, Btu/R

Q_{rev} = reversible heat flow between thermodynamic equilibrium states of the system, 1 and 2 (Fig. 2), Btu/lb

T = absolute temperature, R

Entropy, S, is an extensive property. By dividing by the total mass of the system, it is converted to an inten-

sive property, s, which is also referred to as entropy, although the term "specific entropy" is more rigid.

Reversible and irreversible processes

Reversible thermodynamic processes exist in theory only, but serve an important function of limiting cases for heat flow and work processes which may be represented as total differentials. Reversible thermodynamic processes are confined to paths that describe continuous functional relationships on coordinate systems of thermodynamic properties. These properties, in turn, are homogenous in the sense that there are no variations between any sub-regions of the system. Moreover, during interchanges of heat or work between a system and its surroundings, only corresponding potential gradients of infinitesimal magnitude may exist.

Use of the symbol "δ," instead of the usual differential operator "d," is intended as a reminder that Q depends on the process and is not a property of the system (steam). δQ represents only a small quantity, not a differential. Before (20) is integrated, Q_{rev} must be expressed in terms of properties and a reversible path specified between the prescribed initial and final equilibrium states of the system. For example, when heat flow is reversible and at constant pressure, $Q_{\text{rev}} = c_p dT$. This may represent heat added reversibly to the system from the surroundings, as in a boiler, or the equivalent of internal heat flows due to friction or other irreversibilities. In these two cases ΔS is always positive.

The same qualifications for δ hold in the case of thermodynamic work. There being no exact differential dW_k, small quantities of W_k similar in magnitude to differentials are expressed as δW_k.

All actual processes are classed as irreversible. To occur, they must be under the influence of a finite potential difference measurably different than zero. A temperature difference supplies this drive and direction for heat flow. The work term, on the other hand, is more complicated since there are as many different potentials (generalized forces) as there are forms of work. However, the main concern here is expansion work for which the potential is clearly a pressure difference.

Regardless of whether a process defined for a particular problem is to be considered reversible or accepted as irreversible, it must have specified limits for its solution. Applications of the first and second laws, to follow, require that these limits be equilibrium states. Non-equilibrium thermodynamics is a subject beyond the scope of this chapter. Since the limits of real processes are to be equilibrium states, any process can be approximated by a series of stepwise reversible processes starting and ending at the same states as the real processes. In this way, only equilibrium conditions are considered and the substitute processes can be defined in terms of the system properties. The following table lists the reversible processes for Q and W_k:

Reversible Heat Flow	Reversible Work
Constant pressure, $dp = 0$	Constant pressure, $dp = 0$
Constant temperature, $dT = 0$	Constant temperature, $dT = 0$
Constant volume, $dv = 0$ $W_k = 0$	Constant entropy, $ds = 0$ $Q = 0$

The combined first and second laws, substituting $\delta(Q_{\text{rev}}) = Tds$ for δQ in (19), is:

$$(21) \qquad du = Tds - \delta W_k$$

Since only reversible processes are to be used, δW_k should also be selected with this restriction. Reversible work for the limited case of expansion work can be shown to be:

$$(22) \qquad \delta(W_{\text{rev}}) = pdv$$

Here pressure is in complete equilibrium with external forces acting on the system and is related to v through an equation of state.

Substituting (22) in (21), the combined expression for the first and second laws becomes:

$$(23) \qquad du = Tds - pdv$$

Equation 23, however, applies to a system in which the reversible expansion work is reflected entirely as shaft work. In order to modify this expression for a process where shaft work is the result of a difference between expansion or non-flow work, $(-pdv)$, and flow work, $d(pv)$, the quantity $d(pv)$ is added as externally stored energy to internal energy (du) on the left-hand side of (23) and added as $(pdv + vdp)$ to the expansion work $(-pdv)$ on the right-hand side. The result is:

$$du + d(pv) = Tds - pdv + pdv + vdp$$

$$\text{or} \quad (24) \quad dh = Tds + vdp$$

The work term vdp in (24) now represents reversible shaft work in an open system.

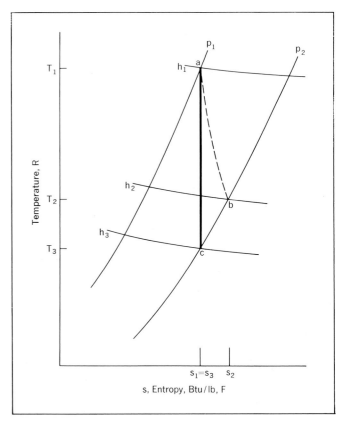

Fig. 3 Irreversible expansion, state a to state b.

Since Tds in equation (24) is equivalent to δQ, its value becomes zero in the case of zero heat transfer to or from the surroundings ($\delta Q = 0$). Since T cannot be zero, it follows that $ds = 0$ and s is constant. Therefore, the maximum possible work from stored energy in an open system during a reversible adiabatic expansion is $\int v\,dp$ at constant entropy. (The term adiabatic refers to zero heat flow between the system and its surroundings.) The work done is equal to the decrease in enthalpy. Likewise for the closed system, the maximum expansion work is $-\int p\,dv$ at constant entropy, equal to the decrease in internal energy. These are important cases of an adiabatic isentropic expansion. Under the section "Work Functions," it is shown how the combined laws can be used to solve problems of reversible work other than expansion work.

The substitution of reversible processes for real processes is illustrated in Fig. 3, which represents the adiabatic expansion of steam in a steam turbine, or any gas expanded from p_1 to p_2 in order to produce shaft work (see Example A, Energy Equations). T_1, p_1 and p_2 are given. The value of h_1 is fixed by T_1 and p_1 for the single-phase problem (vapor) and may be found from the steam tables, a T-s diagram such as Fig. 3 or, more convenient for general use, an h-s diagram or Mollier Chart (see frontispiece to this chapter). From the combined first and second laws it is established that the maximum energy available for work in an adiabatic open system is $h_1 - h_3$ (Fig. 3) where h_3 is found by the adiabatic isentropic expansion (expansion at constant entropy so that $\Delta s = 0$) from p_1 to p_2. It is also a matter of experience that a portion of this available energy, usually about 10 to 15 percent will represent lost work (W_L) of friction and shock, limiting the Δh for shaft work to $h_1 - h_2$. The two reversible paths used to arrive at point b are ac at constant s and cb at constant pressure:

$$(h_1 - h_3) + (h_3 - h_2) = h_1 - h_2$$

Point b now fixes T_2 as well as h_2 and both v_1 and v_2 are available from tabulated values of v, not shown in the figure.

It is of interest to note that Δh_{3-2} can be found from:

$$(25) \qquad \Delta h_{3-2} = \int_2^3 T\,ds$$

or graphically, the area on the T-s diagram (Fig. 3) under the curve p_2 from c to b. Areas bounded by reversible paths on the T-s diagram in general represent Q or heat flow between the system and its surroundings. In this case, however, the path ab is irreversible and the area under ab has no significance. For that matter the area under cb, although it has the form of a reversible quantity, Q, does not represent heat added to the system but its equivalent in internal heat flow. A similar situation applies to the relationship between work and areas under reversible paths on a pv diagram. Considerable care must be exercised in using any graphical interpretation of these areas in cycle analysis.

Returning to Fig. 3 and the path ab, W_L was taken as a percentage of ac. In general the problem should be handled in a stepwise manner (Fig. 4) for the following reason. Point b has a higher enthalpy than point c and, if expansion to a pressure lower than p_2 (Fig. 3) is pos-

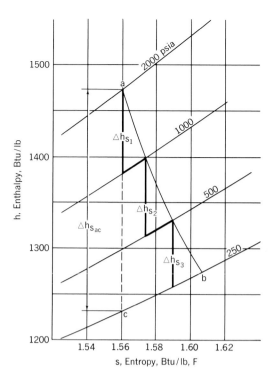

Fig. 4 Three-stage irreversible expansion
$$\Delta h_{s_1} + \Delta h_{s_2} + \Delta h_{s_3} > \Delta h_{s_{ac}}$$

sible, the available energy for this additional expansion is greater than that at point c. In other words a portion of the W_L for the first expansion can be recovered in the next expansion or stage. This is the basis of the reheat factor used in analyzing expansions through a multistage turbine. As the pressure curves are divergent on an h-s or T-s diagram, the sum of the individual Δh_s values (isentropic Δh) for individual increments of Δp or stages in an irreversible expansion is greater than the reversible Δh_s between initial and final pressures (Fig. 4).

Increases in entropy

Although equation (20) gives a quantitative meaning to entropy, there are qualitative aspects of this property which deserve special emphasis. Increases in entropy are a measure of that portion of heat involved in a process which is unavailable for conversion to work. For example, consider the constant pressure reversible addition of heat to a working fluid with the resulting increase in entropy of the system. The minimum portion of this heat flow which is unavailable for shaft work is equal to the entropy increase multiplied by the absolute temperature of the sink to which a part of the heat must be rejected in accordance with the second law. However, inasmuch as reversible addition of heat is not possible, there will also exist additional entropy increases due to internal heat flows as a result of necessary temperature gradients and fluid friction.

Even though the net entropy change in any system executing a cycle of processes is always zero because the cycle requires restoration of all properties to some designated starting point, the sum of all entropy increases has a special significance. These increases in entropy, less any decreases due to recycled heat within a regenerator, multiplied by the appropriate sink temperature (R) are

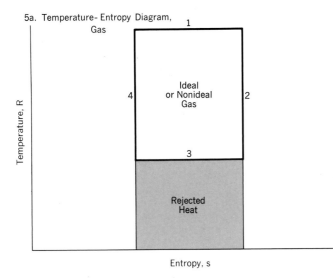

5a. Temperature-Entropy Diagram, Gas

5b. Temperature-Entropy Diagram, Saturated Vapor

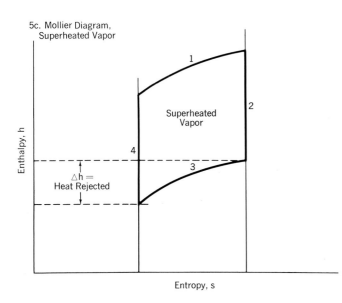

5c. Mollier Diagram, Superheated Vapor

Fig. 5 Carnot cycles.

equal to the heat flow to the sink. In this case the net change of entropy of the system is zero but there is an increase in entropy of the surroundings. Any thermodynamic change which takes place, whether it is a one-time process or cycle of processes, results in a net entropy increase when both the system and its surroundings are considered.

Cycles

Up to this point only thermodynamic processes have been discussed with minor references to the cycle. The next step is to couple processes in some special way in order that heat may be converted to useful work on a more or less continuous basis. This is done by selectively arranging a series of thermodynamic processes in a cycle forming a closed curve on any system of thermodynamic coordinates. Since the main interest here is steam, the following discussion emphasizes expansion or pdv work. This is in keeping with the limited differential expressions given for internal energy (23) and enthalpy (24), although in the broader sense, the subject of thermodynamics recognizes work as energy in transit under any potential other than differential temperature and electromagnetic radiation.

Carnot cycle

We are indebted to Sadi Carnot (1824) for the concepts of the cycle and reversible processes. In fact the "Carnot cycle," so named in his honor, is still used as a comparison for heat engine performance. This cycle, on a temperature-entropy diagram, is shown in Fig. 5a for any gas and in Fig. 5b for a two-phase saturated vapor. Fig. 5c presents this cycle for a nonideal gas such as superheated steam, on Mollier coordinates (entropy vs. enthalpy).

The Carnot cycle consists of the following processes:

1. Heat added to the working medium at constant temperature ($dT = 0$) from an appropriate heat source resulting in expansion work and changes in enthalpy. (For an ideal gas, changes in internal energy and pv are zero and, therefore, changes in enthalpy are zero.)
2. Adiabatic isentropic expansion ($ds = 0$) with expansion work and an equivalent decrease in enthalpy.
3. Constant temperature heat rejection to the surroundings equivalent to the compression work and any changes in enthalpy.
4. Adiabatic isentropic compression back to the starting temperature with compression work and an equivalent increase in enthalpy.

This cycle has no counterpart in practice. The only way to carry out the constant temperature processes in a single-phase system would be to approximate them through a series of isentropic expansions and constant pressure reheats for heat addition and isentropic compressions with a series of intercoolers for heat rejection. Another serious disadvantage of a Carnot gas engine would be the small ratio of net work to gross work (net work refers to the difference between the work of expansion, gross work, and the work of compression). Even a two-phase cycle, such as Fig. 5b, would be subject to the practical difficulties of wet compression and, to a lesser extent, wet expansion.

Nevertheless, the Carnot cycle clearly illustrates the basic principles of thermodynamics. Since the processes are reversible, the Carnot cycle offers maximum thermal efficiency attainable between any given temperatures of heat source and sink. Moreover, this thermal efficiency depends only on these temperatures:

$$(26) \qquad \eta = \frac{T_1 - T_2}{T_1} = 1 - \frac{T_2}{T_1}$$

where:

η = thermal efficiency of heat-to-work conversion.
T_1 = absolute temperature of heat source, R.
T_2 = absolute temperature of heat sink, R.

The efficiency statement of (26) can be extended to cover all reversible cycles where T_1 and T_2 are defined as mean temperatures found by dividing the heats added and rejected reversibly by the Δs in each case. For this reason it can be stated that all reversible cycles have the same efficiencies when considered between the same mean temperature limits of heat source and heat sink.

Rankine cycle

Early thermodynamic developments were centered around the performance of steam engines and, for comparison purposes, it was natural to select a reversible cycle which more nearly approximated the processes related to its operation. The Rankine cycle shown in Fig. 6, proposed independently by Rankine and Clausius, meets this objective. All steps are specified for the system only (working medium) and carried out reversibly in the vapor, liquid and two-phase states as indicated in the figure. Liquid is compressed isentropically from a to b. From b to c heat is added reversibly in the compressed liquid, two-phase and superheat states. Isentropic expansion with shaft work output takes place from c to d and unavailable heat is rejected to the atmospheric sink from d to a.

The main feature of the Rankine cycle is compression confined to the liquid phase only, avoiding the high compression work and mechanical problems of a corresponding Carnot cycle with two-phase compression. This part of the cycle from a to b in Fig. 6 is greatly exaggerated since the difference between the saturated liquid line and reversible heat addition to compressed liquid is too small to show in proper scale. For example, the temperature rise with isentropic compression of water from saturation temperature of 212F and one atmosphere to 1000 psia is less than 1.0F.

If the Rankine cycle is closed in the sense that the same fluid repeatedly executes the various processes, it is termed a condensing cycle. Although the closed condensing Rankine cycle was developed to improve steam engine efficiency, a closed cycle is essential for any toxic or hazardous working fluid. Steam has the important advantage of being inherently safe in these categories. However, close control of water chemistry required in high-pressure high-temperature power cycles also makes it desirable to recirculate steam condensate using a minimum of makeup. (Makeup is used to define water added to the steam cycle to replace leakage and any other withdrawals.) Open steam cycles are still found in small unit sizes and some special process and heating load

applications coupled with power. Usually the condensate from process and heating loads is returned to the power cycle for economic reasons.

The higher efficiency of the condensing steam cycle is a result of the particular pressure-temperature relationship between water and its vapor state, steam. The lowest temperature at which an open or noncondensing steam cycle may reject heat is approximately the saturation temperature of 672R (212F). This corresponds to normal atmospheric pressure of 14.7 psia. The closed or condensing cycle takes advantage of the much lower sink temperature for heat rejection available in natural bodies of water and the atmosphere. Being closed, the back pressure is no longer limited to normal atmospheric pressure but rather to saturation pressure corresponding to a condensing temperature in the neighborhood of 100F and lower. Because the maximum possible pdv work per lb of a compressible fluid is directly related to a function of the pressure ratio available for expansion, as well as the initial absolute temperature, an increase in this pressure ratio means an increase in the available work. A condensing cycle with 1.5 in. Hg absolute pressure in the condenser and starting with the same initial pressure, will have a pressure ratio twenty times greater than the noncondensing cycle expanding to the atmosphere.

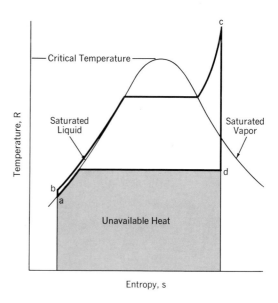

Fig. 6 Temperature-entropy diagram of the ideal Rankine cycle.

Fig. 7 illustrates the difference between an open and closed Rankine cycle (non-ideal) superheated steam. Liquid compression takes place from a to b and heat is added from b to c. The work and heat quantities involved in each of these processes are the same for both cycles. Expansion, and conversion of stored energy to work, is from c to d' for the open cycle and c to d for the closed cycle. Since this process is shown for the irreversible case, there is internal heat flow and an increase in entropy. From d' to a and d to a, heat is rejected. Because this last portion of the two cycles is shown as reversible, the shaded areas are proportional to rejected heat. The larger amount of rejected heat for the open cycle is clearly indicated.

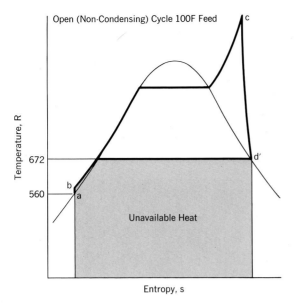

Open (Non-Condensing) Cycle 100F Feed

Temperature, R

672

560

b

a

Unavailable Heat

Entropy, s

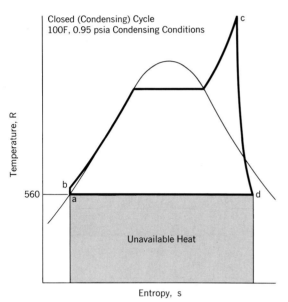

Closed (Condensing) Cycle
100F, 0.95 psia Condensing Conditions

Temperature, R

560

b

a

d

Unavailable Heat

Entropy, s

Fig. 7 Rankine cycles.

Regenerative Rankine cycle

The reversible cycle efficiency given by equation (26), where T_2 and T_1 are mean absolute temperatures for rejecting and adding heat respectively, indicates only three choices for improving ideal cycle efficiency; decreasing T_2, increasing T_1 or both. Not much can be done to reduce T_2 in the Rankine cycle because of the limitations imposed by the normal temperatures of available sinks for rejected heat. There is some leeway available by selecting variable condenser pressures for the very large units with two or more exhaust hoods, since the lowest temperature in a condenser is set by the exit temperature of the cooling water. On the other hand there are many ways to increase T_1 even though the maximum steam temperature may be limited by the materials problems of high temperature corrosion and allowable stress also at elevated temperatures.

One early improvement to the Rankine cycle was the adoption of regenerative feedwater heating. This is done by extracting steam at various stages in the turbine to heat the feedwater as it is pumped from the hot well to the boiler economizer.

Fig. 8 is a cycle diagram of a widely used supercritical steam cycle showing schematically the arrangement of various components including the feedwater heaters. This cycle also employs one stage of steam reheat which is still another method of increasing the mean T_1. Regardless of whether the cycle is high temperature, high pressure or reheat, regeneration is used in all modern condensing steam power plants. It not only improves cycle efficiency but has other advantages, among which are lower volume flow in the final turbine stages and a convenient means of deaerating the feed. The steam power-cycle diagram of Fig. 8 includes a heat-source system which is the combustion products of a fossil fuel. Stored energy is released as heat by the combustion of fuel with air and a portion is then transferred in the boiler for generating and superheating steam. The remaining heat is discharged to the surroundings as indicated. This part of the system also incorporates the principle of regeneration in an air heater to recycle low level (low temperature) heat from the combustion gases which would otherwise be rejected to the atmosphere as an increase in stack loss. Because of the higher feedwater temperatures entering the economizer of a boiler supplying steam to a regenerative Rankine cycle, the amount of low level heat in combustion gases that can be transferred directly to the steam cycle is limited. In other words, these two types of regeneration are not entirely independent with respect to the overall effect on cycle efficiency.

The air heater as a regenerator uses low level heat which otherwise would be rejected from the cycle. Feedwater heaters, on the other hand, utilize heat which could have been partially converted to work by further expansion through the turbine. Both types of regeneration will increase cycle efficiency as long as they can show a net decrease in the entropy production for the system and its surroundings.

The temperature-entropy diagram of Fig. 9 for the steam cycle of Fig. 8 illustrates how the principle of regeneration works in increasing the mean temperature level for heat addition. Instead of heat input starting at the hot well temperature of 91.7F, the lowest temperature for heat addition from the combustion process has been raised to 550F by the bleed heaters.

This same diagram of Fig. 9 also shows that the mean temperature level for heat addition is increased by reheating steam. Where maximum temperatures are limited by physical or economic reasons, reheating after partial expansion of the working fluid can be substituted as an effective means of raising the average T_1. The hypothetical case of an infinite number of reheat and expansion stages approaches a constant temperature heat addition, at least in the superheat region which may in turn be established at the maximum permissible temperature limit of the working medium or its containment. On the other hand, merely increasing T_1 may not improve efficiency. If the entropy increase accompanying reheat causes the final expansion process to terminate in superheated vapor, the mean temperature for heat rejection, T_2, has also been increased unless the superheat can be extracted in a regenerator adding heat to the boiler feed-

water. Such a regenerator would have to operate at the expense of the very effective bleed cycle. All of these factors, plus component design problems, must be considered in any cycle analysis where the objective is to optimize the combination of physical and economic limits, and fuel economy. Overall cycle characteristics, including efficiency, are illustrated more clearly by plotting on a Mollier chart. (*See Fig. 11 and Steam Cycle for Nuclear Plant.*)

The procedure used in preparing Fig. 9 deserves special comment since it illustrates an important function of entropy as a property. All processes on the diagram represent total entropies divided by the high-pressure steam flow rate. Total entropies at any point of the cycle are the product of the flow rate at that point and the entropy per pound corresponding to the pressure, temperature and state of the steam. If a point falls in the two-phase region (wet-steam zone), entropy is calculated from values in the steam tables in the same manner as enthalpy. In either case the value for evaporation is multiplied by the steam quality (fraction of uncondensed steam) and added to the value for water at saturation conditions.

Since there are different flow rates for the various processes of the cycle, small sections of individual *T-s* diagrams are superimposed in Fig. 9 on a base diagram identified by saturated liquid and vapor parameters.

This base actually applies only to those parts of the cycle representing heat addition to high pressure steam and the expansion of this steam down to the first bleed point in the high pressure turbine. At each bleed point the expansion line should show a decrease in entropy due to reduced flow entering the next turbine stage. However, for convenience, the individual "step-backs" in the expansion lines have been shifted to the right in order to show the high pressure steam expansion as one continuous process. The expansion of the reheated steam has also been treated in the same way.

Feedwater heating through the regenerators and compression by the pumps (represented by the zigzag lines in Fig. 9) result in a net increase in entropy. However, two factors are involved — an increase in entropy from the heat added to the feed and a decrease resulting from condensing and cooling the bleed steam and drain flows from higher pressure heaters.

For example, the feedwater heater just before the deaerating heater heats 5,436,519 lb/hr feed from 188.5F to 239.9F. This increases the enthalpy, h, of the feed from 156.4 to 207.1 and the entropy, s, from 0.2762 to 0.3530. The total increase in entropy per lb of high pressure steam flow of 7,860,371 lb/hr is:

$$(0.3530 - 0.2762) \times 5,436,519 \div 7,860,371$$
$$= 0.0531 \text{ Btu/lb, F}$$

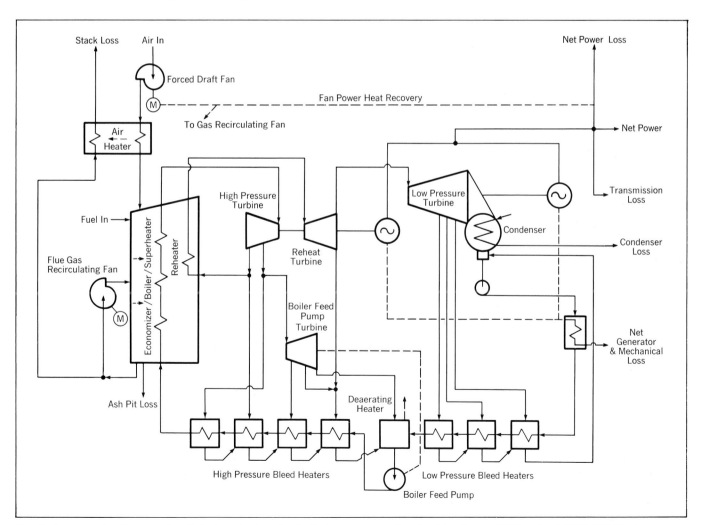

Fig. 8 Power cycle diagram, fossil fuel — single reheat, 8-stage regenerative feed heating — 3515 psia, 1000F/1000F steam.

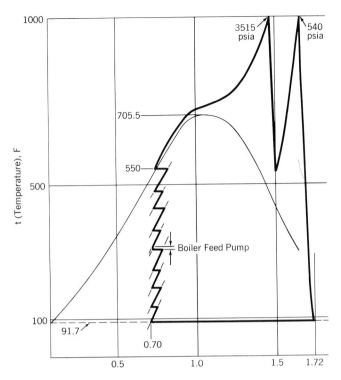

Fig. 9 Steam cycle for fossil fuel — temperature-entropy diagram — single reheat, 8-stage regenerative feed heating — 3515 psia, 1000F/1000F steam. (See pages 2-14 and 2-15.)

Feed temperature rises 51.4F and total heat absorbed is:

$$(207.1 - 156.4) \times 5,436,519 = 275,631,900 \text{ Btu/hr}$$

On the heat-source side of the balance 263,238 lb/hr of steam are bled from the low pressure turbine at 29.1 psia, 1213.2 h and 1.7680 s. This steam is desuperheated, condensed and cooled to:

$$1213.2 - 275,631,900 \div 263,238$$
$$= 166.1 \text{ Btu/lb, at } 198.5F$$

The corresponding entropy of the heater drain is 0.2915 s. Therefore, the entropy decrease is:

$$(1.7680 - 0.2915) \times 263,238 \div 7,860,371$$
$$= 0.0494 \text{ Btu/lb, F}$$

This heater shows a net increase in entropy of 0.0531 − 0.0494 = 0.0037 Btu/lb, F which is a measure of available heat energy loss due to pressure drop required for flow and temperature difference necessary for heat transfer. The product of this entropy increase and the absolute temperature of the sink for receiving rejected heat represents heat rendered unavailable for work by the internal heat flows of irreversible processes.

Available energy. From the foregoing it can be stated that, associated with the property enthalpy, there is a derived quantity, formed by the product of the corresponding entropy and the absolute temperature of the available heat sink, which has the nature of a property. This is the minimum unavailable heat flow to the sink whenever work is extracted from enthalpy. The difference between h (enthalpy) and T_0s is another derived quantity called available energy.

$$(27) \qquad e = h - T_0s$$

where:

e = maximum energy available (sometimes called exergy) from h for useful work, Btu/lb
h = enthalpy, Btu/lb
T_0 = sink absolute temperature, R
s = entropy, Btu/lb, R

The available and unavailable energy are not properties since they are not completely defined by an equation of state but are also dependent on the sink temperature.

Available energy is useful in cycle analysis for optimizing the thermal performance of the various component pieces of equipment relative to overall cycle efficiency. In this way small controllable changes in availability may be weighed against larger fixed unavailable heat quantities which are inherent to the cycle. As an example, an increased pressure drop through a heat exchanger may reduce surface but it also increases capitalized fuel cost by reducing efficiency.

Steam cycle for nuclear plant

Fig. 10 illustrates a Rankine cycle whose thermal energy source is a nuclear steam system. High pressure cooling water (primary loop) from a pressurized water reactor is circulated through a once-through steam generator (boiler) which, in turn, supplies steam for the turbine (see Chapter 21). In this way heat from the fission process absorbed in the primary loop is transferred through the tubes of the steam generator to generate steam at 925 psia on the low-pressure side of the steam generator and superheat it to 570F. This steam is delivered to the high pressure turbine at 900 psia and 566F.

Pressure limitations and especially temperature limitations required for a nuclear reactor mean that expansion lines of the power cycle lie largely in the region of wet steam, in other words, a saturated or nearly saturated steam cycle. The expansion lines for the cycle of Fig. 10 are plotted on an h-s diagram in Fig. 11.

The superheated steam is delivered to the turbine at a temperature only 34F above saturation. Although this amount of superheat does improve cycle efficiency, it does not eliminate the problem (encountered with saturated steam cycles) of having to handle large quantities of condensed moisture in the turbine. For example, if expansion from the initial conditions shown on Fig. 11 proceeded in one step down to the back pressure of 2.0 in. Hg (approximately 1.0 psi) the moisture formed would be in excess of 20 percent. High moisture in the steam not only imposes erosion problems, especially in turbine blades, but also reduces expansion efficiency.

Although there are mechanical losses from momentum exchanges between slow-moving particles of condensate and high velocity steam as well as moving turbine blades, there is also a strictly thermodynamic loss resulting from supersaturation. The expansion of the steam is too rapid to permit equilibrium thermodynamic properties to exist when condensation is occurring. Under this condition the steam becomes subcooled, retaining a part of the available energy which would be released by condensation.

Fig. 10 indicates the two methods of moisture removal utilized in this cycle, and Fig. 11 shows the effect of this moisture removal on the cycle. After expansion in the

high pressure turbine, the steam passes through a moisture separator, which is a low-pressure-drop separator located external to the turbine. After passing through this separator, the steam is reheated in two stages, first by bleed steam and then by high pressure steam to 503F, before entering the low pressure turbine. Here a second method is employed for moisture removal, utilizing grooves on the back of the turbine blades to drain the moisture from certain stages of the low pressure turbine. The separated moisture is then carried off with the bleed steam.

Internal moisture separation not only reduces erosion but also affords a thermodynamic advantage due to the divergence of the constant pressure lines with increasing enthalpy and entropy. This can be shown by the use of available energy, e, in the following manner. Consider the moisture removal stage at 10.8 psia in Fig. 11. After expansion down to 10.8 psia the moisture content of the steam is 8.9%. This is reduced to 8.2% by internal separation. Other properties are as follows:

	End of Expansion	After Moisture Extraction
P	10.8 psia	10.8
h	1057.9 Btu/lb	1064.7
s	1.6491 Btu/lb, F	1.6595
T_0 (@2 in. Hg)	560.8 R	560.8
$T_0 s$	924.8 Btu/lb	930.7
$e = h - T_0 s$	133.1 Btu/lb	134.0

The increase in availablity, Δe, due to moisture extraction is $134.0 - 133.1 = 0.9$ Btu per lb of steam.

The values of moisture and enthalpy listed are given for equilibrium conditions without considering supersaturation, which is accounted for empirically by the isentropic efficiency of the expansion line. Values of enthalpy and entropy used in the example are taken from the ASME Steam Tables where they are listed to five significant figures. Whenever it is necessary to work with small differences between large numbers, it is also necessary to use a sufficient number of significant figures.

Multipurpose steam power plants

In steam power plants operated solely for the generation of electric power, thermal efficiencies that are economically justifiable range up to about 40% in fossil-fuel plants and 34% in nuclear plants, including the optimum use of steam pressure and temperature, reheat, and bleed preheating of feedwater. This means that more than half of the heat released from the fuel is wasted and must be transferred to the environment in some way. This is usually done through a condenser, resulting in the heating of some body of water. As the number of fuel plant installations increases, the heating of streams and bodies of water is approaching undesirable limits in many areas, particularly in the Northeastern part of the U.S.

There is an increasing need for higher efficiency steam plants. Higher efficiency can be obtained by the use of higher steam temperatures but, after many years of re-

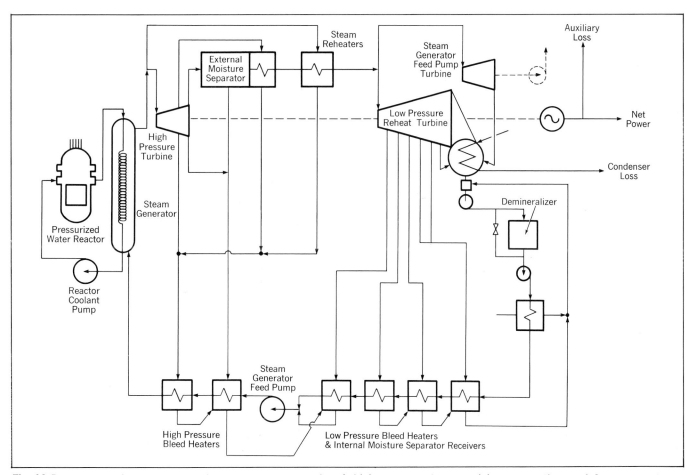

Fig. 10 Power cycle diagram, nuclear fuel — reheat by bleed and high pressure steam, moisture separation, and 6-stage regenerative feed heating — 900 psia, 566F/503F steam.

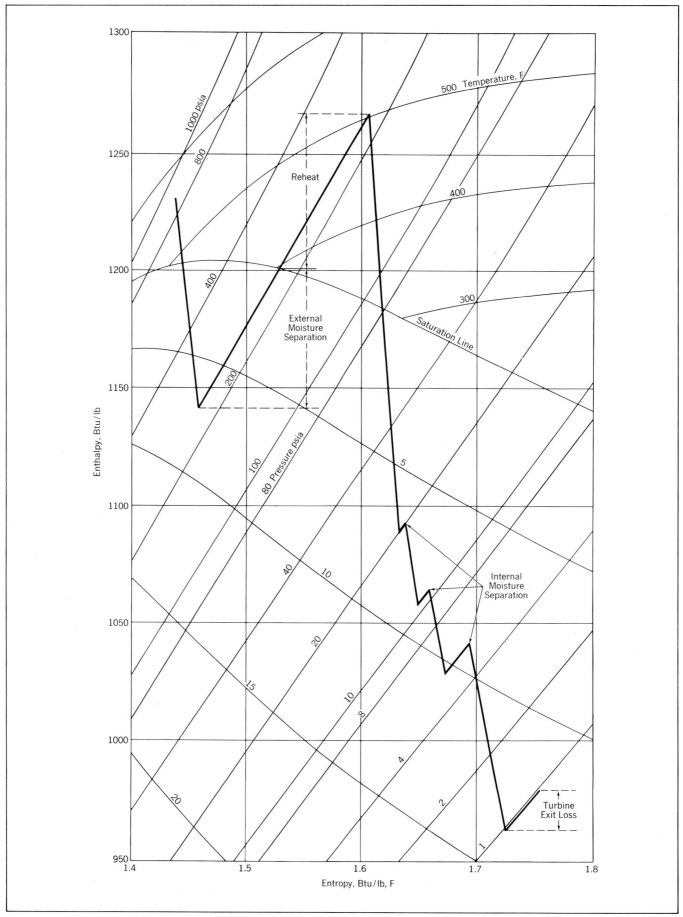

Fig. 11 Steam cycle for nuclear fuel — Mollier chart — reheat by bleed and high pressure steam, moisture separation, and 6-stage regenerative feed heating — 900 psia, 566F/503F steam.

search on high temperature metals, steam temperature is limited economically to about 1000F.

One practical means available for improving the utilization of energy in steam is the use of multipurpose steam plants, where steam is exhausted or extracted from the turbines at a proper pressure level for use in an industrial process. With such arrangements it is possible to obtain an overall thermal utilization between 65 and 70%. The use of combination power-and-process installations has been common in industry for many years, but the demand for process steam is not sufficient to permit the use of these combined cycles in most electric power generating plants.

In recent years, a considerable amount of attention has been devoted, particularly by the U.S. Atomic Energy Commission, to promoting the use of nuclear-fueled plants for power generation combined with the production of steam for process utilization, particularly the desalting of seawater. It is anticipated that dual-purpose nuclear steam plants to supply electrical energy and process steam for industry will be built in the near future.

Work functions

So far only pdv or expansion work has been discussed, although in the definition of internal energy, u, it was pointed out that u could be broadened to cover stored energy for other types of work. The more general case of the combined first and second laws for reversible processes is:

$$(28) \qquad du = Tds - pdv - \Sigma\delta(W'_{rev})$$

The last term $\Sigma\delta(W'_{rev})$ has been added to account for all forms of reversible work other than pdv work.

There are two important thermodynamic properties derived from combinations of other properties just as enthalpy was derived from u, p and v. Together with enthalpy, they are called thermodynamic potentials since in any thermodynamic process, reversible or irreversible, their differences depend only on initial and final properties of the system. These two properties are also known as work functions because of their usefulness in the more generalized viewpoint for work related to constant-temperature or constant-temperature-constant-pressure processes. They are:

$$(29) \qquad A = u - Ts$$

$$(30) \qquad F = h - Ts$$

The first function "A" is sometimes called the total work function because of its relation to equation (23) in a constant temperature process.

$$dA = du - Tds - sdT$$

or (31) where T is constant,
$$dA = du - Tds = -pdv - \Sigma\delta(W'_{rev})$$

In other words the maximum work that can be realized in an isothermal process is equal to the decrease in the property "A."

The second function "F" (equation 30) is the other thermodynamic property associated with work. This is

the Gibbs free energy sometimes referred to as the Gibbs function (G) or more commonly called free energy.[*] Most tabulated values of thermodynamic properties use the symbol "F" for Gibbs free energy.

The differential expression for (30), substituting $u + pv$ for h, is:

$$(32) \qquad dF = du + pdv + vdp - Tds - sdT$$

In calculating the combustion of fossil fuel, it is customary to assume that both reactants and products are at the same temperature and total pressure, i.e., that the process is isothermal and at constant pressure. Hence both dT and dp are zero, and

$$(33) \qquad dF = du + pdv - Tds$$

Combining (28) and (33)

$$(34) \qquad dF = -\Sigma\delta(W'_{rev})$$

Equation (34) shows that the decrease in free energy of a constant-temperature-constant-pressure process is equal to the total reversible work realized from the process less any work due to changes in volume (pdv work). It is evident from (31) and (34) that if the only work of the process is pdv work, $\Sigma\delta(W'_{rev}) = 0$, $dA = -pdv$ and $dF = 0$. On the other hand if work such as the output of a fuel cell is involved, the reversible counterpart of this work is equal to the decrease in free energy between the fuel and oxidant entering and the chemical species leaving. Moreover, as pointed out earlier in defining internal energy u, the free energy reversible work must be accounted for in the stored energy term u which in this case includes so-called heats of formation.

Combustion equilibrium

The important role of free energy in the steam power cycle is in its relationship to the chemical reaction of combustion. Heat absorption rates to the steam cycle from combustion products are very much influenced by the temperature level reached in burning fuel. Therefore, it is helpful to be able to predict limiting temperature levels of a combustion process based on equilibrium concentrations of products. This is often called the problem of dissociation which has a significant effect on adiabatic combustion temperatures above 3000F.

Conditions of equilibrium in a chemical reaction according to the law of mass action applied to ideal gases require a constant relating the species involved in a particular reaction such as a combustion process. This constant is known as the equilibrium constant, K_{eq}, which for ideal gases is given by:

$$(35) \qquad K_{eq} = \frac{(p_C)^c(p_D)^d}{(p_A)^a(p_B)^b}$$

The different p's in (35) are the partial pressures (i.e., the products of total pressure and mole fractions in the mixture) of the reactants and products. Exponents are the number of moles present for each species. The reaction involved is

$$(36) \qquad aA + bB = cC + dD$$

---

[*] Free energy was originally the name applied to the "A" function accredited to Helmholtz but is now widely used to designate the Gibbs function "F."

For nonideal gas reactions the partial pressures are replaced by what is known as fugacities in order to apply the property of free energy as the chemical potential.

Any changes in the partial pressures of A, B, C or D at constant temperature using the ideal gas assumption involve changes in their free energies in accordance with:

$$(37) \qquad F - F^o = RT \log_e (p/p_{\text{ref}})$$

This is derived by substituting (23) for du in (32) and integrating

$$dF = vdp - sdT$$

for the constant temperature case $(dT = 0)$. The use of (23) is possible since the only work involved is reversible expansion work.

$F - F^o$ represents a free energy change per mole at constant temperature when there is a change in concentration or partial pressure of the species. The superscript $(^o)$ is used to designate a property evaluated for the standard state of the species usually taken as its natural state at 298.16K (77F) and one atmosphere. For example, the standard state for steam at 77F and one atmosphere would be the liquid state, water. Since the reference state is to be one atmosphere, p_{ref} in (37) becomes 1.0. Again, p is replaced by fugacity for the nonideal gas.

When (37) is applied to each term of (36), since $\Delta F = 0$ under equilibrium conditions, the result is:

$$(38) \qquad -\Delta F^o = RT \log_e K_{\text{eq}}$$

The last equation provides the useful expression for evaluating the equilibrium constant of a reaction at different temperatures.

Thermodynamic properties and relationships for the compounds and their elements encountered in the combustion process are available in the literature. One of the best sources of this type of information is the "JANAF Thermochemical Tables" published by the United States Department of Commerce. These tables include $\log_{10}$ of the equilibrium constant for temperatures from 0 to 6000 K.

Once the equilibrium composition of the combustion products is calculated for an assumed temperature, this temperature must be checked by a heat balance. One way to do this is first to add together the enthalpies at the assumed temperature T for each product given by $n (H_T^o - H_{298}^o)$ where n is the number of moles of each species. In this case H_T^o does not include heats of formation, $(\Delta H_f)_T^o$, of the various species since this is accounted for in the heat of combustion (fuel heating value) corrected for incomplete combustion of combustibles plus other dissociations such as molecular species to atomic species. Proper allowance must also be made for the evaporation of water formed in the combustion process.

Table 4 outlines a method for calculating equilibrium compositions for an assumed product gas containing 9 species, one of which, nitrogen, has not been included in any reaction and is therefore a constant known quantity. All of these eight simultaneous equations are highly nonlinear except for the mass balance constraints. For this reason the method is very cumbersome even when

the product gas mixture is expected to contain only traces of species other than the six primary constituents (CO_2, CO, H_2O, H_2, O_2 and N_2). A more general method, better adaptable to computer calculations, is a free energy minimization procedure in which differences between assumed species concentrations and the unknown concentrations are successively altered under the constraints of the mass balance, until the sum of the standard free energies of all product species, each multiplied by their number of moles, is a minimum (see: White, Johnson and Dantzig, Journal of Chemical Physics, May 1958, vol. 28, No. 5).

Table 4
Combustion Equilibrium Calculations

Species	Fuel and Air Moles	Combustion Product Moles	Mole Fraction	Eight Unknowns
H	—	u	$u/\Sigma = (H)$	u
H_2	a	v	$v/\Sigma = (H_2)$	v
H_2O	b	w	$w/\Sigma = (H_2O)$	w
OH	—	x	$x/\Sigma = (OH)$	x
C	c	—		
CO	—	y	$y/\Sigma = (CO)$	y
CO_2	—	z	$z/\Sigma = (CO_2)$	z
O_2	d	r	$r/\Sigma = (O_2)$	r
O	—	q	$q/\Sigma = (O)$	q
N_2	n	n	$n/\Sigma = (N_2)$	

$\Sigma = u+v+w+x+y+z+r+q+n$

Mass Balances — **Eight Equations**

Mass Balances		Eq.
Carbon	$c = y+z$	1
Hydrogen	$a+b = v+w+\frac{1}{2}u+\frac{1}{2}x$	2
Oxygen	$\frac{1}{2}b+d = \frac{1}{2}w+\frac{1}{2}x+\frac{1}{2}y+\frac{1}{2}q+z+r$	3

Reaction — **Equilibrium constants (Eq. 35)**

Reaction	Equilibrium constants (Eq. 35)	Eq.
$C+O_2 \rightleftharpoons CO_2$	$\dfrac{(CO_2)}{(O_2)} = K_1$	
$C+\frac{1}{2}O_2 \rightleftharpoons CO$	$\dfrac{p^{1/2}(CO)}{(O_2)^{1/2}} = K_2$	
$CO+\frac{1}{2}O_2 \rightleftharpoons CO_2$	$\dfrac{1}{p^{1/2}}\dfrac{(CO_2)}{(CO)(O_2)^{1/2}} = \dfrac{K_1}{K_2} = K_3$	4
$CO+H_2O \rightleftharpoons CO_2+H_2$	$\dfrac{(CO_2)(H_2)}{(CO)(H_2O)} = \dfrac{K_3}{K_5} = K_4$	5
$H_2+\frac{1}{2}O_2 \rightleftharpoons H_2O$	$\dfrac{1}{p^{1/2}}\dfrac{(H_2O)}{(H_2)(O_2)^{1/2}} = K_5$	
$\frac{1}{2}O_2+\frac{1}{2}H_2 \rightleftharpoons OH$	$\dfrac{(OH)}{(O_2)^{1/2}(H_2)^{1/2}} = K_6$	6
$\frac{1}{2}O_2 \rightleftharpoons O$	$\dfrac{1}{p^{1/2}}\dfrac{(O)}{(O_2)^{1/2}} = K_7$	7
$\frac{1}{2}H_2 \rightleftharpoons H$	$\dfrac{1}{p^{1/2}}\dfrac{(H)}{(H_2)^{1/2}} = K_8$	8

p = system total pressure, atm.

Chapter 3

Fluid dynamics

Problems involving the flow of fluids are encountered in all phases of the production and utilization of steam. The flow of steam and water through pipes, fittings, valves and tube bundles; the flow of air and gases through ducts, tube banks, fans, compressors and turbines; the convection flow and circulation of steam and water; the convection flow of gases due to draft effect; the flow of water and steam through nozzles, orifices, venturi tubes, pumps and turbines—all are processes concerned with fluid flow. The fluid may be either a liquid or gas, but regardless of its state, the essential property is that it yield under the slightest shear stress. This chapter is limited to the discussion of liquids, gases and vapors. These are Newtonian fluids—by definition, fluids in which any shear stress is directly proportional to a velocity gradient normal to the shear force.

Liquids and gases are recognized as states of matter. In the liquid state a fluid is relatively incompressible, having a definite volume. It is also capable of forming a free surface between itself and its vapor or any other fluid with which it is immiscible. On the other hand, a gas is highly compressible and will expand or diffuse indefinitely subject only to the limitations of gravitational forces or any enclosing vessel.

The term vapor, while imprecise and not universally agreed upon, generally implies a gas near saturation conditions where the liquid and the gas phase coexist at essentially the same temperature and pressure. In a similar sense, the term gas is highly superheated vapor.

Energy equation applied to fluid flow

The basic approach to problem solutions in fluid dynamics lies in the application of the conservation laws of mass, energy and momentum. The first two, when used in conjunction with the steady frictionless flow of an incompressible fluid, result in the simplest form of a mechanical energy balance called Bernoulli's equation:

$$(1) \qquad p_1 v + Z_1 g/g_c + \frac{V_1^2}{2g_c} = p_2 v + Z_2 g/g_c + \frac{V_2^2}{2g_c}$$

Each term in this equation must be expressed in a consistent set of units which, in engineering fluid dynamics, is usually ft head (ft lb force per lb mass or ft lb/lb). This is the same as gravitational energy equivalent to a difference in elevation of the flowing fluid, expressed in ft or ft lb/lb. With this system of units, the symbols in equation (1) are defined as follows:

p_1 and $p_2 =$ pressure at locations 1 and 2, lb/sq ft

$v =$ specific volume of fluid, cu ft/lb

Z_1 and $Z_2 =$ elevations of locations 1 and 2, ft

V_1 and $V_2 =$ fluid velocities at locations 1 and 2, ft/sec

$g =$ gravitational acceleration, 32.17 ft/sec^2

$g_c =$ conversion constant (equation 3, Chapter 2)

$\quad = 32.17$ ft lb mass/lb force, sec^2

Briefly, equation (1) states that the total stored mechanical energy present in a mass of flowing fluid is made up of pressure energy, gravity energy and velocity or kinetic energy, each mutually convertible into the other forms. Furthermore, the total of this mechanical energy is constant along any stream-tube, provided there is no friction, heat transfer or shaft work between the points considered. This stream-tube may be an imaginary closed surface bounded by streamlines or it may be the wall of a flow channel, such as a pipe or duct, in which fluid flows without a free surface.

Applications of the mechanical energy balance of equation (1) are found in flow measurements using the velocity head conversion resulting from flow channel area changes. Examples are devices such as the venturi, flow nozzle and various types of orifices. Also, pitot-tube flow measurements depend on being able to compare total head, $pv + Z + V^2/2g_c$ to the static head ($pv + Z$) at a

specific point in the flow channel. Descriptions of metering instruments are found in Chapter 33.

Bernoulli's equation, developed from strictly mechanical energy concepts some 50 years before any precise statement of thermodynamic laws, is a special case of the more general energy equation (2) of Chapter 2 for a compressible fluid repeated here in the form:

$$(2) \quad u_1 + p_1v_1 + V_1^2/2g_c + Z_1 - W_k + Q$$
$$= u_2 + p_2v_2 + Z_2 + V_2^2/2g_c$$

where:

u_1 and u_2 = internally stored energy at locations 1 and 2. (These symbols are used to represent Btu/lb in Chapter 2 but must be expressed in ft lb/lb for consistency in equation (2) above.)

v_1 and v_2 = specific volumes of fluid at locations 1 and 2, cu ft/lb

Q = heat added to the system, ft lb/lb

W_k = work done by the system, ft lb/lb

Applications of equation (2) to fluid flow are given in examples (C) and (D) in the section *Energy Equations*, Chapter 2. Equation (14) of Chapter 2, developed under example D, is:

$$(3) \quad V_2 = 223.9 \sqrt{h_1 - h_2}, \text{ ft/sec}$$

This equation relates fluid velocity to change in enthalpy of the fluid within a compressible fluid under adiabatic conditions. Here h_1 and h_2 represent fluid enthalpy (Btu/lb) at locations 1 and 2. When temperature and pressure at points 1 and 2 are known, h_1 and h_2 can be determined from thermodynamic property tables, such as the ASME Steam Tables (Tables 1, 2 and 3, Chapter 2), or graphically read from a Mollier chart. Then the velocity resulting from a change in pressure within a compressible fluid can be calculated when the initial velocity is zero. Although equation (3) is independent of fluid friction and other flow losses, it is applicable only where $(Z_1 - Z_2)$, W_k and Q are all zero.

If, as is often the case, only the initial state (2 variables) and the final pressure are known, the velocity can be approximated with equation (3) using an adiabatic isentropic expansion to the lower pressure and its associated enthalpy (*see Chapter 2*). This is permissible provided that friction and any other irreversible energy exchanges are negligibly small. The expansion is more readily followed with the aid of a Mollier diagram which will establish the required enthalpy values.

Another convenient method used in solving for velocity changes in a frictionless adiabatic expansion, when enthalpy values are not known or easily obtainable, is to make use of the ideal gas equation of state together with the pressure-volume relationship of constant entropy.

From the established gas laws, the relationship between pressure, volume and temperature of a mole weight (lb-mole) of an ideal gas is expressed by:

$$(4) \quad pv_M = RT$$

$$\text{or } (5) \quad pv_M = MR_gT$$

where:

p = absolute pressure, lb/sq ft

v_M = volume, cu ft/mole of gas

T = absolute temperature, degrees Rankine = F + 460

M = molecular weight of the gas

R_g = specific gas constant, peculiar to each gas

$MR_g = R$ = the "universal gas constant," 1545 ft lb/mole, T

The relationship between pressure and specific volume along any expansion path at constant entropy is given by:

$$(6) \quad pv^k = \text{constant}$$

Since p_1 and v_1 are known, the constant can be taken as $p_1v_1^k$. The exponent, $k = (-v/p)(\delta p/\delta v)_s$, is constant and equal to c_p/c_v for an ideal gas.

where:

c_p = specific heat at constant pressure
c_v = specific heat at constant volume

also $(7) \quad c_v = \dfrac{u_1 - u_2}{T_1 - T_2}$ and $(7a) \quad c_v = \dfrac{1}{k - 1}$

For a process where $Z_2 - Z_1$, W_k and Q are all zero, equations (2), (5), (6), (7) and (7a) can be combined to obtain:

$$(8) \quad V_2^2 - V_1^2 = 2g_c\left(\frac{k}{k-1}\right)p_1v_1\left\{1 - \left(\frac{p_2}{p_1}\right)^{\frac{k-1}{k}}\right\}$$

Where $V_1 = 0$, and substituting $g_c = 32.17$:

$$(9) \quad V_2 = 8.02\sqrt{\left(\frac{k}{k-1}\right)p_1v_1\left\{1 - \left(\frac{p_2}{p_1}\right)^{\frac{k-1}{k}}\right\}}, \text{ ft/sec}$$

Both (8) and (9) can be used for real gases over pressure drop ranges where there is little change in k provided values of k are known or can be calculated. Equation (9) is widely used in problems involving gas flow through orifices, nozzles and flow meters.

It is sufficiently accurate for most purposes to determine velocity differences caused by changes in flow area by treating a compressible fluid as incompressible when the difference in specific volumes at points 1 and 2 is small compared to the final specific volume. The accepted practice is to consider the fluid incompressible where:

$$(10) \quad (v_2 - v_1)/v_2 < 0.05$$

Since equation (1) represents the incompressible energy balance for frictionless adiabatic flow, it may be rearranged to solve for the velocity difference giving:

$$(11) \quad V_2^2 - V_1^2 = 2g_c[\Delta(pv) + \Delta Zg/g_c], \text{ (ft/sec)}^2$$

where:

$\Delta(pv)$ = pressure head difference between stations 1 and 2,
$= (p_1 - p_2)v$, ft

ΔZ = potential head difference (elevation) between stations 1 and 2, ft

Where the approach velocity is approximately zero, equation (11) becomes:

$$(12) \qquad V_2 = \sqrt{2gH} = 8.02 \sqrt{H}, \text{ ft/sec}$$

In this last equation, H, in feet head of the fluid flowing, replaces $\Delta(pv) + \Delta Z$. If pressure difference is measured in psi, it must be converted to lb/sq ft to obtain pv in ft.

Pressure loss from fluid friction

So far only pressure losses associated with changes in the kinetic energy term, $V^2/2g_c$, have been discussed. These occur at constant flow (lb/hr), where there are variations in flow-channel cross-section area. Fluid friction and, in some cases, heat exchanges with the surroundings, also have important effects on pressure and velocity in a flowing fluid. The discussion in the text applies to fluid flowing in channels without a free surface.

When a real fluid flows, molecular diffusion causes interchanges of momentum between layers of the fluid moving at different velocities. These momentum interchanges are not limited to individual molecules; in most flow situations there are also bulk fluid interchanges known as eddy diffusion. The net result of all inelastic momentum exchanges is exhibited in shear stresses between adjacent layers of the fluid. If the fluid is contained in a flow channel, these stresses are eventually transmitted to the walls of the channel. To counterbalance this wall stress, a pressure gradient proportional to the bulk kinetic energy, $V^2/2g_c$, is established in the fluid in the direction of the bulk flow. This is the Quadric Resistance Law. The force balance is:

$$(13) \qquad \pi \frac{D^2}{4}(dp) = \tau_w \pi D (dx)$$

where:

D = tube diameter or equivalent diameter, D_e, ft

$D_e = \dfrac{4 \times \text{flow area}}{\text{duct perimeter}}$, for circular or noncircular cross sections

x = distance in direction of flow, ft

τ_w = shear stress at the tube wall, lb/sq ft

$$\text{or } (14) \qquad \frac{dp}{dx} = \frac{4}{D}\tau_w$$

where:

$\dfrac{dp}{dx}$ = fluid friction pressure gradient, lb force/cu ft

This pressure gradient along the length of the flow channel can be expressed in terms of a certain number of velocity heads, f, lost in a length of pipe equivalent to one tube diameter. The symbol, f, is called the friction factor and, for convenience, the values currently in general use were chosen so that

$$(15) \qquad \tau_w = \frac{f}{4}\frac{1}{v}\frac{V^2}{2g_c}$$

Equation (14) can be rewritten, substituting for τ_w its value from equation (15) as follows:

$$(16) \qquad \frac{dp}{dx} = \frac{4}{D}\left(\frac{f}{4}\frac{1}{v}\frac{V^2}{2g_c}\right) = \frac{f}{D}\frac{1}{v}\frac{V^2}{2g_c}$$

The general energy equation (2) expressed as a differential has the form:

$$du + \frac{VdV}{g_c} + d(pv) = \delta Q - \delta W_k$$

$$\text{or } (17) \qquad du + \frac{VdV}{g_c} + pdv + vdp = \delta Q - \delta W_k$$

Substituting equation (23), Chapter 2 ($du = Tds - pdv$) in equation (17) yields:

$$(18) \qquad Tds + \frac{VdV}{g_c} + vdp = \delta Q - \delta W_k$$

The term Tds represents not only heat exchanged with the surroundings (δQ), but also any heat added internally to the fluid as the result of irreversible processes such as fluid friction or any other irreversible pressure losses resulting from fluid flow. (*See equation (25) and explanation, Chapter 2.*)

$$\text{Hence } (19) \qquad Tds = \delta Q + \delta Q_F$$

where:

δQ_F is the heat equivalent of fluid friction and any shock losses.

Substituting (19) in (18), canceling δQ on both sides of the equation, setting $\delta W_k = 0$ (no shaft work) and rearranging equation (18) reduces to:

$$(20) \qquad dp = -\frac{VdV}{vg_c} - \frac{\delta Q_F}{v}$$

Three significant facts can be deduced from equation (20) and its derivation. First, the general energy equation, of itself, tells nothing about pressure losses due to fluid friction or shock.* To accommodate these pressure losses, equation (20) must be altered on the basis of both the first and second laws of thermodynamics (Chapter 2). Second, equation (20) is not affected by the process of heat transfer except as the latter may change the specific volume, v, along the length of the flow channel. Third, there is also a pressure loss as the result of a velocity change independent of any flow area change and dependent on specific volume changes only. This last item is an acceleration pressure loss, always present in compressible fluids. It is generally zero or neglected in incompressible flow without heat transfer since friction heating has little effect on fluid temperature and the accompanying volume change.

Equation (16) contains no acceleration term and applies only to friction and shock losses. Hence $\delta Q_F/v$ in equation (20) is equivalent to dp of equation (16), or:

$$\frac{\delta Q_F}{v} = f\frac{dx}{D}\frac{V^2}{v\,2g_c}$$

By substitution in equation (20),

$$(21) \qquad dp = -\frac{VdV}{vg_c} - \frac{f}{D}\frac{V^2}{v\,2g_c}dx$$

---

* Shock is defined as the conversion of mechanical energy to heat as a result of eddies and other inelastic momentum exchanges within the fluid.

Under conditions of constant flow-channel area and conservation of mass:

(22) $$\frac{V}{v} = G = \text{constant}$$

where:

G = mass velocity, lb/sq ft, sec (or other consistent units)

Combining (21) and (22):

(23) $$dp = -2\frac{G^2}{2g_c}\,dv - f\frac{G^2}{2g_c}\frac{v}{D}\,dx$$

Integrating (23) between points 1 and 2, located at $x = 0$ and $x = L$ respectively:

(24) $$p_1 - p_2 = 2\frac{G^2}{2g_c}(v_2 - v_1) + f\frac{G^2}{2g_c}\frac{1}{D}\int_0^L v\,dx$$

The second term on the right-hand side of (24) may be integrated provided a functional relationship between v and x can be established. For example, where the heat absorption rate over the length of the flow channel is constant, temperature (T) is approximately linear in (x), or:

(25) $$dx = \frac{L}{T_2 - T_1}\,dT$$

and (26) $$\int_0^L v\,dx = \frac{L}{T_2 - T_1}\int_1^2 v\,dT = Lv_{\text{av}}$$

The term v_{av} is an average specific volume with respect to T.

(27) $$v_{\text{av}} = \phi(v_2 + v_1) = \phi v_1(v_R + 1)$$

where:

$v_R = v_2/v_1$
ϕ = averaging factor

Most engineering problems are concerned with the case where v is almost linear in T and $\phi \approx \frac{1}{2}$.

Combining equations (24) and (26), and rewriting $v_2 - v_1$, as $v_1(v_R - 1)$

(28) $$p_1 - p_2 = 2\frac{G^2}{2g_c}v_1(v_R - 1) + f\frac{L}{D}\frac{G^2}{2g_c}v_1\phi(v_R + 1)$$

Equation (28) is completely general and holds for both compressible and incompressible flow in pipes of constant cross section as long as the function $T = F(x)$ can be assigned. The only limitation is that dp/dx is negative at every point along the pipe. Equation (21) can be solved for dp/dx making use of equation (22) and the fact that p_1v_1 can be considered equal to p_2v_2 for adiabatic flow over a short section of tube length. The result is:

(29) $$\frac{dp}{dx} = \frac{p\,f/2d}{1 - \dfrac{g_c p v}{V^2}}$$

At any point where $V^2 = g_c p v$ the flow becomes choked, since for velocities greater than the $\sqrt{g_c p v}$ the pressure gradient is positive. Essentially the flow is choked by excessive expansion of steam due to the drop in pressure. The minimum downstream pressure which is effective in producing flow in a flow channel is:

(30) $$p_2 = V^2/vg_c = v_2\,G^2/g_c$$

Dividing equation (28) through by $G^2v_1/2g_c$, the pressure loss is expressed in terms of velocity heads. One velocity head equals $(V^2/2g_c)(1/144v)$ for psi units or simply $V^2/2g_c$ for ft head units. In either case f represents the number of velocity heads (N_{vh}) lost in each diameter length of pipe. The term velocity head is sometimes referred to as the Euler number (N_{Eu}).

Two other examples of integrating (23) have wide applications in fluid flow problems. First, consider adiabatic flow through a pipe line. Both h and D are constant and $p_1v_1{}^m = p_2v_2{}^m$ where m is the exponent for constant enthalpy. Values of m for steam are in the range of 1.0 to 0.98. Therefore, the assumption $pv = \text{constant} = p_1v_1$ is sufficiently accurate for pressure drop calculations. This process is sometimes called isothermal pressure drop because a constant-temperature ideal-gas expansion also requires a constant enthalpy. For $pv = p_1v_1$, the integration of (23) reduces to:

(31) $$p_1 - p_2 = 2\frac{G^2}{2g_c}\frac{2v_1v_2}{v_1 + v_2}\log_e\frac{v_2}{v_1} + f\frac{L}{D}\frac{G^2}{2g_c}\frac{2v_1v_2}{v_2 + v_1}$$

Neither p_2 nor v_2 are known in most engineering problems, so equation (31) is solved by iteration. Also, the term $2v_1v_2/(v_2 + v_1)$ can usually be replaced by the numerical average of the specific volumes, $v_{\text{av}} = \frac{1}{2}v_1(p_R + 1)$ where $p_R = p_1/p_2 = v_2/v_1$. The maximum error at $p_R = 1.10$ is plus 0.22% increasing to 1.3% at $p_R = 1.25$. It is common practice to use a numerical average for specific volume in most fluid friction pressure drop calculations. However, where the lines are long, p_2 should be checked by (30). Also, where heat transfer is taking place, it is seldom constant along the flow channel and appropriate averaging factors should be used.

The second important example under adiabatic conditions involves an almost incompressible fluid, i.e., v_1 is approximately equal to v_2 (see equation 10). Substituting v for v_1 and v_2 in (31), the result is:

(32) $$p_1 - p_2 = f\frac{L}{D}\frac{G^2}{2g_c}v$$

All terms in equations (31) and (32) are expressed in a consistent set of units. However, it is general practice and often more convenient to use mixed units. For example a useful form of (32) is:

(33) $$\Delta p = f\frac{L}{d_e}v\left(\frac{G}{10^5}\right)^2$$

where:

Δp = pressure drop of fluid, psi
f = friction factor, i.e., number of velocity heads lost in a length of pipe equal to diameter
L = length, ft
d_e = equivalent diameter of flow channel, in.
v = specific volume of fluid, cu ft/lb
G = mass velocity of fluid, lb/sq ft, hr
   (Note change from units of equation 22)
f = friction factor, Fig. 1

Friction factor

The friction factor, f, introduced in equation (15), is defined as the fluid friction loss in units of velocity heads per diameter length of pipe or equivalent diameter length of flow channel. Earlier correlators in this field, including Fanning, used a friction factor with values of f listed as $\frac{1}{4}$ the magnitude indicated by equation (15). The reason for this is that the shear stress at the wall is proportional to $\frac{1}{4}$ velocity head. All references to f in this book combine the factor 4 in equation (14) with f as has been done by Darcy, Blasius, Moody and others.

Friction factor, f, is plotted in Fig. 1 as a function of Reynolds number, a dimensionless group defined as the ratio of inertial forces to viscous forces (*see Forced Convection and Dimensionless Numbers, Chapter 4*). Reynolds number can be written:

$$\frac{\rho\,VD_e}{\mu} \text{ or } \frac{VD_e}{v\mu} \text{ or } \frac{GD_e}{\mu} \text{ or } \frac{Gd_e}{12\mu}$$

where:

ρ = density of fluid, lb/cu ft
$v = 1/\rho$ = specific volume of fluid, cu ft/lb
μ = absolute viscosity of fluid, lb (mass)/ft, hr
V = velocity of fluid, ft/hr
G = mass velocity of fluid, lb/sq ft, hr
D_e = equivalent diameter of flow channel, ft
d_e = equivalent diameter of flow channel, in.

It is well known that fluid flow inside a closed channel occurs in a viscous or laminar manner at low velocity, but in a turbulent manner at higher velocities.

A large number of experiments on fluid friction pressure drop, examined by dimensional analysis and the laws of similarity, have shown that Reynolds number can be used to characterize a flow pattern. Examination of Fig. 1 shows that flow is laminar at Reynolds numbers less than 2000, generally turbulent at values exceeding

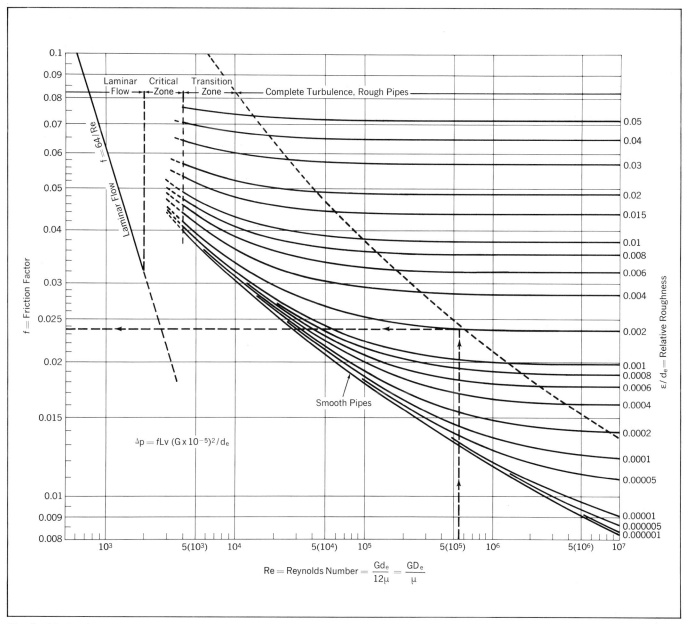

Fig. 1 Friction-factor Reynolds-number relationship for use in determining pressure drop of fluids flowing through closed conduits (pipes and ducts).

4000 and completely turbulent at still higher values. Indeterminate conditions exist in the critical zone between Reynolds number values of 2000 and 4000.

Although the motion of real fluids can be described by a system of simultaneous partial differential equations (Navier-Stokes) the complexity is such that solutions are not possible in any general sense except for the case of laminar or streamline flow where the only momentum exchanges are on a molecular basis. For laminar flow, integration of the Navier-Stokes equation with velocity in the length direction only, gives the following equation for friction factor:

$$(34) \qquad f = 64/\text{Reynolds number}$$

The straight line in the laminar flow region of Fig. 1 is a plot of this equation.

It has been found experimentally that the most rational base for evaluating the friction factor is by using the Reynolds number, Re, to define the flow pattern, and introducing a factor ϵ/d_e for defining the relative roughness of the channel surface. The coefficient, ϵ, expresses the average height of roughness protrusions in in. equivalent to the sand grain roughness established by Nikuradse. The friction factor values in Fig. 1 and the ϵ/d_e values in Fig. 2 are taken from experimental data as correlated by Moody.

Laminar flow

Laminar flow, by definition is characterized through parallel flowing of individual streams without mixing between them except for molecular diffusion from one stream to the other. At least a small layer of fluid next to

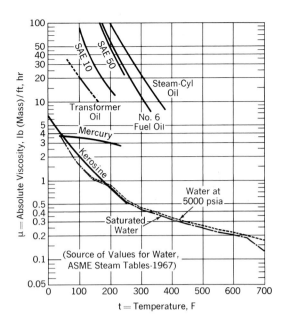

Fig. 3 Absolute viscosities of some common liquids.

the boundary wall has a zero velocity as a result of molecular adhesion forces. This establishes a velocity gradient normal to the main body of flow. Because the only interchanges of momentum in laminar flow are between the molecules of the fluid, the physical condition of the surface has no effect on the velocity gradient and therefore no effect on the friction factor. In commercial equipment, laminar flow is usually encountered only with the more viscous liquids, such as the heavier oils.

Turbulent flow

When turbulence exists, there are interchanges of momentum between masses of fluid induced through secondary velocities with directions not parallel to the axis of flow. In this case the physical condition of the boundary surface does have an effect on the velocity gradient near the wall which in turn affects the friction factor. Heat transfer is substantially greater with turbulent flow (Chapter 4) and, except for viscous liquids, it is generally practicable to employ turbulent flow with steam and water without excessive friction loss. Consequently it is customary to design for Reynolds numbers above the critical zone both on the gas side and the steam-and-water side of steam generating units, as well as in ducts and piping for air, flue gas, water and steam.

Velocity ranges

Table 1 lists the velocity ranges generally encountered in the heat transfer equipment and duct and piping systems in steam generating units. These values, plus the specific volumes of the ASME Steam Tables (see Chapter 2) and Tables 2 and 3 in this chapter for various liquids and gases, are used in establishing mass velocities for calculating Reynolds numbers and fluid friction pressure drop. In addition, values of absolute viscosity, also required in calculating the Reynolds number, are given in Figs. 3, 4 and 5 for selected liquids and gases. Table 4 lists the relationship between various units of viscosity.

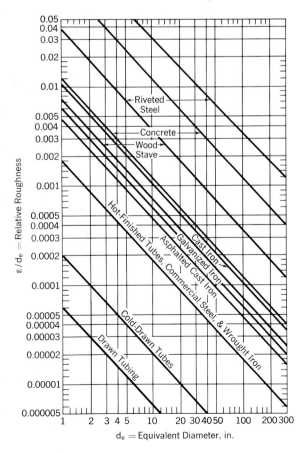

Fig. 2 Relative roughness of various conduit surfaces.

Table 1
Velocities generally used in steam generating systems

Nature of Service	Velocity, ft/min
Air	
Air heater	1000-5000
Coal-and-air lines, pulverized coal	3000-4500
Compressed-air lines	1500-2000
Forced draft ducts	1500-3600
Forced draft ducts, entrance to burners	1500-2000
Register grills	300-600
Ventilating ducts	1000-3000
Crude Oil Lines (6 to 30 in.)	60-360
Flue Gas	
Air heater	1000-5000
Boiler gas passes	3000-6000
Induced draft flues and breeching	2000-3500
Stacks and chimneys	2000-5000
Natural-Gas Lines (large interstate)	1000-1500
Steam	
Steam lines	
High pressure	8000-12,000
Low pressure	12,000-15,000
Vacuum	20,000-40,000
Superheater tubes	2000-5000
Water	
Boiler circulation	70-700
Economizer tubes	150-300
Pressurized water reactors	
Fuel assembly channels	400-1300
Reactor coolant piping	2400-3600
Water lines, general	500-750

Table 2
Physical properties of liquids (at 14.7 psia)

Liquid	Temp, F	Density, lb/cu ft	Sp Vol, cu ft/lb	Sp Ht, c_p
Water	70	62.4	0.0160	1.000
	212	59.9	0.0167	1.000
Automotive oil	70			
SAE 10		55-57	0.0182-0.0175	0.435
SAE 50		57-59	0.0175-0.0170	0.425
Mercury	70	846	0.0018	0.033
Fuel oil, #6	70	60-65	0.0167-0.0154	0.40
	180	60-65	0.0167-0.0154	0.46
Kerosine	70	50-51	0.0200-0.0196	0.47

Table 3
Physical properties of gases (at 14.7 psia)

Gas	Temp, F	Density, lb/cu ft	Sp Vol, cu ft/lb	Instantaneous Sp Ht, c_p	c_v	k, c_p/c_v
Air	70	0.0749	13.36	0.241	0.172	1.40
	200	0.0601	16.63	0.242	0.173	1.40
	500	0.0413	24.19	0.248	0.180	1.38
	1000	0.0272	36.79	0.265	0.197	1.34
CO_2	70	0.1148	8.71	0.202	0.155	1.30
	200	0.0922	10.85	0.216	0.170	1.27
	500	0.0634	15.77	0.247	0.202	1.22
	1000	0.0417	23.98	0.280	0.235	1.19
H_2	70	0.0052	191.2	3.440	2.440	1.41
	200	0.0042	238.0	3.480	2.490	1.40
	500	0.0029	345.0	3.500	2.515	1.39
	1000	0.0019	526.3	3.540	2.560	1.38
Flue gas*	70	0.0776	12.88	0.253	0.187	1.35
	200	0.0623	16.04	0.255	0.189	1.35
	500	0.0429	23.33	0.265	0.199	1.33
	1000	0.0282	35.48	0.283	0.217	1.30
CH_4	70	0.0416	24.05	0.530	0.406	1.30
	200	0.0334	29.95	0.575	0.451	1.27
	500	0.0230	43.50	0.720	0.596	1.21
	1000	0.0151	66.22	0.960	0.836	1.15

* From coal; 120% total air; flue gas molecular weight 30.

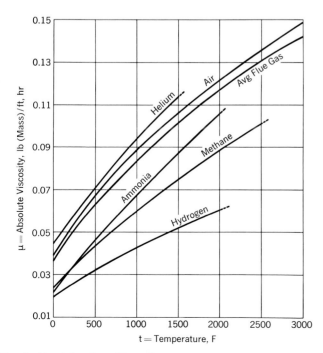

Fig. 4 Absolute viscosities of some common gases at atmospheric pressure.

Resistance to flow in valves and fittings

Pipe lines and duct systems contain many valves and fittings to make a working entity of the assembly. Unless the lines are used to transport fluids over long distances, as in the distribution of process steam at a factory or the cross-country transmission of oil or gas, the straight runs of pipe or duct are relatively short. Water, steam, air and gas lines in a power plant have relatively short runs of straight pipe and many valves and fittings. Consequently, the resistance to flow offered by the valves and fittings is a large, if not major, part of the total resistance.

Table 4
Relationship between various units of viscosity

Absolute (or Dynamic) Viscosity (μ)					Kinematic Viscosity (ν)		
Metric Units		English Units			Metric Units		English Units
Centipoise, 0.01 grams / cm, sec	Poise, grams / cm, sec	lb (mass) / ft, sec	lb (mass) / ft, hr	lb (force), sec / sq ft	Centistoke, 0.01 stoke	Stoke, sq cm / sec	sq ft / sec
1.0	0.01	0.000672	2.42	0.0000209	62.4/ρ	0.624/ρ	0.000672/ρ
100	1.0	0.0672	242	0.00209	6,240/ρ	62.4/ρ	0.0672/ρ
1,488	14.88	1.0	3,600	0.0311	92,900/ρ	929/ρ	1/ρ
0.413	0.00413	0.000278	1.0	0.0000086	25.8/ρ	0.258/ρ	0.000278/ρ
47,900	479	32.2	115,900	1.0	2,990,000/ρ	29,900/ρ	32.2/ρ
0.016ρ	0.00016ρ	0.000011ρ	0.0396ρ	0.00000034ρ	1.0	0.01	0.0000108
1.6ρ	0.016ρ	0.0011ρ	3.96ρ	0.000034ρ	100	1.0	0.00108
1,490ρ	14.9ρ	1.02ρ	3,680ρ	0.032ρ	92,900	929	1.0

ρ = density, lb/cu ft

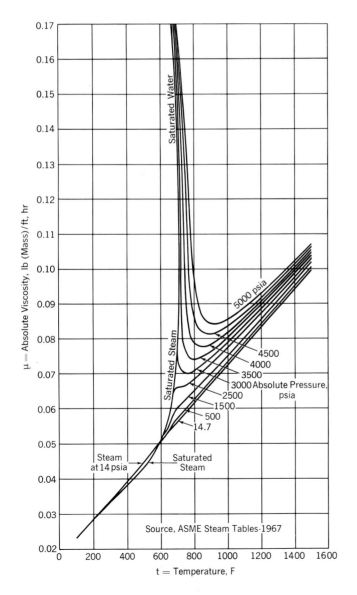

Fig. 5 Absolute viscosity of saturated and superheated steam.

Methods available for estimating the flow resistance in valves and fittings are much less exact than those used in establishing the friction factor for straight-run pipes and ducts. In the latter, pressure drop is considered as the result of the fluid shear stress at the boundary walls of the flow channel leading to relatively simple boundary value problems. On the other hand, pressure losses associated with valves and fittings, and also to a large extent with bends, are mainly the result of impacts and inelastic exchanges of momentum. Even though momentum is conserved, kinetic energies are dissipated as heat. This means that pressure losses are influenced mainly by geometries of valves, fittings and bends. As in the case of turbulent friction factors, pressure losses are determined from empirical correlations of test data either as equivalent pipe lengths or preferably a multiple of velocity heads based on the connecting pipe or tube sizes. Equivalent pipe lengths have the disadvantage of being dependent on the relative roughness (ϵ/d) used in a particular test-data correlation. Because of the almost infinite number of geometries possible in valves and fittings, it is customary to rely on manufacturers for pressure drop coefficients.

It is also customary for manufacturers to supply valve flow coefficients (C_v) for 60F water. These are expressed as ratios of weight or volume flow in the fully open position to the square root of the pressure drop, both given in specified units. These coefficients can be used to relate velocity head losses to a connecting pipe size in the following expression:

$$(35) \qquad N_v = k\, d^4/C_v^2$$

where:

N_v = number of velocity heads lost (dimensionless)
k = constant with a numerical value of 891
d = internal diameter of connecting pipe, in.
C_v = flow coefficient in units compatible with k and d

Strictly speaking, C_v for valves and corresponding values of N_v apply only to incompressible flow. However, they may be extrapolated for compressible conditions using an average specific volume between p_1 and p_2 for Δp values as high as 20% of p_1. This corresponds to a maximum pressure ratio of 1.25. The Δp process for valves, bends and fittings is approximately isothermal and does not require the more stringent limits set by equation (10).

When pressure drop can be expressed as an equivalent number of velocity heads, it can be calculated by the formula:

$$(36) \qquad \Delta p = N_v \frac{v}{12} \left(\frac{G}{10^5} \right)^2$$

where:

Δp = pressure drop, lb/sq in. (psi)
N_v = number of velocity heads equivalent
v = specific volume, cu ft/lb
G = mass velocity, lb/sq ft, hr

Another convenient expression for pressure drop in air (or gas) flow problems is:

$$(37) \qquad \Delta p = N_v \frac{30}{B} \frac{t + 460}{1.73 \times 10^5} \left(\frac{G}{10^3} \right)^2$$

where:

Δp = pressure drop, expressed as in. of water
B = barometric pressure, in. of mercury
t = air (or gas) temperature, F

Equation (37) is based on air, which has a specific volume of 25.2 lb/cu ft at 1000R and a pressure equivalent to 30 in. of mercury. This equation can be used for other gases by correcting for the difference in specific volume.

The range in pressure drop through an assortment of commercial fittings is given in Table 5 in equivalent velocity heads based on the internal diameter of the connecting pipe. As noted, pressure drop through fittings may also be expressed as the loss in equivalent lengths of straight pipe.

Table 5
Resistance to flow of fluids through commercial fittings*

Fitting	Loss in Velocity Heads
Ell, 90° standard sweep	0.3-0.7
Ell, 90° long sweep	0.2-0.5
Tee, flow through run	0.15-0.5
Tee, flow through 90° branch	0.6-1.6
Return bend, close	0.6-1.7
Gate valve, open	0.1-0.2
Check valve, open	2.0-10.0
Globe valve, open	5.0-16.0
Angle valve, 90° open	3.0-7.0
Boiler nonreturn valve, open	1.0-3.0

* See Fig. 9 for loss in velocity heads for flow of fluids through pipe bends. See also "Losses in Pipe and Fittings" by R. J. S. Pigott, *ASME Transactions*, vol. 79, 1957, pp. 1767-1783.

Contraction and enlargement irreversible pressure loss

The simplest sectional change in a conduit is converging or diverging boundaries. Converging boundaries have a tendency to stabilize flow during the change from pressure energy to kinetic energy, and shock losses (inelastic momentum exchanges) can be practically eliminated with proper design. If the included angle of the converging boundaries is 30° or less and the terminal junctions are smooth and tangent, any losses in mechanical energy are largely fluid friction. It is customary practice to take this loss as 0.05 velocity head based on the smaller downstream flow area.

The mechanical energy balance for converging boundaries, when $Z_2 - Z_1 = 0$, becomes:

$$(38) \qquad p_1 v + \frac{V_1^2}{2g_c} = p_2 v + \frac{V_2^2}{2g_c} + N_c \frac{V_2^2}{2g_c}$$

where subscripts 1 and 2 identify the upstream and downstream sections, and N_c, the contraction loss factor, is the number of velocity heads lost by friction and shock in contraction. Fig. 6 lists values of this factor, based on experimental data.

Where there is an enlargement of the conduit section in the direction of flow, the expansion of the flow stream is also subject to a pressure loss depending on geometry and proportional to the kinetic energy of the flowing fluid. Just as in the case of the contraction loss, this is an irreversible energy conversion to heat resulting from inelastic momentum exchanges. Because it is customary to show these losses as coefficients of the higher kinetic energy term, the mechanical energy balance for enlargement loss is:

$$(39) \qquad p_1 v + \frac{V_1^2}{2g_c} = p_2 v + \frac{V_2^2}{2g_c} + N_e \frac{V_1^2}{2g_c}$$

The case of sudden enlargement (angle of divergence = 180°) has been solved mathematically to yield an energy loss of $(V_1 - V_2)^2/2g_c$. This can be expressed

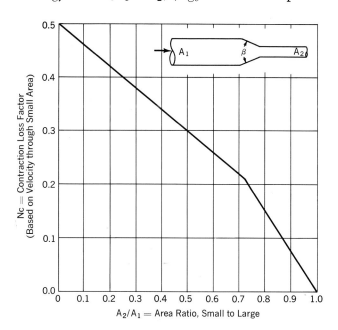

Fig. 6 Contraction loss factor for $\beta > 30°$ ($N_c = 0.05$ for $\beta \leqq 30°$).

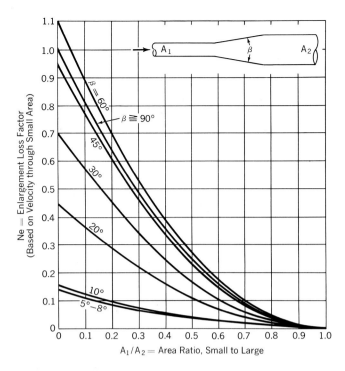

Fig. 7 Enlargement loss factor for various included angles.

as $(1 - A_1/A_2)^2\, V_1^2/2g_c$ where A_1 and A_2 are the upstream and downstream cross-section flow areas ($A_1 < A_2$). Even this solution, based on the conservation laws, depends on qualifying assumptions regarding static pressures at the upstream and downstream faces of the enlargement.

Experimental values of the enlargement loss factor, based on different area ratios and angles of divergence, are given in Fig. 7. The differences in static pressures caused by sudden and gradual changes in section are shown graphically in Fig. 8 in terms of the velocity head at the smaller area plotted against section area ratios.

Flow through bends

Bends in a pipeline or duct system produce pressure losses caused by both fluid friction and momentum exchanges resulting from a change in the direction of flow. Since the axial length of the bend is normally included in the straight-length friction loss of the pipeline or duct system, it is convenient to subtract a calculated equivalent straight-length friction loss from experimentally determined bend-loss factors. These corrected data form the basis of the empirical bend loss factor, N_b.

The pressure losses for bends in round pipe in excess of straight-pipe friction vary slightly with Reynolds numbers below 150,000. For Reynolds numbers above this value they are reasonably constant and depend solely on the dimensionless ratio, r/d, the ratio of the centerline radius of the bend to the internal diameter of the pipe. For commercial pipe, the effect of Reynolds number is negligible. The combined effect of radius ratio and angle of bend, in terms of velocity heads, is shown in Fig. 9.

Flow through coils

A convenient method for calculating the pressure drop in flow through coils is to apply a factor to the drop through

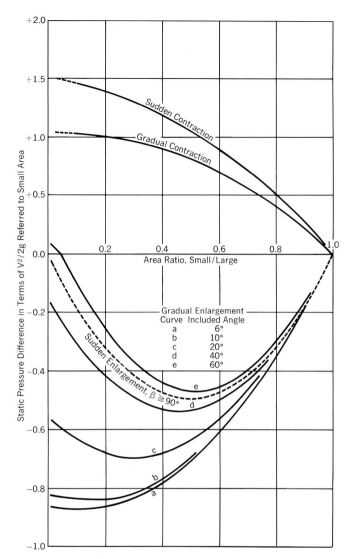

Fig. 8 Static pressure difference resulting from sudden and gradual changes in section.

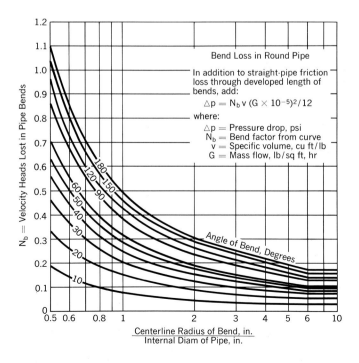

Fig. 9 Bend loss for round pipe, in terms of velocity heads.

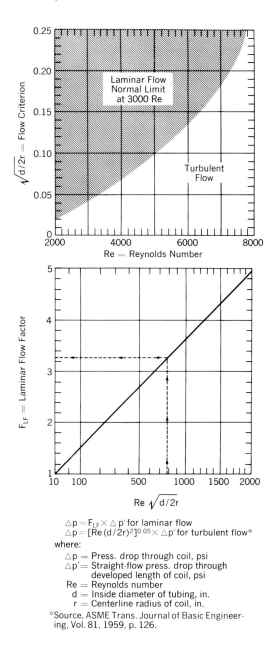

$$\triangle p = F_{LF} \times \triangle p' \text{ for laminar flow}$$
$$\triangle p = [Re (d/2r)^2]^{0.05} \times \triangle p' \text{ for turbulent flow*}$$

where:
  $\triangle p$ = Press. drop through coil, psi
  $\triangle p'$ = Straight-flow press. drop through
        developed length of coil, psi
  Re = Reynolds number
  d = Inside diameter of tubing, in.
  r = Centerline radius of coil, in.
*Source, ASME Trans. Journal of Basic Engineering, Vol. 81, 1959, p. 126.

Fig. 10 Pressure drop for laminar flow and for turbulent flow through coils.

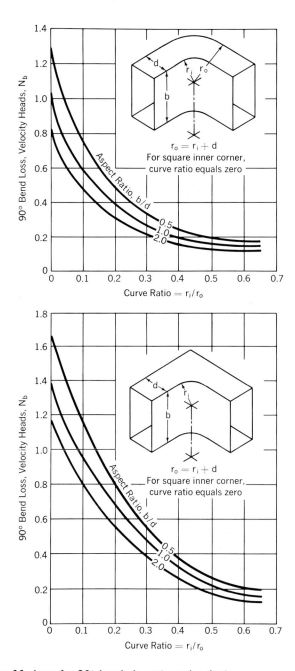

Fig. 11 Loss for 90° bends in rectangular ducts.

an equivalent length of straight pipe. This factor depends on the type of flow, laminar or turbulent, and the radius of the coil. The type of flow and the factors for laminar and turbulent flow can be determined from the curves and formulas of Fig. 10.

Flow through rectangular ducts

The loss of pressure caused by a change of direction in a rectangular duct system is similar to that for cylindrical pipe. However, an additional factor, the shape of the duct in relation to the direction of bend, must be taken into account. This is called the aspect ratio, defined as the ratio of the width to the depth of the duct, i.e., the ratio b/d in Fig. 11. The bend loss for the same radius ratio decreases as the aspect ratio increases, because of the smaller proportionate influence of secondary flows on the stream as a whole. The combined effect of radius and

aspect ratios on 90° duct bends is given in terms of velocity heads in Fig. 11.

The loss factors shown in Fig. 11 are average values of test results on ducts which indicate that, for the given range of aspect ratios, b/d, the losses are relatively independent of the Reynolds number. Outside this range the variation with Reynolds number is erratic. It is therefore recommended that N_b values for $b/d = 0.5$ be used for all aspect ratios less than $b/d = 0.5$ and values for $b/d = 2.0$ be used for ratios greater than $b/d = 2.0$.

Losses for bends other than 90° are customarily taken as proportional to the angle of bend. Bend losses in rectangular ducts can be reduced by the use of splitters, which increase both the aspect ratio and the average radius ratio.

A convenient chart for the calculation of pressure loss resulting from impact losses in duct systems conveying

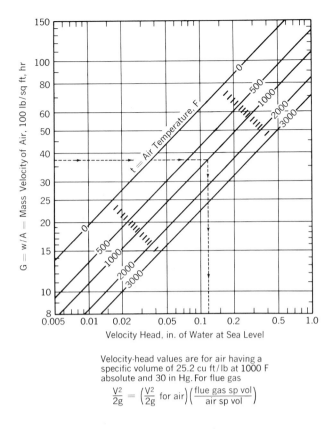

Velocity-head values are for air having a
specific volume of 25.2 cu ft/lb at 1000 F
absolute and 30 in Hg. For flue gas

$$\frac{V^2}{2g} = \left(\frac{V^2}{2g} \text{ for air}\right)\left(\frac{\text{flue gas sp vol}}{\text{air sp vol}}\right)$$

Fig. 12 Mass-velocity velocity-head relationship for air.

air (or flue gas) is Fig. 12. When mass velocity and temperature are known, a base velocity head in inches of water at sea level can be obtained. This is subject to an altitude or pressure correction if such applies. (*See Table 3, Chapter 17.*)

Flow of gases over tube banks

Resistance to the transverse flow of gases across tube banks is an example of repeated major changes of cross section. When the tubes are staggered, both sectional and directional changes affect the resistance. Experimental results and the analytical conclusions of extensive research by B&W indicate that three principal variables other than mass velocity affect this resistance. The primary variable is the number of major restrictions, i.e., the number of tube rows crossed, N. The second variable is the so-called friction factor, f, relatable to the Reynolds number (based on tube diameter), the tube-spacing-diameter ratios and arrangement pattern (in-line or staggered). The third variable is the depth factor, F_d, (Fig. 13), applicable to banks less than 10 rows deep. Friction factors "f" for various in-line tube patterns are given in Fig. 14.

The product of the friction factor, the number of major restrictions (tube rows) and the depth factor is, in effect, the summation of velocity head losses through the tube bank.

$$(40) \qquad N_v = fNF_d$$

The N_v value established by (40) may be used in equation (37) to find the tube bank pressure loss in in. of water. Some test correlations indicate "f" values higher

than the isothermal case for cooling gas and lower for heating gas.

Flow through stacks or chimneys

The flow of gases through stacks or chimneys is established by the natural-draft effect of the stack and/or the mechanical draft produced by a fan. The resistance to this flow or the loss in mechanical energy between the bottom and the top of the stack is a result of the friction and stack exit losses. The algebraic treatment of these losses and examples of actual application are given in Chapter 17.

Pressure loss in two-phase flow

The problem of two-phase or multicomponent flow is one of the most complex in engineering calculations. To date very little progress has been made on a generalized approach. For mixtures of water and steam, a considerable amount of experimental work has been performed in the area of low steam quality. Experiments and correlations by Martinelli and Nelson, and Martinelli and Lockhart in the 1940's are still widely used in the range which they cover.

During the 1950's the United States Atomic Energy Commission sponsored research at Bettis Atomic Power Laboratory (References 1 and 2). This research was limited to nuclear reactor conditions and is valid only between pressures of 1100 to 2000 psi and for steam qualities up to 40%. As a result of this research, corrections to the Martinelli-Nelson two-phase multiplier were developed as a function of quality and mass velocity (*see also Reference 3 and Chapter 21*).

During the 1960's the Water-Tube Boilermakers' Association of Great Britain sponsored two-phase pressure drop investigations at the University of Cambridge. An analysis of these data has been made by J. R. S. Thom, Babcock & Wilcox Ltd. (Reference 4). This analysis covers the pressure range from 15 to 3000 psi and outlet qualities from 3 to 100%.

Although a large amount of experimental work has been done in the two-phase pressure drop area, there is

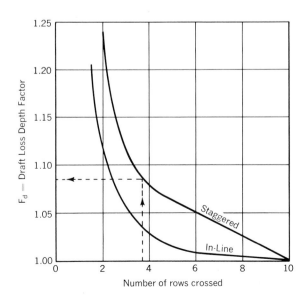

Fig. 13 Draft loss depth factor for number of tube rows crossed in convection banks.

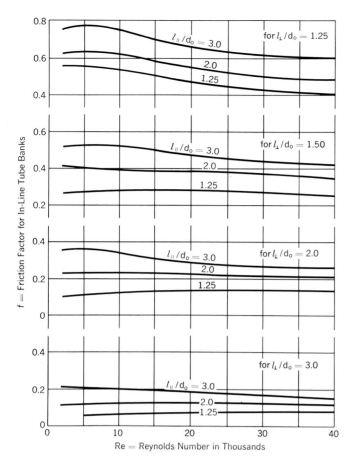

Fig. 14 Friction factor, *f*, as affected by Reynolds number for various in-line tube patterns; crossflow gas or air.

considerable uncertainty in extrapolating the results to geometries and conditions significantly different from the test conditions because of the importance of the flow region (bubbly flow, slug, annular, mist). If experimental data are not directly applicable, prototype testing is recommended where high accuracy is required in the two-phase region.

A simplified approach, for calculating pressure drop in two-phase flow is presented later in this chapter under *Principles of Natural Circulation.* This simplified approach is usually adequate for circulation calculations in natural-circulation fossil-fuel boilers at pressures up to 1500 psi.

Calculation of pressure drop for two-phase flow conditions in pressurized-water nuclear reactors is discussed in Chapter 21. This includes the subcooled-nucleate or local boiling condition (Fig. 1, Chapter 1).

References:

1) Le Tourneau, B. W., and Sher, N. C., "Revised Pressure Drop Recommendations for Pressurized-Water Reactor Design," *WAPD-TH-326.*

2) Sher, N. C., "Estimation of Boiling and Non-Boiling Pressure Drop in Rectangular Channels at 2000 psia," *WAPD-TH-300.*

3) "Boiling Heat Transfer and Two-Phase Flow," L. S. Tong, John Wiley and Sons, Inc.

4) Thom, J. R. S., "Prediction of Pressure Drop During Forced Circulation Boiling of Water," *International Journal of Heat and Mass Transfer,* vol. 7, pp. 709-724.

Entrainment by fluid flow

Collecting or transporting solid particles or a second fluid by the flow of a primary fluid at high velocity is known as entrainment. This is usually accomplished with jets using a small quantity of high-pressure fluid to carry along large quantities of another fluid or of solid particles. The pressure energy of the high-pressure fluid is converted into kinetic energy by nozzles, with a consequent reduction of pressure. The material to be transported is drawn in at the low-pressure zone, where it meets and mixes with the high-velocity jet. Usually the jet is followed by a parallel throat section to equalize the velocity profile. The mixture then enters a diverging section, where kinetic energy is partially reconverted into pressure energy. In this case major fluid flow losses (losses in mechanical energy) are an example of inelastic momentum exchanges occurring within the fluid streams.

The injector is a jet pump that uses condensing steam as the driving fluid to entrain low-pressure water for delivery against a back pressure higher than the pressure of the steam supplied. The ejector, similar to the injector, is designed to entrain gases, liquids, or even mixtures of solids and liquids for delivery against a pressure less than the pressure of the primary fluid. In a water-jet aspirator, water is used to entrain air to obtain a partial vacuum. In the Bunsen-type burner, a jet of gas entrains air for combustion. Steam-jet blowers are sometimes used in the base of stacks of small natural-draft boiler plants to increase the draft for short peak loads.

In several instances, entrainment may be a source of trouble in the operation of steam boilers. Particles of ash, entrained by the products of combustion, when deposited on heating surfaces reduce thermal conductance, erode blades when passing through fans and add to pollution when discharged into the atmosphere. Moisture, carrying solids either in suspension or in solution, is entrained in the stream. The solids may be carried through to the turbine, depositing on the blades and decreasing turbine capacity and efficiency. In downcomers or supply tubes, steam bubbles are entrained in the water when the drag on the bubbles is greater than the buoyant force. This reduces the density in the pumping column of natural-circulation boilers.

Boiler circulation

An adequate flow of water and water-steam mixture is necessary for steam generation and control of tube metal temperatures in all the circuits of a steam-generating unit (Chapter 1). At supercritical pressures, this flow is produced mechanically by means of pumps. At subcritical pressures, circulation is produced either naturally by the action of the force of gravity, by pumps, or by a combination of the two.

The force of gravity available to produce flow in natural circulation comes from the difference between the densities (lb/cu ft) of the fluids in the downcomer (downflow) and riser (upflow) portions of the circuit (Fig. 15). Maximum pumping effect occurs if the fluid in the downcomers is water at or slightly below saturation temperature and free of steam bubbles. Heat-absorbing risers at saturation temperature convey to the boiler drum a water-steam mixture of less density than that of the

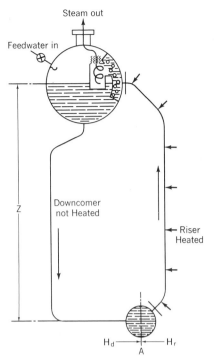

Fig. 15 Simple natural-circulation circuit (diagrammatic) including primary steam separator in drum.

water in the downcomers. This difference in density establishes the force available for circulation.

The flow in the various circuits of boiler units designed for forced circulation at subcritical pressures, is produced by mechanical pumps. There are two general types of forced-circulation systems, a "once-through" system and a "recirculating" system.

The "once-through" forced-circulation type receives water from the feed supply, pumping it to the inlet of the heat-absorbing circuits. Fluid heating and steam generation take place along the length of the circuit until evaporation is complete. Further progress through the heated circuits results in superheating the vapor. Conventionally this type of forced circulation requires no steam-and-water drum. A modification of the "once-through" type evaporates to partial dryness (90% quality) removing the excess water in a separator.

The "recirculating" forced-circulation-type unit has water supplied to the heat-absorbing circuits through a separate circulating pump. The water pumped is considerably in excess of the steam produced and, like a natural-circulation boiler, a steam-and-water drum is required for steam separation. The separated water together with feedwater from the feed pump is returned through downcomer circuits to the circulating pump for another "round trip."

In the recirculating type of forced circulation there is a net thermal loss for the boiler unit because of the separate circulating pump. While practically all the energy required to drive the pumps reappears in the water as added enthalpy, this energy originally came from the fuel at a conversion-to-useful-energy factor of less than 1.0. If an electric motor drive is used, the net energy lost, referred to the fuel input in a plant with 33% thermal efficiency, is about twice the energy supplied to the pump motor.

Natural circulation

In a natural-circulation system, circulation increases with increased heat input (and increased steam output) until a point of maximum fluid flow is reached. Beyond this point, any further increase in heat absorption results in a flow decrease. The form of the curve, shown in Fig. 16, is produced by two opposing forces. An increase in flow results from the increasing difference in the densities of the fluids in downcomers and risers as the heat absorption increases. At the same time, the friction and other flow losses in both downcomers and risers also increase. When the rate of increase in these losses (caused primarily by the increase in specific volume in the riser circuits) becomes greater than the gain from increasing density difference, the flow rate begins to drop. A proper objective, therefore, is to design all the circuits to operate in the region of the rising part of the curve, to the left of the peak in Fig. 16.

When design conditions are limited to the rising portion of the circulation curve, a natural-circulation boiler tends to be self-compensating for the numerous variations in heat-absorption conditions encountered in an operating unit. These include sudden overloads, change in heat-absorbing-surface cleanliness, nonuniform fuel bed or burner conditions, and even the inability to forecast precisely actual conditions over the operating lifetime.

No similar compensating effect is inherent in a forced-circulation unit operating at subcritical pressures, since a large part of the total resistance of the riser circuits, much greater than the natural circulation effect, is caused by flow-distribution devices required at the circuit inlets. Under these conditions, because of the disproportionately large resistance of the distributors, an increase in heat absorption to an individual circuit or group of circuits causes only a slight change in the flow rate.

The method of producing flow in boiler circuits, whether natural or mechanical, has virtually no bearing on the effectiveness of heat-absorbing surfaces as long as the inside surface is wetted at all times by the water in a water-steam mixture of suitable quality to maintain nucleate boiling (Chapter 1). Provided this fundamental requirement is met, the water-film resistance to heat flow is negligibly small, and the overall heat conductance depends on gas-side and tube-wall resistances. Within the nucleate boiling regime, boiler heat-absorbing surface in

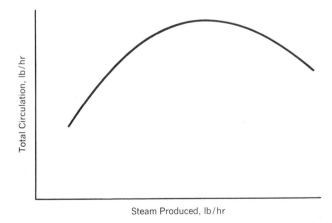

Fig. 16 Typical relationship between circulation in a boiler circuit (at a given pressure) and amount of steam produced (scale arbitrary).

the furnace or convection portion of the unit absorbs substantially the same amount of heat per sq ft regardless of whether the circulating flow is produced by natural methods or by pumps. With either type of circulation, any departure from the nucleate boiling regime (i.e., going beyond the DNB point—Chapter 1) requires special consideration of the forced-convection steam-film heat transfer coefficient and its relation to permissible metal temperatures.

Forced or natural circulation

Under certain conditions forced circulation can be usefully applied to steam generation. Mechanical means to move the fluid within the circuits are employed for boilers designed to operate above or near the critical pressure (3208.2 psia). There are instances, also, in the process and waste-heat fields where temperature control or consolidating heat pickup from widely separated points can be economically effected by the use of pumps.

Natural circulation is most effectively employed when sufficient changes in density occur as the result of heat absorption. Therefore, natural circulation is usually restricted to subcritical pressure designs where there is a considerable difference in density between steam and water. At pressures above 3000 psi a natural-circulation system becomes increasingly large and costly, and a pump may be more economical. The forced-circulation principle, however, is equally operable in both the supercritical and subcritical pressure ranges. The selection of the identifying name "Universal-Pressure" boiler reflects the broad applicability of the once-through forced-circulation principle. Its choice, as opposed to the retention of natural circulation in the subcritical range, is essentially determined by the economics of the installation.

Natural circulation is effective at very high pressures approaching the critical pressure. Natural circulation relies only on the difference between the mean density of the fluid (water) in the downcomers and the mean density of the fluid (steam and water mixture) in the heated tubes. The water in the downcomers is subcooled as the result of mixing the subcooled feedwater from the economizer with the saturated water separated in the steam drum. The fluid in the furnace tubes is a steam and water mixture with lower density than the density of water in the downcomers. The difference in densities provides the pumping head. The available circulating head with natural circulation remains high even at very high pressures approaching the critical pressure as shown in Fig. 17. As long as the maximum effectiveness of this differential is maintained by the efficient separation of the steam from the water in the circulating system, as with the use of the cyclone steam separator, mechanical aid to circulation is not essential.

Circulation design criteria

In the rational design of boiler natural-circulating systems, the primary requisite is to maintain nucleate boiling for all anticipated operating conditions, i.e., to avoid DNB (Chapter 1). Accumulated data on limiting values and design criteria are derived from operating experience and laboratory investigation. These data are based on having boiler water of suitable purity after proper treatment (Chapter 34).

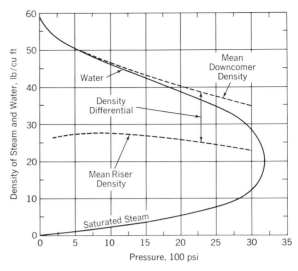

Fig. 17 Effect of pressure on density in downcomers and risers.

In actual design, the riser circuits are normally fixed by the general arrangement of the unit. They form the enclosure of the unit and provide the surface required for heat absorption. There are also dimensional limitations as a result of location, permissible burner clearances and gas velocities. The structural arrangement of the downcomer circuits usually is not as rigidly prescribed as that of the risers. The determination of required flow areas in the various parts of the system, particularly in the downcomer (supply) circuits, is the end result of the circulation calculations.

One design criterion is the acceptable percent steam by volume or the corresponding percent steam by weight, throughout the fluid flow path. This limit is a function of many variables, including pressure, heat flux, and mass velocity. For each pressure and heat flux there is a maximum permissible quality which is dependent on mass velocity. This is the so-called point of departure from nucleate boiling (DNB). Designs resulting in operation at steam qualities in excess of this limit are subject to tube failures when metal temperatures exceed material limitations.

At a constant heat flux and mass velocity, the DNB occurs at a lower percentage of steam by volume as pressure increases. Below 1500 psi (Fig. 18) it is satisfactory to base circulation requirements on quality limits as a function of pressure only. These quality limits are established at the discharge ends of the riser circuits based on the average heat absorption for the entire circuit even though higher local absorption rates are present in lower quality parts of the circuit. This is possible since the absorption rates encountered in boiler units are not a significant factor in DNB limits for low pressures. On the other hand, high-pressure designs require a detailed analysis of the probable distribution of heat fluxes throughout the furnace during operation. These fluxes are a function of heat input, burner location, type of fuel fired, and possible maloperation or operational irregularities. It therefore becomes necessary to investigate all factors which affect the quality, to be assured that the final circulatory arrangement will have an acceptable percentage of steam by weight, not only at the top of the riser circuit, but also incrementally along its length. A

unit with burners located near the top of the riser circuit has high heat fluxes in the high-quality region and must be designed to quality limits different from those of a unit with burners located near the bottom of the riser circuits in a low-quality region. In once-through forced circulation supercritical pressure systems, the primary requisite is to maintain a unique combination of mass velocity and enthalpy at various heat absorption rates such that the fluid film temperature drop is predictable and, in conjunction with local fluid temperature, maintains the furnace enclosure metal temperatures below that at which there would be any threat to integrity of the unit as a result of material limitations.

The quality of the mixture is not the only criterion of proper conditions within the tubes or flow channels. Minimum acceptable internal velocity, which is an interdependent variable with quality and heat flux distribution, is also an important criterion. These values vary widely with the heat absorption rate, quality, manner of heat application and arrangement of tubes in the circuit (see Chapter 1). Sloping tubes in particular, receiving heat on either half or full circumference require adequate velocities in order to prevent separation of the two-phase fluid, steam-blanketing, and eventual tube failure. Adequate velocities are also necessary for sloping tubes receiving heat only from below, to minimize the possibility of solids deposition from the water and the consequent overheating and ultimate failure of the tube metal. Slightly inclined tubes receiving heat only from above, as in a furnace floor, or around the full circumference, as in

a screen, require fluid velocities in the order of 5 to 10 fps entering the heat absorption zone. On the other hand, substantially vertical riser circuits, regardless of heat application, require relatively low entering velocities, approximately 1 to 5 fps.

Another criterion is the relationship between the anticipated density and pressure drop characteristics of the flowing media and those of a static column of saturated liquid of the same vertical height. This ratio is referred to as the percent of saturated-water head. Minimum values can be established from analytical studies or from measured values obtained from operating units. The design of circulatory systems below the established limits could lead to possible problems (tube failures) as a result of recirculation of steam-water mixtures between parallel flow paths.

In the final design of the circulation system all limits must be satisfied. Each circuit will have its own limiting condition, whether it be quality, velocity, or saturated-water head. The limiting condition will be dependent on the overall circuit arrangement, pressure, and heat flux.

The rate of heat absorption must be evaluated from combustion data and from knowledge, based on experience, of the probable performance of the particular arrangement of the heat-absorbing surface. In practice, the heat-input pattern is rarely uniform along the length of the heat-absorbing path, and integrated values of the instantaneous density-height relationship are required to permit precise determination of mean fluid densities.

Analyses of downcomer circuits as compared with riser circuits are less involved. The density of the fluid in the downcomer (preferably all in the liquid phase) is readily determined, since it is at a temperature related to feedwater and saturation temperatures. Steam bubbles in the downcomer circuit seriously affect the head available for natural circulation.

Principles of natural circulation

The elementary circuit, shown in Fig. 15, and the basic relationships noted may be used to demonstrate the principles of natural circulation.

For stabilized flow (system in equilibrium), the weight flow in the downcomer must equal the weight flow in the riser. Also, the net pressure at A, Fig. 15, of the fluid in the downcomer must be balanced by the net pressure of the fluid in the riser, i.e., the net head, H_d, in the downcomer must equal the net head, H_r, in the riser. Another statement of this principle is that the algebraic sum of all the pressures around any closed path of a system in equilibrium must equal zero.

Referring to Fig. 15:

Z = difference in elevation, ft

ρ_d = density of downcomer fluid, lb/cu ft

ρ_{ex} = density of mixture leaving riser, lb/cu ft

ρ_r = mean density of riser fluid, lb/cu ft

$Z\rho_d/62.4$ = downcomer gravity head, ft of std water

$Z\rho_r/62.4$ = riser gravity head, ft of std water

$h_{\Sigma d}$ = sum of downcomer losses (friction, bend, entrance, exit, change of section, baffle, and acceleration), ft of std water

$h_{\Sigma r}$ = sum of riser losses, ft of std water

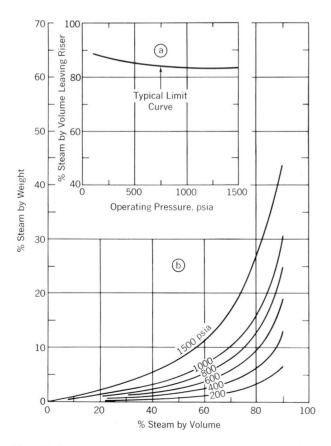

Fig. 18 Diagram (a): Typical maximum percent steam by volume leaving riser at various pressures. Diagram (b): Percent steam by volume corresponding to percent steam by weight for various pressures.

(41) $\quad H_d = H_r$

(42) $\quad H_d = Z\rho_d/62.4 - h_{\Sigma d} =$ downcomer net head, ft of std water

(43) $\quad H_r = Z\rho_r/62.4 + h_{\Sigma r} =$ riser net head, ft of std water

(44) $\quad Z(\rho_d - \rho_r)/62.4 = h_{\Sigma d} + h_{\Sigma r}$, from equations (41), (42) and (43)

The term "std water" refers to water at a density of 62.4 lb/cu ft.

From equation (44) it is evident that the difference between the gravity heads of downcomer and riser is equal to the sum of the circulation losses in the system. The latter, as noted above, include friction losses along the straight flow paths, and bend, entrance, exit, change-of-section, baffle, steam-separator, and acceleration losses.

In general, therefore, the losses in the downcomer portion of the circuit are:

$$h_{\Sigma d} = h_f + h_b + h_{en} + h_{ex} + h_k$$

and similarly for the riser circuit:

$$h_{\Sigma r} = h_f + h_b + h_{en} + h_{ex} + h_k + h_s + h_{ac}$$

The h increments represent the various circulation losses in the downcomer and riser portions of the circuit as enumerated above. h_f refers to fluid friction, h_b to bend loss, h_{en} to entrance loss, h_{ex} to exit loss, h_k to change-in-section loss, h_s to steam separator loss and h_{ac} to acceleration loss. It is convenient to express all "h" values in ft of std water which, in the case of fluid friction, is:

(45) $\qquad h = 2.31 \dfrac{fL}{d_e} \dfrac{1}{\rho} \left(\dfrac{G}{10^5}\right)^2$

Pressure losses normally expressed in N_v are also converted to ft of std water in the following way:

(46) $\qquad h = \dfrac{N_v}{5.2} \dfrac{1}{\rho} \left(\dfrac{G}{10^5}\right)^2$

Units used in both (45) and (46) are:

$\quad f =$ Moody friction factor (Figs. 1 and 2)
$\quad L =$ tube length, ft
$\quad d_e =$ tube equivalent diameter, in.
$\quad \rho =$ fluid density, lb/cu ft
$\quad G =$ mass velocity, lb/sq ft, hr
$\quad N_v =$ velocity head loss factor, dimensionless

The density, ρ_r, in (43) becomes a variable quantity when heat is being added or extracted from a circuit. Because most riser circuits absorb heat and generate steam in some zones, values of $Z\rho_r/62.4$ and values of ρ in (45), as well as h_f, must be average values per ft of vertical height or tube length (in the case of friction). Since heat input varies in the various zones throughout the unit, this problem is normally best handled in a stepwise fashion, assuming uniform heat input or a linear change in steam quality over each increment. On this basis the average value of $1/\rho$ for use in equation (45) is:

(47) $\qquad \left(\dfrac{1}{\rho}\right)_{av} = \dfrac{1}{2} \dfrac{\rho_1 + \rho_2}{\rho_1 \rho_2}$

Also, the average value for ρ_r in (43) is:

(48) $\qquad \rho_{r\,av} = \dfrac{\rho_1}{\rho_1/\rho_2 - 1} \log_e \dfrac{\rho_1}{\rho_2}$

Both (47) and (48) are calculated assuming the same velocity for both the water and steam phases (no slip). In most cases where the increased steam loading of the tube cross section produces an overriding acceleration of the mixture, this assumption is reasonable.

Under certain conditions pressure losses, both friction and shock, for two-phase flow have been observed to be about 1.5 times as great as the single phase case for equal mass velocities if friction factors, based on values of Reynolds number using liquid viscosity and the density of the mixture are used in equations (45) and (46). The factor, 1.5, is used as a direct multiplier in either of these equations for calculating two-phase pressure drop in natural-circulation fossil-fuel boilers. The density of the mixture, ρ_{mix}, is calculated as follows:

(49) $\quad \rho_{mix} = \rho_f - (\rho_f - \rho_g) \dfrac{(\% \text{ steam by volume})}{100}$

where $\rho_f =$ density of water and $\rho_g =$ density of steam.

In high-pressure designs (above about 1500 psi) it is advisable to evaluate pressure losses in two-phase flow by a more detailed procedure, relating local values of heat flux, steam quality and mass velocity. This can be accomplished using the correlation of Martinelli as modified by the results of Thom. See also *Pressure Loss in Two-Phase Flow.*

Furnace of FM-type Integral-Furnace boiler during fabrication in a B&W shop. In the furnace, heat will be transferred primarily by radiation to the tubes shown at the top, bottom, sides and rear. Plastic refractory is being applied to close inspection openings between the furnace and the convection tube bank where heat transfer is primarily by convection. This tube bank is located to the left of the furnace, and combustion gases will enter it at the rear of the furnace (see pages 25-5 to 25-7).

Chapter 4

Heat transfer

Heat transfer deals with the transmission of thermal energy, the source of which may be the combustion of fossil fuels, nuclear fission, or the inevitable losses, such as pressure drop and friction, encountered in transmission or in transformation to other types of energy. Heat transfer is demonstrated in many aspects of everyday life, as in cooking, heating, refrigeration and clothing.

While the fundamentals of heat transfer are simple, practical applications may be extremely complex because of irregular configurations of equipment, simultaneous operation of several different modes of heat transfer, and changes in conditions from moment to moment. In the applications of heat transfer it is, therefore, necessary to combine basic scientific principles with empirical information derived from experience.

Three modes of heat transfer

There are three recognized modes of heat transfer—conduction, radiation and convection. All the varied phases of heat transfer involve one or more of these modes coupled with a temperature difference between a heat source and a heat receiver.

Conduction is the transfer of heat from one part of a body to another part of the same body, or from one body to another in physical contact, without appreciable displacement of the particles of the body or bodies.

Radiation is the transfer of energy between bodies by electromagnetic waves without dependence on the presence of matter in the intervening space. All matter radiates, and the transfer of heat (thermal radiation) is one important manifestation of this phenomenon. The intensity of thermal radiation is dependent on the temperature of the radiating matter. When radiation impinges on a body, some of the radiant energy may be reflected or reradiated, some of it may be transmitted through the body, and the remainder will be absorbed. The portion absorbed is generally converted into heat.

Convection is the transfer of heat from one point to another within a fluid (gas or liquid) by the mixing of one part with another due to the movement of the fluid, or between one fluid and another by the mixing of the fluids, or between a fluid and a solid through relative motion between them. When the movement of the fluid or fluids is caused solely by differences in density resulting from temperature differences within the fluid, the heat transfer is referred to as free or natural convection. When the fluid movement results from some mechanical force, e.g., a pump or fan, the heat transfer is called forced convection.

Conductance and resistance

Conductance is defined as the heat flow through a material or across a boundary per unit of time, per unit of area, and per degree difference in temperature across the material or boundary. Resistance is the reciprocal of conductance. The concepts of conductance and resistance are particularly useful when more than one mode of heat transfer or more than one material or boundary are involved.

When two modes of heat transfer occur simultaneously and independently, such as radiation and convection, the combined conductance, U, is the sum of the individual conductances U_r and U_c, which in effect are in parallel. When the heat flow paths are in series, the resistances, not the conductances, are additive. In all cases the potential force causing the transfer is a temperature difference.

The general equation for heat flow rate by these modes, singly or in combination, may be written:

(1) $q = US\Delta t = S\Delta t/R$

where:

q = rate of heat flow, Btu/hr
U = overall or combined conductance, Btu/sq ft,hr,F
S = surface involved in heat transfer, sq ft
Δt = temp difference causing heat flow, F
$R = 1/U$ = combined resistance of the heat flow path, sq ft,hr,F/Btu

Heat transfer by conduction

If a flat plate is heated on one side and cooled on the other, heat will flow through the plate from the hot side to the cold. The rate of heat flow, q, is conveniently expressed by the equation:

$$(2) \qquad q = \frac{kS\Delta t}{\ell} = \frac{kS(t_1 - t_2)}{\ell}$$

where:

q = rate of heat flow, Btu/hr
k = thermal conductivity, Btu/sq ft, hr,F/in. thickness
S = heating surface, sq ft
Δt = temperature difference causing heat flow = $t_1 - t_2$
t_1 = temperature, F, of heated side of plate
t_2 = temperature, F, of cooled side of plate
ℓ = thickness of plate, in.

Equation (2) is a special form of equation (1) where conductance is expressed as k/ℓ and its reciprocal, ℓ/k, is the resistance.

Metals are good conductors and hence have high thermal conductivities. Certain other materials are poor conductors with low thermal conductivities and are suitable for insulation. Thermal conductivities of a few materials are given in Table 1.

Table 1
Thermal conductivity, k, of selected materials
(Btu/sq ft, hr, F/in. thickness)

Material	k*
Silver	2880
Copper	2640
Carbon steel	350
Alloy steel, 18% Cr-8% Ni	108
First-quality firebrick	4.5
Insulating firebrick	0.8
85% Magnesia block	0.5

* Approximate values at room temperature.

Thermal conductivities of most pure metals decrease with increase in temperature, while conductivities of alloys may either increase or decrease. Thermal conductivities of several steels and alloys are shown in Fig. 1. Thermal conductivities of insulating materials generally increase with increasing temperature as shown in Fig. 7, Chapter 16.

Fig. 2 shows the temperature gradient through a plate where heat flows from a heated side (at higher temperature) to a cooled side (at lower temperature). If the thermal conductivity of the material does not change with change in temperature, the temperature gradient will be a straight line (A); if the conductivity increases with increase in temperature, the temperature gradient will be convex (B); if the conductivity decreases with increase in temperature, the gradient will be concave (C). For most heat transfer calculations it is sufficiently accurate to assume a constant conductivity corresponding to the average temperature of the material.

For example, the rate of heat flow through a flat steel

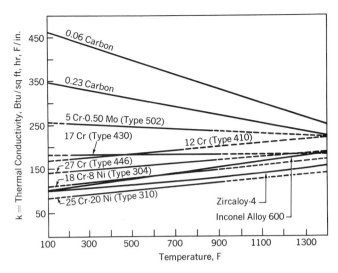

Fig. 1 Thermal conductivity, k, of some commonly used steels and alloys. (*Source of data for Inconel Alloy 600, Huntington Alloy Products Division, The International Nickel Co., Inc.*)

plate ¼ in. thick, 1 sq ft in area, with $\Delta t = 25F$ may be evaluated by equation (2):

$$q = \frac{k\,S\Delta t}{\ell} = \frac{350 \times 1 \times 25}{0.25} = 35,000 \text{ Btu/hr}$$

where k is obtained from Table 1.

Calculation of the heat flow rate through the wall of a steel flue lined on the inside with insulating firebrick and insulated on the outside (Fig. 3) demonstrates the procedure for combining the thermal resistances of different materials (heat flow paths in series) into one overall resistance.

$$q = \frac{k_{12}\,S\Delta t_{12}}{\ell_{12}} = \frac{k_{23}\,S\Delta t_{23}}{\ell_{23}} = \frac{k_{34}\,S\Delta t_{34}}{\ell_{34}}$$

$$\Delta t_{12} = \frac{\ell_{12}}{k_{12}} \times \frac{q}{S}\,;\; \Delta t_{23} = \frac{\ell_{23}}{k_{23}} \times \frac{q}{S}\,;\; \Delta t_{34} = \frac{\ell_{34}}{k_{34}} \times \frac{q}{S}$$

$$(t_1 - t_4) = \frac{q}{S}\left(\frac{\ell_{12}}{k_{12}} + \frac{\ell_{23}}{k_{23}} + \frac{\ell_{34}}{k_{34}}\right)$$

$$q = \frac{S(t_1 - t_4)}{\dfrac{\ell_{12}}{k_{12}} + \dfrac{\ell_{23}}{k_{23}} + \dfrac{\ell_{34}}{k_{34}}}$$

This equation is a form of equation 1.

$$(1) \qquad q = US\Delta t = S\Delta t/R$$

where:

U = combined conductance, Btu/sq ft, hr, F

$$= \frac{1}{\dfrac{\ell_{12}}{k_{12}} + \dfrac{\ell_{23}}{k_{23}} + \dfrac{\ell_{34}}{k_{34}}}$$

R = combined resistance, sq ft, hr, F/Btu

$$= \frac{\ell_{12}}{k_{12}} + \frac{\ell_{23}}{k_{23}} + \frac{\ell_{34}}{k_{34}}$$

$\Delta t = t_1 - t_4$

In addition to the thermal resistance (reciprocal of conductance) of the firebrick, steel and insulation shown in Fig. 3, heat flow through the flue must also be transferred through gas films on both sides of the composite flue structure. Evaluation of gas film conductances is

discussed in detail under convection heat transfer, but it should be recognized that the thermal resistance of the gas films must be combined with the thermal resistance of solid materials. Thus for the example of Fig. 3:

$$U_{05} = \cfrac{1}{\cfrac{1}{U_{01}} + \cfrac{\ell_{12}}{k_{12}} + \cfrac{\ell_{23}}{k_{23}} + \cfrac{\ell_{34}}{k_{34}} + \cfrac{1}{U_{45}}}$$

where:

U_{01} = inside gas film conductance
U_{45} = outside air film conductance

A numerical solution for the example of Fig. 3 is obtained by substituting the following in equation (1):

S = 600 sq ft wall surface
t_0 = 1080F, temperature of hot gas
t_5 = 80F, temperature of room air
$\Delta t = t_0 - t_5$ = 1000F, temperature difference
U_{01} = 5.0 Btu/sq ft, hr, F
k_{12} = 1.08 Btu/sq ft, hr, F/in. for insulating firebrick
k_{23} = 300 Btu/sq ft, hr, F/in. for steel
k_{34} = 0.5 Btu/sq ft, hr, F/in. for insulation
$\ell_{12}, \ell_{23}, \ell_{34}$ = 4 in., ¼ in. and 3 in. thickness respectively
U_{45} = 2.0 Btu/sq ft, hr, F

Then
$$q = US\Delta t = \cfrac{600 \quad \times \quad 1000}{\cfrac{1}{5} + \cfrac{4}{1.08} + \cfrac{0.25}{300} + \cfrac{3}{0.5} + \cfrac{1}{2}}$$
$$= 57{,}690 \text{ Btu/hr}$$

To determine if the correct thermal conductivity was assumed and if the temperature level is within the al-

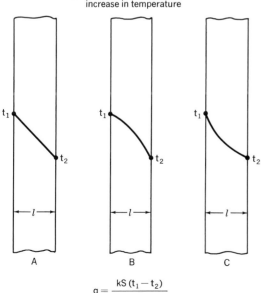

A—k is constant
B—k increases with increase in temperature
C—k decreases with increase in temperature

$$q = \frac{kS(t_1 - t_2)}{l}$$

Fig. 2 Diagrammatic temperature-thickness relationship for different thermal conductivities, *k*.

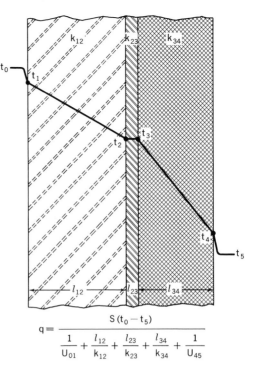

$$q = \cfrac{S(t_0 - t_5)}{\cfrac{1}{U_{01}} + \cfrac{l_{12}}{k_{12}} + \cfrac{l_{23}}{k_{23}} + \cfrac{l_{34}}{k_{34}} + \cfrac{1}{U_{45}}}$$

Fig. 3 Temperature distribution in composite wall (fluid films included).

lowable operating limits of the material, it is necessary to calculate temperatures on both sides of each material. This involves a step-by-step solution of equation (1) as follows:

$$q = US\Delta t \quad \text{or} \quad \Delta t = \frac{q}{US}$$

$$t_0 - t_1 = \frac{q}{U_{01}S} \; ; \; t_1 = 1080 - \frac{57{,}690}{5 \times 600} = 1061\text{F}$$

$$t_1 - t_2 = \frac{q}{\dfrac{k_{12}}{\ell_{12}}S} \; ; \; t_2 = 1061 - \frac{57{,}690 \times 4}{600 \times 1.08} = 705\text{F}$$

$$t_2 - t_3 = \frac{q}{\dfrac{k_{23}}{\ell_{23}}S} \; ; \; t_3 = 705 - \frac{57{,}690 \times 1/4}{600 \times 300} = 705\text{F}$$

$$t_3 - t_4 = \frac{q}{\dfrac{k_{34}}{\ell_{34}}S} \; ; \; t_4 = 705 - \frac{57{,}690 \times 3}{600 \times 0.5} = 128\text{F}$$

$$t_4 - t_5 = \frac{q}{U_{45}S} \; ; \; t_5 = 128 - \frac{57{,}690}{2 \times 600} = 80\text{F}$$

For any case in which heat flows through successive flat layers of material, the reciprocal of the overall conductance equals the sum of the individual resistances. If the successive layers of material do not make good thermal contact with each other, there will be interface resistances due to the air space or film. These resistances may be neglected in composite walls of insulating materials, but become important and must be included in calculations if the resistances of the layers are small in comparison with the interface resistances, such as in heat transfer through a boiler tube having an oxide deposit on the inside of the tube.

When heat is conducted radially through a cylindrical wall, as in heat flow through the wall of a steam line from the inside to the outside of the pipe (Fig. 4), the

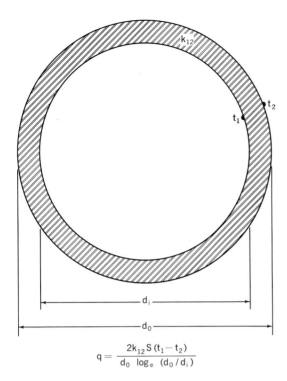

$$q = \frac{2k_{12} S (t_1 - t_2)}{d_0 \log_e (d_0/d_i)}$$

Fig. 4 Heat flow through cylindrical wall (*see equation 4*).

flat-plate equation must be modified, since the heat-flow surface area, S, is no longer a constant but increases as the distance from the center of the pipe increases. If the outside surface area of the pipe is used for the value of S, then it can be shown that the thickness of the pipe wall, corresponding to ℓ in the flat plate equation (equation 2), must be replaced by the equivalent thickness ℓ_e, given by the equation:

(3) $\qquad \ell_e = 0.5 \, d_o \log_e (d_o/d_i)$

where:

$\qquad \ell_e$ = equivalent thickness, in.
$\qquad d_o$ = outside pipe diameter, in.
$\qquad d_i$ = inside pipe diameter, in.

The equation for heat flow through a cylindrical wall thus becomes:

(4) $\qquad q = \frac{k_{12}S(t_1 - t_2)}{\ell_e} = \frac{2k_{12}S(t_1 - t_2)}{d_o \log_e (d_o/d_i)}$

If the heat flows through two successive cylindrical walls, as in an insulated steam pipe, and if the film conductances (*see "Heat Transfer by Convection"*) U_{01} of the steam and U_{34} of the air outside the insulation (Fig. 5) are included, the equation becomes:

(5) $\quad q = \dfrac{S(t_0 - t_4)}{\dfrac{d_3}{d_1} \dfrac{1}{U_{01}} + \dfrac{d_3}{2k_{12}} \log_e \dfrac{d_2}{d_1} + \dfrac{d_3}{2k_{23}} \log_e \dfrac{d_3}{d_2} + \dfrac{1}{U_{34}}}$

where:

$\qquad d_3$ = outside diameter of insulation, in.
$\qquad S$ = outside surface area of insulation, sq ft

Many problems of heat transfer in the power field involve conduction through plane or cylindrical walls and

can be treated by the methods outlined. For other geometrical shapes, such as thick-wall rectangles and ribbed construction, special treatment is required.

Conduction in fluids

Conduction in fluids (liquids and gases) follows the same laws as conduction through solids. In engineering practice, heat transfer by conduction through fluids is small in comparison with convection. However, the thermal conductivity characteristics of fluids and solids affect convection heat transfer. The thermal conductivity of water ranges from 3.9 Btu/sq ft, hr, F/in. at 32F and atmospheric pressure to 1.9 at the critical point. Most of the other nonmetallic liquids have conductivities between 0.60 and 1.80 Btu/sq ft, hr, F/in. Values of thermal conductivity for water and steam are given in the ASME Steam Tables.

Table 2
Thermal conductivity, *k*, of gases
(Btu/sq ft, hr, F/in. thickness)

Gases at Atmospheric Pressure

Temp, F	Air, k	CO_2, k	O_2, k	N_2, k	H_2, k
0	0.168	0.096	0.156	0.168	1.080
500	0.300	0.252	0.312	0.264	2.004
1000	0.408	0.384	0.444	0.336	2.724
1500	0.480	0.516	0.564	0.408	3.360
2000	0.564	0.624	0.672	0.468	3.924
2500	0.636	0.720	0.792	0.528	4.464
3000	0.696	0.804	0.912	–	5.004

Flue Gases from Various Fuels — Atmospheric Pressure

Temp, F	Nat. Gas,* k	Fuel Oil,* k	Coal,† k
0	–	–	–
500	0.264	0.264	0.264
1000	0.360	0.348	0.348
1500	0.444	0.432	0.432
2000	0.528	0.516	0.516
2500	0.612	0.588	0.600

* For 115% total air
† For 120% total air

The thermal conductivities of gases are independent of pressure in the pressure range normally encountered in boiler design, but increase with increasing temperature, the higher values being associated with the lighter and smaller molecules (*see Table 2*). The relatively high conductivity of hydrogen is one factor which makes hydrogen a good cooling medium for electric generators.

Unsteady-state conduction

Thus far the discussion has been limited to steady-state conduction, where temperatures vary from point to point but do not change with time. Unsteady-state conduction occurs in heating or cooling processes where temperatures change with time, as in heating of billets, quenching of steel, regenerative heaters, raising of pressure in a boiler, and warming up and cooling down of steam lines and turbines. With the introduction of time as an

additional variable, the problems of conduction become more complicated. In this complex field, electrical analog models are particularly applicable.

All unsteady-state conduction involves heat storage. For instance, in heating up a furnace, enough heat must be supplied to bring the walls to the operating temperature and also to make up for the steady-state losses of normal operation. In large power boilers that run for long periods of time, heat storage in the walls and boiler metal is an insignificant fraction of the total heat input. In small boilers with refractory settings that are operated only a part of each day, or in heating furnaces that are frequently heated and cooled in batch-process work, heat stored in the walls during start-up may be a considerable proportion of the total heat input. Often in equipment of this type, the use of insulating firebrick of low heat-storage capacity, instead of standard firebrick, is justified by substantial savings in fuel cost and in the time required for start-up, even though the initial cost may be somewhat greater.

Unsteady-state conduction is important in the equalization of temperatures in boiler drums during pressure-raising and -reducing periods. When pressure is raised in a boiler, the water temperature rises and steam generation begins. The inner surface of the steam drum is heated by contact with the water below the waterline and by the condensation of steam above the waterline. The temperatures of the inside and outside of the drum are raised by unsteady-state conduction. It takes time, however, to establish equilibrium temperature conditions, and it is necessary to restrict the rate of pressure rise in thick boiler drums, thus limiting temperature differences in the drum metal to those which will not produce excessive thermal stresses caused by restricting differential expansion (*see Chapters 30 and 34*). During pressure-reducing periods the inside of the drum below the waterline is cooled by boiler water while the top of the drum is cooled only by radiation to the water and by unsteady-state conduction through the metal walls of the drum. The rate of pressure reduction must therefore also be limited.

Heat transfer by radiation

The fractions of radiation reflected, transmitted, and absorbed by a surface are known respectively as the reflectivity, ρ, transmissivity, τ, and absorptivity, α, of the body. The sum of these fractions equals one:

$$\rho + \tau + \alpha = 1$$

Bodies that are good absorbers are equally good emitters of radiation, and it can be shown that at thermal equilibrium their emissivities are equal to their absorptivities. A "blackbody" is defined as one which absorbs all the radiant energy incident upon it, not reflecting or transmitting any of it. The absorptivity and emissivity of a blackbody are each equal to one. In radiant heat transfer parlance, "black" signifies a surface which neither reflects nor transmits radiant energy and has unit absorptivity and emissivity. It does not necessarily mean that the body appears black to the eye. Snow, for instance, absorbs only a small portion of visible light falling upon it, but to the longer wavelengths (the bulk of thermal

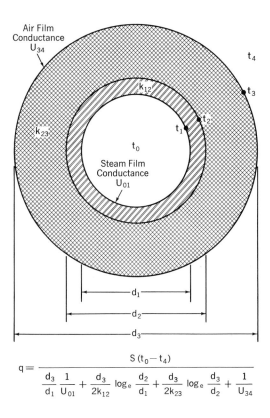

$$q = \frac{S\,(t_0 - t_4)}{\dfrac{d_3}{d_1}\dfrac{1}{U_{01}} + \dfrac{d_3}{2k_{12}}\log_e \dfrac{d_2}{d_1} + \dfrac{d_3}{2k_{23}}\log_e \dfrac{d_3}{d_2} + \dfrac{1}{U_{34}}}$$

Fig. 5 Heat flow through composite cylindrical wall (pipe and insulation) with fluid films included (see *equation 5*).

radiation) snow is almost a blackbody. At a temperature of 2000F a blackbody will glow brightly, since part of its radiation is in the visible range. No actual bodies are completely black, but a hole through the wall of a large enclosure approximates blackbody conditions, since radiation entering the hole will undergo multiple reflections and absorptions so that most of it will be retained inside the enclosure.

The radiation emitted by a blackbody depends upon its surface area and temperature and follows a relationship known as the Stefan-Boltzmann law:

(6) $q = \sigma S T^4$

where:

q = rate of heat flow, Btu/hr
σ = Stefan-Boltzmann constant, 1.71×10^{-9}
    Btu/sq ft, hr, T^4
S = surface area of body, sq ft
T = absolute temperature, $R = F + 460$

This equation is based on the theoretical emissivity value of 1 for a blackbody and must be modified to account for the emissivity of an actual body, as follows:

(7) $q = \sigma \epsilon S T^4$

where ϵ, emissivity, is the ratio of the energy radiated by an actual body to that radiated by a blackbody at the same absolute temperature.

The radiation from a blackbody extends over the whole range of wavelengths, although the bulk of it is concentrated in a moderately narrow band. The wavelength at which the maximum radiation intensity occurs is inversely proportional to the absolute temperature of the

body. Fortunately a number of commercial surfaces, particularly at high temperatures, have emissivities of 0.80 to 0.95 and behave very much like blackbodies. Typical emissivity values are noted in Table 3.

Table 3
Normal emissivities, ϵ, for various surfaces*

Material	Emissivity, ϵ	Temp, F	Description
Aluminum	0.09	212	Commercial sheet
Aluminum oxide	0.63-0.42	530-930	
Aluminum paint	0.27-0.67	212	Varying age and Al content
Brass	0.22	120-660	Dull plate
Copper	0.16-0.13	1970-2330	Molten
Copper	0.023	242	Polished
Cuprous oxide	0.66-0.54	1470-2010	
Iron	0.21	392	Polished, cast
Iron	0.55-0.60	1650-1900	Smooth sheet
Iron	0.24	68	Fresh emeried
Iron oxide	0.85-0.89	930-2190	
Steel	0.79	390-1110	Oxidized at 1100F
Steel	0.66	70	Rolled sheet
Steel	0.28	2910-3270	Molten
Steel (Cr-Ni)	0.44-0.36	420-914	"18-8" rough, after heating
Steel (Cr-Ni)	0.90-0.97	420-980	"25-20" oxidized in service
Brick, red	0.93	70	Rough
Brick, fireclay	0.75	1832	
Carbon, lampblack	0.945	100-700	0.003" or thicker
Water	0.95-0.963	32-212	

* From Hottel

The radiation described above is a function of the temperature and emissivity of the surface of the body and is independent of any other heat exchange mode, i.e., conduction or convection, which may be occurring at the same time.

When two blackbody surfaces are arranged so that all the radiant energy emitted by one is intercepted by the other (as, for example, two infinite parallel planes), the net rate of heat exchange between the hot surface 1 and the cold surface 2 is:

$$(8) \qquad q_{12} = \sigma S \left(T_1^4 - T_2^4\right)$$

where:

q_{12} = Btu/hr
σ = 1.71×10^{-9} Btu/sq ft, hr, T^4
S = surface area of one plane, sq ft
T_1, T_2 = absolute temperatures, R = F + 460, of surfaces 1 and 2

If the two blackbodies are arranged so that all the radiation emitted by one does not fall on the other, it is necessary to introduce an angle factor, F_{12} (less than one), into the equation, which then becomes:

$$(9) \qquad q_{12} = F_{12}\, \sigma S_1 \left(T_1^4 - T_2^4\right)$$

The angle factor depends on the geometry of the arrangement and the body used to define S_1.

If the emissivity of a surface is less than one, but independent of wavelength, the surface is termed a nonselective radiator, or "gray" surface. If the emissivity depends on wavelength, the surface is termed a selective radiator. Exact allowance for the departure of surfaces

from black or ideal radiating characteristics is, in general, too complicated for engineering use. However, if the assumption that all surfaces are gray is permitted, a simpler treatment is possible. This involves introducing an emissivity factor, ϵ, which depends on the geometry, the emissivities involved, and the surface area selected for use as S in the equations. Two special cases are of particular interest:

1. Where one body is completely surrounded by a much larger body (e.g., a steam pipe in a large room), the general equation for the net rate of heat exchange between one surface and another becomes:

$$(10) \qquad q_{12} = \sigma \epsilon_1 S_1 \left(T_1^4 - T_2^4\right)$$

where:

q_{12} = Btu/hr
σ = 1.71×10^{-9} Btu/sq ft, hr, T^4
ϵ_1 = emissivity of smaller surface 1
S_1 = area of smaller surface 1, sq ft
T_1 = absolute temperature of smaller surface 1, R = F + 460
T_2 = absolute temperature of larger surface 2, R = F + 460

2. For the heat exchange between two small gray bodies at considerable distance from one another, the general equation for the net rate of heat exchange between one surface and another becomes:

$$(11) \qquad q_{12} = \sigma \epsilon_1 \epsilon_2 (\omega/2\pi) S_1 (T_1^4 - T_2^4)$$

where:

q_{12} = Btu/hr
σ = 1.71×10^{-9} Btu/sq ft, hr, T^4
ϵ_1, ϵ_2 = emissivities of surfaces 1 and 2
S_1 = area of surface 1, sq ft
ω = solid angle intercepted by body 2 as seen from body 1, steradians (2 steradians comprise a hemispherical solid angle about a point)
π = 3.1416
T_1, T_2 = absolute temperatures of surfaces 1 and 2, R = F + 460

Since the solid angle intercepted by body 2, at a distance from body 1, is something less than 2π steradians, the factor $\omega/2\pi$ is less than unity, and the effective surface area of body 1 becomes $(\omega/2\pi)\,S_1$.

A complicated case of intersolid radiation is encountered in flames made luminous by entrained particles, such as pulverized coal, averaging about 0.001 in. in diameter, or by soot formed by thermal decomposition of hydrocarbons, with particle diameters about 0.00001 in. Radiation from luminous flame is too complex for treatment here.

Radiation from and to gases

Although many gases, such as oxygen and nitrogen, absorb or emit only slight amounts of radiation, others, such as water vapor, carbon dioxide, sulfur dioxide, and carbon monoxide, both absorb and emit. Water vapor and carbon dioxide are important in boiler calculations because of their presence in the combustion products of hydrocarbon fuels. These gases are selective radiators. They emit and absorb radiation only in certain wave-

length bands that lie outside of the visible range, and are consequently identified as nonluminous gas radiators. Whereas solid radiation is a surface phenomenon, a gas both radiates and absorbs (within its absorption bands) at every point throughout the gas body. Furthermore, the emissivity of a gas changes with temperature, and the presence of one radiating gas has an effect on the radiating characteristics of another radiating gas with which it is mixed. The radiant energy emitted by a radiating gaseous mixture depends on gas temperature, the partial pressures of the gaseous radiating constituents, and shape and dimensions of the gas body (*see also Chapter 14*). The fraction of radiant energy emitted by the surroundings, which is absorbed by the gas, depends also on the temperature and surface of the surroundings.

Heat transfer by convection

Heat transfer by convection between a fluid (gas or liquid) and a solid, such as a boiler tube, is expressed in the basic equation:

$$(12) \qquad q_c = U_c S \Delta t$$

where:

q_c = rate of heat flow by convection, Btu/hr
U_c = convection film conductance, Btu/sq ft, hr, F
S = heat transfer surface, sq ft
Δt = temperature difference between fluid bulk temperature and surface temperature of solid

The effect of convection film conductance on the overall heat transfer rate was included in the example of conduction heat transfer given previously. In general, convection film conductance must be determined experimentally using laboratory procedures.

Free convection

The quantity of heat transfer by convection is significantly affected by the type of motion within a fluid. A fluid at rest, exposed to a heated surface, will be at a higher temperature adjacent to the surface than elsewhere. The differences in density, because of this difference in temperature, will cause the fluid to circulate and carry heat from one place to another. This type of heat transfer is known as free or natural convection. It is distinguished from forced convection, where outside mechanical force, change of state of the fluid, or stack induction is used to circulate the fluid. The complex relationships of the numerous variables affecting free-convection heat transfer conductance are fully discussed in texts on the subject. In the power field air and flue gases at atmospheric pressure are the important natural-convection heat transfer media. In this case the following equation is applicable:

$$(13) \qquad U_{fc} = C(\Delta t)^{1/3}$$

where:

U_{fc} = free-convection film conductance, Btu/sq ft, hr, F
C = coefficient, characteristic of shape and position of heat transfer surface
Δt = difference in temperature between the surface and the air or gas, F

Values of C for various surfaces at different attitudes are listed below:

Horizontal plates facing upward	0.22
Vertical plates or pipes more than 1 ft high	0.19
Horizontal pipes	0.18

The flow resulting from the boiling of a liquid at a heating surface should be differentiated from free convection. Whereas the free-convection film conductance for water is about 25-50 Btu/sq ft, hr, F, the heat transfer conductance for boiling water may vary between very wide limits.

Forced convection and dimensionless numbers

In forced-convection heat transfer, flow of the fluid is produced by mechanical means such as a fan, pump, or natural-draft stack.

The correlation of heat transfer data with the fluid flow phenomena is most satisfactorily accomplished by the use of dimensionless numbers. These dimensionless groupings have been developed by many investigators. In the case of forced-convection heat transfer, the best method compares fluid flow, temperature and heat transfer characteristics for geometrically similar systems. The "scale model" is a common example. Here the physical size is changed, but the relative proportions remain constant.

The Reynolds number, $\rho V D/\mu$, is a familiar criterion for similarity in pipes flowing full of fluid, where ρ = fluid density, V = fluid velocity, D = pipe diameter and μ = absolute viscosity. The Reynolds number represents the ratio of inertial forces, F_I, to viscous forces, F_μ, as follows:

$$F_I = \text{mass} \times \text{acceleration} = \rho L^3 V^2/L = \rho L^2 V^2$$
$$F_\mu = \frac{\text{viscosity} \times \text{area}}{\text{time}} = \mu L^2 V/L = \mu L V$$
$$F_I/F_\mu = \rho L^2 V^2/\mu L V = \rho L V/\mu$$

where:

ρ = density of fluid, lb/cu ft
V = mean velocity of fluid, ft/hr
μ = viscosity of fluid, lb/ft, hr
L = characteristic linear dimension, ft

For fluid flowing full in closed conduits, the characteristic linear dimension is the internal diameter for flow in pipe or the equivalent diameter for conduits of non-circular cross section. The equivalent diameter is defined as 4 times the area of the flow cross section divided by the duct perimeter. It can be demonstrated mathematically that, for dynamically similar fluid motion in geometrically similar systems of different size, the Reynolds numbers are equal. In the derivation of the Reynolds number, it is assumed that the fluid is a continuous medium filling the conduit and that gravitational and intermolecular forces are negligible compared with inertial and viscous forces.

Since inertial forces are proportional to velocity squared, and viscous forces are proportional to the first power of velocity, inertial forces dominate the flow pattern at high velocities (high Reynolds number). At low velocities the viscous forces may completely dominate, resulting in what is defined as viscous or laminar flow. Laminar or streamline flow exists if the Reynolds number

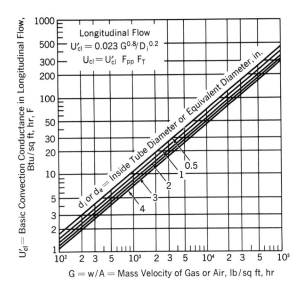

Fig. 6 Basic longitudinal flow convection conductance, U'_{cl}, as related to air, gas or steam mass velocity, G, for various tube diameters.

is less than 2000. At Reynolds numbers greater than 12,000, the inertial forces normally dominate and turbulent flow occurs. Between these limits there is a transition zone where either type of flow may occur.

Another dimensionless group of factors known as the Prandtl number, $c_p\mu/k$, serves as a criterion of temperature gradient similarity. This group can be considered as specific heat, c_p, divided by the ratio of thermal conductivity to viscosity, k/μ. The numerator, c_p, is a measure of the temperature rise of a given mass of fluid for a given heat energy input. The denominator, k/μ, is a measure of the ease of heat transmission through the fluid, since high conductivity or low viscosity stimulates heat transmission.

The dimensionless group known as the Nusselt number, $U_c D/k$, is a criterion of heat transfer similarity and can be considered as a ratio of the size factor, D, to the thickness of the boundary layer of the fluid, which can be expressed as k/U_c.

The dimensionless group known as the Stanton number, $U_c/\rho V c_p$, is the ratio of the conductance to the product of the mass velocity and the specific heat at constant pressure, which is the ratio of the heat absorbed to that available for absorption.

The Nusselt number can be expressed as the product of the Stanton, Reynolds, and Prandtl numbers:

$$(14) \qquad \frac{U_c D}{k} = \left\{\frac{U_c}{\rho V c_p}\right\}\left\{\frac{\rho V D}{\mu}\right\}\left\{\frac{c_p\mu}{k}\right\}$$

where:

$\dfrac{U_c D}{k}$ = Nusselt number, dimensionless

$\dfrac{U_c}{\rho V c_p}$ = Stanton number, dimensionless

$\dfrac{\rho V D}{\mu}$ = Reynolds number, dimensionless

$\dfrac{c_p\mu}{k}$ = Prandtl number, dimensionless

Laminar flow inside tubes. In streamline or laminar flow, the elements or layers of the fluid flow parallel to the axis of the channel, with no appreciable lateral disturbance. For heating or cooling viscous liquids in the laminar-flow region inside horizontal or vertical tubes, the film conductance between fluid and surface, based on the arithmetic mean temperature, can be determined by the following empirical equation from McAdams:

$$(15) \qquad U_{cl} = 1.86\frac{k}{D_i}\left\{\frac{\mu}{\mu_s}\right\}^{0.14}\left\{\frac{GD_i}{\mu}\frac{c_p\mu}{k}\frac{D_i}{L}\right\}^{1/3}$$

where:

U_{cl} = convection film conductance in longitudinal flow, Btu/sq ft, hr, F

D_i = inside tube diameter, ft

k = conductivity of fluid within tube, Btu/sq ft, hr, F/ft

G = mass velocity, or mass flow, of fluid within tubes, lb/hr, sq ft of cross-sectional area

c_p = specific heat at constant pressure, Btu/lb, F

L = heated length of straight tube, ft

μ = absolute fluid viscosity at bulk temperature, lb/ft, hr

μ_s = absolute fluid viscosity at surface temperature, lb/ft, hr

In the case of low-viscosity fluids, such as water and gases, a more complex equation is required to allow for the effects of natural convection at the heat transfer surface. This refinement is of little interest in industrial practice, since it is generally impractical to use water and gases in laminar flow.

Turbulent flow. In turbulent flow, the fluid elements move radially as well as axially. The combination of radial and axial components of flow sets up an eddy motion, which increases the activity within the body of the fluid. Consequently there is a substantial increase in the heat transer with turbulent flow as compared with laminar flow.

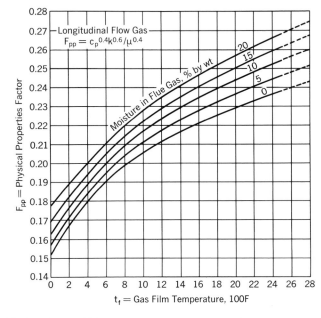

Fig. 7 Effect of film temperature, t_f, on the physical properties factor, F_{pp}, for gas in longitudinal flow.

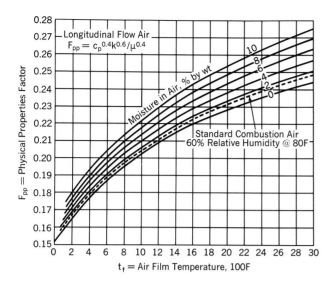

Fig. 8 Effect of film temperature, t_f, on the physical properties factor, F_{pp}, for air in longitudinal flow.

Studies of the velocity gradient across a flowing fluid indicate that in turbulent flow the velocity at the heat transfer surface is zero. In the zone immediately adjacent to the surface, known as the sublaminar layer, the flow is laminar, and the heat leaving or approaching the surface travels by conduction. In the next zone, known as the buffer layer, where the motion is a mixture of laminar and turbulent flow, the heat is transferred partly by convection and partly by conduction. Heat is transferred mainly by convection in the bulk of the stream cross section, known as the turbulent core in the case of flow inside pipes or tubes.

The laminar flow in the sublaminar layer and the laminar component in the buffer layer act as a barrier to the convection transfer of heat to or from the surface. This barrier may be likened to a film, the thickness of which depends, to a certain extent, on the velocity of the fluid. By increasing the velocity a part of this film can be swept away, thus decreasing its thickness and reducing the resistance to heat transfer by conduction.

Turbulent flow inside tubes. Extensive research data on gases and liquids of low viscosity in turbulent flow through long tubes have been correlated using dimensionless numbers resulting in the following equation:

$$(16) \qquad \frac{U_{cl} D_i}{k} = 0.023 \left\{ \frac{GD_i}{\mu} \right\}^{0.8} \left\{ \frac{c_p\mu}{k} \right\}^{0.4} \left\{ \frac{T_b}{T_f} \right\}^{0.8}$$

$$(17) \qquad U_{cl} = 0.023 \left\{ \frac{G^{0.8} c_p{}^{0.4} k^{0.6} T_b{}^{0.8}}{D_i{}^{0.2} \mu^{0.4} T_f{}^{0.8}} \right\}$$

where:

U_{cl} = convection film conductance in longitudinal flow, Btu/sq ft, hr, F

T_b = avg bulk absolute temp of fluid, R = F + 460

T_f = avg film absolute temp

$\quad = \dfrac{\text{surface abs temp} + T_b}{2}$, R = F + 460

Equation (17) applies to both the heating and the cooling of fluids flowing inside clean conduits. For convenience in use, equation (17) is presented in the form:

$$(18) \qquad U_{cl} = U'_{cl} F_{pp} F_T$$

where:

U'_{cl} = basic convection conductance in longitudinal flow
$\quad = 0.023 G^{0.8}/D_i{}^{0.2}$ Btu/sq ft, hr, F (Fig. 6)

F_{pp} = physical properties factor, $c_p{}^{0.4}k^{0.6}/\mu^{0.4}$, evaluated at film temperature, t_f (Figs. 7, 8 and 9)
Where the value of F_{pp} for steam cannot be obtained from Fig. 9, it can be calculated using values of c_p, k and μ from ASME Steam Tables.

$$t_f = \frac{\text{avg surface temp} + \text{avg bulk temp, F}}{2}$$

F_T = temperature factor = $(T_b/T_f)^{0.8}$ (Fig. 10)

Turbulent flow outside tubes. In the steam boiler, the most important application of convection is in the transfer of heat from hot combustion gases to the various

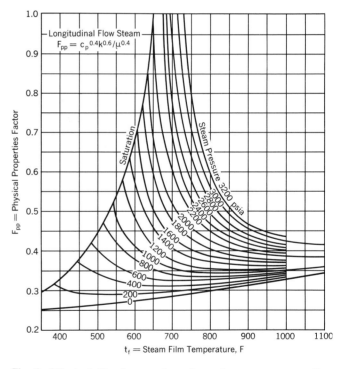

Fig. 9 Effect of film temperature, t_f, and pressure, p, on the physical properties factor, F_{pp}, for steam in longitudinal flow.

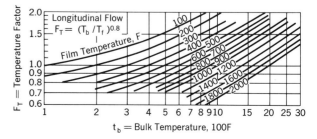

Fig. 10 Temperature factor, F_T, for converting mass velocity from bulk to film basis; longitudinal flow air, gas or steam.

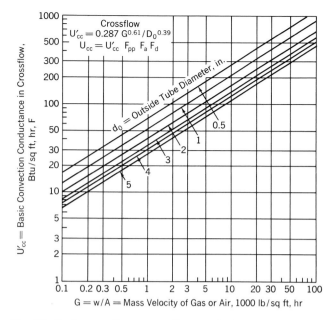

Fig. 11 Basic crossflow convection conductance, U'_{cc}, as related to gas or air mass velocity, G, for various tube diameters.

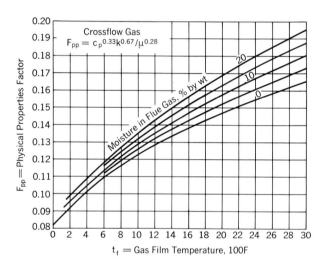

Fig. 12 Effect of film temperature, t_f, on the physical properties factor, F_{pp}, for gas in crossflow.

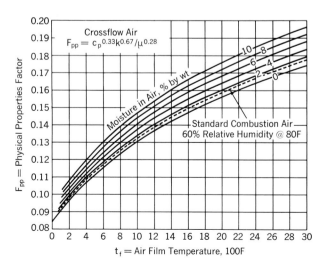

Fig. 13 Effect of film temperature, t_f, on the physical properties factor, F_{pp}, for air in crossflow.

heat-absorbing tubular surfaces. Compared with the extensive research on heat transfer for fluids flowing inside tubes, little has been done to establish convection heat transfer coefficients for crossflow over tube banks. Perhaps the most authoritative and complete data on crossflow heat transfer are those obtained as part of a B&W research program. The following equation was developed from the correlation of these data:

$$(19) \quad \frac{U_{cc} D_o}{k} = 0.287 \left\{ \frac{G D_o}{\mu} \right\}^{0.61} \left\{ \frac{c p \mu}{k} \right\}^{0.33} F_a$$

$$(20) \quad U_{cc} = 0.287 \left\{ \frac{G^{0.61} c_p^{0.33} k^{0.67}}{D_o^{0.39} \mu^{0.28}} \right\} F_a$$

where:

D_o = outside tube diameter, ft

U_{cc} = convection film conductance in crossflow, Btu/sq ft, hr, F

F_a = arrangement factor which corrects for difference in geometric configuration from base arrangement

Equation (20) applies to both the heating and the cooling of fluids flowing outside clean tubes in crossflow. For convenience in use, equation (20) is presented in the form:

$$(21) \quad U_{cc} = U'_{cc} F_{pp} F_a F_d$$

where:

U'_{cc} = basic convection conductance in crossflow
= $0.287 G^{0.61}/D_o^{0.39}$ Btu/sq ft, hr, F (Fig. 11)

F_{pp} = physical properties factor, $c_p^{0.33} k^{0.67}/\mu^{0.28}$, evaluated at film temperature, t_f (Figs. 12 and 13)

F_a = arrangement factor (Fig. 14)

F_d = depth factor (Fig. 15)

t_f = avg film temperature
= $\dfrac{\text{avg surface temp} + \text{avg bulk temp, F}}{2}$

The arrangement factor, F_a, depends on the tube arrangement, the ratios of tube spacing to tube diameter and the Reynolds number. Values for F_a are given in Fig. 14 for various conditions. The mass velocity factor, G, in equation (20) and in the Reynolds numbers for the curves in the figure just mentioned, is calculated on the minimum free area available for fluid flow.

The value of the film conductance, U_{cc} in equation (20) applies to banks of tubes which are 10 or more rows deep in the direction of gas flow. For undisturbed flow (flow is considered undisturbed when it is straight and uninterrupted for at least 4 ft before entering a tube bank) approaching a bank of less than ten rows, the film conductance, U_{cc} must be multiplied by a correction factor, F_d, known as the depth factor, given in Fig. 15. Factor F_d should be taken as unity when the tube bank is preceded by a bend, screen or damper.

Although equations (17) and (18) were developed for flow inside tubes, the same equations can also be developed by correlating the limited data available for flow of gases longitudinally over the outside of tubular surfaces except that an equivalent diameter must be substituted for the tube diameter. For flow along banks of

circular tubes arranged in rectangular spacing, the equivalent diameter is:

$$D_e = \frac{4(L_1 L_2 - 0.785\, D_o{}^2)}{\pi\, D_o}$$

where:

D_e = equivalent diameter, ft
D_o = tube outside diameter, ft
L_1 and L_2 are tube pitches, ft

Combinations of heat transfer mechanisms

In a practical heat exchanger, the transfer of heat usually involves a combination of two, and in many cases all three of the fundamental mechanisms of heat transfer—conduction, convection and radiation. For instance, in the case of a tube wall separating two fluids, the convection conductances for each of the two fluids as well as the conduction conductance through the tube wall must be evaluated. In solving heat transfer problems involving combinations of heat transfer mechanisms, it is advantageous to combine the various conductances into a single overall conductance, U.

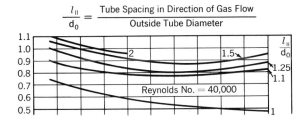

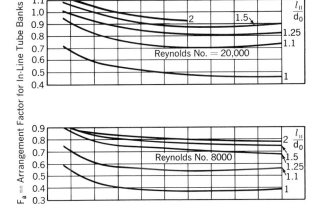

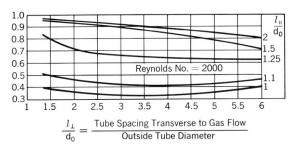

Fig. 14 Arrangement factor, F_a, as affected by Reynolds number for various in-line tube patterns, crossflow gas or air.

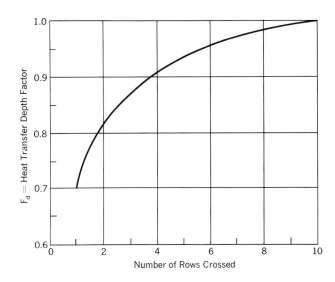

Fig. 15 Heat transfer depth factor for number of tube rows crossed in convection banks.

The flow of thermal energy is analagous to the flow of electrical energy insofar as the concept of resistance to flow is concerned. This analogy is particularly useful in solving complex heat transfer problems through the use of electrical analogues of the heat transfer circuits. As in electrical circuitry, the resistance to flow is the reciprocal of the conductance, or $R = 1/U$, and resistances in series with each other are additive.

Convection and conduction

In Fig. 16 a clean tube wall separates two fluids. The outside fluid temperature is t_o and the inside fluid temperature is t_i. The overall resistance, R, equals $R_{ab} + R_{bc} + R_{cd}$ where R_{ab} is the resistance across the outside film, R_{bc} is the resistance across the tube wall, and R_{cd} is the resistance across the inside film.

Using the definition, $R = 1/U$

$$R_{ab} = \frac{1}{U_{co}};\quad R_{bc} = \frac{0.5\, d_o \log_e d_o/d_i}{k};$$

$$R_{cd} = \frac{1}{U_{ci}\, d_i/d_o}$$

where:

U_{co} = outside film convection conductance, Btu/sq ft, hr, F
k = thermal conductivity of tube material, Btu/sq ft, hr, F/in.
U_{ci} = inside film convection conductance, Btu/sq ft, hr, F
d_o = outside tube diameter, in.
d_i = inside tube diameter, in.

then (22) $\quad R = \dfrac{1}{U_{co}} + \dfrac{0.5\, d_o \log_e d_o/d_i}{k} + \dfrac{1}{U_{ci}\, d_i/d_o}$

A common example of this combination of heat transfer mechanisms in a steam generator is a superheater tube with flue gas on the outside of the tube and steam on the inside of the tube. In this case the resistance to heat flow of the gas and steam films is much greater than the resistance of the tube wall. In evaluating the overall resistance, the metal resistance may be neglected without

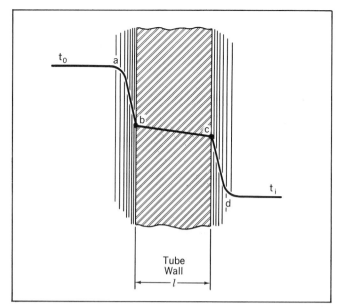

Fig. 16 Temperature gradients through fluid films and tube wall separating two fluids.

serious error. Omitting the metal resistance and with U_{ci} adjusted to the same surface as U_{co}, equation (22) may be revised to define the combined conductance, U, as:

$$(23) \qquad U = \frac{U_{co} \times U_{ci}}{U_{co} + U_{ci}}$$

This is the general equation for the overall convection conductance between two fluids, where resistance to heat flow of the metal separating the fluids is negligible.

Convection and radiation

Carbon dioxide and water vapor, which are found in considerable quantities in the products of combustion of hydrocarbon fuels, absorb and emit radiant energy. Therefore, heat is transferred in tube banks by radiation as well as by convection. The resistance of electrical circuits, in parallel, is the reciprocal of the sum of the reciprocals of the resistance of each circuit, so by analogy the heat transfer resistance, R, can be expressed as:

$$(24) \qquad R = \frac{1}{\dfrac{1}{R_{rg}} + \dfrac{1}{R_{cg}}} + R_{tw} + R_{cs}$$

where:

R_{rg} = resistance of gas film (the hotter fluid) to radiant heat flow

R_{cg} = resistance of gas film (the hotter fluid) to convection heat flow

R_{tw} = resistance of tube wall to conduction heat flow

R_{cs} = resistance of the other fluid film (the colder fluid) to convection heat flow

Substitution of the reciprocals of conductances for the resistances in the electrical analogue gives the relation:

$$\frac{1}{U} = \frac{1}{U_{rg} + U_{cg}} + \frac{1}{U_{cs}}$$

This is predicated on negligible tube wall resistance and on the use of the same surface as the basis of de-

termining all conductances. By rearranging, this may be written:

$$(25) \qquad U = \frac{(U_{rg} + U_{cg})\, U_{cs}}{U_{rg} + U_{cg} + U_{cs}}$$

where:

U = overall conductance, Btu/sq ft, hr, F

U_{rg} = intertube radiation conductance, Btu/sq ft, hr, F

U_{cg} = hotter fluid convection conductance, Btu/sq ft, hr, F

U_{cs} = colder fluid convection conductance, Btu/sq ft, hr, F

In equation (25), U represents the combined conductance for most boiler, economizer, superheater, and air heater heat transfer problems, where the resistance to heat flow through metal (such as tube walls) is small and may be neglected. This usually is true where the quantities of heat transferred and the resulting temperatures of the hotter and colder fluids are to be determined. However, where metal temperatures must be accurately established, it is necessary to include conductance through the metal.

The combined conductance, U, from equation (25) can now be used in the general equation for heat flow, $q = US\Delta t_m$, which is identical with equation (1) with Δt_m, the logarithmic mean temperature difference, substituted for Δt.

Mean temperature difference

The above examples are predicated on the condition that the hot fluid is at one temperature and the cold fluid is at another lower temperature with a specific temperature difference to effect heat transfer from source to receiver. In actual heat transfer equipment, of course, the fluid temperatures change as the fluids pass over the heat transfer surface and many temperature differences exist. It is necessary to determine the mean effective temperature difference for the fluids while in transit through the heat transfer surface. The general expression for mean effective temperature difference, Δt_m, is as follows:

$$(26) \qquad \Delta t_m = \frac{\Delta t_1 - \Delta t_2}{\log_e (\Delta t_1/\Delta t_2)}$$

where:

Δt_1 = initial temperature difference

Δt_2 = final temperature difference

Evaluation of the mean effective temperature difference is dependent on the relative flow of the heat transfer fluids. There are three general arrangements of heat transfer surface insofar as the relative flow of the fluids is concerned. These arrangements are parallel flow, counterflow and crossflow. In parallel flow, both fluids enter at the same relative physical location with respect to the heat transfer surface and flow in generally parallel paths over the heating surface. In counterflow, the two fluids enter at opposite ends of the heat transfer surface and flow in opposite directions over the surface. In crossflow, the flow paths of the two fluids are, in general, perpendicular to one another.

Fig. 17 shows diagrammatically the flow arrangements for parallel flow, counterflow and crossflow. It also presents equation (26) written specifically for each case. For crossflow the counterflow form of the equation is used with a crossflow correction factor, obtained from a set of curves included as Fig. 17d.

Heat transfer in porous materials

Porosity is an important factor in evaluating the effectiveness of materials used in insulation for the reduction of heat losses. In boiler applications, porous materials are backed up by solid walls or casings, so that there is no appreciable fluid flow through the pores of the material.

Heat flow in porous insulating materials is by conduction through the material itself and by the combination of conduction, convection and radiation across the gas filled voids in the material. The relative magnitudes of heat flow from these various mechanisms of heat transfer depend on the porosity of the material, the type of porosity (e.g., cellular or granular), the type of material, the composition and density of gas filling the voids, the temperature gradient through the material, and the absolute temperature of the material.

The analytical evaluation of the separate mechanisms of heat transfer in porous materials is difficult. Overall conductivity values are established experimentally (Fig. 7, Chapter 16). The expression for the quantity of heat flowing through a porous material per unit of time becomes similar to the expression for conduction of heat through a homogeneous substance when an overall con-

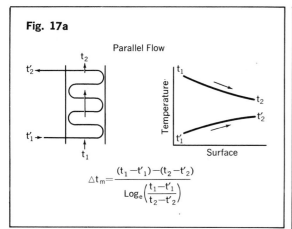

Fig. 17a

Parallel Flow

$$\triangle t_m = \frac{(t_1 - t'_1) - (t_2 - t'_2)}{\mathrm{Log}_e\left(\dfrac{t_1 - t'_1}{t_2 - t'_2}\right)}$$

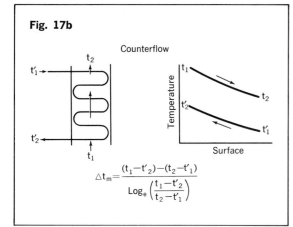

Fig. 17b

Counterflow

$$\triangle t_m = \frac{(t_1 - t'_2) - (t_2 - t'_1)}{\mathrm{Log}_e\left(\dfrac{t_1 - t'_2}{t_2 - t'_1}\right)}$$

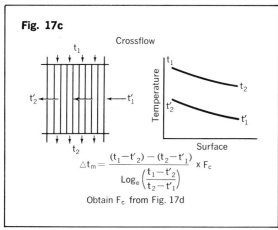

Fig. 17c

Crossflow

$$\triangle t_m = \frac{(t_1 - t'_2) - (t_2 - t'_1)}{\mathrm{Log}_e\left(\dfrac{t_1 - t'_2}{t_2 - t'_1}\right)} \times F_c$$

Obtain F_c from Fig. 17d

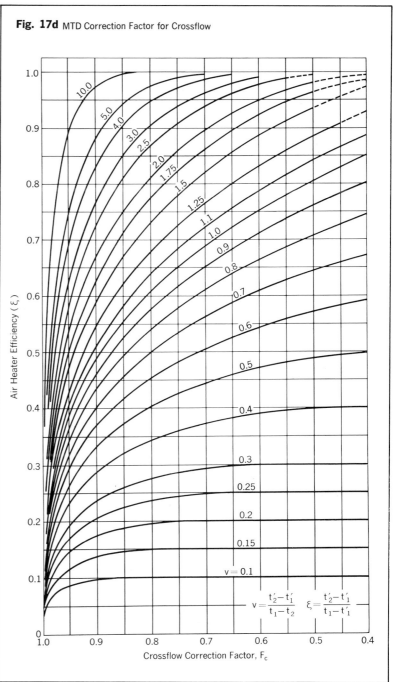

Fig. 17d MTD Correction Factor for Crossflow

$$v = \frac{t'_2 - t'_1}{t_1 - t_2} \qquad \xi = \frac{t'_2 - t'_1}{t_1 - t'_1}$$

Air Heater Efficiency (ξ)

Crossflow Correction Factor, F_c

Fig. 17 Mean effective temperature difference.

ductivity is used. The effect on thermal conductivity of varying the pore size while maintaining approximately a constant density of the material is shown by Fig. 18.

In high-temperature applications, the principal means of heat transfer across the voids is by radiation. Consequently for good insulation, the mean radiating path in the direction of heat flow should be disrupted insofar as possible. In low-temperature applications, heat flow by conduction and convection across the voids approaches in magnitude the heat flow by radiation. It is therefore important not only that the radiation path should be disrupted but also that the pores should be such as to keep the fluid stagnant in pools or pockets, so that heat flow by free convection will also be inhibited.

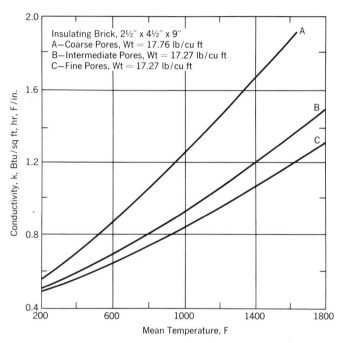

Fig. 18 Effect of pore size on thermal conductivity, *k*, of a porous insulating brick.

Other forms of heat transfer

Condensation—film type

When a pure saturated vapor strikes a surface of lower temperature, the vapor condenses and a film is formed on the surface. If the condensate film flows along the surface because of gravity alone and a condition of laminar flow exists throughout the film thickness, then heat transfer through this film is by conduction only.

Since the heat exchange is by conduction, the thickness of the condensate film has a direct effect on the quantity of heat transferred. The film thickness, in turn, depends on the rate at which the condensate is removed. On a vertical surface, because of drainage, the thickness of the film at the bottom will be greater than at the top. Film thickness increases as a plate surface is inclined from the vertical position.

An increase in the film temperature, which is the mean of the surface and vapor temperatures, decreases film thickness, since the drainage velocity increases with decrease in viscosity. The film thickness is affected by an appreciable velocity of the vapor because of the frictional drag between the vapor and the condensate. The preferable arrangement of the surface, therefore, is such that the vapor flows in the same direction (downward) as the condensate. As heat transfer increases with an increase in the temperature difference between the vapor and the surface, the thickness of the condensate film also increases. The surface conductance of heat transfer, therefore, decreases with an increase in temperature difference, which is an unusual relationship.

Mass transfer and diffusion

There are two related phenomena involved in some types of condensation. When a mixture of condensable vapor and a noncondensable gas is in contact with a surface that is below the dew point of the mixture, some condensation occurs, and a film of liquid is formed on the surface. An example of this phenomenon is the condensation of water vapor on the outside of a glass of iced tea.

The mixture of vapor and noncondensable gas adjacent to the condensate film contains a lower proportion of vapor than the main body of the mixture, since some of the vapor has been removed as condensate. As vapor from the main body of the mixture diffuses through the vapor-lean layer, it is condensed on the cold surface. The rate of condensation is thus governed by the laws of gas diffusion, while the sensible heat transmission is controlled by the laws of heat conduction and convection. This mode of heat transfer is important in the design of equipment such as cooling towers and humidifiers, where mixtures of vapors and noncondensable gases are encountered.

Evaporation or boiling

The phenomenon of boiling is discussed in Chapter 1, where the advantages of nucleate boiling from the standpoint of heat transfer are particularly noted. Natural-circulation fossil fuel boilers are designed to operate in the nucleate boiling range. In this range the film conductance varies from 10,000 to 20,000 Btu/sq ft, hr, F. This is so high that it is not a limiting factor in the design of fossil fuel boilers provided scale and other deposits are prevented by proper water treatment, and provided the design is such as to avoid DNB (departure from nucleate boiling).

In once-through boilers, water is evaporated to dryness in the furnace-wall tubes which are essentially continuous with the superheater tubes. These units must be designed for subcooled nucleate boiling, nucleate boiling, and film boiling, depending on fluid conditions and expected maximum heat absorption rates.

Heat transfer applications

In applying theoretical heat transfer relationships to the design of steam generators, consideration must be given to practical factors, such as (1) available space in a plant, (2) fuel type and firing rate, (3) feedwater quality, (4) operating and maintenance costs, (5) allowable metal temperatures and thickness of drum and tube walls and (6) standards set by boiler manufacturers for a range of tube sizes and arrangements based on operating experience (*see Chapters 12, 13 and 14*).

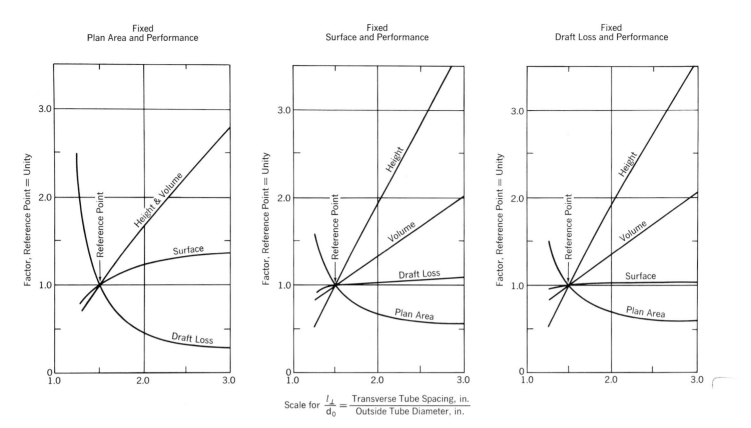

Fixed
Plan Area and Performance

Fixed
Surface and Performance

Fixed
Draft Loss and Performance

Scale for $\dfrac{l_\perp}{d_0} = \dfrac{\text{Transverse Tube Spacing, in.}}{\text{Outside Tube Diameter, in.}}$

Fig. 19 General effect of convection tube arrangement on volume occupied, amount of surface, draft loss, and floor area for selected conditions fixed. Based on tubes in line with longitudinal spacing $l_\| = 2$ x tube OD.

Convection banks

Tube spacing and arrangement. In addition to heat absorption and resistance to gas flow, other important factors to be considered in establishing the optimum tube spacing and arrangement for a convection surface are slagging or fouling of surfaces, accessibility for cleaning, and space occupied. The optimum transverse spacing for in-line or staggered banks should be selected with due regard for these limitations. A large longitudinal spacing in relation to the transverse spacing is usually undesirable, since the length of flow path for the calculated surface may be excessive.

The effect on design of various ratios of transverse tube spacing to outside tube diameter is plotted in Fig. 19 for in-line tube banks and longitudinal spacing equal to two tube diameters. By entering the curves with calculated values for draft loss, heating surface, and space occupied based on an assumed tube diameter and transverse spacing, a pattern best suited to the requirements of the unit can be selected. Similar curves can be plotted for staggered arrangements with a fixed back pitch.

Tube diameter. For turbulent flow, the heat transfer conductance is inversely proportional to some power of the tube diameter. In equations (17) and (20) the exponent for longitudinal flow is 0.20 and for crossflow, 0.39. These equations indicate that the tube diameter should be held to a minimum for most effective heat transfer. However this optimum tube diameter may require an arrangement that is expensive to fabricate, difficult to install and costly to maintain in operating condition. A compromise between heat transfer effectiveness

and manufacturing, erection, and service limitations is thus necessary in the selection of tube diameter.

In oil-fired marine boilers of high rating, 1-in. OD tubes are used in the boiler bank beyond the screen tubes. The higher heat absorption rates in the furnace necessitate an augmented quantity of circulating water. For this reason the screen and water-wall tubes are usually 1½-in. OD.

Penetration of radiation. A convection bank of tubes bordering a furnace or a cavity acts as a blackbody radiant heat absorber. Some of this heat, however, radiates through the spaces between the tubes of the first row and may penetrate beyond the fourth row. The quantity of radiant heat penetration can be established by geometric or analytical methods. The effect of this penetration is especially important in establishing tube temperatures for superheaters located close to a furnace or high-temperature cavity.

Effect of lanes. Lanes in tube banks, formed by the omission of a row of tubes, may decrease the heat absorption considerably. These passages, in effect, act as bypasses for the hot gases through the banks. Although the overall efficiency decreases, the high mass flow and greater gas weight through the lanes increase the absorption rates of the adjacent tubes. Critical tube temperatures in superheaters or steaming conditions in economizers may develop. Whenever possible, lanes should be eliminated both within tube banks and between tube banks and walls. This is not always possible, e.g., with superheaters space must be allowed for additional surface to satisfy future increases in steam temperature. A

calculation for the lanes, taking into account the increased gas weight and mass velocity, is necessary in such cases.

Heat transfer to water

Water-film conductance. The film conductance for water in economizers is so much higher than the gas-side conductance that it is neglected in determining economizer surface.

Boiling-water conductance. The combined gas-side conductance (convection plus intertube radiation) seldom exceeds 30 Btu/sq ft, hr, F in boiler design practice. The film conductance for boiling water (10,000 Btu/sq ft, hr, F) is so much larger that it is generally neglected in calculating the resistance to heat flow.

Effect of oil or scale. Water- and steam-side scale deposits interpose a high resistance to the flow of heat. The additional temperature drop required to maintain a given fluid temperature inside the tube, as the thickness of the scale increases, leads to a high metal temperature and ultimate failure. The high heat-absorption rates in furnace enclosure tubes of high-capacity boilers make it essential to prevent the formation of scale (*see Fig. 13, Chapter 24*) to assure continuity of service. Deposition of scale and other contaminants is prevented by good feedwater treatment and proper operating practices.

Heat transfer to steam

In the design of superheaters, the steam film constitutes a significant resistance to the flow of heat, and although this resistance is much lower than the gas-side resistance, it cannot be neglected in computing the overall resistance to heat flow or the heat transfer rate. It is particularly significant in calculating superheater tube temperatures, since the temperature of the inside tube wall is equal to the steam temperature plus the temperature drop through the steam film.

Steam film conductance is calculated from equation (18) using information from Figs. 6, 9 and 10. If steam-film conductance is designated as U_s, the film temperature drop (Δt_f) is $q/S \div U_s$, where q/S and U_s are expressed in Btu/sq ft, hr and Btu/sq ft, hr, F, respectively, using the outside surface area of the tube as the base in each expression.

It is imperative to prevent scale deposits in superheater tubes because of the magnitude of the resistance to heat flow in the steam film and the elevated temperatures at which superheater tubes operate. Even an extremely thin layer of scale forms an insulating barrier which, together with the steam film, may be sufficient to cause overheating and ultimate failure of a tube.

Furnaces

An analytical solution of the problem of heat transfer in the furnace of a steam-generating unit is extremely complex. It is not possible to calculate furnace outlet temperatures by theoretical methods alone. Nevertheless, the furnace outlet temperature must be predicted correctly since, in a large measure, this temperature determines the design of the remainder of the unit, particularly the superheater. The complexities of the problem are demonstrated in the following discussion.

In the furnace of a steam-generating unit, all of the principal mechanisms of heat transfer take place simultaneously. These mechanisms are: intersolid radiation between solids in fuel beds or suspended solid particles and tubes and refractory materials, nonluminous gas radiation from the products of combustion, convection from the furnace gases to the furnace walls, and conduction through ash deposits on tubes.

Fuel variation is significant. Not only are there important differences inherent in the use of different fuels and in the manner in which they are burned, as in stoker, pulverized-coal, gas, oil, or waste-fuel firing, but there are also differences caused by the use of different types of the same fuel. Coal, for example, may be high volatile or low volatile, and may have much or little ash. The ash fusion temperature may be high or low, and may vary considerably with the oxidizing properties of the furnace atmosphere.

Furnace geometry is complex. Furnaces vary in shape and size, in the location and spacing of burners, in the size of fuel beds, in the disposition and type of cooling surface, in the spacing of tubes in furnace walls, and in the arrangement of arches and hoppers. Flame shape and length also affect the pattern of radiation in the furnace.

Surface characteristics vary. The enclosing furnace walls may include any combination of fuel arrangements,

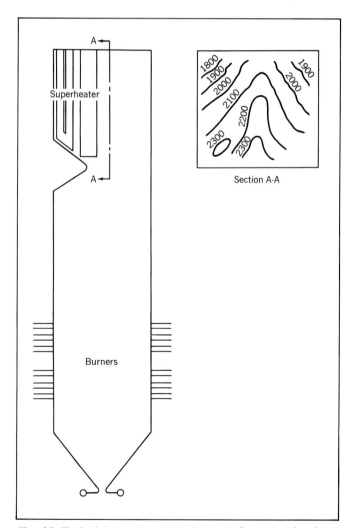

Fig. 20 Typical temperature contours at furnace exit of opposed-fired Radiant boiler.

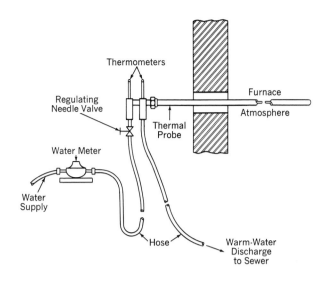

Fig. 21 Special thermal probe or calorimeter (diagrammatic) used to establish the heat absorption rates of surfaces throughout a furnace.

refractory material, studded tubes, spaced tubes backed by refractory, close-spaced tubes, membrane construction or tube banks. Emissivities of various types of surfaces are different. The water-cooled surface may be covered with fluid slag or dry ash in any thickness, or it may be clean. Heat-absorbing surface in a furnace may, when clean, have absorption rates in excess of 175,000 Btu/sq ft, hr. When slag accumulations reach equilibrium, the absorption rate may be reduced to 50,000 Btu/sq ft, hr, or lower.

Temperature varies throughout the furnace. Fuel and air enter at relatively low temperatures, reach a high temperature during combustion, and cool again as the products of combustion give up heat to the furnace enclosure. All temperatures change with load, excess air, burner adjustment and other operating conditions.

Recognizing the need for operating information to supplement theoretical calculation, B&W in the thirties, developed the high-velocity thermocouple to measure furnace gas temperatures (see Chapter 33). Extensive field tests have been conducted for the measurement of gas temperatures in operating units. Fig. 20 shows typical temperature contours of gas leaving a furnace, derived from actual temperature measurements.

The water-cooled thermal probe (Fig. 21) is another useful tool for establishing heat absorption in a furnace. Variations in heat absorption in a boiler furnace are shown in Fig. 22.

The empirical methods for calculating furnace temperature employ test results and data accumulated from operating experience to supplement theoretical analysis based on heat transfer principles.

To correlate data and calculations for different furnaces, it is necessary to have methods for comparing the relative effectiveness of different types of furnace wall surface. The effectiveness of tubes spaced other than touching as compared with completely water-cooled surface is shown in Fig. 23. A wall of flat-studded tubes is considered completely water-cooled. The effectiveness of expected ash covering, as compared with completely water-cooled surface, can also be estimated. The entire

furnace envelope can then be evaluated in terms of equivalent cold surface.

The heat energy supplied by the fuel and by the pre-heated combustion air, corrected for items such as unburned combustible loss, radiation loss and moisture-in-the-fuel loss, may be combined into a single variable known as heat available. Heat available divided by equivalent flat projected water-cooled furnace enclosure surface is called the furnace heat release rate. Heat available divided by the furnace volume is called the furnace liberation rate. Furnace-exit-gas temperature is primarily a function of furnace heat release rate rather than furnace liberation rate. The approximate relation of furnace-exit-gas temperature to heat release rate for three typical fuels is given in Fig. 24.

Furnace-exit-gas temperatures and related heat absorption rates as a function of furnace heat release rate lie within the shaded bands shown in Figs. 25 and 26, respectively, for most pulverized-coal-fired furnaces. The limits indicated are intended to serve only as a general guide. The horizontal scale in each case is heat release rate in thousand Btu per hr per sq ft of water-cooled surface, excluding the floors of slag-tap furnaces. The bands for dry-ash and for slag-tap furnaces overlap between 100,000 and 150,000 heat release rates, but different types of coal are involved. To be suitable for a slag-tap furnace, a coal should have an ash viscosity of 250

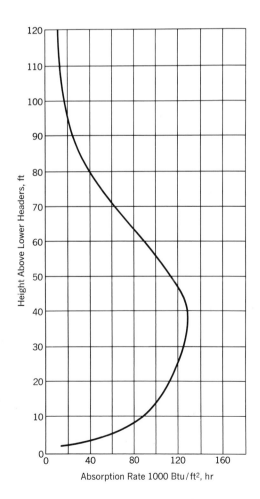

Fig. 22 Heat absorption rates at different elevations in a furnace at maximum output.

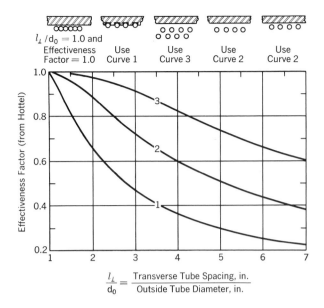

$$\frac{l_\perp}{d_0} = \frac{\text{Transverse Tube Spacing, in.}}{\text{Outside Tube Diameter, in.}}$$

Fig. 23 Furnace-wall area-effectiveness factor (1.0 for completely water-cooled surface). A reduced area (equivalent-cold surface) is determined from these curves for walls not completely water-cooled.

poises at a temperature of 2600F or lower. In the overlapping range, dry-ash and slag-tap both have about the same heat absorption rate, as shown in Fig. 26, or the same "dirtiness" factor. Both bands are rather broad, but they cover a wide range of ash characteristics, considerable diversity in type of water-wall construction and differences in dirtiness resulting from differences in operation, such as mechanical cleaning and load factor.

The quantity of heat leaving the furnace is calculated from the gas weight leaving the furnace and the furnace-exit-gas temperature using gas enthalpy values given in Chapter 6. The quantity of heat absorbed in the furnace is the difference between the heat available from the fuel, including the preheated combustion air, and the quantity of heat leaving the furnace.

Cavities

It is necessary to provide cavities between tube banks of steam generating units for access, for sootblowers and for possible addition of surface. Hot flue gas radiates heat to the boundary surfaces while passing through the cavity. The factors involved in calculating heat transfer in cavities are:

Temperature level. Radiation from nonluminous gases to boundary surfaces and radiation to the gas by the surroundings increase approximately as the fourth power of their respective absolute temperatures.

Gas composition. Carbon dioxide and water vapor are the normal constituents of flue gas which emit nonluminous gas radiation in steam generating units. The concentrations of these constituents depend on the fuel burned and the amount of excess air.

Particles in the gas. The particles carried by dust-laden gases receive heat from the gas by radiation, convection, and conduction, and radiate by inter-solid radiation to the surroundings.

Size of cavity. The quantity of heat transferred per unit of time increases as the size of the cavity increases. Thick layers of gas radiate more vigorously than thin layers. The shape of the cavity also has a complicating effect on heat transfer.

Receiving surface. Refractory surface forming part of a cavity boundary reaches a fairly high temperature by convection and radiation from the flue gas and reradiates to the gas and to the other walls of the enclosure. Reradiation from clean heat-absorbing surface is small unless the receiving surface temperature is high, as it may well be in superheaters and reheaters. Deposits of ash or slag on the tube reduce heat absorption and increase reradiation.

In boiler design there are two significant effects of cavity radiation which are important, (1) the temperature of flue gas drops, sometimes as much as 100F, in passing across a cavity, and (2) gas radiation increases the heat absorption rates for the tubes forming the cavity boundaries. The second effect influences superheater tube temperatures and the selection of alloys.

Insulation

The calculation of heat transfer through insulation follows the principles outlined for conduction through a composite wall. The reader is referred to Chapter 16 for detailed information concerning the properties and application of insulating materials in boiler settings.

Hot-Face temperature. In a boiler furnace with tube-to-tube walls, the hot-face temperature of the insulation may be taken as saturation temperature of the water in the tubes. If the inner face of the furnace wall is refrac-

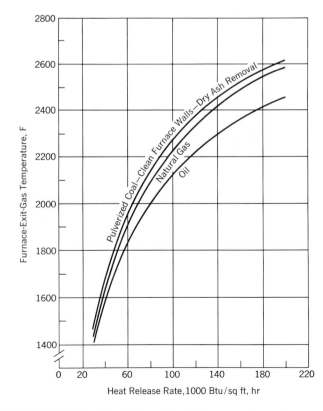

Fig. 24 Approximate relationships of furnace-exit-gas temperature to heat release rate for various fuels.

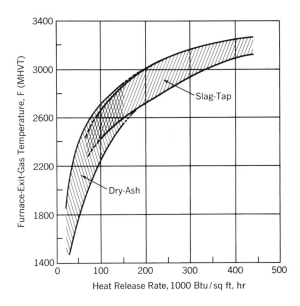

Fig. 25 General range of furnace-exit-gas temperature for dry-ash and slag-tap pulverized-coal firing.

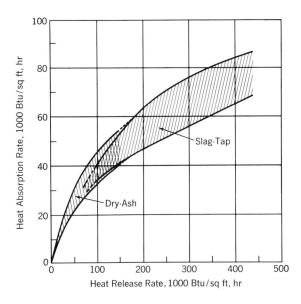

Fig. 26 General range of furnace heat absorption rates in dry-ash and slag-tap pulverized-coal-fired furnaces.

tory, with or without cooling by spaced tubes, the hot-face temperature of the insulation must be calculated or estimated from a knowledge of radiation and convection heat transfer on the gas side of the furnace wall, or from empirical data. Fortunately, a considerable error in calculating the hot-face temperature of the insulation involves a much smaller error in cold-surface temperature and may not introduce significant error into the heat loss calculation. However an error in hot-face temperature may be misleading in the selection of materials.

Heat loss and cold-face temperature. The heat loss to the surroundings and the cold-surface temperature decrease as the thickness of the insulation increases. When the insulation is thick, the change in cold-surface temperature for increase in thickness is small, whereas the cost of the insulation increases steadily with thickness. Standard commercial thicknesses of insulating materials should be used in the composite wall.

The detailed calculation of overall heat loss by radiation and convection from the surfaces of a steam-generating unit (usually called "radiation loss") is tedious and time consuming. A simple approximate method is provided by the chart (Fig. 27) prepared from the ABMA (American Boiler Manufacturers Association) original.

Ambient air conditions. Low ambient air temperature and high air velocities tend to reduce the cold-face temperature, although they have only a small effect on total heat loss, since surface film resistance is a minor part of the total insulation resistance to heat flow. Combined heat loss rates (radiation plus convection) expressed in Btu/sq ft, hr are given in Fig. 8, Chapter 16 for various temperature differences and air velocities. The effect of surface film resistance on casing temperature and heat loss through casings is shown in Fig. 11, Chapter 16.

Temperature-use limits and conductivities. Refractory or insulating material suitable for high-temperature applications is usually more expensive and less effective as insulation than low-temperature materials. It is therefore customary to use several layers of insulation, the lowest cost and most effective insulation in the cool zones and the higher cost materials only where the temperature exceeds the permissible operating limits for low-temperature materials. Thermal conductivities for refractory and insulating materials, at temperatures for which they are suitable, are given in Fig. 7, Chapter 16.

Heat transfer in pressurized-water nuclear reactors

The core of a water-cooled nuclear reactor is designed for a high rate of heat liberation; values of 50 kw/liter (480,000 Btu/cu ft, hr) and higher are common. These high heat liberation rates require high velocities of coolant water which impose considerable pressure drop. In order to keep pressure losses to a minimum, a comprehensive knowledge of the heat transfer characteristics of the nuclear fuel and the water coolant is required.

In a pressurized water reactor the water coolant is maintained under high pressure. It enters at a temperature below the saturation temperature, and in an average flow channel usually leaves at a temperature below saturation. Near the channel entrance the subcooling (saturation temperature minus water temperature) is generally sufficient to assure heat transfer with a complete water film covering the surface of the fuel cladding, i.e., the conditions are those for forced convection as indicated by region *A-B* in Fig. 1, Chapter 1. Conductance through a water film in forced convection is determined from equations such as (17) (*see also Chapter 21*).

At the outlet of the reactor coolant channel there may be some local boiling even though the bulk temperature of the water usually remains below saturation. This means that the conditions are those of the subcooled nucleate boiling region, *B-S* of Fig. 1, Chapter 1. Under these conditions the temperature of the surface of the fuel cladding can be calculated by the Jens and Lottes correlation for subcooled boiling[*] (*see Chapter 21*).

[*] Jens, W. H. and Lottes, P. A. "Analysis of Heat Transfer Burnout, Pressure Drop and Density Data for High-Pressure Water," ANL-4627—May 1951.

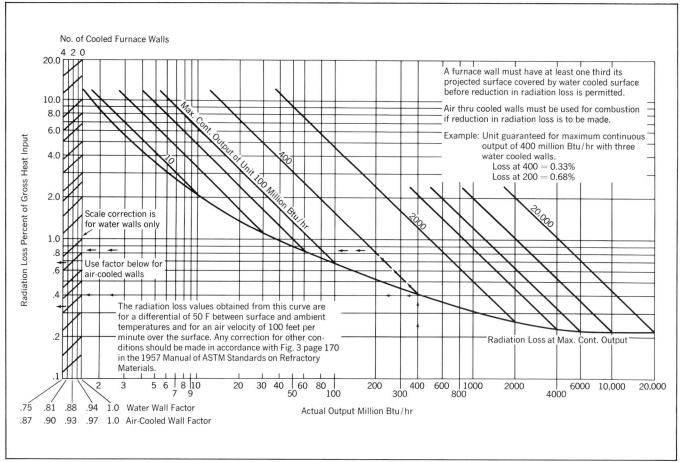

Fig. 27 Radiation loss in percent of gross heat input (American Boiler Manufacturers Association).

A major factor limiting the power that can be removed from a pressurized water reactor is the allowable heat flux at the metal-water interface with nucleate boiling. The limiting or critical heat flux is the DNB (departure from nucleate boiling) discussed in Chapter 1.

In the hotter channels, or during power transients or a situation of reduced flow, conditions near the outlet of some channels may become those of the upper part of the nucleate boiling region, S-C, of Fig. 1, Chapter 1, i.e., the bulk water temperature may reach saturation. Usually only a carefully regulated minimum of bulk boiling would be acceptable in the design of a pressurized water reactor. However, it is necessary to know what margin of safety is available in case an unexpected power transient should increase heat release still further. In such a case the conditions in the water channel would go progressively upward along the full curve in Fig. 1, Chapter 1. Hence it is important in the design of a pressurized water reactor to calculate the DNB (departure from nucleate boiling) and provide a margin of safety against it (Chapter 21).

This critical heat flux is a function of water pressure, enthalpy, velocity, channel dimensions and heat flux distribution. A great amount of experimental data covering the range of these variables has been developed for flow inside tubes or annuli by many investigators during the last twenty years and correlations have been developed from these data. Due to experimental difficulties comparatively little critical heat flux data have been obtained in rod bundle geometries similar to a reactor core. B&W has carried out an experimental critical-heat-flux program (References 1,2)[*] in nine rod bundles with both uniform and nonuniform axial heat flux distributions.

A correlation (Reference 1)[*] has been prepared based on these data. Because the hot channels of a pressurized water reactor operate in the nucleate boiling flow regime, the data obtained in this flow regime were used to develop the correlation. Therefore, the correlation is only valid for operating conditions in the nucleate boiling flow regime. In order to use this critical-heat-flux correlation, the local subchannel (the flow area bounded by 4 fuel rods) mass velocity and steam quality must be obtained from an interchannel mixing computer code which accounts for turbulent crossflow at channel boundaries.

The correlation of Reference 1 does not explain the mechanism of the critical-heat-flux phenomenon. However it correlates the data by means of an equation, which is adapted for use with a computer, and thus is very useful in predicting the critical heat flux in pressurized water reactor designs.

[*] 1) J. S. Gellerstedt, R. A. Lee, W. J. Oberjohn, R. H. Wilson and L. J. Stanek, "Correlation of Critical Heat Flux in a Bundle Cooled by Pressurized Water," Symposium on "Two-Phase Flow and Heat Transfer in Rod Bundles," ASME winter annual meeting, 1969

2) R. H. Wilson, L. J. Stanek, J. S. Gellerstedt and R. A. Lee, "Critical Heat Flux in a Nonuniformly Heated Rod Bundle," Symposium on "Two-Phase Flow and Heat Transfer in Rod Bundles," ASME winter annual meeting, 1969

Steam generation from chemical energy Section II

This section describes the application of the fundamentals of steam generation to the design of boilers, superheaters, economizers and air heaters to generate steam using chemical or fossil fuels.

Chapter 5 discusses the availability of the three major fuels—coal, petroleum, and natural gas—in the world and in the U.S. The characteristics of these fuels, including the classifications of coal, and the relative costs of the three major fuels are summarized. Other fuels included are by-products of coal and petroleum; wood and its by-products and wastes; and other types of vegetation.

The principles of combustion are presented in Chapter 6, including basic chemistry and the weight relationships of fuel, air and combustion products. This chapter discusses the heat of combustion, ignition and adiabatic flame temperatures, and summarizes combustion calculations for solid, liquid and gaseous fuels and the means for measuring total and excess air.

The preparation, transportation, handling and storage of petroleum and natural gas are discussed in Chapter 7. Equipment for burning these fuels is described, and safety precautions necessary in their handling and use are presented.

The processing of coal, including cleaning and sizing, its transportation, and methods of handling and storage at the consumer's plant are discussed in Chapter 8. The firing of coal for the generation of steam is covered in Chapters 9, 10, and 11. Chapter 9 describes the burning of coal in pulverized form, including pulverizing and burning equipment, and safety precautions. Chapter 10 describes the Cyclone-Furnace firing of coal, a method which has significant advantages with coals for which it is suited. Stoker-firing of coals and other solid fuels is treated in Chapter 11.

Chapter 12 presents several current boiler types, and then outlines the basic considerations in boiler design. After fuel selection and determination of the heat requirement, the furnace is designed for proper combustion of the fuel with appropriate provisions for handling the ash in the case of solid fuels. Furnace water-wall surfaces are proportioned to reduce combustion-gas temperature to the level desired at the entrance to the convection banks. The convection surfaces in the boiler,

superheater, and reheater are then designed. The variation of steam temperature with load is discussed for superheaters in various locations. The need for steam-temperature adjustment and control is explained and the means of accomplishment are set forth, including consideration of a number of different methods of control.

Improvements in unit performance by the use of economizers and air heaters are discussed in Chapter 13. Several types of economizers and air heaters are depicted in the text and illustrations, and the problem of sulfur corrosion and means for controlling it are delineated.

The procedure for calculating the performance of a fossil-fired unit is illustrated in Chapter 14 by the detailed calculation of a small unit with a simplified arrangement of heating surfaces. Calculations include heating surface requirements, temperatures and pressure drops in the boiler screen, superheater, boiler convection bank, economizer, and air heater.

The possible effects of fuel-ash from various coals and petroleum on the design and operation of boilers and auxiliary equipment are elaborated in Chapter 15. This chapter highlights the complexities and potential difficulties of fuel-ash effects, and examines the means that are employed in design and operation to provide a unit where the fuels specified can be burned continuously with a minimum of difficulty.

The design requirements for boiler settings are enumerated in Chapter 16. Tube-wall and cased enclosures are depicted. The use of insulation to minimize setting heat loss and the benefits of tight settings in improved unit efficiency are explained.

The use of stacks and fans to provide adequate flow of combustion gases is considered in Chapter 17. The capabilities and limitations of stacks are examined, as are the characteristics of induced and forced draft fans. The advantages of operating with the boiler setting under positive pressure are enumerated.

The disposition of combustion by-products—ash and combustion gases—is considered in Chapter 18. Means now in effect for removing particulate matter and gaseous pollutants from the stack discharge are discussed, and improved procedures and processes in the development stage are examined.

Mine-mouth central station in the Midwest with facilities for conveying coal direct from the mine to the steam plant.

Chapter 5

Sources of chemical energy

The chemical or fossil fuels which occur naturally in the earth are organic materials, largely, if not wholly, the remains of vegetable matter synthesized by solar heat. The energy stored in these fuels thus derives from the nuclear reactions in the sun, such as the transmutation of hydrogen to helium, releasing energy in the form of light and heat. See Einstein's mass-energy equation, Chapter 19.

Estimates indicate that only one two-billionth of the sun's energy reaches the earth, and about half of it is lost by radiation into interstellar space by earth's atmosphere. Also, some of the energy absorbed by the earth by day is lost by radiation at night. The energy received by the earth from the sun is about 40,000 times the estimated annual energy requirements of the world for 1975. The maximum amount of solar energy theoretically recoverable is listed in Table 1.

Table 1
Solar energy annually available to the world from renewable sources*

	Btu/10^{15}
Solar collectors	43,300
Waterfalls	900
Land vegetation	160
Tropical waters	50
Wind	5
Heat pumps	5

* Fossil fuels and fissionable elements are not considered renewable. From *Energy Sources—The Wealth of the World*, Ayres and Scarlott. Copyright © 1952 by McGraw-Hill—used with permission of McGraw-Hill Book Company.

There is a large potential for energy from these renewable sources. However, their use at the present time is at a very low rate. Hence, for the foreseeable future, energy needs will be met largely through the depletion of nonrenewable sources—coal, petroleum, natural gas and oil shale—supplemented by nuclear sources.

The combustion of vegetation, primarily wood, which is replenishable, represents a minor source of energy. The use of petroleum and natural gas as sources of energy is a comparatively recent development. For example, in the U.S. in 1930, about 63.5% of the fuel produced for energy was from coal, 23.5% from petroleum, 9.7% from natural gas, and the remainder from water power. In 1975, coal accounted for only 25.6%, petroleum 51.3%, natural gas 21.4%, water power 1.3% and 0.4% from nuclear power. In the future, however, there will be more energy produced from coal and nuclear power because of the shortage of natural gas and petroleum. Fig. 1 indicates the changing world energy usage. No new utility boilers are being designed to burn oil or natural gas for use in the United States.

World availability of fuels

Coal

World coal reserves and production for 1974, arranged in order of the nine leading countries in each category, are listed in Table 2. According to these statistics more than 90% of the world's reserves lie within three geographical areas—the U.S.S.R., the U.S.A. and China. This table shows the U.S.S.R. leading in coal production during 1974, followed by the U.S.A., China and East Germany.

There is a large tonnage of low-Btu lignite and brown coal mined in the U.S.S.R. and East Germany. Table 3 shows the world production of solid fossil fuels by rank and by nation for 1971.

Petroleum

The distribution of the world's proven recoverable reserves of crude oil and natural gas is summarized in

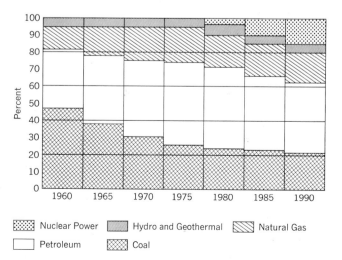

Fig. 1 World energy consumption by source. (*Source, Basic Petroleum Data Book, American Petroleum Institute, 1975.*)

Table 4. The countries in southwest Asia have, by far, most of the known reserves of petroleum with 45.2%. North Africa and Middle South Asia are next with 11.7% and 9.8%. The U.S.S.R. is fourth with 8.9%. North and Middle America, including Alaska and Canada, is sixth with 7.65%.

The Organization of Petroleum Exporting Countries (OPEC) is an international cartel that has gained dominance in the petroleum industry over the past ten years. Table 5 shows how the OPEC nations dominate world oil production. Table 6 shows how their revenues have grown in the years 1971 through 1974. It also gives the member nations of OPEC.

Natural gas

The natural gas reserves are somewhat different with Russia having the greatest amount, 32.6%, and North and Middle America second with 19.88%. See the natural gas tabulation on Table 4.

Oil shale

Oil shale deposits are widely distributed throughout the world with the largest reserves being in the United States and Canada. Table 7 shows the countries with the largest reserves. The production of oil from shale oil has not progressed past the pilot plant stage in the United States. This is primarily because foreign oil is cheaper than oil extracted from shale.

Wood

Forest lands of the world are estimated at 9.6 billion acres, equivalent to about 27% of the land area of the world. The productive forest area is estimated to be about 6.4 billion acres. Of this, about 4 billion acres may be considered as economically accessible.

Until the latter part of the nineteenth century, when it was replaced by coal, wood was the principal source of heat energy. Wood is no longer a major factor as a source of heat energy because of the depletion of the forests and the increasing demands for wood as lumber and in the production of paper, plywood, rayon and other products. Today the burning of wood and bark for steam generation is largely confined to locations where it is available as a by-product or waste from the lumber, furniture, ply-

Table 2
Solid fossil fuel resources by continents and nations with major resources, 1974
(Million metric tons)

Country or Continent	Economic Reserves Recoverable	Economic Reserves Total	Total Resources
U.S.S.R.	136,600	273,200	5,713,600
China, P.R. of	80,000	300,000	1,000,000
Rest of Asia	17,549	40,479	108,053
United States	181,781	363,562	2,924,503
Canada	5,537	9,034	108,777
Latin America	2,803	9,201	32,928
Europe	126,775	319,807	607,521
Africa	15,628	30,291	58,844
Oceania	24,518	74,699	199,654
Total	591,191	1,402,274	10,753,880

Source, World Energy Conference, *Survey of Energy Sources,* 1974.

Table 3
World production of solid fossil fuels by rank and nation, 1971
(Thousand metric tons—2205 lb/ton)

Nation or Area	Anthracite	Bituminous	Brown Coal or Lignite	Peat°	Total	Percent of World Production
U.S.S.R.	79,000	404,000	154,000	57,000	694,000	22.7
United States	8,830	495,300	5,800		509,930	16.7
China, P.R. of	20,000	390,000°°	(Not reported)		410,000	13.5
Canada		14,600	3,000		17,600	0.6
Europe						
Western	27,800	132,300	111,100	320	271,520	8.9
Southern	3,140	8,650	46,270		58,260	1.9
Northern	3,760	143,550	90	5,020	152,420	5.0
Eastern	200	187,700	447,730	50	635,680	20.6
Total	34,900	472,200	605,190	5,390	1,117,680	36.4
India		69,120	3,700		72,820	2.4
Australia		48,920	23,390		72,310	2.4
South Africa	1,680	56,840			58,520	1.9
Japan	1,040	32,940	130		34,110	1.1
North Korea	21,800	6,170°°	(Not reported)		27,970	0.9
South Korea	12,400				12,400	0.4
Turkey		4,180	5,820		10,000	0.3
Rest of Asia	3,000	8,150°°	450		11,600	0.3
Rest of Oceania		1,920	160		2,080	0.1
Rest of Africa	430	4,970			5,400	0.2
Latin America	7	10,970			10,980	0.1
Total	183,090	2,020,280	801,640	62,390	3,067,400	100.0

° Includes peat used for fuel only.

°° Includes some lignite for Peoples Republic of China, Peoples Republic of Korea, Mongolia and Pakistan.

Source, World Energy Conference, *Survey of Energy Sources,* 1974.

wood and pulp industries. In producing lumber from logs, half the wood may be discarded as sawdust, bark, shavings, slabs and ends, all of which can be used as fuel. Also, waste-wood liquors from the pulp industry are burned for the recovery of heat and process chemicals. Various wood wastes are used extensively in other parts of the world, and to a lesser extent in the U.S. to produce alcohol for fuel. New methods of barking logs and producing pulp, however, are continually reducing the quantity of waste available for fuel. More profitable end uses are also reducing the availability of wood for fuel.

Other vegetation

Numerous other types of vegetation, generally in the form of waste or by-products, are used for fuel. In the U.S., however, they are an almost negligible factor in the total energy requirement. As in the case of wood, their use as fuel is diminishing because more profitable uses are being found. One of the more common wastes is bagasse, the fibrous portion of sugar cane after the juice has been extracted.

Availability of fuels in the United States

Coal

Coal reserves in the U.S. have been estimated from drillings, outcroppings, operating mines, and explorations for minerals and oil. The distribution of the coal reserves by states and tonnages at various sulfur levels is shown in Table 8. Since the Clean Air Act of 1970 sulfur has become an important criteria for buying coal.

The states with the greatest reserves do not necessarily

Table 4
Worldwide distribution of proven recoverable reserves of crude oil and natural gas, 1972

	Percent	
	Oil	Gas
Western Africa	1.3	2.4
Middle Africa	1.0	0.7
Northern Africa	11.7	7.6
Total	14.0	10.7
East Asia	1.9	1.3
Middle South Asia (Incl. Iran)	9.8	12.7
South East Asia	2.0	1.2
South West Asia	45.2	8.0
Total	58.9	23.2
Western Europe	0.14	4.7
Eastern Europe	0.41	0.87
Northern Europe	0.84	2.6
Total	1.39	8.17
U.S.S.R.	8.9	32.6
Northern America	7.2	19.3
Middle America	0.45	0.58
Total	7.65	19.88
Tropical South America	7.9	2.4
Oceania	0.25	1.3
Other Regions	1.01	1.75

Source, World Energy Conference, *Survey of Energy Sources*, 1974.

Table 5
World oil production and reserves

Countries	1974 Oil Production (Million Barrels/Day)	Oil Reserves (Billion Barrels)
OPEC nations	31.8	492.9
Communist areas	10.4	111.4
Rest of world	14.5	111.4
World total	56.7	715.7

Source, *International Petroleum Encyclopedia*, 1975.

Table 6
OPEC country revenues
(Millions of dollars)

Country	1971	1972	1973	1974
Algeria	1,221	1,472	2,338	3,600
Ecuador	340	317	532	850
Indonesia	1,174	1,562	2,347	4,600
Iran	1,871	2,410	3,370	6,500
Iraq	694	713	898	2,150
Kuwait	650	797	1,042	1,600
Libya	699	1,038	1,723	2,940
Nigeria	1,511	1,505	1,874	3,000
Qatar	80	124	170	250
Saudi Arabia	806	1,136	1,893	2,850
United Arab Emirates	300	423	784	1,100
Venezuela	2,302	2,436	4,100	4,800
Total	11,648	13,933	21,071	34,240

Source, *International Petroleum Encyclopedia*, 1975.

Table 7
Countries having largest reserves of oil from oil shale and bituminous sands

Country	Type of Resource	Quantity (Million Metric Tons)	Year of Reference
China, P.R. of	Shale	21,000	1973
Canada	Shale	24,860	1965
	Sand	50,250	1963
United States	Shale	145,000	1972
	Sand	2,175	1973
Colombia	Sand	155,400	1971

Source, World Energy Conference, *Survey of Energy Sources*, 1974.

produce the most coal as shown in Table 9, which shows the ten states with the greatest reserves, their total production for 1974, and how they rank in production.

The production of coal in the United States increased only slightly between 1970 and 1974, but the price of coal has changed dramatically. There was a slight increase in price from 1970 through 1973 but the price in 1974 nearly doubled that of 1973. This is shown in Table 10.

Coal fields in the U.S. are shown in Fig. 2. The two great producing regions are the Appalachian, including the states of Pennsylvania, West Virginia, Ohio, western Maryland, eastern Kentucky, Virginia, Tennessee and Alabama; and the Central States region including Illinois, Indiana, western Kentucky, Iowa, Missouri, Kansas, Oklahoma and Arkansas. However, two-thirds of the coal reserves lie in the Great Plains, the Rocky Mountains and the West. These coals are mostly lignites and subbituminous in rank with a small amount of bituminous and anthracite coals found mainly in the Rocky

Table 8
Demonstrated total underground and surface coal reserve base of the United States on January 1, 1974
(Million tons)

State	Sulfur Range, Percent				
	≤1.0	1.1–3.0	>3.0	Unknown	Total[a]
Alabama	624.7	1,099.9	16.4	1,239.4	2,981.8
Alaska	11,458.4	184.2	.0	.0	11,645.4
Arizona	173.3	176.7	.0	.0	350.0
Arkansas	81.2	463.1	46.3	74.3	665.7
Colorado	7,475.5	786.2	47.3	6,547.3	14,869.2
Georgia	0.3	.0	.0	0.2	0.5
Illinois	1,095.1	7,341.4	42,968.9	14,256.2	65,664.8
Indiana	548.8	3,305.8	5,262.4	1,504.1	10,622.6
Iowa	1.5	226.7	2,105.9	549.2	2,884.9
Kansas	.0	309.2	695.6	383.2	1,388.1
Kentucky-East	6,558.4	3,321.8	299.5	2,729.3	12,916.7
Kentucky-West	0.2	564.4	9,243.9	2,815.9	12,623.9
Maryland	135.1	690.5	187.4	34.6	1,048.2
Michigan	4.6	85.4	20.9	7.0	118.2
Missouri	.0	182.0	5,226.0	4,080.5	9,487.3
Montana	101,646.6	4,115.0	502.6	2,116.7	108,396.2
New Mexico	3,575.3	793.4	0.9	27.5	4,394.8
North Carolina	.0	.0	.0	31.7	31.7
North Dakota	5,389.0	10,325.4	268.7	15.0	16,003.0
Ohio	134.4	6,440.9	12,534.3	1,872.0	21,077.2
Oklahoma	275.0	326.6	241.4	450.5	1,294.2
Oregon	1.5	0.3	.0	.0	1.8
Pennsylvania	7,318.3	16,913.6	3,799.6	2,954.2	31,000.6
South Dakota	103.1	287.9	35.9	1.0	428.0
Tennessee	204.8	533.2	156.6	88.0	986.7
Texas	659.8	1,884.6	284.1	444.0	3,271.9
Utah	1,968.5	1,546.7	49.4	478.3	4,042.5
Virginia	2,140.1	1,163.5	14.1	330.0	3,649.9
Washington	603.5	1,265.5	39.0	45.1	1,954.0
West Virginia	14,092.1	14,006.2	6,823.3	4,652.5	39,589.8
Wyoming	33,912.3	14,657.4	1,701.1	3,060.3	53,336.1
Total[a]	200,181.1	92,997.6	92,671.1	50,837.7	436,725.4

[a] Data may not add to totals shown due to independent rounding.
Source, Bureau of Mines bulletin, *Coal—Bituminous and Lignite*, 1974.

Mountain region. These coal fields were not developed in the past because of their distance from major industrial areas. This has changed in the past five years. Most of these coals have low sulfur content and utilities are buying them in much greater quantity because of the Clean Air Act of 1970. Another factor that has had a great impact on the western coal market is the energy crisis and the shortage of low sulfur steam coal. Their

Table 9
Proven coal reserves and production of top ten states with greatest reserves, 1974

State	Demonstrated Proven Reserves (Million Tons)	Production (Thousand Tons)	Production Rank
Montana	108,396.2	14,106	7
Illinois	65,664.8	58,215	4
Wyoming	53,336.1	20,703	6
West Virginia	39,589.8	102,462	2
Pennsylvania	31,000.6	80,462	3
Kentucky	25,540.6	137,197	1
Ohio	21,077.7	45,409	5
North Dakota	16,003.0	7,463	8
Colorado	14,869.2	6,896	9
Alaska	11,645.4	700	10

Source, Bureau of Mines bulletin, *Coal—Bituminous and Lignite*, 1974.

development for use as electric utility fuels and as a source of synthetic liquid fuels is being actively pursued. They also represent a potential source of pipeline gas.

It is estimated that 32 states have 350,000 square miles underlaid with coal. This represents 11% of the total area of the United States.

The electric utilities consumed 70.6% of the total coal used in the United States in 1974 as shown in Table 11. Second to the electric utilities are the oven coke plants for steelmaking. The greatest drop in coal consumption occurred in the railroad industry which used 20.8% in the years 1936 to 1940 but uses such a negligible amount today that it is not even reported. This is the result of conversion to diesel motive power. Practically all transportation in the United States uses petroleum as an energy source today.

Table 12 lists the quantities of coal, oil and natural gas used annually by electric utilities in the United States between 1950 and 1974. In the sixties and early seventies there was an increase in oil and natural gas with a decrease in the use of coal. This will probably change in the future with a great reduction in the use of oil and natural gas—especially natural gas—because of the shortage of these fuels. Coal or manufactured products from coal are expected to be the fuel of tomorrow.

Table 10
Production and value of bituminous coal and lignite in the United States

	1970	1971	1972	1973	1974
Production (Thousand tons)	602,932	552,192	595,386	591,738	603,406
Value (Thousands)	$3,772,662	$3,904,562	$4,561,983	$5,049,612	$9,486,209
Price/ton	$6.26	$7.07	$7.66	$8.53	$15.72

Source, Bureau of Mines bulletin, *Coal—Bituminous and Lignite,* 1974.

Table 11
Consumption of bituminous coal and lignite, by consumer class, and retail deliveries in the United States
(Thousand tons)

Year	Electric Power Utilities	Bunker Lake Vessel and Foreign	Beehive Coke Plants	Oven Coke Plants	Steel and Rolling Mills	Other Mfg. and Mining Industries	Retail Deliveries to Other Consumers	Total of Classes Shown
1970	318,921	298	1,428	94,581	5,410	82,909	12,072	515,619
1971	326,280	207	1,278	81,531	5,560	68,655	11,351	494,862
1972	348,612	163	1,059	86,213	4,850	67,131	8,748	516,776
1973	386,879	116	1,310	92,324	6,356	60,837	8,200	556,130
1974	390,068	80	1,337	88,410	6,155	57,819	8,840	552,709
Percent of 1974 market	70.6	0.01	0.2	16.0	1.1	10.5	1.6	

Source, Bureau of Mines bulletin, *Coal—Bituminous and Lignite,* 1974.

Table 12
Percentages of fuels used in utility steam plants in the United States

	1950	1960	1971	1972	1973	1974
Coal	66.8	65.2	54	54	57	58
Oil	14.1	8.1	16	19	20	20
Gas	19.1	26.7	30	27	23	22

Source, Keystone Coal Industry Manual.

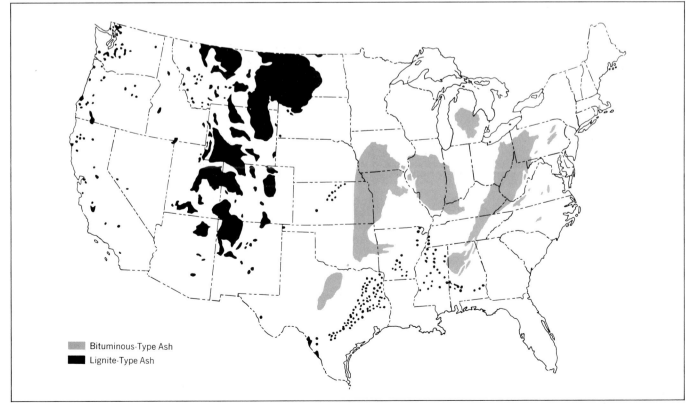

Bituminous-Type Ash
Lignite-Type Ash

Fig. 2 Coal fields of the United States. *(Source, U.S. Geological Survey.)*

Petroleum*

Availability of crude oil is based on the estimated proven reserves in areas where it has actually been found by exploration and drilling. At the end of 1975 the total proven U.S. reserves were 32.68 billion barrels of crude oil. This is an increase from January 1, 1970 of 3.05 billion barrels which reflects reserves of the north slope of Alaska. Since the proven reserves of Northern and Middle America are about 7.65% of the world total, it appears that increasing imports will be needed in the future. In 1975, 1,498,181 thousand barrels of crude oil were imported by the United States.

The eleven states with the highest recoverable petroleum reserves and their production are shown in Table 13. The reserves and production of 1969 and 1975 are shown so a comparison can be made.

Table 13
Recoverable petroleum reserves and production in eleven leading states of United States
(Billion barrels)

	Reserves Jan. 1, 1970	Reserves Dec. 31, 1975	Production 1969	Production 1975
Texas	13.06	10.08	1.11	1.18
Louisiana	5.69	3.83	0.74	0.56
California	4.24	3.65	0.37	0.32
Oklahoma	1.39	1.24	0.22	0.15
Wyoming	1.00	0.88	0.15	0.13
New Mexico	0.84	0.69	0.12	0.09
Kansas	0.56	0.36	0.09	0.06
Alaska	0.43	10.04*	0.07	0.07
Colorado	0.40	0.28	—	0.04
Mississippi	0.36	0.23	0.06	0.05
Illinois	—	0.16	0.05	0.03
Total	27.97	31.34	2.98	2.68
Total in U.S.	29.63	32.68	3.19	2.89

* Alaska Prudhoe Bay reserves included.

Source, American Petroleum Institute and American Gas Association, 1975.

The proportion of petroleum resources actually recovered depends on the rate of withdrawal from existing wells, the economics of continued exploration and drilling and the development or improvement of techniques for economic recovery of more oil from the reservoirs. The rate of discovery of new large fields in the United States is likely to diminish, making it necessary to drill deeper in less favorable areas. The number of dry holes, average drilled depths and costs are increasing.

Recovery of petroleum from the wells is another economic factor. Considerable progress has been made in the past twenty-five years in extraction and recovery of oil. Fig. 3 shows a steady increase per well from 1960 through 1973. There has been a decline since 1973 because oil from a good many wells is becoming more difficult to recover.

After the wells in a reservoir cease to produce oil at an economical rate, artificial methods are used to force the remaining oil to the wells for removal, initiating a secondary economical recovery period. Secondary recovery methods consist of repressuring the reservoirs with water (water flooding), gas or air. More recently, "fire flooding," or in-situ combustion has been used. Briefly, some oil is burned underground to heat the remainder so that

* Source, American Petroleum Institute, 1975.

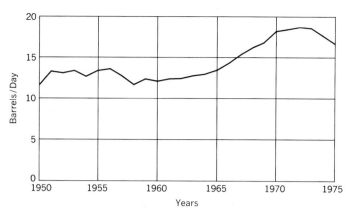

Fig. 3 United States average crude oil production per well per day. (Source, American Petroleum Institute, 1975.)

it may flow more easily and improve recovery. This process may utilize 10 to 15% of the oil as fuel with essentially complete recovery of the remainder.

Many supposedly depleted fields have been restored to commercial production through improved recovery practices, such as gas repressuring of underground reservoirs. Dry gas is pumped into the reservoir to maintain a reservoir pressure, or "drive," at a level which assures an optimum rate of recovery. This gas-cycling method also produces condensate liquids, such as gasoline, butane and propane which are stripped from the gas before it is returned to the reservoir.

Natural gas

The availability of natural gas is based on the estimated proven reserves in areas where it has actually been found by exploration and drilling. Areas containing petroleum can also be expected to yield natural gas, but there are many natural gas wells that do not yield petroleum.

The eleven states with the highest recoverable natural gas reserve and their production are shown in Table 14. The reserves and production for the years 1969 and 1975 are shown so a comparison can be made. Note that natural gas reserves have decreased 17% while production has decreased only 4.8%.

Table 14
Recoverable natural gas reserves and production in eleven leading states of United States
(Trillion cu ft)

	Reserves Jan. 1, 1970	Reserves Dec. 31, 1975	Production 1969	Production 1975
Texas	112.4	71.0	4.6	7.04
Louisiana	85.1	61.3	7.28	7.18
Oklahoma	17.6	13.1	1.68	1.67
New Mexico	14.3	11.8	1.09	1.12
Kansas	14.1	12.7	0.89	0.85
California	6.9	5.5	0.64	0.33
Alaska	5.2	32.0*	—	0.16
Wyoming	3.9	3.7	0.32	0.30
Arkansas	2.6	2.0	0.17	0.12
West Virginia	2.4	2.3	0.21	0.15
Mississippi	—	1.2	0.17	0.08
Total	264.5	216.6	20.11	19.00
Total in U.S.	275.1	228.2	20.72	19.72

* Alaska Prudhoe Bay reserves included.

Source, American Petroleum Institute and American Gas Association, 1975.

Characteristics of coal

How coal was formed

Some of the luxurious vegetation produced by the sun's heat in early geological times has become the coal of today. Great trees and ferns were piled one upon another in circumstances which prevented the free access of air. At intervals, wind and water covered this mass with sediment, sand and dirt to form the overburden now found above coal seams. During millions of years, these layers of vegetation were subjected to moisture, heat and pressure, and portions of the cellulose and other organic materials were converted to carbon and hydrocarbons. In this manner wood and vegetation were changed, perhaps progressively, to peat, brown coals and lignite, subbituminous and bituminous coals, and finally to anthracite.

The intrinsic ash of coal was largely in the vegetation from the beginning. The extraneous ash came from mud deposits of shale and pyrites that filled the cracks and crevices caused by the movement of the earth's crust.

Most of the coal mined in the U.S. comes from seams 3 to 6 ft thick, with the average about 5.5 ft. One seam near Lake De Smet, Johnson County, Wyoming, averages more than 100 feet in thickness and acquires a maximum thickness of 220 ft. The thickest known seam in the world, 425 ft, is in Manchuria.

Sampling of coal

Although the coal consumption in a central station may be measured in thousands of tons per day, the samples used for laboratory analysis are measured in grams. It is therefore important and difficult to obtain representative samples of coal. B&W played a prominent part in resolving this difficulty, and the first ASTM Standard for Sampling Coal (D 21) was based largely on the work of B&W personnel.

ASTM Standard D 492 now in use was developed, adopted in 1948, and reapproved in 1958. In this standard, which is less laborious than the original, allowances are made for the probable ash content of the coal, permitting the use of smaller gross samples for the coals of lower ash content.

Two sampling procedures are recognized in the present standard:

1. Commercial-Sampling Procedure.
2. Special-Purpose Sampling Procedure.

The "Commercial-Sampling Procedure" applies to the average commercial sampling of coal. This procedure is designed to measure the average ash content of a large number of samples within $\pm 10\%$ to a 95% probability.

The "Special-Purpose-Sampling Procedure" applies to the sampling of coal when special accuracy is required. This procedure should be used to supply samples for the classification of coals and the establishment of design or performance parameters. The special-purpose sample can be one of two sizes, either 4 times that of the commercial sample, giving an accuracy of $\pm 5\%$ of the ash content of the coal samples, or 9 times that of the commercial sample, giving an accuracy of $\pm 3.33\%$ of the ash content of the coal sampled.

Standard D 492 also sets procedures for reducing gross samples and for obtaining samples for standard and special moisture determinations. Two additional pertinent publications by the ASTM are: *Symposium on Bulk Sampling* (STP 242, 1958) and *Symposium on Coal Sampling* (STP 162, 1955). A new method has also been adopted in 1968 covering the mechanical sampling of coal, D 2234.

Careful coal sampling is of prime importance since any data resulting from subsequent analyses are only as representative as the sample provided.

Coal analysis

Customary practice in reporting the components of a coal is to use two different analyses, known as "proximate" and "ultimate." The proximate analysis is defined as the determination of moisture, volatile matter, and ash, and the calculation of fixed carbon by difference. The ultimate analysis from a dried sample is defined as the determination of carbon, hydrogen, sulfur, nitrogen and ash, and the estimation of oxygen by difference. The scope of each is indicated in the following analyses of a West Virginia coal, in which the ultimate analysis has been converted to the as-received basis.

Coal analyses on as-received basis
(Pittsburgh Seam Coal, West Virginia)

Proximate Analysis		Ultimate Analysis	
Component	Weight,%	Component	Weight,%
Moisture	2.5	Moisture	2.5
Volatile matter	37.6	Carbon	75.0
Fixed carbon	52.9	Hydrogen	5.0
Ash	7.0	Sulfur	2.3
Total	100.0	Nitrogen	1.5
		Oxygen	6.7
Heating value,		Ash	7.0
Btu/lb	13,000	Total	100.0

The analysis on the as-received basis includes the total moisture content of coal received at the plant. Similarly, the as-fired basis includes the total moisture content of the coal as it enters the boiler furnace or pulverizers. The various values from such analyses are needed to implement the formulas in this chapter and in Chapter 6. Standard laboratory procedures for making these analyses appear in ASTM D 271. A list of other testing standards is given in Table 15.

ASTM classification by rank

Coals are classified in order to identify end use and also to provide data useful in specifying and selecting burning and handling equipment and in the design and arrangement of heat transfer surfaces. Methods and principles of burning are closely associated with specific types of equipment, and reference should be made to Chapters 9, 10 and 11. The nature and effects of impurities in coal are discussed in Chapter 15.

One classification of coal is by rank, i.e., according to the degree of metamorphism, or progressive alteration, in the natural series from lignite to anthracite. Volatile matter, fixed carbon, inherent or bed moisture (equilibrated moisture at 30C and 97% humidity), and oxygen are all indicative of rank, but no one item completely defines it. In the ASTM classification, the basic criteria are the fixed carbon and the calorific values calculated on a mineral-matter-free basis.

It is necessary, in establishing the rank of coals, to use information showing an appreciable and systematic variation with age. For the older coals, a good criterion is the "dry, mineral-matter-free fixed carbon or volatile." However, this value is not suitable for designating the rank of the younger coals. A dependable means of classifying the latter is the "moist, mineral-matter-free Btu,"

which varies little for the older coals but appreciably and systematically for younger coals.

Table 16, ASTM D 388, is used for classification according to rank or age. Older coals are classified by dry, mineral-matter-free fixed carbon, and younger coals by moist, mineral-matter-free Btu. These terms are defined by the Parr formulas (1), (2) and (3). Formulas (4), (5) and (6) are approximate forms of the Parr formulas. Proximate analyses and higher heating values are used in making the calculations.

Parr formulas

(1) Dry, Mm-free $FC =$
$$\frac{FC - 0.15\,S}{100 - (M + 1.08A + 0.55\,S)} \times 100,\ \%$$

(2) Dry, Mm-free $VM =$
$$100 - \text{Dry, } Mm\text{-free } FC,\ \%$$

(3) Moist, Mm-free Btu $=$
$$\frac{\text{Btu} - 50\,S}{100 - (1.08A + 0.55\,S)} \times 100,\ \text{per lb}$$

Approximation formulas

(4) Dry, Mm-free $FC =$
$$\frac{FC}{100 - (M + 1.1A + 0.1\,S)} \times 100,\ \%$$

(5) Dry, Mm-free $VM =$
$$100 - \text{Dry, } Mm\text{-free } FC,\ \%$$

(6) Moist, Mm-free Btu $=$
$$\frac{\text{Btu}}{100 - (1.1A + 0.1\,S)} \times 100,\ \text{per lb}$$

where:
Mm = mineral matter
Btu = heating value per lb
FC = fixed carbon, %
VM = volatile matter, %
M = bed moisture, %
A = ash, %
S = sulfur, %
All for coal on a moist basis.

The term "moist" refers to bed moisture only, and analyses of constituents must be of bed samples collected as prescribed by ASTM D 388. Agglomerating and weathering (or slacking) indices are used to differentiate between certain adjacent groups and are defined in this standard.

Table 17 lists 17 selected U.S. coals, arranged in the order of the ASTM classification. The basis for the two ASTM criteria (the fixed carbon and the calorific values calculated on a moist, mineral-matter-free basis) are shown in Fig. 4 for over 300 typical coals of the U.S. The classes and groups of Table 16 are indicated in Fig. 4. For the anthracitic and low- and medium- volatile bituminous coals, the moist, mineral-matter-free calorific value changes very little; hence the fixed-carbon criterion is used. Conversely, in the case of the high-volatile bituminous, subbituminous and lignitic coals, the moist, mineral-matter-free calorific value is used, since the fixed carbon is almost the same for all classifications.

Table 15
ASTM standards for testing coal, specifications and definitions of terms

ASTM Standards for Testing Coal

*D 1756	Carbon Dioxide in Coal
*D 2361	Chlorine in Coal
°D 291	Cubic Foot Weight of Crushed Bituminous Coal
°D 440	Drop Shatter Test for Coal
°D 547	Dustiness, Index of, of Coal and Coke
°D 1857	Fusibility of Coal Ash
°D 1412	Equilibrium Moisture of Coal at 96 to 97% Relative Humidity and 30C
°D 2014	Expansion or Contraction of Coal by the Sole-Heated Oven
°D 720	Free-Swelling Index of Coal
D 409	Grindability of Coal by the Hardgrove-Machine Method
°D 2015	Gross Calorific Value of Solid Fuel by the Adiabatic Bomb Calorimeter
D 1812	Plastic Properties of Coal by the Gieseler Plastometer
D 2639	Plastic Properties of Coal by the Automatic Gieseler Plastometer
D 197	Sampling and Fineness Test of Powdered Coal
°D 271	Sampling and Analysis, Laboratory, of Coal and Coke
D 492	Sampling Coals Classified According to Ash Content
°D 2234	Sampling, Mechanical, of Coal
°D 2013	Samples, Coal, Preparing of Analysis
°D 410	Screen, Analysis of Coal
D 311	Sieve Analysis of Crushed Bituminous Coal
D 310	Size of Anthracite
°D 431	Size of Coal, Designating from its Screen Analysis
°D 1757	Sulfur in Coal Ash
°D 2492	Sulfur, Forms of, in Coal
°D 441	Tumbler Test for Coal

Specifications

°D 388	Classification of Coals by Rank
°E 11	Wire-Cloth Sieves for Testing Purposes
E 323	Perforated-Plate Sieves for Testing Purposes

Definitions of Terms

°D 121	Coal and Coke
D 2796	Lithological Classes and Physical Components of Coal
°D 407	Gross Calorific Value and Net Calorific Value of Solid and Liquid Fuels

° Approved as American National Standard by the American National Standards Institute.

Table 16
Classification of coals by rank[a] (ASTM D 388)

Class	Group	Fixed Carbon Limits, % (Dry, Mineral-Matter-Free Basis)		Volatile Matter Limits, % (Dry, Mineral-Matter-Free Basis)		Calorific Value Limits, Btu/lb (Moist,[b] Mineral-Matter-Free Basis)		Agglomerating Character
		Equal or Greater Than	Less Than	Greater Than	Equal or Less Than	Equal or Greater Than	Less Than	
I. Anthracitic	1. Meta-anthracite	98	—	—	2	—	—	⎫
	2. Anthracite	92	98	2	8	—	—	⎬ Nonagglomerating
	3. Semianthracite[c]	86	92	8	14	—	—	⎭
II. Bituminous	1. Low volatile bituminous coal	78	86	14	22	—	—	⎫
	2. Medium volatile bituminous coal	69	78	22	31	—	—	⎬ Commonly agglomerating[e]
	3. High volatile A bituminous coal	—	69	31	—	14,000[d]	—	
	4. High volatile B bituminous coal	—	—	—	—	13,000[d]	14,000	⎭
	5. High volatile C bituminous coal	—	—	—	—	{ 11,500	13,000	⎫
		—	—	—	—	{ 10,500[e]	11,500	Agglomerating
III. Subbituminous	1. Subbituminous A coal	—	—	—	—	10,500	11,500	⎫
	2. Subbituminous B coal	—	—	—	—	9,500	10,500	⎬
	3. Subbituminous C coal	—	—	—	—	8,300	9,500	⎬ Nonagglomerating
IV. Lignitic	1. Lignite A	—	—	—	—	6,300	8,300	⎬
	2. Lignite B	—	—	—	—	—	6,300	⎭

[a] This classification does not include a few coals, principally non-banded varieties, which have unusual physical and chemical properties and which come within the limits of fixed carbon or calorific value of the high-volatile bituminous and subbituminous ranks. All of these coals either contain less than 48% dry, mineral-matter-free fixed carbon or have more than 15,500 moist, mineral-matter-free British thermal units per pound.

[b] Moist refers to coal containing its natural inherent moisture but not including visible water on the surface of the coal.

[c] If agglomerating, classify in low-volatile group of the bituminous class.

[d] Coals having 69% or more fixed carbon on the dry, mineral-matter-free basis shall be classified according to fixed carbon, regardless of calorific value.

[e] It is recognized that there may be nonagglomerating varieties in these groups of the bituminous class, and there are notable exceptions in high volatile C bituminous group.

Table 17
Seventeen selected U.S. coals arranged in order of ASTM classification

No.	Coal Rank Class	Coal Rank Group	State	County	M	VM	FC	A	S	Btu	Rank FC	Rank Btu
1	I	1	Pa.	Schuylkill	4.5	1.7	84.1	9.7	0.77	12,745	99.2	14,280
2	I	2	Pa.	Lackawanna	2.5	6.2	79.4	11.9	0.60	12,925	94.1	14,880
3	I	3	Va.	Montgomery	2.0	10.6	67.2	20.2	0.62	11,925	88.7	15,340
4	II	1	W.Va.	McDowell	1.0	16.6	77.3	5.1	0.74	14,715	82.8	15,600
5	II	1	Pa.	Cambria	1.3	17.5	70.9	10.3	1.68	13,800	81.3	15,595
6	II	2	Pa.	Somerset	1.5	20.8	67.5	10.2	1.68	13,720	77.5	15,485
7	II	2	Pa.	Indiana	1.5	23.4	64.9	10.2	2.20	13,800	74.5	15,580
8	II	3	Pa.	Westmoreland	1.5	30.7	56.6	11.2	1.82	13,325	65.8	15,230
9	II	3	Ky.	Pike	2.5	36.7	57.5	3.3	0.70	14,480	61.3	15,040
10	II	3	Ohio	Belmont	3.6	40.0	47.3	9.1	4.00	12,850	55.4	14,380
11	II	4	Ill.	Williamson	5.8	36.2	46.3	11.7	2.70	11,910	57.3	13,710
12	II	4	Utah	Emery	5.2	38.2	50.2	6.4	0.90	12,600	57.3	13,560
13	II	5	Ill.	Vermilion	12.2	38.8	40.0	9.0	3.20	11,340	51.8	12,630
14	III	1	Mont.	Musselshell	14.1	32.2	46.7	7.0	0.43	11,140	59.0	12,075
15	III	2	Wyo.	Sheridan	25.0	30.5	40.8	3.7	0.30	9,345	57.5	9,745
16	III	3	Wyo.	Campbell	31.0	31.4	32.8	4.8	0.55	8,320	51.5	8,790
17	IV	1	N.D.	Mercer	37.0	26.6	32.2	4.2	0.40	7,255	55.2	7,610

Column headers: Coal Analysis, Bed Moisture Basis.

Notes: For definition of Rank Classification according to ASTM requirements, *see Table 16.*

Data on Coal (Bed Moisture Basis)

M = equilibrium moisture, %; VM = volatile matter, %;
FC = fixed carbon, %; A = ash, %; S = sulfur, %;
Btu = Btu per lb, high heating value.

Rank FC = dry, mineral-matter-free fixed carbon, %.
Rank Btu = moist, mineral-matter-free Btu per lb.
Calculations by Parr formulas.

Table 18
International classification of hard coals by type and their statistical grouping

The first figure of the code number indicates the class of the coal, determined by volatile-matter content up to 33% volatile matter and by calorific parameter above 33% volatile matter.
The second figure indicates the group of coal, determined by caking properties.
The third figure indicates the subgroup, determined by coking properties.

Subgroups (Determined by Coking Properties)

Sub-Group Number	Audibert-Arnu Dilatometer	Gray-King
5	>140	>G_8
4	>50-140	G_5-G_8
3	>0-50	G_1-G_4
2	$\geqq$0	E-G
3	$\geqq$0-50	G_1-G_4
2	$\geqq$0	E-G
1	Contraction only	B-D
2	$\geqq$0	E-G
1	Contraction only	B-D
0	Nonsoftening	A

Groups (Determined by Caking Properties) — Alternative Group Parameters

Group Number	Free-swelling Index (Crucible-Swelling Number)	Roga Index
3	>4	>45
2	2½-4	>20-45
1	1-2	>5-20
0	0-½	0-5

Code Numbers

Group / Subgroup	Class 1	Class 2	Class 3	Class 4	Class 5	Class 6	Class 7	Class 8	Class 9
Group 3, Subgroup 5 (VC)				435	535	635			
Group 3, Subgroup 4 (VB)			334 (VA)	434	534	634			
Group 3, Subgroup 3 (VA/VD)			333	433	533	633	733		
Group 3, Subgroup 2			332a / 332b	432	532	632	732	832	
Group 2, Subgroup 3 (VIA)			323	423	523	623	723	823	
Group 2, Subgroup 2			322	422	522	622	722	822	
Group 2, Subgroup 1 (VIB)			321	421	521	621	721	821	
Group 1, Subgroup 2 (IV/III)		212	312	412	512	612	712	812	
Group 1, Subgroup 1 (VII)		211	311	411	511	611	711	811	
Group 0, Subgroup 0 (II / I)	100	200	300	400	500	600	700	800	900

As an indication, the following classes have an approximate volatile-matter content of:
Class 6 33-41% Volatile Matter
Class 7 33-44% Volatile Matter
Class 8 35-50% Volatile Matter
Class 9 42-50% Volatile Matter

Class Parameters

Class Number →	0	1 (A: >3-6.5, B: >6.5-10)	2	3	4	5	6	7	8	9
Volatile Matter (Dry, ash-free) →	0-3	>3-10	>10-14	>14-20	>20-28	>28-33	>33	>33	>33	>33
Calorific Parameter* →	—	—	—	—	—	—	>13,950	>12,960-13,950	>10,980-12,960	>10,260-10,980

Classes: (Determined by volatile matter up to 33% volatile matter and by calorific parameter above 33% volatile matter)

Notes:
(1) Where the ash content of coal is too high to allow classification according to the present systems, it must be reduced by laboratory float-and-sink method (or any other appropriate means). The specific gravity selected for flotation should allow a maximum yield of coal with 5-10% of ash.

(2) 332a >14-16% volatile matter.   332b >16-20% volatile matter.

* Gross calorific value on moist, ash-free basis (86 F/96% relative humidity) Btu/lb.

(Source: Bureau of Mines)

Table 19
Grouping of American coals in international system of classification

The first figure of the code number indicates the class of the coal, determined by volatile-matter content up to 33% volatile matter and by calorific parameter above 33% volatile matter.
The second figure indicates the group of coal, determined by caking properties.
The third figure indicates the subgroup, determined by coking properties.

Group (Caking Properties)	Alt. Group Parameters — Free-swelling Index (Crucible Swelling Number)	Alt. Group Parameters — Roga Index	Sub-Group No. (Coking Properties)	Alt. Subgroup — Audibert-Arnu Dilatometer	Alt. Subgroup — Gray-King	Code Numbers — 000	100 (A / B)	200	300	400	500	600	700	800	900
3	>4	>45	5	>140	>G8					435	535	635			
3	>4	>45	4	>50-140	G5-G8				334	434	534	634	734		
3	>4	>45	3	>0-50	G1-G4				333	433	533	633	733		
3	>4	>45	2	≧0	E-G				332a / 332b	432	532	632	732	832	
2	2½-4	>20-45	3	>0-50	G1-G4				323	423	523	623	723	823	
2	2½-4	>20-45	2	≧0	E-G				322	422	522	622	722	822	
2	2½-4	>20-45	1	Contraction only	B-D				321	421	521	621	721	821	
1	1-2	>5-20	2	≧0	E-G			212	312	412	512	612	712	812	
1	1-2	>5-20	1	Contraction only	B-D			211	311	411	511	611	711	811	
0	0-½	0-5	0	Nonsoftening	A	000	100	200	300	400	500	600	700	800	900

Class Number →	0	1	2	3	4	5	6	7	8	9
Volatile Matter (Dry, ash-free) →	0-3	>3-10 (>3-6.5 / >6.5-10)	>10-14	>14-20	>20-28	>28-33	>33	>33	>33	>33
Calorific Parameter* →	—	—	—	—	—	—	>13,950	>12,960-13,950	>10,980-12,960	>10,260-10,980

Classes: (Determined by volatile matter up to 33% volatile matter and by calorific parameter above 33% volatile matter)

As an indication, the following classes have an approximate volatile-matter content of:
Class 6   33-41% Volatile Matter
Class 7   33-44% Volatile Matter
Class 8   35-50% Volatile Matter
Class 9   42-50% Volatile Matter

Notes:

(1) Where the ash content of coal is too high to allow classification according to the present systems, it must be reduced by laboratory float-and-sink method (or any other appropriate means). The specific gravity selected for flotation should allow a maximum yield of coal with 5-10% of ash.

(2) 332a >14-16% volatile matter.   332b >16-20% volatile matter.

(3) From information available, American coals are represented by open-faced blocks. There are probably no commercial deposits of American coals represented by dotted blocks.

* Gross calorific value on moist, ash-free basis (86 F/96% relative humidity) Btu/lb.

(Source: Bureau of Mines)

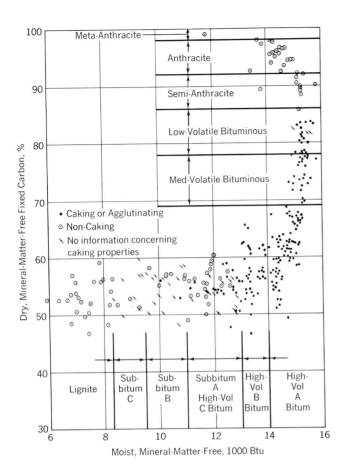

Fig. 4 Distribution plot for over 300 coals of the United States, illustrating ASTM classification by rank as defined in Table 16.

Other classifications of coal by rank

There are classifications of coal by rank (or type) which are currently in limited use on the European Continent. These are the *International Classification of Hard Coals by Type*, and the *International Classification of Brown Coals*. The systems were developed by a Classification Working Party established in 1949 by the Coal Committee of the Economic Commission for Europe.

The classification system of hard coals, which also includes a simplified statistical grouping combining coals having the same general characteristics, appears in Table 18. The term "hard coal" is based on European terminology and is defined as coal with a calorific value of more than 10,260 Btu/lb on the moist, ash-free basis. The term "type" is equivalent to rank in American coal classification terminology and the term "class" approximates the ASTM rank.

The nine classes of coal, based on dry, ash-free volatile matter content and moist, ash-free calorific value, are divided into groups according to their caking properties. Either the free-swelling test or the Roga test may be used to determine caking properties (a measure of the behavior of coal when heated rapidly).

The coal groups are further subdivided into subgroups according to their coking properties, which are a measure of the behavior of the coal when heated slowly. Either the Audibert-Arnu test or the Gray-King coking test may be used to determine these coking properties.

A three-figure code number is used to express coal classification. The first figure indicates the class of the coal, the second figure the group, and the third figure the subgroup. For example, a 635 coal would be a class 6 coal with a free-swelling index greater than 4 and expansion (dilatation) greater than 140.

The rank classification is about the same as ASTM classification except for determination of calorific-value correction. The International system uses the ash-free basis, whereas the ASTM system uses the mineral-matter-free basis. American coals fit in the International classification as shown by the open faced blocks in Table 19. A general comparison of the systems with several American coals is shown in Table 20.

The International Classification of Brown Coals is shown in Table 21, where the term "brown coal" refers to coal containing less than 10,260 Btu/lb on the moist, ash-free basis. The six classes of coal, based on the ash-free equilibrium-moisture content, are divided into groups according to their tar yield on a dry, ash-free basis. This grouping indicates the value of these low-rank coals as fuel and as raw material for chemical purposes. Brown coals with high tar content are generally used as raw material in the chemical industry rather than as fuel.

Other criteria for the classification of coal by rank have been proposed by various authorities.

A method of classifying, by computing the heating value of the residual coal with moisture (M), ash (A), and sulfur (S) removed, has been used by Lord. This is called the "H" value.

$$(7) \qquad H = \frac{\text{Btu} - 4050\,S}{100 - (M + A + S)} \times 100$$

While the H values as listed in Table 22 are of interest, they do not arrange the 17 coals in the same order as the ASTM classification.

Another classification method, reported by Perch and Russell, is based on the following ratio:

$$(8) \qquad \text{Ratio} = \frac{\text{Moist, } Mm\text{-free Btu}}{\text{Dry, } Mm\text{-free } VM}$$

Values of this ratio for the 17 coals listed in Table 17 arrange these coals in Table 22 in exactly the same order as the ASTM method. The very high ratio for coal No. 1 is not shown, since it is of little importance. It is said that this Perch and Russell ratio is closely related to the coking properties of coals used in coke-oven practice.

It may be of interest to consider the validity of other

Table 20
System comparison of selected American coals

State	County	Seam	Classification ASTM	International
W.Va.	McDowell	Pocahontas #3	lvb	333
Pa.	Clearfield	Lower Kittaning	mvb	435
W.Va.	Monongalia	Pittsburgh	hvAb	635
Ill.	Williamson	No. 6	hvBb	734
Ill.	Knox	No. 6	hvCb	821

lvb = low-volatile bituminous
mvb = medium-volatile bituminous
hvAb = high-volatile A bituminous
hvBb = high-volatile B bituminous
hvCb = high-volatile C bituminous

Source, Bureau of Mines.

criteria in the classification of coal by rank based on the dry, ash-free analyses appearing in Table 22. Carbon (C) comes close to lining up the coals in the same order as the ASTM rank. As a criterion, the carbon content would be quite simple, but it cannot be used as a suitable basis for classification. Oxygen (O_2) generally decreases with the age of coals, but it is not consistent. The volatile matter (VM), fixed carbon (FC), hydrogen (H_2), and the Btu do not follow the same order as the ASTM method. Nitrogen (N_2) varies little for all ranks.

Since the quality of the volatile matter in coal is an index of the extent of the conversion of the original carbohydrates to hydrocarbons, studies have been made suggesting that the heating value of the volatile matter will serve as an accurate criterion for classification by rank. This criterion, developed on a "pure coal" basis as calculated in equation (12), is listed in Table 22 under Btu per lb VM_{pc}.

Composition of the fixed carbon in all types of coal is substantially all carbon. The variable constituents of coals can, therefore, be considered as concentrated in the volatile matter. One index of the quality of the volatile matter, its heating value, is perhaps the most important property as far as combustion is concerned and bears a direct relation to the properties of the pure coals (dry, mineral-matter-free). The volatile matter in coals of lower rank, where the conversion of carbohydrates to hydrocarbons has not progressed far, is relatively high in water and CO_2 and, consequently, low in heating

Table 21
International classification of brown coals
(Gross calorific value below 10,260 Btu/lb)*

Group No.	Group Parameter Tar Yield (dry, ash free), %	Code Number					
40	>25	1040	1140	1240	1340	1440	1540
30	>20-25	1030	1130	1230	1330	1430	1530
20	>15-20	1020	1120	1220	1320	1420	1520
10	>10-15	1010	1110	1210	1310	1410	1510
00	10 & less	1000	1100	1200	1300	1400	1500
Class Number		10	11	12	13	14	15
Class Parameter, i.e., Total Moisture, (ash free), %		20 and less	20 to 30	30 to 40	40 to 50	50 to 60	60 to 70

Notes: The total-moisture content refers to freshly mined coal. For internal purposes, coals with a gross calorific value over 10,260 Btu/lb (moist, ash-free basis), considered in the country of origin as brown coals but classified as hard coals for international purposes, may be classified under this system, to ascertain, in particular, their suitability for processing.

When the total-moisture content is over 30%, the gross calorific value is always below 10,260 Btu/lb.

* Moist, ash-free basis (86F/96% relative humidity).

Source, Bureau of Mines.

Table 22
Study of the suitability of other criteria in the classification of coals

Coals Table 17 No.	Btu Lord's H Value	Perch & Russell Ratio	Btu per lb VM_{pc}	Coal Analysis, Dry, Ash-Free Basis							Grind-ability
				VM	FC	C	H_2	O_2	N_2	Btu	
1	14,950	—	—	2.0	98.0	93.9	2.1	2.3	0.3	14,850	37
2	15,180	2520	25,685	7.3	92.7	93.5	2.6	2.3	0.9	15,100	26
3	15,410	1358	23,330	13.6	86.4	90.7	4.2	3.3	1.0	15,325	83
4	15,765	907	21,750	17.7	82.3	90.4	4.8	2.7	1.3	15,670	100
5	15,840	834	21,155	19.8	80.2	89.4	4.8	2.4	1.5	15,615	112
6	15,765	688	19,785	23.5	76.5	88.6	4.8	3.1	1.6	15,540	105
7	15,930	611	19,570	26.5	73.5	87.6	5.2	3.3	1.4	15,630	95
8	15,500	445	17,230	35.2	64.8	85.0	5.4	5.8	1.7	15,265	88
9	15,460	389	16,930	39.0	61.0	85.5	5.5	6.7	1.6	15,370	56
10	15,230	322	15,430	45.8	54.2	80.9	5.7	7.4	1.4	14,730	57
11	14,800	320	14,875	43.8	56.2	80.5	5.5	9.1	1.6	14,430	60
12	14,359	318	14,200	43.2	56.8	79.8	5.6	11.8	1.7	14,260	50
13	14,830	300	14,690	49.3	50.7	79.2	5.7	9.5	1.5	14,400	61
14	14,170	295	13,885	40.8	59.2	80.9	5.1	12.2	1.3	14,110	55
15	13,145	229	11,435	42.8	57.2	75.9	5.1	17.0	1.6	13,100	43
16	13,055	181	11,570	49.0	51.0	74.0	5.6	18.6	0.9	12,970	52
17	12,400	170	9,945	45.3	54.7	72.7	4.9	20.8	0.9	12,330	45

Notes:

For calculations of Lord's H Value and the Perch & Russell ratio, and the heating value of the volatile matter (pure coal basis) refer to equations 7 to 12, inclusive, this chapter.

The subscript pc means on a "pure coal" basis. The dry, ash-free VM may be used, instead of the VM_{pc}, without appreciable error. Grindability is determined by ASTM Method D 409.

value. The volatile matter, in coals of higher rank, is relatively high in hydrocarbons, such as methane (CH_4), and, consequently relatively high in heating value.

The analyses and heating values of the coal must be converted to the mineral-matter-free ("pure coal") basis in order to establish reasonably accurate heating values for volatile matter. The only difference in the conversion used for this method and the conversion used in the ASTM Standard D 388 is that half the sulfur is assumed to be pyritic on the pure coal basis. The assumption that only half the sulfur is pyritic and the remainder organic is in closer agreement with the average for a large number of U.S. coals. The formulas for converting the analyses and coal heating values to the "pure coal" basis and for calculating the heating value of the volatile matter are as follows:

$$(9) \quad VM_{pc} = \frac{VM - (0.08A + 0.2\,S)}{100 - (1.08A + 0.2625\,S + M)} \times 100, \%$$

$$(10) \quad FC_{pc} = \frac{FC - 0.0625\,S}{100 - (1.08A + 0.2625\,S + M)} \times 100, \%$$

$$(11) \quad Btu_{pc} = \frac{Btu - 26.2\,S}{100 - (1.08A + 0.2625\,S + M)} \times 100,$$
$$\text{Btu/lb}$$

$$(12) \quad Btu/lb\ VM_{pc} = \frac{Btu_{pc} - \left(\dfrac{14{,}460}{100} FC_{pc}\right)}{VM_{pc}} \times 100,$$
$$\text{Btu/lb}$$

where:

VM, FC, A, S, M, and Btu are the same as noted previously for the Parr formulas. Subscript pc denotes "pure coal" basis.

The Btu per lb volatile matter, calculated from the above formulas, is given in Table 22 for 16 of the 17 coals listed, covering the entire range of rank. The order of

these values follows generally the ASTM classification of the coals, although the correlation is not as good as with the Perch and Russell ratio. The range of values of Btu per lb volatile matter, from about 8000 to 28,000 (Fig. 5), is large and may serve as a useful classification.

The relation of the heating value of the volatile matter and the heating value of the pure coal is shown in Fig. 5 for a large number of coals. It is evident that a fair line could be drawn, without serious error, to indicate the path of this relationship.

Commercial sizes of coal

Bituminous. Sizes of bituminous coal are not well standardized, but the following sizings are common:

Run of mine. This is coal shipped as it comes from the mine without screening. It is used for both domestic heating and steam production.

Run of mine (8 in.). This is run of mine with oversize lumps broken up.

Lump (5 in.). This size will not go through a 5 in. round hole. It is used for hand firing and domestic purposes.

Egg (5 in. × 2 in.). This size goes through 5 in. and is retained on 2 in. round-hole screens. It is used for hand firing, gas producers, and domestic firing.

Nut (2 in. × 1¼ in.). This size is used for small industrial stokers, gas producers, and hand firing.

Stoker coal (1¼ in. × ¾ in.) is used largely for small industrial stokers and domestic firing.

Slack (¾ in. and under) is used for pulverizers, Cyclone Furnaces, and industrial stokers.

Several other sizes of bituminous coal are prepared by different producers especially for domestic stoker requirements.

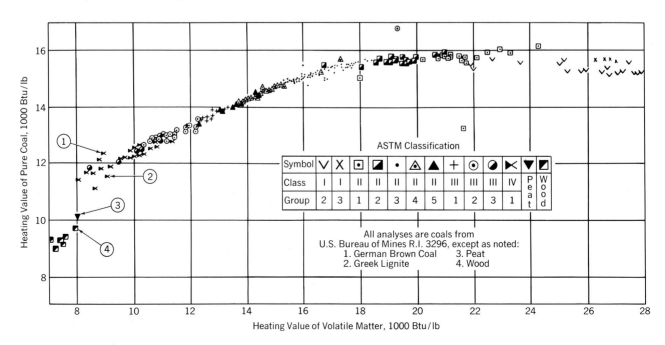

Fig. 5 To illustrate a suggested coal classification using the relationship of the respective heating values of "pure coal" and the volatile matter.

Anthracite. Definite sizes of anthracite are standardized in Table 23. The broken, egg, stove, nut and pea sizes are largely used for hand-fired domestic units and gas producers. Buckwheat and rice are used in mechanical types of firing equipment.

Table 23
Commercial sizes of anthracite (ASTM D 310)
(Graded on round-hole screens)

Trade Name	Diameter of Holes, Inches Through	Retained On
Broken	4-3/8	3-1/4 to 3
Egg	3-1/4 to 3	2-7/16
Stove	2-7/16	1-5/8
Nut	1-5/8	13/16
Pea	13/16	9/16
Buckwheat	9/16	5/16
Rice	5/16	3/16

Moisture determination

Moisture in coal is determined quantitatively by definite prescribed methods. It is preferable to determine the moisture in two steps: 1) prescribed air drying to equilibrium at 10-15C above room temperature, and 2) prescribed oven drying for one hr at 104-110C, after pulverizing (*see also ASTM Standard D 271*).

The air-dried component of the total moisture value should be reported separately, because this information is required in the design and selection of equipment. It is the surface moisture having normal vapor pressure that must be evaporated prior to efficient pulverizing of anthracite and bituminous coal.

ASTM Standard D 1412 provides a means of estimating the bed moisture of either wet coal showing visible surface moisture or coal that may have lost some moisture. It may be used for estimating the surface, or extraneous, moisture of wet coal, i.e., the difference between total moisture, as determined by ASTM Standard D 271, and equilibrium moisture. Also, for classification of coal by rank, the equilibrium moisture of a sample is considered to be equal to the bed or inherent moisture (ASTM Standard D 388).

Table 24
ASTM standard specifications for fuel oils[a]

No. 1 A distillate oil intended for vaporizing pot-type burners and other burners requiring this grade of fuel

No. 2 A distillate oil for general purpose domestic heating for use in burners not requiring No. 1 fuel oil

No. 4 Preheating not usually required for handling or burning

No. 5 (Light) Preheating may be required depending on climate and equipment

No. 5 (Heavy) Preheating may be required for burning and, in cold climates, may be required for handling

No. 6 Preheating required for burning and handling

Grade of Fuel Oil	Flash Point, F (C)	Pour Point, F (C)	Water and Sediment, % by Volume	Carbon Residue on 10% Bottoms, %	Ash, % by Weight	Distillation Temperatures, F (C) 10% Point Max	90% Point Min	90% Point Max	Saybolt Viscosity, sec Universal at 100F (38C) Min	Universal at 100F (38C) Max	Furol at 122F (50C) Min	Furol at 122F (50C) Max	Kinematic Viscosity, centistokes At 100F (38C) Min	At 100F (38C) Max	At 122F (50C) Min	At 122F (50C) Max	Gravity, deg API Min	Copper Strip Corrosion Max
No. 1	100 or legal (38)	0	trace	0.15	—	420 (215)	—	550 (288)	—	—	—	—	1.4	2.2	—	—	35	No. 3
No. 2	100 or legal (38)	20c (−7)	0.10	0.35	—	d	540c (282)	640 (338)	(32.6)f	(37.93)	—	—	2.0e	3.6	—	—	30	—
No. 4	130 or legal (55)	20 (−7)	0.50	—	0.10	—	—	—	45	125	—	—	(5.8)	(26.4)	—	—	—	—
No. 5 (Light)	130 or legal (55)	—	1.00	—	0.10	—	—	—	150	300	—	—	(32)	(65)	—	—	—	—
No. 5 (Heavy)	130 or legal (55)	—	1.00	—	0.10	—	—	—	350	750	(23)	(40)	(75)	(162)	(42)	(81)	—	—
No. 6	150 (65)	—	2.00g	—	—	—	—	—	(900)	(9000)	45	300	—	—	(92)	(638)	—	—

a Recognizing the necessity for low-sulfur fuel oils used in connection with heat-treatment, nonferrous metal, glass, and ceramic furnaces and other special uses, a sulfur requirement may be specified in accordance with the following table:

Grade of Fuel Oil	Sulfur, Max, %
No. 1	0.5
No. 2	0.7
No. 4	no limit
No. 5	no limit
No. 6	no limit

Other sulfur limits may be specified only by mutual agreement between the purchaser and the seller.

b It is the intent of these classifications that failure to meet any requirement of a given grade does not automatically place an oil in the next lower grade unless in fact it meets all requirements of the lower grade.

c Lower or higher pour points may be specified whenever required by conditions of storage or use.

d The 10% distillation temperature point may be specified at 440F (226C) maximum for use in other than atomizing burners.

e When pour point less than 0 F is specified, the minimum viscosity shall be 1.8 cs (32.0 sec, Saybolt Universal) and the minimum 90% point shall be waived.

f Viscosity values in parentheses are for information only and not necessarily limiting.

g The amount of water by distillation plus the sediment by extraction shall not exceed 2.00%. The amount of sediment by extraction shall not exceed 0.50%. A deduction in quantity shall be made for all water and sediment in excess of 1.0%.

Source, ASTM D 396.

Calorific value of coal

The calorific or heating value of coal is determined accurately in an oxygen bomb submerged in cooling water. Several acceptable makes or types of bomb calorimeters are listed in ASTM Standard D 271. A pulverized coal sample is compressed into a hard pellet and ignited in an oxygen atmosphere with a hot wire. The heating value is then determined from the rise in water temperature.

Gross (higher) heating value is defined as the heat released from combustion of unit fuel quantity (mass), with the products in the form of ash, gaseous CO_2, SO_2, N_2, and liquid water exclusive of any water added directly as vapor. The net (lower) heating value is calculated from the gross heating value as the heat produced by a unit quantity of fuel when all water in the products remains as vapor. This calculation (ASTM Standard D 407) is made by deducting 1030° Btu/lb of water derived from the fuel, including both the water originally present as moisture and that formed by combustion. In America the gross calorific value is commonly used in heat balance calculations, while in Europe the net value is generally used.

Grindability of coal

Grindability is a term used to measure the ease of pulverizing a coal in comparison with a standard coal chosen as 100 grindability. For a description of the method of testing to determine grindability of a coal, see "Grindability Index (ASTM D 409)," Chapter 9. Fig. 6 of the same chapter shows the machine used in making the test. The grindability of the 17 representative coals in Table 17 is tabulated in the last column of Table 22.

Free-swelling index

The ASTM Standard Method D 720 is used for obtaining information regarding the free-swelling property of a coal. Since it is a measure of the behavior of rapidly heated coal, it may be used as an indication of the caking characteristics of coal burned as a fuel.

Coal ash

The nature, composition, and properties of coal ash are discussed in Chapter 15.

Characteristics of fuel oil

It is common practice in refining petroleum to produce fuel oils complying with several specifications prepared by the ASTM and adopted as a commercial standard by the U.S. Bureau of Standards. These standards have been revised several times in order to meet changes in supply and demand and further changes may be expected.

The current standards are tabulated in Table 24. Fuel oils are graded according to gravity and viscosity, the lightest being No. 1 and the heaviest No. 6. Grades 5 and 6 generally require heating for satisfactory pumping and burning (see Oil Burners, Chapter 7). Analyses and

---

° The value of 1030 Btu/lb of water, an average figure, corrects for both the latent heat of vaporization and conversion from constant volume conditions of the calorimeter to an equivalent constant pressure basis.

---

relative cost of some selected fuel oils are listed in Table 25. The range of analyses and heating values of the several grades of fuel oils are given in Table 26.

The gross heating values of various fuel oils of different gravity are shown in Fig. 6. The abscissa on this figure is the API (American Petroleum Institute) gravity. Degrees API refer to a hydrometer scale with the following relation to specific gravity:

$$(13) \qquad \text{Degrees API} = \frac{141.5}{\text{sp gr @ 60/60F}} - 131.5$$

where:

sp gr @ 60/60F represents the ratio of oil density at 60F to water density also at 60F.

The heating values, as listed in Fig. 6, are closely related to the gravity of the oil. The heating value for an actual oil is obtained by correcting the Btu/lb value from Fig. 6 as follows:

$$(14) \qquad \frac{\text{Btu/lb} \times [100 - (A + M + S)]}{100} + 40.5\,S$$

where:

Btu/lb is taken from Fig. 6
A = % by wt of ash
M = % by wt of water
S = % by wt of sulfur

The volume percentages of water and sediment can be used without appreciable error in place of weight percentage where the percentages by weight of water and ash are not known.

Fuel oils are generally sold on a volume basis with 60F as the base temperature. Correction factors are

---

Table 25
Selected analyses and relative cost of fuel oils

Grade of Fuel Oil	No. 1	No. 2	No. 4	No. 5	No. 6
Weight, percent					
Sulfur	0.1	0.3	0.8	1.0	2.3
Hydrogen	13.8	12.5	—	—	9.7
Carbon	86.1	87.2	—	—	85.6
Nitrogen	—	0.02	—	— }	2.0
Oxygen	Nil	Nil	—	— }	
Ash	Nil	Nil	0.03	0.03	0.12
Gravity					
Deg API	42	32	20	19	—
Specific	0.815	0.865	0.934	0.940	—
Lb per gal	6.79	7.21	7.78	7.83	—
Pour point, F	−35	−5	+20	+30	—
Viscosity					
Centistokes @ 100F	1.8	2.4	27.5	130	—
SUS @ 100F	—	34	130	—	—
SSF @ 122F	—	—	—	30	—
Water & sediment, vol %	Nil	Nil	0.2	0.3	0.74
Heating value Btu per lb, gross	19,810	19,430	18,860	18,760	18,300°
Relative cost per Btu	118	100	76	60	51

° Bomb calorimeter determination.

given in Fig. 7 for converting known volumes at other temperatures to the 60F standard base. This correction is also dependent on the API (American Petroleum Institute) gravity range as illustrated by the three parametric curves of Fig. 7.

Since handling and especially burning equipment is usually designed for a maximum oil viscosity, it is necessary to know the viscosity characteristics of the fuel oil to be used. If the viscosities of heavy oils are known at two temperatures, viscosities at other temperatures can be closely predicted with negligible error by a linear interpolation between these two values located on the standard ASTM chart of Fig. 8. Viscosity variations with temperature for certain light oils can also be found with the aid of the ASTM chart but in this case knowledge of the viscosity at only one temperature is required. Viscosities of light oils at various temperatures within the region designated as No. 2 fuel oil can be found by drawing a line parallel to the No. 2 boundary lines through the point of known viscosity and temperature. Copies of the chart may be obtained from the ASTM.

Compared with coal, fuel oils are relatively easy to handle and burn. Heating is not required for the lighter oils, and even the heavier oils are relatively simple to handle. There is not as much ash-in-bulk disposal problem as there is with coal, and the amount of ash discharged from the stack is correspondingly small. In most oil burners the oil is atomized to a mist of small particles that mix with combustion air. In the atomized state, the characteristics of oil approaches those of a gas, with consequent similar explosion hazards (*see Safety Precautions, Chapter 7*).

Because of its relatively low cost compared with that of lighter oils, No. 6 fuel oil is the most widely used for steam generation. It can be considered a by-product of the refining process. Its ash content ranges from about 0.01 to 0.5%, which is very low compared with coal. However, despite this low percentage content, ash containing compounds of vanadium, sodium and sulfur can be responsible for a number of serious operating problems (Chapter 15).

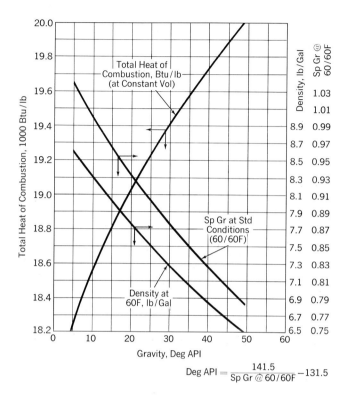

$$\text{Deg API} = \frac{141.5}{\text{Sp Gr @ 60/60F}} - 131.5$$

Fig. 6 Heating value, weight (lb per gal), and specific gravity of fuel oil for a range of API gravities.

Table 26
Range of analyses of fuel oils

Grade of Fuel Oil	No. 1	No. 2	No. 4	No. 5	No. 6
Weight, percent					
Sulfur	0.01-0.5	0.05-1.0	0.2-2.0	0.5-3.0	0.7-3.5
Hydrogen	13.3-14.1	11.8-13.9	(10.6-13.0)°	(10.5-12.0)°	(9.5-12.0)°
Carbon	85.9-86.7	86.1-88.2	(86.5-89.2)°	(86.5-89.2)°	(86.5-90.2)°
Nitrogen	Nil-0.1	Nil-0.1	—	—	—
Oxygen	—	—	—	—	—
Ash	—	—	0-0.1	0-0.1	0.01-0.5
Gravity					
Deg API	40-44	28-40	15-30	14-22	7-22
Specific	0.825-0.806	0.887-0.825	0.966-0.876	0.972-0.922	1.022-0.922
Lb per gal	6.87-6.71	7.39-6.87	8.04-7.30	8.10-7.68	8.51-7.68
Pour point, F	0 to −50	0 to −40	−10 to +50	−10 to +80	+15 to +85
Viscosity					
Centistokes @ 100F	1.4-2.2	1.9-3.0	10.5-65	65-200	260-750
SUS @ 100F	—	32-38	60-300	—	—
SSF @ 122F	—	—	—	20-40	45-300
Water & sediment, vol %	—	0-0.1	tr to 1.0	0.05-1.0	0.05-2.0
Heating value					
Btu per lb, gross (calculated)	19,670-19,860	19,170-19,750	18,280-19,400	18,100-19,020	17,410-18,990

° Estimated.

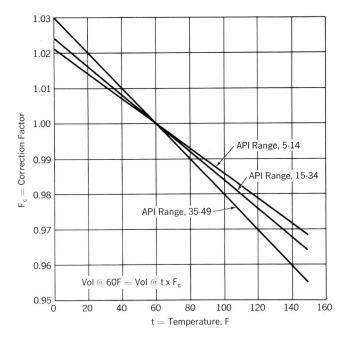

Fig. 7 Temperature-volume correction factor for fuel oil.

Fuel oils generally available on the Eastern seaboard are produced from varying amounts of Venezuelan and Middle East crudes, depending on the relative quantities of shipments and on the blending at the refineries to meet No. 6 fuel-oil viscosity specifications. Fuel oils used on the Gulf and West Coasts are produced largely from domestic crudes, although they may contain some Venezuelan crude. Because of this it is difficult, if not impossible, to identify the source of fuel oils as fired.

Shale oil

An analysis of a typical Green River oil shale from the Colorado-Utah-Wyoming area is given in Table 27. Fuel oils produced from refineries using shale oil feedstock on a commercial scale are unavailable. Characteristics of the fuel oil will depend on the refinery processes to be used and, also, any supplementary crude oil used in the feedstock. At the prevailing cost of producing oil from petroleum, it has not been commercially attractive to produce oil products from oil shale in the U.S.

Characteristics of natural gas

Of all chemical fuels, natural gas is considered the most desirable for steam generation. It is piped directly to the consumer, eliminating the need for storage at the consumer's plant. It is substantially free of ash, and mixes intimately with air to provide complete combustion at low excess air without smoke. Although the total hydrogen content of natural gas is high, the amount of free hydrogen is low. Because of this characteristic, natural gas is not as easy to burn as some manufactured gases with their high free hydrogen content.

The high hydrogen content of natural gas compared with that of oil or coal results in more water vapor produced in the combustion gases with a correspondingly lower efficiency of the steam generating equipment. This can readily be taken into account in the design of the equipment and evaluated in comparing the cost of gas with other fuels.

Analyses of natural gas from several U.S. fields are given in Table 28.

Relative costs of the three major fuels

Costs of all fuels vary from year to year but today the cost of a fuel is not the only criterion used when selecting a fuel for a steam generating plant. Since the passage of the Clean Air Act in 1970, utilities that have been burning high sulfur eastern coals have been investigating other fuels. Various means of removing sulfur from coal before and after it has been burned are being investigated. Most of the methods to remove sulfur are still in the pilot plant stage and are not available for use today. The only one of these methods that can be used presently is flue gas scrubbing, and this method is not without disadvantages. The cost of a scrubber can equal that of the steam generator. There are also other problems such as the disposal of the solid residue obtained after scrubbing. A number of eastern and mid-western utilities are burning or are investigating burning low sulfur western coals. This also is not without its disadvantages. It is mined a long distance from the mid-west and eastern market so transportation is expensive. Most western coals are low ranked as well as having other undesirable char-

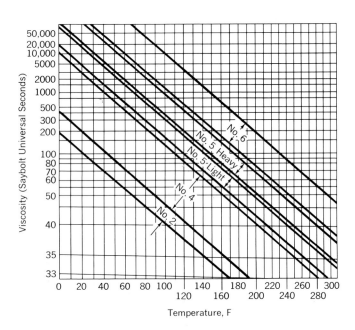

Note: On the scale at the left, find the SUS viscosity at 100F (standard test temperature) for the given oil; move horizontally to the vertical line for 100F. From this intersection move parallel to the diagonal lines to the viscosity required for atomization; the temperature necessary to achieve this viscosity can be read on the bottom scale. The chart, based on U.S. Commerical Standard 12-48 has been developed from data for many fuels and should be sufficiently accurate for most applications.

Fig. 8 Approximate viscosity of fuel oil at various temperatures. *(Source, ASTM.)*

acteristics such as low fusion temperatures, high moisture content, etc.

Another problem that has confused the energy picture is the shortage of natural gas and petroleum—especially natural gas. It no longer matters if natural gas is economical to burn in utility boilers—it is not available. There are no new utility boilers being designed to burn natural gas in the United States.

Table 27
Analysis of a Green River oil shale

Physical properties		
Specific gravity, 60F/60F		2.3
Bulk density, 48 mesh,		
lb/cu ft		67.8
Oil-shale assay,* % by wt		
Oil		10.3
Gas		2.5
Water		1.4
Organic residue		3.1
Mineral residue		82.7
Yield in oil, gal per ton		26.7
Mineral residue, wt %		
of raw shale		
Mineral CO_2 evolved		20.0
Mineral analysis of ash		
Silica	as SiO_2	26.4
Calcium	as CaO	17.1
Magnesium	as MgO	5.4
Aluminum	as Al_2O_3	6.6
Alkalies	as Na_2O & K_2O	3.7
Iron	as Fe_2O_3	2.6
Phosphorus & Vanadium	as P_2O_5 & V_2O_5	0.4
Sulfur	as SO_3	0.5

* Modified Fischer assay.

The shortage of oil for use as a fuel in utility boilers is not as critical but much of this oil is imported. Imported oil is expensive and there is no guarantee of a long range supply. Nearly all large utility plants being designed today are either for coal or nuclear fuel.

Other fuels for combustion

New fuels are being investigated and old ones are being reviewed with new interest.

Among the other fuels used for combustion, those derived from coal are the most important. Also used are petroleum by-products; wood, its by-products and wastes from wood-processing industries; and certain types of vegetation, particularly bagasse.

Coke

When coal is heated in the absence of air or with a large deficiency of air, the lighter constituents are volatilized and the heavier hydrocarbons crack, liberating hydrogen and leaving a residue of carbon. Some of the volatilized portions crack on contact with the hot carbon, leaving an additional quantity of carbon. The carbonaceous residue containing the ash and a part of the sulfur of the original coal is called "coke." The amount of sulfur and the amount and nature of the ash in the coke depend in large measure on the coal from which it is produced and the coking process used. The principal uses for coke are in the production of pig iron in blast furnaces and the charging of iron foundry cupolas. Because it is smokeless in combustion, considerable quantities have been used for space heating.

Undersized coke called "coke breeze," usually passing a 5/8-in. screen, is unsuited for charging blast furnaces

---

Table 28
Selected samples of natural gas from United States fields

	Sample No.	1	2	3	4	5
	Source of Gas	Pa.	So. Cal.	Ohio	La.	Okla.
Analyses						
Constituents, % by vol						
H_2 Hydrogen		—	—	1.82	—	—
CH_4 Methane		83.40	84.00	93.33	90.00	84.10
C_2H_4 Ethylene		—	—	0.25	—	—
C_2H_6 Ethane		15.80	14.80	—	5.00	6.70
CO Carbon monoxide		—	—	0.45	—	—
CO_2 Carbon dioxide		—	0.70	0.22	—	0.80
N_2 Nitrogen		0.80	0.50	3.40	5.00	8.40
O_2 Oxygen		—	—	0.35	—	—
H_2S Hydrogen sulfide		—	—	0.18	—	—
Ultimate, % by wt						
S Sulfur		—	—	0.34	—	—
H_2 Hydrogen		23.53	23.30	23.20	22.68	20.85
C Carbon		75.25	74.72	69.12	69.26	64.84
N_2 Nitrogen		1.22	0.76	5.76	8.06	12.90
O_2 Oxygen		—	1.22	1.58	—	1.41
Specific gravity (rel to air)		0.636	0.636	0.567	0.600	0.630
Higher heat value						
Btu/cu ft @ 60F & 30 in. Hg		1,129	1,116	964	1,002	974
Btu/lb of fuel		23,170	22,904	22,077	21,824	20,160

Table 29
Selected analyses
—bagasse, coke breeze, and fluidized-bed char

Analyses (as fired), % by wt	Bagasse	Coke Breeze	Fluidized-Bed Char
Proximate			
Moisture	52.0	7.3	0.7
Volatile matter	40.2	2.3	14.7
Fixed carbon	6.1	79.4	70.4
Ash	1.7	11.0	14.2
Ultimate			
H_2 Hydrogen	2.8	0.3	—
C Carbon	23.4	80.0	—
S Sulfur	trace	0.6	4.1
N_2 Nitrogen	0.1	0.3	—
O_2 Oxygen	20.0	0.5	—
H_2O Moisture	52.0	7.3	—
A Ash	1.7	11.0	—
Heating value, Btu/lb	4000	11,670	12,100

and is available for steam generation. A typical analysis of coke breeze appears in Table 29. Approximately 4.5% by weight of the coal charged into slot-type coke ovens is recovered as breeze.

Until the late 1940's, roughly three-fourths of the breeze produced at coke oven plants was used by the producing companies for steam generation.

Tars and char

A portion of the coal tars produced as a by-product of the various coking processes may be burned in equipment similar to that used for heavy petroleum oil. Low temperature (900 to 1100F) carbonization processes have been developed for the extraction from coal of valuable tars, bitumens and gases for use as raw materials in the chemical industry. The by-product solid fuel from these processes is called char. Disco char, produced by low temperature carbonization has been sold for use in the domestic and small commercial fuel market. Char which appears to have the greatest commercial significance is that produced by the fluidized-bed method. At present, economics have curtailed the widespread use of any of these processes. A typical analysis of fluidized-bed char is given in Table 29.

Gaseous fuels from coal

A number of gaseous fuels are derived from coal either as by-products or from coal gasification processes. Table 30 lists selected analyses of these gases according to the various types described in the following paragraphs. At the present time they have been largely supplanted by natural gas and oil. However, improvements in coal gasification and wider use of coal in the chemical and liquid fuel industries could reverse this trend.

Coke-oven gas. A considerable portion of coal is converted to gases or vapors in the production of coke. Valuable products recovered from these gaseous portions include ammonium sulfate, oils and tars. The noncondensable portion is called "coke-oven gas." Constituents depend on the nature of the coal and the coking process used (Table 30).

A part of the sulfur from coal may be present in coke-oven gas as hydrogen sulfide and carbon disulfide. These may be removed by scrubbing. Coke-oven gas often contains other impurities that deposit in pipe lines and burners requiring the use of relatively large burner-gas-port openings to reduce plugging. Also, burners are arranged for easy access and cleaning. Coke-oven gas burns readily because of a high free-hydrogen content and presents no problems when used as fuel for steam generation except for the buildup of deposits.

Approximately 14 to 16% by weight of the coal charged into slot-type coke ovens is recovered in the form of a fuel gas. In 1968 a total of 923 billion cu ft of coke-oven gas was formed from 90 million tons of coal averaging 10,251 cu ft per ton of coal carbonized. A breakdown of gas produced in 1968 shows 36.0% used to heat coke ovens, 58.5% used by the producing companies in steel and allied plants and in boilers, 4.0% sold for residential, commercial, and industrial heating, and 1.5% wasted.

Blast-furnace gas. The gas discharged from steel mill blast furnaces is used at the mills in heating furnaces, gas engines, and for steam generation. This gas is quite variable in quality but is generally of high carbon monoxide content and low heating value (Table 30).

The gas is discharged from the furnace at about 500F and contains 5 to 7 grains of entrained dust per cu ft. This gas may be burned directly for steam generation. However, at many mills, entrained dust is first removed by washing or by electrostatic precipitation. Wet washed gas from many types of washers will have a dust loading of 0.1 to 0.2 grains per cu ft.

Both dirty and wet washed gas burned for steam generation can cause trouble by plugging gas lines and burner ports and fouling boiler heating surfaces. Blast-furnace-gas deposits adhere very firmly, and provisions must be made for cleaning boiler heating surfaces. Because of the nature of the deposits, wet washed gas is often more troublesome than hot, dry, dirty gas. Electro-

Table 30
Selected analyses of gaseous fuels derived from coal

Analysis No.	1	2	3	4
Analyses, % by vol				
H_2 Hydrogen	47.9	2.4	34.0	14.0
CH_4 Methane	33.9	0.1	15.5	3.0
C_2H_4 Ethylene	5.2	—	4.7	—
CO Carbon monoxide	6.1	23.3	32.0	27.0
CO_2 Carbon dioxide	2.6	14.4	4.3	4.5
N_2 Nitrogen	3.7	56.4	6.5	50.9
O_2 Oxygen	0.6	—	0.7	0.6
C_6H_6 Benzene	—	—	2.3	—
H_2O Water	—	3.4	—	—
Specific gravity (relative to air)	0.413	1.015	0.666	0.857
Higher heat value—Btu/cu ft				
@ 60F & 30 in. Hg	590	—	534	163
@ 80F & 30 in. Hg	—	83.8	—	—

Anal. No.	Kind of Gas	Anal. No.	Kind of Gas
1	Coke-oven gas	3	Carbureted water gas
2	Blast-furnace gas (lean)	4	Producer gas

statically cleaned gas may or may not cause trouble, depending on the collector efficiency.

When blast-furnace gas is used for steam generation, special safety precautions are required because of fluctuations in gas supply from variations or interruptions in blast furnace operation. Also, an alternate fuel must be immediately available in cases where the steam production rate must be maintained.

Water gas. The gas produced by passing steam through a bed of hot coke is known as water gas. Carbon in the coke combines with the steam to form hydrogen and carbon monoxide. This is an endothermic reaction which cools the coke bed. General practice is to replace steam periodically by air for combustion of coke in order to regain the required bed temperature. While the air is passing through the bed, the discharged products of combustion are diverted to the atmosphere to avoid diluting the water gas with noncombustibles.

Water gas is often enriched with oil by passing the gas through a checkerwork of hot bricks sprayed with oil which in turn is cracked to a gas by the heat. Refinery gas is also used for enrichment. It may either be mixed with the steam and passed through the coke bed or mixed directly with the water gas. Such enriched water gas is called "carbureted water gas" (Table 30) and it is piped for relatively short distances through city mains for industrial and domestic consumption. Where it is so used, it is cleaned at the source to remove sulfur gases and other impurities. In many areas use of carbureted water gas has been replaced by natural gas.

Producer gas. When coal or coke is burned with a deficiency of air and a controlled amount of moisture (steam), a gas known as producer gas is obtained. This gas, after removal of entrained ash and sulfur compounds, is used near its source because of its low heating value (Table 30).

Gasification using in situ combustion of coal has been carried out by the Bureau of Mines on an experimental basis at Gorgas, Alabama. The purpose of these tests was to demonstrate that energy from coal in seams too thin for mining could be made available through underground gasification. The U.S.S.R. has made producer gas for power generation using this process. This means of gasification is not economically competitive in the U.S. at the present time.

Coke from petroleum

The heavy residuals from the various petroleum cracking processes are presently utilized in a number of ways to produce a higher yield of lighter hydrocarbons and a solid residue suitable for fuel. Characteristics of these residues vary widely, depending on the process used. Solid fuels from oil include delayed coke, fluid coke and petroleum pitch. Some selected analyses are given in Table 31.

The delayed coking process uses residual oil heated and pumped to a reactor for coking. Coke is deposited as a solid mass and is subsequently stripped either mechanically or hydraulically, in the form of lumps and granular material. Some of these cokes are easy to pulverize and burn, while others are quite difficult.

Fluid coke is produced by spraying hot residual feed onto externally heated seed coke in a fluid bed. The fluid coke is removed as small particles, which are built up in layers similar to an onion. This coke can be pulverized and burned, or it can be burned in the as-received size in a Cyclone Furnace. Both types of firing require some supplemental fuel to aid ignition.

The process producing petroleum pitch is an alternate to the coking process and yields fuels of various characteristics. Melting points vary considerably and the physical properties vary from soft and gummy to hard and friable. The low melting point pitches may be heated and burned like heavy oil, while those with higher melting points may be pulverized and burned, or crushed and burned in the Cyclone Furnace.

Table 31
Selected analyses of solid fuels derived from oil

Analyses (dry basis), % by wt	Delayed Coke		Fluid Coke	
Proximate				
Volatile matter	10.8	9.0	6.0	6.7
Fixed carbon	88.5	90.9	93.7	93.2
Ash	0.7	0.1	0.3	0.1
Ultimate				
Sulfur	9.9	1.5	4.7	5.7
Heating value, Btu/lb	14,700	15,700	14,160	14,290

Wood

Selected analyses and heating values of several types of wood and analyses of wood ash are given in Table 32. Wood, in common with all types of vegetation, is composed primarily of carbohydrates and consequently has a relatively low heating value compared with bituminous coal and oil.

Wood bark may pick up impurities during transportation. It is common practice to drag the rough logs to central loading points in the logging area. This results in sand pick-up. Where the logs are salt-water borne, bark will absorb sea water with its included salt. Combustion temperatures from burning dry bark may be high enough for impurities to cause fluxing of refractory furnace walls and fouling of boiler heating surfaces, unless sufficient furnace cooling surface is provided. Sand passing through the boiler banks can cause erosion of boiler tubes, particularly if the sand loading of the flue gases is increased by returning collected material to the furnace from hoppers or dust collectors. Such collectors may be required with some type of bark-burning equipment to reduce the stack discharge of incompletely burned bark to acceptable limits.

Wood or bark with a moisture content of 50% or less burns quite well; however, as the moisture content increases above this amount, combustion becomes more difficult. With moisture content about 65%, a large part of the heat in the wood is required to evaporate the moisture, and little remains for steam generation. Burning of this wet bark becomes a means of disposal rather than a source of energy.

"Hogged" wood and bark are very bulky and require relatively large handling and storage equipment (*see Wood Refuse, Chapter 27*). Uninterrupted flow from bunkers or bins through chutes is difficult to maintain,

Table 32
Analyses of wood and wood ash

Wood analyses (dry basis), % by wt	Pine Bark	Oak Bark	Spruce Bark°	Redwood Bark°
Proximate				
Volatile matter	72.9	76.0	69.6	72.6
Fixed carbon	24.2	18.7	26.6	27.0
Ash	2.9	5.3	3.8	0.4
Ultimate				
Hydrogen	5.6	5.4	5.7	5.1
Carbon	53.4	49.7	51.8	51.9
Sulfur	0.1	0.1	0.1	0.1
Nitrogen	0.1	0.2	0.2	0.1
Oxygen	37.9	39.3	38.4	42.4
Ash	2.9	5.3	3.8	0.4
Heating value, Btu/lb	9030	8370	8740	8350
Ash analyses, % by wt				
SiO_2	39.0	11.1	32.0	14.3
Fe_2O_3	3.0	3.3	6.4	3.5
TiO_2	0.2	0.1	0.8	0.3
Al_2O_3	14.0	0.1	11.0	4.0
Mn_3O_4	Trace	Trace	1.5	0.1
CaO	25.5	64.5	25.3	6.0
MgO	6.5	1.2	4.1	6.6
Na_2O	1.3	8.9	8.0	18.0
K_2O	6.0	0.2	2.4	10.6
SO_3	0.3	2.0	2.1	7.4
Cl	Trace	Trace	Trace	18.4
Ash fusibility, F				
Reducing				
Initial deformation	2180	2690		
Softening	2240	2720		
Fluid	2310	2740		
Oxidizing				
Initial deformation	2210	2680		
Softening	2280	2730		
Fluid	2350	2750		

° Salt-water stored.

and available equipment for this purpose is not always satisfactory.

Wood wastes. There are several industries using wood as a raw material where combustible by-products or wastes are available as fuels. The most important of these are the pulp and turpentine industries. The nature and methods of utilization of the combustible by-product from the pulp industry are discussed in Chapter 26.

The residue remaining after the steam distillation of coniferous woods for the production of turpentine is us-able as a fuel. Some of the more easily burned constituents are removed in the distillation process, with the result that the residue is somewhat more difficult to burn. Other than this, fuel properties are much the same as those of the raw wood, and the problems involved in utilization are similar.

Bagasse

Mills grinding sugar cane commonly use bagasse for steam production. The mills normally operate 24 hours per day during the grinding season. The supply of bagasse will easily meet that required to meet the plant steam demands in mills where the sugar is not refined. Consequently, where there is no other market for the bagasse, no particular effort is made to burn it efficiently, and burning equipment is provided that will burn the bagasse as received from the grinders. In plants where refining is done, supplemental fuels are required to provide the increased steam demands. Greater efforts to obtain higher efficiency are justified in these plants. A selected analysis of bagasse is given in Table 29.

Other vegetation wastes

Food and related industries produce numerous vegetable wastes that are usable as fuels. They include such materials as grain hulls, the residue from the production of furfural from corn cobs and grain hulls, coffee grounds from the production of instant coffee and tobacco stems. Fuels of this type are available in such small quantities that they are relatively insignificant in total energy requirements.

Fossil fuels of the future

Two of the more promising fuels that will be available in the near future are solvent refined coal (SRC) and synthetic natural gas (SNG). These fuels are still in the pilot plant stage and are not available in large quantities.

Solvent refined coal

Solvent refined coal is made by dissolving the organic material in coal in a coal derived solvent. The finished product is a solid with a melting point of 140–145C° (284–293F). It can be burned as an oil or a solid.

Synthetic natural gas

Synthetic natural gas is made from coal by one of the many gasification processes to make a low Btu gas and then methanating it. There are many processes currently in the development stage.

° *Investigating the Storage, Handling and Combustion Characteristics of Solvent Refined Coal,* E.P.R.I. Report 1235–1 Final Report October 1975, S. M. Barrick, F. L. Jones and S. J. Vecci.

Chapter 6

Principles of combustion

A boiler requires a source of heat at a sufficient temperature level to produce steam. Fossil fuel, utilized for the generation of steam, is generally burned directly for this purpose in the furnace of the boiler, although it may be used in the form of waste heat from another process.

This chapter is concerned with the combustion of fossil fuels such as coal, oil, gas, wood and their derivatives. It is concerned with the chemistry of combustion and the release of heat by the combustion process.

Combustion may be defined as the rapid chemical combination of oxygen with the combustible elements of a fuel. There are just three combustible chemical elements of significance—carbon, hydrogen and sulfur. Sulfur is usually of minor significance as a source of heat, but it can be of major significance in corrosion and pollution problems. (*See Chapters 15 and 18*).

Carbon and hydrogen when burned to completion with oxygen unite according to the following:

$$C + O_2 = CO_2 + 14{,}100 \text{ Btu/lb of C}$$
$$2H_2 + O_2 = 2H_2O + 61{,}100 \text{ Btu/lb of H}_2$$

Air is the usual source of oxygen for boiler furnaces. These combustion reactions are exothermic and the heat released is about 14,100 Btu/lb of carbon burned and 61,100 Btu/lb of hydrogen burned.

The objective of good combustion is to release all of this heat while minimizing losses from combustion imperfections and superfluous air. The combination of the combustible elements and compounds of a fuel with all the oxygen requires temperature high enough to ignite the constituents, mixing or turbulence, and sufficient time for complete combustion. These factors are often referred to as the "three T's" of combustion.

This chapter details the basic chemistry necessary for understanding the phenomena of combustion in the boiler furnace. Ability to calculate the release of heat in combustion and to determine the amount and nature of the combustion products is essential for the design of a steam generating plant and determination of its performance characteristics.

Table 1 lists the chemical elements and compounds found in fuels generally used in the commercial generation of heat with their molecular weights, heats of combustion, and other combustion constants.

The term "100% total air" used in Table 1 and figures and examples elsewhere in this chapter means 100% of the air theoretically required for combustion without excess. Higher percentages indicate theoretical plus excess air, e.g., 125% total air means 100% theoretical air plus 25% excess.

Concept of the mole

The mass of a substance in pounds equal to its molecular weight is called a pound-mole of the substance or, in power plant practice, simply a mole. For example, carbon (C) has a molecular weight of 12. Therefore a mole of carbon weighs 12 pounds. In the case of gases, the volume occupied by a mole is called the molal volume, and is a constant of 394 cu ft for "ideal" gases at 80F and atmospheric pressure (approximately 14.7 psia or 30 in. Hg). This concept of mass and volume is a valuable tool in combustion calculations.

Fundamental laws

The fundamental physical laws upon which all combustion calculations are based are as follows:

1. Conservation of matter*

Matter is neither destroyed nor created. There must be a weight balance between the sum of the weights entering a process and the sum leaving. In other words A pounds of fuel combined with B pounds of air will always result in A + B pounds of products.

2. Conservation of energy*

Energy is neither destroyed nor created. The sum of the energy (potential, kinetic, thermal, chemical and electrical) entering a process must equal the sum of energy leaving, although the proportionate amounts of each may change. In combustion, chemical energy is exchanged for energy in the form of heat.

---

* While the laws of conservation of matter and energy are not rigorous (*see Chapters 19 and 20*), they are quite adequate for combustion calculations. When a pound of a typical coal is burned, releasing 13,500 Btu, the quantity of mass converted to energy amounts to only 3.5×10^{-10} lb, a loss too small to be measured or considered in combustion calculations.

Table 1   Combustion Constants

No.	Substance	Formula	Molecular Weight	Lb per Cu Ft[b]	Cu Ft per Lb[b]	Sp Gr Air = 1.000[b]	Heat of Combustion[c] Btu per Cu Ft Gross	Net[d]	Btu per Lb Gross	Net[d]	Cu Ft per Cu Ft of Combustible — Required for Combustion O2	N2	Air	Flue Products CO2	H2O	N2	Lb per Lb of Combustible — Required for Combustion O2	N2	Air	Flue Products CO2	H2O	N2	Experimental Error in Heat of Combustion Percent + or −
1	Carbon	C	12.01	—	—	—	—	—	14,093[g]	14,093[g]	—	—	—	—	—	—	2.664	8.863	11.527	3.664	—	8.863	0.012
2	Hydrogen	H_2	2.016	0.005327	187.723	0.06959	325.0	275.0[g]	61,100	51,623	0.5	1.882	2.382	—	1.0	1.882	7.937	26.407	34.344	—	8.937	26.407	0.015
3	Oxygen	O_2	32.000	0.08461	11.819	1.1053	—	—	—	—	—	—	—	—	—	—	—	—	—	—	—	—	—
4	Nitrogen (atm)	N_2	28.016	0.07439[e]	13.443	0.9718[e]	—	—	—	—	—	—	—	—	—	—	—	—	—	—	—	—	—
5	Carbon monoxide	CO	28.01	0.07404	13.506	0.9672	321.8	321.8	4,347	4,347	0.5	1.882	2.382	1.0	—	1.882	0.571	1.900	2.471	1.571	—	1.900	0.045
6	Carbon dioxide	CO_2	44.01	0.1170	8.548	1.5282	—	—	—	—	—	—	—	—	—	—	—	—	—	—	—	—	—
	Paraffin series C_nH_{2n+2}																						
7	Methane	CH_4	16.041	0.04243	23.565	0.5543	1013.2	913.1	23,879	21,520	2.0	7.528	9.528	1.0	2.0	7.528	3.990	13.275	17.265	2.744	2.246	13.275	0.033
8	Ethane	C_2H_6	30.067	0.08029[e]	12.455[e]	1.04882[e]	1792	1641	22,320	20,432	3.5	13.175	16.675	2.0	3.0	13.175	3.725	12.394	16.119	2.927	1.798	12.394	0.030
9	Propane	C_3H_8	44.092	0.1196[e]	8.365[e]	1.5617[e]	2590	2385	21,661	19,944	5.0	18.821	23.821	3.0	4.0	18.821	3.629	12.074	15.703	2.994	1.634	12.074	0.023
10	n-Butane	C_4H_{10}	58.118	0.1582[e]	6.321[e]	2.06654[e]	3370	3113	21,308	19,680	6.5	24.467	30.967	4.0	5.0	24.467	3.579	11.908	15.487	3.029	1.550	11.908	0.022
11	Isobutane	C_4H_{10}	58.118	0.1582[e]	6.321[e]	2.06654[e]	3363	3105	21,257	19,629	6.5	24.467	30.967	4.0	5.0	24.467	3.579	11.908	15.487	3.029	1.550	11.908	0.019
12	n-Pentane	C_5H_{12}	72.144	0.1904[e]	5.252[e]	2.4872[e]	4016	3709	21,091	19,517	8.0	30.114	38.114	5.0	6.0	30.114	3.548	11.805	15.353	3.050	1.498	11.805	0.025
13	Isopentane	C_5H_{12}	72.144	0.1904[e]	5.252[e]	2.4872[e]	4008	3716	21,052	19,478	8.0	30.114	38.114	5.0	6.0	30.114	3.548	11.805	15.353	3.050	1.498	11.805	0.071
14	Neopentane	C_5H_{12}	72.144	0.1904[e]	5.252[e]	2.4872[e]	3993	3693	20,970	19,396	8.0	30.114	38.114	5.0	6.0	30.114	3.548	11.805	15.353	3.050	1.498	11.805	0.11
15	n-Hexane	C_6H_{14}	86.169	0.2274[e]	4.398[e]	2.9704[e]	4762	4412	20,940	19,403	9.5	35.760	45.260	6.0	7.0	35.760	3.528	11.738	15.266	3.064	1.464	11.738	0.05
	Olefin series C_nH_{2n}																						
16	Ethylene	C_2H_4	28.051	0.07456	13.412	0.9740	1613.8	1513.2	21,644	20,295	3.0	11.293	14.293	2.0	2.0	11.293	3.422	11.385	14.807	3.138	1.285	11.385	0.021
17	Propylene	C_3H_6	42.077	0.1110[e]	9.007[e]	1.4504[e]	2336	2186	21,041	19,691	4.5	16.939	21.439	3.0	3.0	16.939	3.422	11.385	14.807	3.138	1.285	11.385	0.031
18	n-Butene (Butylene)	C_4H_8	56.102	0.1480[e]	6.756[e]	1.9336[e]	3084	2885	20,840	19,496	6.0	22.585	28.585	4.0	4.0	22.585	3.422	11.385	14.807	3.138	1.285	11.385	0.031
19	Isobutene	C_4H_8	56.102	0.1480[e]	6.756[e]	1.9336[e]	3068	2869	20,730	19,382	6.0	22.585	28.585	4.0	4.0	22.585	3.422	11.385	14.807	3.138	1.285	11.385	0.031
20	n-Pentene	C_5H_{10}	70.128	0.1852[e]	5.400[e]	2.4190[e]	3836	3586	20,712	19,363	7.5	28.232	35.732	5.0	5.0	28.232	3.422	11.385	14.807	3.138	1.285	11.385	0.037
	Aromatic series C_nH_{2n-6}																						
21	Benzene	C_6H_6	78.107	0.2060[e]	4.852[e]	2.6920[e]	3751	3601	18,210	17,480	7.5	28.232	35.732	6.0	3.0	28.232	3.073	10.224	13.297	3.381	0.692	10.224	0.12
22	Toluene	C_7H_8	92.132	0.2431[e]	4.113[e]	3.1760[e]	4484	4284	18,440	17,620	9.0	33.878	42.878	7.0	4.0	33.878	3.126	10.401	13.527	3.344	0.782	10.401	0.21
23	Xylene	C_8H_{10}	106.158	0.2803[e]	3.567[e]	3.6618[e]	5230	4980	18,650	17,760	10.5	39.524	50.024	8.0	5.0	39.524	3.165	10.530	13.695	3.317	0.849	10.530	0.36
	Miscellaneous gases																						
24	Acetylene	C_2H_2	26.036	0.06971	14.344	0.9107	1499	1448	21,500	20,776	2.5	9.411	11.911	2.0	1.0	9.411	3.073	10.224	13.297	3.381	0.692	10.224	0.16
25	Naphthalene	$C_{10}H_8$	128.162	0.3384[e]	2.955[e]	4.4208[e]	5854[f]	5654[f]	17,298[f]	16,708[f]	12.0	45.170	57.170	10.0	4.0	45.170	2.996	9.968	12.964	3.434	0.562	9.968	—[f]
26	Methyl alcohol	CH_3OH	32.041	0.0846[e]	11.820	1.1052[e]	867.9	768.0	10,259	9,078	1.5	5.646	7.146	1.0	2.0	5.646	1.498	4.984	6.482	1.374	1.125	4.984	0.027
27	Ethyl alcohol	C_2H_5OH	46.067	0.1216[e]	8.221[e]	1.5890[e]	1600.3	1450.5	13,161	11,929	3.0	11.293	14.293	2.0	3.0	11.293	2.084	6.934	9.018	1.922	1.170	6.934	0.030
28	Ammonia	NH_3	17.031	0.0456[e]	21.914[e]	0.5961[e]	441.1	365.1	9,668	8,001	0.75	2.823	3.573	—	1.5	3.323	1.409	4.688	6.097	—	1.587	5.511	0.088
29	Sulfur	S	32.06	—	—	—	—	—	3,983	3,983	—	—	—	—	—	—	0.998	3.287	4.285	1.998 (SO_2)	—	3.287	0.071
30	Hydrogen sulfide	H_2S	34.076	0.09109[e]	10.979[e]	1.1898[e]	647	596	7,100	6,545	1.5	5.646	7.146	1.0 (SO_2)	1.0	5.646	1.409	4.688	6.097	1.880 (SO_2)	0.529	4.688	0.30
31	Sulfur dioxide	SO_2	64.06	0.1733	5.770	2.264	—	—	—	—	—	—	—	—	—	—	—	—	—	—	—	—	—
32	Water vapor	H_2O	18.016	0.04758[e]	21.017[e]	0.6215[e]	—	—	—	—	—	—	—	—	—	—	—	—	—	—	—	—	—
33	Air	—	28.9	0.07655	13.063	1.0000	—	—	—	—	—	—	—	—	—	—	—	—	—	—	—	—	—

All gas volumes corrected to 60F and 30 in. Hg dry. For gases saturated with water at 60F, 1.73% of the Btu value must be deducted.

a Calculated from atomic weights given in "Journal of the American Chemical Society", February 1937.

b Densities calculated from values given in grams per liter at 0C and 760 mm in the International Critical Tables allowing for the known deviations from the gas laws. Where the coefficient of expansion was not available, the assumed value was taken as 0.0037 per °C. Compare this with 0.003662 which is the coefficient for a perfect gas. Where no densities were available the volume of the mol was taken as 22.4115 liters.

c Converted to mean Btu per lb (1/180 of the heat per lb of water from 32F to 212F) from data by Frederick D. Rossini, National Bureau of Standards, letter of April 10, 1937, except as noted.

d Deduction from gross to net heating value determined by deducting 18,919 Btu per pound mol of water in the products of combustion. Osborne, Stimson, and Ginnings, "Mechanical Engineering", p. 163, March 1935, and Osborne, Stimson, and Flock, National Bureau of Standards Research Paper 209.

e Denotes that either the density or the coefficient of expansion has been assumed. Some of the materials cannot exist as gases at 60F and 30 in. Hg pressure, in which case the values are theoretical ones given for ease of calculation of gas problems. Under the actual concentrations in which these materials are present their partial pressure is low enough to keep them as gases.

f From Third Edition of "Combustion."

g National Bureau of Standards, RP 1141.

Reprinted from "Fuel Flue Gases", 1941 Edition, courtesy of American Gas Association.

3. The ideal gas law

The volume of an ideal gas is directly proportional to its absolute temperature and inversely proportional to its absolute pressure. The proportional constant is found to be the same for one mole of any ideal gas, so this law may be expressed as:

$$v_M = \frac{RT}{p}$$

where:

v_M = volume, cu ft / mole of gas
p = absolute pressure, lb/sq ft
T = absolute temperature, degrees Rankine = F + 460
R = universal gas constant, 1545 ft lb/mole, T

This equation states that one mole of all ideal gases occupies the same volume for the same pressure and temperature conditions—394 cu ft at 14.7 psia and 80F. Experiments indicate that most gases approach this ideal.

4. Law of combining weights

All substances combine in accordance with simple definite weight relationships. These relationships are exactly proportional to the molecular weights of the constituents. For example, carbon (molecular wt = 12) combines with oxygen (molecular wt = 32) to form carbon dioxide (molecular wt = 44) so that 12 pounds of C plus 32 pounds of O_2 unite to form 44 pounds of CO_2 (*see Application of Fundamental Laws*).

5. Avogadro's law

Equal volumes of different gases at the same pressure and temperature contain the same number of molecules. From the concept of the mole, a pound-mole of any substance contains a mass equal in pounds to the molecular weight of the substance. Thus the ratio of mole weight to molecular weight is a constant, and a mole of a chemically pure substance contains the same number of molecules, no matter what the substance may be. Since a mole of any ideal gas occupies the same volume at a given pressure and temperature (Ideal gas law), it follows that equal volumes of different gases at the same pressure and temperature contain the same number of molecules.

6. Dalton's law

The total pressure of a mixture of gases is the sum of the partial pressures which would be exerted by each of the constituents if each gas were to occupy alone the same volume as the mixture. In other words, for equal volumes, V, of three gases (A, B and C) all at the same temperature, T, but at different pressures, P_a, P_b and P_c, when all three gases are placed in the space of the volume, V, then the resulting pressure, P, is equal to $P_a + P_b + P_c$. For gases, each gas in a mixture fills the entire volume and exerts a pressure independent of the other gases.

7. Amagat's law

The total volume occupied by a mixture of gases is equal to the sum of the volumes which would be occupied by each of the constituents when at the same pressure and temperature as the mixture. This law is related to Dalton's law, but considers the additive effects of volume instead of pressure. If all three gases are at pressure, P, and temperature, T, but at volumes V_a, V_b and V_c, then, when combined so that T and P are unchanged, the volume of the mixture, $V = V_a + V_b + V_c$.

Application of fundamental laws

Table 2 summarizes the molecular and weight relationships between fuel and oxygen and lists the heat of combustion for the substances commonly involved in combustion. Most of the weight and volume relationships in combustion calculations can be determined by using the information in this table and the seven fundamental laws.

The data for C and H_2 can be expressed as follows:

C	+	O_2	=	CO_2
1 molecule	+ 1 molecule	→ 1 molecule		
1 mole	+ 1 mole	= 1 mole		
*	+ 1 cu ft	→ 1 cu ft		
12 lbs	+ 32 lbs	= 44 lbs		

$2H_2$	+	O_2	=	$2H_2O$
2 molecules	+ 1 molecule	→ 2 molecules		
2 moles	+ 1 mole	= 2 moles		
2 cu ft	+ 1 cu ft	→ 2 cu ft		
4 lbs	+ 32 lbs	= 36 lbs		

While there is a weight balance in these equations, there is not a molecular or volume balance; for example, two cu ft of H_2 unite with one cu ft of O_2 to form only two cu ft of H_2O. This relationship is based on Avogadro's law and the Law of combining weights.

The mole in combustion calculations

Combustion calculations involving gaseous mixtures can be simplified by the use of the mole. Since equal volumes of gases at any given pressure and temperature contain the same number of molecules (Avogadro's law), the weights of equal volumes of gases are proportional to their molecular weights. If M is the molecular weight of the gas, 1 mole equals M lb. Actual values are available from Table 1, e.g.:

1 mole of O_2 = 32 lb O_2
1 mole of H_2 = 2 lb H_2
1 mole of CH_4 = 16 lb CH_4

Data from Table 1 can be used to demonstrate that the volume of 1 mole at a given pressure and temperature is approximately fixed and independent of the kind of gas.

At 60F and atmospheric pressure (30 in. Hg) the specific volume of oxygen is 11.819 cu ft per lb. Therefore, 1 mole of oxygen has a volume of $32 \times 11.819 = 378.21$ cu ft. Similarly, at 60F and atmospheric pressure, the specific volume of hydrogen is 187.723 cu ft per lb, and 1 mole has a volume of $2.016 \times 187.723 = 378.45$ cu ft. This volume, usually taken as 379 cu ft, therefore approximates the volume of 1 mole of any gas at 60F and atmospheric pressure.

---

* When 1 cu ft of oxygen (O_2) combines with carbon (C) it forms 1 cu ft of carbon dioxide (CO_2). If carbon were an ideal gas instead of a solid, 1 cu ft of carbon would be required.

Table 2
Common chemical reactions of combustion

Combustible	Reaction	Moles	Pounds			Heat of Combustion (High) Btu/lb of Fuel
Carbon (to CO)	$2C + O_2 = 2CO$	$2 + 1 = 2$	24 lbs +	32 lbs =	56 lbs	3,960
Carbon (to CO_2)	$C + O_2 = CO_2$	$1 + 1 = 1$	12 +	32 =	44	14,100
Carbon Monoxide	$2CO + O_2 = 2CO_2$	$2 + 1 = 2$	56 +	32 =	88	4,345
Hydrogen	$2H_2 + O_2 = 2H_2O$	$2 + 1 = 2$	4 +	32 =	36	61,100
Sulfur (to SO_2)	$S + O_2 = SO_2$	$1 + 1 = 1$	32 +	32 =	64	3,980
Methane	$CH_4 + 2O_2 = CO_2 + 2H_2O$	$1 + 2 = 1 + 2$	16 +	64 =	80	23,875
Acetylene	$2C_2H_2 + 5O_2 = 4CO_2 + 2H_2O$	$2 + 5 = 4 + 2$	52 +	160 =	212	21,500
Ethylene	$C_2H_4 + 3O_2 = 2CO_2 + 2H_2O$	$1 + 3 = 2 + 2$	28 +	96 =	124	21,635
Ethane	$2C_2H_6 + 7O_2 = 4CO_2 + 6H_2O$	$2 + 7 = 4 + 6$	60 +	224 =	284	22,325
Hydrogen Sulfide	$2H_2S + 3O_2 = 2SO_2 + 2H_2O$	$2 + 3 = 2 + 2$	68 +	96 =	164	7,100

The mole fraction of a component of a mixture is the number of moles of the component divided by the sum of the number of moles of all the components of the mixture. As a mole of every ideal gas occupies the same volume, it follows by Avogadro's law, that in a mixture of ideal gases the mole fraction of a component will exactly equal the volume fraction.

$$\frac{\text{Moles of component}}{\text{Total moles}} = \frac{\text{Volume of component}}{\text{Volume of total mixture}}$$

This is a valuable concept, since the volumetric analysis of a mixture of gases automatically gives the mole fractions of the different components.

So far combustion has been considered only as a process involving fuel and oxygen. In power plant practice the practical source of oxygen is primarily air, which includes with the oxygen a mixture of nitrogen, water vapor and small amounts of inert gases such as argon, neon and helium. Data on the composition of air are given in Table 3.

Table 3
Air composition

	Composition of Dry Air	
	% by Volume	% by Weight
Oxygen—O_2	20.99	23.15
Nitrogen—N_2	78.03	76.85*
Inerts*	0.98	—

Equivalent molecular weight of air = 29.0*
% moisture = 1.3% by wt (standard for the boiler industry—ABMA)†

Moles air/mole oxygen =
cu ft air/cu ft oxygen = $\frac{100}{20.99} = 4.76$

Moles N_2/mole oxygen = $\frac{79.01}{20.99} = 3.76$

lb air (dry)/lb O_2 = $\frac{100}{23.15} = 4.32$

lb N_2/lb O_2 = $\frac{76.85}{23.15} = 3.32$

The information in Table 2 can be used for air instead of O_2 if 3.76 moles of N_2 are added to both left and right side of each equation for every mole of O_2 involved. For example, the burning of CO in air becomes

$$2CO + O_2 + 3.76\,N_2 = 2CO_2 + 3.76\,N_2$$

or for methane, CH_4:

$$CH_4 + 2O_2 + 2(3.76)N_2 = CO_2 + 2H_2O + 7.52\,N_2$$

As indicated by the following example for a fuel gas, molal calculations have a simple and direct application to gaseous fuels, where the analyses are usually reported in percent on a volume basis.

Fuel Gas Analysis
% by Volume

CH_4	85.3
C_2H_6	12.6
CO_2	0.1
N_2	1.7
O_2	0.3
Total	100.0

This analysis may also be expressed as 85.3 moles of CH_4 per 100 moles of fuel; 12.6 moles of C_2H_6 per 100 moles of fuel; etc.

The elemental breakdown of each constituent may also be designated in moles per 100 moles of fuel, as follows:

C in CH_4 = 85.3 × 1 = 85.3 moles
C in C_2H_6 = 12.6 × 2 = 25.2 moles
C in CO_2 = 0.1 × 1 = 0.1 moles

Total C per 100 moles fuel = 110.6 moles

H_2 in CH_4 = 85.3 × 2 = 170.6 moles
H_2 in C_2H_6 = 12.6 × 3 = 37.8 moles

Total H_2 per 100 moles fuel = 208.4 moles

O_2 in CO_2 = 0.1 × 1 = 0.1 moles
O_2 = 0.3 × 1 = 0.3 moles

Total O_2 per 100 moles fuel = 0.4 moles

N_2 per 100 moles fuel = 1.7 moles

* It is convenient in combustion calculations to account for inerts as equivalent nitrogen. The equivalent weight percentage of 76.85 and the equivalent molecular weight of 29.0 have been corrected to account for the extra weight of the inerts.
† Air containing 0.013 lb water/lb dry air is often referred to as standard air.

An analysis of the flue gas produced by burning a gas fuel of the composition given above could be:

Constituent	% by Volume
CO_2	10.4
O_2	2.8
N_2	86.8
Total	100.0

Analyses of flue gases are always reported on a volume basis, *dry*, when an Orsat or other type of gas analysis is used. Flue gases are cooled to room temperature and bubbled through water in most gas analyses, so that the gas becomes saturated with water vapor. This would occur even if no water vapor were formed during combustion. Proportionate parts of the water vapor content of the gas will be absorbed with the different constituents of the gas so that the resulting analysis may be safely assumed to be that of dry gas. These percentages may also be expressed as 10.4 moles CO_2, 2.8 moles O_2 and 86.8 moles N_2; each per 100 moles of dry flue gas.

For each mole of C burned, one mole of CO_2 is formed. From the fuel analysis used there are 110.6 moles C per 100 moles of fuel, and there are also 110.6 moles of CO_2 formed from the 110.6 moles C in the fuel. From the flue gas analysis, there are 100/10.4 = 9.62 moles of dry flue gas per mole of CO_2. The 100 moles of fuel will then yield $110.6 \times 9.62 = 1064$ moles of dry flue gas. By the application of the mole method, an important value has been quickly determined through knowing only the flue gas analysis and the fuel analysis.

From the flue gas analysis, the molecular weight of the dry flue gas can be easily determined, as follows:

10.4 moles of CO_2 weigh 10.4×44 lb =	457.6 lb
2.8 moles of O_2 weigh 2.8×32 lb =	89.6 lb
86.8 moles of N_2 weigh 86.8×28 lb =	2430.4 lb
100.0 moles of dry flue gas	2977.6 lb

Therefore, 1 mole equivalent of dry flue gas = 29.8 lb, or the equivalent molecular weight of the dry flue gas = 29.8. Hence, the weight of 1064 moles of dry flue gas is $1064 \times 29.8 = 31,700$ lb, or 100 moles of fuel yields 31,700 lb of dry flue gas.

The weight of 100 moles of fuel is the sum of the products of each constituent in the fuel and its molecular weight.

CH_4	85.3	$\times$ 16 =	1365
C_2H_6	12.6	$\times$ 30 =	378
CO_2	0.1	$\times$ 44 =	4.4
N_2	1.7	$\times$ 28 =	47.6
O_2	0.3	$\times$ 32 =	9.6
	100.0 moles	=	1804.6 lb

Thus, 1805 lb of gas fuel yield 31,700 lb of dry flue gas, and each lb of gas fuel yields 31,700/1805 = 17.6 lb dry flue gas.

Examples of the application of the mole method in combustion calculations are given later in this chapter.

Heat of combustion

So far we have been concerned principally with the weight and volume relationships between fuel and oxygen or air in the combustion process.

In a boiler furnace (where no mechanical work is done) the heat energy evolved from the union of combustible elements with oxygen depends on the ultimate products of combustion and not on any intermediate combinations that may occur in reaching the final result.

A simple demonstration of this law is the union of 1 lb of carbon with oxygen to produce a specific amount of heat (about 14,100 Btu, Table 2). The union may be in one step to form CO_2, or under certain conditions the union may be in two steps, first to form CO, producing a much smaller amount of heat (3960 Btu/lb carbon) and, second the union of the CO is obtained to form CO_2, releasing 10,140 Btu/lb carbon (4345 Btu/lb CO). However, the sum of the heats released in the two steps equals the 14,100 Btu evolved when carbon is burned in one step to form CO_2 as the final product.

That carbon may enter into these two combinations with oxygen is of utmost importance in the design of combustion equipment. Firing methods must assure complete mixture of fuel and oxygen to be certain that all of the carbon burns to CO_2 and not to CO. Failure to meet this requirement will result in appreciable losses in combustion efficiency and in the amount of heat released by the fuel, since only about 28% of the available heat in the carbon is released if CO is formed instead of CO_2.

Measurement of heat of combustion

In boiler practice the heat of combustion of a fuel is the amount of heat, expressed in Btu, generated by the complete combustion, or oxidation, of a unit weight (1 lb in the United States) of fuel. Calorific value or "fuel Btu value" are terms also used.

The amount of heat generated by complete combustion is a constant for any given combination of combustible elements and compounds and is not affected by the manner in which the combustion takes place, provided it is complete.

The heat of combustion of a fuel is usually determined by direct measurement in a calorimeter of the heat evolved during combustion. Combustion products within a calorimeter are cooled to the initial temperature and the heat absorbed by the cooling medium is measured to determine the higher or gross heat of combustion.

For solid fuels and most liquid fuels, calorimeters of the "bomb" type, in which combustible substances are burned in a constant volume of oxygen, give the most satisfactory results. With bomb calorimeters properly operated, combustion is complete, all of the heat generated is absorbed and measured, and heat from external sources either can be excluded or proper corrections can be applied.

For gaseous fuels, calorimeters of the continuous or constant-flow type are usually accepted as standard. The principle of operation is the same as for the bomb calorimeter except that the heat content is determined at constant pressure rather than at constant volume. For most fuels, the difference in the heating values from the constant-pressure and constant-volume determinations is small and is usually neglected.

The heat of combustion of most gases encountered in boiler practice is given in Table 1. If the content of any gas mixture is known, its heat of combustion can be accurately determined by adding the products of the vol-

ume percentage of each constituent times its heat of combustion.

For accurate heat values of solid and liquid fuels calorimeter determinations are required. However, approximate heat values may be determined for most coals if the ultimate chemical analysis is known. Dulong's formula gives reasonably accurate results (within 2 to 3%) for most coals and is often used as a routine check of values determined by calorimeter:

(1) $Btu/lb = 14,544\ C + 62,028\ (H_2 - O_2/8) + 4050\ S$

In this formula, the symbols represent the proportionate parts by weight of the constituents of the fuel—carbon, hydrogen, oxygen and sulfur—as determined by an ultimate analysis; the coefficients represent the approximate heating values of the constituents in Btu per lb. The term $O_2/8$ is a correction applied to the hydrogen in the fuel to account for the hydrogen already combined with the oxygen in the form of moisture. This formula is not generally suitable for calculating the Btu values of gaseous fuels.

High and low heat values

Water vapor is one of the products of combustion for all fuels which contain hydrogen. The heat content of a fuel depends on whether this water vapor is allowed to remain in the vapor state or is condensed to liquid. In the bomb calorimeter the products of combustion are cooled to the initial temperature and all of the water vapor formed during combustion is condensed to liquid. This gives the high, or gross, heat content of the fuel with the heat of vaporization included in the reported value. For the low, or net heat of combustion, it is assumed that all products of combustion remain in the gaseous state.

While the high, or gross, heat of combustion can be accurately determined by established (ASTM) procedures, direct determination of the low heat of combustion is difficult. Therefore, it is usually calculated using the following formula:

(2) $Q_L = Q_H - 1040\ w$

where:

   Q_L = low heat of combustion of fuel, Btu/lb
   Q_H = high heat of combustion of fuel, Btu/lb
   w = lb water formed per lb of fuel
   1040 = factor to reduce high heat of combustion at constant volume to low heat of combustion at constant pressure

In the United States the practice is to use the high heat of combustion in boiler combustion calculations. In Europe the low heat value is used.

Ignition temperatures

Ignition temperature may be defined as the temperature at which more heat is generated by combustion than is lost to the surroundings so that the combustion process becomes self-sustaining. The term usually applies to rapid combustion in air at atmospheric pressure.

Ignition temperatures of combustible substances vary greatly as indicated in Table 4, which lists minimum temperatures and temperature ranges in air for fuels and for the combustible constituents of fuels commonly used in the commercial generation of heat. Many factors influence ignition temperature so that any tabulation can be used only as a guide. Pressure, velocity, enclosure configuration, catalytic materials, air-fuel-mixture uniformity, and ignition source are only a few of the variables. Ignition temperature usually decreases with rising pressure and increases with increasing moisture content in the air.

The ignition temperatures of the gases of a coal vary considerably and are appreciably higher than the ignition temperatures of the fixed carbon of the coal. However, the ignition temperature of coal may be considered as the ignition temperature of its fixed carbon content, since the gaseous constituents are usually distilled off but not ignited before this temperature is attained.

Table 4
Ignition temperatures of fuels in air
(approximate values and ranges at atmospheric pressure)

Combustible	Formula	Temperature, F
Sulfur	S	470
Charcoal	C	650
Fixed carbon (bituminous coal)	C	765
Fixed carbon (semibituminous coal)	C	870
Fixed carbon (anthracite)	C	840-1115
Acetylene	C_2H_2	580-825
Ethane	C_2H_6	880-1165
Ethylene	C_2H_4	900-1020
Hydrogen	H_2	1065-1095
Methane	CH_4	1170-1380
Carbon Monoxide	CO	1130-1215
Kerosene	–	490-560
Gasoline	–	500-800

Adiabatic flame temperature

The adiabatic flame temperature is the maximum theoretical temperature which can be reached by the products of combustion of a specific fuel and air (or oxygen) combination assuming no loss of heat to the surroundings until combustion is complete. This theoretical temperature also assumes no dissociation, a phenomenon discussed later under this heading. The heat of combustion of the fuel is the major factor in the flame temperature, but increasing the temperature of the air or of the fuel will also have the effect of raising the flame temperature. As would be expected, this adiabatic temperature is a maximum with zero excess air (only enough air chemically required to combine with the fuel), since any excess is not involved in the combustion process and only dilutes the temperature of the products of combustion.

The adiabatic temperature is determined from the adiabatic enthalpy of the flue gas as follows:

$$h_g = \frac{\left(\begin{array}{c}\text{heat of}\\\text{combustion}\end{array}\right)+\left(\begin{array}{c}\text{sensible heat}\\\text{in fuel}\end{array}\right)+\left(\begin{array}{c}\text{sensible heat}\\\text{in air}\end{array}\right)}{\text{weight of products of combustion}}$$

where:

h_g = adiabatic enthalpy (adiabatic heat content of the products of combustion), Btu/lb

Knowing the moisture content of the products of combustion and its enthalpy, the theoretical flame or gas temperature can be obtained from Fig. 1.

The adiabatic temperature is a fictitiously high temperature which does not exist in fact. Actual flame temperatures are lower for two main reasons:

1. Combustion is not instantaneous. Some heat is lost to the surroundings as combustion takes place. The faster the combustion occurs the less heat is lost before combustion is complete. If combustion is slow enough, the gases may be cooled sufficiently for combustion to be incomplete with some of the fuel unburned. This is related to the time factor in the "three *T*'s" of combustion mentioned previously.

2. At temperatures above 3000F, some of the CO_2 and H_2O in the flue gases dissociates, absorbing heat in the process. At 3500F about 10% of the CO_2 in a typical flue gas dissociates to CO and O_2 with a heat absorption of 4345 Btu/lb of CO formed, and about 3% of the H_2O dissociates to H_2 and O_2 with a heat absorption of 61,100 Btu/lb of H_2 formed. As the gas cools, the CO and H_2 dissociated recombine with the O_2 and liberate the heat absorbed in dissociation, so the heat is not lost. However, the effect is to lower the maximum actual flame temperature (*see Combustion Equilibrium, Chapter 2*).

Combustion calculations

The combustion calculations are the starting point for all design and performance determinations for boilers and their related component parts. They establish (a) the quantities of the constituents involved in the chemistry of combustion, (b) the quantity of heat released, and (c) the efficiency of the combustion process under both ideal and actual conditions.

Combustion air

Since carbon, hydrogen and sulfur are the only combustible elements found in the fuels used for commercial steam generation, the air (lb) theoretically required for the complete combustion of 1 lb of fuel is:

(3) $11.53 \, C + 34.34 \, (H_2 - O_2/8) + 4.29 \, S$

where C, H_2, O_2 and S represent the fraction by weight (percent/100) of carbon, hydrogen, oxygen and sulfur, and the constants are those given in Table 1. The factor $O_2/8$ in the term $(H_2 - O_2/8)$ is a correction for the hydrogen already combined with the O_2 in the fuel to form water vapor.

With gaseous fuels, instead of breaking down the hydrocarbons into their constituent elements, it is simpler to use the amount of air for the various compounds directly as given in Table 1. For instance, for a gaseous fuel containing the combustible gases indicated in the expression below, the theoretical air required for complete combustion (lb air/lb fuel) is:

(4) $2.47 \, CO + 34.34 \, H_2 + 17.27 \, CH_4 + 13.30 \, C_2H_2$
     $+ 14.81 \, C_2H_4 + 16.12 \, C_2H_6 + 6.10 \, H_2S - 4.32 \, O_2$

Again, the molecular symbols represent the fraction by weight of the gaseous compounds and elements.

If, as is the usual custom, the analyses of gaseous fuels are given on a volumetric basis, the cu ft of combustion air required as given in Table 1 should be used. Thus for a gaseous fuel containing the combustible gases indicated in the following expression, the cu ft of theoretical air required per cu ft of fuel for complete combustion is:

(5) $2.38 \, (CO + H_2) + 9.53 \, CH_4 + 11.91 \, C_2H_2$
     $+ 14.29 \, C_2H_4 + 16.68 \, C_2H_6 + 7.15 \, H_2S - 4.76 \, O_2$

where the molecular symbols represent the fraction by volume of the gaseous compounds and elements. Note that the total air requirement is reduced if oxygen is one of the constituents of the fuel.

The products of combustion can also be determined from the data given in Table 1. Assuming complete combustion with theoretical air of the fuels ordinarily used for commercial steam generation, the products of combustion in lb (including the nitrogen carried with the combustion air) per lb of fuel are:

$CO_2 = 3.66C$
$H_2O = 8.94 \, H_2 + H_2O^*$
$SO_2 = 2.00 \, S$
$N_2 = 8.86C + 26.41(H_2 - O_2/8) + 3.29S + N_2†$

The moisture introduced with the combustion air must be added to this theoretical quantity to obtain the total weight of combustion products. The molecular symbols represent the fraction by weight of the constituents in the fuel.

Losses

Not all of the Btu in the fuel are converted to heat and absorbed by the steam generation equipment. Some of the fuel may be unburned leaving carbon in the ash or carbon may be burned incompletely to form some CO instead of all CO_2. Usually all of the H_2 in the fuel is burned. By far the greatest heat loss is the loss up the stack. Since the heat in the fuel is determined from a base of ambient temperature, all of the products of combustion must be cooled to the same temperature if all of the heat is to be utilized. Higher temperatures then represent a loss, which is the sum of four items: (1) the sensible heat in dry flue gas, (2) the sensible heat in the moisture in the air, (3) the sensible heat in the H_2O in the fuel and (4) the latent heat of the moisture in the fuel.

It is necessary practically to use more than the theoretical air requirements to assure sufficient oxygen for complete combustion. Excess air would not be required if it were possible to have an ideally perfect union of air and fuel. It is necessary, however, to keep the excess at a minimum in order to hold down the stack loss. The excess air that is not used in the combustion of the fuel leaves

---

* Fraction by weight of H_2O (percent/100) in the fuel as moisture.
† Fraction by weight of N_2 in the fuel as nitrogen.

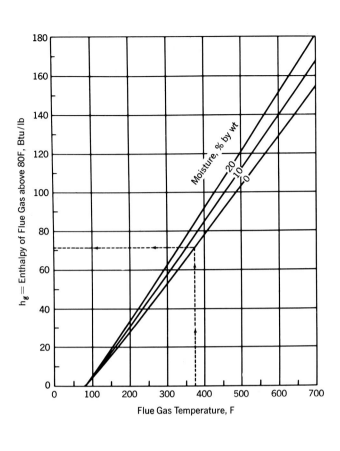

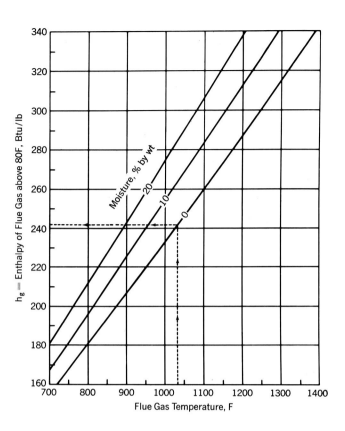

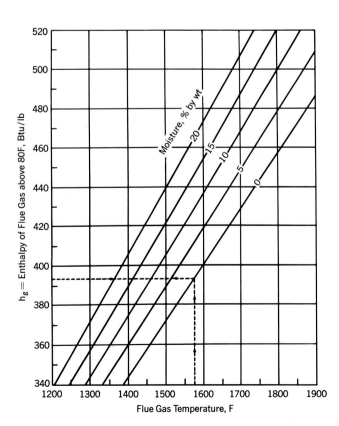

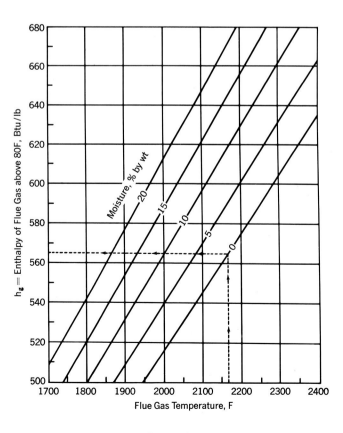

Fig. 1 Enthalpy of flue gas above 80F at 30 in. Hg, Btu per lb.

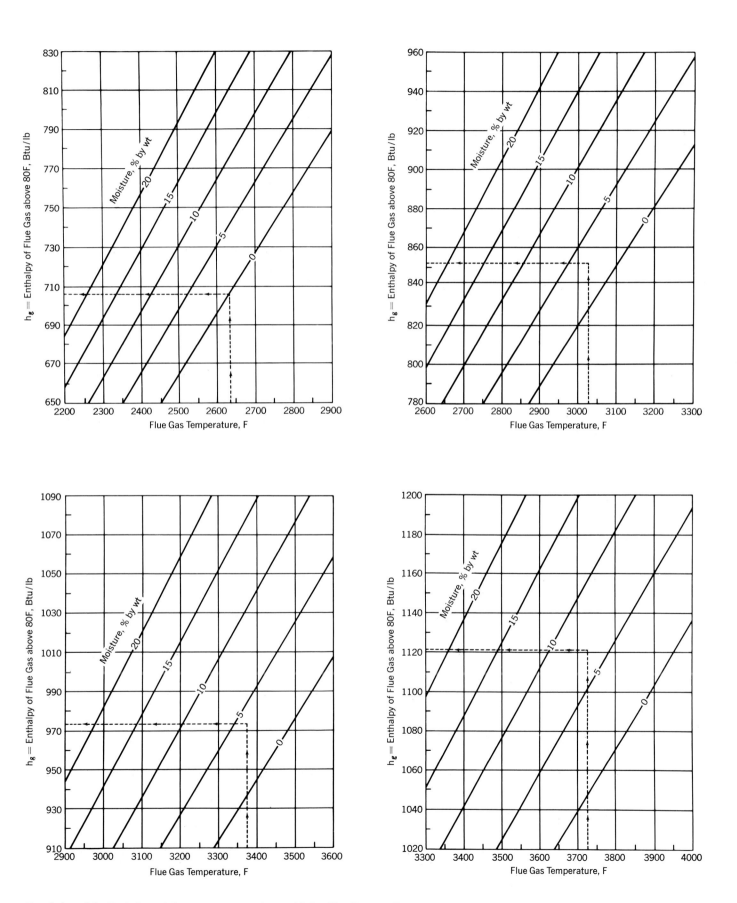

Fig. 1 (cont'd) Enthalpy of flue gas above 80F at 30 in. Hg, Btu per lb.

the unit at stack temperature. The heat required to heat this air from room temperature to stack temperature serves no purpose and is lost heat. Table 5 gives realistic values of excess air for the fuel burning equipment which experience has shown is required to assure complete combustion for various fuels and methods of firing.

In most furnaces operating under suction there is also some leakage of air into the setting, and consequently the excess air leaving the furnace and the unit is greater than that at the fuel burning equipment.

Another loss which must be considered is the radiation loss from the unit setting. This loss is discussed in Chapter 4 (*see Heat Loss and Cold-Face Temperature*) and a simple, approximate method for calculating this loss is provided by Fig. 27, Chapter 4.

Table 5
Usual amount excess air supplied to fuel-burning equipment

Fuel	Type of Furnace or Burners	Excess Air % by Weight
Pulverized coal	Completely water-cooled furnace for slag-tap or dry-ash-removal	15-20
	Partially water-cooled furnace for dry-ash-removal	15-40
Crushed coal	Cyclone Furnace— pressure or suction	10-15
Coal	Spreader stoker	30-60
	Water-cooled vibrating-grate stoker	30-60
	Chain-grate and traveling-grate stokers	15-50
	Underfeed stoker	20-50
Fuel oil	Oil burners, register-type	5-10
	Multifuel burners and flat-flame	10-20
Acid sludge	Cone and flat-flame type burners, steam-atomized	10-15
Natural, coke-oven, and refinery gas	Register-type burners	5-10
	Multifuel burners	7-12
Blast-furnace gas	Intertube nozzle-type burners	15-18
Wood	Dutch oven (10–23% through grates) and Hofft-type	20-25
Bagasse	All furnaces	25-35
Black liquor	Recovery furnaces for kraft and soda-pulping processes	5-7

In summary, there are certain inherent heat losses over which there is no control, and certain others which are subject to some control. The inherent losses are the result of (1) the discharge of the products of combustion at a temperature higher than ambient and (2) the moisture content of the fuel plus the combination of some of the hydrogen with the oxygen in the fuel.

The avoidable heat losses, or those which can be controlled by good design and careful operation, can be minimized by (1) careful control of excess air, (2) tolerating virtually no unburned solid combustible matter in ash or refuse, (3) permitting no unburned gaseous combustibles

in the exit gases and (4) a well-insulated setting for the steam generating unit to reduce radiation loss.

The efficiency of combustion in a heat exchanger or boiler is 100 minus the sum of the heat losses expressed in percent.

Combustion calculations—examples

The detailed steps in the solution of combustion problems are best illustrated by examples. In the examples which follow, the amount of moisture in the combustion air is taken as 0.013 lb per lb of dry air, corresponding to conditions of 80F dry bulb temperature and 60% relative humidity. This value is often used as standard in combustion calculations.

Weight method: The values in the two examples given below are generally developed from the data in Table 1, and the procedure followed is apparent from the execution. These examples determine the quantities and the products of combustion air involved per pound of fuel. In Example 2 (gaseous fuel) the fuel analysis is given on a volume basis, and must be converted to a weight basis. Otherwise the procedure is the same in both examples.

Example 1
Weight method—solid fuel—standard air*
(complete combustion assumed) See Table 1 for multipliers

Ultimate Analysis lb/lb Fuel as Fired			Required for Combustion, lb/lb Fuel @ 100% Total Air	
			O_2	Dry Air
C	0.728	×2.66 and ×11.53	1.936	8.394
H_2	0.048	×7.94 and ×34.34	0.381	1.648
O_2	0.062		—	—
N_2	0.015		—	—
S	0.022	×1.00 and ×4.29	0.022	0.094
H_2O	0.035		—	—
Ash	0.090		—	—
Sum	1.000		2.339	10.136
Less O_2 in fuel (deduct)			−0.062	−0.268†
Required (at 100% total air)			2.277	9.868

† Air equivalent of O_2 in fuel.

		Required for Combustion, lb/lb Fuel @ 125% Total Air	
		O_2	Dry Air
O_2 and air × 125/100, total		2.846	12.335
Excess air = 12.335 − 9.868		—	2.467
Excess O_2 = 2.846 − 2.277		0.569	—

Products of combustion

			lb/lb Fuel @ 125% Total Air
CO_2	0.728	×3.66	2.664
H_2O	0.048	×8.94 + 0.035 +0.013 ×12.335	0.624
SO_2	0.022	×2.00	0.044
O_2	(excess)		0.569
N_2	12.335	×0.7685 + 0.015	9.629
Weight, wet			13.530
Weight, dry = 13.530 − 0.624			12.906

* Air at 60% relative humidity and 80F dry bulb, or 0.013 lb of moisture per lb dry air.

Example 2
Weight method—gaseous fuel—standard air
(complete combustion assumed) See Table 1 for multipliers

Fuel Analysis % by Vol as Fired	lb/100 Moles	lb/lb Fuel		Required for Combustion, lb/lb Fuel @ 100% Total Air	
				O_2	Dry Air
CH$_4$	90.0 × 16 = 1440	0.832	× 3.99	3.320	—
			× 17.27	—	14.370
C$_2$H$_6$	5.0 × 30 = 150	0.087	× 3.73	0.324	—
			× 16.12	—	1.402
N$_2$	5.0 × 28 = 140	0.081		—	—
Sum	100.0 1730	1.000		3.644	15.772
Required (at 100% total air)				3.644	15.772

	Required for Combustion, lb/lb Fuel @ 115% Total Air	
	O_2	Dry Air
O_2 and air ×115/100, total	4.191	18.138
Excess air = 18.138 − 15.772	—	2.366
Excess O_2 = 4.191 − 3.644	0.547	—

Products of combustion

			lb/lb Fuel @ 115% Total Air
CO$_2$	0.832	×2.74 + 0.087 × 2.93	2.535
H$_2$O	0.832	×2.25 + 0.087 × 1.80 +0.013 × 18.138	2.265
O$_2$	(excess)		0.547
N$_2$	18.138	×0.7685 + 0.081	14.020
Weight, wet			19.367
Weight, dry = 19.367 − 2.265			17.102

Mole method: The mole method, as exemplified below, is not quite as direct as the weight method for determining air and flue gas quantities, but is more flexible. It gives the flue gas analysis by only a simple additional step and also gives a better conceptual insight into the basis of the calculations.

Example 3
Mole method—solid fuel—standard air
(complete combustion assumed)
See Table 1 for mol. wt and multipliers

Ultimate Analysis, lb/100 lb Fuel as Fired		Moles per 100 lb Fuel		Required for Combustion, Moles/100 lb Fuel @ 100% Total Air	
				O_2	Dry Air
C	72.8 ÷ 12 = 6.07		×1.00 and ×4.76	6.07	28.89
H$_2$	4.8 ÷ 2.016 = 2.38		×0.5 and ×2.38	1.19	5.66
O$_2$	6.2 ÷ 32 = 0.19			—	—
N$_2$	1.5 ÷ 28 = 0.05			—	—
S	2.2 ÷ 32 = 0.07		×1.00 and ×4.76	0.07	0.33
H$_2$O	3.5 ÷ 18 = 0.19			—	—
Ash	9.0 —			—	—
Sum	100.0	8.95		7.33	34.88
Less O$_2$ in fuel (deduct)				−0.19	−0.90*
Required (at 100% total air)				7.14	33.98

* Air equivalent of O_2 in fuel
= 0.19 × 4.76 = 0.90 moles air/0.19 moles O_2

	Required for Combustion, Moles/100 lb Fuel @ 125% Total Air	
	O_2	Dry Air
O_2 and air × 125/100, total	8.93	42.48
Excess air = 42.48 − 33.98	—	8.50
Excess O_2 = 8.93 − 7.14	1.79	—

Products of combustion

	Moles/100 lb Fuel		Moles/100 lb Fuel	% by Vol, Dry Basis
CO$_2$	6.07	×1	6.07	14.60
H$_2$O	2.38	×1 + 0.19 + 0.89†	3.46	—
SO$_2$	0.07	×1	0.07	0.17
N$_2$	42.48	×0.79	33.56	80.91
O$_2$	(excess)		1.79	4.32
Wet			44.95	
Dry = 44.95 − 3.46			41.49	100.00

† = Moles H_2O in air
= (42.48 × 29 × 0.013) ÷ 18 = 0.89

Example 4
Mole method—gaseous fuel—standard air
(complete combustion assumed)
See Table 1 for multipliers

Fuel Analysis, % by Vol as Fired	Moles per 100 Moles Fuel		Required for Combustion, Moles/100 Moles Fuel @ 100% Total Air	
			O_2	Dry Air
CH$_4$	90.0	90.0	×2.0 and ×9.53	180.0	857.7
C$_2$H$_6$	5.0	5.0	×3.5 and ×16.68	17.5	83.4
N$_2$	5.0	5.0		—	—
Sum	100.0	100.0		197.5	941.1
Required (at 100% total air)			197.5	941.1

	Required for Combustion, Moles/100 Moles Fuel @ 115% Total Air	
	O_2	Dry Air
O_2 and air × 115/100, total	227.1	1082.3
Excess air = 1082.3 − 941.1	—	141.2
Excess O_2 = 227.1 − 197.5	29.6	—

Products of combustion

	Moles/100 Moles Fuel		Moles/100 Moles Fuel @ 115% Total Air	% by Vol, Dry Basis
CO$_2$	90	×1 + 5 × 2.0	100.0	10.11
H$_2$O	90	×2 + 5 × 3 + 22.7*	217.7	—
N$_2$	1082.3	×0.79 + 5.0	860.0	86.90
O$_2$	(excess)		29.6	2.99
Wet			1207.3	
Dry = 1207.3 − 217.7			989.6	100.00

* = Moles H_2O in air
= (1082.3 × 29 × 0.013) ÷ 18 = 22.7

The next step, after the determination of air and flue gas quantities per unit of fuel, is the calculation of the heat input percentage not absorbed by the boiler because of losses.

Table 6 is useful as an aid in this next calculation. It shows the calculations necessary to determine the stack and combustible losses in percent for a selected bituminous coal fired unit. The calculations are predicated on an ultimate analysis of the coal, a flue gas analysis and a stack temperature. The percentage of heat input not absorbed by the boiler and related equipment is computed on the basis of standard air and zero unburned carbon. This loss represents only the lost heat in the stack gases, since there is no carbon unburned.

Table 6 Combustion Calculations—Molal Basis

Conditions—Assigned or Observed and Miscellaneous

Date

Fuel *Bituminous Coal*	L
Source *Ohio*	I
Fuel Unit {100 lb, solid or liquid fuels / 100 moles, gaseous fuels}	N E

	LINE
Fuel Anal. as Fired (AF), % by Wt or Vol	a
C 72.0	
H₂ 4.4	
S 1.6	
O₂ 3.6	b
N₂ 1.4	
H₂O 8.0	
Ash 9.0	
100.0	
CO₂ *15.4* O₂ *3.6* CO *0.0* N₂ *81.0* %†	c
Total air (T.A.) assigned or by ORSAT *120%*	d
Lines f, g, h For Gaseous Fuels	e
Wt, fuel unit = Σ (moles each × mol. wt) lb	f
Mol. wt of fuel = line f ÷ 100	g
Density of fuel @ 80 F & 30 in. = line g/394 lb/cu ft	h
Fuel heat value, Btu/lb *12,800*/cu ft	i
Combustible in refuse, % "C" *0.0%*	j
Carbon unburned, lb/100 lb fuel = % ash in fuel × %"C"/(100 − %"C") *0.0*	k
Exit temp of flue gas, t_2 *345* F	l
Dry-bulb (ambient) temp, t'_1 *80* F	m
Wet-bulb temp F	n
Rel humid. (psychrometric chart) %	o
B*, barometric pressure, in. Hg	p
Sat. press. H₂O at amb temp, in. Hg	q
A*, press. H₂O in air, lines (o × q), in. Hg	r

Fuel, O₂, and Air per Unit of Fuel / Flue Gas (F.G.) Composition Moles per Fuel Unit (AF)

LINE	Fuel Constituent	Per Fuel Unit, lb	Mol. Wt Divisor	Moles Fuel Constituent	O₂ Multiplier	O₂ Moles Theo Reqd	CO₂+SO₂	O₂	N₂	H₂O	CO
1	C to CO₂	72.0	12	6.00	1	6.00	6.00				
2	C to CO		12		.5						
3	CO to CO₂		28		.5						
4	C unburned, line k	0.0	12	0.00							
5	H₂	4.4	2	2.20	.5	1.10				2.20	
6	S	1.6	32	0.05	1	0.05	0.05				
7	O₂ (deduct)	3.6	32	0.11	1	−0.11					
8	N₂	1.4	28	0.05		O			0.05		
9	CO₂		44			O					
10	H₂O	8.0	18	0.44		O				0.44	
11	Ash	9.0				O					
12	Sum	100.0		8.85		7.04					

O₂ and Air, Moles for Total Air = 120% (see line d at right)

LINE							CO₂+SO₂	O₂	N₂	H₂O	CO
13	O₂ (theo) reqd = O₂, line 12					7.04					
14	O₂ (excess) = (T.A. −100)/100 × O₂, line 12					1.41		1.41			
15	O₂ (total) supplied = lines 13 + 14					8.45					
16	N₂ supplied = 3.76 × O₂, line 15					31.77			31.77		
17	Air (dry) supplied = O₂ + N₂					40.22					
18	H₂O in air = moles dry air × A/(B−A) *					0.85				0.85	
19	Air (wet) supplied = lines 17 + 18					41.07					
20	Flue gas constituents = lines 1 to 18, total						6.05	1.41	31.82	3.49	

Total Moles	Wet Flue Gas 42.77	Dry Flue Gas 39.28	s

21 *Note—for air at 80 F and 60% relative humidity, A/(B−A) = 0.0212 is often used as standard.

Determination of Flue Gas and Combustible Losses in Btu per Fuel Unit (AF)

LINE	Flue gas constituents	CO₂+SO₂	O₂	N₂	H₂O	CO	Total
22							
23	Mc_p, mean, t_2 to t'_1 (for t'_1 = 80 F, see Fig. 2)	9.7	10.2	7.15	7.0 8.12		
24	In dry flue gas = moles each, line 20 × Mc_p × ($t_2 − t'_1$)	15,560	2,670	59,000			77,230
25	In H₂O in air = moles H₂O, line 18 × Mc_p × ($t_2 − t'_1$)				1,830		1,830
26	In sens heat, H₂O in fuel = moles, lines (5 + 10) × Mc_p × ($t_2 − t'_1$)				5,680		5,680
27	In latent heat, H₂O in fuel = moles, lines (5 + 10) × 1040 × 18				49,400		49,400
28	Total in wet flue gas						134,140
29	Due to carbon in refuse = line k × 14,100						0
30	Due to unburned CO in flue gas = moles C to CO × 12 × 9,755						0
31	Total flue gas losses + unburned combustible = lines 28 + 29 + 30					Total	134,140
32	Heat value of fuel unit = (100 × line i for solid and liquid fuels)/(394 × line i × 100, for gaseous fuels)						1,280,000
33	Stack and combustible loss, % of heat input = 100 × line 31 ÷ line 32						10.48 %

†Note: Flue gas analysis by ORSAT. If CO is present in flue gases, a carbon balance is used to determine distribution of C, thus: All C in fuel = C in flue gas constituents + C in refuse. Moles C in fuel = % C by analysis ÷ 12. Moles C in refuse = line k ÷ 12. Moles C in CO₂ = (moles C in fuel − moles C in refuse) × % CO₂ by ORSAT ÷ % (CO₂ + CO) by ORSAT. Moles C in CO = moles C in fuel − moles C in refuse − moles C in CO₂.

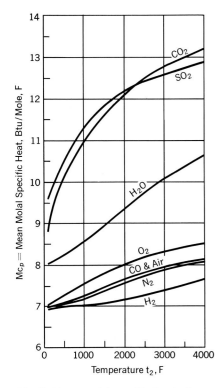

Fig. 2 Mean molal specific heat of gases between final temperature (t_2) and 80F at standard atmospheric pressure.

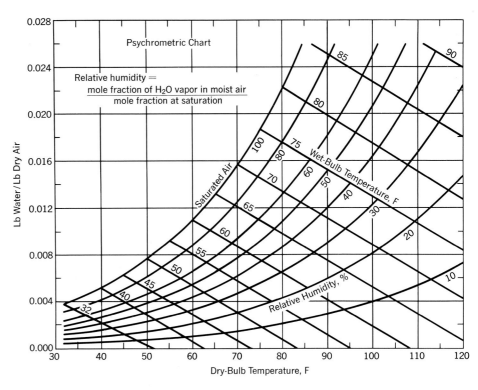

Fig. 3 Water content of air for various wet- and dry-bulb temperatures.

L I N E	Table 7 Molal Quantities—converted to lb units See Combustion Calculations—Molal Basis for line references						L I N E
a^1	Air (dry) supplied per unit of fuel = moles air, line 17 × 29, (mol. wt air)				1166.4	lb	a^1
b^1	H_2O in air supplied per unit of fuel = moles H_2O, line 18 × 18, (mol. wt H_2O)				15.3	lb	b^1
c^1	Wet air supplied per unit of fuel = lines a^1 + b^1				1181.7	lb	c^1
d^1	Wet air supplied per lb of fuel {Line c^1 ÷ 100 for solid or liquid fuels				11.82	lb	d^1
	{Line c^1 ÷ line f for gaseous fuels					lb	
e^1	Flue gas constituent and mol. wt	$CO_2 + SO_2$ 44 64	O_2 32	N_2 28	H_2O 18	CO 28	e^1
f^1	Wet F.G., % by vol = 100 × line 20 ÷ line s (wet)*	14.14	3.30	74.40	8.16		f^1
g^1	Dry F.G., % by vol = 100 × line 20 ÷ line s (dry)*	15.40	3.59	81.01			g^1
h^1	Wt of each constit = line 20 × mol. wt of each, lb	264.0 3.2	45.1	891.0	62.8		h^1
i^1	Total wt flue gas = Σ (line h^1 wet) and Σ (line h^1 dry)	Wet wt 1266.1 lb		Dry wt 1203.3 lb			i^1
j^1	Wet flue gas per lb fuel {Wet wt, line i^1 ÷ 100, solid and liquid fuels				12.66	lb	j^1
	{Wet wt, line i^1 ÷ line f, gaseous fuels					lb	
k^1	Dry flue gas per lb fuel {Dry wt, line i^1 ÷ 100, solid and liquid fuels				12.03	lb	k^1
	{Dry wt, line i^1 ÷ line f, gaseous fuels					lb	
l^1	Molecular wt of wet flue gas = wet wt, line i^1 ÷ wet moles, line s				29.60		l^1
m^1	Molecular wt of dry flue gas = dry wt, line i^1 ÷ dry moles, line s				30.63		m^1
n^1	Density of wet flue gas = line l^1 ÷ 394† (at 80 F and 30 in. Hg)				0.0751 lb/cu ft		n^1
o^1	Density of dry flue gas = line m^1 ÷ 394† (at 80 F and 30 in. Hg)				0.0778 lb/cu ft		o^1

*Flue gas analysis as calculated, based on total air, line d, assigned or observed.
 The calculated values, line g^1, should agree substantially with ORSAT analysis when flue gas is analyzed.
†Volume of 1 mole of any gas at 80 F and 30 in. Hg = 394 cu ft.

Table 8   Combustion Calculations—Molal Basis

Conditions—Assigned or Observed and Miscellaneous

Date

Fuel *Bituminous Coal*
Source *Ohio*
Fuel Unit $\begin{cases}100\text{ lb, solid or liquid fuels} \\ 100\text{ moles, gaseous fuels}\end{cases}$

LINE	Fuel Constituent	Per Fuel Unit, lb	Mol. Wt Divisor	Moles Fuel Constituent	O_2 Multiplier	O_2 Moles Theo Reqd	$CO_2 + SO_2$	O_2	N_2	H_2O	CO
							Flue Gas (F.G.) Composition Moles per Fuel Unit (AF)				
1	C to CO_2	69.6	12	5.80	1	5.80	5.80				
2	C to CO	1.3	12	0.11	.5	0.06					0.11
3	CO to CO_2		28		.5						
4	C unburned, line k	1.1	12	0.09							
5	H_2	4.4	2	2.20	.5	1.10				2.20	
6	S	1.6	32	0.05	1	0.05	0.05				
7	O_2 (deduct)	3.6	32	0.11	1	−0.11					
8	N_2	1.4	28	0.05	0				0.05		
9	CO_2		44		0						
10	H_2O	8.0	18	0.44	0					0.44	
11	Ash	9.0			0						
12	Sum	100.0		8.85		6.90					

O_2 and Air, Moles for Total Air = 120% (see line d at right)

LINE		O_2 Moles Theo Reqd	CO_2+SO_2	O_2	N_2	H_2O	CO
13	O_2 (theo) reqd = O_2, line 12	6.90					
14	O_2 (excess) = $\frac{\text{T.A.}-100}{100}\times O_2$, line 12	1.38		1.38			
15	O_2 (total) supplied = lines 13 + 14	8.28					
16	N_2 supplied = 3.76 × O_2, line 15	31.13			31.13		
17	Air (dry) supplied = $O_2 + N_2$	39.41					
18	H_2O in air = moles dry air × $\frac{A}{B-A}$ *	0.84				0.84	
19	Air (wet) supplied = lines 17 + 18	40.25					
20	Flue gas constituents = lines 1 to 18, total		5.85	1.38	31.18	3.48	0.11

21 *Note—for air at 80 F and 60% relative humidity, $\frac{A}{B-A} = 0.0212$ is often used as standard.

Right side conditions

Fuel Anal. as Fired (AF), % by Wt or Vol — *line a*

			line b
C	72.0		*Moles C/100 lb fuel*
H_2	4.4		C in fuel, 72 ÷ 12 = 6.00
S	1.6		C in refuse, 1.1 ÷ 12 = 0.09
O_2	3.6		C in CO_2 + CO, 6.00 − 0.09 = 5.91
N_2	1.4		C in CO_2, 5.91 × 15.2 ÷ 15.5 = 5.80
H_2O	8.0		C in CO, 5.91 − 5.80 = 0.11
Ash	9.0		
	100.0		

Line		
c	CO_2 15.2 O_2 3.6 CO 0.3 N_2 80.9 %†	
d	Total air (T.A.) assigned or by ORSAT 120%	
e	Lines f, g, h For Gaseous Fuels	
f	Wt, fuel unit = Σ (moles each × mol. wt) lb	
g	Mol. wt of fuel = line f ÷ 100	
h	Density of fuel @ 80 F & 30 in. = $\frac{\text{line g}}{394}$ $\frac{\text{lb}}{\text{cu ft}}$	
i	Fuel heat value, Btu/lb 12,800/cu ft	
j	Combustible in refuse, % "C" 10.6%	
k	Carbon unburned, lb/100 lb fuel = % ash in fuel × $\frac{\%\,"C"}{100-\%\,"C"}$	1.07 (1.1)
l	Exit temp of flue gas, t_2	345 F
m	Dry-bulb (ambient) temp, t'_1	80 F
n	Wet-bulb temp	F
o	Rel humid. (psychrometric chart)	%
p	B*, barometric pressure, in. Hg	
q	Sat. press. H_2O at amb temp, in. Hg	
r	A*, press. H_2O in air, lines (o × q), in. Hg	
s	Total Moles	Wet Flue Gas 42.00	Dry Flue Gas 38.52

Determination of Flue Gas and Combustible Losses in Btu per Fuel Unit (AF)

LINE		CO_2+SO_2	O_2	N_2	H_2O	CO	Total
22	Flue gas constituents						
23	Mc_p, mean, t_2 to t'_1 (for t'_1 = 80 F, see Fig. 2)	9.7 10.2	7.15	7.0	8.12	7.0	
24	In dry flue gas = moles each, line 20 × Mc_p × ($t_2 − t'_1$)	15,040	2,620	57,840		204	75,704
25	In H_2O in air = moles H_2O, line 18 × Mc_p × ($t_2 − t'_1$)				1,810		1,810
26	In sens heat, H_2O in fuel = moles, lines (5 + 10) × Mc_p × ($t_2 − t'_1$)				5,680		5,680
27	In latent heat, H_2O in fuel = moles, lines (5 + 10) × 1040 × 18				49,420		49,420
28	Total in wet flue gas						132,614
29	Due to carbon in refuse = line k × 14,100						15,090
30	Due to unburned CO in flue gas = moles C to CO × 12 × 9,755						12,880
31	Total flue gas losses + unburned combustible = lines 28 + 29 + 30					Total	160,584
32	Heat value of fuel unit = $\frac{100 \times \text{line i for solid and liquid fuels}}{394 \times \text{line i} \times 100\text{, for gaseous fuels}}$						1,280,000
33	Stack and combustible loss, % of heat input = 100 × line 31 ÷ line 32						12.55 %

†Note: Flue gas analysis by ORSAT. If CO is present in flue gases, a carbon balance is used to determine distribution of C, thus:
All C in fuel = C in flue gas constituents + C in refuse. Moles C in fuel = % C by analysis ÷ 12.
Moles C in refuse = line k ÷ 12. Moles C in CO_2 = (moles C in fuel − moles C in refuse) × % CO_2 by ORSAT ÷ % (CO_2 + CO) by ORSAT.
Moles C in CO = moles C in fuel − moles C in refuse − moles C in CO_2.

Table 9 Combustion Calculations—Molal Basis

LINE	Fuel Constituent	Per Fuel Unit, lb	Mol. Wt Divisor	Moles Fuel Constituent	O_2 Multiplier	O_2 Moles Theo Reqd	CO_2 + SO_2	O_2	N_2	H_2O	CO
	Fuel, O_2, and Air per Unit of Fuel						*Flue Gas (F.G.) Composition Moles per Fuel Unit (AF)*				
1	C to CO_2	*87.9*	12	*7.32*	1	*7.32*	*7.32*				
2	C to CO		12		.5						
3	CO to CO_2		28		.5						
4	C unburned, line k		12								
5	H_2	*10.3*	2	*5.15*	.5	*2.58*				*5.15*	
6	S	*1.2*	32	*0.04*	1	*0.04*	*0.04*				
7	O_2 (deduct)	*0.5*	32	*0.02*	1	*−0.02*					
8	N_2	*0.1*	28	*0.00*		0			*0.00*		
9	CO_2		44			0					
10	H_2O		18			0					
11	Ash					0					
12	Sum	*100.0*		*12.53*		*9.92*					
	O_2 and Air, Moles for Total Air = *119%* (see line d at right)										
13	O_2 (theo) reqd = O_2, line 12					*9.92*					
14	O_2 (excess) = $\frac{\text{T.A.} - 100}{100} \times O_2$, line 12					*1.89*		*1.89*			
15	O_2 (total) supplied = lines 13 + 14					*11.81*					
16	N_2 supplied = 3.76 × O_2, line 15					*44.41*			*44.41*		
17	Air (dry) supplied = O_2 + N_2					*56.22*					
18	H_2O in air = moles dry air × $\frac{A}{B-A}$ *					*1.19*				*1.19*	
19	Air (wet) supplied = lines 17 + 18					*57.41*					
20	Flue gas constituents = lines 1 to 18, total						*7.36*	*1.89*	*44.41*	*6.34*	

Conditions—Assigned or Observed and Miscellaneous		LINE
Date		
Fuel *Fuel Oil, Bunker "C"*; Source *California*; Fuel Unit {100 lb, solid or liquid fuels; 100 moles, gaseous fuels}		
Fuel Anal. as Fired (AF), % by Wt or Vol		a
C 87.9; *H_2 10.3*; *S 1.2*; *O_2 0.5*; *N_2 0.1*; *100.0*		b
CO_2 O_2 CO N_2 %†		c
Total air (T.A.) assigned or by ORSAT	*119%*	d
Lines f, g, h For Gaseous Fuels		e
Wt, fuel unit = Σ (moles each × mol. wt) lb		f
Mol. wt of fuel = line f ÷ 100		g
Density of fuel @ 80 F & 30 in. = $\frac{\text{line g}}{394}$ $\frac{\text{lb}}{\text{cu ft}}$		h
Fuel heat value, Btu/lb *18,400*/cu ft		i
Combustible in refuse, % "C"	%	j
Carbon unburned, lb/100 lb fuel = % ash in fuel × $\frac{\text{\% "C"}}{100 - \text{\% "C"}}$	*0.0*	k
Exit temp of flue gas, t_2	*303* F	l
Dry-bulb (ambient) temp, t'_1	*80* F	m
Wet-bulb temp	F	n
Rel humid. (psychrometric chart)	%	o
B*, barometric pressure, in. Hg		p
Sat. press. H_2O at amb temp, in. Hg		q
A*, press. H_2O in air, lines (o × q), in. Hg		r
Total Moles: Wet Flue Gas *60.00*; Dry Flue Gas *53.66*		s

21 *Note—for air at 80 F and 60% relative humidity, $\frac{A}{B-A}$ = 0.0212 is often used as standard.

Determination of Flue Gas and Combustible Losses in Btu per Fuel Unit (AF)

LINE		CO_2+SO_2	O_2	N_2	H_2O	CO	Total
22	Flue gas constituents	CO_2+SO_2	O_2	N_2	H_2O	CO	Total
23	Mc_p, mean, t_2 to t'_1 (for t'_1 = 80 F, see Fig. 2)	*9.5 10.1*	*7.1*	*7.0*	*8.1*		
24	In dry flue gas = moles each, line 20 × Mc_p × ($t_2 - t'_1$)	*15,600*	*2,990*	*69,330*			*87,920*
25	In H_2O in air = moles H_2O, line 18 × Mc_p × ($t_2 - t'_1$)				*2,160*		*2,160*
26	In sens heat, H_2O in fuel = moles, lines (5 + 10) × Mc_p × ($t_2 - t'_1$)				*9,300*		*9,300*
27	In latent heat, H_2O in fuel = moles, lines (5 + 10) × 1040 × 18				*96,400*		*96,400*
28	Total in wet flue gas						*195,780*
29	Due to carbon in refuse = line k × 14,100						*0*
30	Due to unburned CO in flue gas = moles C to CO × 12 × 9,755						*0*
31	Total flue gas losses + unburned combustible = lines 28 + 29 + 30					Total	*195,780*
32	Heat value of fuel unit = 100 × line i for solid and liquid fuels; 394 × line i × 100, for gaseous fuels						*1,840,000*
33	Stack and combustible loss, % of heat input = 100 × line 31 ÷ line 32						*10.64%*

†Note: Flue gas analysis by ORSAT. If CO is present in flue gases, a carbon balance is used to determine distribution of C, thus:
All C in fuel = C in flue gas constituents + C in refuse. Moles C in fuel = % C by analysis ÷ 12.
Moles C in refuse = line k ÷ 12. Moles C in CO_2 = (moles C in fuel − moles C in refuse) × % CO_2 by ORSAT ÷ % (CO_2 + CO) by ORSAT.
Moles C in CO = moles C in fuel − moles C in refuse − moles C in CO_2.

Table 10 Combustion Calculations—Molal Basis

Conditions—Assigned or Observed and Miscellaneous

Date

Fuel *Natural Gas*
Source *California*
Fuel Unit {100 lb, solid or liquid fuels / 100 moles, gaseous fuels}

LINE	Fuel Constituent	Per Fuel Unit, lb	Mol. Wt Divisor	Moles Fuel Constituent	O₂ Multiplier	O₂ Moles Theo Reqd	CO₂+SO₂	O₂	N₂	H₂O	CO
							Flue Gas (F.G.) Composition Moles per Fuel Unit (AF)				
1	C to CO₂	1326.0	12	110.5	1	110.5	110.5				
2	C to CO		12		.5						
3	CO to CO₂		28		.5						
4	C unburned, line k		12								
5	H₂	416.8	2	208.4	.5	104.2				208.4	
6	S		32		1						
7	O₂ (deduct)	9.6	32	0.3	1	−0.3					
8	N₂	47.6	28	1.7	0				1.7		
9	CO₂	4.4	44	0.1	0		0.1				
10	H₂O		18		0						
11	Ash				0						
12	Sum	1804.4		321.0		214.4					

O₂ and Air, Moles for Total Air = 114%
(see line d at right)

13	O₂ (theo) reqd = O₂, line 12		214.4
14	O₂ (excess) = (T.A. −100)/100 × O₂, line 12		30.0
15	O₂ (total) supplied = lines 13 + 14		244.4
16	N₂ supplied = 3.76 × O₂, line 15		918.9
17	Air (dry) supplied = O₂ + N₂		1163.3
18	H₂O in air = moles dry air × A/(B−A) *		24.7
19	Air (wet) supplied = lines 17 + 18		1188.0
20	Flue gas constituents = lines 1 to 18, total		

Line 14: O₂ column = 30.0; Line 16: N₂ = 918.9; Line 18: H₂O = 24.7
Line 20 totals: CO₂+SO₂ 110.6 | O₂ 30.0 | N₂ 920.6 | H₂O 233.1

Right-side data (Conditions):

Fuel Anal. as Fired (AF), % by Wt or Vol — line a

CH₄	85.3		
C₂H₆	12.6	*Moles C & H₂/100 Moles fuel*	
O₂	0.3		C	H₂
N₂	1.7	In CH₄	85.3	170.6
CO₂	0.1	In C₂H₆	25.2	37.8
		Totals	110.5	208.4
100.0		*No unburned fuel*	

(line b)

CO₂	O₂	CO	N₂	%†	c
Total air (T.A.) assigned or by ORSAT 114%					d
Lines f, g, h For Gaseous Fuels					e

Wt, fuel unit = Σ (moles each × mol. wt) lb	f
Mol. wt of fuel = line f ÷ 100 = 18.04	g
Density of fuel @ 80 F & 30 in. = line g/394 lb/cu ft	h
Fuel heat value, Btu/lb /cu ft 1092	i
Combustible in refuse, % "C" 0.0%	j
Carbon unburned, lb/100 lb fuel = % ash in fuel × % "C"/(100 − % "C") = 0.0	k
Exit temp of flue gas, t₂ 304 F	l
Dry-bulb (ambient) temp, t′₁ 80 F	m
Wet-bulb temp F	n
Rel humid. (psychrometric chart) %	o
B*, barometric pressure, in. Hg	p
Sat. press. H₂O at amb temp, in. Hg	q
A*, press. H₂O in air, lines (o × q), in. Hg	r
Total Moles	Wet Flue Gas 1294.3	Dry Flue Gas 1061.2	s

21. *Note—for air at 80 F and 60% relative humidity, A/(B−A) = 0.0212 is often used as standard.

Determination of Flue Gas and Combustible Losses in Btu per Fuel Unit (AF)

		CO₂+SO₂	O₂	N₂	H₂O	CO	Total
22	Flue gas constituents						
23	Mcp, mean, t₂ to t′₁ (for t′₁ = 80 F, see Fig. 2)	9.55	7.12	7.0	8.1		
24	In dry flue gas = moles each, line 20 × Mcp × (t₂ − t′₁)	236,600	47,800	1,443,500			1,727,900
25	In H₂O in air = moles H₂O, line 18 × Mcp × (t₂ − t′₁)				44,800		44,800
26	In sens heat, H₂O in fuel = moles, lines (5 + 10) × Mcp × (t₂ − t′₁)				378,100		378,100
27	In latent heat, H₂O in fuel = moles, lines (5 + 10) × 1040 × 18				3,901,300		3,901,300
28	Total in wet flue gas						6,052,100
29	Due to carbon in refuse = line k × 14,100						0
30	Due to unburned CO in flue gas = moles C to CO × 12 × 9,755						0
31	Total flue gas losses + unburned combustible = lines 28 + 29 + 30					Total	6,052,100
32	Heat value of fuel unit = (100 × line i for solid and liquid fuels)/(394 × line i × 100, for gaseous fuels)						43,024,800
33	Stack and combustible loss, % of heat input = 100 × line 31 ÷ line 32						14.07%

†Note: Flue gas analysis by ORSAT. If CO is present in flue gases, a carbon balance is used to determine distribution of C, thus:
All C in fuel = C in flue gas constituents + C in refuse. Moles C in fuel = % C by analysis ÷ 12.
Moles C in refuse = line k ÷ 12. Moles C in CO₂ = (moles C in fuel − moles C in refuse) × % CO₂ by ORSAT ÷ % (CO₂ + CO) by ORSAT.
Moles C in CO = moles C in fuel − moles C in refuse − moles C in CO₂.

Fig. 2 gives the mean molal specific heat, used on line 23 of Table 6, to determine the heat content of the stack gases between stack temperatures and 80F. Fig. 3 is a psychrometric chart which is useful for the determination of the actual moisture content of air if the standard moisture is not used.

The procedure for converting from molal to pound units is illustrated by Table 7, which tabulates the conversion of the data from Table 6. Line references in Table 7 refer to Tables 6 and 7. Reference in Table 7 to gaseous fuels applies to Table 10 or similar calculations for blast furnace or other types of gaseous fuels.

Tables 8, 9 and 10 show other examples of combustion calculations on the molal basis. Table 8 illustrates bituminous coal for conditions the same as Table 6 except that poor combustion results in some unburned carbon in the ash and some CO in the flue gas. Tables 9 and 10 apply to Bunker "C" fuel oil and natural gas respectively.

Btu method: In many combustion calculations the air required per lb of fuel can be established by using, as a convenient working tool, the theoretical air required per 10,000 Btu heat value of the fuel. Established values for the air requirements on this basis vary slightly for each particular fuel. Accurate values for theoretical air (lb per lb fuel) can be obtained by multiplying the heat content of the fuel expressed as "$\frac{Btu}{10,000}$/lb fuel as fired" by "lb air/$\frac{Btu}{10,000}$". For any fuel of known ultimate analysis, the value for theoretical dry air expressed as lb/$\frac{Btu}{10,000}$ is:

$$(6) \qquad 144 \times \frac{8C + 24\left(H_2 - \frac{O_2}{8}\right) + 3S}{Btu/lb}$$

where:

$$C = \text{Carbon, \% by wt}$$
$$H_2 = \text{Hydrogen, \% by wt}$$
$$O_2 = \text{Oxygen, \% by wt}$$
$$S = \text{Sulfur, \% by wt}$$
$$Btu/lb = \text{Heat value of fuel}$$

This formula should be used only when the exact ultimate analysis and the correct heating value are given for the fuel. Fig. 4 can be used for coal when the proximate analysis is available. Values of the ratio "lb air/$\frac{Btu}{10,000}$" as well as "lb fuel/$\frac{Btu}{10,000}$" and "lb moisture/$\frac{Btu}{10,000}$" are given in Table 11 for a selected heavy fuel oil and a Texas natural gas, having the following analyses:

Heavy Fuel Oil Percent by Wt		Texas Natural Gas Percent by Vol	
S	1.16	CH₄	84.10
H₂	10.33	C₂H₆	6.70
C	87.87	CO₂	0.80
N₂	0.14	N₂	8.40
O₂	0.50	Sp gr	0.630
Btu/lb as fired, 18,400		Btu/cu ft as fired, 974	

Table 11
Theoretical air, fuel, and resulting moisture per 10,000 Btu as fired

Fuel	Theoretical Air* lb/$\frac{Btu}{10,000}$	Fuel lb/$\frac{Btu}{10,000}$	Moisture lb/$\frac{Btu}{10,000}$
Fuel oil	7.46	0.544	0.51
Natural gas	7.19	0.496	0.93
Coal (prox anal.)	*See Fig. 4*	—	—
Coal (ult anal.)	*See Equation (6)*	—	—

* Dry air. To obtain wt of wet air required, moisture in air at standard conditions (0.013 lb per lb dry air @ 60% relative humidity and 80F dry bulb) must be added.

The following two simple examples illustrate the use of the Btu method to determine the amount of air required:

Bituminous Coal

Proximate Analysis as Fired, % by Wt

Moisture	12.0
Volatile matter	25.8
Fixed carbon	46.2
Ash	16.0
Btu/lb	10,900

From this analysis, the volatile matter on a dry ash-free basis is 25.8 × 100 ÷ (25.8 + 46.2) = 35.8 percent. From Fig. 4 theoretical air in lb per 10,000 Btu as fired is 7.57. The required total dry air (for 20% excess air) = 7.57 × 120/100 × 10,900/10,000 = 9.90 per lb of fuel.

From Table 11, for a heavy fuel oil of 18,400 Btu/lb, the theoretical air in lb/10,000 Btu as fired is 7.46, and the required total dry air(for 18% excess air) = 7.46 × 118/100 × 18,400/10,000 = 16.19 lb per lb of fuel.

Tables 12 and 13 present examples of typical combustion calculations for coal and oil using the Btu method.

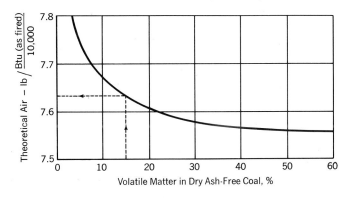

Fig. 4 Theoretical air in lb per 10,000 Btu heat value of coal with a range of volatile.

Measurement of total or excess air

The continuous measurement of combustion air is a necessity in modern practice to accomplish effective control of avoidable heat losses. The amount of air used can be determined by continuously indicated or recorded flue gas analysis and by metering the combustion air or the flue gas.

L I N E	Table 12 Combustion Calculations Based on quantities per 10,000 Btu fuel input			L I N E
1	Fuel—*Bituminous Coal, Virginia*	**Conditions** by test or specification	Date	a
2	Analysis As Fired			
3	Ultimate, % by Wt Proximate, % by Wt	Total air %	*120*	b
4	C 80.31 Moisture 2.90	Air temperature to heater F	*80*	c
5	H₂ 4.47 Volatile 22.05	Air temperature from heater F	*350*	d
6	S 1.54 Fixed carbon 68.50	Flue gas temperature leaving unit F	*280*	e
7	O₂ 2.85 Ash 6.55	H₂O per lb dry air lb	*0.013*	f
8	N₂ 1.38 100.00			g
9	H₂O 2.90	Unburned fuel loss %	*0.4*	h
10	Ash 6.55	Unaccounted loss %	*1.5*	i
11	100.00	Radiation loss (ABMA), Fig. 27, Chapter 4 %	*0.8*	j
12	Btu per lb, as fired, *14,100*			k

13	**Quantities per 10,000 Btu Fuel Input**		13
14	Fuel burned, [100 (100 − line 10) ÷ line 12] − .007 × line h	lb	*0.66*	14
15	Dry air, line b [(value from Fig. 4, Table 11 or Eq. 6) − .08 × line h]	lb	*9.11*	15
16	H₂O in air, line 15 × line f = 9.11 × 0.013	lb	*0.12*	16
17	Wet gas, total, lines (14 + 15 + 16)	lb	*9.89*	17
18	H₂O in fuel, 100 (8.94 × line 5 + line 9) ÷ line 12, or Table 11	lb	*0.30*	18
19	H₂O in flue gas, total, line 16 + line 18	lb	*0.42*	19
20	H₂O in flue gas, total, in percent, (line 19 ÷ line 17) × 100	%	*4.31*	20
21	Dry gas, total, line 17 − line 19	lb	*9.47*	21

22	**Losses per 10,000 Btu Fuel Input**		22
23	Unburned fuel, 10,000 × line h ÷ 100	Btu	*40*	23
24	Unaccounted, 10,000 × line i ÷ 100	Btu	*150*	24
25	Radiation, 10,000 × line j ÷ 100	Btu	*80*	25
26	Latent Heat, H₂O in fuel, 1040 × line 18	Btu	*312*	26
27	Sensible heat, flue gas, line 17 × Btu from Fig. 1 @ line e and line 20 = 9.89 × 50	Btu	*495*	27
28	Total losses, lines (23 + 24 + 25 + 26 + 27)	Btu	*1077*	28
29	Total losses in percent, (line 28 ÷ 10,000) × 100	%	*10.8*	29
30	Efficiency, by difference, 100 − line 29	%	*89.2*	30

31	**Quantities per 10,000 Btu Fuel Input** Combustion temperature, adiabatic		31
32	Heat input from fuel	Btu	*10,000*	32
33	Heat input from air, lines (15 + 16) × Btu from Fig. 8 @ line d temp	Btu	*612*	33
34	Heat input, total, lines 32 + 33	Btu	*10,612*	34
35	Less latent heat loss, H₂O in fuel, line 26	Btu	*−312*	35
36	Heat available, maximum	Btu	*10,300*	36
37	Less (lines 24 + 25) × 0.5*	Btu	*−115*	37
38	Heat available, line 36 − line 37	Btu	*10,185*	38
39	Heat available per lb of flue gas, line 38 ÷ line 17 Btu	*1021*		39
40	Adiabatic temperature, from Fig. 1 for lines 20 & 39 F	*3513*		40

*Note: It is customary to reduce the maximum heat available, line 36, by from ⅓ to ½ of the unaccounted plus radiation losses, on the assumption that a portion of these losses occurs in the combustion zone.

Flue gas analysis

In the continuously recording or indicating flue gas analyzer, gas is continuously drawn from a selected location, and samples are analyzed at intervals of 1 minute or longer. Both the analysis and the indication or recording of the results are automatic. The analysis may or may not include all the constituents of the products of combustion, and instruments are selected accordingly. Many continuously recording instruments give the percentage of CO_2 only, others only the percentage of O_2, and still others the percent of unburned gases. Unburned gases, however, should not be present with proper combustion in the field of heat production.

The amount of O_2 in the flue gases is significant in defining the status of the combustion process. Its presence always means that more oxygen (excess air) is being introduced than is being used. Assuming complete combustion, low values of O_2 in the flue gases reflect moderate (nearly correct) excess air and reduced heat losses to the stack, while higher values of O_2 mean needlessly higher stack losses. The quantitative determination of total air (total air = 100 + percent excess air) admitted to an actual combustion process requires a complete flue gas analysis for CO_2, O_2, CO, and N_2 (by difference) or the direct measurement of the air supplied by a suitable fluid meter.

The approximate percent total air from flue gas analyses may be determined from the curves of Fig. 5. A formula that has long been used for approximating the percent excess air from an Orsat analysis is:

$$(7) \quad \% \text{ Excess air} = 100 \times \frac{O_2 - CO/2}{0.264N_2 - (O_2 - CO/2)}$$

The results are reasonably close for the flue gases from hydrocarbon fuels of low nitrogen content; the error increases with increase in nitrogen content in the fuel.

Fig. 6 is another helpful chart for rapid determination of excess air when a series of gas analyses are taken. From any Orsat analysis, it indicates the kind of fuel being burned. It also indicates relationships between fuels. The various types of fuel are indicated by the reference letters at the upper right of Fig. 6; these are identified in Table 14.

Each Orsat analysis may be plotted as a single point on this chart. For any particular fuel every valid analysis yields a point which falls on a single straight line drawn from the pivot point to the point on the "zero oxygen" line ($O_2 - CO/2 = 0$), where the CO_2 coordinate equals the maximum CO_2 value (percent by volume) obtainable with the particular fuel.

One good Orsat analysis will define the fuel, i.e., the result is plotted as a point on Fig. 6, and a straight line through the pivot and this point is extrapolated to the zero oxygen line. The point of intersection is the maximum CO_2 value possible for the particular fuel, which is identified by the reference fuel letter adjacent to the zero oxygen line.

The maximum CO_2 value can be checked from the following formula:

$$(8) \quad \text{Max } CO_2 = \frac{21.0 \ CO_2}{21.0 - O_2}$$

where chemical symbols represent volume percentages of dry flue gas. Percentages on the right side of the equation are from the Orsat analysis.

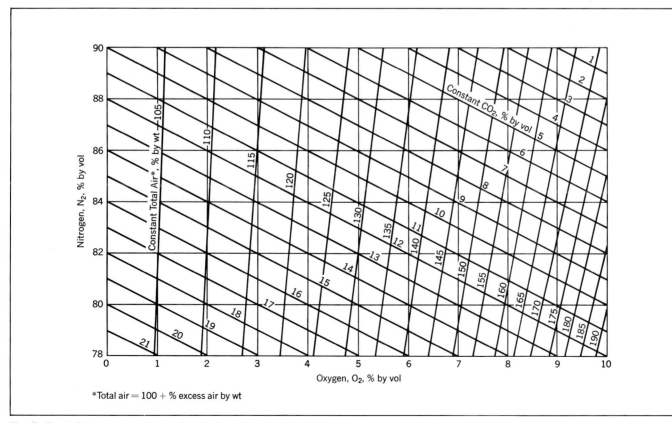

Fig. 5 Chart for approximating total air from flue gas analysis.

Table 13 Combustion Calculations
Based on quantities per 10,000 Btu fuel input

LINE					LINE
1	Fuel—*Fuel Oil, Texas, Heavy*	**Conditions** by test or specification		Date	a
2	Analysis As Fired				
3	Ultimate, % by Wt Proximate, % by Wt	Total air	%	120	b
4	C ⌐ Moisture	Air temperature to heater	F	80	c
5	H₂ Volatile	Air temperature from heater	F	500	d
6	S Fixed carbon	Flue gas temperature leaving unit	F	350	e
7	O₂ ⟩ *Unknown* Ash	H₂O per lb dry air	lb	0.013	f
8	N₂				g
9	H₂O	Unburned fuel loss	%	0.00	h
10	Ash ⌋	Unaccounted loss	%	1.5	i
11		Radiation loss (ABMA), Fig. 27, Chapter 4	%	1.0	j
12	Btu per lb, as fired, *18,500*				k

13	**Quantities per 10,000 Btu Fuel Input**			13
14	Fuel burned, [100 (100 − line 10) ÷ line 12] − .007 × line h	lb	0.54	14
15	Dry air, line b [(value from Fig. 4, Table 11 or Eq. 6) − .08 × line h]	lb	8.95	15
16	H₂O in air, line 15 × line f = 8.95 × 0.013	lb	0.12	16
17	Wet gas, total, lines (14 + 15 + 16)	lb	9.61	17
18	H₂O in fuel, 100 (8.94 × line 5 + line 9) ÷ line 12, or Table 11	lb	0.51	18
19	H₂O in flue gas, total, line 16 + line 18	lb	0.63	19
20	H₂O in flue gas, total, in percent, (line 19 ÷ line 17) × 100	%	6.55	20
21	Dry gas, total, line 17 − line 19	lb	8.98	21

22	**Losses per 10,000 Btu Fuel Input**			22
23	Unburned fuel, 10,000 × line h ÷ 100	Btu	0.0	23
24	Unaccounted, 10,000 × line i ÷ 100	Btu	150.0	24
25	Radiation, 10,000 × line j ÷ 100	Btu	100.0	25
26	Latent Heat, H₂O in fuel, 1040 × line 18	Btu	530.4	26
27	Sensible heat, flue gas, line 17 × Btu from Fig. 1 @ line e and line 20	Btu	673.0	27
28	Total losses, lines (23 + 24 + 25 + 26 + 27)	Btu	1453.4	28
29	Total losses in percent, (line 28 ÷ 10,000) × 100	%	14.5	29
30	Efficiency, by difference, 100 − line 29	%	85.5	30

31	**Quantities per 10,000 Btu Fuel Input** Combustion temperature, adiabatic			31
32	Heat input from fuel	Btu	10,000	32
33	Heat input from air, lines (15 + 16) × Btu from Fig. 8 @ line d temp	Btu	943	33
34	Heat input, total, lines 32 + 33	Btu	10,943	34
35	Less latent heat loss, H₂O in fuel, line 26	Btu	−530	35
36	Heat available, maximum	Btu	10,413	36
37	Less (lines 24 + 25) × 0.5*	Btu	−125	37
38	Heat available, line 36 − line 37	Btu	10,288	38
39	Heat available per lb of flue gas, line 38 ÷ line 17	Btu	1071	39
40	Adiabatic temperature, from Fig. 1 for lines 20 & 39	F	3600	40

*Note: It is customary to reduce the maximum heat available, line 36, by from ⅓ to ½ of the unaccounted plus radiation losses, on the assumption that a portion of these losses occurs in the combustion zone.

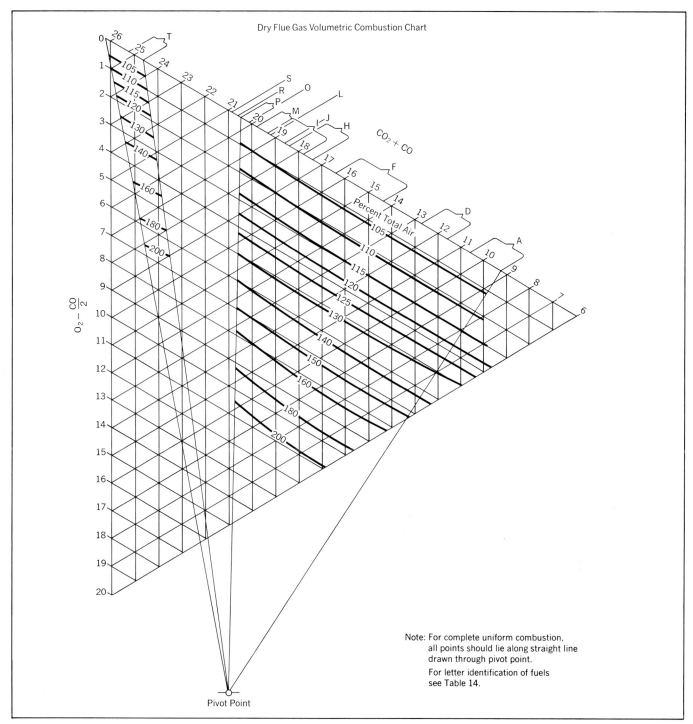

Fig. 6 Dry flue gas volumetric combustion chart.

Maximum CO_2 value can also be computed from the formula:

$$(9)\ \text{Max } CO_2\ (\%\text{ by volume, dry flue gas})$$
$$= \frac{31.3C + 11.5S}{1.504C + 3.55H_2 + 0.56S + 0.13N_2 - 0.45O_2}$$

where chemical symbols other than CO_2 represent weight percentages of each material in the ultimate as-fired analysis of the fuel.

Both of the above equations assume complete combustion. For incomplete combustion with CO and CO_2 (assuming no carbon loss—all carbon burned to either

CO or CO_2) the maximum CO_2 may be computed from the Orsat analysis as follows, where chemical symbols represent volume percentages of dry flue gas as in Equation (8):

$$(10)\qquad \text{Max } CO_2 = \frac{100\ (CO_2 + CO)}{100 - 4.78O_2 + 1.89CO}$$

Fig. 6 should not be used for fuels with more than 6% CO, nor for fuels which contain high amounts of CO_2. However, blast furnace gas may be used, but note it requires the different family of percent-total-air curves included on the left side of Fig. 6.

The following table shows some typical maximum CO_2 ranges for most common fuels:

Table 14
Maximum CO_2 ranges for common fuels

Fuel	% CO_2 by Volume	Reference Letter (Fig. 6)
Coke oven gas (CO 6%)	9.23-10.6	A
Natural gas	11.6 -12.7	D
Oil	14.25-16.35	F
Tar and pitch	17.5 -18.4	H
Bituminous coal	17.7 -19.3	I
Charcoal	18.6	J
Black liquor without saltcake	18.6	J
Lignite, coke	19.2	L
Anthracite coal	19.3 -19.85	M
Tan bark	20.1	O
Wood	20.1 -20.5	P
Bagasse	20.65	R
Pure carbon	20.9	S
Blast furnace gas	24.6 -25.3	T

Flue gas sampling

Great care should be taken to secure truly representative samples of the gas for analysis. The usual practice for a manually operated gas analyzer is to take successive samples from a number of points, laid out in checkerboard fashion over a cross section of the flue or area traversed by the gas. The number of sampling points and their position are best determined by trial analyses of gas samples from tentative locations. If the values from point to point vary widely, more sampling locations across the plane should be used.

Gas samples should be drawn at regular intervals over a relatively long period (during the entire period of a formal test). Unless operating conditions are exceptionally uniform, a few samples drawn at irregular intervals are of little use in obtaining a true analysis.

Fixed-position samplers of the branched-pipe type, extending into the flue area, are likely to give misleading

Fig. 7 Boiler Meter for indicating and recording ratio of air used to Btu input.

results, since the proportion of gas drawn into each branch may not correspond to the flows over the flue cross section. A better arrangement is to insert a single sampling element in the flue, at a location established by thorough preliminary analyses, from which samples can be drawn representing a fair average. Samples for the automatic mechanical gas analyzers are frequently drawn through a single sampling pipe carefully located in this manner.

When the temperatures exceed 900F, gas samples should be drawn through a water-cooled pipe to avoid the loss of O_2 from oxidation of pipe material at such temperature. Uncooled pipes of special steels have been used with fair success, but there is still the uncertainty of the loss of some O_2 to the metal. A properly designed water-cooled sampler can be safely used to obtain gas samples from the hottest regions of a furnace (3000F and above). The completeness of combustion progressively through the furnace is sometimes determined by the analysis of samples taken in this manner. Construction of a water-cooled sampler suitable for this duty is similar to that of the water-cooled portions of the HVT (high velocity thermocouple) probe illustrated in Chapter 33.

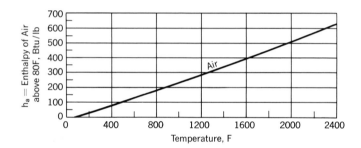

Fig. 8 Enthalpy (above 80F) of air (0.987 lb dry air plus 0.013 lb water vapor per lb mixture) at 30 in. Hg, Btu per lb.

Metering combustion air

Another method of establishing the amount of total air used in a boiler or other similar combustion heat exchanger is to meter the flow of air or the flow of combustion gases through the unit. Furthermore, for a given total air, the flow so measured has a nearly straight-line relationship to the Btu input. In a steam boiler, the steam output (and consequently the Btu output) bears a nearly constant relation to the Btu input. Metered steam is, therefore, a suitable index of Btu input, and the operator may thus proportion the combustion air to the fuel at any rate of steam output.

Instruments recording the air-flow-steam-flow relationship are an important factor in maintaining good boiler efficiency, and are included in most modern boiler installations. The instrument in general use for this function is illustrated in Fig. 7 and is known as the Boiler Meter. Since the air quantity can be adjusted to the fuel quantity in the proper proportion at all times, manually by the operator or by automatic combustion-control equipment, it is not necessary to take and analyze flue gas samples in regular operation. In the initial setting of the Boiler Meter, however, it is necessary to take and to analyze such samples, and most boiler rooms are equipped to make periodic checks with an Orsat analyzer.

Chapter 7

Utilization of oil and gas

Petroleum

Preparation

Petroleum (crude oil) is the most important source of hydrocarbons. It provides an increasingly large number of combinations of hydrogen and carbon in arrangements and proportions ranging from a gas (methane, CH_4) at room temperature through a wide variety of liquids to heavy waxes and asphalts that are solids at room temperature. Crude oil when extracted may contain sufficient water to form an emulsion. Much of this water is removed at the well by electrical or chemical means before delivery to the refinery.

Most petroleum is refined to some extent before use although small amounts are burned without processing. Originally, refining petroleum was simply the process of separating the lighter compounds (higher in hydrogen) from the heavier compounds by fractional distillation. Through the development of refining techniques, such as thermal and catalytic cracking (Fig. 1) and hydrogenation of the heavier hydrocarbons to produce lighter ones, petroleum can now be regarded as a raw-material source of hydrogen and carbon that can be combined as required to meet a variety of end uses. Consequently, the characteristics of the portion available as fuel oil depend more and more on economic and national security requirements rather than the nature of the crude oil from which it comes.

The refining of crude oil yields a number of products having many different applications. Those used as fuel include gasoline, distillate fuel, residual fuel, jet fuels, still gas, liquified gases, kerosine and petroleum coke. Products used for other applications include lubricants and waxes, asphalt, road oil and petrochemical feedstock.

Transportation, handling and storage

Petroleum and its products are widely used. Its high heating value per unit of volume, its varied applications, and its liquid form that facilitates handling have fostered a world-wide system of distribution.

Currently the overall demand for petroleum in the U.S. far exceeds the domestic production. For example, the demand for residual fuel oil is more than twice the domestic production. Imports of residual fuel oil come mostly from South America with smaller amounts from Europe, Central America, the Carribean area, Mexico, the Middle East, Africa and Canada.

Oil from the Gulf is transported to East Coast refineries by tanker and pipeline. A considerable part of the demand in areas near the Mississippi and its tributaries is supplied from the Gulf by barge shipments. Comparatively small quantities are shipped overland by rail and truck because of the relatively higher cost of haulage as compared with water or pipeline transportation. The approximate relative costs of shipping petroleum by various means of transportation, although subject to wide variations, are noted in the following tabulation:

Transportation Method	Relative Cost per Ton-Mile
Water	1
Pipeline	9
Railroad	27
Truck	81

To prevent contamination between crude oils of different composition, precautions must be taken, including cleaning the tanks before loading a new shipment. In pipeline transportation this may necessitate running parallel lines.

The serious hazard from oil-storage-tank failure is overcome by storage in underground tanks or by building cofferdams around surface tanks with sufficient capacity to hold the entire contents of the tank. On the West Coast, crude oil is commonly stored in huge concrete reservoirs holding several million barrels. In the East, oil is usually stored in steel tanks to eliminate evaporation loss and to protect it against fire from lightning. The National Fire Protection Association has prepared a standard set of rules for the storage and handling of oils. These rules serve as the basis for many local ordinances and form an excellent guide to safe practice. Loss of heavy fuel oils in storage is negligible. Lighter products, such as gasoline, may volatilize sufficiently in warm weather to cause appreciable loss, unless special storage tanks are provided.

Fig. 1 Catalytic cracking of petroleum at a Southern refinery.

To facilitate pumping heavy fuel oil, heating equipment is usually provided in storage and transportation facilities. Storage tanks, piping and heaters for heavy oils must be cleaned at intervals because of fouling or sludge formation. Various commercial compounds are helpful in reducing sludge.

Shale oil

Oil shale is not actually a shale nor does it contain oil. It is generally defined as a fine-grained, compact, sedimentary rock containing an organic material called kerogen. Heating the oil shale to about 875F decomposes this material to produce shale oil. There are two methods to produce shale oil—one requires mining the shale and heating it in a retort to decompose the kerogen, the other accomplishes thermal decomposition by underground combustion.

The recovery of oil from shale is not presently a commercial operation in the U.S. Pilot plants have demonstrated that shale oil is a good refinery feedstock. Various grades of gasoline and jet fuel, with low yield of fuel oil, have been produced from shale oil. It is reasonable to anticipate that a commercial plant will begin operation in the 1980's to produce a refinery feedstock and to supplement domestic crude.

Another possible product of oil shale is a fuel gas with high heating value. A hydrogasification process has shown good yields of pipeline gas from Colorado oil shale.

Because of the low combustible content of oil shale it appears certain that the oil will be extracted from the shale close to the source. Commercial use of shale oil will require establishment of distribution systems similar to those for petroleum.

Natural gas

Preparation

Since natural gas almost always accompanies petroleum, it may well be considered as part of the petroleum. To reduce the viscosity of the crude oil and facilitate raising it to the surface and handling, it is desirable to keep the lighter hydrocarbon compounds in solution by subjecting the oil to pressure. When the pressure is released, the light hydrocarbons, including methane (CH_4), ethane (C_2H_6), propane (C_3H_8), and butane (C_4H_{10}) volatilize as gases or vapors. Propane and butane are often separated from the lighter gases and are widely used as bottle gas. They are distributed and stored liquified under pressure. When the pressure is released, the liquid boils, producing gaseous fuel. Some of the portion heavier than butane is distributed as gasoline.

Much of the natural gas produced is suitable for use without further preparation. However, some natural gas may contain enough sand or gaseous sulfur compounds to be troublesome or obnoxious in use. The sand is usually removed at the source. Natural gas containing excessive amounts of hydrogen sulfide is commonly known as "sour" gas. The sulfur is removed before distribution. Where natural gas is used to replace or supplement manufactured gas, it is sometimes "reformed" to bring its heating value in line with the manufactured gas. Natural gas may also be mixed directly with manufactured gas to increase the heating value of the distributed product.

Transportation, handling, and storage

The pipeline is an economical means for transporting natural gas. The rapid increase in consumption throughout the country and in areas remote from the source has resulted from the continued extension of a vast system of long-distance pipelines. The distribution of natural gas is subject to some practical limitations because of the energy required for transportation—about 150 Btu to transmit 1 cu ft of gas 1000 miles.

To accommodate overseas transportation of natural gas, the use of tankers is employed. The gas is liquified under pressure (LNG) to accommodate the transportation method.

In general it is not practical to vary the supply of natural gas to accommodate hourly or daily fluctuations in consumer demand. For economic reasons, long-distance pipelines should operate with a high load factor. The rate of withdrawal from the wells may often be limited for conservation reasons, and the cost of the pipeline to provide the peak rate would be prohibitive. Therefore, to meet fluctuations in demand it is usually necessary to provide local storage or to supplement the supply with manufactured gas for brief periods.

Storage facilities, above ground and underground, are increasing rapidly. Above-ground methods of storage are: a) in the familiar large water-seal tanks; b) in liquid form in insulated steel tanks; c) in liquid form absorbed in a granular substance, released by passing warm gas over the grains; d) in pipe holders (at or near the surface) of commercial gas-line pipe laid parallel and interconnected; and e) using the trunk transmission line as a reservoir by building up the pressure.

In consumer areas where depleted or partially depleted gas and oil wells are available, underground storage of gas pumped back into these wells provides at minimum cost the large storage volume required to meet seasonal variations in demand. This method is coming more and more into use. The closer this storage is to the consumer, the more useful it is.

Oil and gas burning equipment

The *burner* is the principal equipment component for the firing of oil and gas. Burners are normally located in the vertical walls of the furnace. Fig. 2 shows oil burners located in the front wall of a marine boiler unit. Burners, together with the furnaces in which they are installed, are designed to burn the fuel properly in accordance with the principles of combustion outlined in Chapter 6.

The burners introduce the fuel and air into the furnace to sustain the exothermic chemical reactions for the most effective release of heat. That effectiveness is judged by the following:

1. The rate of feed of the fuel and air shall comply with the load demand on the boiler over a predetermined operating range.
2. The efficiency of the combustion process shall be as high as possible with a minimum of unburned combustibles and minimum excess air in the products.
3. The physical size and complexity of the furnace and burners should be such as to minimize the required investment and to meet the limitations on space, weight, and flexibility which are imposed by the service conditions.
4. The design of the burners, including the materials used, shall provide reliable operation under specified service conditions, and shall assure meeting accepted standards of maintenance for the burners and the furnaces in which they are installed.
5. Safety shall be paramount under all conditions of operation of burners, furnace and boiler, including starting, stopping, load changes, and variations in the fuel.

The normal use of a steam generator requires operation at different outputs to meet varying load demands. The specified operating range or "load range" for a burner is the ratio of full load on the burner to the mini-mum load at which the burner is capable of reliable operation. For example, with a boiler of 100,000 lb/hr capacity (steam delivered), a load range of 4 to 1 on the burners means that the unit can be operated from 100,000 lb/hr down to 25,000 lb/hr without changing the number of burners in operation, and with complete combustion.

Combustion air is generally delivered to the burners by fans. It is necessary to supply more than the theoretical air quantity to assure complete combustion of the fuel in the combustion chamber (furnace). The amount of excess air provided should be just enough to burn the fuel completely in order to minimize the sensible heat loss in the stack gases (Chapter 6). The excess air normally required with oil and gas, expressed as percent of theoretical air, is given in Table 5, Chapter 6.

Continuity of service is enhanced by designing the furnace and arranging the burners to minimize slagging and fouling of heat-absorbing surfaces for the normal range of fuels burned.

Maintenance costs of the burner are minimized by (1) the least exposure to furnace heat, and (2) provision for replacement or repair of vulnerable parts while the unit continues in operation.

Modern burner types

The most frequently used burners are the circular type. Fig. 3 shows a single circular register burner for gas and oil firing, and Fig. 4 shows a circular type dual register burner for firing oil or pulverized coal. The circular type dual register burner was developed for NO_x reduction.

The maximum capacity of the individual circular burner ranges up to 300 million Btu/hr dependent upon the atomizer used.

In circular type burners the tangentially disposed "doors" built into the air register provide the turbulence necessary to mix the fuel and air and produce short, compact flames.

While the fuel is introduced to the burner in a fairly dense mixture in the center, the direction and velocity of the air, plus dispersion of the fuel, completely and thoroughly mixes it with the combustion air.

Fig. 5 is a photograph showing circular burners for combination oil and gas firing on a large electric utility in the Southwest.

Oil burners. In order to burn fuel oil at the high rates demanded of modern boiler units it is necessary that the oil be "atomized," i.e., dispersed into the furnace as a fine mist, somewhat like a heavy fog. This exposes a large amount of oil particle surface for contact with the combustion air to assure prompt ignition and rapid combustion. There are many ways of atomizing fuel oil but the two most popular ways are by use of steam or air, and mechanical atomizers.

For proper atomization, oil of grades heavier than No. 2 must be heated to reduce its viscosity to 135-150 SUS (*see Chapter 5*). Steam or electric heaters are required to raise the oil temperature to the required degree, i.e., approximately:

135F for No. 4 oil
185F for No. 5 oil
and 200-220F for No. 6 oil

Fig. 2 Burner front of marine boiler equipped with steam-atomizing oil burners.

With certain oils, better combustion is obtained at somewhat higher temperatures than required for atomization. However, oil temperatures must not be raised to the point where vapor binding occurs in the pump supplying the oil, since this could cause flow interruptions followed by loss of ignition.

It is also important that oil be free from acid, grit and other foreign matter which might clog or injure burners or their control valves.

Steam or air atomizers. Steam (or air) atomizers (Fig. 6) are the most widely used. In general they operate on the principle of producing a steam-fuel (or air-fuel) emulsion which, when released into the furnace, atomizes the oil through the rapid expansion of the steam. The atomizing steam must be dry because moisture causes pulsations which can lead to loss of ignition. Where steam is not available, moisture-free compressed air can be substituted.

Steam atomizers are available in sizes up to 300 million Btu/hr input—about 16,500 lb of oil per hr. Oil pressure is much lower than for mechanical atomizers. The steam and oil pressure required are dependent on the design of the steam atomizer. Maximum oil pressure can be as much as 300 psi and maximum steam pressure 150 psi.

The steam atomizer performs more efficiently over a wider load range than other types. It normally atomizes the fuel properly down to 20 percent of rated capacity, and in some instances steam atomizers have been successfully operated at 5 percent capacity. Frequently these extremes in range cannot be fully utilized because the temperature of the combustion space falls off to such a degree that, despite the excellent quality of atomization, there is not sufficient temperature to complete the combustion process adequately.

A disadvantage of the steam atomizer is its consumption of steam. A good steam atomizer can operate with a steam consumption as low as .02 lb of steam per lb of fuel oil at maximum atomizer capacity. For a large unit this amounts to a sizable quantity of steam and consequent heat loss to the stack. When the boiler unit supplies a substantial amount of steam for a process where condensate recovery is small, the additional makeup for the steam atomizer is inconsequential. However, in a large public utility boiler where turbine losses are low

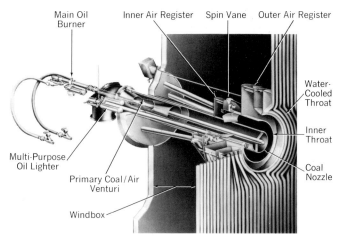

Fig. 4 Circular type dual register burner showing location of burner components.

and there is very little makeup, the use of atomizing steam can have a significant effect on the total makeup requirements. In spite of this the cost of employing a compressed air supply system as a substitute for steam is not always justified.

Mechanical atomizers. In mechanical atomizers the pressure of the fuel itself is used as the means for atomization. Many forms have been developed. However, those with moving parts close to the furnace have lost favor because of the excessive maintenance required to keep them operational.

The return-flow atomizer (Fig. 7) is used in many marine installations and some stationary units where the use of atomizing steam is objectionable or impractical. The oil pressure required at the atomizer for maximum capacity ranges from 600 to 1000 psi, depending on capacity, load range, and fuel. The fuel flows through tangentially disposed slots in a "sprayer plate" (Figs. 8 and 9) into a "whirl" chamber, from which it issues through an orifice of the sprayer plate as a fine conical mist or spray. After the oil passes through the tangentially disposed slots, that which exceeds the boiler input requirements is returned from the base of the whirl chamber to the fuel oil system. Fig. 9 shows characteristic curves for a typical B&W return-flow atomizer.

Mechanical atomizers are available in sizes up to 180 million Btu/hr input—about 10,000 lb oil per hr. The acceptable operating range may be as much as 10 to 1 or as little as 3 to 1 depending on the maximum oil pressure used for the system, the furnace configuration, air temperature and burner throat velocity. Return-flow atomizers are ideally suited for standard grades of fuel oil where it is desired to meet load variations without changing sprayer plates or cutting burners in and out of service.

For good performance over an operating range of 10 to 1, the combustion chamber should be of relatively small cross section at the burner zone, the oil pressure at the burners for full load should be 1000 psi, the temperature of air for combustion should be significantly above ambient throughout the load range, and the air resistance across the burner should be 8 to 12 in. of water at full load, depending upon the size of the particular burner. Departures downward from any of these values

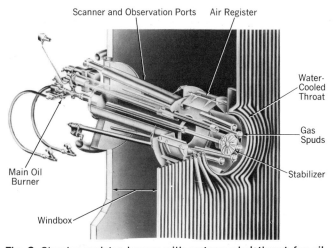

Fig. 3 Circular register burner with water-cooled throat for oil and gas firing.

markedly affect the satisfactory load range obtainable from the burners. In a properly designed and operated system the high pressure return-flow mechanical atomizer will provide combustion efficiency comparable to that obtainable with a good steam atomizer.

Natural gas burners. The variable-mix multispud gas element (Fig. 3) was developed for use with circular type burners for obtaining good ignition stability under most conditions, such as the two-stage combustion technique and vitiated air (by gas recirculation) to the burner. Distinctive features of this gas element are:

1. The individual gas spuds are removable with the boiler in service to enable cleaning or redrilling of the gas nozzles if required.

2. The individual gas spuds can be rotated to orient the gas nozzles for optimum firing conditions with the burner in service.

3. The location of the individual gas spuds with respect to the burner throat can be varied a limited distance to obtain optimum firing conditions with the burner in service.

4. The individual gas spud flame container and gas spud drilling are arranged so as to obtain optimum flame stability.

With the proper selection of control equipment, a multifuel fired burner with a variable-mix multispud type gas element is capable of changing from one fuel to another without a drop in load or boiler pressure. Simultaneous firing of natural gas and oil in the same burner is acceptable on burners equipped with variable-mix multispud type gas elements.

This type element is designed for use with natural gas or other gaseous fuels containing at least:

$$70\% \text{ CH}_4 \quad \text{(methane)}$$
$$\text{or } 70\% \text{ C}_3\text{H}_8 \quad \text{(propane)}$$
$$\text{or } 25\% \text{ H}_2 \quad \text{(hydrogen) by volume}$$

This element is designed for a maximum input of 200 million Btu per hr per burner.

In many respects natural gas is an ideal fuel since it requires no preparation for rapid and intimate mixing with the combustion air flowing through the burner throat. However, this characteristic of easy ignition under most operating conditions has, in some cases, led to operator carelessness with damaging explosions.

To provide safe operation, ignition of a gas burner should remain close to the burner wall throughout the full range of allowable gas pressures, not only with normal air flows, but also with much more air flow through the burner than is theoretically required. Ideally it should be possible at the minimum load to pass full-load air flow through the burner, and at full load as much as 25 percent in excess of theoretical air without loss of ignition. With this latitude in air flow it is not likely that ignition can be lost, even momentarily, during some upset in air flow due to improper operation or error.

Burners for other gases. Many industrial applications utilize coke oven gas, blast furnace gas, refinery gas or other industrial by-product gases. With these gases the heat release per unit volume of fuel gas may be very different from that of natural gas. Hence, gas elements must be designed to accommodate the particular characteristics of the gas to be burned. Also burners must be

Fig. 5 Installation for combination oil and gas firing in a large electric utility boiler located in the Southwest.

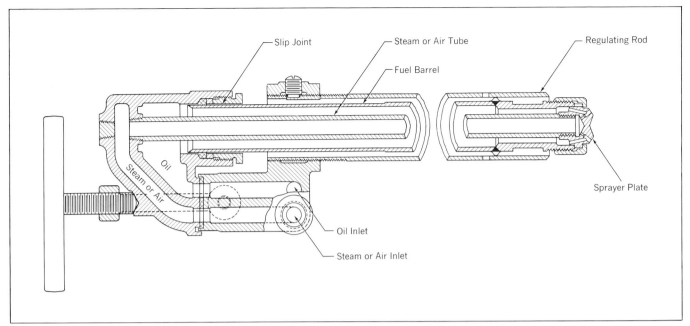

Fig. 6 Steam (or air) oil atomizer assembly.

designed with reference to ignition stability and load range factors which govern in each case. Other special problems may be introduced by the presence of impurities in industrial gases, such as sulfur in coke oven gas, and entrained dust in blast furnace gas (*see Coke Oven Gas and Blast Furnace Gas, Chapter 5*).

Lighters (ignitors) and pilots

Equipment is available, for boiler units ranging from the smallest to the largest, that allows the boiler operator to ignite the main fuel by the simple expedient of pressing a button. This equipment ranges from spark devices that ignite fuel oil directly, to gas or light oil equipment, in itself spark-ignited, which is used for ignition of the main streams of gas and fuel oil. These devices are available with control equipment that ranges from the simplest push button requiring observation of ignition by the operator at the burner, to a fully "programmed" starting sequence, complete with interlocks and flame-sensing equipment, all remotely operated from the boiler control room.

Usually the ignition device is energized only long enough to assure that the main flame is self-sustaining. With the fuel normally used in oil or natural gas burners, ignition should be self-sustaining within one or two seconds after the fuel reaches the combustion air. On a fully automated burner it is customary to allow 10 to 15 seconds "trial for ignition" so that the fuel can reach the burner after the fuel shut-off valve on the burner is opened.

In general, lighters should be used sparingly. Where special fuel is used for the lighters, it is usually more expensive than the fuel used in the regular burners, so unnecessary use adds to operating cost.

However there are applications where a continuously burning lighter or pilot is needed. This is particularly true in the use of a by-product fuel, such as gas from a chemical process. In most installations such fuels are piped directly to the boiler house without an intervening accumulator. The quantity and quality of fuel supplied to the boiler house are subject to any malfunction in the chemical process. Supply pressure may vary beyond the range of main burner stability or the combustible content of the gas may change. Such variations require continuous operation of a pilot. It may be necessary also to provide supplementary fuel to each burner reliably and continuously to keep the process gas burning during abnormal conditions in the process. In these instances the boiler operators have an awareness of the vagaries of the process fuel that does not exist in the operation of conventional oil and natural gas fired boilers. As a consequence, they know the safety of the boiler operation is highly dependent on the reliability of the ignitor and are alert to any malfunction that may occur.

Excess air

When firing oil or natural gas at high loads there normally is no fuel distribution problem but distribution of combustion air in the burner windbox is not perfect, and this dictates the use of some excess air to assure complete combustion from all burners. On most units it is possible to operate with as little as 5 to 7 percent excess air at the furnace outlet at full load, and with extra care in design and operation, some large utility-type boilers have operated with as little as 2.5 percent excess air without excessive unburned combustible loss.

At partial loads on all units regardless of fuel fired, it is necessary to increase the excess air as the load is reduced. If all burners are kept in service, the furnace temperature and the air velocity, which provides burner turbulence, decrease with decrease in load. Raising the excess air tends to compensate for the deterioration of these items as the load drops. Also it may be desirable to operate with higher than normal excess air to maintain steam temperature or minimize corrosion of the "cold" end of the unit. Increased excess air is desirable even when the number of burners in use is reduced at lower

loads. Burner dampers are designed not to close tightly to permit the air to protect the idle burner(s) from overheating by radiant heat from nearby operating burners.

Burner pulsation

One of the most mystifying problems associated with gas burners and, to a much less degree, with oil burners is that of burner pulsation. It appears to result from certain combinations of combustion chamber size and configuration coupled with some characteristic of the burners, perhaps too perfect mixing of fuel and air at the burner. When one or more burners on a large unit start to pulsate, it may become alarmingly violent, at times shaking the whole boiler. Making an adjustment of only one burner may start or stop pulsation. At times only minor burner adjustments eliminate the pulsation. In other instances, it is necessary to alter the burners. This may involve modifying the gas ports, impinging gas streams on one another, or using some other device that effectively alters the mixing of the gas with the air.

To avoid pulsations, burner and boiler manufacturers incorporate the latest information available into the designs of burners and furnaces. However a better understanding of this problem is needed.

Operating range or load range

In the past in particular there have been many claims regarding operating or load range of a particular burner. Erroneous interpretation of test results has led to performance predictions which could not be substantiated. There have been misunderstandings between vendors and users because of interpretation of results. The most persistent differences in opinion are in the acceptability of flame appearance, the length of time the unit is operated at minimum load, and the evaluation of potential hazard from deposits that may occur during the low-load

tests. The following considerations are basic to understanding the difficulties arising from low-load operation.

Large boilers with air heaters have a sizable "heat inertia" which requires more than 2 hours at full load for temperatures throughout the unit to stabilize. Conversely a significant time period is necessary for them to retrograde on dropping load.

A brief drop in load, e.g., for an hour or two, may cause no problems with ignition stability or the deposit of combustible products. However, if the low load is held for a longer period, four hours or more, operation may become intolerable toward the end of the period because of a drop in temperature of the furnace and the combustion air. In rare instances, a load drop for less than an hour may cause trouble. Some boiler installations require carrying low loads consistently over weekends. All such service demands must be taken into account in the design and selection of burners.

Burner testing

It is customary to determine burner performance by testing a single burner in a small furnace. This facilitates flame observation and determination of capacity. However conclusions from such tests, particularly at low loads, must be applied with caution in commercial installations comprising several burners.

On large units with many burners, there may be so little air flow at low loads that severe stratification of air in the windbox results. On tall units the difference in the natural stack effect between the bottom and top rows of burners may alter the quantity of air reaching individual burners.

At extremely low loads, firing oil or gas, the fuel piping itself can introduce poor distribution and, accordingly, affect burner operation. For a given supply pressure some burners may have adequate fuel while others do not receive enough to keep them operating. Thus, from the

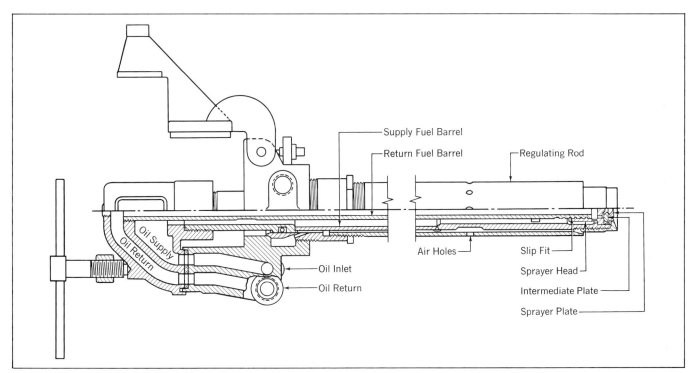

Fig. 7 Mechanical return-flow oil atomizer assembly.

standpoint of fuel and air distribution at low loads, the minimum load possible on a multiple-burner installation usually is higher than that of a single-burner installation.

The design of the furnace has a considerable effect on the minimum safe capacity of a burner, e.g., a small, shallow refractory-walled furnace retains heat longer and preserves ignitability better than a large water-cooled furnace.

Starting cold boilers and operating at low loads

Placing a cold boiler in service requires firing at low heat input for a long period to avoid expansion difficulties and the possible overheating of superheaters or reheaters. Low pressure (200 psi) boilers without superheaters require about an hour, but high pressure, larger units may require 4 to 6 hours for start-up. During this starting period combustion efficiency is poor and, especially with the heavier oils, considerable quantities of unburned combustible may escape.

The low-ignition temperature of gas makes it an ideal fuel for starting purposes. However, extreme care must be taken to avoid a momentary interruption in the flame. Since furnace temperatures are low at these times, there is less latitude for error than when the boiler is in full operation.

Fuel oil probably is potentially more hazardous than gas for starting operations. Generally, there is no problem of ignition stability, and the fire will normally look quite clear especially after the first hour of firing. At this point, low pressure boilers are ready to take the load, and higher pressure boilers, usually equipped with air heaters, are beginning to supply preheated air to the burners which helps the combustion process. However, the furnace temperature is still well below normal and, despite the clean-looking fire, the stack discharge usually will be dark grey in color. Careful inspection may reveal that air heater and economizer surfaces have accumulated significant deposits of oil or oily soot. If such deposits are allowed to accumulate, they are rather easily ignited, and a fire, once started, is difficult to extinguish. To reduce the incidence of fires, some operators use soot-blowers that blow steam continuously on the surfaces of regenerative-type air heaters as they rotate in the flue gas stream.

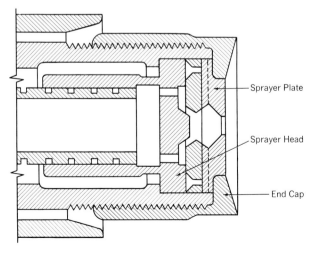

Fig. 8 Mechanical return-flow oil atomizer detail at furnace end of atomizer assembly showing sprayer head, sprayer plate and end cap.

Sprayer Plate

Sprayer Head

End Cap

For those cases where oil must be used for start-up, the following methods of firing are listed, in their order of preference:

1. The safest method producing the cleanest stack, is to use steam atomizers and light fuel oil, No. 1 or 2, with steam or compressed air as the atomizing medium.

2. The second choice is to use steam atomization with fuel oil no heavier than No. 6, heated as required for proper atomization.

3. The third choice is to use steam atomizer nozzles with compressed air for atomization, and fuel oil no heavier than No. 6, heated as required.

Start-up with oil using mechanical atomizers is not recommended because of the amount of oil and soot deposited in economizers and air heaters, creating a fire hazard, particularly in air heaters. Stationary boilers, using mechanical atomizers for oil firing at loads between 20 and 100 percent of maximum, are generally started up with gas or by methods 1, 2 or 3 with oil.

For marine boilers the current practice is to provide steam or air for atomization during start-up. When start-up must be accomplished with mechanical atomizers, No. 6 oil can be used when it is possible to heat this oil to proper viscosity for atomization. Otherwise, No 2 oil is generally used.

Return-flow atomizers are preferable to uniflow mechanical atomizers, as the oil pressure is maintained at higher values giving better atomization when firing rates have to be adjusted downward. A pressure of 600 psi or more is preferred. However, in many marine units, where the maximum oil pressure provided is 300-350 psi, pressures in this range are used for start-up.

Safety precautions

The handling and burning of any fuel is potentially hazardous. Safe handling and operation demand knowledge of the characteristics of the fuel and careful observance of necessary precautions.

Because of the rapid diffusion of gas, any leak of fuel gas into an enclosed space may result in an explosive mixture of air and gas. Oil normally is not in a form where it will disperse readily in air and may have a higher ignition temperature than gas. However, because of the volatile components in fuel oil, explosive mixtures may exist in oil tanks in the space above the oil or in empty tanks, unless they are blanketed with inert gas, which is not normally practicable. Oil tank vents are therefore equipped with a flame-arresting screen to prevent the passage of a flame.

One of the requirements for good combustion (Chapter 6) is intimate mixing of fuel and air. In the case of gaseous fuels and oil (and most other fuels) such mixtures are potentially explosive and can be expected to ignite from a single spark. Therefore these mixtures must never be allowed to exist except inside the combustion chamber at the burner, and then only when the burner is lighted.[*]

This fundamental principle forms the basis for safety precautions and burner lighting and operating sequences.

[*] An exception to this rule is the oil tank, as noted in the preceding paragraph.

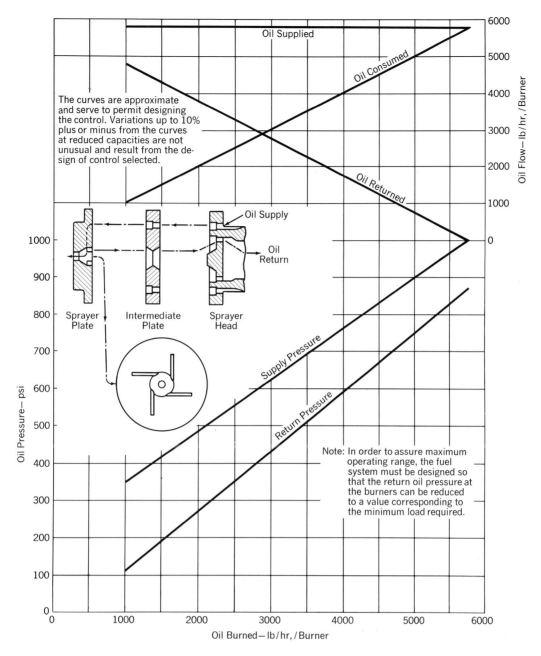

Fig. 9 Characteristic curves for a typical B&W return-flow oil atomizer (mechanical type) based on viscosity required for atomization.

Three rules are of prime importance, whether in a manual or automatic system:

1. Never allow oil or gas to accumulate anywhere, other than in a tank or lines which form part of the fuel supply system. The slightest odor of gas should be cause for alarm. Steps should be taken immediately to ventilate the area thoroughly and then locate the source.

2. Purge the furnace and setting completely before introducing any light or spark, or before relighting after all flame has been extinguished. On a multiple-burner unit, burners may be ignited without a purge if one or more are in service already.

3. Have a lighted torch or spark-producing device in operation before introducing any fuel into a furnace.

To prevent a backfire or flareback of flame into the fireroom or forced air supply system (depending on the installation) the torch or ignitor must be properly placed with respect to the burner and must provide a flame or spark of adequate size continuously until stable ignition of a main burner is accomplished.

Other items essential to safe burner operation are:

4. Maintenance of a positive air flow through the burners, into the furnace, and up the stack.

5. Maintenance of adequate oil pressure and temperature for atomization, and also adequate steam or air pressure in the case of steam or air atomizers.

Compliance with these rules, particularly the first one, requires good housekeeping throughout the plant

and an operating staff alert to any abnormal conditions.

To observe the last four rules, automatic control installations may include:

a) Purge interlocks, e.g., requiring a specified minimum air flow for a specific time period sufficient to purge the setting before the fuel trip valve can be opened.

b) Flame detector. Each burner should have its own flame detector connected to an alarm and interlocked to shut off the fuel to the burner it serves upon flame failure.

c) Closed-position switches for burner shut-off valves, requiring that all shut-off valves be closed to permit opening the fuel trip valve.

d) Shut-off of fuel on failure of forced or induced draft fan.

e) Shut-off of fuel in the event of low fuel pressure (and low steam or air pressure to oil atomizers, where appropriate).

f) Shut-off of fuel in event of low oil temperature.

g) Shut-off of fuel in gas-fired units in event of excessive fuel-gas pressure.

Sealing off air intakes to boiler rooms is a safety violation in plants where combustion air for the burners is supplied from inside the building. In some of these plants, where the air flow is substantial, the boiler room may become uncomfortable for personnel, particularly in extremely cold weather. Personnel comfort should not be provided by reducing air supply to the boiler room, since limiting air supply to the burners causes burner pulsations.

Any of the commonly used fuels can be burned with safety when using the proper equipment with operating skill. The hazard is introduced when, through carelessness or misoperation of a piece of equipment, the fuel is no longer burned in a safe manner. While a malfunction should be corrected promptly, there should be no panic. Investigations of explosions of boiler furnaces equipped with good recording equipment, reveal that the conditions leading to the explosion in most cases had existed for a considerable time—long enough for someone to have taken unhurried corrective action before the accident happened. The old concern that malfunctions of safety equipment cause frequent, unnecessary, unit trips is not consistent with the facts.

Chapter 8

Coal processing and handling

The purpose of coal preparation is to improve the quality of the coal or to make it suitable for a specific purpose by (a) cleaning to remove inorganic impurities, (b) special treatment (such as dedusting), or (c) sizing — crushing and screening, or both.

Economic factors

The properties and quantities of impurities in coal are of major importance in the design and operation of steam generating equipment. Although boilers are often designed and equipped to use a wide range of coals satisfactorily, no boiler installation will perform equally well with all types of coal. All coals have certain properties which place limitations on their most advantageous use. These limitations are particularly stringent for many of the older installations.

To define the limitations of various types of coal-burning equipment in service, specifications covering several important properties of coal are necessary. For certain types of stokers, for instance, a minimum ash-softening temperature, maximum ash content, and maximum sulfur content of the coal are specified to prevent excessive clinkering. For pulverized-coal firing, it may be necessary to specify ash-slagging and ash-fouling parameters for a dry-ash installation. For Cyclone-Furnace firing, it may be necessary, in addition, to specify a maximum viscosity of the slag at a minimum temperature for removal of the liquid slag. Within these and other equipment limitations there is usually a wide range of coals that can be satisfactorily burned in a specific steam boiler, and the choice depends primarily on economics — which coal will produce steam at the lowest overall cost, including cost at the mine, shipment, storage, handling, operating and maintenance costs. To burn a wide range of coals often requires a larger initial investment than would otherwise be necessary. However, fuel cost is usually the predominating factor because it represents so large a part of the overall operating cost. The fuel bill for a year, for instance, may equal the initial cost of the entire steam generating unit.

Cleaning to remove inorganic impurities

Because of a general lowering of quality of raw coal in recent years, the need for coal cleaning has increased. Among the factors contributing to the lowering of coal quality are:

1. Depletion of some of the high-quality coal seams.
2. Greater use of continuous-mining machines.
3. Increased production by strip and auger mining.

In the U.S. the use of mechanical methods in mining bituminous coal and lignite has greatly increased. Mechanical loading of underground production increased from 1% in 1925 to about 96% in 1968. The most important change of recent years was the introduction of continuous-mining machines. Production by these machines increased from three million tons in 1950 to 165 million tons in 1968, or 48 percent of the bituminous coal produced in underground mines. Auger mining, introduced about 1945, accounted for 1.5 million tons of production in 1952 compared with 15.3 million tons, or 2.8% of bituminous coal and lignite production in 1968. In 1925, 3.2% of the bituminous coal and lignite was strip mined compared with 34.1% in 1968.

Growth of mechanical cleaning at bituminous coal and lignite mines in the U.S. has increased continuously from 4% in 1925 to 65.7% in 1960 and 1961. From 1962 to 1969 mechanical cleaning of coal from underground mines increased from 71.3 to 73% and it also increased at auger mines from 14 to 16.8%, but cleaning of coal from strip mines decreased from 53.3 to 47%. Of all U.S. bituminous coal and lignite produced in 1968, 62.5% was mechanically cleaned.

In the anthracite fields of northeastern Pennsylvania during the past several years, the percentage of underground production has decreased. In 1958, 51% of the 21.2 million tons of anthracite produced was from underground mines, 32% from strip mines, 14% from culm banks, and 3% from river dredgings. In 1968, only 21.3% of the 11.5 million tons produced was from underground mines, 41.0% from strip mines, 32.4% from culm banks,

and 5.3% from river dredgings. Most of the fresh-mined anthracite produced in 1967 was mechanically cleaned.

The effect of cleaning on the properties of coal cannot be generalized because of differences in coal characteristics. For example, the ash-fusion temperatures of one coal may be lowered by cleaning and those of another raised. Some reduction in sulfur content is usually obtainable and is invariably a benefit, as experience indicates that the higher the sulfur content of coal the greater the likelihood of spontaneous combustion in storage and corrosion of conveyors, bunkers, and heat-absorbing surfaces in the lower-temperature zones of steam generating equipment.

The principal benefit of cleaning is the reduction in ash content. With ash content reduced, shipping costs and the requirements for storage and handling decrease because of the smaller quantity of coal necessary per unit of heating value. Also, an increase in boiler efficiency may be realized because of less ash deposition on heat-absorbing surfaces.

The cost of cleaning must be balanced against the benefits obtained. Items included in the cleaning costs are cleaning-plant operating costs, capital charges, the value of the coal in the discarded refuse, and the cost of disposing of the refuse. In 1946 about 25 million tons of refuse were discarded by bituminous coal and lignite cleaning plants. This amounted to 15.3% of raw coal supplied to the cleaning plants. In comparison, for the year 1968 the percentage of refuse to raw coal increased to 22.1%, and more than 97 million tons of refuse were discarded. Generally the quantity of coal lost in the refuse increases as the ash content is reduced, hence the "coal loss" portion of cleaning cost is directly related to the ash reduction obtained. A careful evaluation of the benefits from cleaning is required to determine whether this loss plus the other cleaning costs are justified.

By balancing shipping costs against cleaning costs, an optimum reduction in ash content can be established which will give a minimum delivered cost of coal, neglecting differences in handling costs and performance at the steam plant. Because of freight costs, it is generally found that an increase in shipping distance justifies an increase in the cost of cleaning. This is illustrated graphically in Fig. 1 for coal from strip-mine operation.

Nature of impurities in coal

As found in seams, coal is a heterogeneous mixture of organic and inorganic materials. Not only are there large differences in the properties of coal from different seams but also of coal removed from different elevations and different locations in a single seam.

Impurities can be divided into two general classifications—inherent and removable. The inherent impurities are inseparably combined with the coal. The removable impurities are segregated and can be eliminated, by available cleaning methods, to the extent economically justified.

Mineral matter is always present in raw coal and forms ash when the coal is burned. The ash-forming mineral matter is usually classified as either inherent or extraneous. Ash-forming material organically combined with the coal is considered as inherent mineral matter; this portion came from the chemical elements existing in the plants from which the coal was formed. Generally the inherent mineral matter contained in coal is about 2% or less of the total ash. Extraneous mineral matter is ash-forming material that is foreign to the plant material from which the coal was formed; the bulk of this material is from detrital matter which settled into the deposit, crystalline deposits from water that penetrated into the coal through fracture cracks and cleavages both during and after coal formation, or from saline deposits from water before and during formation of peat from which the coal was formed. It consists usually of slate, shale, sandstone, or limestone and includes pieces ranging from microscopic size to thick layers. Mined coal may also include shale, sandstone, clay or other extraneous mineral matter from the roof and floor of the mine.

Sulfur is always present in raw coal in amounts ranging from traces to as high as 8% or more. This results in the emission of sulfur oxides in the stack gases when the coal is burned. Since control of air pollution is now a national concern, some important areas already have laws or regulations prohibiting the use of fuels containing more than a certain amount of sulfur (Chapter 18). As a consequence the demand for low-sulfur coals has increased. Table 1 shows the estimated remaining coal reserves of the U.S. by sulfur content and state as of January 1, 1974.

Three forms of sulfur are recognized as occurring in coal—pyritic sulfur, which is sulfur combined with iron in the form of mineral pyrite or marcasite; organic sulfur, which is sulfur combined with the coal substance; and sulfate sulfur, in the form of calcium or iron sulfate.

Sulfate sulfur in coal as mined is usually not over 0.1% and consequently not very important. Table 2 shows the distribution of pyritic and organic sulfur in several different coals. Pyritic sulfur in coal may occur in lenses,

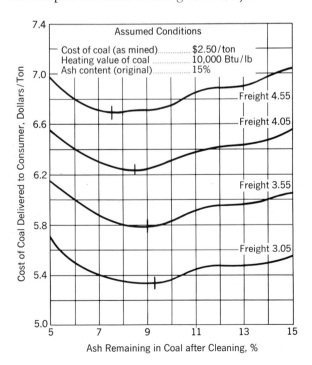

Fig. 1 Optimum reduction in ash content of coal for minimum delivered cost. An increase in cleaning cost is justified as shipping distance increases.

Table 1
Demonstrated total underground and surface coal reserve base
of the United States on January 1, 1974
(Million tons)

State	Sulfur Range, Percent				
	≤1.0	1.1–3.0	>3.0	Unknown	Total[a]
Alabama	624.7	1,099.9	16.4	1,239.4	2,981.8
Alaska	11,458.4	184.2	.0	.0	11,645.4
Arizona	173.3	176.7	.0	.0	350.0
Arkansas	81.2	463.1	46.3	74.3	665.7
Colorado	7,475.5	786.2	47.3	6,547.3	14,869.2
Georgia	0.3	.0	.0	0.2	0.5
Illinois	1,095.1	7,341.4	42,968.9	14,256.2	65,664.8
Indiana	548.8	3,305.8	5,262.4	1,504.1	10,622.6
Iowa	1.5	226.7	2,105.9	549.2	2,884.9
Kansas	.0	309.2	695.6	383.2	1,388.1
Kentucky-East	6,558.4	3,321.8	299.5	2,729.3	12,916.7
Kentucky-West	0.2	564.4	9,243.9	2,815.9	12,623.9
Maryland	135.1	690.5	187.4	34.6	1,048.2
Michigan	4.6	85.4	20.9	7.0	118.2
Missouri	.0	182.0	5,226.0	4,080.5	9,487.3
Montana	101,646.6	4,115.0	502.6	2,116.7	108,396.2
New Mexico	3,575.3	793.4	0.9	27.5	4,394.8
North Carolina	.0	.0	.0	31.7	31.7
North Dakota	5,389.0	10,325.4	268.7	15.0	16,003.0
Ohio	134.4	6,440.9	12,534.3	1,872.0	21,077.2
Oklahoma	275.0	326.6	241.4	450.5	1,294.2
Oregon	1.5	0.3	.0	.0	1.8
Pennsylvania	7,318.3	16,913.6	3,799.6	2,954.2	31,000.6
South Dakota	103.1	287.9	35.9	1.0	428.0
Tennessee	204.8	533.2	156.6	88.0	986.7
Texas	659.8	1,884.6	284.1	444.0	3,271.9
Utah	1,968.5	1,546.7	49.4	478.3	4,042.5
Virginia	2,140.1	1,163.5	14.1	330.0	3,649.9
Washington	603.5	1,265.5	39.0	45.1	1,954.0
West Virginia	14,092.1	14,006.2	6,823.3	4,652.5	39,589.8
Wyoming	33,912.3	14,657.4	1,701.1	3,060.3	53,336.1
Total[a]	200,181.1	92,997.6	92,671.1	50,837.7	436,725.4

[a] Data may not add to totals shown due to independent rounding.
Source, Bureau of Mines bulletin, *Coal—Bituminous and Lignite*, 1974.

Fig. 2 Large quantities of coal are transported to electric utility plants by barge.

Table 2
Chemical distribution of sulfur in various coals*

Location of Mine	Coal Bed	Total Sulfur, %	Pyritic Sulfur, %	Organic Sulfur, %
Washington County, Pa.	Pittsburgh	1.13	0.35	0.78
Franklin County, Ill.	No. 6	2.52	1.50	1.02
Pike County, Ky.	Freeburn	0.46	0.13	0.33
McDowell County, W.Va.	Pocahontas, No.3	0.55	0.08	0.46
Walker County, Ala.	Pratt	1.62	0.81	0.81
Meigs County, Ohio	8A	2.51	1.61	0.86
Clearfield County, Pa.	Upper Freeport	3.56	2.82	0.74
Boone County, W.Va.	Eagle	2.48	1.47	1.01
Clay County, Ind.	No. III	3.92	2.13	1.79
Coshocton County, Ohio	No. 6	4.69	2.63	2.06
Muhlenburg County, W. Ky.	No. 11	5.20	3.20	2.00
Mercer County, N.D.	Lignite	1.00	0.38	0.62
Henry County, Mo.	Tebo	5.40	3.60	1.80
Henry County, Mo.	Bevier	8.20	6.39	1.22
Kittitas County, Wash.	Big Dirty	0.40	0.09	0.31

* Sulfate sulfur not included.

bands, veins, joints, balls, fossils, or finely disseminated particles; pyrites may vary in size from a few microns to balls several feet in diameter. The larger pieces are generally removed in cleaning the coal. However the finely divided pyrites and organic sulfur must be considered, with inherent mineral matter, as nonremovable impurities on the basis of current technology and economics.

Moisture, which is inherent in coal, may be considered to be an impurity. It varies with different ranks of coal, increasing for lower-rank coals from 1 to 2% in anthracite to 45% or more in lignite. Moisture that collects on the exposed surfaces of coal is commonly called "surface moisture" (Chapter 5), and is removable.

Cleaning methods

The principal methods used in the U.S. for cleaning anthracite and bituminous coals are: (a) cleaning at mine face; (b) picking out impurities manually or mechanically; (c) froth flotation; and (d) gravity concentration.

Cleaning at mine face

When manual cutting and loading of coal are used, it is possible to minimize the quantity of impurities. In cutting, the miner can more easily distinguish between coal and rock, and in loading he can often discard visible impurities. With mechanical cutting and loading of coal, the miner has much less control over the product loaded; however, it is often possible to follow mining practices that will reduce the quantity of impurities.

Efforts to reduce the impurities loaded in the mine usually result in increased mining costs, hence economics plays an important part in determining the amount of cleaning done. In general, cleaning at the mine face is greatly reduced when mechanical mining methods are employed. The wide use of continuous-mining machines has resulted in still further reduction in cleaning at the mine face.

Fig. 3 Shaking table used in hand-picking coal.

Picking by hand or mechanical means

Hand picking is the earliest method used in cleaning coal at the mine. A shaking table used for hand picking is shown in Fig. 3. The run-of-mine coal is screened, and only the oversize material, usually 4 in. or more, goes to the picking table. Refuse from hand-picking tables may run from 50 to 60% coal, and it is common practice to crush this refuse and clean it by mechanical means.

Many mechanical picking devices employ differences in physical picking dimensions of coal and impurities as a means of separation. Bituminous coal fractures into rough cubes, whereas slate and shale normally fracture as thin slabs. A slot type of flat picker that can be installed on shaker screens, shaking conveyors, and chutes is shown diagrammatically in Fig. 4.

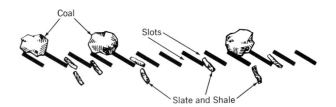

Fig. 4 Rejection of flat refuse by slot shaker.

Froth flotation

While froth-flotation cleaning is of long standing for ore separation and has been widely used in Europe for cleaning coal, its application for this purpose in the U.S. is of recent origin. Its use has greatly increased within the last few years. This method can be used in cleaning smaller sizes, 1/10 in. by 0 and particularly smaller than 48 mesh, a size for which a market has developed.

The incoming coal feed is agitated in a controlled amount of water, air and reagents that cause a surface froth to form, the bubbles of which selectively attach themselves to coal particles and keep them buoyant while the heavier particles of pyrite, slate and shale remain dispersed in the water. The components thus segregated can be suitably diverted to salvage and waste, respectively.

Gravity concentration

Removal of segregated impurities in coal by gravity concentration is the most widely used method of mechanical cleaning. This method is based on the principle that

heavier particles separate from lighter when settling in a fluid. This principle is applicable because most common solid impurities are heavier than coal, (Table 3).

Table 3
Specific gravities of coal and impurities

Material	Specific Gravity
Bituminous coal	1.12-1.35
Bone coal	1.35-1.7
Carbonaceous shale	1.6-2.2
Shale	2.0-2.6
Clay	1.8-2.2
Pyrite	4.8-5.2

The commercial processes used in gravity concentration can be divided into two main classifications—wet and dry (or pneumatic). In the former, water is the separating medium, and in the latter (generally confined to coal sizes ¾ in. or less) air is used as the separating medium.

In gravity concentration it is possible to separate the coal into two or more gravity fractions, subject to the loss of some small particles into the separating medium. Assuming separation is made at a specific gravity of 1.5, particles with a specific gravity less than 1.5 will be recovered as clean coal and particles of higher specific gravity will go to refuse. The quantity of impurities found in the clean coal and the quantity of coal found in the refuse depend on the quantity of impurities in the coal, the specific gravity at which separation is made, and the efficiency of the separation.

Washability characteristics of coal

In the design and operation of coal-cleaning plants, careful studies are made to determine the properties of the various specific-gravity fractions and the variation of these properties with coal sizing.

In most cleaning processes, the low-gravity fractions (below 1.4 sp. gr.) that represent the relatively low-ash coal and the high-gravity impurities (above 1.8 sp. gr.) are easily separated. The middlings material (1.4 to 1.8 sp. gr.) is most difficult to separate.

Where the segregated impurities in the coal are soft compared to the coal, more impurities will be found in the fine-coal sizes. Where the segregated impurities are hard compared to the coal, more of the impurities will be found in the larger-size coal.

There is a general correlation between specific gravity and ash content, although the relation differs for various coals. Ash contents corresponding to various specific gravities for bituminous coal are:

Table 4
Ash contents of various gravity
fractions in bituminous coal

Specific Gravity	Ash Content, %
1.3-1.4	1-5
1.4-1.5	5-10
1.5-1.6	10-35
1.6-1.8	35-60
1.8-1.9	60-75
1.9 & above	75-90

"Float-and-sink" tests run in a laboratory provide data useful for rating and controlling cleaning equipment and evaluating efficiencies obtained, both quantitative and qualitative. However the results from these laboratory tests cannot actually be duplicated in washery operation.

Cleaning by gravity concentration

Wet processes

About 95% of bituminous-coal and lignite cleaning is accomplished by wet processes. Table 5 lists the methods and types of equipment generally used and the extent of application of each method, expressed in percent.

Table 5
Types of wet processes used for cleaning of
bituminous coals and lignite

Equipment or Method Used	Percent of Cleaning Done by Wet Processes
Jigs	46.7
Dense-media method	29.2
Concentrating tables	13.9
Flotation method	2.6
Classifiers	1.4
Launders	1.3
Total	95.1

Jigs. In jigs, pulsating currents of water pass through a bed of coal resting on a screen plate. At the start of the upward flow of water through the coal bed, the coal is at rest. The upward flow, called the "pulsion stroke," opens the bed and brings it into a mobile state. The bed is closed and brought to rest during the downward flow of water, called the "suction stroke." Optimum conditions for classification occur at periods during the pulsation and suction strokes, when the mixture is of high density with freedom of movement between particles. These conditions are utilized to separate the two fractions and divert them into separate streams.

Some types of jigs require rather careful sizing of the feed coal for best results, while with others, such as the Baum jig, which take a wide range of sizing, fair results are possible even for the smaller sizes. The water pulsations in the Baum jig are produced by air pressure. In one application of the Baum jig for cleaning Roslyn bed coal (from Washington State) the ash was reduced from 15.4% in the raw coal to 10.5% in the washed coal. In this case, 95% of the weight of the raw coal washed ranged in screen size from 20 mesh to 1-½in. and over; 73% of this weight ranged in size from ⅜ in. to ½ in. and over. Weight of the refuse from the operation was about 18.7% of the raw coal.

Dense-media method. This method utilizes the principle of the laboratory float-and-sink tests on a commercial basis. Coal is immersed in a medium of specific gravity intermediate between that of coal and refuse. Hence the impurities sink and the coal floats. A well-known type is the Chance-Cone, shown in Fig. 5. The separating medium is a suspension of magnetite or fine sand in water. An upward current of water and stirring are provided to keep the separating medium in the proper suspension to give the specific gravity required for the separation. This

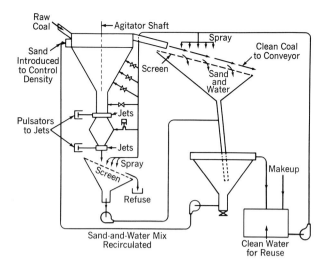

Fig. 5 Chance-Cone dense-media method of cleaning coal.

method is widely accepted for cleaning anthracite, and its use in the bituminous field has increased so that currently about 30% of the bituminous coal cleaned is by this method.

Concentrating tables. Washing or concentrating tables are used primarily for cleaning small coal—down to 50-mesh sizing.

Dry processes

Within recent years pneumatic or dry processes have been used for only 5% of all bituminous coal cleaned in the U.S. and are generally applied to coal ½ in. or less in size. The raw coal is often screened ahead of the cleaning plant so that the oversize may be cleaned by a wet process and the undersize by pneumatic means. For successful results by pneumatic means, the feed coal should have a uniformly low surface-moisture content.

The principal type of pneumatic cleaning process uses tables equipped with riffles with air as the separating medium. Admitted through holes in the tables, the air is blown up through the beds of coal. The motion of the tables plus the air flow segregate the coal and impurities, bringing low-gravity fractions to the top of the beds, whence they move down across the tables in a direction perpendicular to the riffles. The heavy impurities settle in the riffles and move along the riffle troughs, discharging at the end opposite the feed. The middlings move diagonally across the bed. This permits separation of two or three products, at desired specific gravities, by the selection of proper points of withdrawal.

Air used in pneumatic-cleaning methods can be passed through cyclone separators and bag filters for recovery of the fines from the coal. The recovered fines can be remixed in the clean coal if their ash content is not excessive.

Special treatment

Dedusting

Dedusting is a type of air separation with classification according to size. Air passed through the coal entrains a large percentage of the fines. The fine coal is recovered from the air with cyclone separators and bag filters. This process is often employed to remove fines ahead of wet cleaning. The fines, if low enough in ash, may be added to the cleaned coal or disposed of separately.

Before returning the fines to the larger size stream in the cleaning process, it may be necessary to add water to reduce dustiness. The quantity of water required may be decreased by small amounts of commercial wetting agents, such as those made from organic derivatives, which reduce surface tension.

Dewatering—mechanical and heat drying

Dewatering of coal plays an important part in the preparation of coal at the mines. The larger-size coal (above ⅜ in.) can be easily dewatered, and occasionally natural drainage is provided by special hoppers or bins, screen conveyors, perforated-bucket elevators, or fixed screens (radial or bent-sieve screens are finding greater use). However, when the fine sizes must be dried or when lower moisture content is required for the large coal, mechanical dewatering or thermal drying is necessary.

Mechanical dewatering devices may be shaker screens, vibrating screens, filters, centrifuges, and thickening or desliming equipment. Thermal drying is used to obtain low-moisture-content coal, especially for the finer sizes. Various types of thermal dryers are rotary, cascade, reciprocating screen, conveyor, suspension (including flash and venturi dryers), and the fluidized bed. The last type is used for more than half of the coal thermally dried.

Practically all heat dryers require some form of dust collector to recover the fines—especially when the smaller-size coal is dried. Inertial-type collectors, such as the centrifugal cyclones or the wet-type collector, may be used. Final cleanup is done with bag filters or a water-spray system. Some bag filters permit temperatures as high as 550F.

Dustproofing

Oil and calcium chloride are commonly used for dustproofing coal. When coal is sprayed with oil, the film causes some dust particles to adhere to the larger pieces of coal and others to agglomerate into larger lumps not easily airborne. This treatment, usually applied at the mine, is currently in use for about 44 million tons of bituminous coal yearly, representing about 13% of the cleaned coal. Another 1% of cleaned bituminous coal is treated, for allaying dust, with both calcium chloride and oil. Calcium chloride absorbs moisture from the air, providing a wet surface to which the dust adheres.

The amount of oil required for effective dust treatment depends on the coal size, its porosity, and possibly its wetness. For a given coal size and dustiness index, somewhat more oil is required for wet coal. Coals of high porosity require a high-viscosity oil to prevent its absorption into the coal. Small coal sizes require more treatment than larger sizes. In general, the amount of spray oil used ranges from 1 to 8 quarts per ton of coal.

Effective treatment is accomplished by spraying a stream of coal falling from chutes or loading booms. Well-designed hoods prevent waste of oil and insure better treatment. Larger-size coal may be sprayed while on conveyors. In either case, hot or cold oil may be used.

When slack-size steam coal is to be used in high-pressure high-temperature boilers, oil alone is the preferential dust treatment.

Freezeproofing

To prevent freezing of coal during transit or storage, two methods of freezeproofing are recommended. Spray oil may be used and it is applied to the coal in the same manner as dustproofing. Cost of this application may range from 8 to 15 cents per ton of coal. As an alternate and less costly method, the car hoppers may be heavily sprayed with oil. Another freezeproofing method is thermal drying of the fine coal, especially for the high-moisture-content low-rank coals. Addition of salt or calcium chloride is not recommended, since their use may accelerate ash deposition or external corrosion of boiler heating surfaces (*see Chapter 15*).

Sizing by crushing and screening

In the United States, the earliest practice in the sizing of bituminous coal was to hand-load the lump coal and leave the small coal in the mine. Until about 1880, when mechanical stokers were introduced, practically all boilers were hand-fired with lump coal, and in early surface-preparation plants at the mines it was the custom merely to screen out the lump coal and discard the slack. With the adoption of the mechanical stoker, the demand for smaller coal sizes increased, and equipment was installed at the mines to prepare the smaller sizes. The demand for smaller coal sizes again increased with the development of pulverized-coal firing. As early as 1946, approximately 33% of all the bituminous coal shipped was under 2-in. maximum size. Because of this trend toward smaller sizing, the price differential between run-of-mine and slack has been eliminated for many coals.

Sizing operations at steam plants are usually confined to crushing and pulverizing. Except for removing large impurities by the use of simple grids or Bradford breakers, screening at the plant is not generally required. For stoker-fired installations it is customary to specify coal of the proper size to suit the stoker, so that no sizing is necessary at the plant. For pulverized firing, the coal is ground to very fine sizing, after any necessary crushing, in pulverizers generally incorporated as a part of the firing equipment. Crushers are used for the coarser sizing required for Cyclone Furnaces. When intended for pulverized firing, common practice for steam plants is to specify a maximum coal size with no limitation on the percentage of fines, so that the coal delivered will be suitable for crushing and pulverizing in the available equipment.

Some pulverized-coal or stoker-fired boiler plants install crushers for use when a larger coal size such as run-of-mine is more economical. When the more economical coal is a slack that does not require sizing, the crusher may be bypassed. In plants where both pulverized-coal firing and stoker firing are used, all the coal supplied may be sized to suit the stokers, and the portion going to the pulverizers is crushed when necessary. This simplifies the storage and handling facilities.

Because of the wide diversity in use and characteristics of bituminous and lignitic coals, no uniformly accepted sizings have been established. The screen sizes generally employed in specifications conform to the ASTM Standard D 431, *Designating the Size of Coal from its Screen Analysis*. Standard sizings of anthracite are definitely established, as given in ASTM Standard D 310 (*see Table 23, Chapter 5*).

Sizing requirements

Generally acceptable coal sizings for various types of fuel-burning equipment are given in the chapters covering the equipment. The degradation in coal sizing resulting from handling and slacking is an important consideration in establishing sizing specifications for steam plants, where the maximum permissible quantity of fines in the coal is set by firing-equipment limitations.

Crushers and breakers

Many types of crushing and screening equipment are used commercially. Representative types are described below:

Bradford breaker. The Bradford breaker (Fig. 6) breaks the coal to predetermined size and rejects larger refuse and tramp iron. It has a large cylinder rotating at approximately 20 rpm. The cylinder consists of steel screen plates; the size of the screen openings determines the size of the crushed coal. The breaking action is accomplished by dropping the coal. The coal fed at one end of the cylinder is picked up by lifting-shelves and carried up until the angle of the shelf permits the coal to drop. The amount of fines is kept to a minimum because the force (gravity) used in shattering the coal is low. The Bradford breaker may be used at mine or plant.

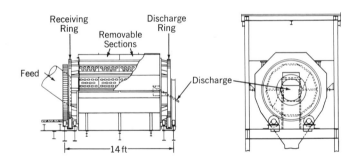

Fig. 6 Bradford breaker, for use at mine and plant.

Single-roll crusher. The elements of a single-roll crusher are illustrated in Fig. 7. This crusher consists of a single roll equipped with teeth designed to force the coal against a plate to produce the crushing action. To prevent jamming by large impurities, such as tramp iron, the roll is permitted to rise or the plate to swing away, allowing the impurities to pass through. The single-roll crusher is one of the older types and is commonly used for reducing run-of-mine bituminous coal to a maximum size of 1-¼ to 6 in. The abrasive action between the coal and the plate produces a relatively large quantity of fines.

Double-roll crusher. In this type (Fig. 8) crushing action is obtained by feeding coal between the two toothed rolls. The mating faces of both rolls move in a downward direction with the coal. The size of the roll teeth and the

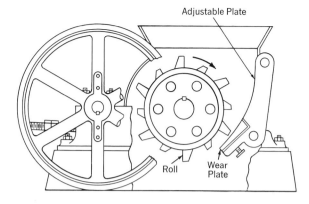

Fig. 7 Single-roll coal crusher—diagrammatic section.

spacing between rolls determine the sizing of the coal. Means for passing impurities is provided by spring-loading one of the rolls. Double-roll crushers are used for reducing run-of-mine coal to smaller sizes at mine-preparation and steam plants.

Hammer mill and ring crusher. Mills of this type (Figs. 9 and 10) employ the centrifugal force of swinging hammers or rings striking the coal to produce the crushing action. The coal is admitted at the top, and the hammers or rings strike the coal downward. The coal discharges through grate bars at the bottom. The spacing of the bars determines the maximum size of the finished product. Usually a trap is provided for collection and removal of tramp iron impurities.

The crushing action produces considerable fines, consequently these mills are not used when fines are objectionable. They are used to reduce run-of-mine coal to sizes such as ¾″ x 0 and for further crushing at both the preparation and steam plants for sizing feed coal for stokers and pulverizers. Reversible hammer mill crushers are used to prepare coal for use in Cyclone Furnaces.

Screens

Gravity bar screen or grizzly. The gravity bar screen was the first type of screening equipment used in the surface preparation of coal. It consists of a number of sloped parallel bars. The width of the openings between bars, the slope, and the length of the bars determine the separating size. The bars have tapered cross sections with openings between bars smaller on the top side than on the bottom; hence, any coal piece entering an opening can drop through freely. Bar screens are used at mine-preparation plants for production of modified run-of-mine or for removal of undersize ahead of a crusher.

Revolving screen. A revolving screen consists of a slowly rotating cylinder set with a slight downward slope parallel to the axis. The envelope of the cylinder is a perforated plate or a wire cloth, the size of the perforations determining the separating size. Because of the repeated tumbling received by the oversize in passing through the cylinder, considerable breakage of coal occurs. For this reason revolving screens are not used for sizes larger than about 3 inches. Since only a small portion of the screen surface is covered with coal, the capacity per sq ft of screen surface is low.

Shaker screen. A shaker screen is a screen mounted in a rectangular frame. This screen may be horizontal or sloped slightly downward from the feed end to the discharge end. If the screen is horizontal, it is given a differential motion to convey the coal along the screen. In the bituminous coal industry, shaker screens are more widely used than any other type for sizing and dewatering larger coal sizes.

Vibrating screen. Vibrating screens are of gravity-feed type with the screen sloped downward from the feed to the discharge end. A high-frequency, low-magnitude vibration is given to the screen by an electric vibrator or other means. The purpose of the vibration is to keep the meshes clear of wedged particles and to stratify the coal so that the fine particles come down in contact with the screen. For screening of fine wet coal, electrical heating of screen cloth is being used more frequently to reduce binding or packing.

Transportation of coal

The total cost, the reliability of supply, and the uniformity of the properties of the coal as received by the consumer are vitally affected by the distance shipped and the means of transportation and local distribution.

In the United States, coal is transported by rail, truck, boat, barge, conveyor belts, or a combination of two or more of these methods. Coal is also transported hydraulically in pipelines. Shipping problems differ widely in different parts of the country. For example, a coal consumer in Wisconsin may be using coal that was transported by rail from West Virginia to Lake Erie where it was reloaded and shipped by boat through the Great Lakes, unloaded, and stored at a dock on Lake Superior. The coal might then be screened to meet a specific requirement, shipped by rail to a local distributing point, and then hauled by truck to the consumer. In contrast to this, a consumer in a coal-producing area might receive coal hauled by truck directly from the mine or receive it via conveyor belt when the mine and plant are within a few miles of each other.

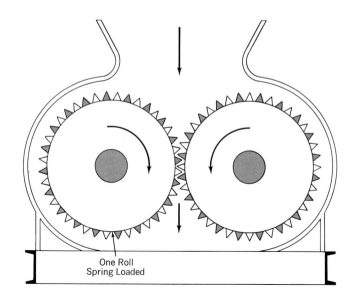

Fig. 8 Double-roll coal crusher—diagrammatic section.

Transportation costs may represent the larger portion of the delivered cost of coal. Roughly 75% of the coal is shipped by rail, and the freight costs may amount to as much as 60 to 70% of the delivered coal cost. To reduce transportation costs, large coal-consuming plants have been located near coal mines (mine mouth) or near rivers where barged coal is available. Electric utilities are now transmitting electricity considerable distances from coal-producing areas to their customers. Use of unit-train shipment of coal, for haulage approaching a thousand miles, is increasing at a rapid rate. During 1968 more than 100 million tons of coal were shipped in unit trains. These trends are expected to continue in order to hold down delivered costs of coal and electrical energy.

Transportation may affect the condition of the coal as received by (1) freezing in transit, (2) change in moisture content, or (3) size degradation.

Where freezing in transit is anticipated, it may be ameliorated, as noted previously, by special treatment of the coal at the point of loading.

Since most coal is shipped at least part of the way in open railroad cars, the moisture content of the coal will depend on sizing, condition at time of loading, and weather conditions during transit. It may be received saturated with moisture or so dry that the fines will blow off as dust. To keep the dust down and minimize loss in transit, the supplier can help by using oil sprays and by demanding tight cars to prevent leakage.

Size degradation depends in large measure on the friability of the coal but it is also affected by the amount of handling and shaking in transit. Fortunately size degradation is not important with pulverized-coal or Cyclone-Furnace firing. To minimize degradation for types of firing equipment where size is important, handling in transit should be reduced by avoiding transfer from one medium to another, where possible.

Handling and storage at consumer's plant

The problems involved in handling and storing coal outside and inside the plant of the consumer have increased almost in proportion to the size of boilers. At a small power plant it may be necessary to handle only 30 tons of coal a day, while many of the larger plants use over 3000 tons a day. Some plants are now being designed to handle about 30,000 tons of coal a day. Intensive efforts have been applied, with fair success, to the development of efficient methods for handling and storing a wide range of tonnage. However, while these methods vary to suit the size of the plant, many of the operations are similar whether the plant is small or large.

Unloading

When the coal is received by rail, the first operation is to unload from the railroad cars. This operation is simple when the coal is dry and flows freely. If the surface moisture of the coal is high, it may be necessary to start the coal flowing by rapping the car sides with a sledge or using a slice bar from above. If this high-moisture coal has been in transit several days in freezing temperatures, it may be frozen into a solid mass, and unloading becomes a real problem. In hot, dry weather the coal, on arrival, may be so dry that a high wind will

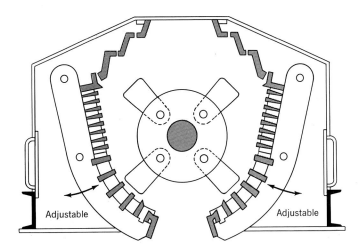

Fig. 9 Hammer-mill coal crusher—diagrammatic section.

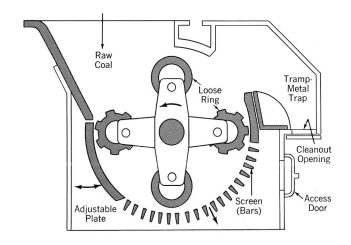

Fig. 10 Ring coal crusher—diagrammatic section.

blow the fines away as dust. The supplier can and does help by using oil sprays to settle the dust in hot, dry weather and for easier handling in freezing weather. The oil treatment does not appreciably affect combustion and does not cause trouble in pulverizers. There is evidence that it tends to reduce hang-ups in bunkers and spouts.

Frozen coal. The need of special equipment for unloading frozen coal will depend on the location and size of a plant. For instance, adequate equipment for this purpose must be provided in a plant located where the temperature is below freezing for an appreciable part of the year, while in a plant located where below-freezing temperatures are infrequent and of short duration manual operations will do.

Several successful mechanically operated methods have been developed for unloading frozen coal. For a permanent installation, probably the most reliable and efficient method is a steam-heated thawing shed. However, new installations are seldom made today because they are expensive. Oil-fired thawing pits, arranged to heat the bottom of the cars without flame impingement, give quite rapid and reliable results. The radiant-electric type railroad car thawer system has also been used effectively at many power plant stations handling unit-train shipments of coal. When the coal has been thawed, two

devices are available to aid in the discharge of the coal. A heavy shear bar, approximately the width of the car in length, is raised by a hoist and dropped on the coal. The other device is a car shakeout, in which a motor-driven eccentric shaker clamped to the top flanges of the car transmits a vibratory action to the car body. The assembly is hung from a hoist and is readily attached to and removed from the car. The shakeout is also very useful in unloading fine wet coal or other materials that do not flow readily.

For smaller plants, expensive equipment is not economically justified, and the methods used depend primarily on manual labor. Slice bars, sledges, portable oil torches, and steam or hot water are the tools used, and the effectiveness of the operation depends on the skill and persistence of the workmen.

Mechanical handling. Extensive equipment, covering the range of plant requirements from a few tons per day to the largest, is available for handling coal from the cars either to outside storage or to inside bunkers or hoppers. Larger plants are compelled to use mechanical handling. To save money, improve plant appearance and cleanliness, release labor for other tasks, and improve employee morale by reducing the drudgery of manual operation, many small plants also find it worthwhile to use mechanical handling.

For the very small plants there are portable screw and belt conveyors to unload cars, fill bunkers, and reclaim coal from outside storage. Portable conveyors of two different types are shown in Fig. 11.

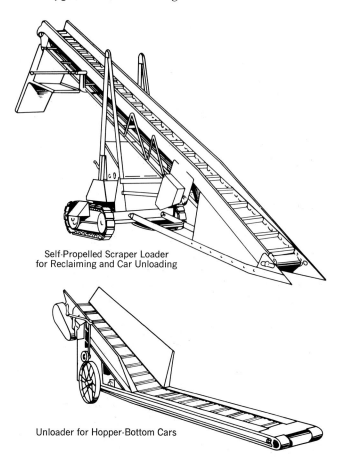

Self-Propelled Scraper Loader for Reclaiming and Car Unloading

Unloader for Hopper-Bottom Cars

Fig. 11 Yard coal-reclaiming and unloading equipment for small plants.

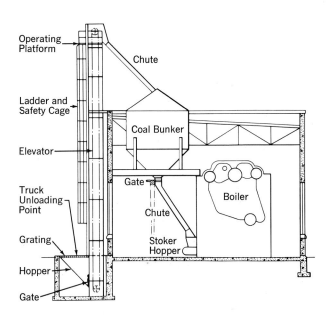

Fig. 12 Coal-handling equipment for truck delivery.

For plants using more than 10 tons of coal per day it is economically necessary to provide complete mechanical coal-handling equipment. The type of equipment depends on the requirements of the plant. When pulverizers are used, it is desirable to include a magnetic separator somewhere in the system, but this is usually not considered necessary for stokers. Frequently a coal crusher will make it economically possible to use locally mined coal that is not screened or sized.

The method of coal delivery, whether by truck or railroad car, may affect the handling arrangements, although a track hopper will serve for either. Some systems are suitable for transferring the coal to either inside or outside storage, while some are limited to one or the other. When determining the capacity of the coal-handling equipment, possible future plant expansion should be kept in mind. In general, the capacity required depends on the time allowed for unloading, and in most plants this is set at from 4 to 6 hr a day.

Where all coal is trucked into the plant, an outside hopper and elevator to the coal bunker (Fig. 12) may be used. It is a simple effective arrangement for a small- to medium-size plant (burning 30 to 300 tons a day) using a minimum of equipment. Care should be taken to keep the angle of the chutes at 60° or above to minimize coal hang-ups.

The arrangement illustrated in Fig. 13 with a track hopper, feeder, elevator, silo, and weigh larry, has a wide application. The silo is arranged with an internal shelf that provides maximum use of storage space. As the coal is used from above the shelf, reserve storage can be reclaimed from the lower part of the silo.

A more elaborate arrangement is shown in Fig. 14. This includes a crusher, magnetic separator, and screw conveyor for distribution along the length of the bunker, usually compartmented.

The arrangement illustrated in Fig. 15 is suitable for large plants, burning 3000 tons per day and over. It includes a car dumper, Bradford breaker, and belt conveyors. In addition to sizing the coal, the breaker will

also remove large pyrites, wood and trash. With this arrangement large quantities of coal (200 tons or more) can be moved per hour.

Outside storage at or near plant

Outside storage of coal at or near the site is often necessary, and in some cases required, to assure continuous plant operation. Coal for an emergency stockpile should be purchased during opportune market conditions. It is important that no more coal be stored than that necessary to meet conditions stated above, because money invested in stored coal cannot be used, changes occurring to the coal during storage may reduce its commercial value, and insurance costs are involved.

The changes that may affect the value of stored coal are loss in heating value, reduction of coking power, reduction of average particle size (weathering or slacking), and, most important, losses from self-ignition or spontaneous combustion. Reduced caking tendencies may actually improve certain coals for chain-grate or underfeed-

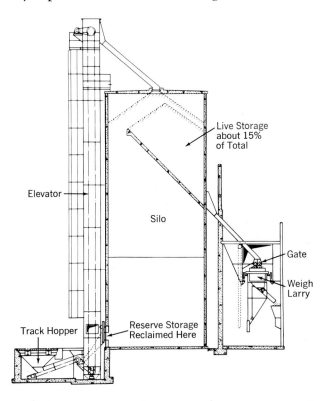

Fig. 13 Coal-handling equipment suitable for railroad-car delivery. Approximate capacity of silo shown, 600 tons.

stoker firing. Reduction of coking power and sizing will not affect pulverized-coal or Cyclone-Furnace firing. Direct loss of stored coal by wind or water erosion is possible and may become a serious nuisance.

Oxidation of coal. All constituents of pure coal begin to oxidize when exposed to air. This oxidation may be considered a very slow, low-temperature combustion process, since the end products, namely, CO_2, CO, H_2O, and heat, are the same as those of coal burned (rapid oxidation) in boiler furnaces. Although there is evidence that bacterial action causes heating of coal, it is believed that heating occurs through a chemical chain process.

Oxidation of coal is affected by the following conditions: length of time exposed to air, coal rank, size or surface area, temperature, petrographic constituents, the amount and size of iron disulfide (pyrites), moisture, and possibly the amount of mineral matter or ash. The rate of absorption of oxygen by coal at constant temperature decreases with time. Higher-rank coals contain less oxygen and oxidize at a slower rate than the higher-oxygen-content lower-rank coals. Oxidation of coal is primarily a surface action, hence the smaller the coal size the greater the surface area and the more rapid the oxidation rate. The rate also increases with temperature, doubling for every 20F rise. The bright components in coal oxidize at a faster rate than the dull. The common banded constituents are listed in probable order of their oxidizability: vitrain or anthraxylon, clarain, durain, and fusain. Pyrites react with oxygen and water to form sulfuric acid, iron sulfate, and heat. It is believed that size degradation of coal as a result of pyrite oxidation is of greater importance than the attendant emission of heat. Moisture content of coal increases with decreasing coal rank; however, the higher oxygen content and greater surface area of very low-rank or young coals are of more importance. Also, the heat of wetting may accelerate oxidation of low-rank coals that had been previously dried. The amount of mineral matter or ash in coal may have a small effect on oxidation, i.e., a high-ash coal has less tendency to oxidize than the same coal with a low-ash content, other conditions being unchanged. The most important factors affecting oxidizability of coal are its rank, surface area, length of exposure to air, and temperature.

Some general conclusions about the storage properties of coals are:

1. High-rank coals, such as anthracite, are easiest to store.
2. Fresh, small-size lignite of high pyrite content is the most difficult to store in hot weather.
3. Once a safe storage pile is established, the rate of oxidation will have decreased considerably; thus coal should be kept in dead storage until an emergency requires its use.
4. Freshly crushed coal has a high oxidation rate; if spontaneous combustion is to be avoided, heat from oxidation of coal should be kept at a low level by retarding oxidation or removing the heat generated thereby.

Protection of bituminous coal or lignite during storage should be considered from the viewpoints of spontaneous combustion and coal deterioration. For example, storing coal loosely in small piles prevents self-ignition, since heat generated by oxidation is released and the temperature of the coal pile does not approach the danger point. However, the coal will suffer loss of both calorific value and coking power as well as size degradation. The safest way to store coal and prevent its oxidation is to submerge it completely in fresh water. However the high cost of underwater storage together with the problems associated with dewatering and handling generally precludes the use of this method. All steam coals may be safely stored, provided proper procedures are used. Coal can be successfully stored by following methods outlined by the Bureau of Mines and practiced by public utilities.

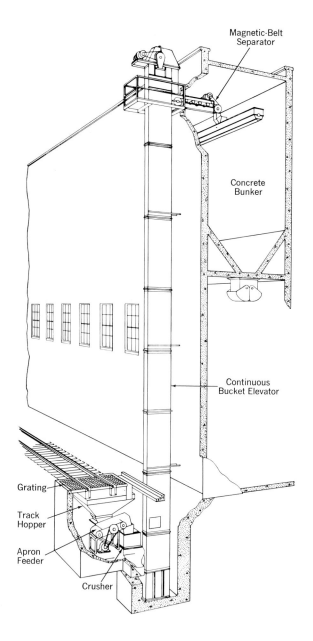

Fig. 14 Coal-handling equipment with distribution along length of bunker.

Selection of storage site. The first important step in the successful storage of coal on the ground is the selection and preparation of the storage site. If possible, the site should be level solid ground. It should be free of loose fill such as ashes or cinders. The site should be cleared of all foreign material, properly graded for drainage, and compacted by a bulldozer. Vents from drains, heat from steam or hot water lines, and high-pressure gas lines that may rupture and explode should not be permitted in the storage area. Consideration should be given to access and provisions for coal delivery and also to protection from prevailing winds, tides, flooded rivers, and spray from salt water.

Storage in small amounts. No special precautions are required for anthracite.

Sized (double-screened) bituminous coals may be stored in small conical piles from 5 to 15 ft high. If a dump truck is used, the depth should not exceed 6 ft to maintain better control over size segregation.

Slack sizes of bituminous coal may be compacted with a bulldozer. It is not necessary to invest in heavy equipment, where labor and equipment can be contracted for when needed. Industrial plants may not have sufficient ground available for an emergency stockpile. In some cases an active storage pile may serve both purposes, using a drag-scraper arrangement of moderate cost.

Subbituminous coal and lignite should be stored in small piles and thoroughly packed. For short-time storage (2 to 3 months), where it is undesirable to pack industrial sizes, oil treatment with about one gallon of heavy oil per ton of lignite will permit safe storage in windrows.

Storage in large amounts. Anthracite is very safe to store in large high piles that permit drainage. They should be capped with larger sizes to prevent loss of fines from wind.

Bituminous coal should be stockpiled in multiple horizontal layers (*see Fig. 16*). The initial layer is spread out from 1 to 2 ft in thickness and thoroughly packed to eliminate air spaces. Well-compacted coal has a bulk density of from 65 to 72 lb/cu ft. Track-type mobile equipment may not give sufficient compaction, and use of a sheepsfoot roller may be required. Rubber-tired, self-powered scrapers may be used to advantage where hauls are more than 200 or 300 ft long. When using these scrapers, a bulldozer is required for trimming the pile. Each succeeding layer is compacted in the same manner. The top is slightly crowned and symmetrical to permit even runoff of water. All sides and the top are covered with a 1-ft compacted layer of fines and then capped with a 1-ft layer of sized lump coal.

Subbituminous coal and lignite should be stockpiled using the same system of layering and compacting, but coal layers should be thinner, not more than 1 ft in thickness, to insure good compaction. It is not practical to seal these piles with coarse coal, since it will weather and slack to small size in a short period of time. The top and sides of the pile are compacted with slack-size coal. Sides should have a shallow slope. Drifting of fines from and around the pile can cause trouble from self-ignition. To prevent this, it is recommended that drift (snow) fences be installed across the pile, normal to the direction of prevailing winds, and the top and sides of the pile be periodically trimmed.

Regardless of the coal stockpiled, the use of material, such as asphalt, for airtight sealing is not recommended. Capping methods described above have proved effective. Sealing with asphalt or road-tar coating may be conducive to self-ignition in those areas near breaks that could cause a "stack effect." Also, the materials are an additional expense, and they may prove difficult to handle or pulverize when the stockpile coal is used.

Visual inspection. Visual inspection for hot spots should be made daily for large storage piles and not less than once a week for smaller piles. In wet weather, a hot area is indicated by rapid drying and a lighter color of the surface coal. On a cold or humid day, streams of vapor and the odor of gas are signs of heating or air entering

the pile. Hot spots may be located by probing with an iron rod and testing its temperature by hand. If the rod in contact with the coal at the hot spot is quickly withdrawn and found to be too hot to hold in the hand, the temperature is at the danger point. Preventing air from entering the pile, by sealing the top and sides near the hot areas with an airtight coating of asphalt or road tar, will usually stop further heating and actually extinguish the fire. Should this method fail to reduce the temperature, the coal must be removed from the hot spot. Water should not be used except in the case of an actual fire.

Inside storage and handling

As the size of single boiler units and the amount of fuel consumed has increased, it has become more difficult to maintain a steady supply of coal to the burning equipment. With bunkers and chutes of proper size and design, the condition of the coal is the all-important factor for easy and efficient handling inside the plant. Dry anthracite flows easily, having an angle of repose as low as 15 degrees. On the other hand, fine, wet coal feeding from a bottom-outlet bunker has a tendency to "rat-hole" or "pipe" all the way to the top surface. Under these conditions the angle of repose may be 90 degrees. When this occurs, coal flow to the feeders is interrupted and spasmodic. Many bunkers and chutes with dents from sledge hammer blows (serving as the only remedy available at the moment) bear evidence of the way fine, wet coal has often been made to flow. Casualties, even fatalities, have resulted from men being caught in slides while trying to get the coal moving in bunkers. In the light of past experience it is universally agreed that no one should be permitted to enter a coal bunker to loosen coal hang-ups. Air lances, manipulated from above or below the bunker, are safer and far more effective.

From studies of actual plant operations it has been found that hang-ups of coal are liable to begin when there is a surface moisture of 5 to 6%. This and other difficulties can best be overcome by improved storage and by careful reclaiming of the coal from storage.

Fig. 16 Coal storage—typical example of thorough packing with minimum of size segregation. This pile contains about 200,000 tons.

Flow of coal through chutes. The following conclusions on the flow of coal through chutes from bunker to pulverizer are drawn from the results of model experiments:

1. A chute should have the shortest possible path in the direction of flow.
2. Tapered or uniformly enlarging round chutes should be used whenever possible.
3. Where two streams of coal must be brought together, this should be accomplished with a minimum angle of convergence. If a sudden change of direction cannot be avoided, a "breakaway" should be used to help re-align the coal. A schematic sketch of such a breakaway is shown in Fig. 17.
4. All angles of chutes should be made as steep as possible, and reductions in cross section should be kept to a minimum.
5. An example of improved layout for bunker discharges, based on model experiments, is shown in Fig. 18.

Bunker design. The inside coal bunker, once built, is essentially a part of the building, and there is little likelihood that it will be modified during the life of the plant. The purpose of the bunker is not only to store a given capacity of coal but also to function efficiently as part of the system in maintaining a continuous supply of fuel to the pulverizer, stoker, or Cyclone Furnace. Therefore, in the design of bunkers, careful consideration should be given to the factors outlined below:

Capacity. Normally, capacity of the bunker or bunkers should be large enough for a 30-hr supply at top load. For plants where coal-handling labor or equipment is

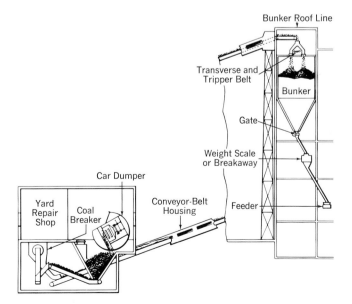

Fig. 15 Coal-handling and distributing equipment for large plants with railroad supply.

not available for 3-day week ends or where the cost is high because of holidays, it is desirable to increase capacity to cover such a period.

Material. Coal bunkers have been built of tile, reinforced concrete, carbon-steel plate, stainless-steel-clad plate, steel plate lined with acid-resisting concrete, and steel plate lined with rubber. Where unlined carbon-steel plate is used, a periodic check should be made to determine the extent of corrosion. Bunkers have been known to collapse because of corrosion.

Shape. The shape of a bunker is usually a compromise between space limitations and the optimum design for coal flow. Dead pockets should be avoided because of the danger of spontaneous combustion. Several shapes of bunkers commonly used are shown in Fig. 19. Note that a breakaway is indicated at the gate at each bunker discharge. This device is quite effective in reducing hang-ups and also provides access to the coal stream to restore flow should clogging occur. Similar breakaways should also be used where there is a material change in the direction of a chute. Many plants use the silo design of coal bunker because it has been found to be less susceptible to rat-holing and hang-ups than other shapes. This design is equally suitable for small and large plants.

Location. The coal bunker should be so located that the flow to the fuel-consuming equipment is as nearly vertical as possible. It should also be as far as possible from flues, hot-air ducts, steam pipes, or other external sources of heat that could start bunker fires.

For large plants, the cost of bunkers may be high because of the large coal weight requirements, necessitating considerable structural steel, and increased building volume. Therefore, the current trend is to replace bunkers with silos which require less building volume and structural steel.

Fig. 20 shows a schematic arrangement of a modern coal-handling system, serving an electric generating plant having two 500 Mw steam generators. This figure is reproduced from ASME Publication 65-PWR-7, *Innovations in Coal Handling Designed for Union Electric's Sioux Plant*, by P. D. Harrington. The system shown handles crushed coal delivered by integral-train operation in self-unloading bottom-dump cars. It is designed with a large "live storage" coal pile and an automatic continuous-modulated (controlled) reclaim system. The system is automated so that a two-man crew can handle 7000 tons of coal per day, 5 days per week. All of the equipment from the reclaim feeders to the in-plant silos and boiler are unmanned and controlled automatically by the central control-room operator. The plan view of the system in Fig. 20 shows two rows of five silos each. These ten silos serve one boiler, which is fired from both sides. There are two other rows of silos diametrically opposite, which serve the other boiler.

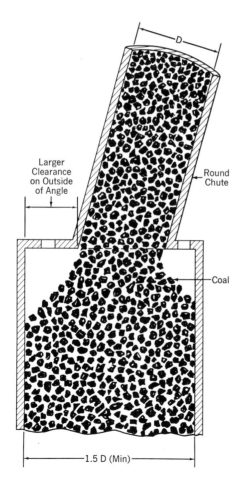

Fig. 17 Arrangement of "breakaway" in coal chute to relieve lateral pressure and pipe friction.

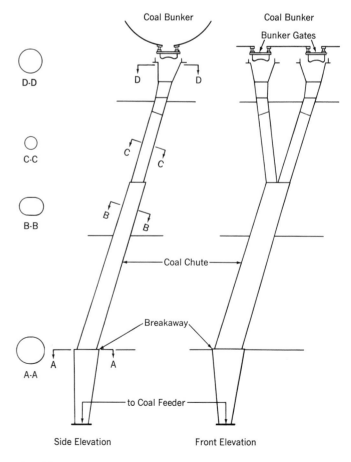

Fig. 18 Arrangement of bunker discharge with desirable features of breakaways and gradual enlargement of chutes.

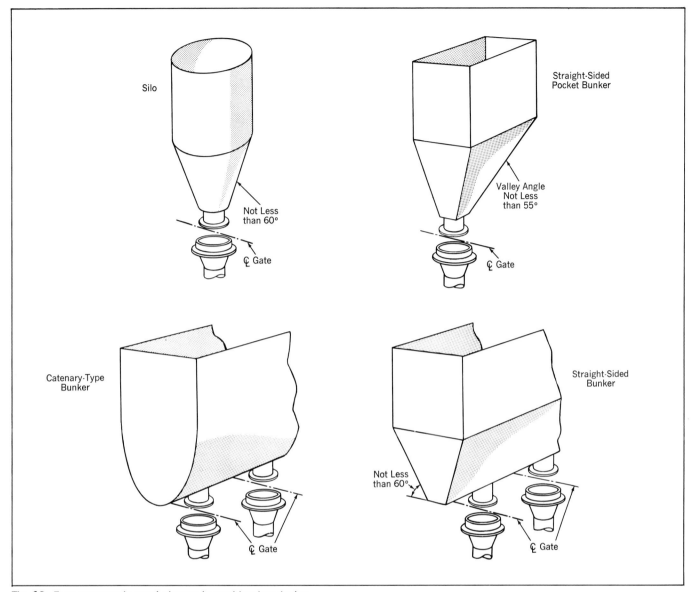

Fig. 19 Four commonly used shapes in coal-bunker design.

Bunker fires — a serious danger. A fire in the coal bunker should be recognized at once as a serious danger to personnel and equipment and should be dealt with promptly and adequately. As long as there is fire in the bunker, there is danger of a possible explosion of combustible gases, and steps should be taken to smother the fire. Steam or carbon dioxide may be piped in directly to covered bunkers and to the affected areas in open-top bunkers. While the fire is being smothered with steam or carbon dioxide, the hot coal should be run through the fuel-burning equipment, whether pulverizer or stoker, until the bunker is empty. While feeding the raw coal, special care should be taken to feed uniformly, without interruption, and at as high a rate as the plant load requirements will permit. Continuity of feed at this time is especially important.

If the hot coal from the bunker is fed to a pulverizer, cold air should be used to reduce mill-outlet temperature. Should the feed to the pulverizer stop for any reason, the pulverizing equipment must be shut down immediately, and all valves in connection with the pulverizer should be closed to prevent a draft through the pulverizer. After it has been established by inspection of the pulverizing unit that no fire is present and the cause of the feed interruption has been removed, the unit should again be placed in service until the bunker is empty. Operation after a stoppage should be supervised with the same care as before the interruption. The important safeguard in the case of stokers is to maintain a continuous coal flow to the stoker hopper so that the chute is sealed, thus preventing air flow back into the bunker.

While it is highly desirable to extinguish completely all fire in the bunker before it is emptied, this is rarely possible because of load demands and because it is extremely difficult to do. However, the use of steam or carbon dioxide in smothering the fire will minimize the danger, and it is common practice to continue feeding hot or even burning coal from the bunker at the highest possible rate so that the bunker may be quickly emptied.

Carbon dioxide is very useful in fighting bunker fires, and in some plants permanent connections for the use of this gas have been fitted to the bottom of bunkers. Distri-

bution of dry ice over the top of the fuel in the bunker has been very effective in smothering fires because the heavier carbon dioxide displaces air.

It is necessary to empty completely a bunker in which a fire has occurred before adding new coal because a few hot pieces will start a new fire. The cause of the bunker fire should be established. The fire may have started from coal already overheated or burning in storage or, more likely, the cause may be spontaneous combustion because of long-term storage in the bunker itself. Dead pockets within a bunker should be eliminated. To reduce the effect of external heat from adjacent steam lines or breechings, insulation should be fitted and ventilation provided around the bunker. Care should be taken to avoid loading the bunker with overheated coal.

No one must be allowed to enter a bunker in which there has been a fire until it is completely empty and the gases generated have been dissipated. Even then, only an experienced person equipped with an oxygen supply should enter the bunker, and he should be attended by helpers outside the bunker to whom he is connected by lifelines.

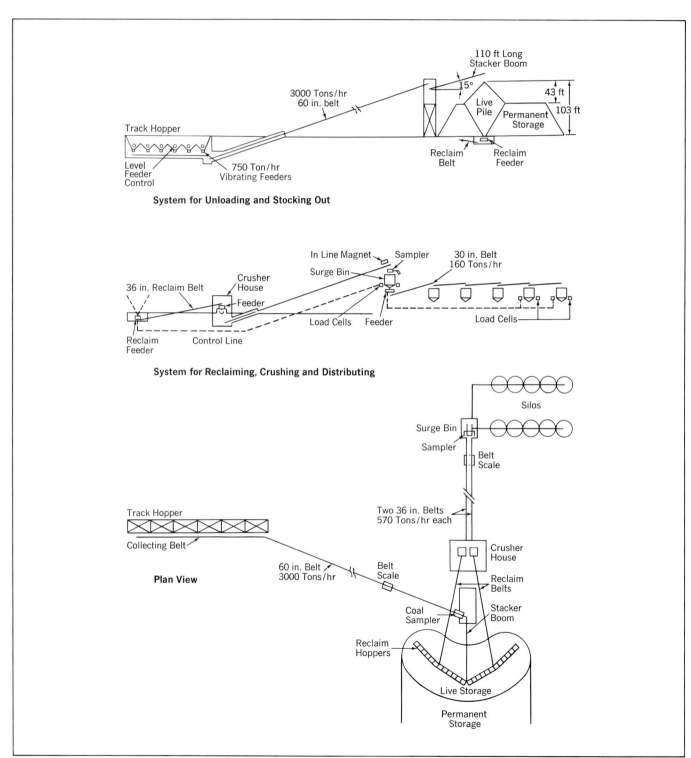

Fig. 20 Coal-handling system for 1000 Mw plant.

Chapter 9   Preparation and utilization of pulverized coal

Consumption of coal for the power industry in the United States has begun to increase significantly as oil and gas supplies are held for domestic heating and other uses. A disproportionate increase over previous levels in the production of subbituminous and lignite coals has been necessary for industrial and utility users to meet government air pollution requirements. Increases in bituminous coal production costs have also made use of low rank coals mined from larger seams economically attractive. Solid fossil fuels from anthracite to peat are all possible energy sources depending upon the economics for special application. Preparation and firing of these fuels in pulverized form is the major method used for new power installations.

The preparation and firing of pulverized coal is covered in this chapter, Cyclone-Furnace firing in Chapter 10, and stoker firing in Chapter 11. Hand firing is essentially obsolete.

Selection of coal-burning equipment

The selection of the most suitable equipment for a particular job consists of balancing the investment, operating characteristics, efficiency, and type of coal to give the most economical installation (see *Selection of Steam Generating Equipment, Chapter 22*).

Almost any coal can be burned successfully in pulverized form or on some type of stoker. Cyclone-Furnace firing has special advantages for certain coals for which it is suited.

The capacity limitations imposed by stokers have been overcome by the development of pulverized-coal systems using increased pulverizer sizes. These improved methods of burning coal also provide:

1. Ability to use coal from fines up to 2-in. maximum size.
2. Improved response to load changes.
3. Increase in thermal efficiency because of lower excess air for combustion and lower carbon loss than with stoker firing.
4. A reduction in manpower required for operation.
5. Improved ability to burn coal in combination with oil and gas.

Experience shows that stoker firing is more economical for steam generating units of capacity less than 100,000 lb of steam per hr, where the lower efficiency of a stoker can be tolerated. In larger plants, where fuel cost is a larger fraction of the operating cost, pulverized-coal or Cyclone-Furnace firing is more economical except in special cases.

Operating characteristics may be of controlling significance in the choice of firing methods. For example, where unit size is suitable for pulverized-coal, Cyclone-Furnace, or stoker firing, an extremely wide load range may make stoker firing preferable as a result of minimal control actions required in operation. Where rotary kilns and industrial furnaces are fired by coal, the required high fineness levels necessitates use of pulverized-coal firing.

The type of coal influences the choice of the method of firing for boiler furnaces with the primary considerations as follows:

Pulverized-coal firing: grindability, rank, moisture, volatile matter, and ash.

Stoker firing: rank of coal, volatile matter, ash, and ash-softening temperature.

Cyclone-Furnace firing: volatile matter, ash, and ash viscosity.

Convenient approximations for the selection of bituminous coals for the firing of boilers are given in Table 1.

Table 1
Coal characteristics and the method of firing

	Stoker	Pulverized Coal	Cyclone Furnace**
Max. total moisture* (as fired), %	15–20	15	20
Min. volatile matter (dry basis), %	15	15	15
Max. total ash (dry basis), %	20	20	25
Max. sulfur (as fired), %	5	—	—

* These limits are exceeded for lower rank, higher inherent-moisture-content coals, i.e., subbituminous and lignite.

** See *Suitability of Fuels for the Cyclone Furnace*, Chapter 10.

Pulverized-coal systems

The function of a pulverized-coal system is to pulverize the coal, deliver it to the fuel-burning equipment, and accomplish complete combustion in the furnace with a minimum of excess air. The system must operate as a continuous process and, within specified design limitations, the coal supply or feed can be varied as rapidly and as widely as required by the combustion process.

A small portion of the air required for combustion (15 to 20% in current installations) is used to transport the coal to the burner. This is known as primary air (see Chapter 13). In the direct-firing system, primary air is also used to dry the coal in the pulverizer. The remainder of the combustion air (80 to 85%) is introduced at the burner and is known as secondary air.

The two basic equipment components of a pulverized-coal system are:

1. The pulverizer which pulverizes the coal to the fineness required.
2. The burner which accomplishes the mixing of the pulverized-coal-primary-air mixture with secondary air in the right proportions at the furnace.

Other necessary requirements are:

3. Hot air for drying the coal for effective pulverization.
4. Fan(s) to supply air to the pulverizer and deliver the coal-air mixture to the burner(s).
5. Coal feeder to control the rate of coal feed to each pulverizer.
6. Coal and air conveying lines.
7. Pyrites reject system.
8. Measuring and control elements.

Two principal systems—the bin system and the direct-firing system—have been used for processing, distributing and burning pulverized coal. The direct-firing system is the one being installed almost exclusively today.

Bin system

The bin system is primarily of historical interest, although a large number of units of this type remain in operation. Its use was required before pulverizing equipment had reached the stage of development where it could be relied upon for uninterrupted operation, flexibility and consistent performance.

In this system the coal is processed at a location apart from the furnace, and the end product is pneumatically conveyed to cyclone collectors which recover the fines and clean the moisture-laden air before returning it to the atmosphere. The pulverized coal is discharged into storage bins and later conveyed by pneumatic transport through pipelines to utilization bins which may be as far as 5,000 ft from the point of preparation. A bin system is illustrated in Fig. 1 and a transport system in Fig. 2.

For the coal-air transport system, a differential-pitch screw pump, Fig. 3, is provided to feed pulverized coal continuously into a pipeline, where coal is aerated or fluidized at the entrance so that it flows through the pipe somewhat like a viscous fluid. Through a system of two-way valves (Fig. 2) the coal can be distributed to any number of bins. The system may be arranged for manual, remote or automatic control. These air-transport systems have been built in sizes from 1 to 100 tons of coal per hour. For successful operation, the surface moisture in the pulverized coal must not exceed 3%, and the fineness should not be less than 90% through a 50-mesh sieve.

Although bin systems installed in older plants are still operating quite satisfactorily, this system is no longer competitive with the direct-firing system. Furthermore, the drying, transportation and storage of pulverized coal, other than anthracite, involves a fire hazard from spontaneous combustion.

Direct-firing system

The bin system has been superseded by the direct-firing system because of greater simplicity, lower initial investment, lower operating cost, and less space requirement.

The pulverizing equipment developed for the direct-firing system permits continuous utilization of raw coal directly from the bunkers with a storage capacity compatible with plant operation. This is accomplished by feeding coal prepared to a maximum top size directly into the pulverizer, where it is dried as well as pulverized, and then delivering it to the burners in a single continuous operation.

Components of the direct-firing system (Figs. 4 and 5) are as follows (see also Fig. 19):

1. Raw-coal feeder.
2. Source (steam or gas air heater) to supply hot primary air to the pulverizer for drying the coal.
3. Pulverizer fan, also known as the primary-air fan, arranged as a blower (or exhauster).
4. Pulverizer arranged to operate under pressure (or suction).
5. Coal-and-air conveying lines.
6. Burners.

There are two direct-firing methods in use—the pressure type, which is more commonly used, and the suction

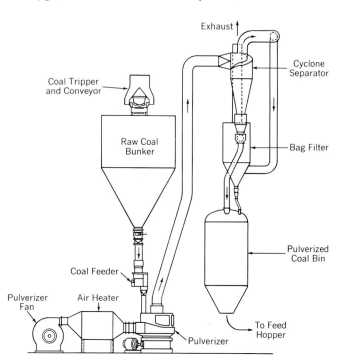

Fig. 1 Bin system for pulverized coal.

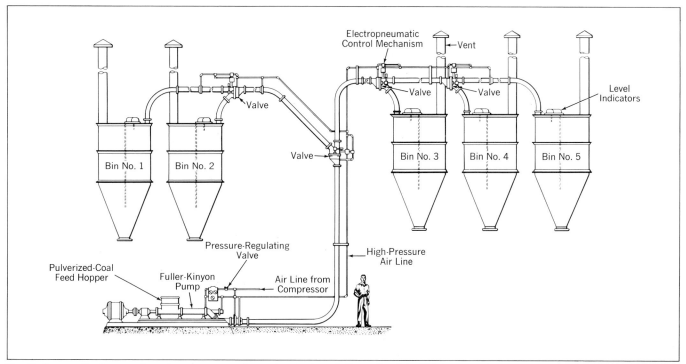

Fig. 2 Pneumatic transport system for conveying pulverized coal. Capacity, 1 to 100 tons per hour.

type. The principal differences between the two methods are summarized in Table 2.

Table 2
Comparative features of direct-firing pressure and suction systems

System	Pressure	Suction
Type of fan	Blower	Exhauster
Location of fan	Pulverizer inlet	Pulverizer outlet
Fan construction	Standard	Explosion-proof
Fan handles	Air only	Pulverized coal and air
Relative fan efficiency	High	Low
Fan wear	Low to none	High
Pulverized coal distribution to burners	Direct distribution	Distributor required

In the pressure method, the primary-air fan, located on the inlet side of the pulverizer, forces the hot primary air through the pulverizer where it picks up the pulverized coal, and delivers the proper coal-air mixture to the burners. On large installations, primary-air fans operating on cold air, force the air through the air heater first and then the pulverizer. In either event, the coal is delivered to the burners by a fan operating entirely on air, so that minimal entrained dust passes through the fan. One pulverizer generally furnishes the coal for several burners. With the pressure method, it is usual to supply each burner with a single conveying line direct from the pulverizer although on larger installations, burner line arrangements may favor use of a distributor.

In the suction method, the air and entrained coal are drawn through the pulverizer under negative pressure by an exhauster located on the outlet side of the pulverizer. With this arrangement the fan handles a mixture of coal and air, and distribution of the mixture to more than one burner must be obtained by a distributor beyond the fan discharge. Exhausters tend to concentrate the coal leaving and proper distribution is required to balance flow in coal air piping. Suction type mills usually operate at a constant air flow over the pulverizer load range which results in poorer fineness levels at lower loads.

The feeding of coal and air to the pulverizer is controlled by either of two methods: (1) The coal feed is proportioned to the load demand, and the primary-air supply is adjusted to the rate of coal feed; or (2) the primary air through the pulverizer is proportioned to the load demand, and the coal feed is adjusted to the rate of air flow. In either case, a predetermined air-coal ratio is maintained for any given load.

The direct-firing system, in addition to eliminating separately fired dryers and storage facilities for pulverized coal, permits the use of inlet air temperatures to the

Fig. 3 Fuller-Kinyon pump for transporting pulverized coal.

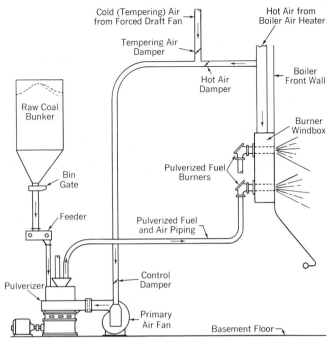

Fig. 4 Direct-firing system for pulverized coal.

pulverizer up to 650F and higher for drying high-moisture coals (total moisture 20%, surface moisture 15%) or high-moisture lignites (20 to 40% total moisture) in the pulverizer.

In the direct-firing system the operating range of a pulverizer is usually not more than 3 to 1 (without change in the number of burners in service) because the air velocities in lines and other parts of the system must be maintained above the minimum values to keep the coal in suspension. In practice most boiler units are provided with more than one pulverizer, each feeding multiple burners. Load variations beyond 3 to 1 are generally accommodated by shutting down (or starting up) a pulverizer and the burners it supplies.

Pulverizers

Design fundamentals

A) *Feeding.* In direct-firing systems the fuel rate must be capable of automatic control by the boiler load demand. Pulverizer air flow is controlled in proportion to fuel rate to provide the correct fuel-air ratio for proper drying, fineness and velocity required for transporting the fuel to the burners.

B&W uses a control that maintains a predetermined variable air-fuel ratio over the entire operating range of the pulverizer. Air flow is measured by an orifice or a pitot tube in the duct supplying air to the pulverizer and fuel flow is measured by feeder speed in a gravimetric type feeder.

B) *Drying.* In order to pulverize and circulate fuel pneumatically within a pulverizer, enough of the moisture must be removed to leave the fuel dry and dusty. For most commercially available coals, preheated air to the pulverizer is required. Drying is accomplished quickly as the coal is being circulated and ground. The mixture of tempering and hot primary air is used to control the temperature of the fuel-air mixture in the range suitable for burning.

C) *Grinding.* The pulverizer must do adequate work on each passage of the material through the grinding zone and without the production of excessive superfines. This is best accomplished by internal recirculation of coarse material. The pulverizer should maintain its grinding ability over the life cycle of the grinding elements and be able to reject foreign matter that enters with the feed. These objectives should be attained without excessive wear and power consumption.

The grinding elements of B&W pulverizers are spring loaded to provide the necessary grinding force throughout the life of the elements. Controlled grinding elements furnish adequate grinding surface, allow rapid material flow, and facilitate the discharge of foreign material.

D) *Circulating.* Circulation of coal within a pulverizer is required (1) to promote rapid drying by mixing the incoming feed with dry material in the pulverizer, (2) to keep the grinding elements loaded at all times, and (3) to remove pulverized material from around the grinding elements.

Rapid circulation is maintained in B&W pulverizers by utilizing the pulverizer air in combination with centrifugal force and gravity to move the material as desired.

E) *Classifying.* It is not feasible to grind all the coal to the desired fineness in a single passage through the grinding elements. Therefore a device called a "classifier" is provided. Coal pulverized to the proper fineness leaves the pulverizer and goes to the

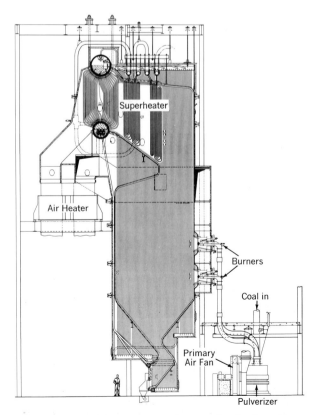

Fig. 5 Two-drum boiler direct-fired with pulverized coal.

burners. Oversize coal is separated out by the classifier and returned to the grinding zone.

If separation is not discriminative, oversize particles will go to the furnace causing high unburned combustible loss and slagging. Separation must be effective over the entire operating range, and the classifier must be adjustable for product size, since the required fineness is not the same for all applications.

The stationary, multiple-inlet-cyclone-type classifier used in the B&W pulverizer meets these requirements. The shrouded discharge prevents reentrainment of oversize particles. Fineness varies inversely with rating so that the highest fineness is obtained at the lowest load. The movable inlet vanes permit adjusting the classifier for the fineness desired.

F) *Transporting.* The velocity in pulverizer discharge lines must be sufficiently high to prevent settling of coal. At the burners the air-coal mixture must be uniform and the velocity suitable.

The B&W system of decreasing air flow with coal flow (Fig. 18) results in an increase in fineness as the transport line velocity decreases. The integral turret distributor provides uniform discharge from the classifier to the transport lines. The pressure loss through the transport lines can be balanced by orificing. This will assure proper distribution of coal-air flow between burners.

Pulverizer requirements

1. Rapid response to load change and adaptability to automatic control.
2. Continuous service for long operating periods.
3. Maintenance of prescribed performance throughout the life of pulverizer grinding elements.
4. A wide variety of coal properties should be acceptable.
5. Ease of maintenance with the minimum number and variety of parts, and space adequate for access.
6. Minimum building volume required.

The rank of coal and its end use govern the fineness to which coal must be ground. The data of Table 3 are helpful in this specification.

Table 3
Required pulverized fuel fineness
Percent through 200 U.S. sieve*

ASTM Classification of Coals by Rank

Type of Furnace	Fixed Carbon, %			Fixed Carbon below 69%		
	97.9-86 (Petroleum coke)	85.9-78	77.9-69	Btu/lb above 13,000	Btu/lb 12,900-11,000	Btu/lb below 11,000
Water-cooled	80	75	70	70	65**	60**
Cement kiln	90	85	80	80	80	—
Metallurgical	(As determined by process, generally from 80 to 90%)					

* The 200-mesh screen (sieve) has 200 openings per linear inch or 40,000 openings per square inch. For U.S. and ASTM sieve series, the nominal aperture for 200 mesh is 0.0029 in. or 0.074 mm. The ASTM designation for 200 mesh is 74 microns.
** Extremely high ash content coals will require higher fineness than indicated.

Grindability index (ASTM D-409)

Some coals are harder and hence more difficult to pulverize than others. The grindability of a coal is expressed as an index showing the relative hardness of that coal compared with a standard coal chosen as 100 (unity) grindability. Thus a coal is harder or easier to grind if its grindability index is less or greater, respectively, than 100. The capacity of a pulverizer is related to the grindability index of the coal.

A method of testing to determine the grindability index of coal is described in ASTM Standard D-409. The method is based on the premise that "the work done in pulverizing is proportional to the new surface produced." A definite amount of grinding energy is applied to a prepared sample in a miniature pulverizer (Hardgrove Grindability Machine, Fig. 6) and the new surface is determined by sieving.

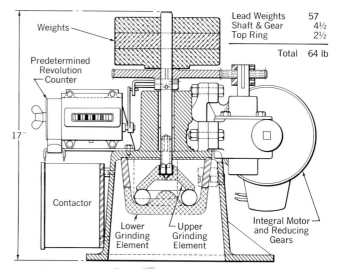

Fig. 6 Hardgrove grindability machine.

On lower rank coals, a modified ASTM 409 procedure has been used to predict actual pulverizer performance where the standard procedure failed. Several prepared samples are dried to different moisture levels and the grindability determined at each. The grindability value selected is that at the moisture level expected of the coal around the grinding elements. On some lignites, even this modified procedure has been inaccurate. On coals without prior experience, grinding a sample in an actual pulverizer may be necessary to assure that adequate milling capability is designed into the new installation.

Types of pulverizers

The reduction of materials to a fine particle size for countless human needs is one of the oldest arts of civilization. Coal-pulverizing equipment may be said to be based, in general, on rock and mineral-ore grinding machinery. The principles involved in all pulverizing machinery are grinding by impact, by attrition, by compression, or by a combination of two or more of these.

The principal types of coal pulverizers may be classified under high, slow, and medium speeds:

1. Medium speed (75-225 rpm)
   (a) Ball-and-race pulverizer
   (b) Roller type pulverizer

2. Slow speed (below 75 rpm)
   (a) Ball-and-race pulverizer
   (b) Roll-and-race type pulverizer
   (c) Roller type mill
      i) Saucer mill
   (d) Tube mill
3. High speed (above 225 rpm)
   (a) Impact mill

Medium-speed pulverizers. There are two groups of medium-speed pulverizers, classified as ball-and-race and roller type. The same principle of pulverizing by a combination of crushing under pressure, impact, and attrition between grinding surfaces and material, is used in each group, but the method is different. In both groups air is the predominant means for circulating the material through the grinding zone and conveying the finished product to the burners or cyclone collectors.

Medium-speed ball-and-race pulverizers. The ball-and-race pulverizer works on the ball-bearing principle. The grinding elements constitute the distinguishing feature. In the ball-and-race pulverizer these elements consist of a row of balls with one race below them and another above. High load circulation through the grinding zone, very desirable for effective drying and classification of the finished product, is a feature of this type of pulverizer.

B&W Type EL pulverizer. The Type EL pulverizer, illustrated in Fig. 7, has one stationary top ring, one rotating bottom ring, and one set of balls that comprise the grinding elements. The pressure required for efficient grinding is obtained from externally adjustable dual purpose springs. The bottom ring is driven by the yoke which is attached to the vertical main shaft of the pulverizer. The top ring is held stationary by the dual purpose springs.

Raw coal is fed into the grinding zone where it mixes with partially ground coal that forms the circu-

lating load. Pulverizer air causes the coal to circulate through the grinding elements where some of it is pulverized in each pass through the row of balls. As the coal becomes fine enough to be picked up by the air it is carried to the classifier where coal of the desired fineness is separated from the stream entering the classifier and is carried out with the air. Oversize material is returned to the grinding zone.

The classifier is a multiple-inlet cyclone with adjustable inlet vanes to permit varying inlet velocity as required to obtain the desired fineness of the pulverized coal.

The pulverizer is driven by spiral bevel gears located in the base. Both the vertical main shaft and the horizontal pinion shaft are mounted in roller bearings. Forced lubrication is provided for the entire gear drive by an oil pump submerged in the oil reservoir and gear-driven from the pinion shaft. Since it is not necessary to shut the pulverizer down for lubrication or to adjust spring pressure, it may be operated continuously over long periods of time.

The Type EL pulverizer is manufactured in 18 sizes, from EL-17 (balls located on a 17-in. pitch circle) to EL-76 (76-in. pitch circle of balls) with capacities from 1½ to 20 tons per hour of 50 grindability (ASTM) coal with a product fineness of 70% through a 200-mesh sieve (*see Grindability Index*).

Table 4
Characteristics of B&W Types EL and MPS pulverizers
Bituminous coal at 50 grindability (ASTM)
and 70% through 200 mesh

	Type EL Ball-and-Race	Type MPS Roll-and-Race
Size range	EL-17 to EL-76	MPS-67 to MPS-118
Output, max tons/hr	1½-20	20-105
Speed	Medium	Slow
Rpm of main shaft, range	231-90	21-29
Operates under	Pressure	Pressure
Fan location	Pulverizer inlet	Pulverizer inlet
Load circulation	High	High
Classification	Internal	Internal
Classification control	Mechanical adjustment	Mechanical adjustment
Drying, range of moisture°	Up to 20% total, 15% surface	Up to 20% total, 15% surface
Effect of surface moisture on output	None up to 15%, if air is hot enough	None up to 10%, slight reduction above this
Effect of wear on fineness	None	Slight
Method of control	Control primary air, which controls coal feed	Parallel control of primary air and coal feed
Response to load change	Fast	Fast
Power input per unit output, including fan	Low, 14 kwhr/ton	Low, 14 kwhr/ton
Noise level	Medium	Low

° On lower rank coals, moisture levels over 40% can be handled.

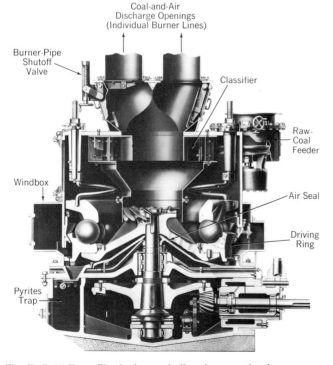

Fig. 7 B&W Type EL single-row ball-and-race pulverizer.

Coal-and-Air
Discharge Openings
(Individual Burner Lines)

Burner-Pipe
Shutoff
Valve

Classifier

Raw-
Coal
Feeder

Windbox

Air Seal

Driving
Ring

Pyrites
Trap

An outstanding feature of the ball-and-race type of pulverizer is its operation under positive pressure, with drying and conveying air supplied by the primary-air fan, and its consequent avoidance of wear on the fan rotor and housing. Wide latitude in the selection of a high-efficiency fan follows. A further advantage is better and more uniform coal-and-air distribution to a plurality of burners in a direct-firing system, since each burner is supplied from a common source. High surface moisture levels in the coal do not cause this type of pulverizer to lose capacity as with a roller type.

Table 4 shows a comparison of characteristics of the EL pulverizer with the larger-capacity MPS type (*see B&W Type MPS Pulverizer*).

Medium-speed roller type pulverizers. This type of pulverizer can be of two designs (1) where the ring is stationary and the rolls rotate; and (2) where the rolls are mounted off the mill housing and the ring rotates.

Type 1 mill. Grinding elements of three or more cylindrical rolls, suspended from driving arms, revolve in a horizontally positioned replaceable race. The pressure exerted by the rolls against the race is proportional to the centrifugal force resulting from the speed of the main shaft. Pulverizers of this type have been used in processing coal for the bin system and for grinding various materials in the ceramic and chemical industries. Both integral cyclone and rotating whizzer type classifiers can be used depending on fineness levels desired. The pulverizer has been normally designed to operate under suction.

Type 2 mill. The principal components of the bowl mill are a rotating bowl equipped with a replaceable grinding ring, two or more tapered rolls in stationary journals, a classifier, and a main drive. Instead of depending on centrifugal force for the grinding action, the rolls in the bowl mill are held in position relative to the grinding ring by mechanical springs, and centrifugal force is used only to feed the coal between the race and the rolls. The classifier is an internal cone type, housed in a high-sided chamber, and provided with adjustable vanes and a reject discharge trap at the bottom. Coal fineness is externally controlled by adjusting the entrance vanes in the classifier and by adjusting the compression springs to control the pressure of the rolls on the material.

The bowl mill is usually designed to operate under suction, and the pulverizer fan is placed on the outlet side of the classifier. Heavy scroll liners and rotor blades are generally provided to withstand the abrasive action of the material on the fan. These mills are used in direct-firing systems, for steam boilers, and for cement kilns.

Slow-speed pulverizers. Slow-speed pulverizers include ball-and-race, roll-and-race, roller, and tube mill types.

B&W Type MPS pulverizer. The MPS pulverizer, illustrated in Fig. 8, is a roll-and-race type utilizing three large contoured grinding rolls equally spaced around the mill pitch diameter. The roll assemblies are attached through a patented pivot connection to a triangular

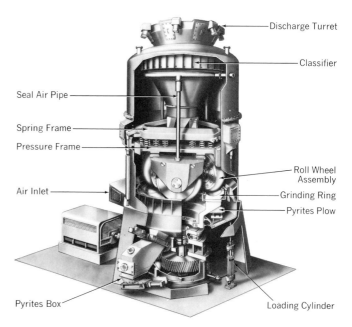

Fig. 8 Babcock & Wilcox Type MPS mill.

frame-loading system that keeps the rolls from planetating within the housing. This frame system also applies the spring pressure applied through the roller bracket axle system to positively load the rolls against the rotating grinding table and material carried under the rolls because of this rotation. The grinding ring runs at low speed and is shaped to form a race in which the rolls run.

Raw coal is fed through a center raw coal pipe. It immediately mixes with the partially ground coal that is circulated within the grinding zone by the air flow through the pulverizer. As the coal is reduced in size, the air carries it to the classifier similar to that used in the Type EL pulverizer. The fine coal, along with the air, leaves the pulverizer through the outlet pipes. The oversize is returned to the grinding zone through the classifier-discharge seal.

The pulverizer is driven through a triple reduction gear drive by a horizontal shaft motor. All shafts in the gear drive are supported on roller bearings, and lubrication is supplied under pressure from an external, separately driven, pump.

The Type MPS pulverizer, size 89 (89-in. pitch circle of the rolls where they contact the ring) weighs 150 tons, is 27 ft high and is about 12 ft across. Each roll assembly weighs 10 tons. The pulverizer is driven by a 700 horsepower motor.

The MPS pulverizer like the EL operates under pressure and provides the benefits noted. The slow table speed of the MPS results in quiet and smooth operation. The use of large diameter rollers results in high installed volumes of wear material and when combined with the contoured shape, high utilization of this material and long wear life occurs. The large tires also permit feeding larger raw coal size. The roller-race design maintains mill capacity over the wear life.

Saucer mill. This machine is a roller type, similar to the bowl mill in construction and operation. The principal differences are that the bowl has been flattened into a disc and the replaceable ring segments are essentially

Labels on figure: Discharge Turret, Classifier, Seal Air Pipe, Spring Frame, Pressure Frame, Air Inlet, Roll Wheel Assembly, Grinding Ring, Pyrites Plow, Pyrites Box, Loading Cylinder

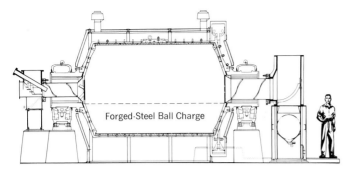

Fig. 9 Tube mill pulverizer.

flat. There are two or more tapered rollers loaded by external springs or by hydraulic cylinders to produce the desired pressure between the rollers and the coal bed. These pulverizers are equipped with an integral classifier of the cyclone type. A disadvantage of this type of pulverizer is that the clearance between roller and race results in loss of capacity as wear progresses.

Tube mill. One of the oldest practical pulverizers is the tube mill (Fig. 9), in which a charge of mixed-size forged-steel balls in a horizontally supported grinding cylinder is activated by gravity as the cylinder is rotated. The coal is pulverized by attrition and impact as the ball charge ascends and falls within the coal. Air is circulated over the charge to convey the finished product to the classifiers. The coal rejected in the classifiers returns to the grinding zone by gravity. Both pressure and suction operated tube mills have been used in the industry. The conical-end feature of the grinding cylinder causes size segregation in both ball charge and material within the grinding zone.

The outstanding features of the tube mill are dependability and low maintenance as a result of the simple arrangement of liners and ball charge in the grinding zone. No provision is required for removing tramp iron from the raw coal. Because of its simple and sturdy construction, low maintenance costs at rated capacities, and ability to grind very abrasive materials, the tube mill is still being used for wet and dry grinding of mineral ores and cement raw material, and for the dry grinding of the cement kiln product (clinker). Power evaluations are creating a trend to vertical spindle mills in these industries.

For any given capacity the tube mill is larger in size and heavier in construction than high- or medium-speed pulverizers using different principles of grinding. The tube mill requires more power per unit output than other types. Because of the absence of load circulation within the mill, the excessive amount of fine product within the ball charge, and circulation of preheated air over the top of the charge, it is not as efficient in drying the coal as medium-speed pulverizers with high air circulation through the grinding zone. This results in capacity reduction when handling wet coal.

The tube mill is still successfully applied to the grinding of coal where there is ample room for installation and where power cost is not the governing portion of the operating cost. For the most part, however, the tube mill has been replaced by more efficient modern machines for grinding coal.

High-speed pulverizers. High-speed pulverizers use impact as a primary means of grinding through the use of hammer like beaters, wear resistant pegs rotating within a cage and fan blades integral with the pulverizer shaft. These pulverizers have been called attrition type and have the advantage of very low storage. However, a disadvantage is their susceptibility to damage caused by foreign material.

Selecting pulverizer equipment

A number of factors must be considered when selecting pulverizer equipment. If selection anticipates the use of a variety of coals, the pulverizer should be sized for the coal that gives the highest "base capacity." Base capacity is the desired capacity divided by the capacity factor. The latter is a function of the grindability of the coal and the fineness required (see Fig. 10).

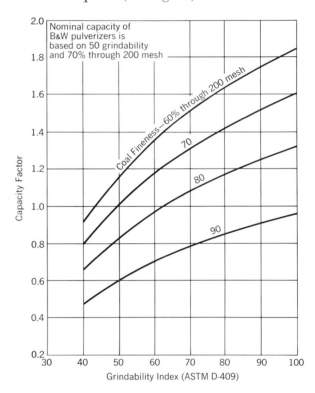

Fig. 10 Effect of grindability and fineness on pulverizer capacity.

The extent of drying in a given pulverizer depends upon its design and the method used to introduce preheated air into the grinding zone. Raw coal with very high surface moisture, over 15%, can be efficiently dried when fed into the grinding zone of a pulverizer designed for a high internal circulating load, i.e., a high ratio of coal recirculated to coal feed. As the recirculated material is dry, the more of it there is, the less effect the wet fuel has on the performance of the mill (see *Design Fundamentals, Circulating*).

As a practical matter, temperature is the only variable for controlling the heat input for drying, since the weight of primary air is usually a fixed quantity at any given output. As moisture levels increase, so does the amount of moisture evaporated. This is true on the transition from bituminous to lower rank coals with a noticeable increase in mill inlet temperatures.

The percentage of volatile matter in the fuel has a direct bearing on the recommended primary-air-fuel mixture temperature for combustion. The generally accepted safe values for pulverizer exit fuel-air temperatures are given in Table 5.

Table 5
Prevalent pulverizer exit primary-air-fuel temperature

Fuel	Exit Temp, F
Lignite	120-140
High-volatile bituminous	150
Low-volatile bituminous	150-175
Anthracite	175-212

The temperature of the primary air entering the pulverizer may run 650F or more, depending on the amount of moisture and the type of pulverizer.

Fine grinding of coal is necessary to assure complete combustion of the carbon for maximum efficiency and to minimize the deposit of ash and carbon on the heat-absorbing surfaces. This applies not only in the firing of steam boilers but also in other applications where close temperature control and the avoidance of carbon contamination are important. Chemical and metallurgical processes using pulverized coal as a source of thermal or chemical energy generally require very finely ground coal to assure the optimum reaction in a limited combustion zone and often under difficult firing conditions.

Fineness is expressed as the percentage of the product passing through various sizes of sieves, graded from No. 16 to No. 325 in the ASTM designation. Coal classification by rank and the end use of the product determine the fineness to which coal should be ground (Table 3). The effect of fineness on capacity is indicated in Fig. 10, where the capacity factor is given as a function of the fineness factor and the grindability index.

The range through which the equipment will operate must be considered in selecting pulverizing equipment for direct firing. The range through which a single pulverizer can operate is an inherent feature of the pulverizer system. B&W systems normally operate with a 3 to 1 range. However, the range of safe operation depends on the number of burners, size of burner lines and type of fuel.

When B&W pulverizers are operated at fractional loads, the fineness of the product increases automatically as the air flow is decreased. This is beneficial to low-load operation as it assists in ignition and flame stability.

Pulverizer auxiliary equipment

Control equipment. The B&W pulverizer is controlled by proportioning coal feed and pulverizer air flow to load demand (*see Table 4*). Air flow indication is obtained from modified pitot tubes, orifice, or venturi installed in the air duct ahead of the pulverizer. The air-metering device is calibrated on the job and adjusted so that all pulverizers on a unit show the same coal flow for the same air flow. Coal-feed rate is obtained from feeder speed on a volumetric feeder or actual rate as generated by a gravimetric feeder. The control equipment converts the primary-air differential from a square root to a linear value and balances it against the coal-feed signal. The control is adjustable so that the desired air-fuel ratio can

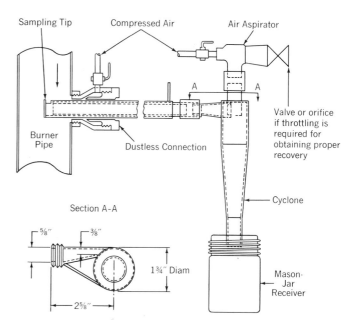

Fig. 11 Recommended arrangement for sampling pulverized coal in a direct-firing system using cyclone collector.

be maintained over the complete operating range of the pulverizer.

Sampling equipment. There is no universally adopted procedure for sampling pulverized coal, but the procedures given in ASME PTC 4.2 (Performance Test Code for Coal Pulverizers) and ASTM Standard D-197 may be considered as good practice. Fig. 11 shows the latest testing probe.

The results of sieve analyses of pulverized-coal samples should be plotted on a Rosin and Rammler chart, Fig. 12.

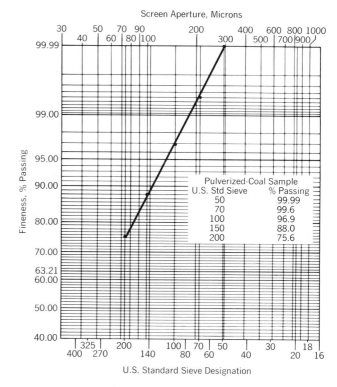

Fig. 12 Rosin and Rammler chart for plotting pulverized-coal-sample sieve analyses.

This graphical form of presenting size distribution is explained in The Bureau of Mines Information Circular 7346 (1946). If the points fall on a relatively straight line, the sample can be considered as representative. If there is a sharp or abrupt break in the curve, the sample should be discarded.

Exhausters and blowers. Primary air is required for conveying the pulverized coal to the burners. In the direct-firing system the primary air is supplied through the pulverizers. With a pressure system (*see Direct-Firing System*), the primary-air fan handles clean air and is not subjected to abrasion by the pulverized coal. In this case a high-efficiency fan can be used since the conditions permit an efficient rotor design and high tip speed.

With a suction system, the fan or exhauster must handle pulverized-coal-laden air. To comply with the National Fire Protection Association strength requirements, the exhauster housing must be designed to withstand an explosion within the fan. Furthermore, since the exhauster is subject to excessive wear, the design is limited to a paddle-wheel type of heavy construction and hard-metal or other protective-surface coatings. All of these construction features are detrimental to the mechanical efficiency of the fan.

Exhauster type fans are generally direct drive off the mill drive shaft and have considerably lower rotational speeds due to limits in tip speeds.

Power consumption of the pulverizer fan is an important item in the operating cost, and the selection of the fan should receive careful consideration. For a direct-firing installation, the fan must overcome the flow resistances through the pulverizers and burner lines as well as provide the pressure required at the burner. The resistance through the pulverizer depends on the inherent characteristics of the pulverizer and the amount of drying accomplished in it. The resistance through the discharge lines is a function of their length and the air-coal velocity (Table 6) that must be maintained to prevent settling.

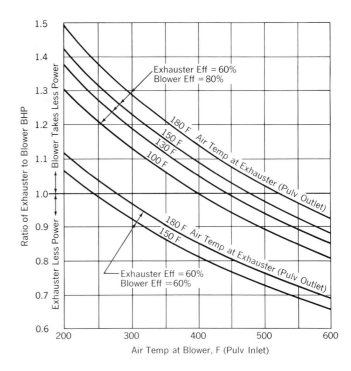

Note: Exhauster BHP increases 15% over clean-air power because of separation of coal on fan blades and direct acceleration of the coal. Assumed same pressure drops for both systems.

Fig. 13 Comparison between power consumption of blower and exhauster for given set of conditions.

Table 6
Average velocity of primary air and coal mixture through conveying pipes
Air-coal ratio, 2 lb air/lb coal

Pulverized-coal fineness, % through 200-mesh sieve	70	80	85
Normal velocity, fpm	5000	4500	4000
Minimum velocity, fpm	3000	3000	3000

Fig. 13 shows average relative power consumption, under given conditions, for a standard commercial blower handling clean air and a fan used as an exhauster handling coal-laden air.

Cost of pulverizing coal

The operating costs per unit of output are affected by (a) size of the installation, (b) characteristics of the coal, and (c) fineness of the finished product.

The life of the grinding elements of a pulverizer may vary from 6000 to 32,000 hours of operation or more. The rate of wear is generally a function of the pyrite sulfur levels and free silica in the coal. This may be com-

pounded by increased ash levels. The operating cost per unit of output is a function of the total coal pulverized during the life of the grinding elements. The maintenance cost is usually expressed in cost per ton of coal pulverized. For direct-firing systems, the power consumption per ton of coal delivered to the burners is the sum of the power required to drive (a) the auxiliaries delivering coal to the pulverizer, (b) the pulverizer, and (c) the fan delivering air to the pulverizer and coal to the burners.

Pulverized-coal burning equipment

As for oil and gas, the burner is the principal equipment component for the firing of pulverized coal, and much of the discussion relative to the burning of oil and gas (Chapter 7) is basically applicable to pulverized coal. However, the use of solid fuel in pulverized form presents additional problems in the design of boilers and furnaces.

As oil must be atomized to expose a large amount of oil particle surface to combustion air, so coal must be pulverized to the point where particles are small enough, i.e., surface is sufficiently large per unit of mass to assure proper combustion. Fineness requirements are listed in Table 3. Low 50 mesh fineness levels indicate proper classification and low unburned combustible losses.

In the direct-firing system the coal is dried and delivered to the burner in suspension in the primary air, and this mixture must be adequately mixed with the secondary air at the burner (*see Pulverized-Coal Systems and Direct-Firing System*).

Piping and nozzle sizing requirements

Size selection of pulverized-coal piping and burner nozzles requires flow velocities that are high enough to keep the coal particles in suspension in the primary air stream.

Modern pulverizers generally use 40 to 70% of their full-load air-flow requirement at zero output. Horizontally arranged burner nozzles should be sized for no less than 3000 fpm at the minimum pulverizer capacity. Vertically disposed coal nozzles may be sized for velocities as low as 2200 fpm, the actual value depending on the burner configuration used (*see Application of Pulverized-Coal Systems*).

Stability of ignition

To assure stability of ignition the temperature of the primary air and coal leaving the pulverizer must be at least 130F for units burning coal with 30 + percent volatile matter, going up to temperatures as high as 180F where the volatile matter of the coal is as low as 22%.

Standards of burner performance

Operators of pulverized-coal equipment should expect burner performance to meet the following conditions:

1. The rate of feed of the coal and air must comply with the load demand over a predetermined operating range. For most modern applications ignition of the pulverized coal should be stable, without the use of supporting fuel, over a load range of approximately 3 to 1. Most steam boilers are equipped with a multiplicity of burners so that a wider capacity range is readily obtained by varying the number of burners and pulverizers in use.

2. Unburned combustible loss should be less than 2%. With most well designed and coordinated installations it is possible to keep the unburned combustible loss under 1% with excess air in the range of 15 to 22%, measured at the furnace outlet.

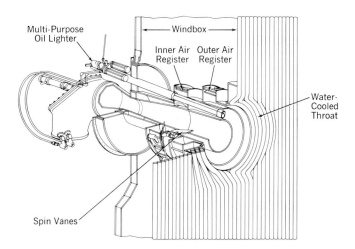

Fig. 15 Circular dual register pulverized coal burner.

3. The burner should not require adjustments to maintain flame shape. The design should avoid the formation of deposits that may interfere with the continued efficient and reliable performance of the burner over the operating range.

4. Only minor repairs should be necessary during the annual overhaul. Burner parts subject to abrasion may require replacement at more frequent intervals. Alloy steel should be used for parts that cannot be protected by cooling or other means, to avoid damage from high temperatures.

5. Safety must be paramount under all conditions of operation.

Modern burner types

As with oil and gas, the most frequently used burners are the circular types. Fig. 14 shows a circular single register type burner and Fig. 15 shows a circular dual register type burner, both designed for firing pulverized coal only. They can be used singly or in multiples. The dual register type was developed for NO_x reduction (*see Oxides of Nitrogen, Chapter 18*). Either of these burner types can be equipped to fire any combination of the three principal fuels. However, combination pulverized-coal firing with oil in the same burner should be restricted to short emergency periods. It is not recommended for long operating periods due to possible coke formation on the pulverized-coal element.

The maximum nozzle input per individual burner is 165 million Btu per hr. The secondary-air port velocity at full load on the boiler ranges from 4000 fpm for small boilers where unheated secondary air is used, to 6000 fpm for a dry-ash-removal furnace with 600F air. When circular burners are installed in slag tap furnaces velocities of 7500 fpm are common.

Fig. 16 shows the arrangement of pulverized-coal-firing equipment for an electric utility boiler in the West. Fig. 17 is a photograph of pulverized-coal burners installed in a steam-electric generating plant in the Central Appalachian region.

Lighters (ignitors) and pilots

Ignition and control equipment available for pulverized-coal firing is similar to that for oil and gas, although

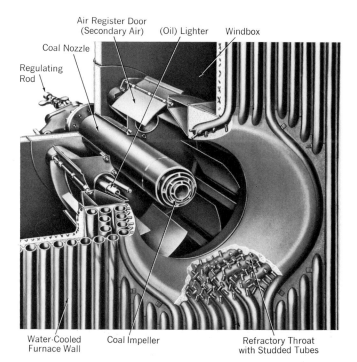

Fig. 14 Circular register burner for pulverized-coal firing.

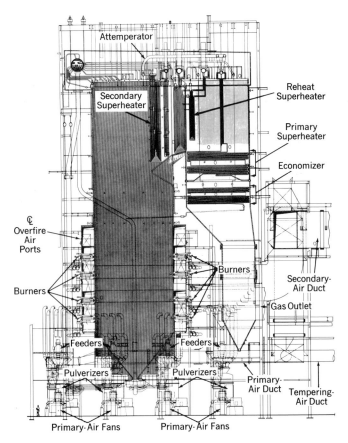

Fig. 16 Radiant boiler fired with pulverized coal in the Rocky Mountain area.

there are differences in the way it is used. In the case of starting up on pulverized coal, it may be necessary to keep the ignitors in operation until the temperature in the combustion zone becomes high enough to assure self-sustaining ignition of the main fuel.

The self-igniting characteristics of pulverized coal vary from one fuel to another, but on most coals it should be possible to maintain ignition without auxiliary fuel down to one-third capacity of the boiler. In some instances completely reliable ignition is obtained down to a quarter load. When firing pulverized coal with volatile matter less than 25%, it may be necessary to activate the ignitors even at high loads. This can occur with any coal if it is excessively wet, or feeding sporadically into the pulverizers. If the ignitor is not activated during the intervals when coal is not reaching the pulverizer, or is reaching it in small amounts, ignition of the burner may be lost momentarily; then upon reestablishing coal flow, the burner may ignite with explosive force from an adjacent burner.

Excess air

Pulverized coal requires more excess air for satisfactory combustion than either oil or natural gas (Table 5, Chapter 6). One reason for this is the inherent maldistribution of coal both to individual burner pipes and to the fuel discharge nozzles. The minimum acceptable quantity of unburned combustible is usually obtained with 15% excess air as measured at the furnace outlet at high loads. This allows for the normal maldistribution of both primary-air-coal and secondary air. Higher ex-

cess air values may be necessary to avoid slagging or fouling of the heat absorption equipment.

In the design of the burner and furnace of a pulverized-coal-fired unit, consideration must be given to the burner arrangement and furnace configuration to minimize slagging or fouling from coal ash. Increasing excess air will permit most designs to perform satisfactorily but this can be an uneconomical long-time substitute for good basic design.

Operating range or load range

In general, the pulverizer-burner combination can operate satisfactorily from full load to approximately 40% of full load with all pulverizers and burners in service. In some installations a pulverizer and set of burners, in addition to the number actually required, is provided to assure availability of the boiler unit in case of unscheduled outage of a pulverizer. Where spares are provided, it is generally most economical to operate with the greatest number of burners and pulverizers in service consistent with the capacity demand on the unit. Although the use of this excess equipment raises the minimum load which can be obtained without cutting out pulverizers and burners, other benefits offset this disadvantage.

It is easier to pick up load with an operating pulverizer than to bring an idle unit into service. Also, at high loads on a boiler unit air leakage through idle burners raises the overall excess air in the unit as this leakage does not enter into the combustion reaction but is excess air which lowers the boiler efficiency.

As the output of the boiler unit is reduced from full load, it is desirable to reduce the number of pulverizers and burners in service to avoid settling of pulverized coal in the burner piping or burner nozzles. It may also be necessary or advisable to activate the ignition fuel to sustain ignition of the coal fire because of the reduced furnace temperature that prevails at the lower load.

Where a unit has no more than two pulverizers it is usually satisfactory to take individual burners out of service as the boiler load is reduced and thus maintain adequate burner line and nozzle velocities. For units with three pulverizers or more, it is better to take a pulverizer and its full complement of burners out of service or bring it back into service, on a change in load.

Idle burners are subject to considerable radiant heat from the furnace and can attain temperatures above the coking temperatures of the coals. The use of alloy metals provides longer life for burner parts. However, if they are not adequately cooled below the coking temperature before being placed in service, coke may form and cause severe damage to the parts. The easiest way to cool the nozzle is to run cold primary air through the pulverizer and burners for five to ten minutes and then immediately feed coal before the nozzles can reheat. It is for this reason that a pulverizer and its group of burners should be operated as a unit rather than as individual burners. There is no simple way to air cool individual burners before bringing them into service.

Large boilers with air heaters have a sizable "heat inertia" which requires upward of 6 hours at full load for temperatures throughout the unit to stabilize. Conversely, a significant time period is necessary for them to retrograde on dropping load. When a fuel containing

Fig. 17 Installation for pulverized coal firing in an electric utility boiler located in the Central Appalachian region.

ash—either oil or pulverized coal—is burned, the length of time for temperatures to stabilize increases.

Starting cold boilers and operating at low loads

Starting with pulverized coal probably is next safest to gas. While coal is difficult to ignite and probably will require continuous operation of the ignitors, the unburned fuel that escapes is dry dust with a high-ignition temperature. It does not cling readily to surfaces and is carried out of the unit with the products of combustion. The only potential problem is dust that accumulates in hoppers under boiler components or in dust collectors. These should be emptied frequently so the unburned material cannot build up to a point where it may ignite and burn with damaging effect.

Oil ignitors that use steam or air to atomize can be used for sustaining ignition of pulverized coal during start-ups with little risk of air heater fires. Only a small amount of oil is used and the resulting deposits are inconsequential.

Application of pulverized-coal systems

Coordination of pulverizers and burners

To design a system for pulverized coal, components must be chosen to function together over the load range desired. In a storage system all auxiliary equipment must be selected to operate at its most efficient point when the pulverizer is at maximum rating. In a direct-firing system the pulverizer and its burners have to be considered as a unit and selected not only to meet maximum load requirements but also to provide a stable operating minimum load. Because of variations in coal, in job requirements, and in equipment ratings, each application must be considered separately.

Pulverizer and burner coordination curves, (Fig. 18) can be plotted to show the maximum capability, the operating range, and the permissible limits of both the pulverizer and its burners. The curves shown in Fig. 18 have been developed for B&W equipment and design parameters.

1. *Curve A.* The maximum steam flow must be known. In this example 2,800,000 pounds per hour is used. The heat input to the furnace divided by the Btu per pound coal, as fired, gives the coal rate (lb/hr) required for the boiler. The number of pulverizers is then determined. The choice is then made on the basis of operating load range or permissible loss of load if one pulverizer is out of service, or on available pulverizer size. Five pulverizers are selected to meet all the customer specifications. The performance coal required per pulverizer is 97,300 pounds per hour with all five pulverizers in service. The pulverizer capacity is fixed by the fineness of the pulverized coal (Table 3) and its grindability. A fineness of 70% through a 200 mesh screen and a grindability of 49 are used in the example. Figure 10 gives a capacity factor of 0.98 for these values. Dividing the coal required by the capacity factor gives the base capacity required for the pulverizer, i.e., 99,300 pounds per hour. A pulverizer with a base capacity of 124,000 pounds per hour is required to meet the customer's specifications when firing other fuels. Curve "A" can now be plotted as a straight line by drawing a line from zero through 97,300 pounds of coal and extending this line to 122,000 pounds of coal per hour. 122,000 is the pulverizer capacity on the performance coal.

2. *Curve B.* Each size of pulverizer is designed to operate at a specific air flow. The full-load air flow for the MPS-89 is 55,800 outlet cfm at 150F coal-air temperature. The air flow curve is a straight line from 100% coal flow down to 50% air flow at 16% coal

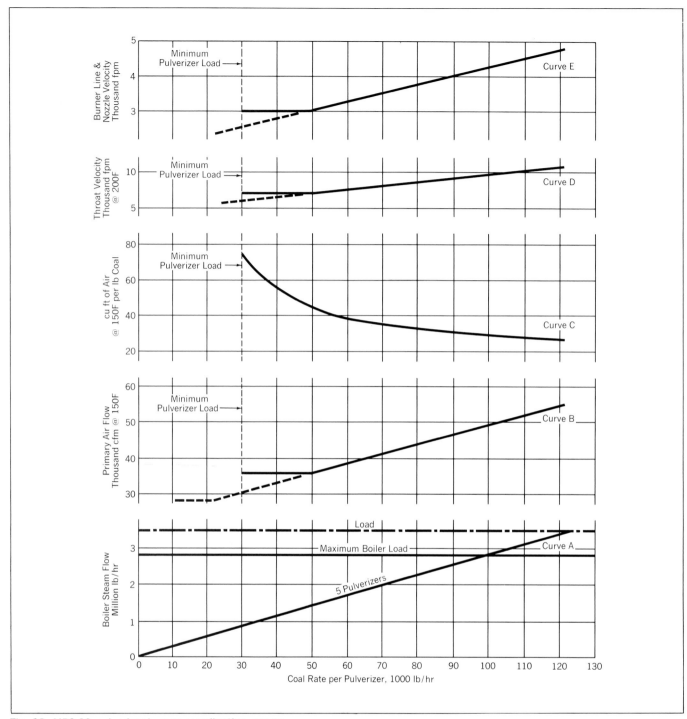

Fig. 18 MPS-89 pulverizer-burner coordination curves.

flow. The minimum pulverizer air flow may be higher than 50%. The minimum pulverizer air flow is the largest of the air flows for the following three values: (a) minimum burner line velocity of 3000 fpm, (b) minimum pulverizer throat velocity of 7000 fpm with 200F, or (c) maximum ft³ air per pound coal reached. This value is based on the type of coal being burned. In this case the maximum ft³ air per pound of coal is 70. This curve shows the primary air going through each pulverizer and with all burners in service.

3. *Curve C*. This air-fuel ratio curve is obtained by dividing air flow rate by coal per unit of time. This

curve is helpful in showing when the mixture gets too "lean" for stable ignition. The limit is a function of the volatile matter in the coal. For the coal used in this example, 70 cubic feet of 150F air is possible with stable ignition. The limit line can be drawn at this point.

4. *Curve D*. The passage where the air enters the pulverizer grinding zone is called the throat. The velocity of the air at this point prevents coal from falling down through the throat and being rejected from the bottom of the pulverizer. The minimum throat velocity for an MPS-89 is 7000 fpm based on 200F air.

5. *Curve E.* This curve has more sizing criteria than the others. The number of burners per pulverizer is based on the pulverizer capacity and the Btu content of the fuel. This is due to the fact that the Btu dual register burner is limited to 125,000,000 Btu input with all burners in service. In this example, the burner line velocities and burner nozzle velocities are the same. This is not always the case. Burner lines are sized based on 5500 fpm maximum velocity and a minimum of 3000 fpm. In the case of the MPS-89, the minimum air flow should not be lower than 50%. The burner nozzle velocity is limited to 5500 fpm also. This example is based on six 20-in. OD ½-in. wall burner lines with 20-in. burner nozzles per pulverizer.

The coordination curves developed above show that the pulverizer air flow is decreased linearly from a maximum pulverizer capacity of 122,000 pounds per hour down to 49,000 pounds per hour coal flow. Below 49,000 coal flow the air flow is held constant. This air flow relationship is due to the requirement of a minimum burner line velocity of 3000 fpm. A smaller size burner line would allow us to lower the pulverizer air flow, however, the higher velocities at a given load would result in increased fan power and burner line erosion. The minimum pulverizer load of 30,000 coal flow is due to the ft³ air per pound of coal reaching the maximum

value of 70. This range should be entirely possible on automatic control with little or no attention from the operator. Under starting conditions, with extremely low firing rates, some burners may be shut off to permit operation of a pulverizer at a lower rating. Where coals of different characteristics must be fired, as is frequently the case, pulverizer and burner performance on each coal should be plotted on the coordination curves. When the coals vary widely, flexibility of operation of the boiler may be severely curtailed.

Pulverized coal in the metals and cement industries

Application of pulverized-coal firing to copper- and nickel-ore smelting and refining has been standard practice for many years. With the use of pulverized coal, high-purity metal can be obtained since the furnace atmosphere and temperature can be easily controlled. Beside a possible price differential favoring pulverized coal over other fuels, the advantages of pulverized coal are the high rate of smelting and refining and the ready ability to oxidize the sulfur.

Copper reverberatory furnaces for both smelting and refining are fitted with waste-heat boilers for the generation of steam. These boilers supply a substantial portion of power for auxiliary equipment and also provide the means for cooling the gases leaving the furnace. A typical

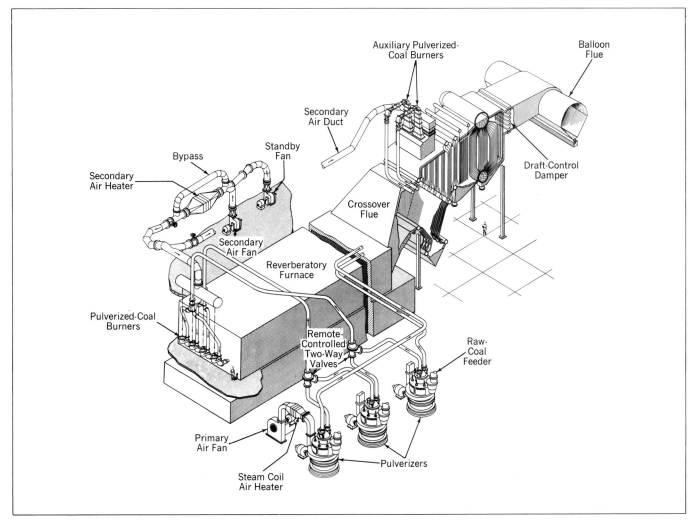

Fig. 19 Direct-fired copper-reverberatory-furnace and waste-heat-boiler arrangement.

direct-firing copper reverberatory furnace with waste-heat-boiler arrangement is shown in Fig. 19.

An interesting application of pulverized coal is as a reducing agent in the recovery of zinc from lead blast-furnace and copper-reverberatory-furnace slags. Lead-bearing ores contain an appreciable amount of zinc and other metals that remain in the slag after smelting. The slag-fuming process by which these metals are recovered is not new. However, by applying modern methods of preparing, distributing, and firing pulverized coal, the fuming can now be done directly, automatically, and more efficiently.

Approximately 65 to 70% of all the malleable-iron tonnage produced in this country is made from white cast iron that is melted in a low-head air furnace of the reverberatory type, burning pulverized coal in a direct-firing system with forced-draft burners. In producing malleable iron castings, the hard white iron is converted to a tough, ductile, machineable iron by annealing, which transforms the combined carbon (iron carbide) to free carbon, known as temper-carbon. Pulverized coal is especially suitable for this purpose because of better heat distribution and greater economy than with oil or gas.

In the production of cement, fuel cost is one of the major items of expense. The first consideration, therefore, in deciding on the type of firing in the manufacture of cement is the price of fuel. In general, except in locations where the cost differential is in favor of oil or gas, pulverized coal is universally used in the industry. Direct firing, with a single pulverizer delivering coal to a single burner, is common practice in the majority of the cement plants in this country. The waste-heat air from the clinker cooler, taken from the top of the kiln hood through a suitable dust collector, usually serves as the preheated air for drying the coal in the pulverizer.

A new field for the use of pulverized coal is in the steel industry where it is injected into the blast furnace tuyeres. The pulverized coal thus injected replaces approximately an equal weight of higher-priced coke. Theoretically 40% of the coke could be replaced by pulverized coal.

Safety precautions

Since a mixture of pulverized coal in air can be readily burned to accomplish complete combustion, it is not surprising that suspension of coal dust in air can be explosive. Hence, it is basic that dispersion of pulverized coal or dust in air must not exist except at locations where it is essential to the process and where conditions are understood and controlled at all times. (Reference applicable National Fire Protection Association code).

Since fine dust can be lifted into the air by means which are not always expected or predictable, it is important to avoid accumulation of coal dust anywhere in the plant except in coal storage spaces. Even there the suspension of dust in the air must be avoided. In general, it is hazardous to blow dust off surfaces with air lances. Vacuum cleaners are preferred.

The fundamental principles forming the basis for safety precautions and burner lighting and operating sequences are basically the same with pulverized coal as with oil and gas (Chapter 7).

These rules can be stated for coal in abbreviated form:

1. Never allow coal dust to accumulate except in specified storage facilities.

2. Never allow a mixture of coal or dust suspension in air to exist except in drying, pulverizing or burner equipment and the necessary transportation ducts.

3. Purge the furnace and setting before introducing any light or spark.

4. Have a lighted torch or spark-producing device in operation before introducing fuel into a furnace.

5. Maintain a positive flow of secondary air through the burners into the furnace and up the stack.

6. Maintain a positive primary-air-coal flow to burners.

Compliance with these rules requires an alert operating staff and good housekeeping throughout the plant.

Automatic installations include interlocks, a flame detector, and shutoff provisions paralleling those listed for oil and gas firing in Chapter 7.

Chapter 10

Cyclone Furnaces

Over the years continuing advances have been made in the methods of burning coal. The introduction of pulverized-coal firing in the 1920's was a major advance, providing advantages over stoker firing as listed in Chapter 9. Today, pulverized-coal firing is highly developed and is still the best way to burn many types of coal, particularly the higher grades and ranks.

Another method of burning coal, the Cyclone Furnace, has been developed and is now widely used.

The Cyclone Furnace is applicable to coals having a slag viscosity of 250 poises at 2600F or lower, provided the ash analysis does not indicate excessive formation of iron or iron pyrites (*see Suitability of Fuels for the Cyclone Furnace*). With these coals, Cyclone-Furnace firing provides the benefits obtainable with pulverized-coal firing plus the following advantages:

1. Reduction in fly ash content in the flue gas.
2. Saving in the cost of fuel preparation, since only crushing is required instead of pulverization.
3. Reduction in furnace size.

For further understanding a discussion of the combustion of coal particles may be helpful, particularly if this is considered in the framework of the "three T's" of combustion (Chapter 6) with special emphasis on turbulence (mixing) and time.

When coal is burned in boiler furnaces, the combustion of hydrogen is accomplished without difficulty, but successful combustion of carbon to CO_2 requires special measures to assure a continuing supply of oxygen in contact with carbon particles as long as they remain unburned. Not only must there be intimate mixing of the coal particles and air; there must also be sufficient turbulence to remove the combustion products as they form at the surface of the fuel and provide fresh air at the fuel surface to continue combustion. The greater the turbulence the more rapid the process; hence less time is required for combustion.

With pulverized-coal firing, the coal is reduced to a powder, so fine that approximately 70 percent will pass a 200-mesh screen. The finely pulverized coal is then very intimately mixed with combustion air in the burner; however, after this initial mixing the tiny coal particles are merely carried along in the air stream, and very little additional scrubbing by the air occurs. Thus, further contact of oxygen with the coal must be largely by diffusion. The furnace consequently has to be relatively large to give the necessary retention time for oxygen to diffuse through the blanketing CO_2 layer to reach the coal particles and, at the same time, temperatures must be sufficiently high to complete combustion. After combustion, since the residual ash particles are much smaller than even the original tiny pulverized-coal particles, the former are easily carried along with the flue gases from the furnace and through the boiler setting.

At the same time the pulverized-coal-fired boiler furnace also has the function of cooling the combustion

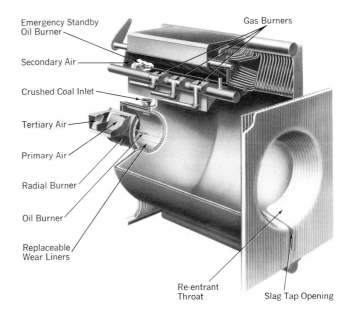

Emergency Standby Oil Burner

Secondary Air

Crushed Coal Inlet

Tertiary Air

Primary Air

Radial Burner

Oil Burner

Replaceable Wear Liners

Gas Burners

Re-entrant Throat

Slag Tap Opening

Fig. 1 The Cyclone Furnace, in the form of a horizontal cylinder, is completely water cooled by connection to the main boiler circulation. All combustion gases leave through the re-entrant throat at the rear. Molten slag drains from the bottom at the rear through a small opening into the adjacent boiler furnace.

gases, so that when they enter the convection surfaces they are below the temperature at which slagging occurs. This function conflicts with that of maintaining the high temperatures necessary to complete combustion. It would therefore be advantageous to separate these functions by providing a separate small combustion chamber where high turbulence and temperature may be maintained, and using the main boiler furnace primarily to cool the combustion gases.

For many years engineers recognized this need and actively explored basic changes in the design of furnaces and fuel-burning equipment to improve combustion and furnace performance. In addition, significant changes in availability and use of coal further increased the need for new designs, e.g., demands for higher grades of coal have depleted many seams, and others have been reserved for metallurgical and other uses.

Washing is widely used to lower ash and sulfur contents; however, this is an added expense (*see Chapter 8*). The industrial growth of the Western portion of the country, rich in reserves of subbituminous and lignitic coal, is rapidly increasing the consumption of these lower ranks of coal. This has furthered the need for equipment fully suitable for the lower grades and ranks of high-ash, low-fusion-temperature coal. The Cyclone Furnace is an outgrowth of efforts to meet these needs and to overcome difficulties encountered with other firing methods.

Principle of operation

The Cyclone Furnace (Fig. 1) is a water-cooled horizontal cylinder in which fuel is fired, heat is released at extremely high rates, and combustion is completed. Its water-cooled surfaces are studded, and covered with refractory over most of their area (*see Chapter 16*). Coal crushed in a simple crusher, so that approximately 95 percent will pass a 4-mesh screen, is introduced into the burner end of the cyclone. About 20 percent of the combustion air, termed primary air, also enters the burner tangentially and imparts a whirling motion to the incoming coal. Secondary air with a velocity of approximately 300 fps is admitted in the same direction tangentially at the roof of the main barrel of the cyclone and imparts a further whirling or centrifugal action to the

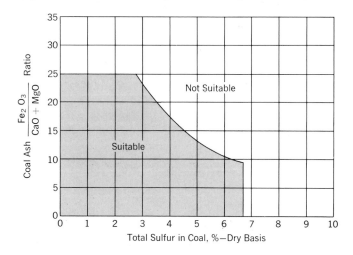

Fig. 2 Coal suitability for Cyclone Furnaces based on tendency to form iron and iron sulfide.

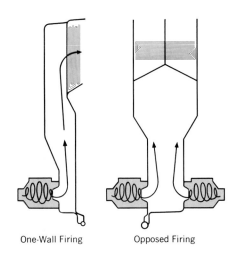

One-Wall Firing   Opposed Firing

Fig. 3 Firing arrangements used with Cyclone Furnaces.

coal particles. A small amount of air (up to about 5%) is admitted at the center of the burner. This is known as "tertiary" air (Fig. 1).

The combustible is burned from the fuel at heat release rates of 450,000 to 800,000 Btu/cu ft, hr, and gas temperatures exceeding 3000F are developed. These temperatures are sufficiently high to melt the ash into a liquid slag, which forms a layer on the walls of the cyclone. The incoming coal particles (except for a few fines that are burned in suspension) are thrown to the walls by centrifugal force, held in the slag, and scrubbed by the high-velocity tangential secondary air. Thus the air required to burn the coal is quickly supplied, and the products of combustion are rapidly removed.

The release of heat per cu ft in the Cyclone Furnace is very high. However, there is only a small amount of surface in the cyclone and this surface is partially insulated by the covering slag layer. Heat absorption rates range from 40,000 to 80,000 Btu/sq ft, hr. This combination of high heat release and low heat absorption assures the high temperatures necessary to complete combustion and to provide the desired liquid slag covering of the surface.

The gaseous products of combustion are discharged through the water-cooled re-entrant throat of the cyclone (Fig. 1) into the gas-cooling boiler furnace. Molten slag in excess of the thin layer retained on the walls continually drains away from the burner end and discharges through the slag tap opening, shown in Fig. 1, to the boiler furnace, from which it is tapped into a slag tank, solidified, and disintegrated for disposal (*see Slag Handling Equipment*).

By this method of combustion the fuel is burned quickly and completely in the small cyclone chamber, and the boiler furnace is used only for cooling the flue gases. Most of the ash is retained as a liquid slag and tapped into the slag tank under the boiler furnace. Thus, the quantity of fly-ash is low.

Suitability of fuels for the Cyclone Furnace

The Cyclone Furnace is capable of burning successfully a large variety of fuels. A wide range of coals varying in rank from low volatile bituminous to lignite may be successfully burned, and in addition other solid fuels such

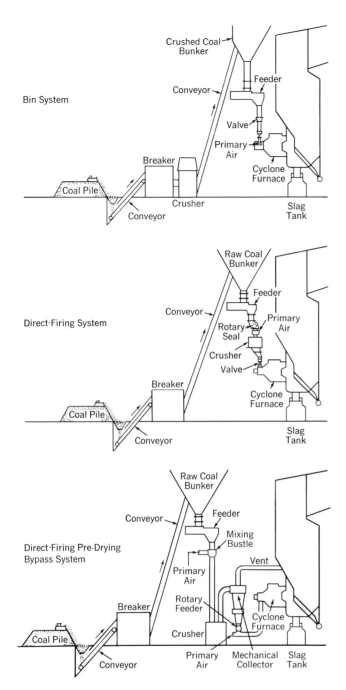

Fig. 4 Bin, direct-firing, and direct-firing pre-drying bypass systems for coal preparation and feeding to the Cyclone Furnace (schematic).

as wood, bark, coal chars, refuse, and petroleum coke may be satisfactorily fired in combinations with other fossil fuels. Fuel oils and gases are also suitable for firing.

The suitability of coals is dependent on the moisture, ash and volatile contents of the coal together with the chemical composition of the ash. The volatile matter should be higher than 15 percent, on a dry basis, to obtain the required high combustion rate. The ash content should be a minimum of about 6 percent to provide a proper slag coating in the cyclone and can be as high as 25 percent on a dry basis. A wide range of moisture content is permissible depending on coal rank, secondary air temperature and fuel preparation equipment that may include capability for pre-drying the fuel.

One of the two important criteria for coal suitability is the total amount of sulfur compared to the ratio of iron to calcium and magnesium (Fig. 2). This comparison gives an indication of the tendency of the coal to form iron and iron sulfide, both of which are very undesirable in the Cyclone Furnace. Coals with too high sulfur content and/or a high iron ratio are not considered suitable.

The other important criterion for establishing the suitability of coal for firing in the cyclone is the viscosity of the slag formed from the ash. Since satisfactory combustion of coal depends on the formation of a liquid slag layer in the cyclone, and since ash is removed from the cyclone and primary furnace in fluid form, the viscosity of the slag must permit slag flow at the temperatures experienced in the cyclone and primary furnace. Field experience with many different coals together with extensive investigation of ash characteristics has provided information for evaluating coal suitability, from a slag tapping standpoint.

Slag will just flow on a horizontal surface at a viscosity of 250 poises. The temperature at which this viscosity occurs (T_{250}) is used as the criterion to determine the suitability of a coal from this point of view. The T_{250} is calculated from a chemical analysis of the coal ash, and a value of 2600F is considered maximum (*see Viscosity of Coal-Ash Slag, Chapter 15*). Somewhat lower temperatures may be desirable for fuels with high moisture contents and low heating values.

The suitability of other solid fuels such as wood, bark, refuse, petroleum coke or chars must be considered on an individual basis and the amount of supplementary fuel carefully calculated.

Design features

Boiler furnace

The two general firing arrangements used for the Cyclone Furnace are one-wall firing and opposed firing. These are shown in Fig. 3. For smaller units, sufficient firing capacity is usually attained with Cyclone Furnaces located in only one wall. For large units, furnace width can often be reduced by using opposed firing.

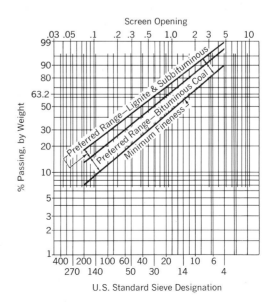

Fig. 5 Sizing of crushed coal fired in the Cyclone Furnace.

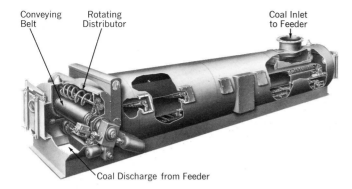

Fig. 6 Belt-type coal feeder for the Cyclone Furnace.

Cyclone Furnace capacities

The size and number of Cyclone Furnaces used to fire a given boiler depend primarily on the boiler size and the load flexibility required. They are built commercially in sizes ranging from 6 ft diameter through 10 ft diameter, with an allowable maximum heat input per furnace of about 160 million to 425 million Btu/hr, respectively.

Coal preparation

There are two general types of coal preparation and feeding (see Fig. 4), the bin or storage system and the direct-firing system. The former is preferred for most bituminous coals when the plant layout permits. The range of sizing of crushed coal required with either system is given in Fig. 5.

With the bin system, coal is crushed in a central preparation plant to a size suitable for firing, and the crushed coal is delivered to the bunker. Because the crushed coal is relatively large in particle size, the hazards associated with pulverized-coal systems do not exist. The only precaution necessary is to provide adequate venting of the bunkers to assure removal of the small amounts of combustible gases released from freshly crushed coal of certain types. With the bin system there is less equipment in the boiler room, and short crusher outages can be accommodated without interrupting boiler operation.

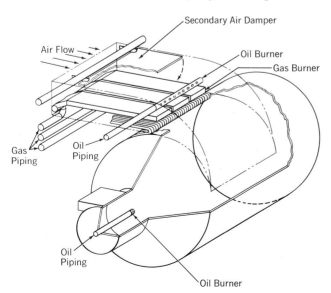

Fig. 7 Arrangement of gas and oil burner in Cyclone Furnace.

The second method of coal preparation is the direct-firing system, which has a separate crusher located between the feeder and the burner of each Cyclone Furnace. The crusher is swept by hot air, and the intimate mixing of coal and hot air in the crusher helps to dry the coal. This improves crusher performance and ignition with high moisture coals. It is often easier to accommodate the direct-firing system in existing plants, where the coal handling equipment cannot readily be adapted to the bin system.

The direct-firing, pre-drying, bypass system (Fig. 4) is a variation of the second method, incorporating a mechanical dust collector between the crusher and the Cyclone Furnace. The collector is vented to the boiler furnace. This system is used when firing extremely high moisture coals. Its advantage is that moisture is removed from the coal during crushing and then vented to the boiler furnace instead of the Cyclone Furnace. This maintains maximum temperature in the cyclone with improved performance and slag tapping characteristics.

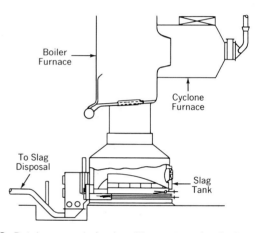

Fig. 8 Batch-removal slag-handling system for Cyclone-Furnace boiler.

Coal feeders

The coal feeders normally used are of the belt type, illustrated in Fig. 6. A rotating distributor is provided at the coal discharge from the feeder to assure a continuous and uniform rate of feed. This is necessary because the coal is burned almost instantaneously when it reaches the Cyclone Furnace, and fluctuations in feed are reflected in combustion conditions. The rapidity of combustion makes the Cyclone Furnace very responsive to load demands, and it has been demonstrated that boiler output can be made to respond very quickly to demand by changing coal-feeder speed. Continuous weighing devices can be applied to the belt feeder so that it can serve the dual function of coal scale and feeder.

Feeders of other types may also be used. Some are equipped with an angled cutoff plate at the coal discharge from the feeder to provide a uniform rate of feed.

Oil and gas burners

Oil and gas, as previously noted, are satisfactory cyclone fuels. These fuels can be burned at ratings and with performance equal to those with coal firing. Oil may be injected either into the secondary air stream or through the center of the front coal burner (see Fig. 7), where

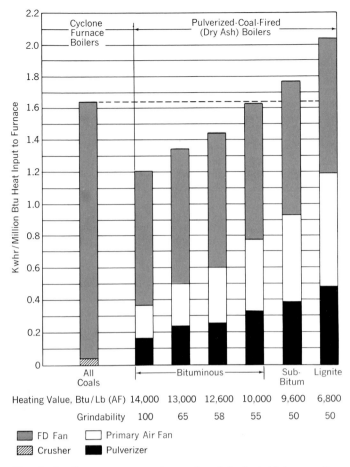

Fig. 9 Auxiliary power requirements of typical high-capacity pressure-fired Cyclone-Furnace and pulverized-coal units.

the oil is picked up and atomized by the high velocity air stream. Gas is fired through flat ports located in the secondary air entrance to the cyclone. The gas burners and the oil burners located in the secondary air inlet may be left in place when coal is fired. This facilitates changing from one fuel to another by remote control without removal of the Cyclone Furnace from service. This feature makes the Cyclone Furnace most attractive for the firing of multiple fuels. However Cyclone Furnaces are not normally competitive with other firing methods unless coal is to be a principal fuel (*see Cyclone-Furnace Firing, Chapter 22*).

Slag handling equipment

Slag handling equipment for a Cyclone-Furnace boiler unit is similar to that for a pulverized-coal slag-tap unit. The capacity of the slag-handling equipment must be greater since the percentage of ash recovered in the Cyclone Furnace is higher. The batch-removal system, illustrated in Fig. 8, is the system generally used. Storage tanks into which slag is continuously tapped, quenched and accumulated are located under the furnace floor. Slag is withdrawn at intervals and discharged to a storage area, from which it may be removed at will (*see Design and Operation of Slag-Tap Units, Chapter 15*).

Combustion controls

Automatic combustion controls for Cyclone-Furnace boilers are generally based on maintaining equal coal

weights and equal total air flows in the proper proportion to each Cyclone Furnace. Where volumetric type feeders are used, equal coal weights are obtained by maintaining equal feeder speeds. Where gravimetric type feeders are used, they measure and control the coal weights to the Cyclone Furnaces.

Combustion air flow is measured separately to each cyclone. Where individual ducts supply combustion air to individual cyclones, a venturi throat in each duct measures the air to each cyclone. Where cyclones are installed in a common windbox, secondary air flow is measured at the bell-mouth section of the secondary air port of each cyclone, then added to the primary and tertiary air flows of that cyclone. These flows are measured at orifices in the individual ducts.

Using these measurements, the controls maintain equal coal rates and air flows to each Cyclone Furnace.

Operating results

Fuels burned

The first commercial Cyclone-Furnace boiler was designed to burn Central Illinois coal and was installed at the Calumet Station of the Commonwealth Edison Company, Chicago, in 1944. Since then over 765 Cyclone-Furnace units have been installed in boilers throughout the United States and Europe. In this country coals of the following constituent range have been burned in commercial Cyclone-Furnace boilers:

Moisture, %	2 to 40
Volatile matter (dry), %	18 to 45
Fixed carbon (dry), %	35 to 75
Ash (dry), %	4 to 25

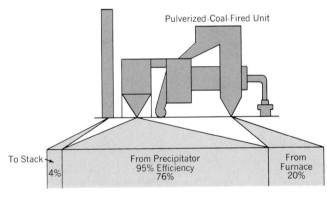

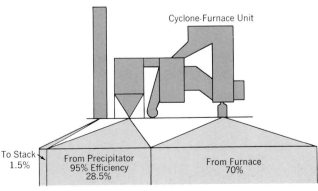

Fig. 10 Comparison of fly-ash emission from typical large dry-ash-removal pulverized-coal-fired unit and Cyclone-Furnace unit.

As mentioned previously, a number of by-products from petroleum and many waste fuels, such as bark, can be successfully burned. The petroleum products range in volatile matter from 5% for some petroleum coke to 60% for pitch. Because of the very low ash content of these petroleum by-products, it is usually necessary to add a slag-forming material or to mix the pitch with a coal having suitable ash characteristics to provide the necessary slag coating of the cyclone barrel. It may also be necessary to stabilize ignition of the low volatile coke by burning 5 to 10% auxiliary oil or gas.

Coal chars, resulting from the low-temperature carbonization of bituminous or lignitic coals having sufficient ash and volatile matter, are suitable for firing, provided the ash viscosity characteristics are suitable.

Two units designed to burn bark and bituminous coal in amounts up to approximately 50% by weight of each are in operation in a large Southern paper mill. To burn the bark successfully, it is necessary to fire sufficient coal to supply the slag coating in the cyclone and to maintain sufficiently high temperatures to provide the necessary fluidity of the slag. A chopper, or "hog", is used to reduce the bark to chips of a size suitable to the Cyclone Furnace. The chips are screened after "hogging" and oversize pieces are recycled.

Power requirements

Since the only coal preparation is crushing, the power required is low compared with that for pulverizing coal. To offset this, the forced draft fan power required is relatively high, Cyclone Furnace air pressure drop being in the range of 20 to 40 in. of water compared with 2 to

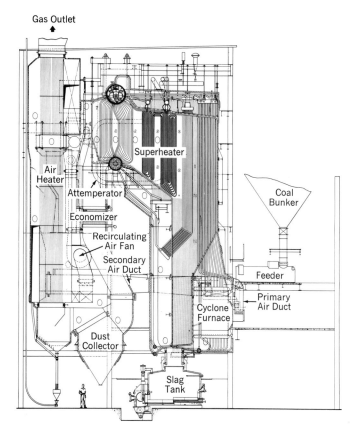

Fig. 11 Two-drum boiler with Cyclone Furnaces (one-wall) and bin system for coal preparation and feeding.

10 in. of water for pulverized-coal burners. Fig. 9 shows that the comparative power requirements vary considerably for different types of bituminous coals and lignite. For high-heating value, high-grindability bituminous coals, the Cyclone Furnace requires more power. However, for the low-heating value, low-grindability bituminous and lignite coals, for which the Cyclone Furnace is usually best suited, the power requirements are less than with pulverized-coal firing.

Combustion efficiency

The excess air required for satisfactory combustion of an individual Cyclone Furnace is less than 10 percent. However, where automatic controls are used and particularly where there are several Cyclone Furnaces for one boiler, excess air is usually maintained between 10 and 15% to assure that no individual cyclone is operating with insufficient air. When operating with coal of suitable sizing and with 10 percent excess air, the loss in efficiency from unburned combustible has been found to be less than 0.1 percent with most coals.

Ash recovery and dust collectors

The dust loading of the flue gas from coal-fired cyclone units is in the range of 20 to 30 percent of the ash in the coal, compared with about 80 percent for a dry-ash pulverized-coal-fired unit. This means that, if both units are equipped with 95 percent efficient precipitators or dust collectors, the ash discharged from the stack of a cyclone-fired unit will be less than half that from the stack of a dry-ash pulverized-coal-fired unit.

This comparison is illustrated in Fig. 10 for a large utility Cyclone-Furnace unit and a pulverized-coal unit arranged for dry ash removal. Both units are 600-megawatt capacity, each consuming approximately 7,000 tons of coal per day and producing 970 tons of ash. With pulverized-coal firing about 4 percent of the ash or 39 tons per day is discharged from the stack. Under similar operating conditions with the Cyclone-Furnace-fired unit only approximately 1.5 percent of the ash or 15 tons per day is discharged from the stack. On a Cyclone-Furnace-fired unit the fly ash collected in the precipitator may be returned to the Cyclone Furnace and recovered as slag. The slag from the furnace is chemically inert and disposal is relatively simple.

Typical Installations

Although Cyclone-Furnace units were first installed in central stations, their use has been extended to a wide variety of industries. Fig. 11 shows a unit installed in a large Northern industrial plant. The unit incorporates the bin system with one-wall firing. It is designed to produce 440,000 lb/hr of steam at 1350 psi and 905F superheat.

The designs of Cyclone-Furnace units have followed the general trend of the power industry to higher steam temperatures and pressures and larger capacities. Fig. 12 shows a Radiant boiler with one-wall firing. This unit produces 1,250,000 lb/hr of steam at 1900 psi and 1005F, with reheat to 1005F. Fig. 13 shows a Universal-Pressure once-through unit with opposed Cyclone-Furnace firing; the capacity of this unit is 8,000,000 lb of steam per hr at 3650 psi and 1003F, with 1003F reheat temperature.

Operation

Start-up

The Cyclone Furnace can be started by the continuous firing of coal, oil or gas. Coal is ignited by a permanently installed gas-lighting torch or a retractable oil-lighting torch inserted into the front of the secondary air port. With coal firing, the usual load range for good operation of an individual furnace is from 50 to 100% of rated capacity, depending on the ash characteristics; however, for short periods, such as start-up, loads of 20 to 25% can be carried with some increase in unburned combustible. The load range for continuous operation of the entire Cyclone-Furnace unit is from full to approximately half load, again depending on the ash characteristics and the furnace arrangement. For short periods such as overnight load drops, lower ratings can be carried by allowing the slag tapped from the Cyclone Furnace to accumulate and solidify on the boiler furnace floor. When the load is increased, this slag will melt and tap in the usual manner.

Maintenance

The principal items requiring maintenance are the coal crusher and the Cyclone-Furnace burner. Crusher maintenance includes replacement of hammers and grid bars at yearly or less frequent intervals, depending on the arrangement and the type of coal fired. In the burner, the coal is accelerated to the high velocity necessary to throw it against the slagged surfaces of the cyclone barrel. This high velocity causes erosion of the burner, which is minimized by the use of tungsten carbide or other erosion-resistant wear liners (Fig. 14). Since these liners normally last a year or more, they can be replaced or built up during regularly scheduled annual outages.

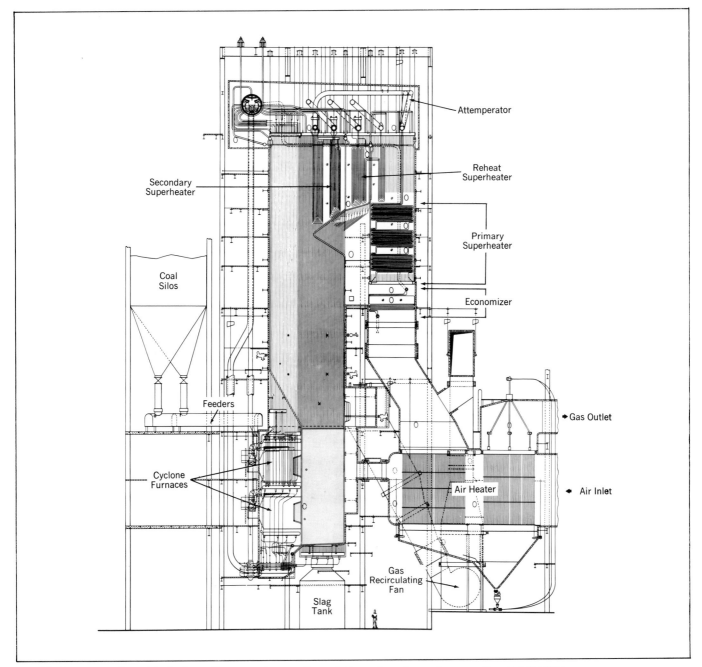

Fig. 12 Radiant boiler with Cyclone Furnaces (one-wall) and bin system for coal preparation and feeding.

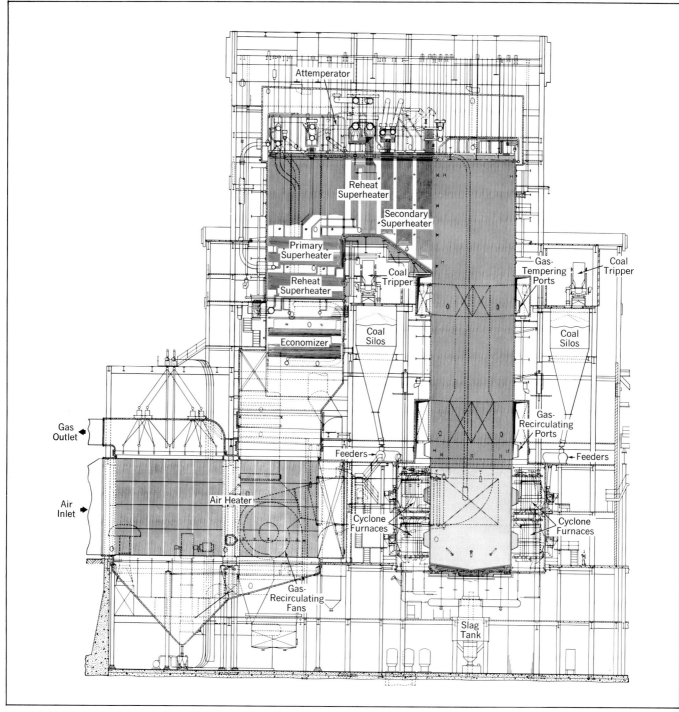

Fig. 13 Universal-Pressure boiler with opposed Cyclone Furnaces and bin system for coal preparation and feeding.

Summary

The Cyclone Furnace has made a significant contribution to the steam-power industry by improving combustion and furnace performance, by permitting the economic utilization of the lower grades and ranks of coal, and by alleviating the problems caused by coal ash. Because of this, it has gained wide acceptance in the U.S. and abroad. By 1976 about 765 Cyclone Furnaces were in service, under construction or on order for installation in the United States. These Cyclone Furnaces serve more than 155 boilers with a combined capacity of more than 220 million lb of steam per hr.

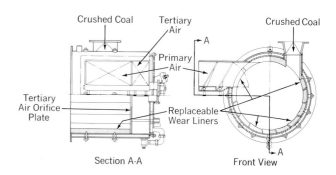

Fig. 14 Burner of Cyclone Furnace showing replaceable wear liners.

Chapter 11

Stokers

Mechanical stokers, as an improvement over hand firing, were developed early in the history of the steam boiler. Today many small and medium size boilers are fired with stokers, and several types of stokers are available. All are designed to feed fuel onto a grate within the furnace and to remove the ash residue. Higher rates of combustion are possible than with hand firing, and the continuous process of stoker firing permits good control and high efficiency.

A successful stoker installation requires the selection of the correct type and size for the fuel to be used and the desired capacity. Also, the associated boiler unit should have the necessary instruments for the proper control of the stoker. The grate area required for a given stoker type and capacity is determined from allowable rates established by experience. Table 1 lists allowable fuel burning rates (Btu/sq ft, hr) for various types of stokers, based on using coals suited to the stoker type in each case.

Table 1
Maximum allowable fuel burning rates

Type of Stoker	Btu/sq ft, hr
Spreader – stationary and dumping grate	450,000
Spreader – traveling grate	750,000
Spreader – vibrating grate	400,000
Underfeed – single or double retort	425,000
Underfeed – multiple retort	600,000
Water-cooled vibrating grate	400,000
Chain grate and traveling grate	500,000

For a boiler of a given steam capacity, these maximum fuel burning rates determine the plan area for a stoker-fired furnace. As boiler unit size is increased, practical considerations limit stoker size and, consequently, the maximum rate of steam generation with this method of firing. Because of the greater flexibility in furnace design with pulverized-coal and Cyclone-Furnace firing and the trend toward larger boiler units, the present market for stokers is less than in former years. The practical steam-output limit of boilers equipped with mechanical stokers is about 400,000 lb/hr, although many engineers limit the application of stokers to lower steam capacities. However, within their capacity range, mechanical stokers are an important and valued element of modern equipment for the production of steam or hot water. When applicable, stokers are often preferred over pulverizers because of their greater operating range, capability of burning a wide range of solid fuels, and lower power requirements.

Almost any coal can be burned successfully on some type of stoker. In addition, many by-products and waste fuels, such as coke breeze, wood wastes, pulpwood bark and bagasse can be used either as a base or auxiliary fuel.

Mechanical stokers can be classified in four main groups, based on the method of introducing fuel to the furnace:

1. Spreader stokers.
2. Underfeed stokers.
3. Water-cooled vibrating-grate stokers.
4. Chain-grate and traveling-grate stokers.

Among these several types, the spreader stoker is the most generally used in the capacity range from 75,000 to 400,000 lb of steam per hr, because it responds rapidly to load swings and can burn a wide range of fuels.

Underfeed stokers of the single-retort, ram-feed, side-ash-discharge type are used principally for heating and for small industrial units of less than 30,000 lb of steam per hr capacity. Larger size underfeed stokers of multiple-retort, rear-ash-discharge type have been largely displaced by spreader stokers and by the water-cooled vibrating-grate stokers in the intermediate range. Chain- and traveling-grate stokers, while still used in some areas, are gradually being displaced by the spreader and vibrating-grate types.

Spreader stokers

The spreader stoker is capable of burning a wide range of coals, from high-rank Eastern bituminous to lignite or brown coal and a variety of by-product waste fuels.

As the name implies, the spreader stoker projects fuel into the furnace over the fire with a uniform spreading action, permitting suspension burning of the fine fuel

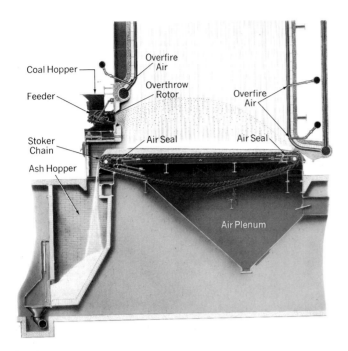

Fig. 1 Traveling-grate spreader stoker with front ash discharge.

particles (Fig. 1). The heavier pieces, that cannot be supported in the gas flow, fall to the grate for combustion in a thin fast-burning bed. This method of firing provides extreme sensitivity to load fluctuations as ignition is almost instantaneous on increase of firing rate and the thin fuel bed can be burned out rapidly when desired.

The modern spreader stoker installation consists of feeder-distributor units in widths and numbers as required to distribute the fuel uniformly over the width of the grate, specifically designed air-metering grates, forced draft fans for both undergrate and overfire air, dust collecting and reinjecting equipment, and combustion controls to coordinate fuel and air supply with load demand.

Spreader mechanism

Fig. 2 illustrates a fuel feeder-distributor unit of the variable stroke, reciprocating-feed-plate type. The reciprocating-feed plate moves coal from the supply hopper over an adjustable spill plate to fall onto an overthrow rotor. This rotor is equipped with curved blades for uniform coal distribution over the furnace area.

While the details of the several means used to feed and distribute the coal may vary with different manufacturers, the overthrow rotor design illustrated has the widest usage. The object in all cases is to provide a continuous well-distributed supply of fuel at a variable rate as required by the load demand.

Grates for spreader stoker

Spreader-stoker firing is old in principle and based on many experiments conducted over the years. It became practical in the early 1930's when specially designed high-resistance air-metering grates were coupled with adequate spreader-feeder mechanisms. The first of these metering grates was a stationary type, with the ash removed manually through the front doors. This limited application to boilers of 20,000 to 30,000 lb of steam per hr capacity.

Stationary grates were soon followed by dumping-grate designs in which grate sections are provided for each feeder, and the undergrate air plenum chambers are correspondingly divided. This permits the temporary discontinuance of fuel and air supply to a grate section for ash removal without affecting other sections of the stoker.

Introduction of the continuous-ash-discharge traveling grate of the air-metering design in the later 1930's brought the spreader stoker into immediate and widespread popularity. Since there are no interruptions for removing ashes, and because of the thin, fast-burning fuel bed, average burning rates were increased approximately 70% over the stationary and dumping grate types. This type stoker is generally competitive in sizes up to about 525 sq ft of grate area, corresponding to steam capacity somewhat over 400,000 lb of steam per hr. The furnace width required for stokers above this size usually results in increased boiler costs as compared to pulverized-coal- or Cyclone-Furnace-fired units with narrower and higher furnaces.

Although continuous-cleaning grates of reciprocating and vibrating designs have also been developed, the continuous-ash-discharge traveling-grate stoker is preferred for large boilers because of its higher burning rates.

The normal practice of all continuous-ash-discharge spreader stokers is to remove the ashes at the front or feeding end of the stoker. This permits the most satisfactory fuel distribution pattern and provides maximum residence time on the grates for complete combustion of the fuel.

The traveling-grate spreader stoker (Fig. 1) has self-adjusting air seals at both the front and rear of the grate. These effectively reduce leakage and stratification of air along the front and rear furnace walls, where it cannot be efficiently utilized in the combustion process.

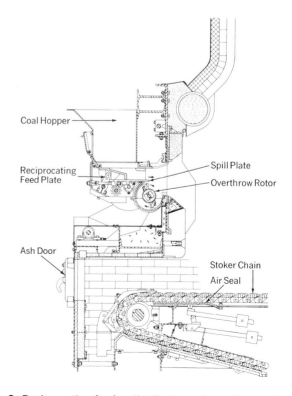

Fig. 2 Reciprocating-feeder distributor and overthrow rotor for spreader stokers.

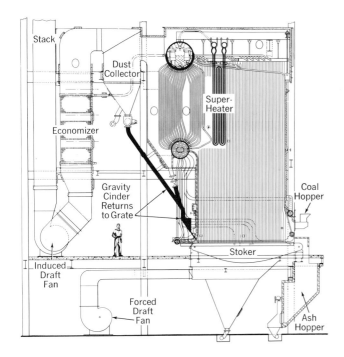

Fig. 3 Spreader-stoker installation with gravity fly-carbon return.

Furnace design

An example of good furnace design is shown in Fig. 3 which also illustrates the fly-carbon reinjection system, discussed later in this chapter. This unit has water-cooled walls which are actually a necessity for traveling or continuous-cleaning spreader-stoker grates where slag or clinker formation adjacent to the stoker would interfere with movement of the fuel bed. Furnaces with refractory walls are sometimes installed with stationary or intermittent dumping-grate spreader stokers, but the high maintenance cost of such refractories makes this application questionable. The water walls are usually vertical, or nearly so, as arches are not desirable.

An overfire air system, with pressures from 27 to 30 in. of water (gage), is essential to successful suspension burning. It is customary to provide at least two rows of evenly spaced high-pressure-air jets in the furnace rear wall and one in the front wall (Fig. 1). This air mixes with the furnace gases and creates the turbulence required to complete combustion.

Fly-carbon collection and reinjection systems

Partial suspension burning results in a greater carryover of particulate matter in the flue gas than with other types of stokers. Particulate collection equipment, depending on local emission standards, is therefore required.

In general, the arrangement of the collection equipment is such that the coarse carbon-bearing particles can be returned to the furnace for further burning and the fine material discharged to the ash removal system.

When plant physical layout permits locating the collecting and settling hopper outlets at a sufficient height, the fly carbon flows by gravity to a distributing hopper directly behind the rear wall of the furnace (Fig. 3).

Pneumatic systems, using high pressure air as the conveying medium, have been extensively used for rein-

jection of the fly carbon into the furnace in the high temperature zone just above the fuel bed. The overfire-air system may be adapted to return the fly carbon.

Reintroducing the fly carbon into the furnace results in an increase in boiler efficiency of 2 to 3%.

Fuels and fuel bed

All spreader stokers, and in particular the traveling-grate spreader type, have an extraordinary ability to burn fuels with a wide range of burning characteristics, including coals with caking tendencies. High-moisture, free-burning bituminous and lignite coals are commonly used, and some low volatile fuels, such as coke breeze, have been burned in a mixture with higher volatile coal. Anthracite coal, however, is not a satisfactory fuel for spreader-stoker firing.

Coal size segregation is a problem with any type of stoker, but the spreader stoker can tolerate a small amount of segregation because the feeding rate of the individual feeder-distributors can be varied. Size segregation, where fine and coarse coal are not distributed evenly over the grate, produces a ragged fire and poor efficiency.

The ideal fuel and ash bed for coal-fired spreader stokers is evenly distributed and from 2 to 4 inches thick. Maximum heat release rates are from 450,000 Btu/sq ft, hr on stationary or dumping grates, to 750,000 Btu/sq ft, hr on traveling-grate spreader stokers. Higher releases are practical with certain of the waste fuels, such as pulpwood bark.

The ash and moisture content in bituminous coals are factors to be considered in the selection of the grate type. If the ash content of the coal exceeds 10% (as-fired basis), stationary or dumping grates should not be considered unless heat release rates are reduced at least 25%. Traveling grates have no limits for maximum ash content.

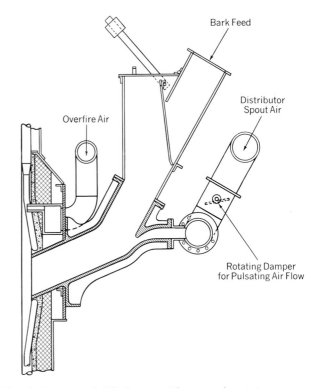

Fig. 4 Air-swept distributor spout for spreader stoker.

Residue handling

With stationary grates, the ash is removed from the grates one section at a time by hoe or rake through suitable doors at the grate level. Intermittent-dumping-grate stokers discharge the ash to pits. These may be shallow for firing-floor cleanout in the absence of basement space.

The practical maximum net length or length open to air flow for a stationary grate is about 9 ft. With a dump grate arranged for floor cleaning, the net length should be held under 12 ft. In the case of an arrangement with a basement ash pit this dimension may be 15 ft.

Traveling-grate continuous-ash-discharge stokers usually require either a basement ash pit or elevation of the firing level to obtain equivalent ash storage space.

The recommended maximum net length of reciprocating and vibrating grates for spreader stokers is 15 feet, while for traveling grates it is about 18 feet with current designs.

Ashes may be removed from the ash pits for final disposal by means of any of the conventional ash-transport systems such as pneumatic conveyors and sluices.

Control

With its sensitivity to adjustment for varying loads, the spreader stoker requires close control of fuel and air supply to achieve best results. There are many types of automatic combustion controls available, from simple positioning types sometimes used on relatively small installations, to the more elaborate air-flow-steam-flow equipment found in larger plants.

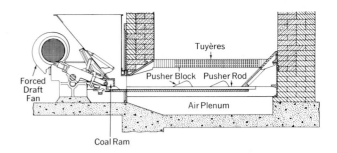

Fig. 6 Single-retort, horizontal-feed, side-ash-discharge underfeed stoker.

Spreader stoker firing of by-product waste fuels

In many manufacturing processes, by-product wastes are produced having considerable calorific value which can be recovered by using the wastes as a base fuel or as a supplementary fuel in the generation of steam for power, heating or industrial processes. Bark from wood pulping operations and bagasse from sugar refineries are good examples. Others include coffee-ground residue from instant coffee manufacture, corn cobs, coconut and peanut hulls, furfural, and bark and sawdust from woodworking plants. Spreader-stoker firing provides an excellent way to burn these wastes. The feeding and distributing units may employ an overthrow rotor similar to the arrangement shown for coal firing in Fig. 2, or an air swept distributor, Fig. 4. Depending on the moisture content and the fuel fineness, combustion takes place both in suspension and on the grates. Fig. 5 shows a unit arranged to burn bark in combination with oil and gas. Burners for oil and gas are located on the side opposite the fuel chute for bark feed. Coal could also be fired on the stoker as an alternate fuel, but a feeder and distributor suitable for coal would be required.

Waste fuels with high moisture content may present problems in maintaining combustion unless there is enough auxiliary fuel to maintain the average moisture of the total fuel input at a maximum of about 50%.

Preheated air, at temperatures dependent on the fuel moisture content, aids in drying and igniting the fuel as it is fed into the furnace. Air temperatures up to 450F are in common use on bark-fired units. High air temperatures may require the use of alloy grate materials in order to reduce maintenance.

Grate construction for firing waste fuels is substantially the same as for coal. The traveling grate is the most popular, but dumping and vibrating grates are also used.

A greater proportion by weight of the more common waste fuels can be burned in suspension than is possible with coal. Thus a higher burning rate per sq ft of grate can be tolerated, and up to 1,000,000 Btu/sq ft, hr is not unusual. The higher allowable heat release rate significantly affects the design of the boiler, furnace and overfire-air system. During operation, it is particularly important that an adequate bed of ash be maintained on the grate as protection against the radiant heat of the furnace.

Underfeed stokers

Underfeed stokers are generally of two types—the horizontal-feed, side-ash-discharge type, Fig. 6; and the

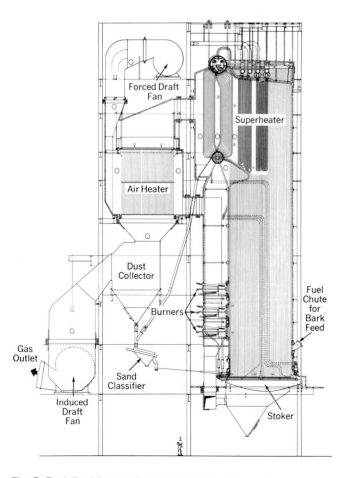

Fig. 5 Bark-fired boiler unit with auxiliary oil and gas burners.

gravity-feed, rear-ash-discharge type, Fig. 7.

In the side-ash-discharge underfeed stoker (Fig. 6), fuel is fed from the hopper by means of a reciprocating ram to a central trough called the retort. On very small heating stokers, a screw conveys the coal from the hopper to the retort. A series of small auxiliary pushers in the bottom of the retort assist in moving the fuel rearward and, as the retort is filled, the fuel is moved upward to spread to each side over the air-admitting tuyeres and side grates.

As the fuel rises in the retort and is subjected to heat from the burning fuel above, volatile gases are distilled off and mixed with air supplied through the tuyeres above each side of the retort and through the side grates. The volatile mixture burns as it passes upward through the incandescent zone, sustaining ignition of the rising fuel. Burning continues as the incoming raw coal continually forces the fuel bed to each side. Combustion is completed by the time the bed reaches the side-dumping grates. The ash is intermittently discharged to shallow pits, quenched and removed through doors at the front of the stoker.

The single (and double) retort, horizontal-type stokers are generally limited to 25,000 to 30,000 lb steam per hr with burning rates of 425,000 Btu/sq ft, hr in furnaces with water-cooled walls. For refractory-walled furnaces, the maximum rate should be reduced to about 300,000 Btu/sq ft, hr. The multiple retort, rear-end-cleaning type (Fig. 7), has a retort and grate inclination of 20 to 25 degrees. This type of stoker can be designed for boiler units generating up to 500,000 lb steam per hr. Burning rates up to 600,000 Btu/sq ft, hr are practicable.

The multiple-retort inclined underfeed stoker is still being used in many plants with relatively constant loads, or light loads of long duration which can be handled without objectionable smoke more easily than with the spreader stoker.

The burning rates for underfeed stokers are directly related to the ash-softening temperature. For coals with ash-softening temperature below 2400F, the burning rates are progressively reduced.

With multiple-retort stokers, overfire-air systems are frequently provided with a separate high pressure fan, developing a pressure of approximately 16 in. of water (gage), to be operated intermittently to prevent smoke at low loads, or on sudden increase of firing rate and consequent distillation of a large quantity of volatile gases.

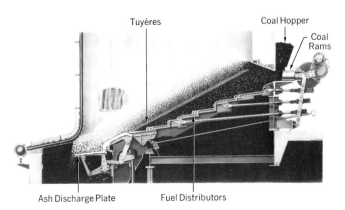

Fig. 7 Multiple-retort gravity-feed type of rear-ash-discharge underfeed stoker.

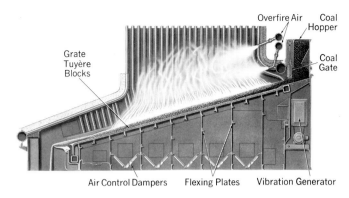

Fig. 8 Water-cooled vibrating-grate stoker.

The size of the coal has a marked effect on the relative capacity and efficiency of an underfeed stoker. The most desirable size consists of 1¼ in. × 0 nut, pea, and slack in equal proportion. A reduction in the percentage of fines helps to keep the fuel bed more porous and extends the range of coals with a high coking index.

In general, underfeed stokers are able to burn caking coals. The range of agitation imparted to the fuel bed in different stoker designs permits the use of coals with varying degrees of caking properties. The only certain way to select suitable coal is by actual field tests for a given unit. The ash-fusion temperature is an important factor in the selection of the coals. Usually, the lower the ash-fusion temperature, the greater the possibility of clinker trouble.

Combustion control

Many small underfeed stokers, handling relatively steady heating loads, operate with a start-stop control. Stokers operating to suit a varying load should be equipped with modulating combustion control that varies the coal-feeding rate and air supply in step with the steam demand. This should include control of the furnace draft through operation of the boiler outlet damper.

Water-cooled vibrating-grate stokers

Several manufacturers build spreader stokers with air-cooled vibrating or oscillating grates. An entirely different design of stoker is the water-cooled vibrating-grate hopper-feed type, Fig. 8. An adaptation of an original European design used successfully with many of the low ranking lignite and brown coals found in Central Europe, this type of stoker is equally successful in burning the better grades of coal. Since introduction to the American market in the middle fifties, it has found steadily increasing acceptance because of simplicity, inherent low fly-ash carry-over characteristics and very low maintenance.

The water-cooled vibrating-grate stoker consists of a tuyere grate surface mounted on, and in intimate contact with, a grid of water tubes interconnected with the boiler circulation system for positive cooling. The entire structure is supported by a number of flexing plates allowing the grid and its grate to move freely in a vibrating action that conveys coal from the feeding hopper onto the grate and gradually to the rear of the stoker. Ashes are automatically discharged to either a shallow or basement ash pit.

Vibration of the grates is intermittent, and the frequency of the vibration periods is regulated by a timing device. Timing is regulated by the automatic combustion control system to conform to load variations, synchronizing the fuel feeding rate with the air supply.

Furnace design

The water-cooled vibrating-grate stoker is suitable for burning a wide range of bituminous and lignite coals. Even with coals having a high free-swelling index, the gentle agitation and compaction of the fuel bed tends to keep the bed porous without the formation of large clinkers generally associated with low ash-fusion coals. A well distributed, uniform fuel bed is maintained without blow holes or thin spots.

The furnace design for this stoker should include water-cooled walls to prevent slag formation adjacent to the stoker. A rear arch extending over approximately one third of the stoker length directs the gases forward to mix with the rich volatile gases released in the ignition zone. A short front arch is adequate for most bituminous fuels. The use of high pressure air jets—from 27 to 30 in. of water (gage)—through the front arch provides turbulent gas mixing and promotes combustion. In rare cases, with extremely low-volatile fuels, some refractory facing of the front water-cooled arch may be desirable to increase the temperature over the ignition section.

Burning rates of these stokers vary with different fuels but, in general, the maximum heat release rate should not exceed 400,000 Btu/sq ft, hr. In this range, fly-carbon carry-over is held to a minimum.

Water cooling of the grates makes this stoker especially adaptable to multiple-fuel firing, as a shift to oil or gas does not require special provision for protection of the grates. A normal bed of ash left as a cover gives adequate protection from furnace radiation.

The strategic placement of burners in this type of furnace configuration may, in many cases, permit operation with a bare grate without exceeding safe metal temperature limits.

Chain-grate and traveling-grate stokers

Traveling-grate stokers, including the specific type known as the chain-grate stoker, have assembled links, grates, or keys joined together in endless belt arrangements that pass over the sprockets or return bends located at the front and the rear of the furnace. Coal, fed from the hopper (Fig. 9), onto the moving assembly, enters the furnace after passing under an adjustable gate to regulate the thickness of the fuel bed. The layer of coal on the grate, as it enters the furnace, is heated by radiation from the furnace gases and is ignited together with the hydrocarbon and other combustible gases driven off by distillation. The fuel bed continues to burn as it moves along,

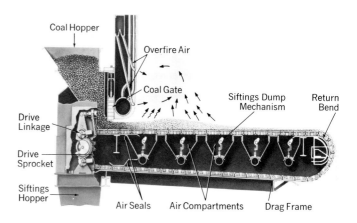

Fig. 9 Chain-grate stoker. (*Courtesy Laclede Stoker Co.*)

with the bed growing progressively thinner as combustion continues. At the far end of the travel, ash is discharged from the end of the grate into the ash pit. Although there are structural differences, the operation of the chain-grate and other traveling-grate types are quite similar. Generally these stokers used furnace arches (front and/or rear) to improve combustion by reflecting heat onto the fuel bed. The front arch also serves to break up and mix rich streams of volatile gases that might otherwise travel through the unit unburned.

In 1954, a chain-grate stoker was developed, which eliminated the need of a front arch (Fig. 9). Two rows of overfire-air jets, located in the front wall, are particularly effective in completing the combustion of the rich, volatile gases over the first two compartments, which are blasted more heavily than is permissible with an arch.

Chain- and traveling-grate stokers can burn a wide variety of fuels. Almost any solid fuel—peat, lignite, subbituminous, free-burning bituminous, anthracite and coke breeze—of suitable size can be burned on these stokers. When burning anthracite and coke breeze, which are low in volatile constituents, rear arches are used to deflect and direct incandescent fuel particles and combustion gases toward the front of the stoker, where they assist in the ignition of the incoming raw fuel.

Chain- and traveling-grate stokers are offered for a maximum continuous burning rate of 425,000 Btu/sq ft, hr with high-moisture (20%), high-ash (20%) bituminous coal, and 500,000 Btu/sq ft, hr with lower-moisture (10%), lower-ash (8 to 12%) bituminous coal. For anthracite, the corresponding burning rate is 350,000 Btu/sq ft, hr. Chain- and traveling-grate stokers are particularly effective in burning low-volatile fuel and have a minimum of fly-ash carry-over. Spreader stokers with traveling grates require less grate area for a given boiler size and have a better response to load changes.

Chapter 12

Boilers, superheaters and reheaters

In a modern steam generator, various components are arranged to absorb heat efficiently from the products of combustion. These components are generally described as boiler, superheater, reheater, economizer and air heater.

Boilers

Boiler surface may be defined as those parts of tubes, drums and shells which are part of the boiler circulatory system and which are in contact with the hot gases on one side and water or a mixture of water and steam on the other side. Although the term boiler may refer to the overall steam generating unit, the term "boiler surface" does not include the economizer or any component other than the boiler itself. Boilers may be broadly classified as shell, fire-tube and water-tube types. The development of the various boiler types is described under *History of Steam Generation and Use* in the *Introduction to Steam*.

Modern boilers are of the water-tube type. The safety and dependability of operation that characterize the boilers of today had their beginning in the introduction of this boiler type. In the water-tube boiler, the water and steam are inside the tubes, and the hot gases are in contact with the outer tube surfaces. The boiler is constructed of a number of sections of tubes, headers and drums joined together in such a way that circulation of water is provided for adequate cooling of all parts, and the large indeterminate stresses of the fire-tube boilers are eliminated. With water-tube designs it is possible to protect thick drums from the hot gases and resultant high thermal stresses. Steam-side explosion failures have been essentially eliminated with water-tube boilers. Further the water space is divided into sections so arranged that, should any section fail, no general explosion occurs and the destructive effects are limited.

The water-tube construction facilitates obtaining greater boiler capacity, and the use of higher pressure. In addition, the water-tube boiler offers greater versatility in arrangement and this permits the most efficient use of the furnace, superheater, reheater and other heat recovery components.

Water-tube boilers may be classified as straight-tube and bent-tube. Straight-tube boilers, illustrated in Figs. 12 and 14, *Introduction to Steam*, have been supplanted by modern designs of bent-tube boilers, which are more economical and serviceable than the straight-tube designs.

Bent-tube boilers

Many important modern designs of boilers, such as the two-drum Stirling, the Integral-Furnace, the Radiant, and the Universal Pressure are included in the "bent-tube" classification. All bent-tube boilers today, with the exception of those with stoker or flat refractory floors, have water-cooled walls and floors or hoppers. The principal designs referred to are illustrated in Figs. 1-6.

Integral-Furnace boiler. The Integral-Furnace boiler is a two-drum boiler which, in the smaller capacities, is adaptable to shop assembly and shipment as a package. Fig. 1 shows a low-capacity Type FM Integral-Furnace

Fig. 1 Type FM Integral-Furnace boiler. Shop-assembled unit, complete and ready to operate.

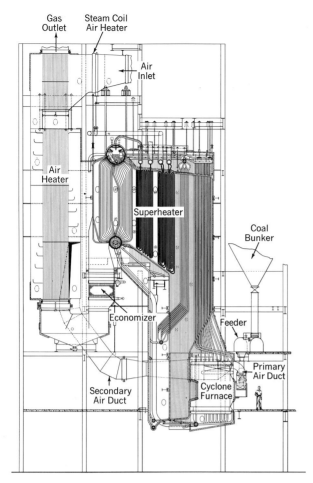

Fig. 2 Two-drum Stirling boiler for Cyclone-Furnace firing. Design pressure 1575 psi; steam temperature 900F; maximum continuous steam output 550,000 lb/hr.

boiler designed for shop assembly. This package boiler is shipped complete with support steel, casing, forced draft fan (unmounted in larger sizes), firing equipment, and controls, ready for operation when water, fuel, and electrical connections are made. Only a stub stack is required. It is built for outputs from 10,000 to 180,000 lb of steam per hr. Steam pressures range to 925 psi and temperatures to 825F. Units can be fired with oil, gas, or a combination of the two.

Only a forced draft fan is required, as the casing is airtight (welded) and the combustion gases are under pressure. Size of the unit is varied principally by changes in setting depth and drum length. Larger size FM boilers and Integral-Furnace boilers of the PFI and PFT types are described and illustrated in Chapter 25.

Two-drum Stirling boiler. The simple arrangement possible for the connecting tubes, with one upper steam drum directly over one lower drum, led to the development of a series of designs known as the two-drum Stirling boiler, Fig. 2. These designs are standardized over a wide range of capacities and pressures with steam flows varying from 200,000 to 1,200,000 lb/hr, design pressures to 1750 psi and steam temperatures to 1000F. The firing may be by Cyclone Furnace, pulverized coal, oil or gas.

The two-drum Stirling boiler is furnished for industrial and utility application.

High-pressure and high-temperature boilers

In the rapid development of power-plant economy, the single-boiler, single-turbine combination has been adopted for the central station and where electric power is the end product of heat transformation. There is an incentive to use very large electrical generators, since the investment and labor costs decrease as size increases. In the design of large boiler units for this application, the important factors are: (a) high steam pressure, (b) high steam temperature, (c) bleed feedwater heating and, (d) reheat. High steam pressure means high saturation temperature and low temperature difference between steam and exit gas. High steam temperature means high initial temperature and, usually, reheating to high temperature for reuse of the steam. Bleed feedwater heating lowers the temperature difference in an economizer and increases the gas temperature leaving the economizer. An air heater is then required to lower the exit-gas temperature. These factors and, above all, the economic need for continuity of operation to realize an optimum return on the large investment involved have combined to produce boiler units different in many respects from earlier concepts. Thus the principle of the integrated boiler unit is firmly established for very large boilers, as well as for boilers of smaller outputs.

As steam pressures have increased, steam temperatures also have increased. This necessitates proportionally more superheating surface and less boiler surface. When pressures exceed 1500 psi in a drum-type boiler, the heat absorbed in furnace and boiler-screen tubes is normally almost enough to generate the steam. Thus it is usually more economical to use economizer surface for any additional evaporation required as well as to raise the feedwater to saturation. All the steam is then generated in the furnace, water-cooled wall enclosures of superheater and economizer, boiler screen, division walls, and in some cases the outlet end of a steaming economizer.

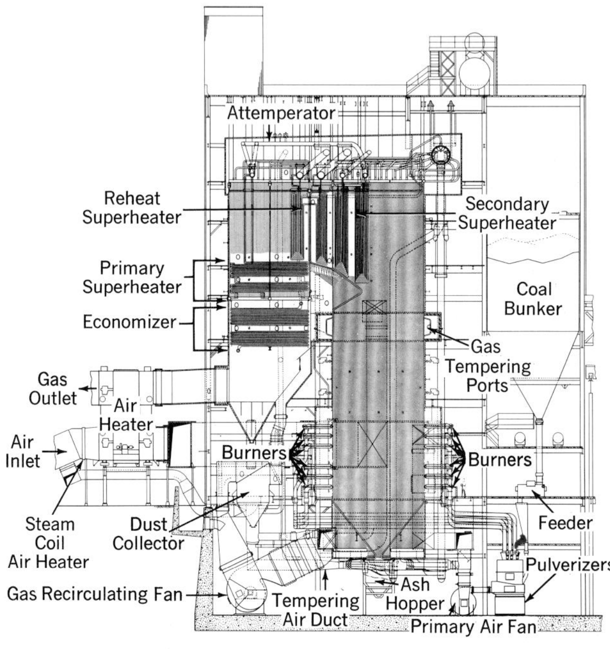

Fig. 3 Carolina-type Radiant boiler for pulverized-coal firing. Design pressure 2875 psi; primary and reheat steam temperatures 1000F; maximum continuous steam output 1,750,000 lb/hr.

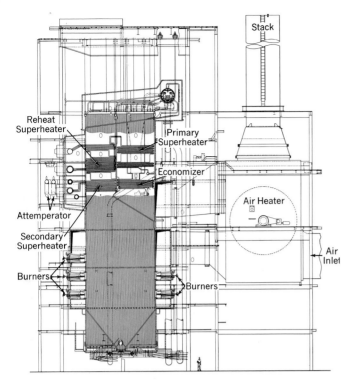

Fig. 4 El Paso-type Radiant boiler for natural-gas and oil firing. Superheater outlet pressure 2625 psi; primary and reheat steam temperatures 1005F; capacity 3,770,000 lb steam per hr.

Radiant boiler. The Radiant (RB) boiler (Figs. 3 and 4) is a high-pressure, high-temperature, high-capacity boiler of the drum type. It is adaptable to pulverized-coal or Cyclone-Furnace firing, and also to natural-gas and oil firing. Boiler convection surface is a minimum in these units.

The Carolina-type Radiant boiler illustrated in Fig. 3 is a pulverized-coal-fired unit with hopper-bottom construction for dry-ash removal. Components, such as furnaces, superheaters, reheaters, economizers and air heaters are integrated to coordinate the fuel fired with the turbine throttle requirements. Sizes are available in reasonable increments of width and height to permit selection of economical units for the required steam conditions and capacity.

Fig. 4 illustrates the El Paso-type Radiant boiler, a unit developed for natural-gas and oil firing. This compact and economical design is suitable for these fuels because of the cleanliness of natural gas and the relatively minor ash problems encountered with oil as compared to coal (*see Chapter 15*).

A more comprehensive description of the Radiant boiler is given in Chapter 22, including capacity, performance characteristics, application, and illustrations.

Universal-Pressure boiler. The Universal-Pressure boiler (Figs. 5 and 6) is a high-capacity, high-temperature boiler of the "once-through" or "Benson" type. Functionally applicable at any boiler pressure, it is applicable economically in the pressure range from 2000 to 4000 psi. Firing may be by coal, either pulverized or Cyclone-Furnace-fired, or by natural gas or oil.

The working fluid is pumped into the unit as liquid, passes sequentially through all the pressure-part heating

surfaces, where it is converted to steam as it absorbs heat, and leaves as steam at the desired temperature. There is no recirculation of water within the unit and, for this reason, a drum is not required to separate water from steam. The Universal-Pressure boiler may be designed to operate at either subcritical or supercritical pressures.

Fig. 5 illustrates a pulverized-coal-fired Universal-Pressure boiler for a 1300 Mw capacity electric generating unit. Fig. 6 is a natural-gas-fired installation, supplying steam for a 750 Mw generator.

Chapter 22 contains a more detailed description and additional illustrations of the Universal-Pressure boiler.

Boiler design

A boiler may be a unit complete in itself without auxiliary heat absorbing equipment, or it may constitute a rather small part of a large steam generating complex in which the steam is generated primarily in the furnace tubes, and the convection surface consists of a superheater, reheater, steaming economizer and air heater. In the latter case, a drum-type boiler comprises only the steam drum and the screen tubes between the furnace and the superheater. However, the furnace water-wall tubes, and usually a number of side-wall and support tubes in the convection portion of the unit, discharge steam into the drum and therefore effectively form a part of the boiler.

In the case of the Universal-Pressure boiler, there is no steam drum, but rather an arrangement of tubes in which steam is generated and superheated. Whether the boiler is a drum- or once-through type, whether it is an individual unit or a small part of a large complex, it is necessary in design to give proper consideration to the performance required from the total complex of the

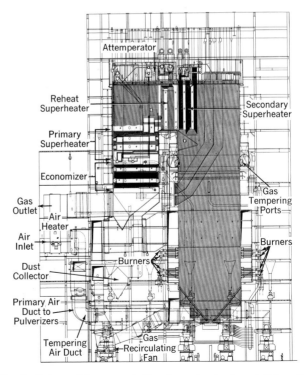

Fig. 5 Universal-Pressure boiler for pulverized-coal firing. Superheater outlet pressure 3650 psi; primary and reheat steam temperatures 1003F; capacity 9,300,000 lb steam per hr.

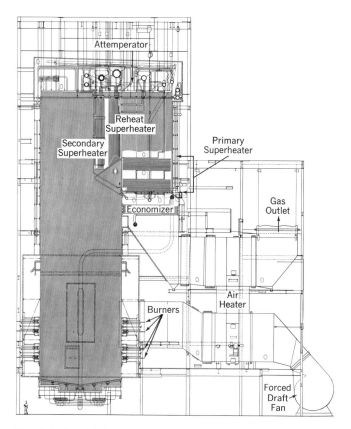

Fig. 6 Universal-Pressure boiler for natural-gas firing. Superheater outlet pressure 3850 psi; primary and reheat steam temperatures 1005F; capacity 5,455,000 lb steam per hr.

steam generating unit. Within this framework, the important items which must be accomplished in boiler design are the following:

1. Determine the heat to be absorbed in the boiler and other heat transfer equipment, the optimum efficiency to use, and the type of fuel or fuels for which the unit is to be designed. When a particular fuel is selected, determine the amount of fuel required, the necessary or preferred preheated air temperature and the quantities of air required and flue gas to be generated.

2. Determine the size and shape required for the furnace, giving consideration to location, the space requirements of burners or fuel bed, and incorporating sufficient furnace volume to accomplish complete combustion. Provision must also be made for proper handling of the ash contained in the fuel, and water-cooled surface must be provided in the furnace walls to reduce the gas temperature leaving the furnace to the desired value.

3. The general disposition of convection heating surfaces must be so planned that the superheater and reheater, when provided, are located at the optimum temperature zone where the gas temperature is high enough to afford good heat transfer from the gas to the steam, yet not so high as to result in excessive tube temperatures or excessive fouling from ash in the fuel.

While there is flexibility in the location of saturation or boiler surface, there must be enough total convection surface either before or after the superheater to transfer the heat required to heat the feedwater to

saturation temperature and to generate the remainder of the steam required which is not generated in the furnace. This can be accomplished without an economizer, or an economizer can be provided to heat the feedwater to saturation temperature or even to generate up to 20% of the full-load steam requirement.

The foregoing must be accomplished in a design that provides for proper cleanliness of heating surfaces without buildup of slag or ash deposits and without corrosion of pressure parts.

4. Pressure parts must be designed in accordance with applicable codes using approved materials with stresses not exceeding those allowable at the temperatures experienced during operation.

5. A tight boiler setting or enclosure must be constructed around the furnace, boiler, superheater, reheater and air heater, and gastight flues or ducts must be provided to convey the gases of combustion to the stack.

6. Supports for pressure parts and setting must be designed with adequate consideration for expansion and local requirements, including wind and earthquake loading.

Combustion data

The requirements and conditions that form the basis for the designer's selection of equipment are outlined in *Boiler Designer's Requirements*, Chapter 22.

These include factors involved in the selection of fuels. In most areas there are several fuels available and their availability and cost may be expected to change during the lifetime of the plant, with the result that the unit must be designed to burn more than one fuel. It is usually possible to determine which fuel is the most difficult from the standpoint of combustion and ash handling, and the unit is therefore designed for the most difficult fuel which will be used.

Procedures for optimizing parameters such as steam pressure and evaluating the worth of auxiliary equipment for a given application are outlined in Chapter 22. After the steam requirements—steam flow, steam pressure and temperature—and boiler feedwater temperature are determined, the required rate of heat absorption, q, is determined from the equation:

$$(1) \qquad q = w'(h_2' - h_1') + w''(h_2'' - h_1'')$$

where:

q = rate of heat absorption, Btu/hr
w' = primary steam or feedwater flow, lb/hr
w'' = reheat steam flow, lb/hr
h_1' = enthalpy of feedwater entering, Btu/lb
h_2' = enthalpy of primary steam leaving superheater, Btu/lb
h_1'' = enthalpy of steam entering reheater, Btu/lb
h_2'' = enthalpy of steam leaving reheater, Btu/lb

To determine unit efficiency, it is necessary to know the temperature of the flue gas leaving the unit. This temperature may be set at the point where further addition of heating surface to reduce gas temperature would not be justified by the increased economy obtained. In the case of sulfur-bearing fuels, flue gas tem-

perature is usually kept above the dew point to avoid sulfur corrosion of economizer or air heater surfaces.

The efficiency of combustion is 100 minus the sum of the heat losses expressed in percent. For a fuel with known characteristics and a given flue gas temperature, heat losses are evaluated by methods described under *Combustion Calculations* in Chapter 6. The fuel input rate is then determined from equation (2):

$$(2) \qquad w_F = q/(Q_H \times \text{eff})$$

where:

w_F = fuel input rate, lb/hr
Q_H = high heat value of fuel, Btu/lb
eff = efficiency, %/100

From the quantity of fuel to be burned per hr, the corresponding weight of air required and the weight of combustion gases produced are determined.

Furnace design

When pulverized-coal or Cyclone-Furnace firing is used, the wall(s) in which the burners or cyclones are located must be designed to accommodate them and the necessary fuel- and air-supply lines. Minimum clearances, established by experience, must be maintained between burners to avoid interference of the fuel streams from the various burners with each other. Minimum clearances must also be provided between burners and side walls and between each burner and the opposite wall to avoid flame impingement on furnace walls with consequent possible overheating of wall tubes or excessive deposits of ash or slag.

Where fuel is burned on stokers or hearths, the size of the furnace is usually set by providing a plan area based on a specified release of heat per sq ft of grate area per hr. These fuel burning rates are based on experience and vary for different types of stokers (*see Chapter 11*).

The furnace must also be proportioned so that combustion is completed with due regard to the factors of temperature, turbulence and time.

Adequate combustion temperature is partly a function of burner (or other fuel-burning equipment) design, i.e., the burner equipment must be designed to provide the proper mixing of air and gas, and it must be sized for the job to be done so that the burner is not over- or underloaded. Likewise, there must not be too much cooling surface in the furnace in proportion to the fuel to be burned. Preheated air is beneficial in obtaining adequate combustion temperature, and is required for pulverized-coal and Cyclone-Furnace firing, as well as for residual or heavy oils.

Turbulence is primarily a function of the fuel-burning equipment, and its importance lies in supplying air, not only to individual fuel particles but also to any unburned or partially burned gases until combustion is completed.

The time factor is fulfilled primarily by providing sufficient furnace volume so that the combustion gases remain in the furnace long enough to assure completeness of combustion.

Water-cooled walls. Most modern boiler furnaces have all walls water-cooled. This not only reduces maintenance on the furnace walls, but also serves to reduce the gas temperature entering the convection bank to the point where slag deposit and superheater corrosion can be controlled by sootblowers.

Furnace wall tubes are spaced on close centers to obtain maximum heat absorption. Tangent tube construction, used in earlier units, has been replaced with "membrane walls" in which a steel bar or membrane is welded between adjacent tubes (Fig. 7). This construction, used in both natural- and forced-circulation units for all types of firing, consists of flat wall sections composed of panels of single rows of tubes on centers wider than a tube diameter connected by means of a membrane bar securely welded to the tube on its centerline. This results in a continuous wall surface of rugged, pressure-tight construction capable of transferring a desirable amount of heat to the tube. The individual panels are of a width and length suitable for economical manufacture and assembly, with bottom and top headers attached in the shop prior to shipment for field assembly. Membrane walls with refractory lining are used in the lower furnace walls of cyclone-fired units. Membrane walls are described under *Tube Wall Enclosures*, Chapter 16 and illustrated in Figs. 1 to 3 of that chapter.

Handling of ash. In the case of coal and, to a lesser extent with oil, an extremely important consideration is the presence of ash in the fuel. If this ash is not properly considered in the design and operation, it can and does deposit not only on furnace walls and floor, but through the convection banks. This not only reduces the heat absorbed by the unit, but increases draft loss, corrodes pressure parts, and eventually can cause shutdown of the unit for cleaning and repairs. This subject is discussed in detail in Chapter 15, *Fuel Ash Effects on Boiler Design and Operation.* With certain fuels the proper handling of ash constitutes an overriding consideration in the design of furnaces, boilers, and other heat transfer equipment.

In coal-fired furnaces the ash problems are more severe. There are two approaches to the handling of ash, namely, the dry-ash furnace and the slag-tap furnace. (*See Use of Dry-Ash or Slag-Tap Units, Chapter 15.*)

Dry-ash furnace. In the dry-ash furnace, which is particularly applicable to coals with high ash fusion temperatures, the furnace is provided with a hopper bottom (*see Figs. 3 and 5*) and with sufficient cooling surface so that the ash impinging on furnace walls or hopper bottom is solid and dry and can be removed essentially as dry particles. When pulverized coal is burned in a dry-ash furnace, about 80% of the ash is carried through the convection banks; most of this fly ash is normally removed by particulate-removal equipment located just ahead of the stack.

Slag-tap furnace. With many coals having low ash fusion temperatures, it is difficult to utilize a dry-bottom furnace because the slag is either molten or sticky and tends to cling and build up on furnace walls and bottom. The slag-tap furnace has been developed to handle coals of these types. The most successful form of the slag-tap furnace is that used in conjunction with Cyclone-Furnace firing (*see Fig. 2, and also Figs. 3 and 6, Chapter 22*). The furnace comprises a two-stage arrangement. In the lower part of the furnace, gas temperature is maintained high enough so that the slag drops in liquid form onto a

Fig. 7 Membrane-wall construction applied to a burner wall.

floor where a pool of liquid slag is maintained and tapped into a slag tank containing water (*see Design and Operation of Slag-Tap Units, Chapter 15*). In the upper part of the furnace, the gases are cooled below the ash fusion point so that ash carried over into the convection banks is dry and does not adhere.

Convection boiler surface

The gas temperature leaving the furnace or entering the boiler depends mainly on the ratio of the heat released to the amount of furnace-wall cooling surface installed (*see Furnaces, Chapter 4*). Because the cost of furnace-wall cooling surface is relatively higher than that of boiler surface, the furnace size and surface are limited to the amount required to lower the gas temperature entering the convection tube banks sufficiently to avoid ash deposits.

The first few rows of tubes in the convection bank may be boiler tubes widely spaced to provide gas lanes wide enough to prevent plugging with ash and slag and to facilitate cleaning. These widely spaced boiler tubes are known as the slag screen or boiler screen. In many large units they are used to support the furnace rear wall tubes. These screen tubes receive heat by radiation from the furnace, and by radiation and convection from the combustion gases passing through them (*Chapter 14*).

In the larger current units, the superheater generally replaces the boiler screen or, if not, is located immediately beyond it (Fig. 8). The gas temperature entering the superheater must be high enough to give the superheat desired with a reasonable amount of heating surface and the use of economical materials. The arrangement shown in Fig. 8 shows two or three rows of boiler-screen tubes ahead of superheater tubes on close spacing.

However it may also be necessary to locate several rows of superheater tubes on wide spacing (*see Cleaning — External*).

Design of boiler surface after the superheater will depend on the particular type of unit selected, desired gas temperature drop, and acceptable gas pressure drop (draft loss) through the boiler surface. Typical arrangements of boiler surface for various types of boilers have been illustrated. The object in the design of convection heating surfaces is to establish the combination of tube diameter, tube spacing, length of tubes, number of tubes wide and deep, and gas baffling that will give the desired gas temperature drop with the pressure drop permissible.

Heating surface and pressure drop are directly interrelated since both are primarily dependent on gas mass velocity. If either heating surface or pressure drop is increased, the other must decrease in order to maintain the desired gas temperature drop (heat transfer). Hence there is an optimum gas mass velocity which results in the optimum combination of heating surface and gas pressure drop.

For a given gas mass velocity (lb of gas per hr per sq ft of gas flow channel) or for a given gas velocity, a considerably higher gas film conductance, heat absorption, and draft loss result when the gases flow at right angles to the tubes (crossflow) than when they flow parallel to the tubes (longitudinal flow). Gas turns between tube banks generally add draft loss with little or no benefit to heat absorption and should be designed for easy flow.

From a long record of experience, given sets of conditions for each fuel to be burned have been effectively established as the conditions of economic practice. While these conditions vary as improvements occur over a period of years, at any particular time competitive economics acts to hold most of the variables involved within a fairly limited range.

Determination of the amount of convection boiler surface required for a given transfer of heat is explained and illustrated in Chapter 14 in a step-by-step calculation of an example unit.

Design of pressure parts

Boilers have achieved the safety and reliability which they now have through the use of sound materials and safe practices for determining acceptable stresses in tubes, drums and other pressure parts. Boilers are always

designed to applicable codes. Most stationary boilers in the U.S. are designed to the ASME Code. Tables 2 and 4 of Chapter 29 list the allowable stresses for plate and tube steels respectively. In each case, the stress allowable depends on the maximum temperature to which the part is subjected, and therefore it is important that pressure parts be so designed that design temperatures are known and are not exceeded in operation. In boilers, the material temperatures are normally designed to be only a few degrees above the saturation temperature corresponding to the boiler pressure. In boiler tubes, this is accomplished by providing sufficient water to avoid the occurrence of a DNB, or departure from nucleate boiling (*see Factors Affecting DNB, Chapter 1*). This means that an adequate supply of water must be provided for each tube, and this is particularly important in furnace and screen tubes where heat input is high (*see also Boiler Circulation, Chapter 3*).

The methods used in the stress analysis of large pressure vessels, including boiler drums, are described in Chapter 30. Because steam drums have thick walls, it is necessary to limit the heat flow through them to avoid excessively high thermal gradients. Where the drum is penetrated by a number of tube holes, the flow of water through these holes serves to cool the ligaments between. Where the heat input through a drum would be too high, because of high gas temperature or velocity, insulation may be provided on the outside of the drum. This is particularly necessary where there are no tube penetrations to provide cooling.

In a drum-type boiler, equipment is provided in the steam drum for the reduction of moisture and solids in the steam to acceptable values (*see Steam Separation and Purity, Chapter 1*). In once-through boilers, all moisture is evaporated in the tubes where boiling and superheating occur sequentially. In boilers of this type, steam purity depends on maintaining adequate purity of the feedwater.

The boiler safety valve constitutes a very important item in the safety of modern boilers. By law, the boiler design pressure for which the pressure parts must be designed cannot be less than the safety-valve relief pressure. As a practical matter, to avoid unnecessary losses and maintenance from frequent action of the safety valves, the first safety valve should be set to relieve at not less than the desired boiler operating pressure plus about 5%. The operating pressure in the boiler steam drum, in turn, depends on the pressure required at the point of use and the intervening pressure drop. As an example, where the steam is used in a turbine, the boiler operating pressure is determined by adding to the turbine throttle pressure and pressure drop through the steam piping, nonreturn valve, superheater, and drum internals at maximum steam flow.

Boiler enclosure

The methods used to provide a tight boiler setting and a tight enclosure around the superheater, reheater, economizer and air heater are described in Chapter 16.

Boiler supports

Boiler and furnace wall tubes are usually supported by the drums or headers to which they are connected. In the

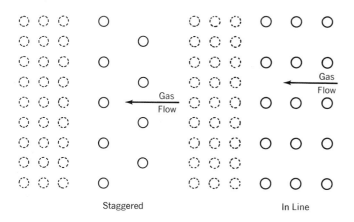

Staggered   In Line

Fig. 8 Diagrammatic arrangement of slag screens ahead of tube banks.

design of proper supports the following considerations are important:

1. The tubes must be so arranged that they will not be subject to excessive bending-moment stresses in carrying the weight of the tubes, drums, other parts which they support, and contained water. When the unit is bottom supported, the tubes must satisfy column requirements.

2. The holding strength of the tube seats must not be exceeded.

3. Provision must be made to accommodate the required expansion of the pressure parts. For a top-supported unit, the hanger rods must be designed to swing at the proper angle, and they must be long enough to take the movement without excessive stresses in either the rods or the pressure parts. Bottom-supported boilers should be anchored only at one point, guided along one line, and allowed to expand freely in all other directions. To reduce the frictional forces and resultant stresses in the pressure parts, roller saddles or mountings are desirable for bottom-supported heavy loads.

For more detailed discussion of support, see *Structural Design, Fossil-Fuel Steam Generators*, Chapter 30. The support of boiler setting or enclosure is discussed under *Support* in Chapter 16.

Superheaters and reheaters

Early in the eighteenth century, it was demonstrated that substantial savings in fuel could be experienced when steam engines were run with some superheat in the steam. In the late 1800's, lubrication problems were encountered with reciprocating engines, but once these were overcome, development of superheaters continued.

Commercial development of the steam turbine hastened the general use of superheat. By 1920 steam temperatures of 650F, representing superheats of 250F, were generally accepted. In the early 1920's the regenerative cycle, using steam bled from turbines for feedwater heating, was developed to improve station economy without going to higher steam temperatures. At the same time, superheater development permitted raising the steam temperature to 725F. A further gain in economy by still higher temperature was at that time limited by allowable superheater tube-metal temperature. This led to the commercial use of reheat, where the steam leaving the high-pressure stage of the turbine was reheated in a separate reheat superheater and returned at higher temperature and enthalpy to the low-pressure stage.

The first reheat unit for a central station was proposed in 1922 and went into service in September, 1924. It was designed for 650 psi and operated at 550 psi and 725F. Exhaust steam from the high-pressure turbine was reheated to 725F at 135 psi.

A much higher-pressure reheat unit, designed in 1924 for 1200 psi and 700F primary steam temperature with reheat at 360 psi and 700F, went into service in December, 1925 (*see Fig. 14, Introduction to Steam*).

Advantages of superheat and reheat

When saturated steam is utilized in a steam turbine, the work done results in a loss of energy by the steam and consequent condensation of a portion of the steam, even though there is a drop in pressure. The amount of work that can be done by the turbine is limited by the amount of moisture which can be handled by the turbine without excessive wear on the turbine blades. This is normally somewhere between 10 and 15%. It is possible to increase the amount of work done by moisture separation between turbine stages, but this is economical only in special cases. Even with moisture separation, the total energy that can be transformed to work in the turbine is small compared to the amount of heat required to raise the water from feedwater temperature to saturation and then evaporate it. Thus moisture constitutes the basic limitation in turbine design.

Because a turbine generally transforms the heat of superheat into work without forming moisture, the heat of superheat is essentially all recoverable in the turbine. This is illustrated in the temperature-entropy diagram of the ideal Rankine cycle (Fig. 6, Chapter 2), where the heat added to the right of the saturated vapor line is shown as 100% recoverable. While this is not always entirely correct, the Rankine cycle diagrams in Fig. 7, Chapter 2 indicate that this is essentially true in practical cycles. Fig. 9 of Chapter 2 shows this same benefit from superheat in a regenerative cycle plus an additional substantial benefit from reheat, which also embodies the principle of high utilization of heat added above the saturated vapor line.

The foregoing discussion is not specifically applicable at steam pressures in the vicinity of the critical point. The term "superheat" is not really appropriate in defining the temperature of the working fluid at or above the critical point. However, even at pressures exceeding 3208 psia, heat added at temperatures above 705F is essentially all recoverable in a turbine.

The benefits of superheat are illustrated graphically in Fig. 9, which shows the reduction in cycle heat rate by increasing the steam temperature from 900 to 1100F at pressures from 1800 to 3500 psi.

Superheater types

The original and somewhat basic type of superheater and reheater was the convection unit, for gas temperatures where heat transfer by radiation was very small. With a unit of this type the steam temperature leaving the superheater increases with boiler output because of the decreasing percentage of heat input that is absorbed in the furnace, leaving more heat available for superheater absorption. Since convection heat transfer rates are almost a direct function of output, the total absorption in the superheater per lb of steam increases with increase in boiler output (*see Fig. 10*). This effect is increasingly pronounced the further the superheater is removed from the furnace, i.e., the lower the gas temperature entering the superheater.

On the other hand, the radiant superheater receives its heat through radiation and practically none from convection. Because the heat absorption of furnace surfaces does not increase in direct proportion to boiler output but at a considerably lesser rate, the curve of radiant superheat as a function of load slopes downward with increase in boiler output.

In certain cases the two opposite-sloping curves have

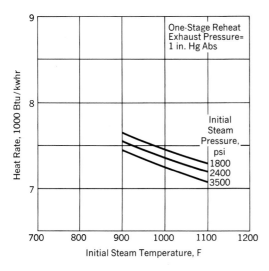

Fig. 9 Effect of changes in steam temperature and pressure on performance of ideal Rankine cycle with one-stage reheat.

been coordinated by the combination of radiant and convection superheaters to give flat superheat curves over wide ranges in load, as typically indicated in Fig. 10. A separately fired superheater (see Fig. 15) has the characteristic that it can be fired to produce a flat superheat curve.

Development of superheaters

The early convection superheaters were placed above or behind a deep bank of boiler tubes in order to shield them from the fire or from the higher temperature gases. The greater heat absorption required in the superheater for higher steam temperatures made it necessary to move the superheater closer to the fire. This new location brought with it problems which were not apparent with the superheaters located in the original lower-gas-temperature zone. Steam- and gas-distribution difficulties and instances of general overheating of tube metal were ultimately resolved by improved superheater design, including higher mass velocity of the steam. This increased the heat conductance through the steam film, resulting in lower tube-metal temperatures, and also improved steam distribution by increasing pressure drop through the tubes.

Steam mass velocity in modern superheaters ranges from as low as 100,000 to 1,000,000 lb/sq ft, hr or higher depending on pressure, steam and gas temperatures, and the tolerable pressure drop in the superheater.

The fundamental considerations governing superheater design apply also to reheater design. However, the pressure drop in reheaters is critical because the gain in heat rate with the reheat cycle can be completely nullified by too much pressure drop through the reheater system. Hence, steam mass flows are generally somewhat lower in the reheater.

Tube sizes. Plain cylindrical tubes of 2-in. or 2½-in. outside diameter predominate in superheaters and reheaters in stationary practice. Smaller diameters (1-in. or 1¼-in.) are used to conserve weight and space in marine units. Steam pressure drop is higher and alignment more difficult with the smaller diameters. Larger diameters bring about higher pressure stresses.

Recent designs have called for greater spans between supports for horizontal superheater tubes, and for wider tube spacing or fewer tubes per row to avoid slag accumulation. The 2½-in. tube has met these new conditions with a minimum sacrifice of the smaller-tube advantages, and 3-in. tubes are used to advantage in some cases. When steam temperatures increase, the allowable stresses may force a return to the smaller-diameter thinner-wall tube.

Plain tubes are used almost exclusively in modern superheater practice. Extended surface on superheater tubes in the form of fins, rings, or studs not only makes gas-side cleaning difficult, but the added thickness increases metal temperature and thermal stress beyond tolerable limits.

Relationships in superheater design

Effective superheater design calls for the resolution of several factors. The outstanding considerations are:

1. The steam temperature desired.
2. The superheater surface required to give this steam temperature.
3. The gas temperature zone in which the surface is to be located.
4. The type of steel, alloy, or other material best suited to make up the surface and the supports.
5. The rate of steam flow through the tubes (mass velocity), which is limited by the permissible steam pressure drop but which, in turn, exerts a dominant control over tube-metal temperatures.
6. The arrangement of surface to meet the characteristics of the fuels anticipated, with particular reference to the spacing of the tubes to prevent accumulations of ash and slag or to provide for the removal of such formations in their early stages.
7. The physical design and type of superheater as a structure.

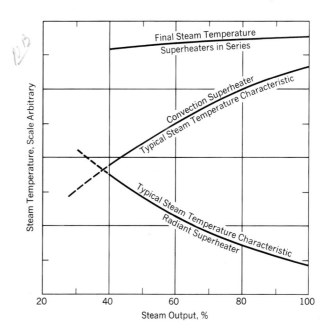

Fig. 10 A substantially uniform final steam temperature over a range of output can be attained by a series arrangement of radiant and convection superheater components.

A change in any one of the first six items will call for a counterbalancing change in all other items.

The steam temperature desired in advanced power station design is the maximum for which the superheater designer and manufacturer can produce an economical structure. Economics in this case requires the resolution of two interrelated factors—first, or investment cost and the later cost of upkeep for minimum operating troubles, outages, and replacements. A higher first cost is warranted if the upkeep cost is thereby reduced sufficiently to cover, in a reasonable time, the extra initial cost. The steam temperature desired is, therefore, based on the complete coordinated knowledge available for the optimum evaluation of the combination of the other five items and the necessities of the particular project. Operating experience in recent years has resulted in the use of approximately 1000F steam temperature both for primary superheat and reheat in nearly all large units purchased for installation in the U.S.

After the steam temperature desired is actually set or specified, the next consideration is the amount of surface necessary to give this superheat. The amount of superheater surface required is dependent on the four remaining items and, since there is no single correlation, the amount of surface must be determined by trial, locating it in a zone of gas temperature that is likely to be satisfactory. In the so-called standard boilers, the zone is fairly well established by the physical arrangements and by the space preempted for superheater surface.

Steam mass velocity, steam pressure drop, and superheater tube-metal temperatures are calculated after the amount of surface is established for the trial location and the trial tube spacing. The proper type of material is then selected for the component tubes, headers, and other parts. It may be necessary to compare several arrangements to obtain an optimum combination that will:

1. Require an alloy of lesser cost.
2. Give a more reasonable steam pressure drop without jeopardizing the tube temperatures.
3. Give a higher steam mass velocity in order to lower the tube temperatures.
4. Give a different spacing of tubes that will provide more protection against the ash accumulations with uncertain types of fuel.
5. Permit closer spacing of the tubes, thereby making a more economical arrangement for a fuel supply that is known to be favorable.
6. Give an arrangement of tubes which will reduce the draft loss for an installation where draft loss evaluation is crucial.
7. Permit the superheater surface to be located in a zone of a higher gas temperature, with a consequent saving in surface, that will compensate for deviation from a standard arrangement.

It is possible to achieve a practical design with optimum economic and operational characteristics and with all criteria reasonably satisfied, but a large measure of experience and the application of sound physical principles are required for satisfactory results. The methods of calculation for superheater performance are given in Chapter 14.

Relationships in reheater design

The same general similarity exists between superheater and reheater considerations, but the reheater is limited in ruggedness of design by the permissible steam pressure

Table 1
High temperature tubes
Maximum allowable design stress, lb per sq in.*

| Material | ASME Spec. Number | Grade | For metal temperatures not exceeding degrees F | | | | | | | |
			900	950	1,000	1,050	1,100	1,150	1,200	1,300
Carbon Steel	SA210	A1	5,000	3,000	1,500					
Carbon Moly	SA209	T1a	13,700	8,200	4,800					
Croloy ½	SA213	T2	12,500	10,000	6,200					
Croloy 1¼	SA213	T11	13,100	11,000	6,500	4,000	3,000	2,500	1,200	
Croloy 2¼	SA213	T22	13,100	11,000	7,800	5,800	4,200	3,000	1,600	
Croloy 5	SA213	T5	10,300	7,600	5,600	4,100	3,000	2,000	1,300	
Croloy 9M	SA213	T9	12,000	10,800	8,500	5,500	3,300	2,200	1,500	
Croloy 18-8	SA213	TP304H			9,700	9,500	8,800	7,700	6,000	3,700
Croloy 18-8	SA213	TP321H			10,400	10,100	8,800	6,900	5,300	3,100

* The stress values listed herein are reproduced from Table PG-23.1 of the 1974 *ASME Boiler and Pressure Vessel Code*, Section I, Power Boilers, and include addenda through the addendum issued December 31, 1975. The stress values listed and the use of this material is subject to the same variations as required by the notes forming an integral part of Table PG-23.1 of the *ASME Boiler and Pressure Vessel Code*, Section I, Power Boilers, December 31, 1975 addenda.

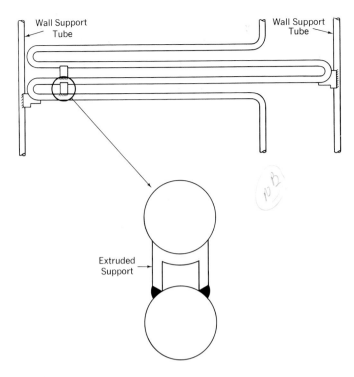

Fig. 11 Horizontal superheater section end-supported on walls.

drop. Steam mass velocities in reheater tubes should be sufficient to keep the steam-film temperature drop below 150F. Ordinarily this may be done with less than 5% pressure drop through the reheater tubes. This allows another 5% pressure drop for the reheater piping and valves without exceeding the usual 10% total allowable.

Metals for tubes

Oxidation resistance, maximum allowable stress, and economics determine the choice of materials for superheater and reheater tubes. The use of carbon steel should be extended as far as these considerations permit. Beyond this point, carefully selected alloy steels should be used. The steels commonly used for this application are shown in Table 1, which also lists the maximum allowable stress values in accordance with the *ASME Boiler and Pressure Vessel Code*, Section I, Power Boilers, December 31, 1975 addenda. Additional information on these materials is given in Table 4, Chapter 29. Table 3, Chapter 29 lists the maximum allowable metal temperatures recommended by B&W for these materials.

Supports for superheaters and reheaters

Because superheaters and reheaters are located in zones of relatively high gas temperature, it is preferable to have the major support loads carried by the tubes themselves. In horizontal superheaters the support load is usually transferred to the boiler or wall tubes by means of lugs, one welded to the boiler tubes and the other to the superheater tubes, Fig. 11. In many cases, these lugs are made of high-chromium-nickel alloy. They must slide on one another to provide relative movement between the boiler tubes and the superheater tubes. Supports of the saddle type, also shown in Fig. 11, provide for relative movement between adjacent components of the superheater itself.

As units grow in size, the span of the superheater tubes may become so great that it is inadequate to support them only at the ends. Most of the larger size units utilize "stringer" tubes, generally from the economizer outlet, to support the superheater tubes as indicated in Fig. 12. Tube spacing within the section is maintained by the use of saddle-type supports.

With pendant superheaters, the major support points are located outside of the gas stream with the pendant loops supporting themselves in simple tension. Fig. 13 shows a standard support arrangement for a pendant-superheater outlet section with major section supports above the roof line. Where adequate side spacing is available, steam-cooled wrap-around ties are used, thus radically reducing the amount of attachment to tubes and assuring maximum flexibility for accommodation of differential thermal expansion of individual loops within a section. In addition, in the higher gas temperature zones, steam-cooled side-to-side ties are utilized to maintain side spacings. For closer side-spaced elements, steam-cooled wrap-arounds are not practical, and mechanical ties are used to maintain alignment (Fig. 14). In this case the clear back-spacing between tubes and the size of attachments have been kept to a minimum. This serves to reduce the operating temperatures of the attachment and also to reduce the thermal stresses imposed on the tube wall. Fig. 14 shows a typical arrangement of a pendant reheater section and illustrates the support of a separated bank by a special loop of reheater which permits all major supports to be kept above the roof and out of the gas stream.

Cleaning—internal

In the early designs of superheaters and reheaters, access to tube ends was provided, and the tubes were so arranged that they could be turbined for internal cleaning. Current designs of superheaters and reheaters provide for internal cleaning when such provision does not

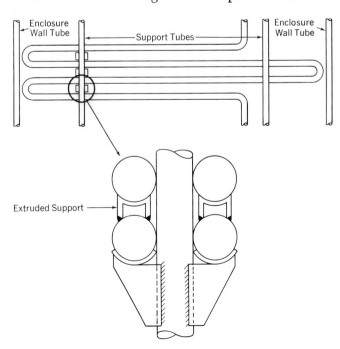

Fig. 12 Horizontal superheater section with intermediate stringer supports.

Re ason for controlleig

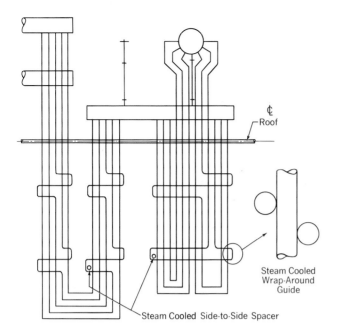

Fig. 13 Pendant superheater section.

adversely affect other important features. Access for internal cleaning of the tubes is now subordinated to permit greater freedom in design, so necessary for good performance. The infrequent cleaning required can normally be accomplished by washing with water.

Cleaning—external

In the early designs of superheaters and reheaters, the importance of maintaining clean surfaces was not stressed as it is today. The units designed today are furnished for continuous operation, in some cases for eighteen to twenty-four months between outages. Usually one year between outages is considered acceptable.

The superheater sections (platens) of modern standard utility units are spaced according to the zone of gas temperature and the fuel fired. For pulverized-coal- and Cyclone-Furnace-fired units, a transverse spacing of 18 in. has been found satisfactory in the high-temperature-gas zone at the furnace exit. With progressive gas cooling, the spacing is decreased, usually varying from 18 to 9 and from 9 to 6 in. and, as the horizontal surface is crossed, the tubes are spaced on $4\frac{1}{2}$ and possibly 4 in. across the gas flow. The back spacing in the direction of gas flow is usually set to allow $\frac{1}{2}$ to $\frac{3}{4}$ in. clear space between tubes in the high temperature zones with an increase allowable in the 1500F gas-temperature zone of the horizontal surface. These spacings are empirical, based on tube-fouling and erosion experience, and on manufacturing requirements.

Steam-temperature adjustment and control

Improvement in the heat rate of the modern boiler unit and turbine results in large part from the high cycle efficiency possible with high steam temperatures. The importance of regulating steam temperature within narrow limits is evident from Fig. 9, which shows that a change of 35 to 40F corresponds to a change of about 1% in heat rate at pressures from 1800 to 3500 psi.

Other important reasons for accurate regulation of steam temperature are to prevent failures from overheating parts of the superheater, reheater, or turbine, to prevent thermal expansion from reducing turbine clearances to the danger point, and to avoid erosion from excessive moisture in the last stages of the turbine.

The control of fluctuations in temperature from uncertainties of operation, such as slag or ash accumulation, is important. However superheat and reheat steam temperatures in steam generation are mainly affected by variations in steam output (*see Fig. 10*).

With drum-type boilers, steam output and pressure are maintained constant by firing rate, while the resulting superheat and reheat steam temperatures depend on basic design and other important operating variables, such as the ratio of convection to radiant heat-absorbing surface, excess air, feedwater temperature, changes in fuel that affect burning characteristics and ash deposits on the heating surfaces, and the specific burner combination in service. In the Universal-Pressure once-through boiler, which has a variable transition zone, steam output and pressure are controlled by the boiler feed pump and steam temperature by the firing rate, leaving reheat steam temperature as a dependent variable (*see Chapter 35*). Standard performance practice for steam generating equipment permits a tolerance of ± 10F in a specified steam temperature.

Meanings of terms used

Adjustment. A change in the arrangement of equipment which affects steam temperature but cannot be used to vary steam temperature during operation. Example—removal of superheater tubes.

Control. Regulation of steam temperature during operation without changing the arrangement of equipment. Example—operation of an attemperator.

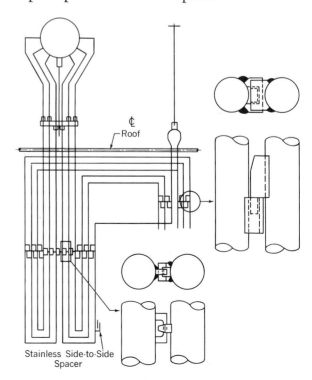

Fig. 14 Pendant reheater section.

Attemperator. Apparatus for reducing and controlling the temperature of a superheated vapor or of a fluid passing through it. Example—a bank of tubes, submerged in the boiler water, through which all or a part of the superheated steam is diverted to give up some of its heat, thereby regulating the final steam temperature.

Radiant superheater or reheater. Heating surface containing steam and receiving heat primarily by radiation. Example—tubes which form part of a furnace enclosure and within which steam is flowing.

Convection superheater or reheater. Heating surface containing steam and receiving heat primarily by convection. Example—a bank of tubes within which steam is flowing and across or along which hot gases pass.

Effect of operating variables

Many operating variables affect steam temperatures in drum- or separator-type units. To maintain constant steam temperature, means must be provided to compensate for the effect of such variables, the most important of which are:

Load. As the load increases, the quantity and temperature of combustion gases increase (*see Superheater Types*). In a convection superheater, steam temperature increases with load, the slope of the curve being less steep as superheater location is brought closer to the furnace. In a radiant superheater, steam temperature decreases as load increases. Sometimes a convection and a radiant superheater of proper proportions are installed in series in a single steam generating unit to maintain substantially constant steam temperature over a considerable range of load (*see Fig. 10*).

Excess air. For a change in the amount of excess air entering at the burners there is a corresponding change in the quantity of gas flowing over a convection superheater, and therefore an increase in excess air tends to raise the steam temperature.

Feedwater temperature. Increase in feedwater temperature causes a reduction in superheat since, for a given steam flow, less fuel is fired and less gas passes over the superheater.

Heating-surface cleanliness. Removal of ash or slag deposits from heat-absorbing surfaces ahead of the superheater will reduce gas temperature and steam temperature. Removal of deposits from superheater surface will increase superheater absorption and raise steam temperature.

Use of saturated steam. If saturated steam from the boiler is used for sootblowers or for auxiliaries, such as pumps and fans, an increased firing rate is required to maintain constant main steam output, and this raises the steam temperature.

Blowdown. The effect of blowdown is similar to the use of saturated steam but in lesser degree because of the low enthalpy of water as compared with steam.

Burner operation. The distribution of heat input among burners at different positions or a change in the adjustment of a burner usually has an effect on steam temperature through changes in furnace heat-absorption rate.

Fuel. Variations in steam temperature may result from changing the type of fuel burned or from changes in the characteristics of a given fuel from time to time.

Regulation of steam temperature

As noted above under *Meanings of Terms Used,* "Adjustment" and "Control" are the two methods by which steam temperature can be regulated. Everything affecting the regulation of steam temperature belongs in either one or the other of these two classifications.

Adjustment

Why adjustment is necessary. A power-generating unit represents a large capital investment, and means should be provided at a reasonable cost for the regulation of steam temperature to meet changed conditions that may be more or less permanent in nature. For instance, if a fuel change that has a considerable effect on steam temperature is anticipated, it is good engineering to design for compensating physical alterations of the equipment. This is not necessarily so, however, if the type and range of control provided are adequate to meet the varied requirements without loss in boiler efficiency.

Adjustment for regulating steam temperature is required when the actual operating conditions depart, as they often do, from the conditions on which the design is based. To provide for ultimate adjustment to meet such variations in operation, allowance should be made in the design for the required change at minimum expense.

Quite often a plant is designed with some future change in mind that would affect steam temperature, as, for example, a different fuel or a higher operating pressure. Here again the superheater (and reheater if used) must be so designed that an economical adjustment can be effected.

Means of adjustment. The basic method of adjustment for regulating steam temperature is by the addition or the removal of superheater and/or reheater surface. A good design should provide for an economical way of doing so.

Adjustment is also possible by a reduction or increase in the amount of saturated surface ahead of the steam-heating elements. Such alterations will modify the gas temperature at the inlet to these elements. If saturated surface is removed to increase steam temperature, this type of adjustment is relatively simple and, in general, will cost less than the addition of steam-heating elements. However, the addition of saturated surface in order to decrease steam temperature is liable to be difficult and expensive, or even impractical.

The gas temperature at the superheater inlet can be increased or decreased, without altering the convection surface ahead of the superheater, by changing the effectiveness of the heat-absorbing surface in the furnace. This is accomplished by the addition or removal of refractory covering on parts of the furnace surface. While a refractory coating on water-cooled furnace surfaces can have a favorable effect on combustion and carbon loss, refractory should not be added in areas where undesirable ash would deposit.

One of the simplest, least expensive, and most effective means of adjustment in regulating steam temperature is to change the gas mass velocity over the steam-

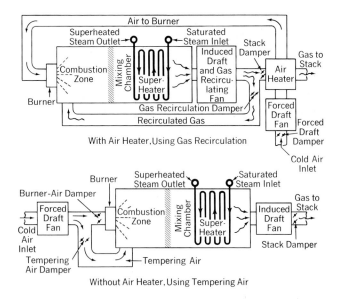

Fig. 15 Typical arrangements for separately fired superheater.

heating elements by baffle changes, if the design of the unit will permit such changes. Several of the standardized boilers, especially in the smaller sizes, have an adjustable baffle suitable for steam-temperature regulation. By means of this design it is possible to vary the steam-temperature range as much as 20%. The limit of variation is the effect on draft loss and efficiency. A 10F change in the temperature of the gas at the exit end of the boiler unit will alter efficiency by about 0.25%.

Control

Why control is necessary. Regulating steam temperature within required limits by means of control is necessary to correct fluctuations caused by operating variables. Probably the most frequent cause for the need of control in regulating steam temperature is the deposit of ash in some form on the surface of saturated and steam-heating elements. This condition can usually be corrected by simple changes in the operating schedules of soot- and slag-blowers.

To hold the optimum heat rate of a turbine designed to utilize full first-stage pressure over a given load range, it is essential to regulate steam temperature over this range by an effective means of control.

The time in which a turbine may be brought to full load is established by the turbine manufacturer in accordance with a safe steam temperature-time curve. Since the temperature of the steam is directly related to the degree of expansion of the turbine elements, and consequently the maintenance of safe clearances, it must be regulated within permissible limits by some means of accurate control.

The removal of feedwater heaters for servicing may be cited as an instance of variable operation. To maintain the same load, with the feedwater heaters out, will require an increase in the heat input to the boiler unit, with a corresponding increase in superheater or reheater absorption. Unless some means of control is available for regulating steam temperature to cover this condition, a drop in load might be required to protect both the steam-heating elements and the turbine.

Means of control. Among the means of control for regulating steam temperature are:

Separately fired superheater
Excess air
Gas recirculation
Divided furnace differentially fired
Burner selection
Movable burners
Gas bypass
Attemperation

Separately fired superheater. A superheater completely separate from the steam generating unit and independently fired may serve one or several saturated steam boilers. This arrangement is not generally economical for power generation, where a large quantity of high-temperature steam is needed, and its use is largely confined to process industries, such as chemical manufacture and petroleum refining, to meet special requirements. Since heat absorption can be varied independently of the quantity of steam delivered, the separately fired superheater has great flexibility in operation and a wide range of steam-temperature regulation at all loads. Either oil or natural gas is customarily used as fuel.

A separately fired superheater usually requires some means of reducing the temperature of the combustion gases entering the tube bank, to avoid excessive use of expensive alloys. Entering gas temperatures normally range from 1500 to 1900F, dependent on the economies involved. One method of tempering the combustion gases is to operate with high excess air. This increases the stack loss and lowers efficiency. If a higher efficiency is desired and the cost of additional equipment is justified, the combustion gases may be tempered with recirculated flue gas withdrawn from the setting beyond the superheater. Both methods are indicated in Fig. 15.

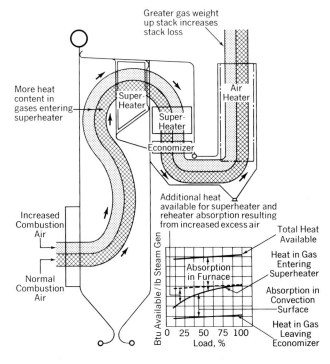

Fig. 16 Steam-temperature control by use of increased excess air.

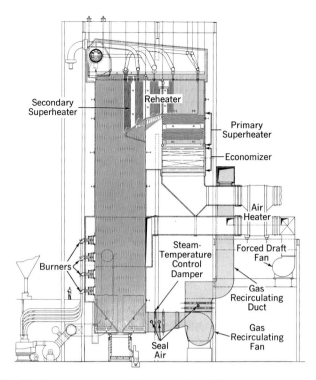

Fig. 17 One arrangement for gas recirculation.

Excess air. Boiler operators have long known that the steam outlet temperature of a convection superheater on a drum- or separator-type unit can be increased at fractional loads by decreasing the furnace heat absorption through an increase in the amount of excess combustion air. The resulting greater gas weight to the stack increases the stack loss, but the drop in boiler efficiency is usually unimportant since the increase in turbine efficiency may offset this higher loss. Such an arrangement is diagrammatically illustrated in Fig. 16.

Gas recirculation. One of the most attractive methods of controlling superheat or reheat, both from economic and operational viewpoints, is gas recirculation. As the name implies, this involves a method by which gas from the boiler, economizer, or air heater outlet is reintroduced to the furnace by means of a suitable fan and ducts. For the sake of clarity, recirculated gas introduced in the immediate vicinity of the initial burning zone of the furnace and used for steam-temperature control will be referred to as "gas recirculation," and recirculated gas introduced near the furnace outlet and used for control of gas temperature will be referred to as "gas tempering." Fig. 17 shows an application of gas recirculation on a hopper-bottom Radiant boiler. In most instances the gas is obtained from the economizer outlet. The point of reintroduction is dictated by the effect which is desired. The recirculated gas should be introduced into the furnace in such manner as to avoid interference with the combustion of the fuel. The amount of recirculated gas is generally expressed as a percentage of the gas that remains after the point of takeoff of the recirculated gas.

While recirculated gas may be used for several purposes, its basic function is to provide a means of altering the heat-absorption pattern within a steam generating unit in a manner advantageous to both designer and operator. Recirculated gas has the special advantage of providing a means of heat-absorption adjustment that may be used both as a design factor in initial surface arrangement and as a method of controlling the heat-absorption pattern under varying operating conditions.

An important feature of recirculated gas is that its use changes only the pattern of heat absorption through a boiler and has a negligible effect on the total boiler heat absorption, the gas weight up the stack, and the boiler efficiency.

The thermal effect of recirculated gas depends on the amount of gas recirculated, the location of gas introduction, and the furnace rating.

Fig. 18 shows the variation in heat absorption with gas recirculation introduced into the hopper. Introduction of gas at this location produces a marked reduction in furnace absorption and increases the absorption of the convection section. The total heat absorption remains unchanged.

Furnace heat absorption is primarily a function of the gas temperatures and gas-temperature patterns throughout the furnace, since the heat is mainly transferred by radiation. Hence, the introduction of gas recirculation into the furnace hopper reduces furnace absorption by altering the gas-temperature pattern.

The major portion of the heat absorbed in the superheater, reheater, and economizer is transferred by convection, which depends on gas temperature and gas mass velocity. Both are affected by gas recirculation. Therefore, when the gas mass velocity through a convection bank is increased by gas recirculation, the amount of heat transferred may increase, decrease, or remain unchanged,

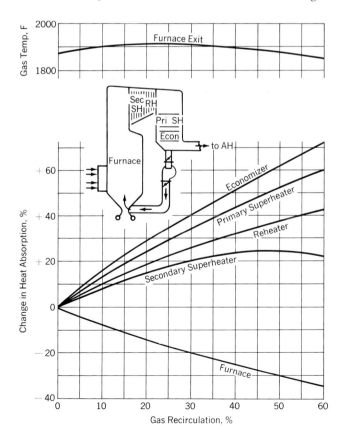

Fig. 18 Effect of gas recirculation on heat-absorption pattern at a constant firing rate.

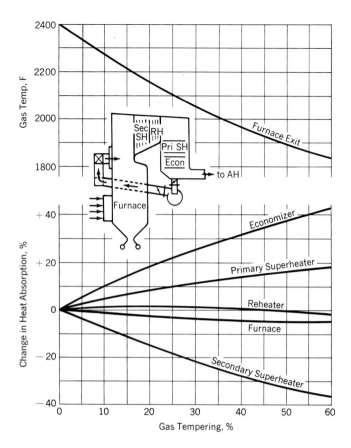

Fig. 19 Effect of gas tempering on heat-absorption pattern at a constant firing rate.

depending on the changes in the relationship between gas temperature and gas weight entering the bank. Fig. 18 illustrates a condition in which the gas temperature entering the secondary superheater (furnace exit temperature) is relatively unchanged by gas recirculation. Increasing the amount of gas recirculation, therefore, increases the heat absorption in the secondary superheater. The heat absorption in the reheater, primary superheater, and economizer is also increased, with the greatest increase occurring at the cold end of the unit. This is a typical example of variation in the convection-pass heat-absorption pattern by gas recirculation.

While gas recirculation into the hopper always reduces furnace heat absorption, its effect on furnace-exit-gas temperature depends mainly on furnace rating. The furnace-exit-gas temperature may increase, decrease, or, as shown in Fig. 18 be essentially unchanged by gas recirculation. In general, recirculated gas introduced in the hopper will decrease the furnace-exit-gas temperature of a unit operating at high furnace loading and increase this gas temperature at low loading.

Fig. 19 illustrates the effect of introducing tempering gas at a point near the furnace exit. Since the portion of the furnace in which the bulk of heat absorption occurs is unaffected by the recirculated gas, the furnace heat absorption is decreased only slightly. There is, however, quite a large decrease in furnace-exit-gas temperature, caused by dilution of the hot combustion gases with colder recirculated gas.

In the case of tempering gas introduced near the furnace outlet, the reduction in furnace-exit-gas tempera-

ture is usually sufficient to overbalance the effect of gas weight increase, and the heat absorption in the secondary superheater is decreased. The effect of gas tempering on the primary superheater and the economizer follows the pattern that was shown in Fig. 18, with the greatest change in heat absorption again occurring at the cold end. Because of the physical location of the reheater in Fig. 19, its absorption remains constant regardless of the percentage of gas tempering.

Figs. 18 and 19 illustrate the effect on heat distribution and gas temperature of introducing recirculated gas either into the hopper or at a point adjacent to the furnace exit. Introduction of gas at intermediate points will result in heat absorptions and gas temperatures between those shown. In order to show the effect of recirculated gas only, Figs. 18 and 19 have been based on constant firing rates.

A modern Universal-Pressure boiler with both gas tempering for gas-temperature control and gas recirculation for furnace heat-absorption control is illustrated in Fig. 20. In addition to gas recirculation, units of this type can employ spray attemperation in the reheater for reheat control.

Divided furnace differentially fired. In some divided furnaces, the superheater receives heat from one section of the furnace only, while the other section of the furnace generates only saturated steam. Steam temperature is regulated by changing the proportion of fuel input between the two furnaces. This arrangement, similar in principle to the separately fired superheater, was formerly used widely in marine practice, where a considerable amount of saturated steam is required for auxiliaries, for maneuvering at sea, and for port operation when the

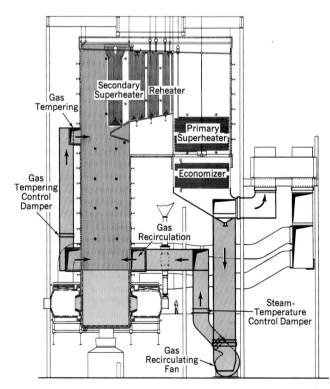

Fig. 20 Universal-Pressure boiler with gas tempering for gas-temperature control and gas recirculation for control of furnace absorption and reheat temperature.

direct contact - passing
of surface - passing through the condensate
surface

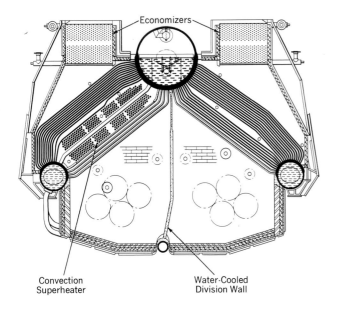

Fig. 21 Two-furnace marine boiler with superheat controlled by adjusting furnace firing rates.

main propulsion machinery is idle. The differentially fired divided-furnace method of steam-temperature control has also been used in a number of stationary power plants. A typical application of the principle to marine boilers is illustrated in Fig. 21.

Burner selection. It is often possible to regulate steam temperature by selective burner operation. Higher steam temperatures may be obtained at less than full load by operating only the burners giving the highest furnace outlet temperature. When lower steam temperatures are required, firing may be shifted to the other burners. This method of control can be improved by distributing the burners over a considerable height of the burner wall or by installing a special burner near the furnace outlet.

Movable burners. Regulation of steam temperature by changing the furnace absorption pattern can also be effected by the use of movable burners operated to shift the main combustion zone in the furnace. Tiltable burners are used for this purpose.

Gas bypass. If the convection banks of a steam generating unit are separated by gastight baffles into two or more parallel gas passes isolating portions of the superheater and reheater surfaces, the proportion of gas flow over all or part of the superheater and reheater may be varied by regulating dampers. An example of a two-pass arrangement for the control of superheat is shown in Fig. 22. This method has the advantage of low first cost, and high-purity spray water is not required as with a spray attemperator. Disadvantages may be listed as follows:

1. It is difficult to keep the dampers operable unless they are placed in a cool gas zone.

2. Draft loss through the unit is increased for some designs, particularly if control is desired with alternate fuels.

3. Control is more sluggish than with attemperators.

4. High gas temperature exists at the bypass dampers unless there is heat-absorbing surface in the pass.

Attemperation. All of the foregoing methods of control in regulating steam temperature are based on variation in the amount of heat absorbed by the steam-heating elements. In the two general types of attemperators commonly used, steam temperature is regulated by removing heat from the steam or by diluting high-temperature steam with low-temperature water.

The attemperator may be located in one of three places: between the saturated-steam outlet and the superheater; at some intermediate point between two sections of the superheater; or at the superheater outlet.

An attemperator located before the superheater will condense some of the saturated steam passing through it and will deliver wet steam of reduced enthalpy to the superheater.

There are important advantages in locating an attemperator between two stages of a superheater. With this arrangement the average steam temperature never exceeds the final steam temperature desired, and the steam from the various circuits of the first-stage superheater is so thoroughly mixed that it enters the second-stage superheater at a uniform temperature. This is, therefore, the most usual location, and the only disadvantage is the amount of piping required—from the first-stage superheater to the attemperator and from the latter to the second-stage superheater.

A surface-type attemperator located at the superheater outlet will be somewhat smaller than an interstage attemperator serving the same superheater, since it is handling higher temperature steam. The piping will be simpler. To keep the cost of alloys required in the attemperator, superheater, and piping within reasonable limits, this location should be selected only for moderately high steam temperatures.

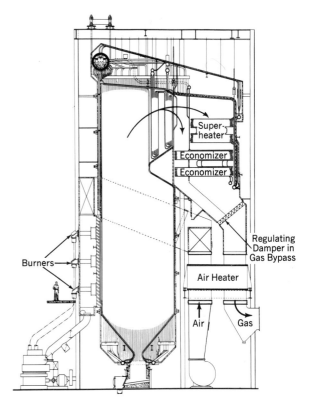

Fig. 22 Superheat control by damper regulation of gas flow over superheater.

Attemperators may be classified in two types—surface and direct-contact. In the surface type, the steam is isolated from the cooling medium by the heat-exchanger surface. In the direct-contact type, the steam and the cooling medium (water) are mixed. The surface attemperator includes the shell type, and the drum type. The direct-contact attemperator is exemplified by the spray type.

When a shell or drum type of attemperator is used interstage, a part of the steam from the primary superheater is diverted to it by an automatic valve. The diverted steam is reduced in temperature by giving up heat to the boiler water, and it is then mixed with the rest of the steam from the primary superheater and passes on to the secondary superheater. The final temperature of the steam is regulated by the position of the automatically operated valve that controls the amount of steam diverted through the attemperator.

In the shell type of surface attemperator, a bundle of tubes through which the superheated steam flows is fitted in a cylindrical shell through which cooling water circulates. A valve in the base of the shell diverts through the tubes the proper proportion of the superheated steam to give the final steam temperature desired. A positive flow of water in the shell at all times is assured by connection to the boiler circulating system. Thermal-sleeve ferrules at the steam-inlet ends connect the tubes to an inlet box which protects the tubesheets from severe thermal stresses. Disadvantages of this type of attemperator are the relative inaccessibility of the tubes and tubesheet for inspection of possible sludge deposition.

A more satisfactory design of surface attemperator is the drum type (Fig. 23), in which tube loops are submerged in one of the boiler drums and the required portion of superheated steam passes through the tubes. Difficulties with boiler-water deposits are avoided, and an additional high-pressure shell is not required. It may be necessary, however, to increase the size of the boiler drum to accommodate the attemperator tubes. Where this is not advisable, the amount of attemperation and, therefore, the range of steam-temperature control are

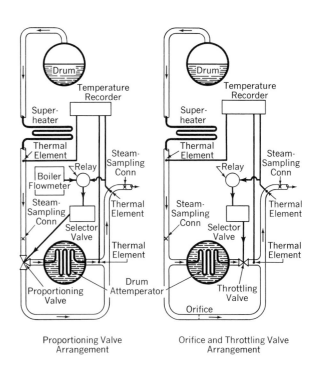

Fig. 24 Automatic controls for drum-type attemperator.

limited by the number and length of tubes for which space is available.

In the drum type, steam temperature is regulated by control of the proportion of total superheated steam flow through the attemperator. In one method of control, a proportioning valve receives all of the superheated steam, diverting some of it to the attemperator while the remainder goes through a bypass. In another method, suitable for comparatively low temperatures, an orifice is fitted in the bypass line to give the pressure drop required to divert some of the superheated steam through the attemperator, and a throttling valve is located at the attemperator outlet. By this method a simple valve is used in place of a more elaborate proportioning valve, and, since only attemperated steam flows through it, construction suitable for high temperature is not required. The two methods are illustrated in Fig. 24. An example of steam-temperature regulation using both gas recirculation and attemperation is shown in Fig. 25.

Of the direct-contact type as differentiated from the surface type, the spray attemperator, illustrated in Fig. 26, has proved most satisfactory for regulating steam temperature. Water of high purity is introduced into the superheated-steam line through a spray nozzle at the throat of a venturi section within the line. Because of the spray action at the nozzle and the high velocity of the steam through the venturi throat, the water vaporizes, mixes with, and cools the superheated steam. An important feature of construction is the continuation of the venturi section into a thermal sleeve, downstream from the spray nozzle, to protect the high-temperature piping from thermal shock that could result from any incompletely evaporated water droplets striking the hot surface of the piping.

The spray attemperator provides a quick-acting and sensitive means of control for regulating steam temperature. The curves of Fig. 25 are actually based on a spray

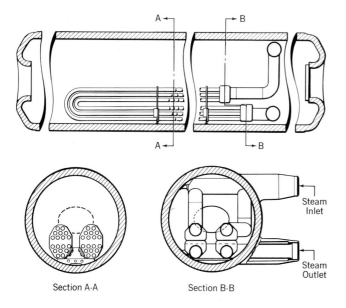

Fig. 23 B&W drum type of surface attemperator.

attemperator, although applicable to a surface type. It is important that the spray water be of highest purity, since solids entrained in the spray water enter the steam and may, if excessive, cause troublesome deposits on superheater tubes, piping, or turbine blades. High-pressure heater drains are a source of extremely pure water but require a separate high-pressure corrosion-resistant pump if used for attemperator supply. Boiler feedwater may be satisfactory, provided condenser leakage or makeup does not introduce too much contamination. The total solids concentration in the spray water should not exceed 2.5 ppm.

Reheat steam temperature

The need for regulating the temperature of reheated steam and the methods of adjustment and control to do so are, in general, the same as for superheated steam. However, the designer does not have the same freedom of action as when only the superheater is used. For instance, in a drum-type unit the removal of heating surface ahead of the superheater as a means of adjustment to increase superheated steam temperature will also increase the reheat steam temperature, which may be undesirable. Furthermore, to reduce gas temperature below slagging limits for convection tube banks and to give the desired steam temperature, such a large proportion of the total input must be absorbed in the furnace and in the superheater and reheater that the boiler is practically eliminated. When this is so, boiler surface ahead of the superheater is not available for adjustment purposes.

Most of the means of control described for regulating steam temperature will also affect the reheat temperature if a reheater is incorporated.

When a spray attemperator is proposed for superheater and reheater steam-temperature control, it is necessary to weigh the convenience and good control characteristics of the spray attemperator against reduction in cycle efficiency resulting from diversion of reheater attemperator spray water around the high-pressure turbine.

Instruments and their application

Instruments are required to tell the operator how the equipment is performing and to guide him in adjusting the controls to produce the desired results. Among these are instruments for automatic and manual control, indicating, recording, alarm, and for use at test connections.

Instruments for automatic control. A single thermal element actuated by the final steam temperature is the sim-

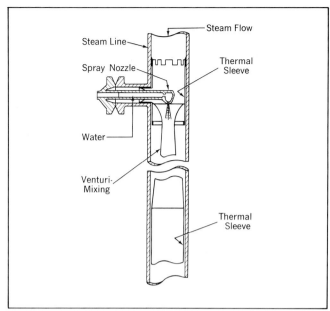

Fig. 26 Spray attemperator showing thermal sleeve.

plest and least expensive type of automatic control for adjusting the means provided to give the temperature desired. The temperature-sensitive element may be a thermocouple, resistance thermometer, or bulblike pyrometer, located in the steam line beyond the superheater outlet. Variation of final steam temperature from the desired standard initiates a correction by adjusting the opening of a gas bypass damper, moving a proportioning valve to allow a larger or smaller proportion of the total steam flow through a submerged attemperator, or changing the quantity of water supplied to a spray attemperator. A schematic diagram of the elements of such a control system is shown in the view at the right in Fig. 24. This type of control is satisfactory for many applications, particularly where steam temperature responds quickly to an adjustment of the regulating mechanism, as in the case of an attemperator at the superheater outlet.

Where the response of steam temperature to the adjustment of the regulating mechanism is slow, as in the case of damper control or because of the thermal inertia in large superheaters, an anticipating type of control is preferable. This feature is included in the two-element control, in which either steam flow or air flow (latter usually preferred) governs the initial adjustment of the control mechanism. The final adjustment must always be by final steam temperature.

A schematic diagram of a two-element control system is shown in the view at the left in Fig. 24. With this type of control, quick action follows a change in load because the proportioning valve is immediately set to the approximate new position required without waiting for a change in final steam temperature to take place.

A three-element control (Fig. 27) often used with spray attemperators is an improvement on the two-element control because of a more accurate initial adjustment of the regulating mechanism, in this case the spray-water valve. The steam temperature at the outlet of the spray attemperator is used as the third element of the control. However, final adjustment must always be by final steam temperature.

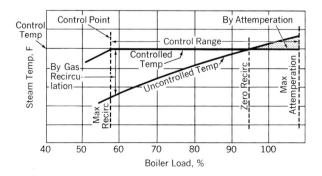

Fig. 25 Control of superheated steam temperature by both gas recirculation and attemperation.

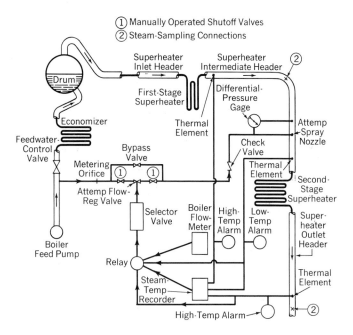

① Manually Operated Shutoff Valves
② Steam-Sampling Connections

Fig. 27 Three-element control for spray attemperator.

Indicating, recording, and alarm. How far to go in providing instruments for indicating and recording temperature and for alarms depends on the steam generating equipment furnished and on the judgment of the design- or operating-engineer. In a small installation with moderate steam temperature, a simple instrument for indicating final steam temperature may be all that is necessary. For a large unit with high steam temperature, where deviation from design conditions may cause serious loss in efficiency or failure of equipment, a complete set of instruments for all necessary functions should be provided.

The arrangement shown in Fig. 27 will serve as a basis for illustrating the need for and the functions of a typical set of instruments. Of first importance is the correct determination of final steam temperature, since satisfactory operation and safety of equipment beyond the boiler, as well as protection of the superheater, depend on this temperature. This measurement is also needed for actuating the automatic control system.

A high-temperature alarm is recommended as an additional safety feature, even though the careful attention given to final steam temperature by both boiler and turbine operators is usually considered sufficient protection.

Measurement of steam temperature with a low-temperature alarm at the spray-attemperator outlet will protect the second-stage superheater from the thermal shock of quenching by preventing over-attemperation and the consequent discharge of saturated steam and water into the hot superheater elements. Measurement of steam temperature with a high-temperature alarm at the first-stage superheater outlet protects this stage from overheating should slagging or other upset conditions alter the distribution of heat absorption between first- and second-stage superheaters to such an extent that the primary steam temperature becomes excessive.

It is desirable to have a spare thermometer well in the steam line adjacent to each thermal element of the control system so that these elements may be checked periodically for accuracy. A steam-sampling connection should be installed in the steam line between the steam drum and the attemperator to check the purity of steam leaving the drum. It is also desirable to install a steam-sampling connection in the steam line after the attemperator to check for leakage of boiler water into the line in the case of a submerged attemperator, or for excessive solids carried over in the spray water of a spray-type attemperator.

Chapter 13

Economizers and air heaters

In a boiler operating at subcritical pressure, the temperature of the gases leaving the steam generating surfaces of the boiler is essentially determined by the saturation temperature of the boiling water. The higher the steam pressure the higher will be this saturation temperature. The flue gases must be at a still higher temperature level, usually from 700 to 1000F, to permit transfer of heat from the gases to the steam generating surfaces. If the flue gases were exhausted to the atmosphere at such temperatures, the resultant loss in boiler efficiency could be intolerable. Feedwater on its way to the boiler at temperatures substantially below saturation, or air on its way to the furnace offers opportunity to absorb much of the residual, low-grade heat in the gases leaving the boiler with substantial improvement in overall efficiency. Historically, when this heat was absorbed by feedwater, the heat exchange device was logically called an "economizer." It served to improve the economy in the use of fuel.

Subsequently, it was found desirable and profitable to recover some or all of this low-grade heat in air heaters which raised the temperature of the air supplied for combustion. This not only improved boiler efficiency by lowering stack temperatures but it also improved the combustion conditions in the furnace. Higher heat release rates and higher furnace temperatures improved the economics of the boiler installation. Air heaters and economizers are consequently often called "heat traps." Modern boilers make full use of these devices for lowering the cost and improving the reliability of steam supply. The details of the design, selection and use of economizers and air heaters are discussed in this chapter.

Economizers

The early economizers were installed in boiler units operating on natural draft. They generally utilized tubes of equal or larger diameter than the boiler tubes, and widely spaced to reduce resistance to gas flow.

Cast iron proved to be an acceptable material for economizers because of its inherent resistance to corrosion, both internal and external. Cast iron fins were used in some designs of economizers to give extended heat transfer surface on the gas side and to minimize the effects of external corrosion.

Steel was early adapted to successful use in boilers but at first could not be used in economizers because of the corrosive effects of free oxygen. In the boiler, most of the dissolved oxygen in the feedwater was driven off in the steam drum with the steam, and the corrosive effect on the boiler tubes was accordingly reduced. In the economizer, as the temperature of the feedwater rose, the oxygen was gradually driven out of solution and attacked the inside of the tubes. Also the temperature of the water in the boiler, at saturation temperature, was above the dew point of the flue gases, while in the economizer, the feedwater, often entering at a temperature as low as 100F, cooled the surrounding flue gases so much that moisture condensed on the outside of the tubes. This moisture, with some of the sulfur dioxide and sulfur trioxide from the flue gas, caused corrosion. The moisture also formed a bond for the collection of ash on the tubes, restricting the gas passages and reducing the heat transfer. Cleaning apparatus had to be used to remove this deposit. Early economizers of cast iron were equipped with mechanical scrapers. Cast iron economizers of this type are still in use with some low pressure boilers.

When feedwater temperatures were increased by the introduction of stage bleeding of turbines and extraction feed heating, the minimum operating temperature for the economizer was increased, thus eliminating gas-side condensation with its attendant corrosion and fouling. Feedwater was treated and oxygen removed by deaeration to reduce internal corrosion. These improvements made it possible to use steel for economizer tubes, thus permitting the use of economizers at high pressures. Soot blowing was developed to keep gas-side surfaces clean. Induced and forced draft replaced natural draft, allowing more compact and economical surface arrangements.

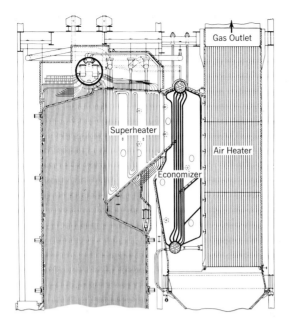

Fig. 1 Two-drum bent-tube economizer arranged with three gas passes.

One of the earliest straight-tube steel economizers of B&W design was built to ASME standards in 1915. A successful two-drum bent-tube type of economizer was developed early in 1917. A later version of this type applied to a Radiant boiler is illustrated in Fig. 1. The tube diameters and spacing can be the same as for the boiler, or they can be modified to improve heat absorption, draft loss, water velocities and the conditions for external cleaning. Water is fed into the lower drum and flows up through the tubes to the upper drum. Gases flow either along the tubes, preferably entering at the top and flowing down counter to the water flow, or across the tubes in single or multiple passes.

Smaller tube economizers (2-in. OD) were introduced about 1920 and, since that time, have come to be widely used. The small-tube economizer requires less space, is easier to manufacture, and uses less steel for tubes and casing than the larger tube units. It is particularly suitable for high pressures.

The early 2-in. tube economizers were generally made with straight horizontal tubes rolled into horizontal square headers. Handhole fittings were provided in the headers opposite the ends of the tubes so that every tube could be inspected and mechanically cleaned internally. Water fed into the bottom header flowed up through the tubes from header to header and then from the top header into the boiler. Gas entered the top of the economizer and flowed down across the staggered tubes, leaving at the bottom (see Fig. 14, *Introduction to Steam*). This type of economizer was used with the first 650 psi boiler units in 1922, and with coal-fired high-pressure units shortly afterward.

An improved design of the horizontal steel tube economizer, frequently used when it was necessary to clean the inside of the tubes mechanically, was also developed during the 1920's. The 2-in. OD tubes were bent through 180 degrees at one end. The other end was equipped with a special flanged and bolted return-bend fitting.

Heating surface design

The use of inhibited acid to clean internal surfaces (*see Chapter 36*) has materially simplified the design of economizers. The tubes can be continuous from inlet to outlet headers with terminals rolled or welded. They can be made any length and any diameter. Diameters commonly used range from $1\frac{3}{4}$- to $2\frac{3}{4}$-in. OD. All high pressure and most intermediate and low pressure economizers are now designed with continuous tubes, each tube having several horizontal sections connected vertically by 180-degree bends to permit draining.

The tubes in a bare tube economizer are usually arranged in line. Side spacing of tube sections, except for "clean" fuel firing (e.g., natural gas), is limited to a minimum of $1\frac{3}{4}$- to 2-in. lanes, depending on the characteristics of the fuel ash. In many large units, greater side spacings are selected based on the overall economic evaluation of equipment cost and draft loss. Back spacings of rows are less critical from a cleaning standpoint and are therefore usually set by a similar economic evaluation.

Steaming economizer

Sometimes there is an advantage in producing part of the steam in an economizer rather than in the boiler surface. Basically there is no operating limit to the percentage of water flow that may be evaporated in a steaming economizer. However, in practice it is customary to limit the steam generation in the economizer to a maximum of about 20% of the feed at full boiler output. This percentage will be less as the load decreases because of lower gas temperatures in the economizer. Since 1924, steaming economizers have been installed in a great number of new boiler units. Steaming economizers cannot be used to advantage where a high feed makeup is required because of the practical difficulties in treating a high percentage of the feedwater to a suitable condition.

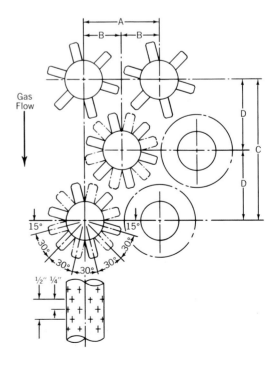

Fig. 2 Economizer tube arrangement and stud pattern.

Economizer size

Economizer surface can be justified only where it can absorb the same heat at less cost than other types of surface. Steaming in the economizer can be justified only when economizer surface costs less than boiler surface. In the non-steaming sections, the economizer surface operates at a lower temperature than boiler surface. Hence, for a given gas temperature a greater temperature difference is available for heat transfer in the non-steaming sections of the economizer than in the boiler, and more heat can be transferred in the economizer for a given amount of heating surface. The correct balance of boiler and economizer surface requires a cost evaluation.

Extended surface economizers have economic advantages over bare tube surface in lower first cost and smaller space required for installation. They are especially well suited for gas fired units and units without air heaters, such as those with combined steam and gas turbine cycles. Extended surface tubes are normally installed horizontally in a staggered pattern. A typical tube arrangement and stud pattern is shown in Fig. 2.

In units with air heaters the stack temperature and the amount of economizer and air heater surfaces are usually set by the overall economic evaluation of the equipment, fuel, and draft and air resistance costs. For a given stack gas temperature, there is an optimum gas temperature leaving the economizer, since an increase in the economizer exit gas temperature decreases the size of the economizer and increases the size of the air heater. In some cases, the size of the economizer is limited and the air heater increased by the need for high temperature air for adequate fuel drying or for good combustion.

The amount of economizer surface required varies with the incoming feedwater temperature which usually ranges from 212 to 560F. For high pressure units, the temperature of the feed to the economizer is determined by the number of turbine extraction points. It rises as the pressure increases. The turbine extraction points, feedwater heaters and resulting feed temperatures are set by an economic evaluation of equipment, fuel and operating costs for the overall plant.

Location, arrangement and cleaning

Location of the economizer varies with the overall design of the boiler unit. Where air heaters are not installed, as in many small boilers of standardized types, economizers are located in the gas flue between the boiler gas exit and the fan or stack. It is always preferable for the gas from the boiler to flow down across the economizer tubes and for the water to enter at the bottom and flow up through the tubes. This counterflow design reduces to a minimum both the surface and the draft loss. Up-flow of water eliminates unstable water flow, gives the most uniform gas distribution, and makes possible the proper use of a "steaming economizer" where some steam is generated in a portion of the water-outlet end.

In many high pressure units, location of the economizer in an upward-flowing gas stream is fixed by the layout. In such cases small economizers can be installed for all-parallel flow. Large economizers require special consideration and should be installed counterflow for the water-inlet section and parallel flow for the water-outlet section (*see Fig. 3*).

The air heater, when installed, is usually the final heat trap, i.e., the economizer is generally located ahead of the air heater in the gas stream. In some cases where very low exit gas temperatures and high air temperatures are desired, it may be necessary to divide the air heater and place the economizer between the air heater sections.

In large high pressure units when high efficiency is desired, low temperature economizers, called "stack coolers," are placed after the air heater. The stack cooler replaces one of the low pressure feedwater heaters. Water temperatures at full load are about 160 to 180F.

When ash-bearing fuels are to be fired and tenacious ash deposits are liable to form on the tubes, the economizer should be located directly over a hopper so that water-soluble constituents of the deposits can be dissolved and washed off during out-of-service periods.

In addition to washing, the external surface of economizers may be cleaned with the same type of equipment used to clean boiler surfaces. Economizers are designed with tube spacing and depths of banks best suited for external cleaning by either steam or air blowers. The design details depend upon the fuel ash characteristics, feedwater temperature, gas temperature, gas flow and type of surface (bare tube or extended).

External corrosion

External corrosion of economizers may occur when water vapor in the flue gas condenses on the tubes. If the flue gas also contains combustion products of sulfur, corrosion will be accelerated. The rate of corrosion increases as the metal temperature is reduced. The dew point and the potential rate of corrosion both increase as the sulfur content of the fuel increases. Pulverized-coal ash seems to act as an inhibitor in retarding the corrosion rate. Experience indicates that the corrosion rate can be reduced to safe limits if the temperature of the feedwater to the economizer is kept above certain minimum values. Minimum safe values of tube-metal temperatures for varying percentages of sulfur and for several types of firing are indicated by the curves in Fig. 4. When sulfur is burned in a boiler, as in one sulfuric acid manufacturing process, the dew point is so high that all steel surfaces must be above 450F to assure a reasonable life. For such applications, an economizer is not furnished.

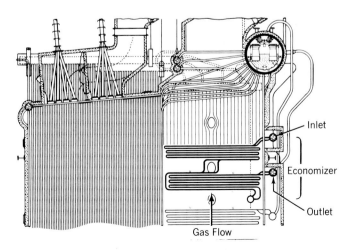

Fig. 3 Continuous-tube economizer arranged for part counterflow and part parallel flow.

Internal corrosion

Economizers are also subject to internal corrosion from dissolved oxygen and low hydroxyl ion concentration (a low pH). Oxygen corrosion can be eliminated by deaeration to essentially zero oxygen (*see Chapter 34*). Feedwater is usually deaerated with the deaerator at or above 212F to avoid stray air leaks into the system. Steel in the economizer is attacked faster by pure water, which has equal hydrogen and hydroxyl ion concentrations (pH = 7), than by water which has a higher hydroxyl ion concentration. It is therefore necessary to maintain a pH value between 8 and 9 for the water passing through the economizer. If necessary, some boiler water may be recirculated to the inlet end of the economizer to maintain the desired pH value in the economizer.

Air heaters

The air heater in a steam generating unit reclaims some heat (which would otherwise be lost) from the flue gas and adds that heat to the air required for the combustion of the fuel.

As in the case of economizers, air heaters originated in Europe before they were used in the United States. Early patent files reveal the invention of air heaters long before the industry had developed to the stage where they could be used economically.

The first air heater to be installed in a commercial boiler unit in the United States was built in 1922. Flat parallel steel plates formed alternate gas and air passages. It was necessary that the passes be completely separate from each other, since any air leakage into the gas stream not only reduced the efficiency of the air heater but increased the load on the forced and induced draft fans. Plate air heaters (recuperative type) are still in use but are not as suitable as tubular or regenerative heaters for the higher gas and air pressures which are now common practice.

Placing its first tubular air heater in service early in 1923, B&W built a total of 50 air heaters during 1923 and 1924. The demand at that time arose as a result of increases in boiler pressure and size. Before 1922 the highest pressures commonly used in power generation

ranged from 350 to 400 psi. In 1922 units of 650 psi were developed to generate more kilowatt-hours per pound of steam. The increase in steam pressure made larger units possible. The larger units and higher pressures made extraction steam feedwater heating economical, and the higher feed pressures and temperatures in turn made the addition of air heaters economical.

Before 1920 practically all coal used in the production of steam was burned on stokers or grates. Furnace walls were generally all refractory or, in a few instances, partly water cooled. Hot air supplied to the fire improved stoker performance by raising the temperature level in the combustion zone, although this increased maintenance costs of stoker parts and furnace surfaces. The development of water-cooled furnace walls that could withstand high combustion temperatures contributed greatly to the effective use of air heaters in boiler units.

In the early 1920's there was a tremendous increase in the development and use of pulverized-coal firing in central stations. For this type of firing, hot air was ideal for drying, transporting and burning the coal in suspension. Demand for air heaters was thus established.

Advantages of preheated air

Practically all pulverized-coal-fired units require preheated air at 300 to 600F for drying the fuel. The larger stoker-fired units burning bituminous coal operate more efficiently with air preheated to about 350F (not too hot for stoker parts). Preheated air is not essential for the smaller stoker-fired units. Service requirements and conditions will primarily influence the decision to install an air heater.

The size of heater chosen will depend upon economic and engineering factors. The major economic factors are the original cost of the air heater, the operating costs for fuel and fan power, and the maintenance cost. The principal engineering factors are the space available, the characteristics of the fuel used, and the desired temperatures for the preheated air and the exit gas.

With the common fuels (coal, oil and gas) and identical furnace conditions, the efficiency of a steam generating unit as a whole will increase about 2.5% for every 100F decrease in exit gas temperature. This corresponds to an increase of about 2% in efficiency for each 100F increase in air temperature. An air heater providing combustion air at temperatures ranging upward from 300F will often effect savings in fuel ranging from 5 to 10%, as indicated by the curve in Fig. 5. While temperatures above the maximum in the graph (600F) have been and are used in boiler practice, it is increasingly difficult above this limit to arrange the boiler unit satisfactorily or to obtain economical materials suitable for the temperature.

The use of preheated air improves combustion conditions and efficiency at all loads. In a new installation, the use of an air heater frequently permits a reduction in the physical size of the boiler.

Classification of air heaters

Air heaters may be classified according to the principle of their operation as (a) recuperative and (b) regenerative. Heat is transferred to the air from the flue gases of the boiler or from other sources. Air heaters operating on

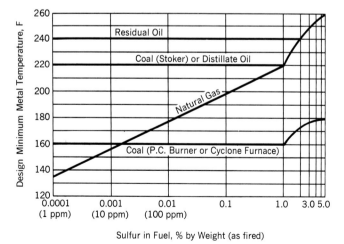

Fig. 4 Limiting tube-metal temperatures to avoid external corrosion in economizers or air heaters when burning fuels containing sulfur.

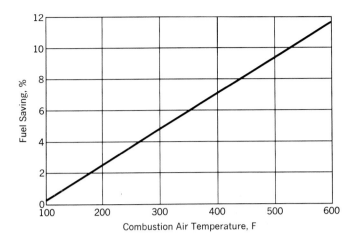

Fig. 5 Approximate improvement in efficiency when heated combustion air is used in boiler units.

the recuperative principle are generally tubular type, although some are plate type. Heat is provided by 1) the flue gases of the boiler, 2) steam in coils, or 3) separately fired furnaces. Among air heaters operating on the regenerative principle are the rotary regenerative and stationary regenerative types with heat provided by the flue gases or a separate furnace.

In a recuperative design, the heat is transferred directly from the hot gases or steam on one side of the surface to air on the other side.

In a regenerative heater, the heat is transferred indirectly from the hot gases to the air through some intermediate heat-storage medium. Use of the principle of regeneration is not new. Regenerative air heaters were used in other industries before they were used in steam generation. For open-hearth furnaces, it was common practice to control the gas flow from the furnace and the air flow to the furnace by dampers, so that the gas flow would alternately heat one flue and then the other. With the brickwork in the flues acting as the heat-storage medium, the air, flowing through the hot flues alternately, would be heated to over 1000F before entering the combustion chamber.

Corrosion control

Experience indicates that corrosion may occur in air heaters when metal temperature falls below the limits given in Fig. 4. Sulfur content of the fuel, moisture content of the gases and type of firing are all important factors which must be considered. Relationships between the minimum metal temperature, the gas and air temperatures, the fuel and the design of the air heater are established by design calculations using data from operation and engineering tests.

Requisite metal temperatures may be controlled by one or more of the following methods:

1. Bypass a portion, or all, of the inlet air around a portion or all of the heating surface. This is particularly effective for start-up or low load operation.
2. Recirculate a portion of the hot air from the air heater outlet back to the forced draft fan inlet to increase the air temperature entering the heater.

3. Use steam extracted from turbine or plant process as the heat source in a steam coil heater located in the air duct ahead of the air heater (gas-to-air) to increase the air temperature entering the air heater.

Metal temperatures may be increased by:
1. Employing parallel flow air and gas in the heater. This is often used for stoker-fired units and for chemical recovery units in the paper industry.
2. Designing the first air pass of the tubular heaters for varying air velocity with lowest velocity at the air entrance.

Corrosion may be reduced and service life increased by using corrosive resistant materials and coatings in the low temperature sections of the heater, such as low grade alloy steel and coated surfaces.

Recuperative air heater — tubular

The B&W tubular air heater utilizes the heat from the products of combustion after they leave the boiler, superheater or economizer. It is essentially a nest of straight tubes expanded into tube sheets and enclosed in a suitably reinforced steel casing. This casing functions to contain the air or gas and is provided with air and gas inlet and outlet openings and the necessary hoppers and structural steel supporting members. The vertical type, suspended from above, is illustrated in Fig. 6. The casing is made of flanged steel plate panels welded to stiffening

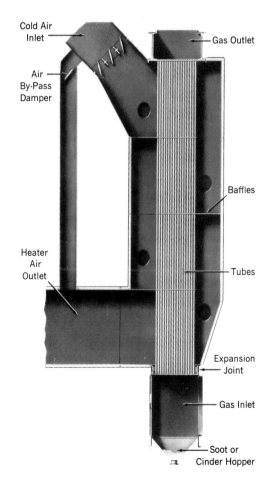

Fig. 6 Tubular air heater arranged for counterflow of gas and air, with an air bypass to control metal temperature at air inlet end.

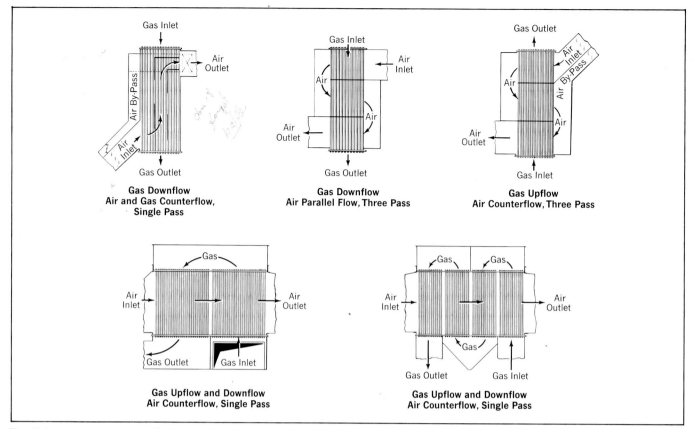

Fig. 7 Some arrangements of tubular air heaters to suit various directions of gas and air flow.

bars and supported by a frame of steel bars, angles and channels. The frame also carries the flanged air-inlet and air-outlet boxes. Dust and cinder disposal hoppers as required are provided under the tubes to suit flue arrangements.

In the modern tubular air heater the tubes are expanded into tube sheets at both ends. To provide for expansion, one tube sheet should be free to move with respect to the casing, and this must be accomplished without air leakage. One method is to fit a flexible bellows-type expansion joint connection as indicated at the bottom tube sheet of the air heater illustrated in Fig. 6. Tests made in actual operation with this type show negligible leakage as reflected in excess air or CO_2 determinations. For overall tightness of the air heater it is preferable to weld the panel joints of the casing and hoppers. Air leakage is undesirable because it increases the fan power in direct proportion to leakage. If it occurs at the gas inlet it also impairs the efficiency of the air heater.

For pulverized-coal firing, tubular air heaters are used as secondary air heaters with a single air pass, two gas pass arrangement. Water washing is provided at the cold end for secondary air heaters exceeding 25 ft in length. The water washing is intended to be utilized for out-of-service operation only. When firing lignite or subbituminous coal on secondary air heaters, the arrangement should be restricted and tubes above 25 ft in length should be provided with straight line type air heaters equipped to water wash the hot end only. In addition, service should be provided for water washing the cold end of the heater when out of service.

Sootblowers are located so that a jet of steam, air (or water in some instances with the boiler out of service) can be blown through each tube as required.

Tube sizes. In building tubular air heaters, tubes from 1½-in. to 4-in. OD have been used in various units, including marine plants. The smaller the tube diameter, the shorter the tube length and the greater the number of tubes required for a given performance. The arrangement of air and gas passages, space available for the air heater and, from a cleaning standpoint, the type of fuel fired are factors involved in establishing the diameter of the air heater tubes. Generally, the smaller the diameter, the more compact the heater and the less space required. For a given performance, overall cost of the heater (including the manufacture, shipment, and erection of the tubes, casing and supports, and building costs) is a minimum for some particular size of tube. In stationary boiler practice, the 2½-in. and 2-in. tubes are now generally used, and in marine practice, where space and weight are limited, the 2-in. or 1½-in. tubes prove to be more economical.

Adaptability for installation. Adaptability of the air heater to space limitations and to the arrangement of flues and ducts between the heater and the boiler is an important factor in the overall design of a steam generating unit. The tubular air heater, as indicated in Fig. 7, can be arranged to suit a wide variety of space conditions and duct layouts. It can be adapted for vertical or horizontal applications and for multipass flow of either gas or air, or both. Where the forced draft fan is located at a

distance from the boiler, the tubular air heater has frequently been used as a flue, thus saving the expense of additional ductwork.

Primary air heating. Occasionally, for pulverized-coal-fired units it is desirable to have a separate section in the air heater for heating the primary air to the pulverizers, particularly when the temperature leaving the main heater is lower than that required for drying very wet coal, such as a Midwest coal with more than 10 to 12% surface moisture requiring air temperatures up to 650F. This arrangement has the additional advantage of permitting use of a smaller forced draft fan for the secondary air, since a single fan handling clean cold air is used for all pulverizers of a unit. However, because of complications in the air heater design, a separate primary heater is seldom recommended when the air temperature leaving the main heater is high enough for the pulverizers.

Primary air heaters on any coal fuel with tubes over 25 ft long are provided for out-of-service water washing at the cold end of the air heater only.

Recuperative air heater – plate

Plate type air heaters use thin, flat, parallel plates with alternate wide and narrow spacing to match the ratio of gas weight to air weight. Thus the flue gas is made to pass through the wider spaced passages (1 in. to ½ in.) and the air through the narrower passages (¾ in. to ¼ in.) generally in counterflow relation. To obtain more heating surface for a given volume, the gas space is made as small as possible within the limits required for cleaning. Commercial designs have differed chiefly in the method of sealing the air spaces from the gas spaces.

Recuperative air heater – steam coil

After the development of pulverized fuel there was some demand to substitute this type of firing for existing boilers. This application required hot air, and it was not always possible to install a flue gas air heater. In such cases commercially available steam-to-air heat exchangers were successfully adapted to supply the heat to dry and burn the fuel. Steam coil heaters are used today to increase the minimum tube metal temperatures to reduce corrosion by heating the combustion air before it enters the main air heater.

Recuperative air heater – separately fired

Hot air is sometimes required for industrial use. Air at atmospheric or higher pressure may be heated to the desired temperature by using a separately fired air heater. The separately fired air heater usually consists of a refractory furnace with a tubular heater arranged for a number of gas and air passes.

To prevent overheating of the tubes, it is essential to control the gas temperatures entering the heater. This may be done by (a) diluting the gas with excess air or by (b) recirculating the gas from the air heater outlet to the furnace, thus reducing the temperature of the furnace gases. The unit is more efficient when the latter method is used.

Regenerative air heater – rotating plate

In the rotating-plate-type regenerative air heater, heat-storage plate elements are heated progressively in a flow-ing gas stream, and then progressively rotated by mechanical means into a flowing air stream where the stored heat is released to the air before the plates are returned to the gas stream. The use of steel plates as a heat-storage medium in a regenerative air heater was developed and first applied in Europe. The first rotary air heater of this type in the United States was installed in 1923. Since then, this type and the tubular (recuperative) type have been the two principal air heater designs used in steam generating systems.

The general features of a rotary regenerative air heater are shown in Fig. 8. A rotor, supported by bearings at shaft extremes, is mounted within a box housing. The rotor structure is provided with cavities for the location of segmental baskets containing the heating surface in the form of plates. As the slowly moving rotor turns, the heating surface is placed in the gas stream, passes through the fixed band containing the axial and radial seals, and is then placed in the air stream. The seal system reduces both infiltration and bypass leakage. Gas flues and air ducts attached to the housing confine the air and gas to the desired flow paths.

The turbulent-surface type is applicable to coal, oil and gas-fired systems. In this type air heater, the plates are wide spaced to minimize pluggage and turbulent flow results. The shaft may be horizontal or vertical.

Ash particulate residues from coal or oil firing are cleaned from the heat-storage plates by means of a soot-blowing device that uses either steam or air as a cleaning medium. During low load operation, when deposits tend

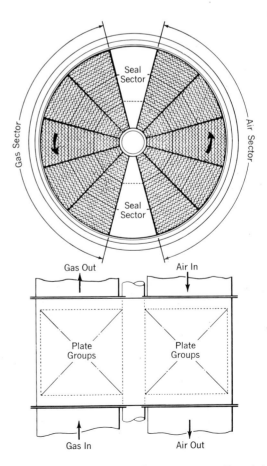

Fig. 8 Diagrammatic illustration of rotary regenerative air heater (vertical shaft arrangement) with gas and air counterflow.

to increase because of low metal temperatures, the heater can be bypassed on the air side or air can be recirculated.

Rotary regenerative air heaters are made in a number of standard diameters and with various depths of heat-storage plates to obtain the desired performance in various applications to steam generating systems.

Regenerative air heater — stationary plate

The Babcock & Wilcox type Rothemuhle regenerative air heater, illustrated in Fig. 9, utilizes heat-storage plate elements contained in a stationary stator in the flowing gas stream and two symmetrical air hoods progressively rotated over the stator to direct the flowing air stream so the stored heat is transferred to the air. The reliability of the Rothemuhle type regenerative air heater stems in part from the rotating mass being minimized to only 15 to 25% of the total air heater weight and in part from the slow rotation speed (less than 1 rotation per minute). The stationary stator permits selection of acid-resistant materials including enameled steel and ceramic materials to provide resistance to corrosion. Since the major part of the mass remains static, the load is distributed to a number of structural steel supports equally spaced around the stator and adjacent duct loads can be taken through the stator housing directly into the structural steel.

The sealing system is spring mounted to the hoods and is designed to adapt to the stator curvature, maintaining a constant seal. The hot end sealing devices are thermally self adjusting to provide constant adjustment as thermal changes expand or contract the stator. The heating surface can be continuously monitored for cold end metal temperature in order to minimize the potential for corrosion and pluggage. A permanent fire detection system can be embedded in the stationary stator to provide an early warning in the event of fire.

The Rothemuhle type regenerative air heater can be applied in a variety of designs and arrangements for optimum adaptation to each boiler system.

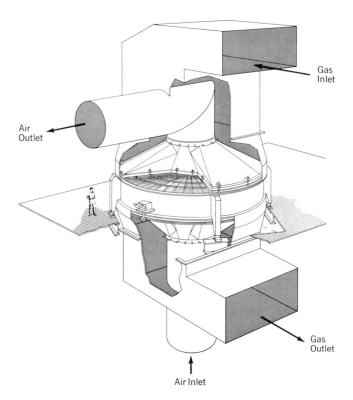

Fig. 9 Arrangement of counterflow regenerative air heater with stationary plates.

Chapter 14

Temperature, surface and pressure drop calculations

In evaluating the performance of a steam generating unit for a given set of conditions, a number of complex factors must be considered, as indicated by the material in the preceding chapters. Only a few of these factors are subject to precise analysis. Many others must be determined by empirical rules and from correlation of test data from operating units. The most serious complications are the effects of ash from coal, and to a lesser extent from oil, as discussed in Chapter 15. In spite of these complications large units are built and operated in conformity with design specifications.

When furnace and firing equipment are properly designed and operated so that combustion is completed within the furnace, the gas temperature leaving the furnace can be predicted by methods discussed under *Furnaces* in Chapter 4. These methods depend essentially on curves such as Figs. 24, 25 and 26 of Chapter 4, which are based on theory with empirical corrections. These curves relate heat available (Chapters 4 and 6) to the amount of cooling surface in the furnace and the quantity of combustion gases leaving the furnace. Corrections must be made for the nature and disposition of the fur-

nace surface, and the kind of fuel and firing method used.

In determining the disposition of the heating surfaces beyond the furnace, a primary problem is to attain an optimum interrelationship among three principal factors: gas temperature drop, surface, and pressure drop (draft loss) of the gas.

Heating surfaces may be disposed in a great variety of arrangements, each affecting temperature and pressure drop. Sizes and spacings of tubes are the result of a compromise between the requirements of heat transfer, pressure drop of the gas, fouling characteristics of fuels, erosive velocities and other considerations (Chapter 12).

In most steam generators the hotter medium of heat transfer consists of flue gases that are the products of combustion of various fuels. The cooler medium in the steam generating section of the boiler is a mixture of water and steam at constant temperature of saturation (Case I, Fig. 1). In the superheater and economizer sections, the cooling medium is steam and water respectively, and either Case II or III of Fig. 1 may apply, i.e., either a parallel flow or counterflow arrangement may be used (*see Mean Temperature Difference, Chapter 4*).

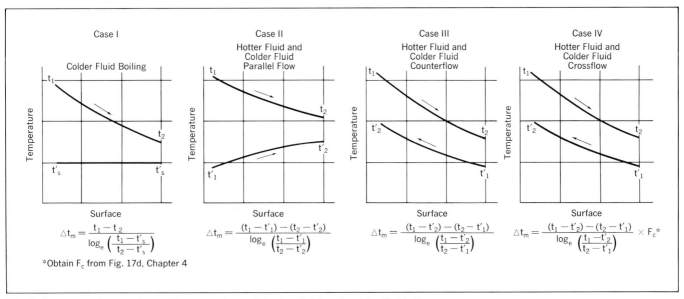

Fig. 1 Log mean temperature difference, Δt_m, of hotter fluid and colder fluid, F.

In the air heater the cooling medium is air, generally with a counterflow or crossflow arrangement (Cases III or IV, Fig. 1).

To illustrate the general procedure of performance calculation, a small unit (Fig. 2) with a simplified arrangement of heating surfaces will serve as an example. The procedures described are applicable to the more complex arrangements found in large modern steam generating units.

As the combustion gases leave the furnace of Fig. 2, they pass successively through a screen (boiler tubes), superheater, boiler, economizer and air heater. The characteristics and extent of the heating surface in each of these areas are summarized in Table 1.

Table 1
Arrangement and extent of heating surfaces in example unit of Fig. 2

Screen
  2 rows of 2½-in. OD tubes, approx 18 ft long
  Rows in line and spaced on 6-in. centers
  23 tubes per row spaced on 6-in. centers
  $S = 542$ sq ft
  $A_g = 129$ sq ft

Superheater
  12 rows of 2½-in. OD tubes (0.165-in. thick), 17.44 ft long
  Rows in line and spaced on 3¼-in. centers
  23 tubes per row spaced on 6-in. centers
  $S = 3150$ sq ft
  $A_g = 133$ sq ft

Boiler
  25 rows of 2½-in. OD tubes, approx 18 ft long
  Rows in line and spaced on 3¼-in. centers
  35 tubes per row spaced on 4-in. centers
  $S = 10,300$ sq ft
  $A_g = 85.0$ sq ft

Economizer
  10 rows of 2-in. OD tubes (0.148-in. thick), approx 10 ft long
  Rows in line and spaced on 3-in. centers
  47 tubes per row spaced on 3-in. centers
  $S = 2460$ sq ft
  $A_g = 42$ sq ft

Air Heater
  53 rows of 2-in. OD tubes (0.083-in. thick), approx 13 ft long
  Rows in line and spaced on 2½-in. centers
  41 tubes per row spaced on 3½-in. centers
  $S = 14,800$ sq ft
  A_g (total internal cross section area of 2173 tubes) $= 39.3$ sq ft
  A_a (clear area between tubes for crossflow of air) $= 70$ sq ft
  Air temperature entering air heater = 80F

Heating surface, S, is the external area of the tubes exposed to the combustion gases. For example, the superheater heating surface is:

$$12 \times 23 \times 17.44 \times \pi \times 2.5/12 = 3150 \text{ sq ft}$$

Except in the air heater, the gas flows through the heating surfaces in a direction perpendicular to tube length, and the free gas-flow area, A_g, is the minimum clear area between the faces of the tubes in the direction of the passage of the gas flow. The gas-flow area for the superheater is:

$$(18 \times 12) - (23 \times 17.44 \times 2.5/12) = 133 \text{ sq ft}$$

This chapter deals primarily with heat transfer and pressure drop calculations:

1. Heat transfer calculations to relate an amount of heat transferred under given conditions and the corresponding amount of heating surface of a given type and disposition.

2. Calculations to determine the amount of pressure drop sustained by a given quantity of flue gas, air, steam, or water flowing through or across a given tube arrangement.

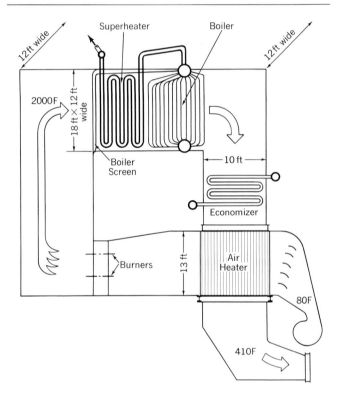

Fig. 2 Example unit (sectional side view).

Output of the unit

The example unit is expected to generate 250,000 lb/hr of superheated steam at 450 psia and 650F ($h = 1332.5$), when feedwater at 220F ($h = 189.2$) enters the economizer. (Enthalpy values are taken from *ASME Steam Tables*, 1967. Selected values from these tables are listed in Table 3, Chapter 2.) The efficiency of the boiler is such that the temperature of the gases leaving the air heater will not exceed 410F when the boiler is fired with No. 6 fuel oil of approximately 18,500 Btu/lb heating value with 80F inlet air and 13% excess air.

The following information is calculated by applying the principles of combustion to the burning of fuel oil, as described in Chapter 6:

Table 2

Heat absorbed by water and steam
$= 250,000 \ (1332.5 - 189.2) = 285.8 \times 10^6$ Btu/hr

Unit efficiency	$= 85.2\%$
Fuel input	$= 335.5 \times 10^6$ Btu/hr
Weight of flue gas	$= 304,000$ lb/hr
Weight of air	$= 287,000$ lb/hr
Moisture in flue gas	$= 6.8\%$

Heat transfer

The general equation for heat flow rate is stated in equation (1), Chapter 4, as follows:

(1) $\quad q = US\Delta t$

where:

q = rate of heat flow, Btu/hr
U = overall or combined conductance, Btu/sq ft, hr, F
S = heat transfer surface, sq ft
Δt = temperature difference causing heat flow, F

From equation (25), Chapter 4:

(2) $\quad U = (U_{cg} + U_{rg}) \times U_{cs}/(U_{cg} + U_{rg} + U_{cs})$

where:

U_{cg} = hotter fluid convection conductance, Btu/sq ft, hr, F
U_{rg} = intertube radiation conductance, Btu/sq ft, hr, F
U_{cs} = colder fluid convection conductance, Btu/sq ft, hr, F

Equation (1) can be expanded as follows to state the quantitative relationship in the transfer of heat from a heating to a cooling fluid:

(3) $\quad q = US\Delta t_m = wc(t_1 - t_2) = w'c'(t'_2 - t'_1)$
$$= w'(h'_2 - h'_1)$$

where:

Δt_m = mean temperature difference between the heating and cooling fluids (*see Fig. 1, also Mean Temperature Difference, Chapter 4*)
w = weight of hotter fluid, lb/hr
c = mean specific heat of hotter fluid, Btu/lb, F (normally c_p)
t_1, t_2 = temperature of hotter fluid entering and leaving heat transfer surface, F
w' = weight of colder fluid, lb/hr
c' = mean specific heat of colder fluid, Btu/lb, F (normally c_p)
t'_1, t'_2 = temperature of colder fluid entering and leaving heat transfer area, F
h'_1, h'_2 = enthalpy of colder fluid entering and leaving, Btu/lb

The foregoing heat transfer formulas can be used in two general ways:

1. To determine how much heat is absorbed by a tube bank of given description.

2. To determine how much heating surface is required to transfer a predetermined amount of heat with a given tube size and arrangement. Both of these approaches will be used in the examples to follow. In determining the value of U or Δt_m, it is necessary to assume a value for t_2. This involves reiteration of calculations. It is possible to derive "operative" equations that would reduce the effect of assumptions. However, the above equations are satisfactory to illustrate basic procedure.

Calculation of conductance

Chapter 4 contains formulas and charts for calculating the convection component (U_c) of conductance. Equation (21) and Figs. 11-15 of Chapter 4 apply to cross-flow; equation (18) and Figs. 6-10 of Chapter 4 apply to longitudinal flow.

Intertube and cavity radiation. Radiation originating from the radiating gaseous constituents of combustion gases (in cavities and in the spaces between tubes) is described in *Radiation from and to Gases*, Chapter 4. This gaseous radiation can be expressed in terms of conductance by use of equation (4) in conjunction with Figs. 3-6.

(4) $\qquad\qquad U_{rg} = U'_r K$

U'_r is obtained from Fig. 3, entering with Δt_m and tube temperature.

K is obtained from Fig. 4 by entering with values of the product of p_r and L. Values of p_r are obtained

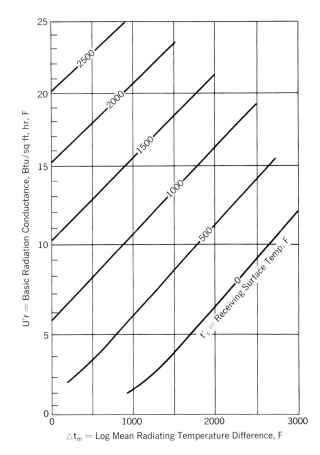

Fig. 3 Basic radiation conductance, U'_r, vs log mean temperature difference, Δt_m, and receiving surface temperature, t'_s.

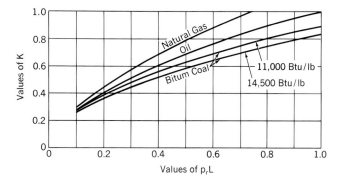

Fig. 4 Effect of fuel and mean radiating length on radiation conductance.

from Fig. 5. In the case of intertube radiation, L is obtained from Fig. 6. For cavity radiation, L is obtained from the following equation:

(5) $\quad L = 3.4\, V_L/A$

where:

$\quad L =$ mean radiating length for cavity, ft
$\quad V_L =$ volume of cavity, cu ft
$\quad A =$ total flat projected surface of enclosing boundaries, sq ft

Cleanliness factors. Current values of heat conductance, as described in Chapters 4 and 14, apply to oil- and coal-fired units with heating surfaces that are kept free from slag and deposits. No "cleanliness factor" as such is included in these formulas, i.e., in effect, a cleanliness factor of 1.0 is used.

In gas-fired units experience indicates that gas-side conductances are higher as a result of the higher cleanliness of the heating surfaces. In recognition of this experience, gas-side conductances increased by a cleanliness factor of 1.2 are used in the design of gas-fired units. Likewise, in coal-fired units where slag and deposits are difficult to remove, a cleanliness factor less than 1.0 may be required.

Pressure drop

Crossflow outside tubes

Pressure loss in gas or air flowing across a bank of tubes can be obtained from equation (6) which is derived by combining equations (37) and (40) of Chapter 3.

(6) $\quad \Delta p = (f N F_d) \left(\dfrac{30}{B} \right) \left(\dfrac{t + 460}{1.73 \times 10^5} \right) \left(\dfrac{G}{10^3} \right)^2$

where:

$\quad \Delta p =$ pressure drop (draft loss), in. of water
$\quad f =$ friction factor, given in Fig. 7 (and Fig. 14, Chapter 3) for various in-line tube patterns
$\quad N =$ number of tube rows crossed
$\quad F_d =$ depth factor applicable to tube banks less than 10 rows deep, Fig. 8 (and Fig. 13, Chapter 3)
$\quad B =$ barometric pressure, in. of mercury (30 in. at sea level)
$\quad t =$ effective gas or air temperature, F
$\quad G =$ mass velocity (w/A) of gas or air figured on the minimum clear area between tubes, lb/sq ft, hr

Under most conditions a good approximation for t is:

(7) $\quad t = 0.95(t_1 + t_2)/2$ for flue gas
$\quad t = (t_1 + t_2)/(2 \times 0.95)$ for air in air heater

where t_1 and t_2 are temperatures entering and leaving, F.

For each 1000 ft elevation above sea level, the value of Δp should be increased about 4% (Table 3, Chapter 17).

Flow inside tubes

Pressure drop for flow inside tubes can be calculated by equation (33), Chapter 3. Additional allowances for entrance, exit and bend losses are made as fractions of a velocity head (equation 36, Chapter 3).

Draft loss inside tubes — gas. Pressure drop (draft loss) of gas resulting from friction losses in straight tubes is conveniently obtained from equation (8). This is a modification of equation (33), Chapter 3, in which pressure drop is expressed as in. of water and specific volume of the gas is expressed in terms of average gas temperature.

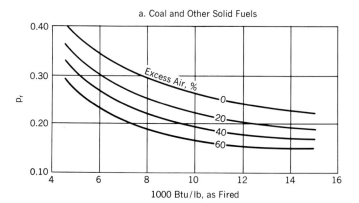

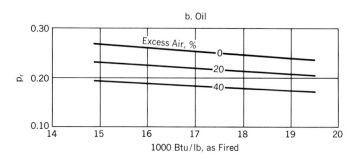

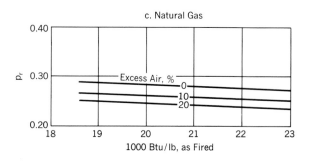

Fig. 5 Partial pressure, p_r, of principal radiating constituents $(CO_2 + H_2O)$ of combustion gases for various fuels, heat values, and excess airs.

(8) $\Delta p_f = f(L/d_i)[460 + (t_1 + 2t_2)/3](G_g/10^3)^2/14,400$

where:

Δp_f = pressure drop (draft loss) in straight tube, in. of water

L = tube length, ft

d_i = internal diameter of tube, in.

G_g = mass velocity of gas (w/A_g), based on internal cross section of tubes, lb/sq ft, hr

t_1 and t_2 = gas entering and leaving, F

$(t_1 + 2t_2)/3$ = an approximation used for mean gas temperature

f = friction factor (Fig. 1, Chapter 3), corresponding to various values of Re and ϵ/d_e (*see also Friction Factor, Chapter 3*)

Re = Reynolds number = $Gd_e/12\mu$

d_e = equivalent diameter = d_i for round tubes

μ = absolute viscosity, lb mass/ft, hr (Fig. 4, Chapter 3)

ϵ/d_e = relative roughness (Fig. 2, Chapter 3). Assume hot-finished tubes unless specified to the contrary.

Combined entrance and exit losses in inches of water, taken as 1.5 velocity heads, are obtained from equation (9), which is a modification of equation (37), Chapter 3:

(9) $\Delta p_e = 1.5[460 + 1/3(t_1 + 2t_2)](G_g/10^3)^2/173,000$

Total pressure drop is the sum of the values obtained from equations (8) and (9). The value of Δp should be increased about 4% for each 1000 ft elevation above sea level, as for flow outside of tubes.

Pressure drop inside tubes — all fluids. For flow inside tubes, pressure drop in psi is obtained by the summation of three components, i.e., pressure drop due to friction in straight tubes, entrance and exit losses, and additional pressure drop due to bends. Values of these three components expressed in psi are obtained from equations (10), (11) and (12) respectively:

(10) $\Delta p'_f = (fL/d_i)\, v\, (G/10^5)^2$

(11) $\Delta p'_e = (1.5\, v/12)\, (G/10^5)^2$

(12) $\Delta p'_b = (N_b\, v/12)\, (G/10^5)^2$

where:

$\Delta p'_f$ = pressure drop from friction in straight tube, psi

$\Delta p'_e$ = pressure drop from entrance and exit losses, equivalent to 1.5 velocity head, psi

$\Delta p'_b$ = additional pressure drop due to bends, psi

L = developed length of tube in one circuit, ft

d_i = internal diameter of tube, in.

v = average specific volume of fluid (Tables 1, 2 and 3, Chapter 2 for steam and water)

G = fluid mass velocity (w/A), based on internal cross section area of tubes, lb/sq ft, hr

N_b = total number of velocity heads lost in bends (Fig. 9, Chapter 3)

f = friction factor, Fig. 1, Chapter 3, for Reynolds number = $Gd_i/12\mu$. Relative roughness values (ϵ/d_e) are obtained from Fig. 2, Chapter 3 (*see also Friction Factor, Chapter 3*).

μ = absolute viscosity, lb mass/ft, hr (Figs. 3, 4 and 5, Chapter 3 for liquids, gases and steam).

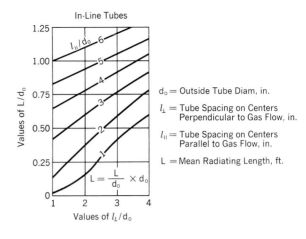

Fig. 6 Mean radiating length, *L*, for various tube diameters and arrangements.

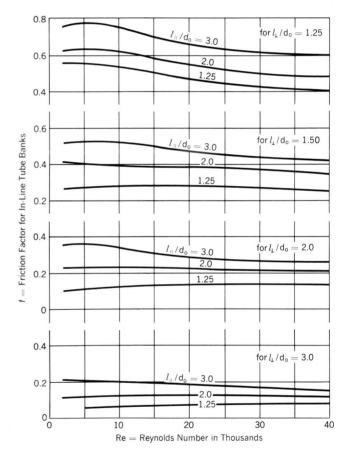

Fig. 7 Friction factor, f, as affected by Reynolds number for various in-line tube patterns; crossflow gas or air.

Furnace radiation to convection bank

The surface of the furnace is proportioned to reduce the temperature of the gases to 2000F at the furnace outlet. Radiation from the furnace to the convection bank is calculated from equation (8), Chapter 4, using the 2000F gas temperature and multiplying by an effectiveness factor of 0.2, which accounts for the emissivities of the furnace gases and the heating surface. The result is a radiation heat transfer rate to the convection bank of 12,250 Btu/sq ft, hr.

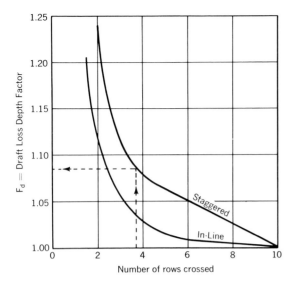

Fig. 8 Draft loss depth factor for number of tube rows crossed in convection banks.

The convection bank is 18 ft high and 12 ft wide. Hence the heat transferred to it by radiation from the furnace is $18 \times 12 \times 12,250$, or 2.65×10^6 Btu/hr. Not all of this heat is absorbed in the furnace screen, since the screen consists of only two rows of 2.5-in. OD tubes spaced on 6-in. centers. In Fig. 23, Chapter 4, curve 1 indicates that 55% of the radiation from the furnace is absorbed by the first row of screen tubes. In turn, 55% of the remaining 45%, which passes through the first row, is absorbed by the second row. The screen, therefore, absorbs 2.11×10^6 Btu/hr. The rest of the furnace radiation to the convection bank (0.54×10^6 Btu/hr) is absorbed by the superheater.

Screen

Heat transfer

Heat transfer to the screen tubes by convection and intertube radiation can be calculated from equation (3).

Δt_m is calculated from the Case I formula of Fig. 1, using 460F temperature of saturated steam (corresponding to 465 psia drum pressure), and 2000F gas temperature entering. It is necessary to assume the gas temperature leaving. If this is taken as $t_2 = 1915F$,

$$\Delta t_m = \frac{(2000 - 460) - (1910 - 460)}{\log_e[(2000 - 460)/(1910 - 460)]} = 1496F$$

Resistance to heat transfer on the waterside is negligible compared to that on the gas side. Hence U can be taken as equal to $U_{cg} + U_{rg}$ (see equation 2).

To obtain U_{cg} it is necessary to know gas mass velocity, G_g, and Reynolds number, Re. With a gas weight of 304,000 lb/hr (Table 2) and a value of $A_g = 129$ sq ft (Table 1):

$$G_g = w/A_g = \frac{304,000}{129} = 2355 \text{ lb/sq ft, hr}$$

Reynolds number is calculated from K_{Re}, which is obtained from Fig. 9, taking gas film temperature, t_f, as:

$$t_f = \text{sat. temp} + \Delta t_m/2 = 460 + 1496/2 = 1208F$$

Reynolds number, $\text{Re} = K_{Re} \times G = 2.3 \times 2355 = 5420$

With these values of G_g and Re and a value of 6.8% moisture in flue gases (Table 2), U_{cg} can be obtained from equation (21), Chapter 4, using Figs. 11, 12, 14 and 15 of Chapter 4.

Thus $U_{cg} = U'_{cc} F_{pp} F_a F_d$
$= 60 \times 0.133 \times 0.92 \times 1.0 = 7.36$

In this calculation, the value of F_d is taken as 1.0, because the screen is preceded by a bend as the combustion gases leave the furnace.

As noted under *Intertube and Cavity Radiation*, values of U_{rg} can be obtained from Figs. 3-6 inclusive. The intertube radiation within the screen must be corrected for furnace radiation. It was shown that 55% +55% of 45%, i.e., 80% of the furnace radiation acting on the plane at the furnace outlet was absorbed by the screen surface. It may be assumed that this acted on 80% of the plane area of the furnace outlet or on $0.80 \times 12 \times 18 = 172.5$ sq ft. The total heating surface of the screen is 542 sq ft. Hence it is assumed that $542 - 172.5 = 369.5$ sq ft of the screen surface is affected by intertube radiation and 172.5 sq ft by furnace radiation. From this, an effectiveness factor for intertube radiation applicable to the total surface is obtained:

$$F_s = \frac{\text{effective surface}}{\text{total surface}} = \frac{369.5}{542} = 0.682$$

From Figs. 3-6, $U_{rg} = 8.15 \times 0.48$

$$U_{rg} F_s = 8.15 \times 0.48 \times 0.682 = 2.67$$

$$U = U_{cg} + U_{rg} F_s = 7.36 + 2.67 = 10.03$$

From equation (3), $q = US\Delta t_m = 10.03 \times 542 \times 1496 = 8.14 \times 10^6$ Btu/hr

Gas temperature drop through the screen is now obtained from equation (3):

$$q = US\Delta t_m = wc(t_1 - t_2)$$

or (13) $t_1 - t_2 = US\Delta t_m/wc$

w is obtained from Table 2 and c from Fig. 10

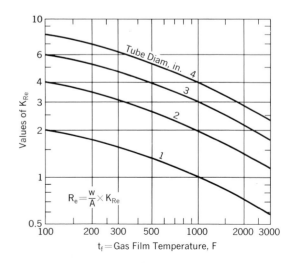

Fig. 9 Determination of Reynolds number, Re (using gas mass velocity, w/A) for various tube diameters and gas film temperatures.

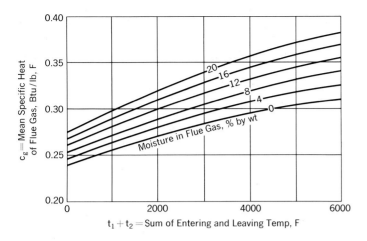

Fig. 10 Approximate mean specific heat, c_g, of flue gases.

Then $t_1 - t_2 = 8.14 \times 10^6/(304,000 \times 0.316) = 85F$
$$t_2 = 2000 - 85 = 1915F$$

The estimated value of t_2 (1915F) is equal to the calculated value, so recalculation will not be required.

Draft loss

Resistance to gas flow is calculated from equation (6), obtaining "f" from Fig. 7. The factor $30/B$ is eliminated from the equation on the assumption that the unit is located approximately at sea level.

$$\Delta p = \frac{0.216 \times 2 \times 1.0 \times 2318(2.355)^2}{173,000} = 0.0322 \text{ in.}$$
$$\text{of water}$$

Superheater

Design steam conditions are:

$$
\begin{array}{lll}
t'_2 = 650F & p'_2 = 450 \text{ psia} & h'_2 = 1332.5 \\
t'_1 = 459F & p'_1 = 460 \text{ psia} & h'_1 = 1204.8 \\
& & h'_2 - h'_1 = \overline{127.7}
\end{array}
$$

From equation (3) $q = w'(h'_2 - h'_1) =$
$250,000 \times 127.7 = 31.9 \times 10^6$ Btu/hr

Furnace radiation contributes 0.54×10^6 Btu/hr, leaving 31.36×10^6 Btu/hr to be absorbed by convection and intertube radiation.

Gas temperature leaving the superheater, t_2, can be obtained from equation (3), i.e.,

$$q = wc(t_1 - t_2) \text{ or } (t_1 - t_2) = q/wc$$

Temperature t_1 is 1915F, the temperature leaving the superheater. With an assumed value of 1590F for t_2, a value of $c = 0.311$ is obtained from Fig. 10.

$$\text{Then, } q = wc(t_1 - t_2) \text{ or } t_1 - t_2 = q/wc$$

Hence $t_1 - t_2 = 31.36 \times 10^6/(304,000 \times 0.311) = 332F$
$$t_2 = t_1 - 332F = 1915 - 332 = 1583F$$

Δt_m can now be obtained from the formula of Case III, Fig. 1, or:

$$\Delta t_m = \frac{(1915 - 650) - (1583 - 459)}{\log_e\left(\dfrac{1915 - 650}{1583 - 459}\right)} = 1190F$$

Then, average film temperature, t_f, $= (650 + 459)/2 + 1190/2 = 1150F$

Tube material is selected according to ASME Code procedure. In this instance, a thickness of 0.165 in. is required for bending and manufacturing reasons and is greater than the requirements of stress and temperature. With allowance for shop tolerances, the average inside diameter of the tubes is taken as 2.12 in. corresponding to a flow area of 3.52 sq in. per tube. Total steam flow area, A_s, is $2 \times 23 \times 3.52/144 = 1.13$ sq ft. Steam mass velocity, G_s, is $250,000/1.13 = 222,000$ lb/sq ft, hr.

Heat transfer

U_{cg} is obtained from gas mass velocity, G_g, and Reynolds number, Re.

$$G_g = w/A_g = 304,000/133 = 2285$$

To obtain Reynolds number, a value of $K_{Re} = 2.4$ is obtained by entering Fig. 9 with a t_f value of 1150F. Then:

$$\text{Re} = 2.4 \times 2285 = 5480$$

From equation (21), Chapter 4 and Figs. 11, 12, 14 and 15, Chapter 4:

$$U_{cg} = 59 \times 0.133 \times 0.74 \times 1.0 = 5.80$$

To obtain U_{rg}, a factor, F_s, must be included as in the case of the screen. Since 20% of the furnace radiation to the convection bank is assumed to be absorbed in the superheater, it can be assumed that $0.20 \times 12 \times 18 = 43.2$ sq ft of superheater surface receives furnace radiation and the remainder, or $3150 - 43.2 = 3106.8$ sq ft, receives intertube radiation. As in the screen calculation,

$$F_s = \frac{\text{effective surface}}{\text{total surface}} = \frac{3150 - 43.2}{3150} = 0.985$$

Then, from Figs. 3-6 inclusive:

(14) $\qquad U_{rg} F_s = 7.5 \times 0.40 \times 0.985 = 2.96$

The resistance to heat transfer through the steam film inside the superheater tubes is sufficiently high that it cannot be neglected as it is on the waterside of the screen and boiler tubes. Hence, in calculating conductance, U, from equation (2), the U_{cs} term must be included, and is obtained from the equation:

(15) $\quad U_{cs} = U'_{cl} \times F_{pp} \times F_T \times d_i/d_o$ *(See equation 18, Chapter 4)*

where:

U'_{cl} = basic convection conductance in longitudinal flow from Fig. 6, Chapter 4

F_{pp} is the physical properties factor from Fig. 9, Chapter 4 (t_f for steam can be taken as average steam temperature).

F_T is taken as 1.0. This factor is not normally significant in superheated steam heat transfer unless heat absorption rates are very high.

The ratio d_i/d_o converts the conductance to the outside diameter of the tube so that all components of U will be based on outside tube diameter.

Then, $U_{cs} = 612 \times 0.34 \times 1.0 \times (2.12/2.50) = 176$

It is now possible to determine U from equation (2) by substituting values of U_{cg} and U_{cs}, and taking U_{rg} as equal to $U_{rg} F_s$ in equation (14).

$$U = \frac{(5.80 + 2.96) \times 176}{5.80 + 2.96 + 176} = 8.35$$

From equation (3), $q = US\Delta t_m = 8.35 \times 3150 \times 1190 = 31.30 \times 10^6$ Btu/hr, which can be considered close enough to the desired absorption of 31.36×10^6 Btu/hr. From equation (13), $t_1 - t_2 = 31.30 \times 10^6/(304,000 \times 0.311) = 331$F,

$$\text{and } t_2 = 1915 - 331 = 1584\text{F}$$

Including cavity radiation, the heat absorbed in the steam $= (31.30 + 0.54) \times 10^6$ or 31.84×10^6 Btu/hr. From the relationship of equation (3), $q = w'(h'_2 - h'_1)$, it can be deduced that a final steam temperature of 649.5F corresponds to the value of 31.84×10^6 Btu/hr for q.

Draft loss

Resistance to gas flow from equation (6), obtaining "f" from Fig. 7, is:

$$\Delta p = 0.088 \times 12 \times 1.0 \times 2120 \times (2.285)^2/173,000$$
$$= 0.068 \text{ in. water}$$

Steam pressure drop

Steam pressure drop is calculated from equations (10), (11) and (12) as follows:

$$\begin{aligned}
\Delta p'_f &= (0.019 \times 130/2.12) \times 1.20 \times (2.21)^2 = 6.83 \text{ psi} \\
\Delta p'_e &= (1.5 \times 1.20/12) \times (2.21)^2 = 0.73 \\
\Delta p'_b &= (2.94^* \times 1.20/12) \times (2.21)^2 = 1.44 \\
&\text{Total pressure drop} \quad \overline{9.00} \text{ psi}
\end{aligned}$$

Boiler

Assume $t_2 = 822$F

From Case I, Fig. 1, $\Delta t_m = \dfrac{1584 - 822}{\log_e \dfrac{1584 - 460}{822 - 460}} = 672$F

$$\begin{aligned}
t_f &= 460 + 672/2 = 796\text{F} \\
G_g &= 304,000/85.0 = 3575 \\
\text{and Re (from Fig. 9)} &= 2.7 \times 3575 = 9650
\end{aligned}$$

Heat transfer

$$U_{cg} = 78 \times 0.122 \times 0.92 \times 1.0 = 8.76$$

In calculating U_{rg}, an effectiveness factor is derived to account for gaseous radiation from the boiler area to the large cavity in the rear of the boiler.

$$F_s = \frac{\text{effective surface}}{\text{total surface}} = \frac{10,300 - (12 \times 18)}{10,300} = 0.98$$

$$U_{rg} F_s = 4.4 \times 0.25 \times 0.98 = 1.08$$

As in the screen, water-film resistance is not significant.

Hence, $U = U_{cg} + U_{rg} F_s = 8.76 + 1.08 = 9.84$
$$\begin{aligned}
q &= US\Delta t_m = 9.84 \times 10,300 \times 672 \\
&= 68.2 \times 10^6 \text{ Btu/hr}
\end{aligned}$$
and $\quad t_1 - t_2 = 68.2 \times 10^6/(304,000 \times 0.294) = 762$F
$$t_2 = 1584 - 762 = 822\text{F}$$

---

* N_b = Losses in bends (Fig. 9, Chapter 3)

3 180-degree bends R/D = 0.77	3 × 0.64	= 1.92
2 180-degree bends R/D = 2.3	2 × 0.28	= 0.56
2 90-degree bends R/D = 2.3	2 × 0.23	= 0.46
	Total	$\overline{2.94}$

Draft loss

$$\Delta p = 0.236 \times 25 \times 1.0 \times 1602(3.575)^2/173,000 = 0.70 \text{ in. of water}$$

Rear cavity radiation

Gas radiation from the large cavity between the boiler and economizer is sufficient to reduce the gas temperature by only 6F. However the calculation of this cavity radiation will illustrate the procedure which is of more significance for cavities with higher gas temperature.

$$\Delta t_m = \frac{822 + 816}{2} - 460 = 359\text{F} \quad \text{(to boiler)}$$

$$\Delta t_m = \frac{822 + 816}{2} - 280 = 539\text{F} \quad \text{(to economizer)}$$

As noted under *Intertube and Cavity Radiation*, values of U_{rg} for cavity radiation can be obtained from Figs. 3, 4 and 5, using a value of L obtained from equation (5):

$$L = \frac{3.4(12 \times 10 \times 18)}{2(12 \times 10) + 2(10 \times 18) + 2(12 \times 18)} = 7.1$$

From Fig. 5, $p_r = 0.23$ and $p_r L = 0.23 \times 7.1 = 1.63$
From Fig. 4, (extrapolated) $K = 1.2$
From Fig. 3, $U'_r = 3.0$ (to boiler)
$\qquad\qquad\quad = 2.5$ (to economizer)

From equation (4), $U_{rg} = U'_r K$
$$\begin{aligned}
&= 3.0 \times 1.2 = 3.6 \text{ (to boiler)} \\
&= 2.5 \times 1.2 = 3.0 \text{ (to economizer)}
\end{aligned}$$

Heat radiated to boiler tube bank =

$$3.6 (12 \times 18) \times 359 = 279,000 \text{ Btu/hr}$$

and heat radiated to economizer tube bank =

$$3.0 (12 \times 10) \times 539 = 194,000 \text{ Btu/hr}$$
Total $q = 473,000$ Btu/hr
$t_1 - t_2 = q/wc = 473,000/(304,000 \times 0.281) = 6$F approx
$t_2 = 822 - 6 = 816$F

Economizer

Assume $t_2 = 627$F. In designing a unit, gas temperature leaving the economizer is usually determined by working back from the gas temperature leaving the air heater and the absorption required to obtain the required temperature of preheated air. In the example unit, the unit efficiency of 85.2% corresponds to 410F gas temperature leaving the air heater. An air temperature of approximately 335F (255F above an 80F ambient) is desired, and this corresponds to about 627F gas entering the air heater, as can be seen from the heat balance calculations in the *Air Heater* section.

If $t_2 = 627$F, the heat transferred in the economizer can be calculated from equation (3):

$$\begin{aligned}
q = wc(t_1 - t_2) &= 304,000 \times 0.270 \times (816 - 627) \\
&= 15.51 \times 10^6 \text{ Btu/hr}
\end{aligned}$$

Adding to this the cavity radiation previously calculated, the total economizer absorption is

$$15.51 \times 10^6 + 194,000 = 15.71 \times 10^6 \text{ Btu/hr.}$$

$$\frac{15.71 \times 10^6 \text{ Btu/hr}}{250,000 \text{ lb/hr (water)}} = 62.84 \text{ Btu/lb added to the water}$$

Enthalpy $h'_1 = 189.2$, corresponding to 220F water temperature entering the economizer.

Hence, $h'_2 = 189.2 + 62.8 = 252.0$ Btu/lb leaving the economizer, or $t'_2 = 282F$, (Table 3, Chapter 2). By Case III, Fig. 1:

$$\Delta t_m = \frac{(816 - 282) - (627 - 220)}{\log_e\left(\dfrac{816 - 282}{627 - 220}\right)} = 468F$$

Average film temperature, $t_f = (220 + 282)/2 + 468/2$
$$= 485F$$

$$G_g = w/A_g = 304,000/42.0 = 7240 \text{ lb/sq ft, hr}$$

and Re (from Fig. 9) = 18,800

Heat transfer

$$U_{cg} = 120 \times 0.105 \times 1.03 \times 1.0 = 13.00$$

The effectiveness factor for cavity radiation is:

$$F_s = \frac{\text{effectiveness factor}}{\text{total surface}} = \frac{3450 - (12 \times 10)}{3450} = 0.965$$

$$U_{rg} F_s = 2.1 \times 0.24 \times 0.965 = 0.49$$

Water film resistance is negligible, and

$$U = U_{cg} + U_{rg} F_s = 13.00 + 0.49 = 13.49$$

Then, $q = US\Delta t_m = 13.49 \times 2460 \times 468$
$$= 15.5 \times 10^6 \text{ Btu/hr, and}$$
$$t_2 - t_1 = 15.5 \times 10^6/(304,000 \times 0.270) = 189F$$
$$t_2 = 816 - 189 = 627F$$

Total heat absorbed by the water = 15.50×10^6 Btu/hr + 194,000 Btu/hr (from cavity radiation) = 15.69×10^6 Btu/hr, or 62.8 Btu/lb of water. Hence, $h'_2 = 189.2 + 62.8 = 252.0$, and $t'_2 = 282F$.

Draft loss

$$\Delta p = 0.316 \times 10 \times 1.0 \times 1146 \times (7.24)^2/173,000$$
$$= 1.10 \text{ in. water}$$

Pressure drop of water

The water flows parallel through ninety-four 2-in. OD tubes 0.148-in. thick. With allowance for tolerances, the internal diameter of the tubes is taken as 1.66 in., corresponding to a water flow area of 2.16 sq in. per tube. The total water flow area is $2.16 \times 94/144 = 1.41$ sq ft, and

$$G_w = 250,000/1.41 = 177,000 \text{ lb/sq ft, hr}$$

Water pressure drop can now be calculated from formulas (10), (11) and (12) as follows:

$$\Delta p'_f = (0.024 \times 50/1.66) \times 0.017\,(1.77)^2 = 0.038 \text{ psi}$$
$$\Delta p'_e = (1.5 \times 0.017/12) \times (1.77)^2 = 0.007$$
$$\Delta p'_b = (2 \times 0.44 + 2 \times 0.34) \times \frac{0.017}{12}(1.77)^2 = 0.007$$

Total pressure drop is negligible, i.e., 0.052 psi

Height from the economizer inlet header to the steam drum is 30 ft, and the corresponding static head is $30 \div (0.017 \times 144) = 12.25$ psi. Hence, the total pressure differential between the economizer and steam drum is $12.25 + 0.052 = 12.302$ psi. (This assumes negligible friction loss between the economizer outlet and boiler steam drum.)

Air heater

The air heater is proportioned to take the flue gases leaving the economizer and reduce their temperature to 410F. The heat removed is transferred to preheat the air for combustion from 80F to approximately 335F.

With gases entering the air heater at 627F, the heat removed from the gases is:

$$q = wc(t_1 - t_2) = 304,000 \times 0.27(627 - 410)$$
$$= 17.8 \times 10^6 \text{ Btu/hr}$$

Rise in air temperature can be obtained from an equation (3) relationship:

$$q = w'c'(t'_2 - t'_1), \text{ or } t'_2 - t'_1 = q/(w'c')$$

From Table 2, the weight of air, $w' = 287,000$ lb/hr. From Fig. 11, the specific heat of air over the temperature range between 335 and 80F is 0.244.

Hence, $t'_2 - t'_1 = 17.8 \times 10^6/(287,000 \times 0.244) = 255F.$
$$t'_1 = 80F \text{ and } t'_2 = 80 + 255 = 335F$$

Since this is a crossflow air heater, the value of Δt_m is obtained from Case IV, Fig. 1. The value of F_c for use in this formula is obtained from Fig. 17d, Chapter 4, and in this case is 0.93.

$$\Delta t_m = \frac{(627 - 335) - (410 - 80)}{\log_e \dfrac{627 - 335}{410 - 80}} \times 0.93 = 289F$$

Since conductance across the air and gas films is approximately equal, it is sufficiently accurate to express the mean temperature of gas and air as follows:

(16)   Gas $t_f = (t_1 + t_2)/2 - \Delta t_m/4 = 441F$

(17)   Air $t'_f = (t'_1 + t'_2)/2 + \Delta t_m/4 = 284F$

The gas flows in parallel through 2173 tubes (53 rows of 41 tubes each). These tubes are 2-in. OD and 0.083-in. thick. With allowance for tolerances, the average inside diameter of the tubes is taken as 1.822 in., corresponding to a flow area of 2.61 sq in. per tube. Total gas flow area is $2173 \times 2.61/144 = 39.4$ sq ft.

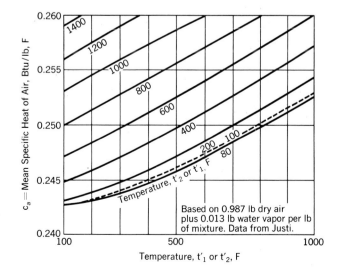

Fig. 11 Mean specific heat of air, c_a, between any two temperatures, t'_1 and t'_2, at a constant pressure of one atmosphere.

Hence, $G_g = 304,000/39.4 = 7720$ lb/sq ft, hr.

From Table 1, the clear area for air flow across the tubes is 70 sq ft.

$G_a = 287,000/70 = 4100$ and Re for air = 12,700

Heat transfer

Gas-side conductance is the sum of the convection conductance from longitudinal gas flow inside the tube plus a small amount of gaseous radiation originating inside the tube.

U_{cg} is obtained from equation (18), Chapter 4, and Figs. 6, 7 and 10 respectively of Chapter 4. The ratio d_i/d_o converts to external tube diameter and surface. U_{rg} inside a tube is obtained as for intertube radiation (see *Intertube and Cavity Radiation*), except that the inside diameter in ft is used for L.

$$U_{cg} = 43.3 \times 0.185 \times 1.138 \,(1.822/2.0) = 8.32$$

$$U_{rg} = 1.1 \times 0.20 = 0.22$$

U_{ca}, the crossflow convection conductance for air, is obtained from equation (21) and Figs. 11, 13, 14 and 15 of Chapter 4 as follows:

$$U_{ca} = 91.0 \times 0.103 \times 0.88 \times 1.0 = 8.25$$

Overall conductance, U, is then obtained from equation (2), substituting U_{ca} for U_{cs}.

$$U = (8.32 + 0.22) \times 8.25/(8.32 + 0.22 + 8.25) = 4.2$$
$q = US\Delta t_m = 4.2 \times 14,800 \times 289 = 17.95 \times 10^6$ Btu/hr, which checks closely the desired heat exchange.

Pressure drop

Gas inside tubes. Pressure drop (draft loss) is calculated from formulas (8) and (9).

$$\text{Re} = \frac{Gd_i}{12\mu} = \frac{7720 \times 1.822}{12 \times 0.06} = 19,600$$

Then f is 0.021 for cold-drawn tubes

$$\Delta p_f = 0.021(13/1.822)[460 + (627 + 2 \\ \times 410)/3](7.72)^2/14,400 = 0.58 \text{ in. of water}$$

$$\Delta p_e = 1.5[460 + (627 + 2 \times 410)/3] \\ (7.72)^2/173,000 = 0.49 \text{ in. of water}$$

Then the total gas draft loss through the air heater is $0.58 + 0.49 = 1.07$ in. of water.

Air outside tubes. Pressure drop of the air in crossflow across the tubes is calculated from equation (6).

$$\Delta p = 0.19 \times 53 \times 1.0[460 + (80 + 335)/ \\ (2 \times 0.95)] \frac{(4.1)^2}{173,000} = 0.66 \text{ in. of water}$$

Steam generation

It is necessary to confirm that the total boiler absorption is sufficient to generate 250,000 lb/hr of steam from water at 300F supplied by the economizer. To do this requires the addition of 953.2 Btu/lb of water as indicated by the following tabulation:

$$\begin{aligned} h'_2 \text{ for saturated steam at 460 psia} &= 1204.8 \\ h'_1 \text{ for water at 282F} &= 251.6 \\ \hline h'_2 - h'_1 &= 953.2 \end{aligned}$$

The required heat absorption is therefore 953.2 Btu/lb × 250,000 lb/hr = 238.3×10^6 Btu/hr. The heat to generate this steam is absorbed in three areas—furnace tubes, screen tubes and boiler bank. Heat absorbed in the furnace tubes is tabulated in Table 3, and is determined in the following manner.

The heat input to the furnace is equal to the fuel input plus the heat added to the combustion air in the air heater. Net heat available, q_a, equals heat input less the losses from moisture and hydrogen in the fuel. Heat absorbed in the furnace tubes equals net heat available less the heat in the combustion gases leaving the furnace. These gases at 2000F and 6.8% moisture contain 548 Btu/lb of heat above 80F (Fig. 1, Chapter 6), and the gas weight is 304,000 lb/hr. Hence the heat contained is $548 \times 304,000 = 166.5 \times 10^6$ Btu/hr. The heat absorption in the furnace tubes is then 161.9×10^6 Btu/hr.

Heat absorbed in the screen by convection and intertube radiation is 8.1×10^6 Btu/hr. Heat absorbed in the boiler bank is 68.5×10^6 Btu, including 68.2×10^6 Btu/hr by convection and intertube radiation, and 0.3×10^6 by cavity radiation.

The total heat absorbed for the generation of steam is 238.6×10^6 Btu/hr (Table 3). This checks closely with the required heat absorption of 238.3×10^6 Btu/hr.

Table 3
Heat absorbed in the example unit
for the generation of steam, millions of Btu/hr

Fuel input (Table 2)	335.5
Heat absorbed in air heater	18.0
Total heat input to furnace	353.5
Deduct moisture and hydrogen losses	25.0
Net heat available to the furnace	328.5
Deduct heat in combustion gases leaving furnace	166.5
Absorption in the furnace tubes	162.0
Add absorption in the screen from convection and intertube radiation	8.1
Add boiler bank absorption, 68.2 + 0.3	68.5
Total heat absorbed for the generation of steam	238.6

Chapter 15 Fuel-ash effects on boiler design and operation

From the beginning of the application of combustion of fossil fuels for the production of power, much attention has been devoted to the problems created by the residues of such combustion, broadly known as "ash." The complexity of these problems has increased with the size and rating of modern units. When burned, all but a few fuels have solid residues, and in some instances the quantity is considerable.

For continuous operation, removal of ash is essential to all methods of firing. In stoker firing with a fuel bed this is accomplished by the intermittent shaking or dumping of grate sections or by the continuous movement of the ash residue toward a point of discharge. In suspension firing the ash particles are carried out of the furnace by the gas stream or retained in part by settling or by adhering to boiler surfaces. Retained material of solid form is removed by periodic cleaning. If temperatures are sufficiently high, the retained ash is molten and may be drained continuously from the furnace. Some of the ash may form deposits of slag on the furnace walls (slagging), and a portion of the ash that is carried from the furnace by the flue gases may form deposits on the tubes in the gas passes (fouling). Also, under some conditions, the deposits may lead to corrosion of these surfaces. The nature and the amount of ash in the fuel to be used are, therefore, of major concern to the designer and the operator.

The following discussion is concerned primarily with the importance of coal ash in the design and operation of boilers, but consideration is also given to the importance of ash residue from petroleum fuels. Commercial fuels containing ash, and others with little or no ash, are listed in Table 1.

Some means must be provided to handle and dispose of the ash since ash in its various forms may seriously interfere with operation or even cause shutdown.

Ash content of coal

The ash content of coals varies over a wide range. This variation occurs not only in coal from different parts of the world or from different seams in the same region but also in coal from different parts of the same mine. Some rock and earthy materials find their way into the mined product. Before marketing, some commercial coals are cleaned or washed to remove a portion of what would be reported as ash in laboratory determinations (see Chapter 8). In any case, the ash determinations of significance to the user are those made at the point of use, and the values noted below are on that basis.

The bulk of bituminous coal used for power generation in the U.S. has an ash content within the range of 6 to 20%. Low values of 3 or 4% are encountered infrequently, and such coals find other commercial uses, particularly in the metallurgical field. On the other hand, some coals may have an ash content as high as 30%. Many high-ash fuels are successfully burned in the Cyclone Furnace as well as in pulverized-coal-fired units. Their use is increasing in localities where the fuel costs indicate a favorable overall economy.

Nature of coal ash

The presence of ash is accounted for by minerals associated with initial vegetal growth or those which entered the coal seam from external sources during or after the period of coal formation. Appreciable quantities of inorganic material may be contributed to the commercial fuel by partial inclusion of adjacent rock strata in the process of mining.

Since quantitative evaluation of mineral forms is extremely difficult, the composition of the coal ash is

Table 1
Commercial fuels for power production

Fuels Containing Ash	Fuels Containing Little or No Ash
All coals	Natural gas
Fuel oil—"Bunker C"	Manufactured gas
Refinery sludge	Coke-oven gas (clean)
Tank residues	Refinery gas
Refinery coke	Distillates (most)
Most tars	
Wood and wood products	
Other vegetational products	
Waste-heat gases (most)	
Blast-furnace gas	
Cement-kiln gases	

Table 2
Ash content and ash fusion temperatures of some U.S. coals and lignite

Rank:	Low Volatile Bituminous	High Volatile Bituminous				Sub-bituminous	Lignite
Seam	Pocahontas No. 3	No. 9	Pittsburgh	No. 6			
Location	West Virginia	Ohio	West Virginia	Illinois	Utah	Wyoming	Texas
Ash, dry basis, %	12.3	14.10	10.87	17.36	6.6	6.6	12.8
Sulfur, dry basis, %	0.7	3.30	3.53	4.17	0.5	1.0	1.1
Analysis of ash, % by wt							
SiO_2	60.0	47.27	37.64	47.52	48.0	24.0	41.8
Al_2O_3	30.0	22.96	20.11	17.87	11.5	20.0	13.6
TiO_2	1.6	1.00	0.81	0.78	0.6	0.7	1.5
Fe_2O_3	4.0	22.81	29.28	20.13	7.0	11.0	6.6
CaO	0.6	1.30	4.25	5.75	25.0	26.0	17.6
MgO	0.6	0.85	1.25	1.02	4.0	4.0	2.5
Na_2O	0.5	0.28	0.80	0.36	1.2	0.2	0.6
K_2O	1.5	1.97	1.60	1.77	0.2	0.5	0.1
Total	98.8	98.44	95.74	95.20	97.5	86.4	84.3
Ash fusibility							
Initial deformation temperature, F							
Reducing	2900+	2030	2030	2000	2060	1990	1975
Oxidizing	2900+	2420	2265	2300	2120	2190	2070
Softening temperature, F							
Reducing		2450	2175	2160		2180	2130
Oxidizing		2605	2385	2430		2220	2190
Hemispherical temperature, F							
Reducing		2480	2225	2180	2140	2250	2150
Oxidizing		2620	2450	2450	2220	2240	2210
Fluid temperature, F							
Reducing		2620	2370	2320	2250	2290	2240
Oxidizing		2670	2540	2610	2460	2300	2290

customarily determined by chemical analysis of the residue produced by burning a sample of coal at a slow rate and at moderate temperature (1350F) under oxidizing conditions in a laboratory furnace. It is thus found to be composed chiefly of compounds of silicon, aluminum, iron, and calcium, with smaller amounts of magnesium, titanium, sodium and potassium. The analyses of coal ash in Table 2 indicate what may be expected of some coals from various areas of the United States. A comparison of analysis of ash from wood and from two low-ash-content lignite coals is indicated in Table 3. The ash analyses do not always total 100%, since the analysis does not include all constituents.

The element sulfur is present in practically all coal, and its effect on equipment performance has been given much attention. Sulfur itself burns as a fuel with a relatively low heating value (3980 Btu/lb when burned to SO_2), but its reputation, which is nearly all bad, results from the effect of its chemical combination with other elements. Under certain conditions some of these compounds corrode boiler components; others contribute to the fouling and slagging of gas passages and heating surfaces.

Some of the sulfur in coal is in combination with iron as FeS_2. Sulfur may also be present in the form of complex organic compounds and, in minor amounts, in combination with the alkaline earths (calcium and magne-

sium). When the fuel is burned, the sulfur compounds are normally converted to more or less stable mineral oxides and sulfur dioxide gas, SO_2. A very small part of the SO_2 thus formed is further oxidized to SO_3. These sulfur gases are carried along with the other combustion gases, and their presence, under certain conditions, can contribute to corrosion of boiler heating surfaces and to air pollution problems (Chapter 18).

Table 3
Comparison of ash from two lignites with wood ash

	Lignite-Type Ash		Wood Ash
Ash, dry basis, %	5.0	6.0	1.0
Sulfur, dry basis, %	1.0	1.0	0.1
Analysis of ash, % by wt*			
SiO_2	17.9	18.9	33.8
Al_2O_3	13.2	19.5	2.6
TiO_2	0.5	0.6	0.2
Fe_2O_3	6.0	6.4	1.6
CaO	59.7	40.8	56.5
MgO	2.0	12.7	4.7
Na_2O	0.2	1.0	0.5
K_2O	0.5	0.1	0.1
Total	100.0	100.0	100.0
Ash Fusibility—Hemispherical Temperature, F			
Reducing	2680	2470	2580
Oxidizing	2650	2470	2550

* Adjusted to 100%

Coals may be classified into two groups based on the nature of their ash constituents. One is the bituminous-type ash and the other is the lignite-type ash. The term "lignite-type" ash is defined as an ash having more CaO plus MgO than Fe_2O_3. By contrast, the "bituminous-type" ash will have more Fe_2O_3 than CaO plus MgO.

Locations of U.S. deposits of coals are shown in Fig. 2, Chapter 5. The coal fields labeled "bituminous-type ash" include all those of Triassic age and older coals. The fields shown for "lignite-type ash" include all those of Jurassic age and younger coals, and all ranks of coals in these deposits.

Ash fusibility

The preferred procedure for the determination of ash fusion temperatures is outlined in ASTM Standard D-1857. Earlier procedure used only a reducing atmosphere for ash-fusibility determination whereas the standard adopted in 1968 offers the use of both reducing and oxidizing atmospheres. The previous method had loosely defined softening and fluid critical points; the new procedure uses improved definitions, as follows:

Initial deformation temperature, at which the first rounding of the apex of the cone occurs.

Softening temperature, at which the cone has fused down to a spherical lump in which the height is equal to the width at the base.

Hemispherical temperature, at which the cone has fused down to a hemispherical lump at which point the height is one half the width of the base.

Fluid temperature, at which the fused mass has spread out in a nearly flat layer with a maximum height of one-sixteenth in.

The determination of ash fusion temperatures is strictly a laboratory procedure, developed in standardized form, which experience shows can be duplicated with some degree of accuracy. For example, the permissible differences of reproducibility between two furnace runs may range from 100 to 150F. However, some bituminous-type ash, containing relatively large amounts of silica, may exhibit low ash-softening temperatures, yet exhibits high viscosity characteristics in its plastic range. Some lignite-type ash, containing large amounts of calcium and magnesium, may react with the refractory base (kaolin and alumina), or it may evolve gaseous products and swell, thereby causing changes in density of the ash cone. Methods for determining fusibility of coal ash used by countries outside the U.S. may also vary considerably. Thus, ash fusibility data should be used with care and its limitations recognized.

Ash melts when heated to a sufficiently high temperature. Following combustion, individual ash particles are generally in the form of tiny spheres (cenospheres) that appear hollow when viewed under a microscope, as illustrated in Fig. 1. The form of the ash particles indicates that, during combustion of the coal, the particles were actually liquid and the spheres were formed as tiny bubbles by evolved gases trying to escape. What happens to these particles depends on their physical and chemical characteristics and on furnace conditions. If

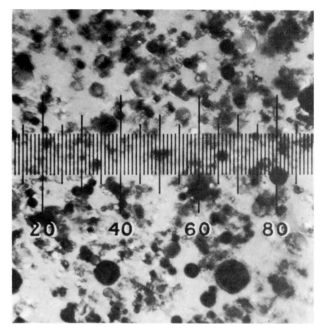

Fig. 1 Ash cenospheres (485x) formed in burning pulverized coal.

cooled promptly and sufficiently, the result is a dusty ash that may travel through the equipment, lodge on heating surfaces, drop out in soot hoppers and along flues, or collect at the base of the stack. Those particles that remain in suspension are carried out with the flue gases to the particulate-removal equipment (Chapter 18) and stack.

The individual ash particles do not, however, always cool quickly to a solid state. If insufficiently cooled, they remain molten or sticky and tend to coalesce into large masses in the boiler furnace or other heat-absorption surfaces. This problem is dealt with by adequate design of burners and furnace arrangement for the fuels to be burned and by proper attention to boiler operation.

Viscosity of coal-ash slag

Viscosity of coal-ash slag is measured in a high-temperature rotating-bob viscometer (Figs. 2 and 3), similar to one originally developed by the U.S. Bureau of Mines. The control panel is shown at the left in Fig. 2 and the furnace with its measuring element is at the right. A section through the furnace is shown in Fig. 3. The molten-slag sample is placed in a platinum crucible. There is an optical electronic device for measuring the torsional deflection of the calibrated wire, and the torque is recorded on a chart. Provision is made for controlling the atmosphere within the furnace.

Ash is introduced into the crucible at an elevated temperature (2600-2800F) and held at that temperature until it becomes uniformly fluid and all decomposition gases have been expelled. The temperature is then decreased in predetermined steps, and the viscosity is measured at each temperature.

Measurement of viscosity of coal-ash slags provides reliable data that can be used for determining suitability of coals for use in slag-tap type boilers. Since viscosity measurements require a considerable amount of coal ash that may not be readily available and, in addition,

Fig. 2 High-temperature viscometer for determining the viscosity of molten coal ash.

are costly and time consuming, it is desirable to calculate viscosity from chemical analysis of the coal ash. It has been feasible to remove liquid slag from operating furnaces for slags having a viscosity at or below 250 poise. A reasonable temperature limit, to provide ample reduced load operation, has been found to be 2600F. Thus, a dependable guide for suitability of coal-ash slag may be referred to as the T_{250} or the temperature in degrees F to obtain a 250-poise viscosity.

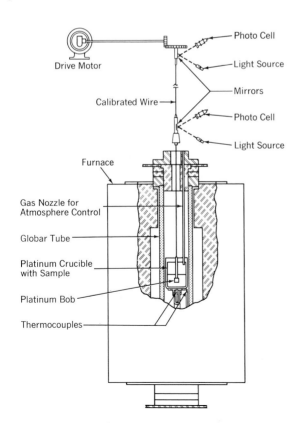

Fig. 3 Section through furnace of high-temperature viscometer.

Laboratory studies and field investigations, supplementing investigations by the Bureau of Mines, resulted in a calculation method for determining the T_{250} of slag from coals in the eastern United States. This method employs the ash fusibility (hemispherical temperature) in a reducing atmosphere and the "silica ratio" of the coal, where the

$$\text{Silica ratio} = \frac{SiO_2 \times 100}{SiO_2 + Fe_2O_3 + CaO + MgO}$$

The use of this method is illustrated in Fig. 4 where the T_{250} is obtained by entering with the silica ratio and the hemispherical temperature in a reducing atmosphere plus 200F. For example, for a coal ash having a silica ratio of 62 and a hemispherical temperature of 2300F, locate this point at the intersection of the 2500F line and the 62 silica ratio. From this point extend a straight line at a 10-degree slope from the vertical to the 250-poise value; this slag thus has a calculated T_{250} of 2450F.

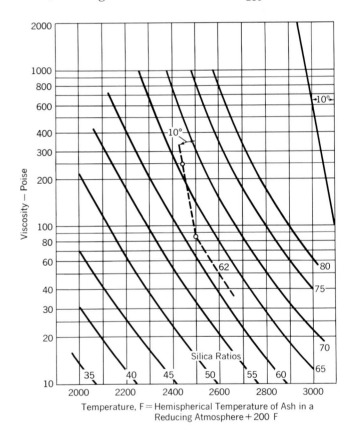

Fig. 4 Slag viscosity from ash analysis.

The constituents of a coal ash can be classed as either basic or acidic. Basic constituents are the Fe_2O_3, CaO, MgO, Na_2O, and K_2O; the acidic constituents are SiO_2, Al_2O_3 and TiO_2. Laboratory studies have shown that the relative amounts of the basic and acidic constituents in the ash can be used as a means of predicting the viscosity of the slag (see Fig. 5). The viscosity of a slag decreases as the base-to-acid ratio increases to 1.0 where

$$\text{Base-to-acid ratio} = \frac{Fe_2O_3 + CaO + MgO + Na_2O + K_2O}{SiO_2 + Al_2O_3 + TiO_2}$$

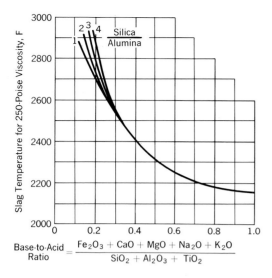

Fig. 5 Plot of temperature for 250-poise viscosity vs base-to-acid ratio—based on a ferric percentage of 20.

This correlation takes into account the SiO_2 to Al_2O_3 ratio which has an effect with slags having a low base-to-acid ratio. For bituminous-type coal ash and for lignite-type ash having an acidic content in excess of 60%, the base-to-acid ratio method is used in preference to the silica-ratio method to estimate the T_{250}.

For coals with lignite-type ash and an acidic content less than 60%, the dolomite percentage method is used (*see Fig. 6*).

Dolomite percentage =
$$\frac{(CaO + MgO)100}{Fe_2O_3 + CaO + MgO + Na_2O + K_2O}$$

where the sum of the basic and acidic constituents is adjusted to equal 100%.

Effect of iron on ash behavior

Coals having bituminous-type ash usually contain iron and its compounds as a principal component; the iron may exist in more than one state, i.e., metallic (Fe), ferrous (FeO) or ferric (Fe_2O_3). The Fe_2O_3 reported in an analysis of ash is actually the equivalent Fe_2O_3 representing the sum of Fe, FeO and Fe_2O_3 expressed as Fe_2O_3. Experience indicates that iron has a dominating influence on the behavior of ash in the furnace, as indicated by its effect on the ash softening temperature.

The specific effect of iron in coal ash is interesting. In completely oxidized form (Fe_2O_3) iron tends to raise all four values of ash fusion temperatures, initial deformation, softening, hemispherical and fluid, while in the lesser oxidized form (FeO) it tends to lower all four of these values. The effect of iron, in each of the two forms, on initial deformation and hemispherical temperatures is indicated in Fig. 7 plotted for a large number of ash samples from U.S. coals. Data in Fig. 7 show that as the amount of iron in the ash increases there is a greater difference in ash fusibility between oxidizing and reducing conditions. This effect may be negligible with coal ash containing small amounts of iron. Lignite-type ash generally contains small amounts of iron and the ash fusion temperatures are affected

very little by the state of oxidation of the iron in the slag. In fact, lignite-type ash having a high basic content and high dolomite percentage may have ash fusion temperatures that are lower on an oxidizing basis than a reducing basis. Ash hemispherical temperatures and ash analyses of lignites appearing in Table 3 illustrate this effect.

The iron content of a slag and the degree of oxidation of the iron also have a great influence on the viscosity of the slag. The degree of iron oxidation is normally expressed as the ferric percentage where

$$\text{Ferric percentage} = \frac{Fe_2O_3 \times 100}{Fe_2O_3 + 1.11FeO + 1.43\ Fe}$$

In stating the viscosity of a slag containing a significant amount of iron, it is important that the degree of oxidation, or ferric percentage, be expressed. Experience indicates that slags from boiler furnaces operating under normal conditions have an average ferric percentage of 20. The curves appearing in Fig. 5 are based on a ferric percentage of 20. Fig. 8 shows viscosity curves for a typical slag with various stages of oxidation of the iron. For coal ash having small amounts of iron, such as a lignite-type ash, this effect will be greatly diminished.

Furnace design

A properly designed furnace has two functions: (1) to burn the fuel completely and (2) to cool the products of combustion sufficiently so that the convection passes of the boiler unit may be maintained in a satisfactory condition of cleanliness, with a reasonable amount of sootblowing (*see also Chapter 12*). The products of combustion include all the impurities either in the solid, liquid or gaseous state. Experience and tests indicate that when the average gas temperature leaving a coal-fired furnace is too high, the ash particles are molten or

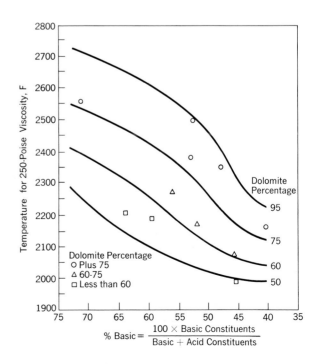

Fig. 6 Basic content and dolomite percentage of ash vs temperature for 250-poise viscosity.

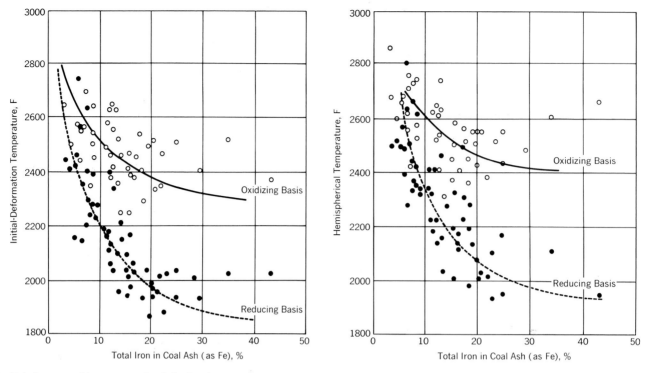

Fig. 7 Influence of iron on coal ash fusion temperatures.

sticky, and the need for cleaning the ash deposits from the upper-furnace and high-temperature zones in the convection passes may become excessive. This is, of course, subject to some latitude, because what constitutes excessive cleaning depends largely on the opinions of the individual operating crews.

In establishing the proper functional design of a furnace, two methods of cooling the products of combustion must be considered, namely, radiation and gas tempering.

Cooling gas by radiation

For many years the method used to cool the products of combustion has been that of providing radiant furnace-cooling surface. Sufficient surface is installed to assure a reduction in gas temperature to a level where convection passes can be kept reasonably clean. There is a general relationship between the average desired furnace-exit-gas temperature and the slagging and fouling potential of the coal ash. There can be a considerable variation in the gas temperature at the furnace outlet (*see Furnaces, Chapter 4*) and the maximum gas temperature can be considerably higher than the average. The usual design criterion of furnace size when using this method of cooling gases is "heat release rate," which is defined as heat available per hour per sq ft of equivalent flat projected water-cooled furnace enclosure surface (*see Chapter 4*).

Heat available, in turn, is defined as the amount of energy released in the furnace and available for increasing the temperature of the products of combustion. It is equal to (heat input in fuel + heat in air) − (heat required to evaporate moisture in fuel + ½ radiation loss). The assumption that half of the radiation loss occurs from the furnace is an acceptable approximation.

The relationship between furnace release rates and furnace-exit-gas temperatures has been developed from field test data. Factors affecting this relationship include type of furnace design, method of firing, fuel, burner location, burner input, and furnace wall construction.

From information obtained over a number of years, desirable heat release rates have been established for different types of coals. In general, units using coals having low or medium ash-slagging tendencies can have the highest heat release rates. A boiler designed to burn this type of coal is shown in Fig. 9. Units using coals hav-

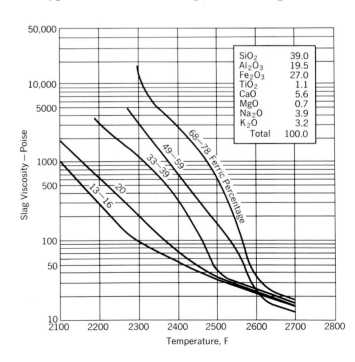

SiO_2	39.0
Al_2O_3	19.5
Fe_2O_3	27.0
TiO_2	1.1
CaO	5.6
MgO	0.7
Na_2O	3.9
K_2O	3.2
Total	100.0

Fig. 8 Viscosity-temperature plots of a typical slag showing effect of ferric percentage.

ing high or severe ash-slagging tendencies will require furnaces with heat release rates about 10 to 15% lower. Units designed for some very severe ash-slagging coals, such as North Dakota lignites, may require furnace heat release rates reduced by 30% as compared with furnaces designed for low- and medium-slagging-type coals.

With current use of high-volume type train shipments, coal from one source only may be considered for the life of the power plant; it may be shipped, for example, from northern West Virginia to New England. Thus, for best overall operation, units should be designed for the ash characteristics of the coal to be fired.

Furnaces fired with oil are generally designed for high heat release rates. Convection-pass tube spacing can be set in design so as to overcome ash-deposition problems when high-ash oils are fired. With these high heat releases, designs must take into consideration economic factors of tube metals, furnace proportions and high-temperature corrosion.

Gas tempering

The second method of cooling hot furnace gas is that known as "gas tempering," in which relatively cool gas from the economizer outlet is mixed with the hot furnace gas near the furnace outlet (Figs. 9 and 10). The tempering gas supply is normally taken from the top of the main gas-recirculation duct. Gas recirculation for superheater control is discussed in Chapter 12.

Gas tempering provides the operator with a control of furnace-exit-gas temperature with little or no effect on superheater and reheater absorption. Thus, if a high-fouling type coal is fired, the amount of tempering gas is increased to lower the gas temperature leaving the furnace to a level at which the convection surface is free from fouling. On the other hand, if a low-fouling type coal is fired, the amount of tempering gas is decreased, thereby reducing fan power. With some coals, tempering may be reduced to zero where experience indicates that it is not needed.

Gas tempering thus provides a positive means of controlling gas temperature at the furnace outlet. With this method of design, furnaces may be held to a reasonable height. Overall building requirements, steam piping, structural steel, and platforms are all decreased with no sacrifice in quality or performance of equipment. Rather, performance has been upgraded, since the gas temperature leaving the furnace is subject to positive control and is not dependent on furnace cleanliness. When gases are cooled only by radiation, the upper furnace cooling surfaces may be covered with slag from low-fusion coal and will not do the required cooling.

With gas tempering, the combustion gases are cooled uniformly across the width of the furnace, minimizing the large temperature variation customary with older designs. The possibility of localized slagging and fouling and excessive superheater-metal temperatures is therefore reduced.

With high steam temperatures and pressures it may be necessary to resort either to steam-cooling the walls or locating steam-cooled surface in high gas-temperature zones in the furnace subject to radiant heat. Gas tempering eliminates these requirements in most cases, and thus improves the reliability and availability of units.

Gas tempering reduces the furnace height required to obtain an equivalent furnace-exit-gas temperature and permits engineers to design high capacity units that occupy less space and reduce overall plant costs. The Universal-Pressure boiler (Fig. 10), has operated successfully with dry-ash removal with a furnace-exit-gas temperature of 2210F and 20% gas tempering at full load.

Gas tempering permits engineers to design high-capacity units that occupy less space and have greater reliability, lower maintenance, safer operation, and reduced overall plant costs.

Ash from pulverized-coal firing

No matter how fine the pulverization, the fuel fed to the furnace still has all its original ash. However, the final ash product ejected from a pulverized-coal-fired unit differs in appearance from the refuse of a stoker-fired unit. With pulverized coal, nearly all the ash particles are formed in suspension and tend to remain in suspension in a dry-ash furnace, with the individual particles well dispersed and very much smaller than those from spreader-stoker firing. In the slag-tap furnace, a portion of the ash particles coalesces on walls or other suitably designed surfaces and drains to the furnace bottom.

When pulverized coal is burned in a dry-ash furnace (e.g., Fig. 10), about 80% of the ash originally in the coal leaves the furnace entrained in the flue gas. On the other hand, with pulverized coal burned in a slag-tap furnace, as much as 50% of the ash may be retained in the furnace. The other 50% of total ash in the coal leaves the unit in the form of dust. With the Cyclone Furnace 70 to 80% of the total ash is retained, and only 20 to 30% leaves the furnace as dry ash in the flue gas (*see Ash Recovery and Dust Collectors, Chapter 10*). Particulate-removal equipment is placed ahead of the stack to prevent the ejection of large quantities of this ash to the atmosphere (Chapter 18).

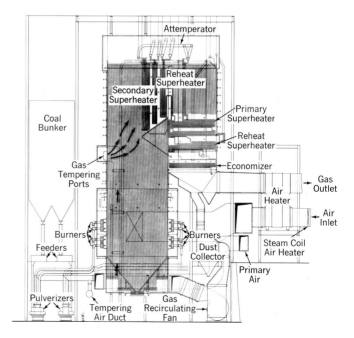

Fig. 9 Universal-Pressure boiler with gas tempering in front wall.

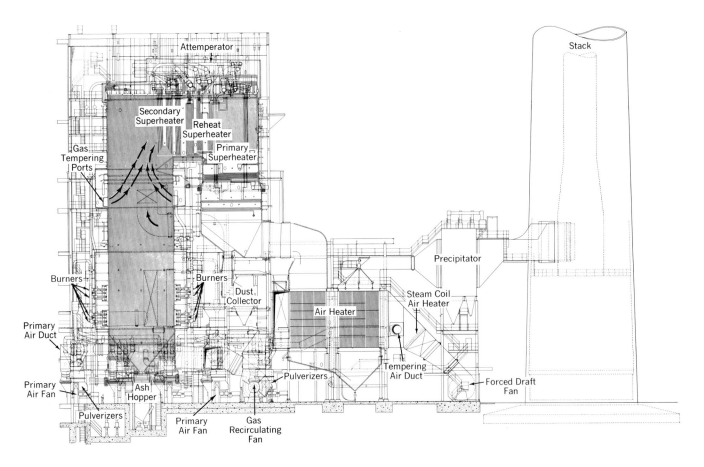

Fig. 10 Universal-Pressure boiler with gas tempering in front and rear walls.

Ash produced by stokers

In the fuel bed of a stoker, whether of the spreader, underfeed, or chain-grate type, ash particles tend to become fused together. In a properly operating stoker burning a suitable coal, the passage of air and the agitation of the fuel bed serve to keep ash accumulations more or less porous, and the ash is discharged to an ashpit in fairly large pieces varying from popcorn size upward.

Not all the ash is retained in a fuel bed. With the types of stokers mentioned, and particularly the spreader stoker, some of the fuel is burned in suspension. A considerable quantity of ash particles, containing some unburned and some still-burning fuel, is consequently carried over with the gases. With the spreader stoker this material is usually collected in hoppers provided for the purpose and is reinjected into the furnace for further burning of any combustible that it may contain (*see Chapter 11*). Reinjection is also used occasionally with other types of stokers.

Use of dry-ash or slag-tap units

Considered answers to the following pertinent questions relating to fuel are essential in initiating the design of a successful coal-fired unit:

1. Has the particular coal selected been burned extensively, so that its combustion and ash characteristics are well known?
2. Will the source of coal and the characteristics of the coal remain substantially constant during most of the life of the equipment. What is likely to be the "worst" fuel supplied?
3. What auxiliary fuel may be made available during periods of temporary suspension of coal delivery?
4. What type of equipment is best suited to the experience of the operating personnel?
5. In the public interest, for better public relations, or to comply with civil regulations, what is required to limit atmospheric pollution from dust?
6. What method of final refuse disposal is available?

Answers to these questions make it possible to select proper equipment for the specific method of utilizing the coal. For instance, coal should not be burned in a slag-tap furnace if the ash fusion temperature and viscosity are higher than experience indicates they should be for successful tapping. Slag-tap furnaces are rarely suitable for an ash viscosity greater than 250 poise at 2600F. If the ash viscosity of the coal selected is too high or marginal, equipment permitting the ash to be removed in dry form is indicated.

Ash erosion

Ash erosion must not be ignored even though coal-ash particles may be exceedingly fine. Where ash particles are concentrated in a local region, such as in a gas turn, erosion is a potential problem. The induced draft fan is a well-known example, and erosion is an important fac-

tor to be considered in selecting the type of fan and its performance characteristics. Blade wear is relatively low at fan-blade-tip speeds under 22,000 ft/min. Above this tip speed the wear from erosion increases very rapidly and higher speeds should not be considered in designs having a high concentration of entrained ash. Local high concentrations of ash through the boiler setting may cause erosion of highly critical pressure parts. This action is liable to be found where ash tends to concentrate in streams, as at turns formed by baffles within boiler banks. In this case the remedy is to limit gas velocities and to eliminate baffles if possible. The elimination of baffles has been the trend in the development of coal-fired boiler units, as illustrated in Fig. 11, where the gas flow continues horizontally through the tube banks without turns. Maximum allowable gas velocities with various fuels are given in Table 4.

Table 4
Design gas velocity, fps, through net free flow area in tube banks to prevent flue-dust erosion

| | Baffle Arrangement | |
Type of Firing or Fuel	Multi-pass	Single pass
Pulverized coal	75	65*
Spreader stoker	50	60
Chain-grate stoker, anthracite	60	75
Chain-grate stoker, coke breeze	60	75
Chain-grate stoker, bituminous	100	100
Underfeed stoker	75	100
Blast-furnace gas	75	100
Cyclone Furnace	—	85
Wood or other waste fuels containing:		
Sand	50	60
Cement dust	—	45
Bagasse	60	75

*For PC units burning fuels having more than 30% ash on a dry basis, limit the maximum velocity through the free flow area to 60 fps. For PC units burning coals producing fly ash with known high abrasive tendencies, such as Korean or Central Indian coals, limit the maximum velocity through free flow area to 45 fps.

Erosion may also be a problem in slag- and ash-handling equipment. If the unit is of the slag-tap variety, the molten refuse or slag tapped from the furnace must be cooled to be conveniently handled. This is done with water and the quenched product is usually small particles, like coarse sand, which, regardless of the mode of transport, tend to wear the surfaces of the conveying system. When water is used for transport, the pump, pipe lining, and turns in pipes or sluices are especially subject to localized wear and are usually protected by replaceable linings of alloy steel or chilled cast iron.

Design and operation of slag-tap units

The method of disposal of coal ash by tapping from a boiler furnace was evolved in 1926, more by accident than by design, in a boiler furnace originally expected to operate under dry-ash disposal conditions. During operation, the low-fusion ash melted, collected in a pool at the bottom of the furnace, and was drained at intervals by means of an improvised arrangement.

Many features of this furnace, the forerunner of later slag-tap furnaces, were totally inadequate for the for-

mation, retention and disposal of fluid ash. The furnace bottom was of ordinary brick that quickly disintegrated under the chemical action of the molten slag. It was also apparent that the proper handling of a stream of molten slag was a difficult undertaking. Nevertheless, this early experience opened the way to the development of a method for easier handling and disposal of refuse in furnace operations. Some of the important requirements for adequate slag-tap furnace design that evolved from this development are:

1. The slag in the furnace must be kept fluid. The furnace temperature must be high and the slag-tap furnace should be designed to withstand the maximum temperature reached during combustion, which is usually in excess of 3000F.

2. Since fluid slag is heavy as well as extremely hot, it must be securely contained in those regions of the furnace where it tends to collect.

3. The interior surface of the furnace must be chemically inactive to the constituents of the hot slag.

4. Means must be provided to drain slag from the furnace as fast as it is formed, or at least at frequent intervals.

5. Once the molten slag has left the furnace, it must be cooled to a temperature that renders it suitable for ultimate disposal.

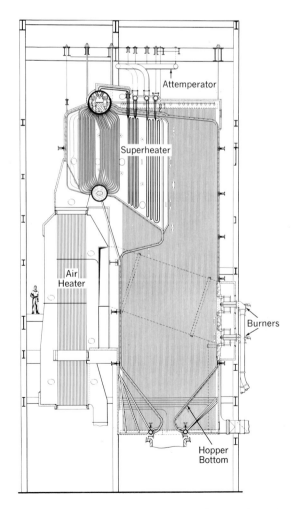

Fig. 11 Boiler with dry-ash furnace designed for horizontal gas flow through tube banks without baffles.

To withstand the high temperatures noted above, all sides and the floor of the furnace are water cooled. More or less unsuccessful attempts were made at different times to employ other arrangements, including solid refractories in brick and molded form, air-cooled refractories, and water-cooled tubes on various centers embedded in a variety of refractories.

The continuous-tap arrangement for withdrawing molten slag from the furnace is illustrated in Fig. 12. The molten slag disintegrates as it comes in contact with water in the slag tank, and this final slag product is conveyed to disposal.

The difficulty in tapping slag of high fluid temperature is most evident during low-load operation. Under these conditions, even a coal with a slag of medium fluid temperature may not be suitable for slag-tapping, since the furnace temperature may not be sufficiently high to attain the degree of fluidity necessary for tapping.

One of the most important attributes of the slag-tap furnace is the coating of sticky ash that covers a portion of the furnace walls near the bottom. The sticky surface of molten ash, deliberately maintained in selected high temperature zones, serves to entrain other transient particles. The ash so collected drains continuously toward the furnace bottom and is removed through the tap holes. The consequent reduction in the quantity of dust and ash leaving the boiler unit has a definite practical value, since it decreases the amount of dust to be handled by collectors and therefore decreases the size and cost of the dust collecting equipment.

It may be possible to reduce building costs in housing units with slag-tap furnaces, since they are usually built with flat floors, thus requiring less building height. In planning new buildings, this may be a significant factor in total first cost. Even in outdoor installations the height of the supporting steel structure can be reduced. Also, slag-tap units may be installed in older plants where it would be difficult, because of the greater height required, to install a unit designed for dry ash removal.

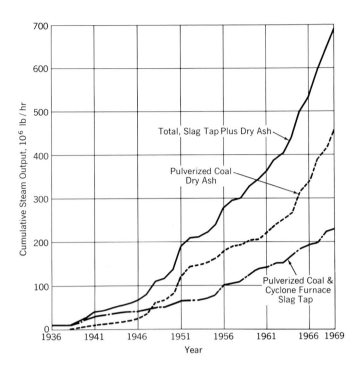

Fig. 13 Steam capacity of B&W slag-tap and dry-ash boiler units of 300,000 lb/hr and above, for a 34-yr period.

Dry-ash and slag-tap furnace installations

For the 34-year period 1936 through 1969, B&W sold 567 slag-tap and dry-ash boiler units in sizes of 300,000 lb of steam per hr and above, for a total capacity of over 683,000,000 lb of steam per hr. Of these, 208 units for 228,000,000 lb/hr, or 33% of the total, were of the slag-tap type, and 359 units for 455,000,000 lb of steam per hr were of the dry-ash type. In the size range considered, the steam output of B&W dry-ash and slag-tap units by years is shown graphically in Fig. 13. In the earlier years of the period, the greater part of the steam output was produced with slag-tap units. In the middle years of the period, the proportion of dry-ash units steadily increased, and in 1948 virtually an equal amount of steam was produced by each type. In the years 1948 through 1969 more steam was produced by dry-ash units than by the slag-tap type.

The statistics plotted in Fig. 13 for the units included in the study, indicate a steep increase in the application of the dry-ash method of burning pulverized coal after the early period. One important reason for this increase is the fact that boiler designers, by improvements in burners, furnace proportions, and the arrangement of heating surfaces to preclude slagging and fouling, largely overcame the earlier difficulty of keeping the dry-ash unit free of slag or troublesome ash.

Ash and slag removal from heating surfaces

Furnace walls and convection-pass surfaces can be cleaned of ash and slag while in operation by the use of sootblowers using steam or air as a blowing medium. Tubular air heaters having tubes 20 feet long or less can be cleaned by air or steam blowers. Tubular air heaters having tubes over 20 feet long would undoubtedly require out-of-service water washing.

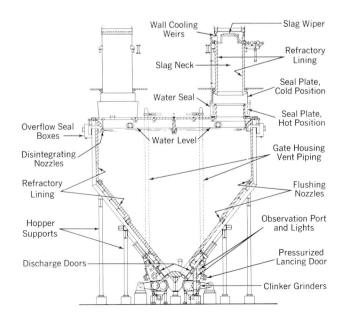

Fig. 12 Slag tank for a large utility unit for collecting low-viscosity molten ash when burning a midwestern coal. (Courtesy Allen-Sherman-Hoff Company.)

Coal-ash deposition

Ash deposition in various boiler zones is an important factor to be considered by the boiler designer and operator. Initially, ash deposits on furnace walls act as insulation, thereby delaying cooling of flue gases. This can cause an increase in steam temperature and is one factor that can cause the deposits to advance into normally cooler parts of the boiler. If the deposits are not removed during operation, accumulations forming on furnace walls may cause excessive gas temperatures downstream, or in some cases, these accumulations may fall and damage pressure components. Accumulations in tube banks may block gas passes and require a boiler outage for manual cleaning.

The occurrence and severity of ash deposition depend largely on the coal-ash composition and amount of coal ash, but can be strongly influenced by the method of firing, design of equipment, and the operating conditions. Some of the influencing conditions are shown in Table 5. In practice, the design parameters and operating conditions are determined by the characteristics of the ash. For example, if the ash does not tend to form troublesome deposits, the furnace wall surfaces will require few, if any, sootblowers for cleaning. The boiler can be designed with deep banks of closely spaced superheater or reheater tubes located in high-gas-temperature zones. Relatively few sootblowers will be required and these can be operated at high speeds, with small nozzles and low pressures.

On the other hand, if the ash produces hard, massive deposits, the superheater and reheater tube banks are designed to permit ease of deposit removal. For instance, lateral tube spacing is increased, tube bank depth is decreased, and the banks are located in cooler-gas-temperature zones. Additional sootblowers, operating at maximum capability, may be required.

It is therefore essential to identify the factors responsible for the fouling characteristics of various coals, so that the optimum design can be achieved with the coal or coals being burned. This has required a large amount of research into the nature of coal and coal ash, the extent and nature of ash deposits, the relationship between coal-ash composition and ash deposition, and the effect of boiler operating variables. The results of some of this research were discussed earlier in the chapter when it was noted that coal ash was derived from mineral matter associated with the coal-forming plants and from inorganic constituents added to the coal deposit from outside sources during or following coal formation. These materials are usually referred to as inherent and adventitious mineral matter, respectively. They occur in many forms, including shales, kaolins, sulfides, carbonates, chlorides and others. Identification of the mineral species is difficult for a variety of reasons. However, the presence of several of them has long been associated with severe ash deposition, fouling, and corrosion, after the organic material is burned and the inorganic constituents are carried through the boiler by the flue gases.

An obvious answer to the problem is to remove all of the coal ash. Although some ash removal is possible and actually accomplished commercially, the task is very difficult, and economic and technical limits are encountered. Therefore, it is imperative to acquire a comprehensive understanding of the nature of coal ash and its behavior during and following the combustion process. This is being accomplished through laboratory, pilot-plant, and field investigations being carried out in the U.S. and abroad.

The results of some of these investigations are given in the following section which briefly reviews some of the ash-deposit types and their effect on boiler operation, outlines some of the factors affecting ash deposition, and describes techniques used to assess deposit severity.

Ash-deposit types

A portion of the coal ash and its combustion products is carried by the flue gases through the boiler, regardless of the method of coal firing. Much of the ash passes through the boiler without depositing or, in the case of the slag-tap furnace, is removed as molten slag. The ash passing through the boiler is subject to various chemical reactions and physical forces which lead to deposition on stationary surfaces. Flue-gas, particle and surface temperatures, gas velocity, flow patterns, as well as other factors such as particle size and composition, influence the amount and nature of ash depositing on cooled surfaces. Deposits are frequently divided into three broad types:

1. Fused slag deposits forming on furnace walls and other surfaces exposed to predominantly radiant heat transfer.
2. High-temperature bonded deposits occurring on convection heating surfaces, especially superheaters and reheaters.
3. Low-temperature deposits occurring on air heaters and economizers.

Fused slag deposits

Slag deposits are usually associated with physical transport of molten or tacky particles by the flue gases. Condensation of species vaporized by the flame also can occur as the gases cool, causing enrichment of certain elements in the wall-slag deposits. For slag-tap furnaces, a portion of the furnace is usually designed to provide a continuous layer of slag near or in the combustion zone. Beyond the slagging zone, and in dry-ash pulverized coal boilers, accumulation of deposits can cause the problems described earlier. Fig. 14 shows an example of severe slagging encountered on one boiler. Deposits forming beyond the slagging zone are normally removed with short retractable sootblowers. Removal of some slags can be very difficult, depending on several factors that are discussed later.

High-temperature bonded deposits

The formation of deposits on convection heating surfaces has been the subject of a great deal of research. The extent of these deposits varies greatly from coal to coal and with changes in the furnace wall condition. They can be very troublesome because they can obstruct gas passages, and are sometimes very difficult to remove with normal in-service cleaning equipment.

Investigators have identified several types of bonded deposits, including alkali, calcium, phosphorus, and silica

Table 5
Design parameters—coal and coal ash

Fuel characteristics

1. Properties of coal substance

a. Physical, including density, hardness, specific heat, thermal expansion and thermal conductivity.

b. Chemical—behavior during heating, i.e., carbonization, gasification, and combustion.

Technological properties

1. Proximate analysis
2. Ultimate analysis
3. Free-swelling index
4. Differential thermal analysis
5. Thermogravimetric analysis
6. Effluent gas analysis
7. Grindability
8. Calorific value
9. Sieve analysis
10. Ignitability
11. Abrasiveness

2. Properties of coal ash

Determined by the concentration and type of minerals in the coal containing the following elements:

a. Alkalis   e. Calcium-Magnesium
b. Sulfur   f. Iron
c. Chlorine   g. Silica
d. Phosphorus   h. Alumina

Technological properties

1. Fusion temperatures
2. Viscosity of slag
3. Surface tension of slag
4. Volatility of constituents in slag
5. Sintering temperature and strength of ash

Boiler design and operation

1. Firing method
   a. Slag tap, PC and cyclone
   b. Dry ash, PC
   c. Fuel bed, chain-grate, and spreader stoker

2. Furnace design
   a. Rating
   b. Wall construction
   c. Type, number and arrangement of burners
   d. Furnace geometry
   e. Exit-gas temperature

3. Tube bank design
   a. Horizontal or vertical tubes
   b. Spacing, side and back
   c. Depth of bank
   d. Alignment
   e. Freedom of tube movement

4. Combustion conditions
   a. Excess air
   b. Air temperature
   c. Load cycles
   d. Residence time

5. Properties of flue gases
   a. Temperature
   b. Flow patterns
   c. Composition

6. Properties of entrained ash
   a. Dust loading
   b. Size consist
   c. Composition
   d. Microstructure

Sootblower design and operation

1. Blowing medium
   a. Air or steam
   b. Pressure
   c. Temperature

2. Type of sootblower
   a. Short retractable
   b. Long retractable
   c. Fixed position rotating
   d. Traveling frame

3. Location and spacing of sootblowers

4. Sootblower nozzles
   a. Type
   b. Size
   c. Number
   d. Angle of attack

5. Lance-tube speed
   a. Rotational
   b. Axial

6. Frequency of blower operation

Fig. 14 Furnace-wall slag deposits.

Table 6
Analysis of superheater deposits vs fly ash
from a boiler firing an Illinois coal

Constituents of Ash, % by Wt	Fly Ash	Superheater Deposits	
		Outer Layer	Inner Layer
SiO_2	37.4	36.2	15.8
Al_2O_3	15.3	12.9	9.0
Fe_2O_3	20.8	19.9	11.8
TiO_2	1.0	1.1	0.5
CaO	5.2	9.1	3.9
MgO	0.9	1.0	0.8
Na_2O	3.8	4.3	5.9
K_2O	2.7	2.4	9.0
SO_3	9.6	13.1	43.3
Not Determined	3.3	0.0	0.0
Total	100.0	100.0	100.0
Water Solubility, %	—	12	60

the normal alkali equivalent, which is attributed to the formation of complex iron and aluminum sulfates. Investigations carried out by B&W indicate that this white inner layer is formed over a period of time as a reaction product of the gaseous sulfur oxides and fly ash depositing on tube surfaces. Inspections and analyses were made of deposits forming on an air-cooled probe in a boiler firing an Illinois coal. After one week of exposure to flue gases at approximately 2000F, the deposit formed on the metal surface, controlled at 1050F, consisted of loosely held fly ash with no evidence of a white bonding material. The white layer began forming after two weeks and its thickness progressively increased throughout the remainder of the 11-week test period.

The white layer not only provides a bond for the bulk fly-ash deposit, but can also be responsible for corrosion of high temperature tubes. This is discussed in a subsequent section in this chapter.

The nature and amount of bulk deposit forming on the tube are functions of fly-ash characteristics, which in turn are related to the coal-ash composition, firing method, and furnace operating conditions. For fly ash with similar properties, the rate of ash deposition is proportional to the amount of fly ash being transported by the flue gases.

types, depending on the bonding agent. They appear to be associated with vaporization of coal ash constituents during combustion and subsequent condensation on fly-ash particles on surfaces. The alkali and calcium-bonded deposits are more common in the United States, whereas problems with these and the other types have been described by investigators in other countries. The occurrence and severity of fouling by these bonded deposits depend chiefly on the composition of the coal ash, but are influenced by the method of firing, the design of equipment, and the conditions of operation.

Since the alkali-bonded deposits are generally acknowledged as the most prevalent, especially with U.S. bituminous coals, they will be treated more extensively in the following sections. An example of severe fouling on superheater tubes is shown in Fig. 15.

Deposits found in the superheater and reheater regions of the boiler are typically composed of a thin inner layer with a characteristic composition and appearance distinctive from the outer layer, which has a composition similar to the fly ash. Table 6 gives a comparison of the two deposit layers and the fly ash from a boiler firing an Illinois coal.

The inner layer is normally tightly attached to the tube surface and there is strong evidence that a liquid phase exists within the layer at operating temperatures. This layer provides a bond between the superheater tube and the outer layer of sintered fly ash which forms the bulk of the deposit and becomes massive under certain conditions.

It is apparent that the inner layer is rich in sodium and potassium, and it usually contains sulfate in excess of

Fig. 15 Ash deposits on secondary superheater tubes.

Low-temperature deposits

Formation of deposits in the low-temperature zones such as the economizer and air heater is usually associated with condensation of acid or water vapor on cooled surfaces. Other types of deposits, especially in the economizer of boilers with bed-type combustion systems, have also been reported while firing coals with relatively small amounts of phosphorus. Phosphatic deposits have been extremely hard, but the problem is restricted to a limited number of boilers, located mostly in Europe.

Condensation of acid or water vapor can be encountered when metal surfaces are allowed to cool below the acid or water dew points. The sulfuric acid dew point depends on the amount of sulfur trioxide present in the flue gases, but it is usually between 250 and 300F for SO_3 concentrations of 15-30 parts per million. The water dew point depends on the coal and air moisture levels, the hydrogen in the coal, the excess air, and the amount of steam used in sootblowing. It is usually in the range of 105-115F for coal firing. On air heaters, where metal temperature is a function of both air and flue gas temperatures, condensation on low temperature surfaces of tubular heaters can occur on tubes near the air inlet and flue gas outlet or on cold-end baskets on regenerative heaters as they are being heated by the flue gases on each cycle. Several factors, such as maldistribution of air or flue gases, excessively low exit-gas temperatures and very low air temperatures can aggravate the problem of condensation. Low gas flow during low load, start-up and other similar periods can also result in condensation of water and acid.

The deposits themselves can be composed of three types of material. First, the acid attack can produce various amounts of corrosion product next to the metal depending on the amount of acid available, the temperature, and the type of metal. Second, this wet deposit can trap fly ash which adds to the bulk of the deposit. Third, the acid can react with constituents such as iron, sodium and calcium in the fly ash to form sulfates, which increase the deposit bulk.

The deposits are usually characterized by low pH (highly acidic); many contain hydrated salts, and for most bituminous coals they are water soluble. In this case, deposits can sometimes be water washed from low-temperature surfaces. However, in some cases when the coal ash contains large amounts of materials such as calcium, the reaction product $CaSO_4$ is nearly insoluble. The deposits that form are very hard and difficult to remove by washing. Complete plugging of gas passes also makes removal by water washing more difficult, even when the deposits are water soluble.

Deposition can be eliminated by operating the metal temperatures well above the acid dew point temperature of the flue gas, but this would result in a significant loss in boiler efficiency. Improvements in design to get more uniform air and gas distribution, better materials of construction and improved cleaning systems have been combined to minimize the low-temperature deposit problem while operating at relatively low exit-gas temperatures.

Evaluation techniques

The development of laboratory techniques for evaluating the slagging and fouling tendencies of coals is an important and necessary step in providing optimum boiler designs for each fuel type. Typical ASTM tests are usually inadequate to distinguish fouling tendencies of various coals. Extremes in ash fusion temperatures may be indicative of differences in fouling and slagging potential, but most coal ash falls within a narrower range and the fusion temperatures are therefore inadequate. Operating experience from commercial boilers is essential in establishing the actual behavior of coals, but controlled testing of large boilers is unwieldy and expensive. Furthermore, it is impossible in these large boilers to examine very small coal samples, such as core drillings from a new mine. Thus, information that would be of value in establishing boiler and cleaning equipment design parameters might be delayed, probably until a new mine is operating, and the boiler has already been designed. It is therefore essential that laboratory tests be available to evaluate the behavior of coals. Several methods have been developed by B&W to aid in providing optimum design parameters for various coal-ash types.

Wall slagging

The deposit forming on water-cooled furnace walls usually varies in appearance, depending on the composition, atmosphere, and slag temperature. Adjacent to the tube surface, it is frequently porous and relatively loosely adherent to the tube surface. As the deposit builds in thickness, the surface exposed to the flue gases becomes plastic, then fluid, if temperatures are high enough when it reaches an equilibrium thickness. However, the plastic slag is more difficult to remove as sootblowers can be almost ineffective in penetrating the viscous plastic shell that sometimes forms at the outside surface of the wall slag.

Various methods have been used in attempting to predict the slagging tendencies of a coal ash. Ash fusion temperatures, in some cases, provide an indication of the potential problems that might be encountered with a particular coal. For example, coal ash with extremely high fusion temperatures remains dry and little or no deposit forms on furnace walls. However, for coals with lower ash fusion temperatures, other factors are important. Coal-ash composition has also been shown to influence the slagging behavior of coal ash and formulas have been proposed to calculate softening temperature from ash composition, but here too, no correlation has been developed to enable prediction of wall-slagging tendency.

Extensive field tests, during which time-lapse movies and other observations were made, confirmed that the slags that were plastic were very difficult to remove. Viscosity measurements, usually made to determine flow characteristics for slag-tap performance, were extended to higher viscosity levels. These measurements showed that the slags most difficult to remove were plastic over a broad temperature range, whereas slags that were easy to remove were plastic over a relatively narrow temperature range (see Fig. 16). This relationship was observed for a number of coal-ash slags and efforts are

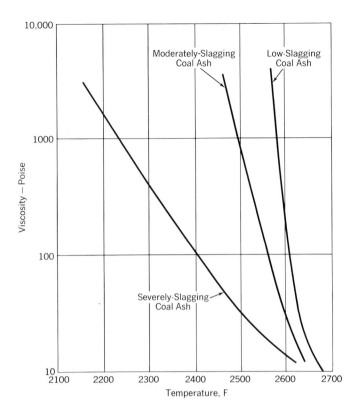

Fig. 16 Viscosity of wall slags (oxidizing atmosphere).

now being made to develop a correlation giving coal-ash viscosity in the plastic region as a function of temperature and slag composition, including relative amounts of FeO and Fe_2O_3. The influence of the iron oxidation state is very strong and the change in oxidation level may be due to changes in excess air. Fig. 17 shows the effect on viscosity by changing from an oxidizing to a reducing atmosphere over the slag melt. Flame impingement on furnace water walls can be responsible for creating a strongly reducing condition of the slag and causing severe wall slagging.

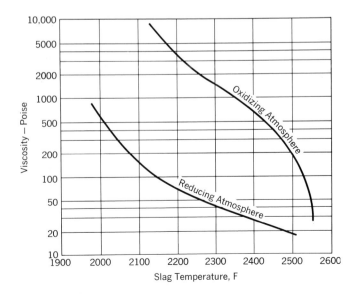

Fig. 17 Viscosity-temperature relationship.

High-temperature bonded deposits

Early research effort in this area was directed toward alleviating ash deposition by modifying boiler design, injecting additives, and improving boiler cleaning equipment. During this time, numerous coal analyses were obtained in an effort to isolate troublesome coal constituents, and concurrently to develop laboratory techniques for assessing the deposit-forming tendency of a coal. One technique, developed some time ago, has proved to be very useful and is still in use today. This technique, called the sintering test, determines the relative strength of a deposit. In this test, the fly-ash samples collected from the flue gases are passed through a 60-mesh U.S. Standard screen to remove particles of slag and are then ignited to constant weight at 900F to remove any carbon that might be present. The ignited fly ash is then reduced to a minus 100-mesh size, and at least 24 cylindrical specimens (0.6-in. diameter by 0.75-in. long) are formed in a hand press at a pressure of 150 psi. At least six specimens are heated in air, usually at each of four temperature levels (1500, 1600, 1700 and 1800F) for 15 hours.

After the specimens have cooled slowly in the furnace, they are removed, measured, and then crushed in a standard metallurgical testing machine. The sintered or compression strength is then computed from the applied force and the cross-sectional area of the sintered specimen. The average strength of six specimens is used as the strength of the sintered fly ash at a particular sintering temperature.

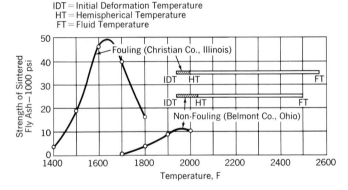

Fig. 18 A comparison of sintered strengths and ash fusion temperatures for a fouling and a non-fouling coal.

Extensive application of this method, combined with observation of operating boilers, showed that coals with a tendency to form troublesome deposits produced fly ash with high sintered strength. Conversely, low-strength fly ash was associated with non-fouling coals. The two extremes are illustrated in Fig. 18 which shows the strength of sintered fly ash for two coals having similar ash fusibility but widely varying fouling characteristics. This figure shows that ash fusion temperatures bear little relation to the tendency to form bonded deposits.

Coal samples were also obtained while the sintering information was being compiled. A relationship between total alkali content (Na_2O and K_2O, expressed as equivalent total Na_2O) and fly-ash sintered strength was observed for the samples collected. This trend is shown in

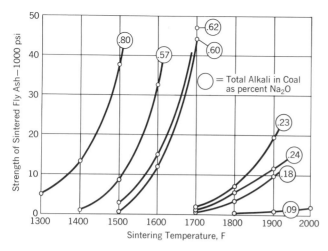

Fig. 19 Effect of alkali content in coal.

Fig. 19, which illustrates the higher coal-alkali content associated with high-strength fly ash. As knowledge of the factors affecting ash deposition increased, guidelines were established to arrive at suitable equipment designs for various fuels. The first such guideline, called a "fouling index," used total alkali content in the coal as a criterion. This index divided coal into three categories, based on the alkali content. Coals with 0.4% alkali or lower produced deposits that could easily be removed by sootblowers, but superheater fouling increased markedly when the alkali content of the dry coal was more than 0.6%. Between these two levels, intermediate fouling was encountered.

During this period, it was also learned that additives such as dolomite and magnesia have a pronounced effect on the strength of fly ash. For bituminous coals, which normally contain more acidic than basic constituents, magnesia was the most effective additive tested. Fig. 20 shows the effect of several additives. Subsequent field tests in which magnesia and high-magnesium dolomite were injected into boilers, confirmed that these additives could substantially lower sintered strength and reduce fouling with bituminous coals.

Development of laboratory tests

The fouling guidelines were improved as information was acquired from operating experience, sintering data, and coal analyses. However, the acquisition of data for improving guidelines was slow and expensive because it was dependent on field tests. This, of course, meant full-scale boiler tests under constant conditions with a large, consistent coal supply which became more difficult as unit size increased. In an effort to improve the efficiency and accuracy of obtaining data, a research program was initiated to develop a technique to evaluate the fouling potential of a coal based on information developed in the laboratory. The primary requirement for this step was the production of suitable fly ash for evaluation by the sintering test. This was accomplished by building a small coal-fired pilot plant.

Tests made in the pilot plant confirmed field experience, indicating that it could be used as a tool for evaluating ash-fouling tendency. Fig. 21 shows that fly ash from this pilot plant had widely differing strengths; those strengths related well with fouling history.

Numerous tests have been made with a variety of domestic and foreign coals. These coals were selected to provide a wide range of analyses and fouling potential when this information was known. The actual ranges of concentrations of coal-ash constituents for all coals and for the bituminous coals tested in this and other programs are compared in Table 7 with the ranges typical of U.S. coals:

Table 7
Coal-ash constituents of pilot plant coals vs typical U.S. coals
Percent by weight

	All Coals Tested	Bituminous Coals Tested	Typical U.S. Coals
SiO_2	3.3–61	37 –61	20 –60
Al_2O_3	<5.0–43	13 –43	10 –35
Fe_2O_3	2.6–30	2.6–30	5 –35
TiO_2	0.3– 1.4	0.7– 1.4	0.5– 2.5
CaO	0.9–33	0.9– 9.2	1 –20
MgO	0.4–10+	0.4– 2.4	0.3– 4
Na_2O	0.1–14	0.1– 2.4	}1 – 4
K_2O	0.2– 3.0	0.3– 3.5	
SO_3	1 –23	–	0.1–12

This comparison shows that information has been acquired for coals with constituent concentration ranges in some cases greater than those typical of U.S. coals, and thus indicates a very wide range of coal-ash compositions.

These experiments have demonstrated that sodium is the most important single factor affecting ash fouling. Potassium, which had been included in previous alkali-fouling indices, makes no perceptible contribution to sintered strength. The amount of water-soluble sodium, which is related to the more readily vaporized sodium, was shown to have a major effect on sintered strength.

This result was achieved by washing the coal with hot condensate in the laboratory to remove the water-soluble sodium which is related to the more readily vaporized

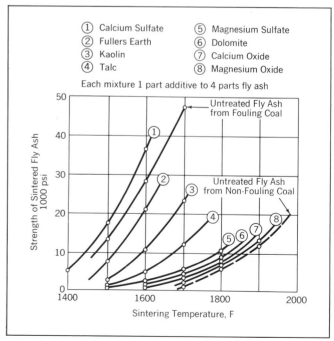

Fig. 20 Effect of additives.

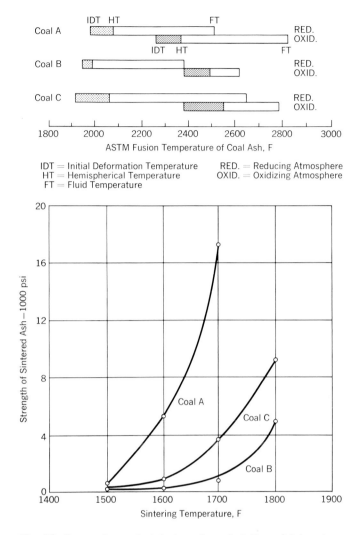

IDT = Initial Deformation Temperature   RED. = Reducing Atmosphere
HT = Hemispherical Temperature   OXID. = Oxidizing Atmosphere
FT = Fluid Temperature

Fig. 21 Comparison of sintering characteristics of laboratory fly ash.

become very high (approximately 15,000 psi) at temperatures of 1900F if the Na_2O content of the ash is high. Since this ash contains large amounts of alkaline materials, which react with sulfur dioxide to form sulfates, the bond is probably a sulfate type. These ashes become very hard when exposed to temperatures of 1500 to 2000F for long periods of time.

Effect of operating variables

Although the predominant factors affecting ash deposition are the amount and composition of the coal ash, boiler operating conditions have also been demonstrated to affect deposition. Some of the factors that have been studied are excess air, firing method, and deposit-time temperature, which is a function of the gas-tube temperature relationship as well as ash properties.

The effect of excess air variation on viscosity is indicated in Fig. 17. It was noted earlier that plastic slag is most difficult to remove from furnace walls, and this figure shows that variations in atmosphere from reducing to oxidizing have a major effect on the nature of the ash. In practical terms, this means that care must be exercised in maintaining proper coal/air ratios at all times. If imbalances are allowed to occur, the slagging may be aggravated. Flame impingement on furnace walls, or operating several burners with less than theoretical air required for combustion and others at high excess-air levels, are typical ways in which this can occur. Increased slagging can also raise temperatures entering the convection bank, which leads to higher gas and deposit temperatures, thereby increasing deposit strength (see Fig. 19). Thus, although excess air has no direct effect on deposit strength, the higher gas temperatures caused by increased furnace wall slagging do affect superheater deposition.

Since deposition appears to be associated with vaporization of coal ash constituents, this phenomenon has been studied extensively. Vaporization is strongly dependent on mineral-matter type and on time and combustion temperature. Combustion temperature in turn is affected by heat release rate (including firing method),

sodium. The washed coal was then fired in the pilot plant and sintered at various temperatures. In one case a fouling coal washed with hot condensate and sintered at 1700F had a fly-ash strength only 10% of the value obtained with an unwashed sample at the same sintering temperature.

Information from the tests carried out thus far is being processed to develop correlations between fly-ash sintered strength and coal-ash composition, using both total and water-soluble sodium.

Lignites

Tests with several North Dakota and Canadian lignites and with Australian brown coal, all of which have ash with high alkaline contents (CaO, MgO, Na_2O, K_2O), have shown that fly ash from these coals will sinter at low temperatures; however, sintered strengths will remain low regardless of fouling tendency if the sintering method used is the same as for United States Eastern coals (sintering at 1700F for 15 hours). Further testing has shown that the sintering strengths of North Dakota lignites do not become high until they approach the initial deformation fusion temperature. These coal ashes become harder as the sodium content of the ash increases. The fusion temperatures also become lower as the Na_2O content increases. The sintering strength can

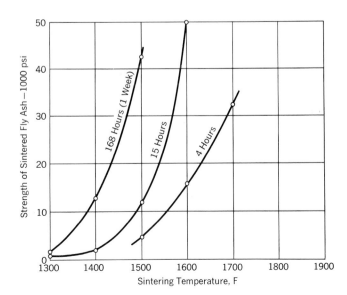

Fig. 22 Effect of sintering time.

excess air, combustion air temperature, and coal characteristics. The rate of deposition is proportional to the amount of ash suspended in the flue gases and actual operation can be more severe for the lower strength deposits because of the higher rate of deposition. For bituminous coals only a small amount, usually less than 5%, of the suspended ash is deposited on convection banks, but for lignites this figure may be much greater.

Sintering time or reaction time is also a very important factor in determining deposit characteristics. Fig. 22 shows that, if a deposit is not removed promptly, the strength of the deposit increases many times. Thus, establishing sootblower operating frequency and coverage is also an extremely important facet of the overall problem of ash deposition.

Coal-ash corrosion

Serious external wastage or corrosion of high-temperature superheater and reheater tubes was first encountered in coal-fired boilers in 1955. Tube failures resulting from excessive thinning of the tube walls, as shown in Fig. 23, occurred almost simultaneously in the reheater of a dry-ash furnace boiler and the secondary superheater of a slag-tap furnace unit. Corrosion was confined to the outlet tube sections of the reheater and the secondary superheater, which were made from chrome-ferritic and stainless steel alloys, respectively.

Significantly, these boilers were among the first to be designed for 1050F main and reheat steam temperatures; also, both units burned high-sulfur, high-alkali coals from central and southern Illinois, which were causing chronic ash-fouling problems at the time.

Early investigations showed that corrosion was found on tube surfaces beneath bulky layers of ash and slag. When dry, the complex sulfates were relatively innocuous; but when semi-molten (1100-1350F), they corroded most of the alloy steels that might be used in superheater construction, as well as other normally corrosion-resistant materials.

At first, it appeared that coal-ash corrosion might be confined to boilers burning high-alkali coals, but complex sulfate corrosion was soon found on superheaters and reheaters of several boilers burning low-to-medium alkali coals. Where there was no corrosion, the complex sulfates were either absent or the tube-metal temperatures were moderate (less than 1100F). The general conclusions drawn from this survey of corrosion were:

1. All bituminous coals contain enough sulfur and alkali metals to produce corrosive ash deposits on superheaters and reheaters, and those containing more than 3.5% sulfur and 0.25% chlorine may be particularly troublesome.

2. Deposit temperature adjacent to the tube surface is the dominant factor affecting rate of corrosion. Experience has shown that the combination of tube-metal temperature and gas temperature provides a practical criterion for estimating deposit temperature and for establishing design temperature limits. Fig. 24, which is used as a guide in design, indicates stable and corrosive zones of fuel-ash corrosion as a function of gas and metal temperatures.

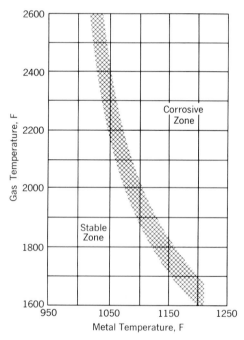

Fig. 24 Fuel-ash corrosion—stable and corrosive zones.

Based on this information, B&W modified the design of its boilers to reduce greatly the corrosion of superheaters and reheaters. These modifications included changes in furnace geometry, burner configuration, superheater arrangement, and the use of gas tempering, all of which reduced metal and gas temperatures and reduced temperature unbalances. Experience from these installations has shown that it is possible to operate boilers with main and reheat steam temperatures up to 1050F with little, if any, corrosion.

Meanwhile, there was a gradual return to the 1000F steam conditions for new plants, due primarily to economic factors and secondarily to coal-ash corrosion. This temperature level permits the use of lower-cost alloys in the boiler, steam piping, and turbine with sub-

Left Side of Tube   Right Side of Tube

Fig. 23 Typical corroded 18Cr-8Ni tube from secondary superheater.

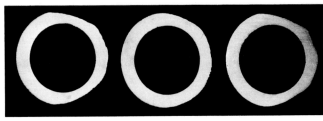

— Direction of Gas Flow

Fig. 25 Transverse sections of corroded tubes from secondary superheater platens.

stantial savings in investment costs, and it also provides a greater margin of safety to avoid corrosion. Steam temperatures will therefore probably remain on the current 1000F plateau until economics dictates the use of high-temperature alloys and until methods are developed for avoiding corrosion at higher steam temperatures.

General characteristics of corrosion

External corrosion of superheaters and reheaters is concentrated on the upstream side of the tube, as shown in Fig. 25. The greatest metal loss usually occurs on the 10 and 2 o'clock sectors of the tubes and it tapers off to little or none on the back side of the tubes. The corroded surface of the tube is highly sculptured by a shallow macropitting type of attack. The amount of corrosion, as measured by reduction in tube wall thickness, varies considerably along the length of the tube, depending on local conditions, i.e., the position of the tube in the bank or platen, the proximity of sootblowers, the composition of ash deposits and, most importantly, the gas and metal temperatures.

The corrosion rate is a nonlinear function of metal temperature (Fig. 26). The corrosion of both chrome-ferritic and 18Cr-8Ni stainless steels increases sharply above a temperature of 1150F, passes through a broad maximum between 1250 and 1350F, and then decreases rapidly at still higher temperatures.

The highest corrosion rates are generally found on the outlet tubes of radiant superheater or reheater platens opposite retractable sootblowers. Values ranging from

50 to 250 mils/year have been observed on 18Cr-8Ni stainless steel tubes under these adverse conditions. When similar high-temperature surfaces (1100-1175F) are arranged in convection tube banks so they are shielded from direct furnace radiation and sootblower action, corrosion rates are much lower, ranging between 5 and 20 mils/year.

Corrosive ash deposits

Corrosion is rarely found on superheater or reheater tubes having only dusty deposits. It is nearly always associated with sintered or slag-type deposits that are strongly bonded to the tubes. Such deposits consist of at least three distinct layers. The outer layer, shown diagrammatically in Fig. 27, constitutes the bulk of the deposit and has an elemental composition similar to that of fly ash. Though often hard and brittle, this layer is a porous structure through which gases may diffuse. Innocuous by itself, it plays an important part in the formation of an intermediate layer that contains the corrosive agents.

The intermediate layer, frequently called the white layer, is a white-to-yellow colored material which varies in thickness from $\frac{1}{32}$ to $\frac{1}{4}$ in. It usually has a chalky texture where corrosion is mild or nonexistent but is fused and semi-glossy where corrosion is severe. In the latter condition this layer is difficult to remove as it is so firmly bonded to the corroded surface beneath.

Upon heating in air, the intermediate layer melts around 1000F and slowly discolors and hardens into a hard mass resembling rust. Chemical analyses of this layer show that it contains higher concentrations of potassium, sodium and sulfur than does the parent coal

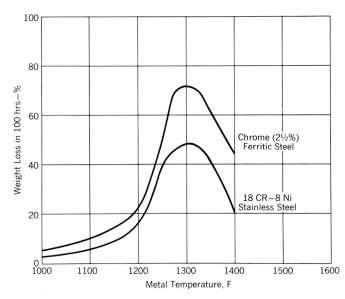

Fig. 26 Effect of temperature on corrosion rate.

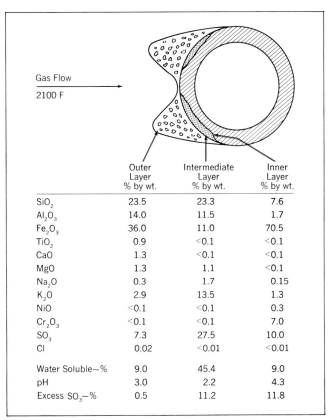

	Outer Layer % by wt.	Intermediate Layer % by wt.	Inner Layer % by wt.
SiO_2	23.5	23.3	7.6
Al_2O_3	14.0	11.5	1.7
Fe_2O_3	36.0	11.0	70.5
TiO_2	0.9	<0.1	<0.1
CaO	1.3	<0.1	<0.1
MgO	1.3	1.1	<0.1
Na_2O	0.3	1.7	0.15
K_2O	2.9	13.5	1.3
NiO	<0.1	<0.1	0.3
Cr_2O_3	<0.1	<0.1	7.0
SO_3	7.3	27.5	10.0
Cl	0.02	<0.01	<0.01
Water Soluble—%	9.0	45.4	9.0
pH	3.0	2.2	4.3
Excess SO_3—%	0.5	11.2	11.8

Fig. 27 Analyses of typical ash deposit from 18Cr-8Ni superheater tube.

ash. A large part of this deposit is water soluble and the water-soluble fraction is always acidic. The identification of compounds making up the intermediate layer is difficult because its constituents are not well crystallized. The normal sulfates are conspicuously absent and the complex alkali sulfates are detected irregularly. The most common compounds found are $Na_3Fe(SO_4)_3$ and $KAl(SO_4)_2$ although other complex sulfates are thought to be present.

Laboratory studies have shown that complex alkali sulfates, when molten, rapidly corrode most, if not all, superheater alloys. Corrosion begins between 1000 and 1150F, depending on the relative amounts of complex sodium and potassium sulfates present, and whether these are predominantly iron or aluminum-base compounds. Corrosion usually begins at the lower temperature where the sodium-iron-sulfate system is the major part of the intermediate layer, but corrosion is more severe and persists into a higher temperature range when the potassium-aluminum-sulfate system is the dominant one.

If the intermediate layer is carefully removed, a black, glassy inner layer is revealed, which appears to have replaced the normally protective oxide on the tube. This layer is composed primarily of corrosion products, i.e., oxides, sulfides and sulfates of iron, and other alloying constituents in the tube metal. It seldom exceeds $\frac{1}{16}$ in. thickness on corroded 18Cr-8Ni stainless steel tubes, probably because of its strong tendency to spall off when the tube cools. The layer containing corrosion products from chrome-ferritic alloys often reaches $\frac{1}{8}$ in. thickness and exhibits little tendency to spall as the tube cools.

Corrosion mechanisms

The elements involved in coal-ash corrosion (sodium, potassium, aluminum, sulfur, and iron) are derived from the mineral matter in coal. The minerals supplying these elements include shales, clays and pyrite, which are commonly found in all coals.

During the combustion of coal, these minerals are exposed to high temperatures and strongly reducing effects of carbon for very short periods of time. Although comparatively stable, the mineral matter undergoes rapid decomposition under these conditions. Some of the alkalies are released or volatilized as relatively simple compounds, which have "dew points" in the 1000-1300F range. Furthermore, the pyrite is oxidized, releasing SO_2 with the formation of a small amount of SO_3, leaving a residue of iron oxide (Fe_2O_3).

By far the largest portion of the mineral matter or its derived species react to form the glassy particulates of fly ash. The fly ash and volatile species in the flue gases tend to deposit on the tube surfaces in a selective manner and subsequent reactions between these materials occur over long periods of time.

In the formation of corrosive deposits, fly ash first deposits on the superheater and reheater tubes. Slowly, over a period of weeks, the alkalies and the sulfur oxides diffuse through the layer of fly ash toward the tube surface. In the lower temperature zone of the ash deposit, chemical reactions between the alkalies, the sulfur oxides, and the iron and aluminum components

of the fly ash result in the formation of the complex alkali sulfates as follows:

$$(1) \qquad 3K_2SO_4 + Fe_2O_3 + 3SO_3 \rightarrow 2K_3Fe(SO_4)_3$$

and (2) $K_2SO_4 + Al_2O_3 + 3SO_3 \rightarrow 2KAl(SO_4)_2$

Similar reactions occur with sodium sulfate (Na_2SO_4), although the complex sodium sulfates are less apt to form at high temperatures because of their lower stability.

Recent work at B&W's Research Center has shown that SO_3 concentrations in ash deposits must be very high (1000-1500 ppm), compared to the level in the flue gas (10-25 ppm) in order to form the complex alkali sulfates in the intermediate layer. Hence the bulk of the SO_3 must come from the catalytic oxidation of SO_2 in the outer layer of the deposit.

When the SO_3 produced in the outer deposit exceeds the partial pressure of SO_3 over the intermediate deposit, the complex sulfates form via reactions (1) and (2) above. When the opposite is true, the complex sulfates begin to decompose, according to the reverse of reactions (1) and (2), until a new equilibrium is reached. Since the formation of SO_3 is temperature dependent, the reversibility of these reactions is also temperature dependent. As shown in Fig. 26, the corrosion rate increases with temperature, passes through a maximum between 1250 and 1350F, and then falls to a comparatively low level at higher temperatures.

The destructive reactions between the complex alkali sulfates and the tube metal and its oxides have not been fully defined. A number of theories have been advanced to account for the composition of the corrosion products and the high rate of metal wastage. One that has been tentatively accepted is shown below:

$$(3) \qquad 3Fe \quad + \quad SO_4^= \quad \rightarrow Fe_3O_4 + S^=$$
(Tube Metal)   (Molten Complex   (Black Glassy
Sulfate)   Layer)

The temperature range of this rapid liquid-phase attack is bracketed by (a) the melting temperature of the mixture of complex alkali sulfates present, and (b) their thermal-stability limits. The extreme width of this temperature band is approximately 400F, or corrosion due to the complex alkali sulfates may range from as low as 1000F to a maximum of 1400F, depending on the species present in the intermediate layer.

Corrective measures

Various methods of combatting corrosion of superheater and reheater tubes have been used or suggested, including the following:

1. The use of stainless steel shields to protect the most vulnerable tubes.
2. Coal selectivity and the grinding of coals to a finer size.
3. Improve combustion conditions, i.e., provide fast ignition, good mixing, and proper excess air.
4. Injection of additives (mainly magnesium- and calcium-bearing minerals) into furnace gases or directly on the tubes through sootblowers.

5. The use of more corrosion-resistant alloys and ceramic coatings on the most vulnerable superheater and reheater tubes.

Low temperature coal-ash corrosion is covered in Chapter 13.

Fuel-oil ash

The ash content of residual fuel oil seldom exceeds 0.2%, an exceedingly small amount compared to that in coal. Nevertheless, even this small quantity of ash is capable of causing severe problems of external deposits and corrosion in boilers. Of the many elements that may appear in oil-ash deposits, the most important are vanadium, sodium, and sulfur. Compounds of these elements are found in almost every deposit in boilers fired by residual fuel oil and often constitute the major portion of these deposits.

Origin of ash

As with coal, some of the ash-forming constituents in the crude oil had their origin in animal and vegetable matter from which the oil was derived. The remainder is extraneous material resulting from contact of the crude oil with rock structures and salt brines, or picked up during refining processes, storage and transportation.

In general, the ash content increases with increasing asphaltic constituents in which the sulfur acts largely as a bridge between aromatic rings. Elemental sulfur and hydrogen sulfide have been identified in crude oil, and simpler sulfur compounds are found in the distillates of crude oil including thio-esters, disulfides, thiophenes and mercaptans.

Vanadium, iron, sodium, nickel and calcium in fuel oil were probably derived from the rock strata but some elements such as vanadium, nickel, zinc and copper probably came from organic matter from which the petroleum was derived. Vanadium and nickel especially, are known to be present in organo-metallic compounds known as porphyrins which are characteristic of certain forms of animal life. Table 8 indicates the amounts of vanadium, nickel and sodium present in residual fuel oils from various crudes.

Table 8
Vanadium, nickel and sodium content
of residual fuel oils
(parts per million by weight)

Source of Crude Oil	Vanadium	Nickel	Sodium
Africa			
1	5.5	5	22
2	1	5	—
Middle East			
3	7	—	1
4	173	51	—
5	47	10	8
United States			
6	13	—	350
7	6	2.5	120
8	11	—	84
Venezuela			
9	—	6	480
10	57	13	72
11	380	60	70
12	113	21	49
13	93	—	38

Crude oil as such is not normally used as a fuel but is further processed to yield a wide range of more valuable products. For example, in a modern U.S. refinery the average product yield, as a percentage of total throughput, is:

Gasoline	44.4
Lube oil fraction	16.4
Jet fuel	6.2
Kerosine	2.9
Distillates	22.5
Residual fuel	7.6

Virtually all metallic compounds and a large part of the sulfur compounds are concentrated in the distillation residue, as illustrated for sulfur in Table 9. Where low-sulfur residual fuel oils are required, they are obtained by blending with suitable stocks, including both heavy distillates and distillation from low-sulfur crudes. This procedure is also used occasionally if a residual fuel oil must meet specifications such as vanadium, or ash content.

Table 9
Sulfur content in fractions of Kuwait crude oil

Fraction	Distillation Range, F	Total Sulfur % by Weight
Crude oil	—	2.55
Gasoline	124-253	0.05
Light naphtha	257-300	0.05
Heavy naphtha	307-387	0.11
Kerosine	405-460	0.45
Light gas oil	477-516	0.85
Heavy gas oil	538-583	1.15
Residual oil	588-928	3.70

Source, Article by F. E. Hixon, Shell Refining and Marketing Co., Ltd., *Chemistry and Industry*, March 26, 1955, page 333.

Release of ash during combustion

Residual fuel oil is preheated and atomized to provide enough reactive surface so that it will burn completely within the boiler furnace. The atomized fuel oil burns in two stages. In the first stage the volatile portion burns and leaves a porous coke residue, and in the second stage the coke residue burns. In general, the rate of combustion of the coke residue is inversely proportional to the square of its diameter, which in turn is related to the droplet diameter. Thus, small fuel droplets give rise to coke residues that burn very rapidly and the ash-forming constituents are exposed to the highest temperatures in the flame envelope. The ash-forming constituents in the larger coke residues from the larger fuel droplets are heated more slowly, partly in association with carbon. Release of the ash from these residues is determined by the rate of oxidation of the carbon.

During combustion, the organic vanadium compounds in the residual fuel oil thermally decompose and oxidize in the gas stream to V_2O_3, V_2O_4 and finally V_2O_5. Although complete oxidation may not occur and there may be some dissociation, a large part of the vanadium originally present in the oil exists as vapor phase V_2O_5 in the flue gas. The sodium, usually present as chloride in the oil, vaporizes and reacts with sulfur oxides either in the gas stream or after deposition on tube surfaces.

Subsequently, reactions take place between the vanadium and sodium compounds with the formation of complex vanadates having melting points lower than those of the parent compounds, for example:

$$(4) \qquad Na_2SO_4 + V_2O_5 \rightarrow 2NaVO_3 + SO_3 \uparrow$$

Melting Points   1625F   1275F   1165F

Excess vanadium or sodium in the ash deposit, above that necessary for the formation of the sodium vanadates (or vanadyl vanadates), may be present as V_2O_5 and Na_2SO_4, respectively.

The sulfur in residual fuel is progressively released during combustion and is promptly oxidized to sulfur dioxide (SO_2). A small amount of sulfur dioxide is further oxidized to SO_3 by a small amount of atomic oxygen present in the hottest part of the flame. Also, catalytic oxidation of SO_2 to SO_3 may occur as the flue gases pass over vanadium-rich ash deposits on high-temperature superheater tubes and refractories.

Oil-slag formation and deposits

The deposition of oil-ash constituents on the furnace walls and superheater surfaces has been a serious problem in recent years. This deposition, coupled with corrosion of superheater and reheater tubes by deposits, was largely responsible for the break in the trend towards higher steam temperatures that occurred in the early 1960's.

Practically all boiler installations are now designed for steam temperatures in the 1000-1015F range to minimize those problems and to avoid the higher capital costs of the more expensive alloys required in tubes, steam piping, and turbine for 1050-1100F steam conditions.

There are many factors affecting oil-ash deposition on boiler heat absorbing surfaces. These factors may be grouped into the following interrelated categories:

1. Characteristics of the fuel oil.
2. Design of the boiler.
3. Operation of the boiler.

Characteristics of fuel-oil ash

Sodium and vanadium are the most significant elements in the fuel oil because they can form complex compounds having low melting temperatures, 480-1250F, as shown in Table 10. Such temperatures fall within the range of tube-metal temperatures generally encountered in furnace and superheater tube banks of many oil-fired boilers. However, because of its complex chemical composition, fuel-oil ash seldom has a single sharp melting point, but rather softens and melts over a wide temperature range.

An ash particle that is in a sticky, semi-molten state at the tube-surface temperature may adhere to the tube if it is brought into contact by the gas flow over the tube. Even a dry ash particle may adhere due to mutual attraction or surface roughness. Such an initial deposit layer will be at a higher temperature than that of the tube surface because of its relatively low thermal conductivity. This increased temperature promotes the formation of adherent deposits. Thus, fouling will continue until the deposit-surface temperature reaches a level at which all of the ash in the gas stream is in a

Table 10
Melting points of some oil-ash constituents

Compound	Melting Point, F
Aluminum oxide, Al_2O_3	3720
Aluminum sulfate, $Al_2(SO_4)_3$	1420*
Calcium oxide, CaO	4662
Calcium sulfate, $CaSO_4$	2640
Ferric oxide, Fe_2O_3	2850
Ferric sulfate, $Fe_2(SO_4)_3$	895*
Nickel oxide, NiO	3795
Nickel sulfate, $NiSO_4$	1545*
Silicon dioxide, SiO_2	3130
Sodium sulfate, Na_2SO_4	1625
Sodium bisulfate, $NaHSO_4$	480*
Sodium pyrosulfate, $Na_2S_2O_7$	750*
Sodium ferric sulfate, $Na_3Fe(SO_4)_3$	1000
Vanadium trioxide, V_2O_3	3580
Vanadium tetroxide, V_2O_4	3580
Vanadium pentoxide, V_2O_5	1275
Sodium metavanadate, $Na_2O \cdot V_2O_5 (NaVO_3)$	1165
Sodium pyrovanadate, $2Na_2O \cdot V_2O_5$	1185
Sodium orthovanadate, $3Na_2O \cdot V_2O_5$	1560
Sodium vanadylvanadates, $Na_2O \cdot V_2O_4 \cdot V_2O_5$	1160
$5Na_2O \cdot V_2O_4 \cdot 11V_2O_5$	995

* Decomposes at a temperature around the melting point.

molten state so that the surface is merely washed by the liquid without freezing and continued buildup.

In experimental furnaces it has been found that the initial rate of ash buildup was greatest when the sodium-vanadium ratio in the fuel oil was 1 to 6, but an equilibrium thickness of deposit ($\frac{1}{8}$ to $\frac{1}{4}$ in. thick) was reached in approximately 100 hours of operation. When the fuel oil contained more refractory constituents such as silica, alumina, and iron oxide in addition to sodium and vanadium, an equilibrium condition was not reached and the tube banks ultimately plugged with ash deposits. However, these ash deposits were less dense, i.e., more friable than the glassy slags encountered with a 1 to 6 sodium-vanadium fuel oil. Both the rate of ash buildup and the ultimate thickness of the deposits are also influenced by physical factors such as the velocity and temperature of the flue gases and particularly the tube-metal temperature.

In predicting the behavior of a residual oil insofar as slagging and tube-bank fouling are concerned, several fuel variables are considered including (1) ash content, (2) ash analysis, particularly the sodium and vanadium levels and the concentration of major constituents, (3) melting and freezing temperatures of the ash, and (4) the total sulfur content of the oil. Applying this information in boiler design is largely a matter of experience.

Boiler design

Generally speaking, progressive fouling of furnaces and superheaters should not occur if the tube-metal temperatures do not exceed 1000F. If such trouble is encountered, the solution can usually be found in improving combustion conditions in the furnace and/or modifying the sootblowing procedures.

Studies on both laboratory and field installations have shown that the rate of ash deposition is approximately

proportional to the velocity and temperature of the flue gases, and the concentration of oil-ash constituents in the flue gases. The geometry of the furnace and the spacing of tubes in the convection banks are selected in the design of a boiler to minimize the rate of deposition. It is common practice to use in-line tube arrangements with progressively wider lateral spacings for tubes located in higher gas-temperature zones. This makes bridging of ash deposits between tubes less likely and facilitates cleaning of tube banks by the sootblowers.

Boiler operation

Poor atomization of the fuel oil results in longer flames and frequently increases the rate of slag buildup on furnace walls which, in turn, makes it more difficult to keep the convection sections of the boiler clean. Completing combustion before the gases pass over the first row of tubes is especially important. Relatively large carbonaceous particles have a far greater tendency to impinge on the tubes than do the smaller ash particles. If these larger particles are in a sticky state, they will adhere to the tubes where oxidation will proceed at a slow rate with consequent formation of ash. Fouling from this cause is difficult to detect by inspection during boiler outages because the carbonaceous material has usually disappeared completely. It can generally be detected during operation since flames are usually long and smoky and sparklers may be carried along in the flue gases.

Regular and thorough sootblowing can have a decisive effect on superheater and reheater fouling. To be fully effective, however, sootblowing cycles should be

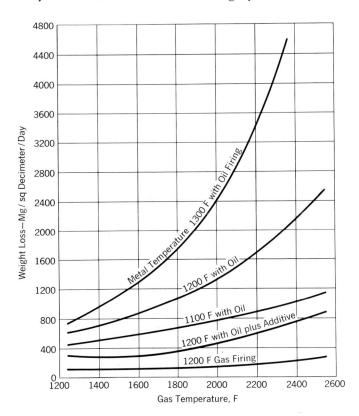

frequent enough so that ash deposits cannot build up to a thickness where their surfaces become semi-molten. If this point is reached, complete removal of the ash deposit can be very difficult because the sootblowers now have a dual task to perform: (1) to cool the surface of the deposit below its freezing temperature and (2) to shatter the now solid mass of slag and break its bond to the tube surface. In instances of extreme slagging, it is sometimes necessary to relocate sootblowers, install additional sootblowers to control deposition in a critical zone, or to use additives.

The boiler load cycle can also have a significant effect on the severity of slagging and superheater fouling. A unit that is base-loaded for long periods is more apt to have fouling problems on a borderline fuel oil than a unit that takes daily swings in load. In the latter instance, the furnace generally remains cleaner due to periodic shedding of slag, with the result that the gas temperatures through the superheaters are appreciably lower. This eases the burden on the sootblowers and goes a long way towards controlling ash-deposit formation in the superheater-reheater tube banks. Overloading the boiler, even for an hour or two a day, should be avoided, especially if excess air has to be lowered to the point where some of the burners are starved of air. The furnace is apt to become slagged and ash deposition creeps into the superheater and reheater tube banks.

Oil-ash corrosion
High-temperature corrosion

The sodium-vanadium complexes, usually found in oil-ash deposits, are corrosive when molten. The corrosion mechanism is probably one of accelerated oxidation of metal brought about by oxygen transfer to its surface by the constituents in the molten ash, accompanied by the removal by the ash of the normal protective oxide coating on the metal surface.

Corrosion can also be caused by sulfate attack, particularly when sodium (or some other) chloride is also present in the fuel oil, and this may occur at metal temperatures as low as 1000F. This type of corrosion is more apt to be encountered on boilers burning a low-vanadium fuel oil but containing several hundred ppm of sodium chloride. Even when the chloride content of the fuel oil is negligible, sulfate corrosion may still be severe when reducing or alternating oxidizing-reducing conditions prevail around the tubes.

A measurable corrosion rate can be observed over a wide range of metal and gas temperatures, depending on the amount and composition of the oil-ash deposit. Fig. 28 shows the combined gas and metal temperature effects on corrosion for a specific fuel oil composition of 150 ppm vanadium, 70 ppm sodium, and 2.5% sulfur. As the vanadium concentration of the fuel oil varies, the amount of corrosion, compared to a 150-ppm vanadium fuel, will increase or decrease according to the curve shown in Fig. 29.

The effect of the sodium level in the fuel oil is not quite so clear-cut because combustion conditions and the chloride content of the fuel oil may be controlling. The sodium content does, however, definitely affect the minimum metal temperature at which corrosion will be significant.

Fig. 28 Effect of gas and metal temperatures on corrosion of 304, 316, and 321 alloys in a unit fired with oil containing 150 ppm vanadium, 70 ppm sodium, and 2.5% sulfur. Test duration 100 hours.

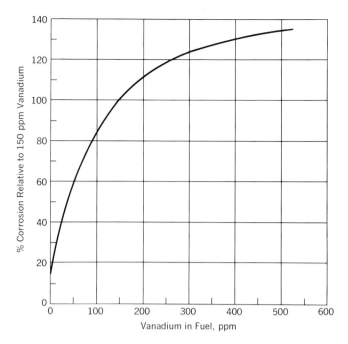

Fig. 29 Effect of vanadium concentration on oil-ash corrosion.

At the present time there does not appear to be any alloy that is immune to oil-ash corrosion. In general, the higher the chromium content of the alloy the more resistant it is to attack. This is the main reason for the use of 18Cr-8Ni alloys for high-temperature superheater tubes. High chromium contents, greater than 30%, give added corrosion resistance but at the expense of physical properties; 25Cr-20Ni has been used as a tube cladding but even this alloy has not provided complete protection. The presence of nickel in high-temperature alloys is needed for strength. High-nickel alloys may be fairly resistant to oil-ash attack under oxidizing conditions but they are liable to sulfide attack brought about by local reducing conditions or by the presence of chloride in the ash deposit. Since it is difficult to avoid such conditions entirely, high-nickel content of alloys may be of limited value. In any event, the higher material cost must be justified by longer life, which is not always predictable.

Low-temperature corrosion

In oil-fired boilers the problem of low-temperature corrosion resulting from the formation and condensation of sulfuric acid from the flue gases is similar to that previously described for coal firing.

Oil-fired boilers are more susceptible to low-temperature corrosion than are most coal-fired units for two reasons: (1) the vanadium in the oil-ash deposits is a good catalyst for the conversion of SO_2 to SO_3 and (2) there is a smaller quantity of ash in the flue gases. Ash particles in the flue gas reduce the amount of SO_3 vapor in the gas. Since oil has considerably less ash than coal, significant differences would be expected. Furthermore, coal ash is more basic than oil ash and tends to neutralize any acid deposited; oil ash generally lacks this capability.

Under certain conditions, oil-fired boilers may emit acidic particulates from their stacks that stain or etch

painted surfaces in the neighborhood of the plant. The acidic deposits or smuts are generally caused by metallic surfaces (air heaters, flues and stacks) operating well below the acid dew point of the flue gases or by soot which has absorbed sulfuric acid vapor in its passage through the boiler. Methods that can be used to prevent acid-smut emission include:

1. Minimize SO_3 formation in the flue gases,
2. Neutralize SO_3 in flue gases,
3. Maintain all surfaces in contact with the flue gases above about 250F and,
4. Completely burn fuel oil to eliminate soot particles.

Methods of control

The methods of control that have been used or proposed to control fouling and corrosion in oil-fired boilers are summarized in Table 11, but in every instance economics governs their applicability. There is no doubt that reducing the amount of ash and sulfur entering the furnace is the surest means of control, and that minimizing the effects of the ash constituents, once they have deposited on the tubes, is the least reliable. Since the severity of fouling and corrosion depends not only on the fuel-oil characteristics but also on boiler design and operating variables, a generalized solution to these problems cannot be prescribed.

Table 11
Classification of methods for controlling fouling
and corrosion in oil-fired boilers

	Fuel Oil Supply
Reduce amount of fuel ash constituents to the furnace	Selection Blending Purification

	Design
Minimize amounts of fuel ash constituents reaching heat transfer surfaces	Furnace geometry Tube bank arrangement Metal temperature Gas temperature Sootblower arrangement

	Operation
Minimize effects of bonding and corrosive compounds in ash deposits	Load cycle Sootblowing schedule Combustion—Excess air Additives Water washing

Fuel oil supply

Although fuel selection and blending are practiced to some extent in this country, it is done to provide safe and reliable handling and storage at the user's plant rather than to avoid fouling difficulties. Since the threshold limits of sodium, sulfur and vanadium are not accurately defined for either fouling or corrosion, utilization of these means of control cannot be fully exploited.

Processes are available for both the desulfurization and de-ashing of fuel oils. Water washing of residual fuel oil has been successfully applied to a few marine-type boilers, but it is doubtful that it will be widely used because only sodium and sediment, mainly rust and

sand, are removed by the process. Use of low-sulfur, low-ash crudes and desulfurized fuel oil is expected to increase (*see also Chapter 18*).

Fuel oil additives

The practice of water washing out of service and, to a limited extent, in service has been beneficial in overcoming some of the troubles experienced with present oil fuels. In addition, continued study of the problem has revealed another approach that is effective where the fuel-oil ash is most troublesome. In brief, the method involves adding to the fuel or furnace small amounts of materials that change the character of the ash sufficiently to permit its removal by steam or air sootblowers or air lances.

Additives are effective in reducing the troubles associated with superheater fouling, high-temperature ash corrosion, and low-temperature sulfuric acid corrosion. Most effective are alumina, dolomite and magnesia. Kaolin is also a source of alumina. Analyses of typical superheater deposits from a troublesome fuel oil, before and after treating it with alumina or dolomite, are shown in three bar graphs at the left in Fig. 30. The results for a different oil treated with magnesia are shown in the bar graph at the right.

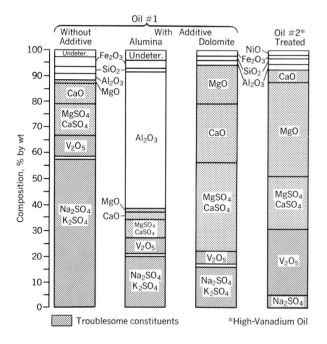

Fig. 30 Effect of fuel-oil additives on composition of oil-ash deposit.

The reduction of fouling and high-temperature corrosion is accomplished basically by producing a high-melting-point ash deposit that is powdery or friable and easily removed by sootblowers or lances. When the ash is dry, corrosion is considerably reduced.

Low-temperature sulfuric-acid corrosion is reduced by the formation of refractory sulfates by reaction with the SO_3 gas in the flue-gas stream. By thus removing the SO_3 gas, the dew point of the flue gases is sufficiently reduced to protect the metal surfaces. The sulfate compounds formed are relatively dry and easily removed by the normal cleaning equipment.

In general, the amount of additive used should be about equal to the ash content of the fuel oil. In some instances, slightly different proportions may be required for best results, especially for high-temperature corrosion reduction, in which it is generally accepted that the additive should be used in weight ratios of 2 or 3 to 1, based on the vanadium content of the oil.

Several methods have been successfully used to introduce the additive materials into the furnace. The one in general use consists of metering a controlled amount of an additive oil slurry into the burner supply line. The additive material should be pulverized to 100% through a 325-mesh screen (44 microns) for good dispersion and minimum atomizer wear.

For a boiler fired by a high-pressure return-flow oil system, it has been found advantageous to introduce the additive powders by blowing them into the furnace at the desired locations. The powder has to be 100% through a 325-mesh screen for good dispersion.

A third, and more recent method, is to introduce the additive as a water slurry through specially adapted sootblowers or lances. This method offers the advantage of applying the additive in exactly the location desired, with a possible reduction in the quantity required. Some caution should be observed with this system to prevent possible thermal shock (quench-cracking) damage to the hot tubes. The presence of chlorides in the water slurry, from either the water or the additive material, could possibly produce stress-corrosion cracking of austenitic tubing and should be considered.

The choice of the particular additive material depends on its availability and cost to the individual plant and the method of application chosen. For example, alumina

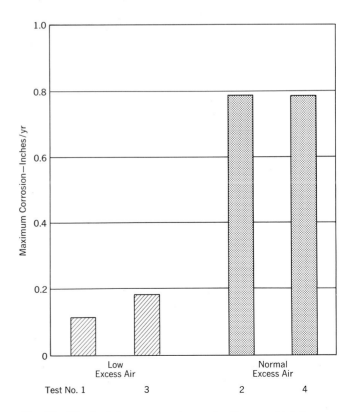

Fig. 31 Effect of low excess-air combustion on high-temperature oil-ash corrosion.

causes greater sprayer-plate wear than the other materials when used in an oil slurry.

The quantity of deposit formed is, of course, an important consideration for each individual unit from the aspect of cleaning. A comparison of the amounts of deposit formed with different additives shows that dolomite produces the greatest quantity because of its sulfating ability, alumina and kaolin form the least, and magnesia is intermediate. However, when adequate cleaning facilities are available, the deposits are easily removed, and the quantities formed should not be a problem.

Excess-air control

As mentioned previously the problems encountered in the combustion of residual fuels—high-temperature deposits (fouling), high-temperature corrosion, and low-temperature sulfuric-acid corrosion—all arise from the presence of vanadium and sulfur in their highest states of oxidation. By reducing the excess air from 7% to 1 or 2%, it is possible to avoid the formation of fully oxidized vanadium and sulfur compounds and, thereby, reduce boiler fouling and corrosion problems.

In a series of tests on an experimental boiler, it was found that the maximum corrosion rate of type 304 stainless steel superheater alloy held at 1250F in 2100F flue gas was reduced more than 75% (see Fig. 31) when the excess air was reduced from an average of 7% to a level of 1 to 2%. Moreover, the ash deposits that formed on the superheater bank were soft and powdery, in contrast to hard, dense deposits that adhered tenaciously to the tubes when the excess air was around 7%. Also, the rate of ash buildup was only half as great. Operation at the 1 to 2% excess air level practically eliminated low-temperature corrosion of carbon steel at all metal temperatures above the water dew point of the flue gases (Fig. 32). However, much of the beneficial effects of low excess-air combustion are lost if the excess air at the burner fluctuates even for short periods of time

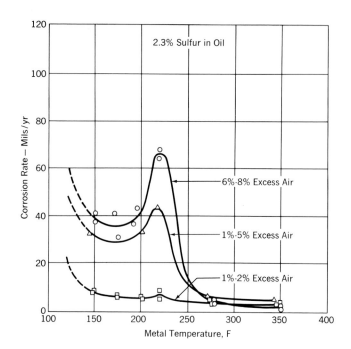

Fig. 32 Effect of excess air on low-temperature corrosion of carbon steel.

to a level of about 5%. Carbon loss values for low excess air were approximately 0.5%, which is generally acceptable for electric utility and industrial practice.

A number of large industrial boilers both in this country and in Europe have been operating with low excess air for several years. As a result, the benefits of reducing low-temperature corrosion are well established. However the benefits on high-temperature slagging and corrosion are not wholly conclusive. In any event, great care must be exercised to distribute the air and fuel oil equally to the burners, and combustion conditions must be continuously monitored to assure that combustion of the fuel is complete before the combustion gases enter the convection tube banks.

Chapter 16   Boiler enclosures, insulation and casing

Boiler settings

The term *boiler setting* was originally applied to the brick walls enclosing the furnace and heating surface of the boiler. As the demand grew for larger capacity steam generating units, the brick walls gave way to air-cooled refractory walls and then to water-cooled tube walls. The water-cooled wall progressed in turn through the Bailey-block-covered tube, the tube with flat studs backed with refractory and the tangent tube, to the present membrane wall construction. The term *boiler setting* comprises all the walls that form the boiler and furnace enclosure, and includes the insulation and lagging of these walls. The term *enclosure* may refer either to the entire setting or to a section of it.

Casing is sheet or plate attached to pressure parts for the purpose of supporting insulation or forming a tight closure.

Lagging is an outer covering over a wall for the purpose of protecting insulation or improving appearance.

Design requirements

Settings must safely contain high temperature gases and air. Leakage, heat loss and maintenance must be reduced to acceptable values. A number of factors require consideration in the design of settings:

1. Enclosures must withstand the effects of high temperature, ranging up to 3500F in some cases.

2. The action of ash and slag (molten ash) must be considered from the following viewpoints:

   a) Destructive chemical reactions between slag and metal or refractory can occur under certain conditions.

   b) Accumulations of ash on the water walls can significantly reduce heat absorption.

   c) Ash accumulations can fall from a height and cause injury to personnel or damage to apparatus.

   d) High-velocity ash particles can erode the pressure parts.

3. Provisions must be made for the expansion of enclosures and for differential expansion of component parts.

4. Supports must be designed to accommodate the effects of thermal expansion, temperature and pressure stresses, and wind and earthquake loadings appropriate to the plant site.

5. The effect of explosions as well as implosions must be taken into account to lessen the probability of injury and damage.

6. Vibrations caused by combustion pulsations and the flow characteristics of gas and air must be limited to acceptable values.

7. The insulation of the enclosures should limit the heat loss to an economic minimum.

8. The surface temperature or the ambient air temperature must not cause discomfort or hazard to the operating personnel.

9. Enclosures must be gastight to minimize leakage into or out of the setting.

10. The design must be adequate to meet the corrosive effects of ash and gases.

11. Settings of outdoor units must be weatherproof.

12. Settings must be designed for economical fabrication and erection.

13. Serviceability, including access for inspection and maintenance, is essential.

14. Good appearance, consistent with cost and maintenance requirements, is always desirable.

Tube wall enclosures

In modern units, water- or steam-cooled tubes are utilized as the basic structure of the enclosure in high temperature areas of the setting. Three important types of water-cooled enclosures are discussed in this section—membrane walls, membrane walls with refractory lining, and flat-stud-tube walls. Fig. 1 illustrates locations where two of these are used in the setting of a modern boiler.

Membrane walls

Fig. 2 illustrates a typical furnace wall using membrane construction. These membrane walls are water-cooled walls, constructed of bare tubes joined together by thin membrane bars. The walls thus formed are gastight and require no inner casing to contain the products of combustion. Insulation is provided on the outer side of the wall, and metal lagging to protect the insulation. Membrane wall construction is used for furnace walls (Fig. 1).

Membrane walls with refractory lining

The lower furnace walls of cyclone-fired units consist of membrane walls with the tubes covered with refractory held in place by cylindrical (pin) studs on the hot side

(Fig. 3). The studs are welded to the tubes at close intervals and covered with a slag-resistant refractory material.

The purpose of this construction, is to increase furnace temperatures to maintain the coal, peat or lignite ash in a liquid state. The external surface is insulated and lagged as in Fig. 2.

Flat-stud-tube walls

These walls consist of tubes with small flat bar studs welded at the sides (Fig. 4). These flat-studded tubes are backed by refractory and a welded inner casing forming a gastight enclosure. This casing is supported from channel tie bars welded to tubes at each buckstay

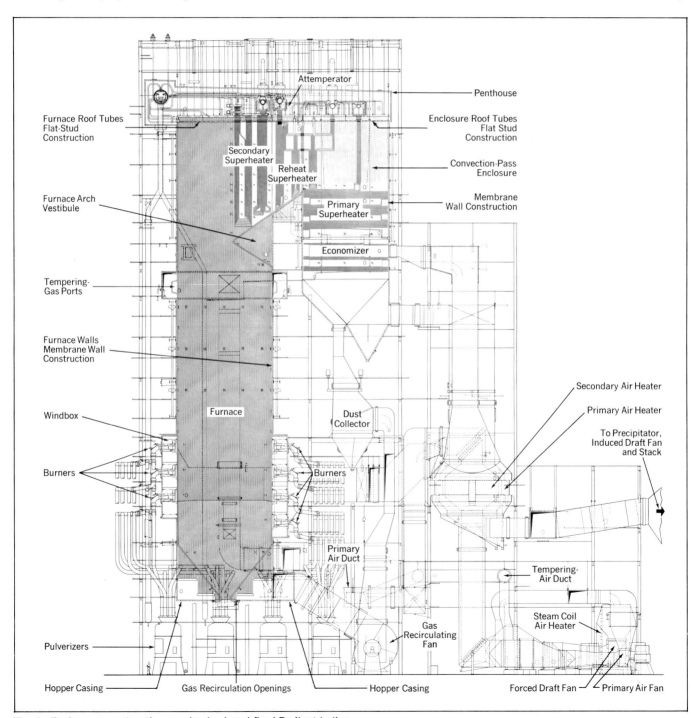

Fig. 1 Enclosure constructions–pulverized-coal-fired Radiant boiler.

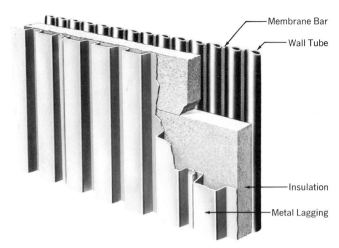

Fig. 2 Membrane wall construction.

row. The walls are reinforced with buckstays and the inner casing is reinforced with stiffeners to withstand the design pressure of the walls between buckstays. Insulation is applied to the outer face of the inner casing and protected with a metal lagging. This construction is used in the area of the convection tube banks and the convection pass enclosure.

While the construction of the casing described in the preceding paragraph applies to areas of horizontal buckstay reinforcement, some industrial designs require vertical casing reinforcement and the tie bar is welded vertically to a bar between the tubes.

Cased enclosures

A boiler unit contains many non-water-cooled or cased enclosures. These must be designed to withstand relatively high temperatures and at the same time to have external wall temperatures low enough to minimize heat loss and to be safe for contact by operating personnel. Important cased enclosures include (*see Fig. 1*):

Hopper casing

This casing forms the gastight enclosure at the bottom of the furnace for dry-bottom units. It also serves as an insulation retainer and generally improves the appearance of the steam generator in this area. The enclosure provided by the hopper casing may also serve as a flue for the recirculating gas which enters the furnace through openings between tubes.

Windbox

This is a reinforced cased enclosure housing the burners and functioning as a distributor of combustion air. The windbox may be located on one burner wall or on all furnace walls with a wraparound configuration. The top, outer side and bottom of the windbox are made of metal casing while the furnace tube wall forms the inner side. The attachment to the furnace wall must be gastight and also permit differential thermal expansion between the tubes and the casing.

For large capacity boilers, the windbox is compartmented and is only on the front and rear walls of the furnace. The windboxes are compartmented for better matching of the air to the fuel requirements.

Tempering gas plenum

This enclosure is similar to a windbox with economizer exit gas flowing through it instead of air. This gas is used to temper the furnace gases and thus control ash fouling of the heating surfaces. The construction of the plenum is similar to that of the windbox but the tempering gas plenum is much smaller. The reinforced casing construction is normally unprotected on the inside except for stainless steel shields located opposite the gas ports.

Penthouse casing

This casing forms the enclosure for all miscellaneous pressure parts located above the furnace and convection pass roofs. It is gastight, with the roof tubes forming the bottom of the enclosure. Many seals, dependent on the penthouse size and thermal conditions, are used with this gastight enclosure, such as cylindrical bellows or flexible cans sealing the suspension hangers or large fold (pagoda) seals around steam leads. This top enclosure composed of a series of reinforced flat panels welded together, is either pressurized with air to form a secondary seal for furnace and convection pass roof tubes or the furnace and convection pass roof tubes are covered by a gastight casing.

Inner casing is used over wall surfaces that would not be gastight without this covering. The inner casing may be applied directly to the external face of the walls or remotely, as in the area between the convection pass and furnace rear wall, for economical insulation coverage. In general the casing consists of flanged panels seal welded to be gastight.

Casings are constructed of light gage sheet or thin plate, suitably reinforced with stiffeners to withstand the required pressure and temperature. When the casing is directly attached to the furnace walls, expansion elements are provided to accommodate differential thermal expansion of the tubes and casing.

Pressure-fired units require gastight construction. Each unit is considered tight when all welded joints are inspected visually and tested under pressure (*see "Leakage"*). Suction or negative-pressure-fired units are also of welded gastight construction.

Resistance to ash and slag

Ash has a tendency to shed from a cold metal surface, particularly when the temperature of the ash itself is well below its softening point. Wall-type blowers remove ash in high temperature areas, where it tends to adhere to the walls.

Extensive areas of exposed refractory should not be used because of the tendency for slag adhesion. Damage or injury from the falling of large slag accumulations into the furnace is thus avoided. Also, crotches formed by tubes bent out of the plane of the wall should be designed to prevent ash accumulation.

Erosion of pressure parts is reduced by limiting the gas velocity through the unit. However, low average gas velocities do not preclude local high velocities which can still occur in areas where gas bypasses baffles or heating surface. These high-velocity lanes must be eliminated by proper design, baffle installation and maintenance.

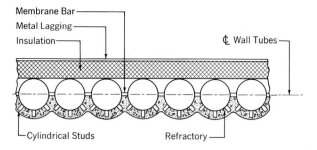

Fig. 3 Fully studded membrane walls.

Expansion

With the inner-cased unit, Fig. 4, small temperature differentials can occur between the casing and the tubes during start-up. Expansion of the wall in the horizontal direction is governed by the temperature of the tie channel. Since the casing and the channels are at the same temperature, they can be welded together. Vertical expansion differences are taken in the slight bending of the casing flanges at the top and bottom of each section of the casing.

With a bottom-supported unit, such as the type PFI Integral-Furnace boiler (Fig. 5), which is designed for pressure firing, the structure is fixed at a point at one end of the lower drum. Clearances, seals and supports are designed for known expansions in all directions.

With the top-supported unit, Fig. 1, the expansion occurs downwards from one elevation. Unless one of the walls is fixed to the building steel, the expansion will occur outwards from the center of the unit.

Flues and ducts, piping, ash tanks, and burner lines must be designed with expansion joints or seals to accommodate the relative movements involved. Flexible metal bellows are used in flues and ducts; metal hoses and sliding or toggling gasketed couplings in piping. Water seals are generally used between ash hoppers or slag tanks and the associated furnace. With large units, the expansion may be as much as 12 in. between adjacent parts, yet joints must be maintained pressure-tight.

Support

The support of steam generators is discussed in Chapter 30. It is generally more economical to support the smaller size units from the bottom and the larger units from the top. In either case the boiler setting is formed by the water walls where these are available (Figs. 2, 3 and 4).

For bottom-supported units, other parts of the enclosure are usually supported from a common foundation with the boiler (Fig. 5). For top-supported units, similar portions of the enclosure are supported from the pressure parts except that the cased enclosure at the top of the unit is supported directly from the structural steel by the hanger rods (Fig. 1).

Explosions

In the design of settings, the effect of possible explosions must be taken into account to eliminate the possibilities of injury and serious damage. Historically, the rupture of pressure parts in boilers was a serious menace. Such disastrous explosions have been largely eliminated by better understanding of the technical problems and the development of adequate design and operating codes. More recently the firing of large units with fluid or fluidized fuels has introduced a new hazard from the ignition of explosive fuel and air mixtures within the setting. Explosion pressures may range as high as 50 psi in some parts of the setting. It is not feasible to build structures to meet bursting pressures of this magnitude. The enclosure is normally designed to withstand common puffs and minor explosions. In the event of a major furnace explosion, the design should provide for failure of studs, stud attachments, and welds rather than the tube walls themselves. This practice minimizes the danger of releasing large quantities of steam in the event of a furnace explosion.

The loading from furnace puffs and from normal operating negative or positive furnace pressure is contained by the use of bars and channels welded to tubes to form continuous bands around the setting. Beams, called buckstays, are attached to the tie bars with slip connections and keep the walls from bowing inward or outward.

Since the buckstays are outside the insulation, special corner connections are required (*see Fig. 6*) that will allow the walls to expand and at the same time tie together the corners, where the force of an explosion is concentrated. These corner connections must be tight during starting-up periods when the walls have not fully expanded, as well as at the normal operating fully expanded position. Furnace puffs caused by incorrect fuel-and-air mixtures are often associated with starting-up operations.

The tube span between the buckstays acts as a beam to resist the internal furnace pressure. The larger the tube diameter and the heavier the tube wall, the farther apart the buckstays may be spaced. The size of the buckstay beam is determined by the permissible deflection and the positive or negative pressure loading.

Explosion doors are now seldom used to relieve exces-

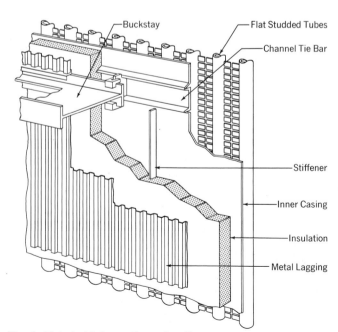

Fig. 4 Flat-stud-tube wall construction.

sive internal furnace pressure. Except in very small furnaces, they cannot fulfill their purpose, because the internal pressure from a fuel explosion is not significantly relieved by the opening of a door. Actually, explosion doors may be more of a hazard than a safety feature because, in the event of a puff, they may discharge hot gases that would otherwise be completely contained within the setting.

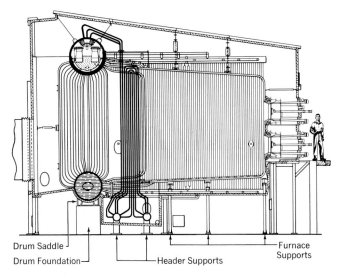

Drum Saddle
Drum Foundation
Header Supports
Furnace Supports

Fig. 5 Bottom-supported unit.

Implosions

In the design of settings, the effect of possible implosions must also be taken into account to eliminate the possibilities of injury and serious damage. Implosions are usually caused by 1) improper operation of dampers on units with high static pressure induced draft fans or 2) an extremely rapid decay of furnace pressure due to sudden termination of fuel supply (usually oil valve closing too rapidly). Due to the high draft loss requirements of back end cleanup systems which result in induced draft fans with high static pressure capability, it is not economical to design the setting to withstand the full developed negative head of the fan. Accordingly, settings are designed for a transient condition of a positive or negative pressure of 20 in. H₂O at 80% yield strength. In addition, induced draft fan controls are specified as to minimize possible operating or control errors and to reduce the degree of furnace draft excursion following a fuel trip.

Vibration

Excessive vibration in boiler settings can cause failures of the insulation, casing and supports. This vibration can be produced 1) by external rotating equipment, such as turbines and fans, and transmitted to the setting through building steel, piping, flues or ducts; 2) by furnace pulsations from the uneven combustion of the fuel; and 3) by turbulence in the flowing streams of air or gas in flues, ducts and tube banks.

The walls, flues and ducts are designed to limit vibration to low values for normal operating conditions. For the walls, the section modulus of buckstays is usually

selected to limit wall deflection at its midpoint to 1/16 in. with a pressure change of 1 in. of water. Flues, ducts and casings are similarly stiffened by bars or structural shapes to prevent excessive vibration. This stiffening is particularly necessary in sections of flues and ducts where the flow is highly turbulent as in the fan-discharge connecting piece. Every effort should be made to eliminate the sources of severe vibration, such as unbalanced rotating equipment, poor combustion, and highly turbulent air or gas flow.

Heat loss

Heat loss from a boiler setting is reduced by the installation of insulation, usually as an integral part of the boiler enclosure (Figs. 2, 3 and 4). From the standpoint of heat loss there is an economic balance between the value of the heat lost and the cost of insulation and its installation.

For steam generating units located outdoors it is customary to install the amount of insulation required for maximum economy, since natural ventilation is normally adequate to remove the heat losses without discomfort to operating personnel.

For indoor units ventilation is required for operator comfort, and the heat losses must be removed from the boiler room by means of the ventilating air. This generally requires more insulation than could be justified by the heat loss criterion alone.

The basic materials most frequently used in heat insulation for steam generators are listed below together with some of the commercial forms of insulation made from these materials and their limitations.

1. *Mineral wool.* This material comprises molten slag, glass or rock, blown into fibers by steam or air jet or spun by high-speed wheels.

   (a) *Mineral-wool-base block.* Mineral-wool fibers and clay, molded under heat and pressure, are used to insulate membrane tube walls and boiler casing up to a temperature limit of 850, 1200 or 1800F depending upon the grade.

   (b) *Mineral-wool blanket.* Mineral-wool fibers compressed into blanket form, and held in shape by retention between hexagonal wire mesh or expanded metal lath, are used on all types of enclosures with external metal lagging or casing and for piping inside cased enclosures. The temperature limit is normally 1200F.

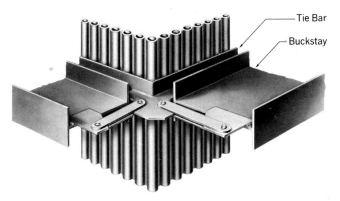

Tie Bar
Buckstay

Fig. 6 Tie bar and buckstay arrangement at corner of furnace.

2. *Calcium silicate block.* Reacted hydrous calcium silicate block is used on enclosures and piping, generally below 1200F.

3. *High temperature plastic.* Insulating cement made of mineral-wool fibers processed into nodules and then dry-mixed with clay forms a tough fibrous monolithic insulation in final dried condition. Drying shrinkage is as much as 40% and there is a tendency to crack upon drying. This material is used principally on irregularly shaped valves and fittings, and heated tanks up to a temperature of 1500F.

4. *Ceramic fiber.* High purity ceramic fibers with melting points above 3000F are occasionally used for tube enclosure seals where resiliency is required.

Heat loss calculations

Calculations of the heat flow through a composite wall are discussed in Chapter 4 (Fig. 3 and related text). Thermal conductivities of a wide range of commercial refractory and insulating materials, at the temperatures for which they are suitable, are given in Fig. 7. Combined heat losses (radiation plus convection) per sq ft of outer wall surface are given in Fig. 8 for various ambient air velocities and various temperature differences between surface and air. The ABMA radiation loss chart (Fig. 27,

Chapter 4) provides a quick approximation for radiation loss, expressed as a percentage of gross heat input.

Ventilation, surface temperature, and working conditions

To maintain satisfactory working conditions around a boiler installed indoors, the insulation must be thick enough to keep the outside surface temperature of the wall reasonably low, and to prevent excessive increase in the boiler room temperature by heat loss through the wall. A cold face temperature of 130 to 160F is usually considered satisfactory for an indoor installation. Heat losses, corresponding to these surface temperatures, range between 70 and 180 Btu/sq ft, hr, which can be readily absorbed by the air circulation generally provided in present day boiler rooms.

Insulating a boiler to reduce the heat loss to a value that can readily be absorbed by the total volume of room air does not in itself assure comfortable working conditions. Good air circulation around all parts of the boiler is also necessary to prevent the accumulation of heat in the areas frequented by the operating personnel. This can be aided by the substitution of grating for solid floors, by ample aisle space between adjacent boilers, by the location of fans to assist the circulation of air around the boiler, and by the addition of ventilating equipment to assure adequate air change.

Fortunately on modern units good ventilation does not greatly increase the overall heat loss. Air velocity affects the surface conductance (q/S ÷ temperature difference); this can be verified by data from Fig. 8. However, surface conductance is only a small part of the total resistance to heat flow. For example, an increase in air velocity from 1 to 10 fps, for the conditions given in Fig. 9, will increase the heat loss rate through the wall only 3 Btu from 144 to 147 Btu/sq ft, hr. This is approximately 2% for a tenfold increase in air velocity.

Unlike heat loss, outer surface temperature is affected considerably by the surrounding conditions. In a situation such as that shown in Fig. 10 where two walls of similar temperature are close together, the radiant heat transfer from either wall is negligible. The natural circulation of air through such a cavity is inadequate to cool the walls to a temperature suitable for personnel working in the vicinity. From Fig. 11 it will be seen that a considerable change in surface film resistance will cause an appreciable change in lagging or surface temperature while not affecting the heat loss through the wall to any extent.

Increased insulation thickness would not significantly reduce the surface temperature in the cavity in Fig. 10. Cavities should therefore be avoided in areas where operators work. Ventilating ducts can be installed, if necessary, to reduce the air temperature in such a cavity.

Leakage

Continuing efforts have been made over the years to reduce air infiltration into boiler settings. Such leakage increases gas flow and the heat rejected to the stack, thus lowering the boiler efficiency (*see Combustion Calculations, Chapter 6*) and increasing induced draft fan power.

The constant goal of higher efficiency has led to the

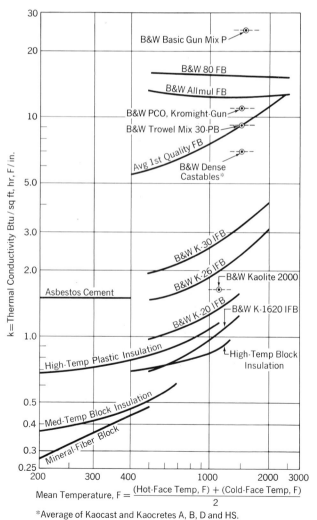

Fig. 7 Thermal conductivity of various refractory materials.

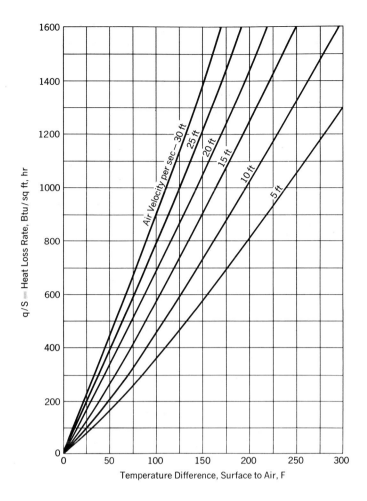

Fig. 8 Heat loss from wall surfaces (radiation + convection). (*Source—ASTM Standards, Part 13, 1969*)

development of pressurized firing. With this system leakage is reduced to a minimum, the induced draft fan is eliminated, and the cost of fans and fan power is lowered considerably. The all-welded casing, directly behind the tube enclosures with the insulation on the outside of the casing (Fig. 4), and the membrane wall (Figs. 2 and 3) were developed for pressurized firing. The casing temperature is approximately the same as the temperature of the tube walls so that all-welded seals can be used around openings. For rotating sootblowers and some inspection doors, seal air, from the forced draft fan, at a pressure higher than internal, is provided to prevent gas leakage and to furnish some cooling. This seal air usually amounts to 1 or 2% of the theoretical air required for combustion.

The same type of inner casing is also used for many suction-fired boilers to obtain the benefits of minimum leakage. This amounts to about 1 to 2% of the theoretical air required.

A rigorous test is made to check the tightness of the inner casing of a pressurized unit. All inlets and outlets to the boiler setting are sealed temporarily with welded closures, and the setting is pressurized to 20 in. of water or 1.5 times the design pressure, whichever is the lower. Welds are examined for air leakage, and the rate of pressure drop within the setting is noted. A rate of 5 in. of water pressure drop in 10 minutes is usually considered acceptable depending upon the size of the unit.

Leakage tests of negative-pressure-fired units are made by visual inspection with the unit under pressure from the forced draft fan.

Gas leakage through walls separating zones of different pressure must be prevented. Such leakage can overheat inner or outer casings as well as other structural parts. Walls that become saturated with ash and sulfur may undergo corrosion of outer casings. Enclosures around headers and drums may accumulate large quantities of troublesome ash. A good seal directly behind or in line with the tube wall prevents these difficulties (Fig. 2). All openings through walls must be sealed by tight sleeves. Barriers in walls may be necessary to prevent gas flow through insulation between zones of different pressure.

Corrosion

One of the advantages of the membrane wall is that it eliminates flue-gas corrosion in the enclosure walls.

Most flue gases contain sulfur, and metal parts of the setting must be kept either above the dew point of the gases or out of contact with the gases if the metal is below the dew point (Chapter 13). The dew point generally ranges between 150 and 250F and is dependent on the fuel, its sulfur content, and the firing method.

Flues carrying low-temperature spent gases should be insulated on the outside to inhibit corrosion. This is particularly necessary on outdoor units. Water-cooled doors and slag-tap coils require water temperatures above 150F to keep the cooling coils above the dew point.

When casing is located outside of insulation or refractory, it is still subject to the action of the flue gases. When this type of casing is subjected to temperatures below the dew point, an asphalt mastic coating is required to protect the casing from corrosion on the inside. The same is true of the metal in a cased enclosure. This prob-

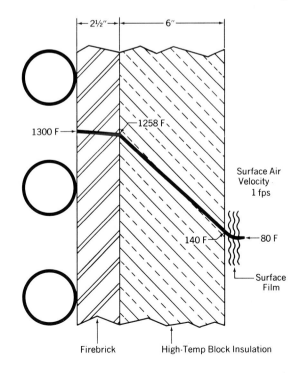

Fig. 9 Temperature gradients through tube-and-brick wall.

lem requires special attention in the design of outdoor installations where temperatures may at times be low.

With the use of inner casing, corrosion problems are greatly reduced, since the flue gases are completely contained by a metal "skin" that is well above the dew point. Even with the inner casing, however, care must be exercised to insulate seals and expansion joints properly to avoid cold spots and the consequent corrosion.

Resistance to weather

In recent years, outdoor boiler installations have gained in popularity, particularly in mild climates. Although the initial cost of the plant is reduced, maintenance of the boiler and auxiliary equipment must be considered. Severe weather can extend outage time and increase maintenance expense. These units must have sufficient reinforcement to withstand the pressure and suction forces of the wind.

It is relatively simple to make a metal-lagged unit rainproof. Joints and flange connections are overlapped, and flashings are used around openings. Welding of joints or the use of mastic compounds is necessary in areas difficult to seal.

Sloping roofs are required and are particularly important on aluminum lagging as pockets of water would eventually stain the surface. Direct contact between aluminum and steel must be avoided to prevent galvanic corrosion of the aluminum in the presence of moisture. Copper lines or roof flashings should be so designed that water runoff does not wet the aluminum.

All outdoor jobs should have the connections between the water-gage assembly and the drum insulated, except for approximately 4 ft of the upper connection adjacent to the assembly. This area is left uninsulated to assure circulation of the condensate. Water columns must also be insulated. In climates where freezing weather is experienced, the drain lines for the water-gage assembly

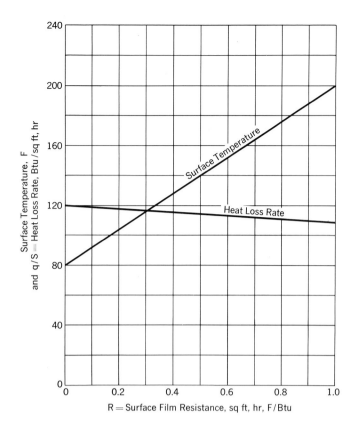

Fig. 11 Effect of surface film resistance on surface temperature and heat loss rate.

must be insulated and protected. The water gage and its illuminator will provide ample warmth within the water-gage housing.

Weather hoods should be used to keep rain, snow and ice from contact with outdoor safety valves. Nozzles and valve necks must be insulated and protected with sheet metal or other waterproof covering.

Outdoor control lines containing air or flue gas, drain and sampling lines, and intermittently operated steam and water lines should be insulated and protected by electric-resistance-heating wires. Steam pipe tracer lines may be substituted in some cases. Dry air should be supplied for control lines and sootblowers. Steam and water lines outside the setting must be completely drainable.

Fabrication and assembly

The setting must be designed for economical fabrication and field assembly. This requires integration of all shop and field methods and practices. Small units can be completely shop-assembled. For larger units the trend has been toward shop subassembly of large components.

Shipping clearances limit the size of shop-assembled wall panels to approximately 10 ft wide and 65 ft long. Shop assembly of components permits better quality control of the more complicated parts such as burners and Cyclone Furnace throats.

Advances in welding methods and the development of shop machinery have greatly influenced the design of enclosures. Flues, ducts, expansion joints and inner casings are welded. Tube connections to headers, tie bars, doors and other attachments are generally welded. New

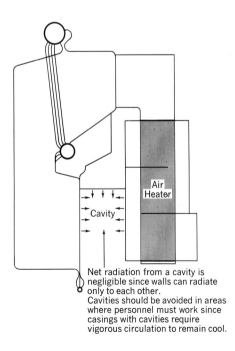

Net radiation from a cavity is negligible since walls can radiate only to each other.
Cavities should be avoided in areas where personnel must work since casings with cavities require vigorous circulation to remain cool.

Fig. 10 Cavities tend to raise wall-surface temperature.

and improved materials and attachment methods reduce the man-hour requirements for insulating boilers and installing metal lagging.

Serviceability

Many setting design details must be resolved to simplify operation and maintenance. Working areas around the unit should have adequate lighting and comfortable temperatures. Clearances for servicing and removing parts should be provided. Access through the setting is necessary for inspection of boiler internals. Suitable platforms for access doors, sootblowers, instruments and controls are essential.

Inspection doors permit observation of combustion conditions and the cleanliness of heat-absorbing surfaces. They facilitate good operation and should be safe and easily opened. Fig. 12 illustrates an inspection door for a pressurized setting. Safety is provided by two types of interlocks which assure that compressed air is properly aspirating the aperture before the door is opened. A feature of this door is that the aspirating jet does not restrict the comparatively wide view angle.

The tube bends that form openings in high-duty furnaces must be of the smallest possible radius. In some cases die-formed tube bends are used. The length of the stud-plate closures around the opening is thus minimized, so that the plates can be adequately cooled by welded contact to the tubes.

Appearance

The setting should present a good appearance initially and be designed so that the good appearance can be retained indefinitely with a minimum of housekeeping. The outer surface should be easily cleanable. Equipment

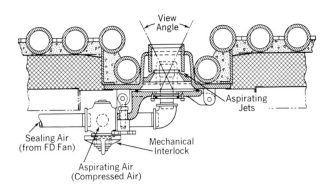

Fig. 12 Inspection door for pressurized furnace.

handling flue gas, coal, ash, or oil should be designed to contain these materials without leakage.

Light-gage metal lagging is generally used for outer covering. This is particularly true for outdoor units, where it is relatively simple to make the metal lagging watertight. Many types of covering are still found in older installations. These include plastic insulation, cement finishes, canvas and asbestos cloth, welded steel casing, and asbestos lumber.

Figs. 2, 3 and 4 show metal-lagged units. Light-gage galvanized-steel or clad-aluminum sheets are commonly used for lagging. Galvanized steel is generally less expensive than the aluminum, but for outdoor units it may be necessary to paint the galvanized steel after weathering, unless the climate is dry. If much painting is required, the clad aluminum may be preferable, since it does not require painting except under the more severe conditions. Since the lagging is fabricated at the job site, the cost is less than it would be for metal casings shop-manufactured from drawings.

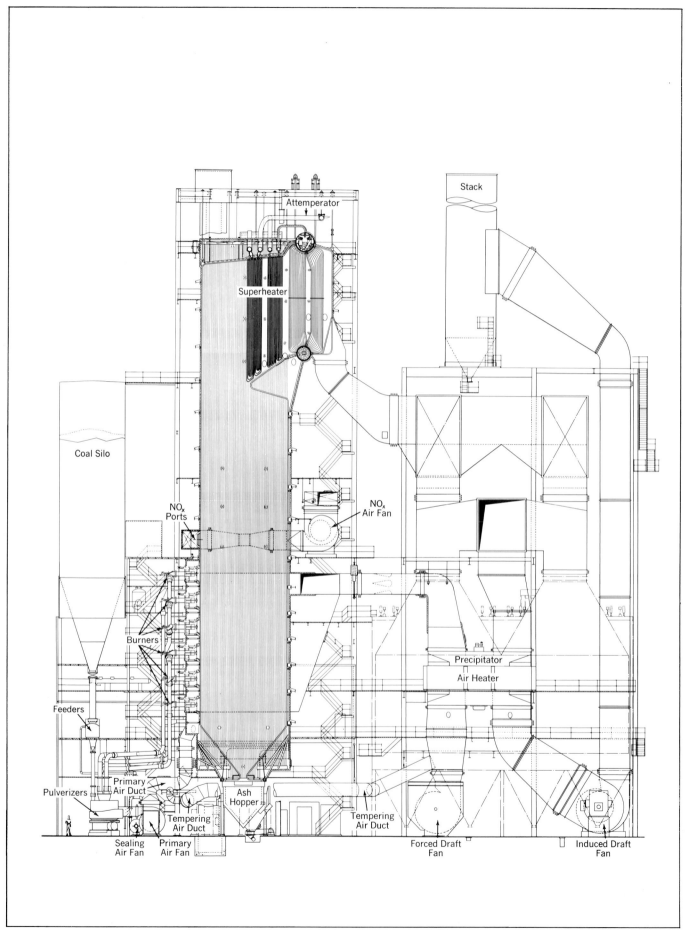

Arrangement of forced and induced draft fans for a boiler unit of 800,000 lb of steam per hr capacity.

Chapter 17

Stacks, fans and draft

A flow of air and combustion gases in steam generating units is required to supply the proper amount of combustion air and to remove the gaseous combustion products. This flow, confined to ducts, boiler settings, heat exchangers, flues and stacks, is created and sustained by stacks and fans. Either the stack alone or a combination of stack and fans must produce the required pressure differential for the flow.

Draft

Draft is a term commonly used to designate static pressure in a furnace, air or gas passage, or stack. It is also accepted practice to speak of draft in any one of the four categories: forced draft, induced draft, balanced draft and natural draft.

The term "forced draft" is used when air or flue gases flowing in a unit are maintained at pressures above atmospheric. This will generally imply the use of a forced draft fan.

When air or the products of combustion flow in a unit under the influence of a progressively decreasing pressure below atmospheric, the system is operating under induced draft. This is the case where stacks alone furnish sufficient natural draft to meet low draft loss requirements or where stacks are supplemented with induced draft fans to meet higher pressure differentials.

The term "natural draft" in conjunction with stacks is used to designate a pressure differential caused by gravity. In this case, a difference in density between the hot gas in the stack and the colder air of the surrounding atmosphere results in a negative pressure, or natural draft, at the stack entrance.

Balanced draft refers to a point in the system where the draft is zero (static pressure = atmospheric pressure). It is also used to describe a unit in which the top of the furnace operates at slightly less than atmospheric pressure.

Pressures and flows

Whereas draft refers to static pressure, it is also important to be able to determine the total pressure at any point. This is the static pressure plus the velocity pressure, where velocity pressure is the equivalent of the kinetic energy of the flowing air or gas in ft lb/lb divided by specific volume:

$$(1) \qquad p_v = \frac{V^2}{2g_c} \cdot \frac{1}{v}$$

where:

p_v = velocity pressure, lb/sq ft
V = fluid velocity, ft/sec
g_c = conversion constant, 32.2 ft/sec^2
v = specific volume of the air or gas, cu ft/lb

The units of p_v in equation (1) are lb/sq ft. However, it is customary to designate drafts and associated pressures in inches of water because measurements made with Pitot or static tubes are conveniently indicated in inches of water with a simple U-tube gage.* Thus, converting equation (1) to inches of water:

$$(2) \qquad H_w = \frac{12}{62.4} \, p_v = \frac{1}{5.2v} \cdot \frac{V^2}{2g_c}$$

Knowledge of the average velocity pressure permits determination of the quantity of air or gas flowing in a duct or flue. Solving for V in equation (2) and since flow rate, Q, is 60 AV:

$$(3) \qquad Q = 1098A\sqrt{H_w v}$$

where:

Q = flow rate, cu ft/min
A = flue or duct area normal to the flow, sq ft
H_w = velocity pressure, in. water
v = specific volume of air or gas, cu ft/lb

Specific volumes for air and combustion gases at a pressure of one standard atmosphere (approximately 30 inches mercury) and a temperature of 1000 degrees Rankine are listed in Table 1.

* Inches of water, feet of water or inches of mercury are energy terms which have pressure equivalents when multiplied by the density of the measuring fluid.

Table 1

Gas	Equivalent Molecular Weight	Base Specific Volume, cu ft/lb at one atmosphere and 1000R
Dry Air	29.0	25.2
Combustion Air (0.013 lb water/lb dry air)	28.7	25.4
Flue Gas 3% water by weight	30.0	24.3
Flue Gas 5% water by weight	29.5	24.7
Flue Gas 10% water by weight	28.3	25.7

It is sufficiently accurate to determine the specific volume at any other set of conditions by using the ideal gas laws:

$$(4) \qquad v = v_b \cdot \frac{t_F + 460}{1000} \cdot \frac{30}{B}$$

where:

v = specific volume at t_F and B, cu ft/lb
t_F = fluid temperature (air or gas), F
B = barometric pressure, in. mercury
v_b = specific volume at 1000R and one atmosphere, cu ft/lb

The molecular weights and specific volumes listed in Table 1 for flue gas are approximate only. More accurate values can be obtained from a flue gas analysis.

The composition of air used is based on 0.2095 moles O_2 and 0.7905 moles equivalent N_2. Assumed molecular weight of equivalent N_2 is 28.16 to account for other inert gases and CO_2. The mole volume used in Table 1 is 359 cu ft at 32F and one atmosphere.

Equation (3) can also be expressed as:

$$(5) \qquad G = 65880 \sqrt{\frac{H_w}{v}}$$

where G = mass velocity, lb/sq ft, hr

Stack effect

Stack effect, or chimney action, is the difference in pressure caused solely by the difference in elevation between two locations in vertical ducts or passages conveying heated gases. Like natural draft, it is the result of the action of gravity. The intensity and distribution of this pressure difference depend on the height and arrangement of ducts and passages, and on the gas temperature in each.

Fig. 1 illustrates the procedure used in calculating stack effect, which can either assist or resist the gas flow through the unit. The three gas passages of height AB, CB and CD contain heat absorbing surface; therefore, gases within these passages are at different temperatures. For illustrative purposes, assume atmospheric pressure (draft = 0) at point D.

Stack effect always assists up-flowing gas and resists down-flowing gas. To establish stack effect in each passage, plus signs are assigned to up-flows and minus signs

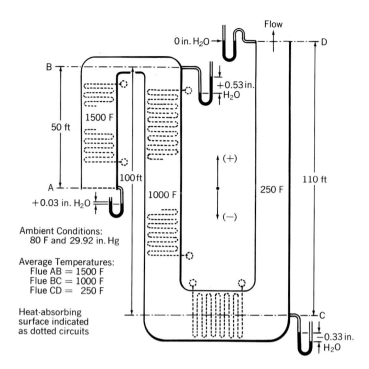

Fig. 1 Diagram illustrating stack effect, or chimney action, in three vertical gas passes arranged in series.

to down-flows. Using values from Table 2 for an ambient air temperature of 80F, the stack effect in inches of water for each passage is:

Stack effect C to D = +(110 × 0.0030) = +0.33 in.
Stack effect B to C = −(100 × 0.0086) = −0.86 in.
Stack effect A to B = + (50 × 0.0100) = +0.50 in.

If draft gages, one end open to the atmosphere, are placed at locations A, B, C and D of Fig. 1 the theoretical zero-flow draft readings are:

Draft at D = 0 in.
Draft at C = draft at D minus stack effect C to D
= 0 − (+0.33) = −0.33 in.
Draft at B = draft at C minus stack effect C to B
= −0.33 − (−0.86) = +0.53 in.
Draft at A = draft at B minus stack effect A to B
= +0.53 − (+0.50) = +0.03 in.

Table 2
Stack effect or pressure differential
for each foot of vertical height, in. water

v, wet flue gas (0.04 lb water/lb dry gas)
= 13.23 cu ft/lb at 80F and 30 in. Hg
v, std. air (0.013 lb water/lb dry air)
= 13.70 cu ft/lb at 80F and 30 in. Hg

Avg. Temp. in Flue or Stack	Ambient Air Temperature, F			
F	40	60	80	100
250	.0041	.0035	.0030	.0025
500	.0070	.0064	.0058	.0053
1000	.0098	.0092	.0086	.0081
1500	.0111	.0106	.0100	.0095
2000	.0120	.0114	.0108	.0103
2500	.0125	.0119	.0114	.0109

Note that, in the example, since the direction of the summations is opposite to the gas flow, stack effects are subtracted in calculating static pressures or drafts. If the summation is made in the direction of gas flow, stack effects should be added.

The net stack effect from A to D in Fig. 1 is the sum of all three stack effects and is −0.03 inches. Since this net is negative it opposes gas flow. For this reason, fans or stack height must be selected not only to provide the necessary draft to overcome flow losses through the unit, but also to allow for the net stack effect of the system.

In some boiler settings, gases leak outward from the upper portions when the unit is operating at very low loads or when it is taken out of service. The leakage can occur even though the outlet flue may show a substantial negative draft. The preceding example illustrates this condition, with a suction or negative pressure at the bottom of the uptake flue CD and positive pressures at both points A and B.

The chimney or stack

All early boilers operated with natural draft supplied by the stack effect of the stack to meet the total draft requirement. This is also true for many of the smaller modern units. However, for larger units equipped with superheaters, economizers and especially air heaters, it is not practical, or economical, to draft the entire unit only from stack induced draft. These units require fans in addition to the stack, either with the entire unit under pressure supplied by a forced draft fan or using both induced and forced draft fans for balanced draft operation. The combination of only an induced draft fan and stack is not commonly used.

The required height and diameter of stacks for natural draft units depend upon:

1. Draft loss through the boiler from the point of balanced draft to the stack entrance.
2. Average temperature of the gases passing up the stack and the temperature of the surrounding air.
3. Required gas flow from the stack.
4. Barometric pressure.
   The influence of altitude on barometric pressure is indicated in Table 3.

Table 3
Barometric pressure (effect of altitude)

Ft Above Sea Level	Pressure In. Hg	Ft Above Sea Level	Pressure In. Hg
0	29.92	6,000	23.98
1,000	28.86	7,000	23.09
2,000	27.82	8,000	22.22
3,000	26.82	9,000	21.39
4,000	25.84	10,000	20.58
5,000	24.90	15,000	16.89

Values from Publication 99, 1967, Air Moving and Conditioning Association, Inc.

No formula satisfactorily covers all of the many factors involved in a determination of the stack height and diameter. For practical purposes, the most important points to consider are: (a) temperature of the surround-ing atmosphere and temperature of the gases entering the stack; (b) drop in temperature of the gases within the stack because of the heat loss to the atmosphere and air infiltration; and (c) stack draft losses associated with the gas flow rate (due to fluid friction within the stack and the kinetic energy of gases leaving the stack).

Theoretical stack draft

The suction at the base of the stack, neglecting the effect of flow losses, is the theoretical stack draft. It is due to the previously discussed stack effect of the stack. For example, if the atmospheric temperature is 60F and the average temperature of the gases in the stack is 500F, the stack effect per foot of stack height is 0.0064 in. from Table 2. If the stack is 100 feet high the theoretical stack draft would be 0.64 inches of water.

Since the theoretical stack draft is the result of a difference between the average density of gases in the stack and the density of the surrounding air, it may also be calculated as follows:

$$(6) \qquad \text{Stack draft} = \frac{L}{5.2}\left(\frac{1}{v_a} - \frac{1}{v_g}\right)$$

where:

Stack draft = induced draft, in. water
L = stack height above gas entrance, ft
v_a = specific volume of atmospheric air, cu ft/lb
v_g = average specific volume of stack gases, cu ft/lb

For standard air with 0.013 lb water per lb of dry air ($v_a = 25.4$ at 1000R and 30 in. Hg) and a typical flue gas ($v_g = 24.5$ at 1000R and 30 in. Hg):

$$(7) \qquad \text{Stack draft} = 7.57L\left(\frac{1}{T_a} - \frac{1}{0.965T_g}\right)\frac{B}{30}$$

where:

B = barometric pressure (Table 3), in. Hg
T_a = absolute temperature of surrounding air, R
T_g = average absolute temperature of stack gas, R

For 80F air (7) becomes:

$$(8) \qquad \text{Stack draft} = 7.84L\left(0.00179 - \frac{1}{T_g}\right)\frac{B}{30}$$

Average stack temperature

The average stack gas temperature used in equations (7) and (8) is assumed to be the arithmetic average of the temperatures entering and leaving the stack. Gases flowing through the stack lose some heat to the outside atmosphere by heat transfer through the shell. Also, infiltration of cold air may lower stack temperatures an appreciable amount. The total loss in temperature depends upon the type of stack, stack diameter and height, and a number of variables influencing the outside atmosphere. Fig. 2 indicates an approximate stack exit temperature for a given stack relative to height, diameter and inlet gas temperature.

Stack flow loss

The net stack draft, or available induced draft at the stack entrance is the difference between the theoretical draft calculated by equations (6), (7), or (8) and the

pressure losses due to gas flow through the stack. The fluid friction pressure loss, based on Moody's friction factor, is represented by the first term of equation (9), and the pressure equivalent of the mean kinetic energy of the gases leaving the stack, by the second term.

(9)   Stack flow loss =

$$\frac{2.76}{B} f\, T_g \frac{L}{D_i{}^5}\left(\frac{W}{10^5}\right)^2 + \frac{2.76}{B}\frac{T_g}{D_i{}^4}\left(\frac{W}{10^5}\right)^2$$

$$= \frac{2.76}{B}\cdot\frac{T_g}{D_i{}^4}\left(\frac{W}{10^5}\right)^2\left(\frac{fL}{D_i}+1\right)$$

where:

stack flow loss is in in. of water
W = mass flow rate of gas, lb/hr
D_i = internal stack diameter, ft
L = stack height above gas entrance, ft
f = Moody friction factor from Fig. 3, dimensionless
T_g = average absolute gas temperature, R
B = barometric pressure, in. Hg

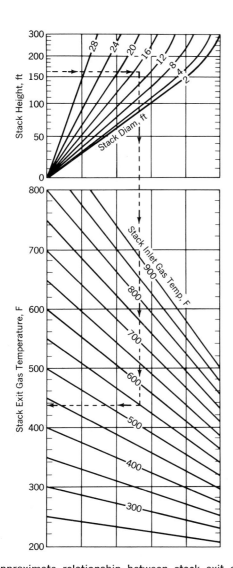

Fig. 2 Approximate relationship between stack exit gas temperature and stack dimensions.

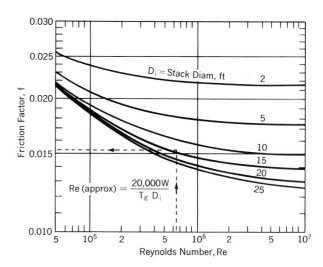

Fig. 3 Friction factor, f, as related to Reynolds number and stack diameter.

Stack flow losses for natural draft units are customarily less than 5% of the theoretical stack draft. Also, that part of the loss due to unrecoverable kinetic energy of flow (exit loss) is from 3 to 7 times greater than the friction loss, depending on stack height and diameter.

Selection of stack size

Tentative stack diameter and height for a given draft requirement may be established with the aid of Figs. 2, 4 and 5 and an assumed stack exit gas temperature. Adjustments to these values are then made as required by verification of the assumed stack exit temperature, a flow loss check and altitude correction (if necessary). The following example illustrates this sizing procedure:

Unit Specifications:

Fuel	Pulverized coal
Steam generated, lb/hr	360,000
Stack gas flow, lb/hr	450,000
Stack inlet gas temp., F	550
Required stack draft (from point of balanced draft to stack gas entrance), in. water	1.0
Plant altitude	Sea level

Initial Assumption:

Stack exit gas temperature, F	450

If the stack gas flow is not specified the following approximate ratios may be used:

Type of Firing	Approx. Gas Weight lb/lb of Steam
Oil or gas	1.15
Pulverized coal	1.25
Stoker	1.50

The stack diameter to the nearest 6-in. increment from Fig. 5 for 450,000 lb/hr stack gas flow is 14 ft 6 in. For the required stack draft of 1.0 in. (increased to 1.1 in. for safety) and an average stack gas temperature of 500F, based on the specified inlet temperature of 550F and assumed exit temperature of 450F, Fig. 4 gives an approximate height of 187 ft. A check of the assumed

stack exit temperature is obtained from Fig. 2, with the tentative height of 187 ft, diameter of 14 ft 6 in. and inlet temperature of 550F. This result is 430F, or an average stack temperature of 490F. With the revised average temperature of 490F and draft of 1.1 in. of water, Fig. 4 is again used to establish a stack height neglecting stack flow losses. This height is 190 ft.

Assuming a stack flow loss of 5%, the final required stack height is 200 ft, (190/0.95). This represents the active height to which must be added the height of any inactive section from foundation to stack entrance.

The stack flow loss may be checked by using the above values for diameter, height, average gas temperature, and gas flow in equation (9). A check of available net draft, using equation (6), indicates that the 1.0 in. draft requirement is amply covered.

If the plant is not located at sea level, the draft requirement of the unit should be increased by multiplying the draft by the altitude factor 30/B and the theoretical stack draft decreased by multiplying the theoretical draft by B/30, where B is the normal barometric pressure, inches of mercury, at the boiler site (Table 3).

External factors affecting stack height

The stack also functions to disperse combustion gases. Increasing stack height enlarges the area of dispersion. In narrow valleys or locations where there is a concentration of industry, it may be necessary to provide increased stack height in the interest of the comfort and health of the community. (*See Chapter 18.*)

Some power plants located near airports, are prohibited from using stacks high enough to provide adequate dispersion. In such cases the stack may be necked down at the top to increase the discharge velocity, simulating the effect of the higher stack. However, necking down the stack adds an appreciable amount of flow re-

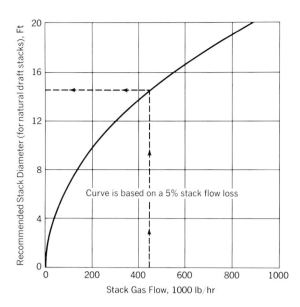

Fig. 5 Recommended stack diameter for a range of gas flows.

sistance which can only be accommodated in a mechanical-draft system.

Stack design

After the correct stack height and diameter are established, there are economic and structural factors to consider in designing the stack. For example, stack material selection is influenced by material and erection costs, stack height, means of support (i.e., whether the stack is supported from a steel structure or a foundation) and erosive and corrosive constituents in the flue gas. After selecting the material, the stack is checked for structural adequacy, making both a static and a dynamic analysis of the loads.

A static analysis is made to determine the stack dead weight load, the horizontal load due to wind and, in some cases, the effect of earthquake forces. The stack thickness, base ring design and anchor bolt requirements are determined by these loads, subject to dynamic analysis to check deflections.

It has long been recognized, especially with welded steel stacks, that some constructions will vibrate, producing large deflections normal to the wind direction at wind velocities much less than the maximum wind velocity used in the static check. This phenomenon results from the von Karman vortices that form around a stack whenever a steady wind is present. The effect of the vortex shedding is to set up periodic pressure pulsations. When the frequency of these pulsations is near the stack's natural frequency, a resonant condition exists which results in large stack deflections. For stability, the diameter required for a tall stack is so great that the large volume in its base, up to the elevation of the gas entry, has been economically used for material storage, condensate storage, air-raid shelters and control rooms.

Stack maintenance

All connections to the stack should be air tight and protected against leakage by reasonably tight dampers when not in use. Cold air leakage to the stack not only lowers the stack temperature and available draft, but also in-

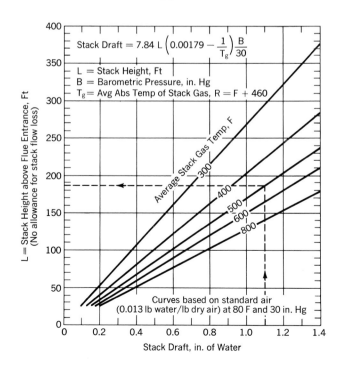

Fig. 4 Stack height required for a range of stack drafts and average stack gas temperatures.

creases the quantity of gas that the stack must handle. In some cases factory wastes are discharged through a boiler stack for dispersion high into the atmosphere. This procedure requires careful consideration from the stand-points of air pollution and possible cost increase for stack maintenance.

A stack is subject to the erosive action of ash in the flue gases, to acid corrosion by sulfur products, and to deterioration from continuous exposure to the weather.

Erosion or wastage of stack material normally occurs at the stack entrance or throats and necked-down sections, where there is a change in the direction or the velocity of the gas. These sections may require replacement after long-period operation. Reduction in stack maintenance justifies use of abrasive-resistant materials.

Low exit gas temperature from a boiler unit is desirable from an efficiency standpoint. Too low a temperature, however, may result in the condensation of sulfuric acid. This, in turn, corrodes steel or steel-lined stacks. The limit to which flue gases can be cooled without condensation depends upon the sulfur trioxide and moisture content of the flue gas.

Acid corrosion has destroyed steel stacks within a few months. Corrosion resistant metals, refractory coatings, and high temperature acid resistant paints all help to prolong life. Refractory stacks also are subject to deterioration from the chemicals and water vapor in the gases. Long exposure in wet weather (during out-of-service periods) and insufficient drying on start-up contributes to increased maintenance cost.

Fans

A fan moves a quantity of air or gas by adding sufficient energy to the stream to initiate motion and overcome all resistance to flow. The fan consists of a bladed rotor, or impeller, which does the actual work, and usually a housing to collect and direct the air or gas discharged by the impeller. The power required depends upon the volume of air or gas moved in unit time, the pressure difference across the fan and the efficiency of the fan and its drives.

Power may be expressed as shaft horsepower, input horsepower to motor terminals, if motor driven or theoretical horsepower computed by thermodynamic meth-

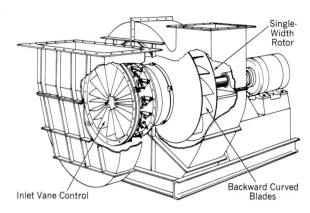

Fig. 7 Single-width single-inlet centrifugal fan with backward curved blades and inlet vane control.

ods. Each has its own significance. As far as the fan is concerned, the important factors are the power input to the shaft and the power dictated by thermodynamic calculations.

Fan performance

Stacks seldom provide sufficient natural draft to cover the requirements of modern boiler units. The 200 foot high stack of the previous example with a 490F average gas temperature will develop a theoretical natural draft of approximately 1.15 in. of water, whereas resistances to gas and air flow may be as high as 50 inches. These higher draft loss systems require the use of mechanical draft equipment and a wide variety of fan designs and types is available to meet this need, Figs. 6 and 7.

There are essentially two different kinds of fans:

1. The centrifugal fan in which gas or air accelerates radially outward in a rotor from heel to tip of blades, discharging into a surrounding scroll casing, Figs. 6 and 7.

2. The axial flow fan in which the fluid is accelerated parallel to the fan axis, Fig. 9.

Fan performance is best expressed in graphical form, such as Fig. 8. These functional relations are the fan characteristic curves. In the figure, capacity in cfm is shown horizontally as the independent variable and head (static pressure), shaft horsepower and static efficiency are dependent variables plotted vertically. Fan speed (rpm) is constant. Since fan operation for a given capacity must match single values of head and horsepower on the characteristic curves, a balance between fan static pressure and system resistance is required. If the system resistance for a given capacity is less than the head indicated on the fan characteristic curve, additional variable flow resistance, such as an inlet control vane must be added to the system.

Varying the operating speed (rpm), to yield a family of curves, as shown in Figs. 10a and b, will change the numerical performance values of the characteristics. However, the nature of the curves remains substantially unaltered. Performance at different speeds for the same efficiency can be related by the following:

1. Capacity is directly proportional to speed.
2. Head is directly proportional to speed squared.
3. Power input is directly proportional to speed cubed.

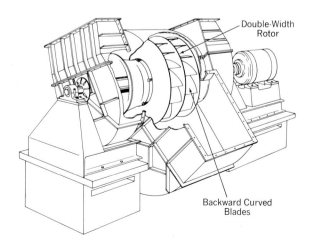

Fig. 6 Double-width double-inlet centrifugal fan with backward curved blades.

System resistance is plotted in Figs. 10a and b along with the fan characteristic of static pressures at various speeds, both as functions of volumetric flow rate. If the fan operates at constant speed, any output less than that shown at the intersection of the system resistance and specified rpm curves must be obtained by throttling the excess fan head. This represents a waste in power that can be avoided by using an inlet control vane or a variable speed drive.

Plotting characteristics on a percentage basis shows some of the many variations available in different fan designs. Fig. 11 is such a plot with 100% rated capacity selected at the point of maximum efficiency. Some fans give steep head characteristics, while others give flat head characteristics. Some horsepower characteristics are concave upward, others are concave downward. The latter have the advantage of being self-limiting, so that there is little danger of burning out the driver or little need for the alternative of overmotoring.

A steep head characteristic limits the effect of system resistance, minimizes errors in fan selection and provides better equalization of loads in parallel fan operation, but

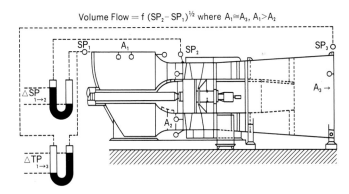

$$\text{Volume Flow} = f\,(SP_2 - SP_1)^{1/2} \text{ where } A_1 \cong A_3,\ A_1 > A_2$$

Fig. 9 Flow and head determination of axial flow fan.

requires high tip speeds for the specified head. Fans with flat head characteristics handle larger volumes for a given wheel diameter and head.

Centrifugal fans, which are heavy-duty fans, usually are equipped with wear liners and are used for induced draft when there is heavy dust loadings in the gas. This type is also used as exhausters for pulverizing mills which handle a mixture of coal and air.

Fan testing

It is difficult to obtain consistent data from field tests of fans installed in flue and duct systems because straight sections are seldom long enough to eliminate flow disturbances from such things as bends, change in section and dampers. Structural arrangements at the fan entrance and discharge also materially affect field performance results. The user should expect the supplier to meet a given performance and who but the fan supplier should be able to anticipate fan performance.

Admittedly, the consistent way to verify fan performance is on a test stand as shown in Fig. 12. TLT-Babcock's Brunswick, Ga. facility is laid out and equipped to permit full-scale testing of the manufacturer's full line of variable pitch axial flow fans, to demonstrate, as required (1) proper mechanical functioning (2) guaranteed operating-performance conditions and (3) aerodynamic (including noise) characteristics.

Control of fan output — centrifugal fan

Very few applications permit fans to operate continuously at the same pressure and volume discharge rate. Therefore, to meet requirements of the system, some convenient means of varying the fan output becomes necessary. Common methods of controlling fan output are inlet damper, inlet vane control and variable speed.

Damper control introduces sufficient variable resistance in the system to alter the fan output as required. However, damper control causes wasted power because of the excess pressure energy which must be dissipated by throttling. Advantages are:

1. Lowest first cost of all control types.
2. Ease of operation or adaptation to automatic control.
3. Least expensive type of fan drive; a constant-speed induction-type a-c motor may be used.
4. Continuous rather than a step type of control. This makes it effective throughout the entire range of fan operation.

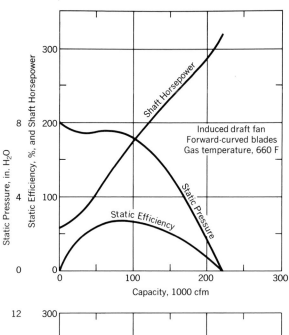

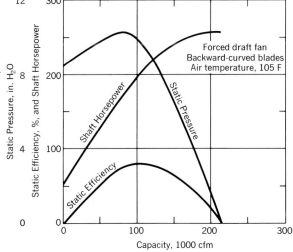

Fig. 8 Characteristic curves for two types of centrifugal fans operating at 5500-ft elevation and 965 rpm.

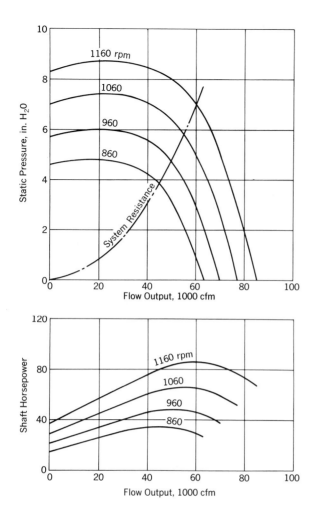

Fig. 10a Graph to show how desired output and static pressure can be obtained economically by varying fan speed to avoid large throttling losses.

The most economical control of centrifugal fans is accomplished with inlet vanes. Inlet vanes are designed for use on dirty gas as well as clean air.

Operating experience on forced draft, primary air and induced draft fans has proven that the inlet vane control is reliable and reduces operating cost. It also controls stability, controls accuracy and minimizes hysteresis.

Inlet vane control (Fig. 10b) regulates air flow entering the fan and requires less horsepower at fractional loads than outlet damper control. The inlet vane gives the air a varying degree of spin in the direction of wheel rotation enabling the fan to produce the required head at proportionately lower power. Although vane control offers considerable savings in efficiency over damper control at any reduced load, it is most effective for moderate changes close to net load operation. The initial cost is more than for damper control but less than that for variable speed control.

Speed control results in some loss in efficiency since no variable speed driver works as efficiently throughout the entire fan load range as a direct connected constant speed a-c motor. The loss in efficiency depends upon the type of speed variation.

A number of commonly used variable speed arrangements are: (a) hydraulic coupling, (b) variable speed d-c motor, and (c) variable speed steam turbine.

Fan drives

Electric motors are normally used for fan drives because they are less expensive and more efficient than any other type of drive. For fans of more than a few horsepower, squirrel-cage induction motors predominate. This type of motor is relatively inexpensive, reliable and highly efficient over a wide load range. It is frequently used in large sizes with a magnetic or hydraulic coupling for variable speed installations.

For some variable speed installations, particularly in the smaller sizes, wound-rotor (slip-ring) induction motors are used. If a d-c motor is required, the compound type is usually selected. The steam turbine drive costs more than a squirrel-cage motor, but is less expensive than any of the variable speed electric motor arrangements in sizes over 50 hp. A steam turbine may be more economical than the electric motor drive in plants where exhaust steam is needed for process, or on large utility units using the exhaust steam for feedwater heating.

Fan safety factors

To make sure that the fans will not limit a boiler's performance, margins of safety are added to the calculated or net fan requirements to arrive at a satisfactory test block specification. These margins are intended to cover conditions encountered in operation that cannot be specifically evaluated. For example, variation in fuel ash characteristics or unusual operating conditions may foul heating surfaces. The unit then requires additional draft. Stoker-fired boilers, burning improperly sized coal, may require more than normal pressure to force air through the fuel bed. A need for rapid load increase or a short emergency overload often calls for over-capacity of the fans. The customary margins to allow for such conditions are 10 to 15% increase in the net weight flow of air or gas, 20 to 32% increase in the net head, and 25F increase in the air or gas temperature at the fan inlet.

Forced draft fan

Boilers operating with both forced and induced draft use the forced draft fan to push air through the combus-

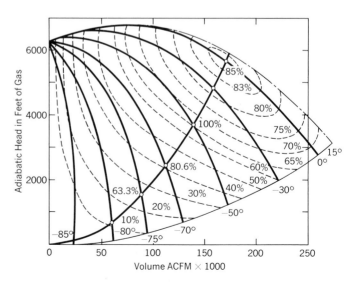

Fig. 10b Inlet vane control.

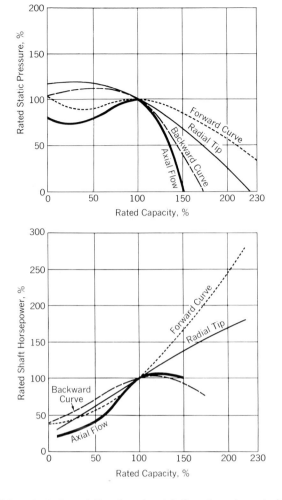

Fig. 11 Selected centrifugal and axial flow fan characteristic curves — percentage basis.

tion air supply system into the furnace. The fan must have a discharge pressure high enough to equal the total resistance of air ducts, air heater, burners or fuel bed and any other resistance between the fan discharge and the furnace. This makes the furnace the point of balanced draft or zero pressure. Volume output of the forced draft fan must equal the total quantity of air required for combustion plus air heater leakage. In many boiler installations, greater reliability is obtained by division of the total fan capacity between two fans operating in parallel. If one fan is out of service, the other usually can carry 60% or more of full boiler load, depending on how the fans are sized.

To establish the required characteristics of the forced draft fan, the system resistance from fan to furnace is calculated for the actual weight of air required for combustion plus the expected leakage from the air side of the air heater. It is usual boiler design practice to base all calculations on 80F air temperature entering the fan. The results are the net requirements which are then adjusted to test block specifications by the safety factors previously discussed.

For pressurized units without an induced draft fan, the forced draft fan is sized for the entire system.

A forced draft fan for boiler service operates under far more stringent conditions than the ordinary ventilat-

ing fan and selection should consider the following general requirements:

Reliability. Modern boilers must operate continuously for long periods (up to 18 months in some instances) without shutdown for repairs or maintenance. Thus the fan must have a rugged rotor and housing and conservatively loaded bearings. The fan must also be well balanced, and the blades so shaped that they will not collect dirt and disturb this balance.

Efficiency. High efficiency over a wide range of output is necessary because boilers operate under varying load conditions.

Stability. Fan pressure should vary uniformly with volume over the capacity range. This facilitates boiler control and assures minimum disturbance of air flow when minor adjustments to the fuel-burning equipment change the system resistance. When two or more fans operate in parallel, the pressure-output curves should have characteristics similar to the radial tip or backward-curved blade fans in order to share the load equally near the shutoff point.

Overloading. It is desirable for motor driven fans to have self-limiting horsepower characteristics, so that the driving motor cannot overload. This means that the horsepower should reach a peak and then drop off near the full-load fan output (Fig. 10a).

Induced draft fan

Units designed to operate with balanced furnace draft or without a forced draft fan require induced draft to move the gaseous products of combustion over convection heating surfaces and through the gas passages between the furnace and stack. Where it is not practical or economical to design for natural draft, induced draft fans discharging essentially at atmospheric pressure are used to provide the necessary negative static pressure.

The gas weight used to calculate net induced draft

Fig. 12 TLT-Babcock's Brunswick facility permits full scale testing of variable pitch axial flow fans.

requirements is the weight of combustion product gas at maximum boiler load plus any air leakage into the boiler setting from the surroundings and from the air side to the gas side of the air heater. Net gas temperatures are based on the calculated unit performance at maximum load. Induced draft fan test block specifications of gas weight, negative static pressure and gas temperature are obtained by adjusting from net values by margins similar to those used for forced draft fans.

An induced draft fan has the same basic requirements as a forced draft fan except that it handles higher temperature gas which may contain erosive ash. Excessive maintenance from erosion is sometimes avoided by protecting casing and blades with replaceable wear strips. (Bearings, usually water-cooled, have radiation shields on the shaft between rotor and bearings, to avoid overheating.)

Gas recirculating fan

Gas recirculating fans are used variously for controlling steam temperature, furnace heat absorption and slagging of heating surfaces, are generally located to extract gas at the economizer outlet and inject it into the furnace at locations depending on the intended function. This multiple purpose is also an important consideration in properly sizing and specifying gas recirculating fans. This selection may be dictated by the high static pressure required for tempering furnace temperatures at full load on the boiler unit, or by the high volume requirement at partial loads for steam temperature control.

Even though gas recirculating fans have the same basic requirements as induced draft fans, the designer or engineer must consider additional factors. Since the gas recirculating fan operates at higher gas temperatures, intermittent service may cause thermal shock or unbalance. When the fan is not in service, suitable protection in the form of tight shut-off dampers and sealing air must be provided to prevent the backflow of hot furnace gas and a turning gear is often used on large fans to rotate the rotor slowly to avoid distortion.

Fan selection

The method of establishing fan characteristics for a boiler unit is illustrated by the following example:

Data, assigned or from calculated performance
(boiler unit with pressure-tight setting)

Steam flow, lb/hr	325,000
Input to furnace, Btu/hr	416,000,000
Air flow through unit, lb/hr	
Theoretical air for combustion	310,340
Excess air required at burner, 5%	15,520
Infiltration, furnace and convection enclosure, 2%	6,210
Leakage, air to gas in air heater, 10%	31,030
Fuel oil consumption, lb/hr	22,500
Temperature, F	
Air entering air heater	80
Gas leaving air heater (corrected for air heater leakage)	335
Atmospheric pressure, in. of mercury	29.9
Air resistance, in. of water (includes stack effect)	
Air heater	3.3
Ducts and steam coil air heater	2.0
Burners and windbox	5.0
Total air resistance	10.3
Draft loss, in. of water (includes stack effect)	
Furnace	0.1
Boiler and superheater	1.3
Economizer	1.9
Air heater	4.4
Flues	0.9
Total draft loss	8.6

Selection of forced draft fan

(a) Weight of air to be handled by fan, lb/hr

Theoretical air for combustion	310,340
Excess air required at burner	15,520
Leakage, air to gas in air heater	31,030
Total net wt requirement	356,890
Add 10% safety margin	35,690
Test block wt requirement	392,580

(b) Static pressure at fan discharge, in. of water

Total air-resistance, fan to furnace	10.3
Add 25% safety margin	2.6
Test block pressure requirement	12.9

(c) Temperature of air to be handled by fan, F

Net temp. requirement, air to fan	80
Add 25F safety margin	25
Test block temperature requirement	105

Selection of induced draft fan

(a) Weight of gas to be handled by fan, lb/hr

Theoretical air for combustion	310,340
Excess air required at burner	15,520
Fuel burned (assume no ash)	22,500
Infiltration	6,210
Leakage, air to gas in air heater	31,030
Total net wt requirement (gas wt leaving air heater)	385,600
Add 10% safety margin	38,560
Test block wt requirement	424,160

(b) Draft to be provided by fan, in. of water

Total net draft requirement	8.6
Add 25% safety margin	2.2
Test block draft requirement	10.8

(c) Temperature of gas to be handled by fan, F

Net temp. requirement, gas leaving air heater	335
Add 25F safety margin	25
Test block temp. requirement	360

Fan maintenance

The service of fans as components of a boiler unit, like that of all running equipment, requires frequent inspection to detect and correct irregularities that might cause trouble. The period of continuous operation of fans should be long compared with that of other power plant equipment. This continuity of operation can be assured by proper lubrication and cooling of fan shafts, couplings and bearings.

Fan bearings and couplings must be carefully aligned with the driving equipment, making proper allowance for the small vertical movement of the fan rotor due to temperature rise of the bearing supports from cold to running conditions. End clearances must be provided for oil slingers at the floating bearing and at the coupling to compensate for the increased shaft length due to heat expansion. The bumping action of a poorly aligned bearing becomes progressively worse with each revolution and rapidly destroys the bearing.

A fan requires proper balance, both static and dynamic, to assure smooth and lasting service. This balance should be checked after each maintenance shutdown by running the fan at full speed, first with no air flow and second with full air flow. Special instruments may be required, especially with larger fans, to establish the amount and location of weight to be added for static balance. Fans can be thrown out of balance by the uneven shedding of deposits from the blades. This condition is usually self-correcting, but, to guard against serious mechanical damage to the equipment, any out of balance operation should be under careful observation.

Fans handling gases with entrained abrasive dust particles are subject to erosion of the blades and the housing near the discharge. Abrasive-resistant materials and liners can be used to reduce such wear. In some cases, beads of weld metal are applied to build up eroded surfaces.

Specific operation and maintenance requirements for variable pitch axial fans are covered under the axial fan heading.

Axial flow fans

A demonstrated way to reduce auxiliary power is to install variable pitch axial flow fans in fossil power generating systems.

Fig. 13 compares the power consumption of the primary air (PA), forced draft (FD) and induced draft (ID) fans for a typical 900 Mw coal-fired unit using variable pitch axial flow fans with the same unit using backward curved, inlet vane controlled centrifugal fans.

At 100% unit load the auxiliary power savings using a variable pitch axial flow fan will be 4000 kw, or about 7% of the total auxiliary power consumption. At control load, 50% of full load, the power savings will be 6000 kw or about 15% of total auxiliary power consumption. Assuming a 73% unit load factor, the annual savings will be 30,540 Mwh. Assuming a 10,800 Btu/lb coal and a unit heat rate of 9000 Btu/kwhr, the resulting annual savings will be 12,730 tons of coal.

Aerodynamic characteristics

Fig. 14 shows a fan type selection diagram used to determine the type most economical for a given set of

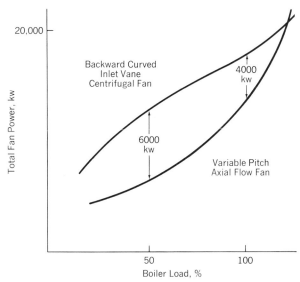

Fig. 13 Power savings.

performance conditions. The diagram is based on the calculation of fan specific speed which is:

$$n_q = n_x \cdot \frac{V^{1/2}}{H^{3/4}},$$

where the given set of performance conditions are as follows:

n_x = operating speed (rpm)
V = volume flow (m³/sec)
H = adiabatic head (m)*

The performance requirements of a two-fan arrangement (ID, FD and PA) for a 900 Mw coal-fired boiler are superimposed on the fan type selection diagram.

When specific speed increases, the diameter ratio of a centrifugal fan increases toward unity. As unity is approached the design becomes less practical. Axial flow fans are practical in the high specific speed range since their diameter ratios decrease.

The diagram shows that by increasing volume flow with a constant head and by using a reasonable operating speed, a higher specific speed results. Unit sizes are steadily increasing, however, air- and gas-side resistance (head) has remained relatively constant. These are the two fundamental reasons why four centrifugal fans are required for the same conditions that can be satisfied by two axial fans.

Performance and control characteristics

Fig. 15 shows the characteristic performance field of a variable pitch axial flow fan. Two of the major benefits are:

1. The areas (eggs) of constant efficiency run parallel to the boiler resistance line. High efficiency is maintained over a wide boiler range.

   There is a large control range above, as well as below, the area of maximum efficiency. This permits

---

*For precise calculations, adiabatic head, H, must be used to account for variations in density due to temperature, altitude, and compressibility factor (Kp).

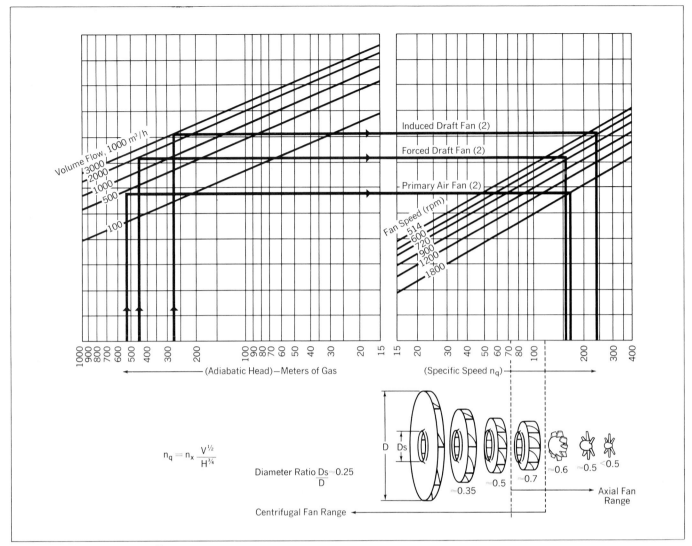

Fig. 14 Fan type selection diagram.

the fan to be designed for net boiler conditions, while the test block point remains within the control range.

2. The lines of constant blade angle are actually individual fan curves for a given blade setting. Because the curves are very steep, a change in resistance produces very little volume change.

As the blade angle is adjusted from minimum to maximum position the flow change is nearly linear, as shown in Fig. 16.

These two characteristics provide stable fan and boiler control.

Parallel operation

Variable pitch axial flow fans can be operated in parallel, provided that care is taken to avoid operating either fan in the stall area which will be discussed later in this section. With two fans in operation, the resistance line for one fan is influenced by the other fan, as well as by the boiler conditions. Two fans together will develop the pressure required to overcome the boiler resistance, but their individual volume flows need not be equal.

Fig. 17 shows a typical performance field for two variable pitch axial flow fans. In this curve Point 1 shows the total volume flow required by the boiler at net con-

ditions. Point 2 shows the individual fan operating point with proper parallel operation. At net boiler conditions the two fans may operate individually anywhere on the line from Points 1 to 3 provided they do not operate in the range above the stall line ("X-Y"), and the total volume flow produced is equivalent to Point 1. To obtain the most efficient fan operation and to avoid operation in a range close to the stall line, it is best to keep both fans operating at Point 2.

If the fans and motors are sized so that it is possible to operate one fan at Point 1, then it will be necessary to reduce load slightly to put the second fan into operation. The load reduction is to lower the boiler resistance. If the resistance is not lowered, the second fan must start up at Point 3 and then move horizontally to Point 2. When the second fan reaches "X," it will stall.

Axial fans are connected to the boiler control system with an 180 degree stroke, 25 ft-lb positioner. The positioner moves a pilot valve in the hydraulic blade adjustment system which positions the blades with minimum hysteresis. This system is explained under the caption *Maintenance and Reliability*.

The suggested control logic for starting, stopping, and supervising the operation of variable pitch axial flow FD

and ID fans is very similar to that of the centrifugal fan.

An additional requirement of the logic is to prevent damage to the fan while always maintaining an open flow path through the boiler to prevent furnace pressure excursions.

Stall characteristics

Axial flow fans have a unique characteristic called stall. Stall is the aerodynamic phenomenon which occurs when a fan is asked to operate beyond its performance limits. When the fan blades are required to provide more lift than they are designed to produce, flow separation occurs around the blade. If this happens the fan becomes unstable and no longer operates on its normal performance curve. This characteristic must be understood and considered in boiler operation as it can have an important effect on boiler design.

The curves in Fig. 18, marked "A," are the normal fan performance curves for a constant blade angle.

Each blade angle curve has its individual stall point, identified as "I" on the diagram. The curve "C" connects all the stall points "I" and is generally referred to as the "stall line."

The dotted curves, "B," are the characteristic stall curves for three different blade angles. The curves show the path that the fan will follow when operating in a stalled condition.

Fig. 19 explains the stall phenomenon in relation to the fan and boiler system.

If the normal boiler system resistance (Curve "B") increases for any reason (for instance, a furnace pressure excursion caused by a main fuel trip) the normal operating point "X" will change to meet a new higher system resistance (Curve "B₁") by traveling along the fan performance Curve "A." If the operating point arrives at point "I," the fan will stall. Because of the relationship between the fan performance Curve "D" in the stall area and the upset system resistance (Curve "B₁"), a new operating point "X₁" will be found where the system resistance (Curve "B₁") and the stall Curve "D" intersect.

If the system resistance remains high (Curve "B₁"), the fan will continue to operate at point "X₁" in an unstable stall condition.

When the system resistance comes down, the fan will recover from the stall condition and return to its normal performance Curve "A."

In the case of an upset as described above, the blade angle can be reduced until the fan regains stability. The fan will be stable when the new performance Curve "A₁" provides a stall point "I," which is higher than the upset system resistance (Curve "B₁").

If stabilization cannot be attained by blade adjustment, the fan must be shut down. When operating in stall condition flow vibrations occur which are unpredictable in energy and frequency and can cause damage to the rotating blades.

The maximum stable negative furnace pressure generated by an ID fan (pressure differential between the fan stall line and the boiler resistance line) occurs at the condition of zero flow. For variable pitch axial flow fan, the maximum zero flow static pressure usually approxi-

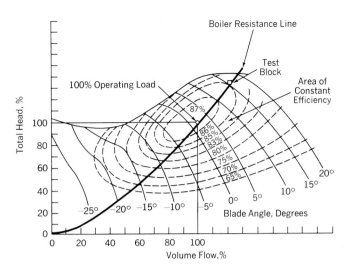

Fig. 15 Performance field for variable pitch axial flow fan.

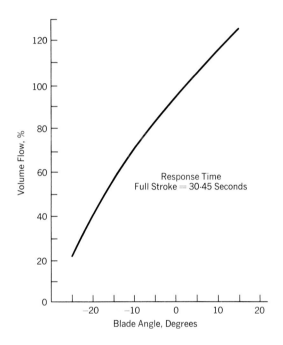

Fig. 16 Variable pitch blade control characteristics.

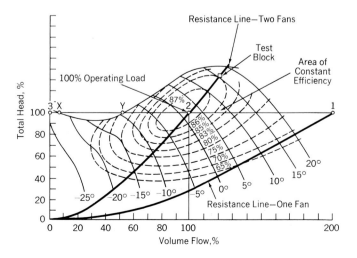

Fig. 17 Performance field for parallel operation.

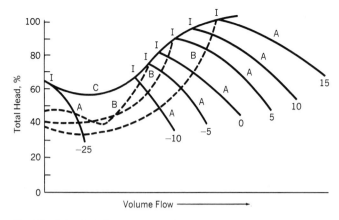

Fig. 18 Actual stall curves.

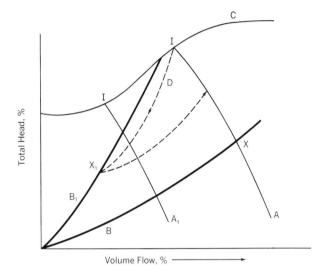

Fig. 19 Stall as related to the boiler.

mates the net boiler resistance. This inherent characteristic of the variable pitch axial flow fan allows the structural designer to use lower design pressures for the furnace, flues, ducts and precipitator.

Stall prevention

When axial fans are sized properly and the system resistance line is parabolic in shape the probability of experiencing stall is low.

The possibility of experiencing a stall increases if a fan is oversized (Fig. 20), if the system resistance increases significantly, or if the fans are operated improperly.

The degree of stall protection desired in the control system depends on individual utility philosophy. A visual indication of head and volume (or blade angle) in the control room is a minimum requirement for satisfactory operation.

To prevent the occurrence of stall, either the operator or the control system must know where the fan is operating with respect to its stall curve. This can be accomplished in several ways, depending on the degree of protection desired.

1. By monitoring blade angle and head (ΔP compensated for temperature), the operator will be visually

aware of his operating point. Actual blade position can be transmitted electrically to the control room. Pressure increase across the fan is measured and also transmitted to the control room.

These two inputs when compared to the fan's predetermined (by actual job site testing) performance field will enable the operator to judge his operating point relative to the stall line.

2. The next step is to monitor and transmit a flow signal to the control room, along with the pressure increase. This flow signal is readily available because the inlet nozzle of the fan is a calibrated venturi (Fig. 9). These two signals can be manually compared to the performance field by the operator.

3. By putting the head and flow signals into an "X-Y" plotter with the fan performance field already engraved on the plotter (Fig. 21), the operator can scan his operating point with respect to the stall line.

4. A further refinement of Step 3 is to place an alarm mechanism on the "X-Y" plotter.

5. The final step is to utilize a function generator to place the stall curve into the control system. The generated curve is compared to the head and volume inputs. When the operating point approaches the stall line an alarm is sounded. If travel toward stall continues, the controls will automatically reduce the blade angle on both fans.

It is necessary to close the blades of both fans to prevent fan "B" (Fig. 22) from maintaining the system flow while fan "A" is being run back.

If fan "B" is permitted to maintain system flow, system resistance will be maintained and fan "A" under run-back control will be forced to the left and into the stall line.

Fan arrangement

Axial flow fans designed for today's large fossil fueled steam generating systems are compact and relatively light. By concentrating the load carrying parts of the rotor on a small radius, a low Wk^2 is obtained. The low weight, unbalanced forces, and inertia of the axial flow fan permits either horizontal or vertical arrangement on steel construction. This provides greater arrangement flexibility. The normal grade installation can be accomplished with reduced concrete requirements.

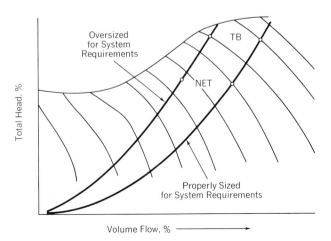

Fig. 20 Proper fan selection.

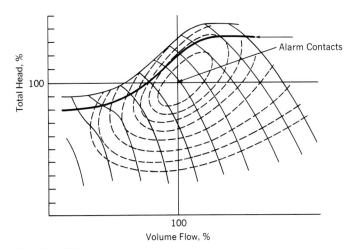

Fig. 21 X-Y plotter.

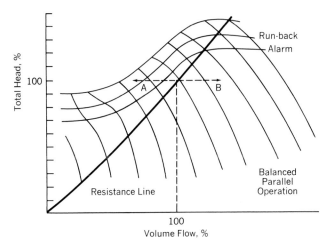

Fig. 22 Run-back control.

A horizontal fan arrangement is generally the economic preference for forced draft and primary air fans. Induced draft fans can be arranged horizontally, or vertically inside the *stack*. Vertical arrangements offer additional benefits:

Simplifying the flues (straight horizontal connection between precipitator outlet and fan inlet box is possible).

Reducing draft losses in turning bends.

Eliminating the need for sound enclosure (fan, drive, and auxiliary equipment).

Eliminating the need for additional fan space by utilizing existing unused space.

Acoustics

Fans produce two distinct types of noise:

1. Single tone noise is generated when the concentrated fluid flow channels leaving the rotating blades pass a stationary object (straightener vanes or nose). The distance from the rotating blades to the stationary objects affect the sound intensity, with the blade passing frequency and its first harmonic being most predominant. Economic and aerodynamic considerations usually override achieving the optimum acoustic design.

2. Broad band noise is produced by high velocity fluid "rushing" through the fan housing, and as the name implies, covers a wide frequency range.

From the outside, the apparent source of both types of fan noise is the fan housing. The sound travels out of the inlet box opening through the discharge duct work, and through the casing of the fan. All three "leaks" must be acoustically analyzed and treated individually to achieve an acceptable installation.

Inlet noise

FD and PA fans normally have inlets open to either a boiler room or to the plant exterior. The noise emitted to these areas is almost always above desired values.

Installation of an absorption type silencer is the most common way to lower inlet sound pressure level to desired values. This type of silencer is a large box filled with aerodynamically shaped panels (named coulissen) made with perforated plate skin and filled with absorptive mineral wool. The acoustic effectiveness of this type of silencer increases with higher frequency noise up to about 2000 Hz (Fig. 23).

The single tone base and first harmonic frequencies of the axial fan are usually twice the frequencies of an equivalent centrifugal fan. The silenced sound pressure level of an axial fan with a given length silencer will usually be comparable to the silenced sound pressure level of an equivalent centrifugal fan using the same silencer.

Noise through the fan casing

Application of absorptive mineral wool insulation and acoustic lagging on axial fan casing is effective in re-

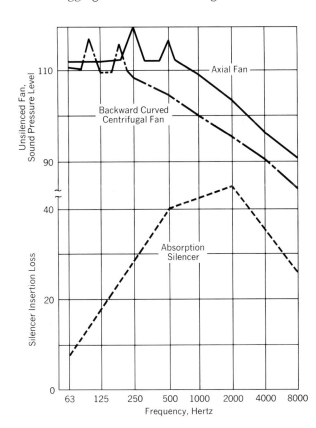

Fig. 23 Acoustic performance.

ducing the sound to acceptable levels. This method avoids the use of expensive sound rooms often used to suppress the lower frequency noise of centrifugal fans. It also permits access to the fan and its auxiliary equipment without exposure to damaging noise.

Discharge noise

The determination of the best method to quiet fan discharge noise requires an evaluation of the duct arrangement, fan application, auxiliary power costs, and fan unsilenced sound pressure level.

The most common method of attenuating FD fan discharge noise is to apply acoustic insulation and lagging to the discharge duct from the fan outlet to the air heater inlet. Where a long run of duct work is used, i.e., the tempering air duct in a cold PA system, a discharge silencer may be more economical.

For an axial flow ID fan the thermal insulation and lagging applied to the flues before and after the fan are usually adequate to control both inlet and discharge noise. On ID fans in residential areas it may be necessary to reduce the stack discharge noise level by using an ID fan discharge silencer. In these cases the objectional noise is the single tone sound at base frequency and first harmonic. A resonant type silencer is effective for silencing single tone noise. Its performance does not deteriorate with service, absorptive type silencers tend to plug with fly ash and become less effective.

Maintenance and reliability

Maintenance and reliability are discussed together because they are closely related. Axial fan reliability has been demonstrated in Europe where this type fan has been used successfully in power plant applications for

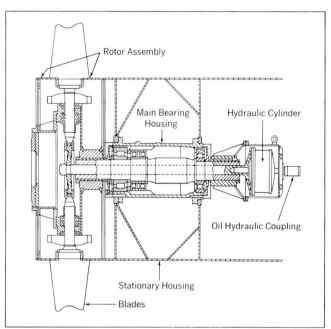

Fig. 24 Rotor assembly.

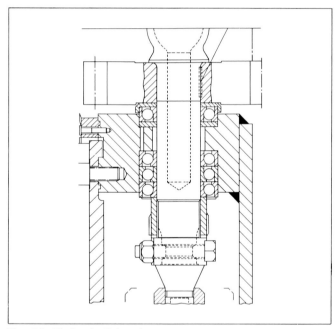

Fig. 26 Blade shaft bearings.

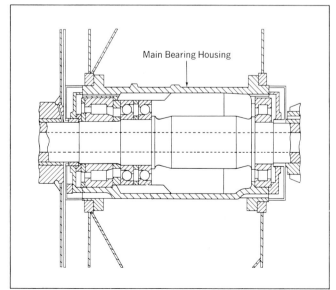

Fig. 25 Main bearings.

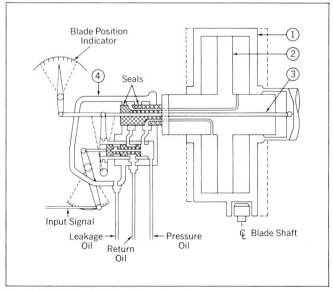

Fig. 27 Blade adjustment mechanism.

over 20 years. Design improvements have been made to the fan during this time period. This result is a mature design which is compatible with the utility industry's need for high reliability.

With a proper preventative maintenance program the variable pitch axial flow fan will provide continued reliable service. The items requiring preventative maintenance are as follows:

Main bearings. The bearings are designed for the radial and thrust loadings of the fan at its test block rating. Because the rotors are mounted close to the bearings (Fig. 24), and the rotating weight is low, conservative catalog anti-friction bearings can be and are selected (Fig. 25).

Sleeve bearings, commonly used in centrifugal fans, can be used in axial flow fans but are uneconomical because the axial thrust loading requires the use of a Kingsbury type thrust bearing.

Lubrication of the main bearings is achieved with an oil splash bath. The bath is continuously circulated through an oil cooling and filtering lube set. In addition, cooling air is circulated across the main bearing housing by utilizing the pressure differential available between the inlet nozzle and atmosphere (FD and PA fans), or by an auxiliary cooling air fan. Forced outages resulting from a failure of the oil circulating system are minimized since the oil reservoir in the bearing housing is capable of maintaining lubrication for extended periods with the system out of service.

The fan main bearings are designed to have a minimum "B-10" life of 40,000 hours at the test block condition. Depending upon actual operation (power input and temperature) the bearings should be changed on a three to five year cycle to prevent a "B-10" type failure.

One main bearing and shaft assembly is relatively inexpensive and should be stocked with each fan type to facilitate maintenance. With this assembly, a main bearing can be changed in two shifts with a two-man crew.

Blade shaft bearings. Blade shaft bearings are used to minimize the friction in the blade adjustment system. They transfer the centrifugal force due to the blade weight to the fan hub. These bearings are designed for static thrust loading because they operate only through the blade adjustment range, an arc of about 50 degrees.

Stacked angular contact ball thrust bearings (Fig. 26) are used for this application because the load is shared equally by each bearing. The required number of bearings is a function of the bearing static load coefficient and the thrust. The thrust is a function of angular speed, blade material and blade size.

Prolonged operation with relatively little blade adjustment can cause fretting of the bearing race. Therefore, inspection is recommended after two years. Some owners replace the bearings at this time. Depending on the specific design and operating conditions, the bearings may last considerably longer than two years.

The bearings are *not* an item which fails suddenly

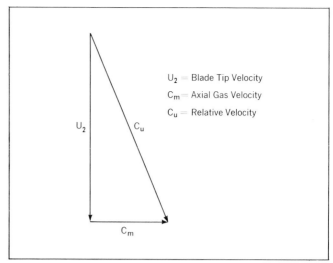

U_2 = Blade Tip Velocity
C_m = Axial Gas Velocity
C_u = Relative Velocity

Fig. 28 Relative velocity diagram.

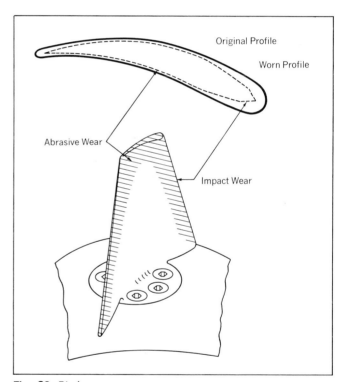

Original Profile
Worn Profile
Abrasive Wear
Impact Wear

Fig. 29 Blade wear.

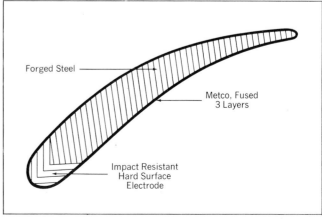

Forged Steel
Metco, Fused 3 Layers
Impact Resistant Hard Surface Electrode

Fig. 30 Induced draft fan blade hard surfacing.

and an indication of their condition can be monitored by recording the hydraulic pressure required to move the blades. If fretting occurs, the force required to move the blade increases. When this force is plotted in terms of hydraulic pressure versus time, a fan outage for blade shaft bearing maintenance can be scheduled to coincide with the next unit outage.

The replacement time is approximately five shifts with two men.

Hydraulic adjustment device

The hydraulic blade adjustment system (Fig. 27) consists of the following main elements:

1. An adjusting cylinder which moves axially along the fan's centerline and rotates with the fan rotor. This cylinder moves the individual blade adjustment levers.
2. A piston inside the cylinder which is also rotating, but fixed axially.
3. A positive feedback position rod which mechanically measures the cylinder position.
4. A stationary hydraulic servo-mechanism is mounted to the rotating piston rod. Alignment is maintained with anti-friction bearings.

This unit serves the following three functions:

a) It serves as the transition piece between the stationary control system and rotating fan system. This transition is accomplished at the smallest possible diameter to reduce relative speed and seal wear.
b) The pilot valve in the unit translates the mechanical input signal from the fan control positioner to a hydraulic signal which drives the adjusting cylinder.
c) The unit mechanically reads the feedback position and readjusts the hydraulic signal to the cylinder. It also transmits an indication of actual blade position to the exterior of the fan.

Should the hydraulic pressure be lost because of electrical or mechanical failure, the blades are counterweighted to open gradually to their maximum position increasing air flow to its maximum value. The flow through the parallel fan can be adjusted within its performance field so that the unit load is controlled until an outage is scheduled.

Induced draft fan blade wear

Fan blade wear is a function of:

1. Dust loading.
2. Particle size distribution.
3. Particle hardness.
4. Particle concentration.
5. The relative velocity at which the particles pass the blade.
6. The blade material.
7. Angle of attack.

The fan designer has no control over the first three parameters. He can only influence the blade life by varying the other parameters.

The blades of a variable pitch axial flow fan are subjected to a relatively uniform velocity across the entire blade surface.

The wear is evenly distributed over the blade of a variable pitch axial fan, since there are no inlet vanes utilized or 90 degree direction changes which concentrate dust particles.

Fig. 28 indicates that relative velocity is a function of blade tip speed and axial gas velocity. By selecting a two-stage fan the blade tip velocity is reduced by a factor of 1.4, and the axial velocity is reduced by a similar factor. Wear is a function of relative velocity to the 2.5 to 3.5 power.

Angle of attack influences the type of wear experienced (Fig. 29). Material is removed in the following two ways:

1. Impact wear (high angle of attack).
2. Sliding abrasion (low angle of attack).

To resist sliding abrasion, Metco 32C is fused to the blade prior to final machining.

Even with the above protection and conservative design, wear can occur due to precipitator malperformance. Should blade wear be experienced, the blade set can be unbolted (Fig. 29) and a new set installed in one and a half shifts. Worn blades can be taken to the shop and repaired by rewelding the nose and recoating with Metco.

To prevent impact wear an impact resistance wear metal is deposited by stick electrode to the leading edge of the steel blade (Fig. 30).

Chapter 18

Combustion by-products

The by-products of combustion are stack gases, which are present with all fossil fuels, and ash, which is present in substantial quantity with coal and in lesser quantity with oil.

Much of the ash, and in some cases most of it, is removed via the ash pit or slag-tap for disposal. On the other hand, in the case of pulverized-coal firing with dry-ash furnaces, about 80 to 90% of the ash remains as fly ash in the combustion gases.

Thus stack gases contain particulate matter as well as certain gaseous products of combustion which produce air pollution if discharged in sufficient quantity. Stack gases may contain carbon monoxide and carbon particles but, with proper operation, these can be, and normally are, largely eliminated in boilers for electric power generation and industrial application. The problems with stack gases arise principally from fly ash and oxides of sulfur and nitrogen.

Air pollution control

The control of atmospheric pollution is one part of a prime present-day problem—environmental control. The by-products from boiler furnaces are by no means the major factor in producing air pollution. In the larger cities, other factors, particularly the automobile and industrial or manufacturing processes, produce the larger share of air pollution. Generally power plant stacks contribute only about 15% of the total weight of atmospheric contaminants emitted from all sources.

While air pollution has been increasingly present since the beginning of the industrial revolution, it is particularly in the last 25 years that the total release of pollutants from all sources has signaled a national air pollution problem of increasing proportions, indicating the necessity for remedial measures. Even though the combustion products from boiler furnaces constitute a small part of total air pollutants, the growth of industry indicates an increasing need for remedial measures. Some of these measures are currently available and in general use. Others are in the development stage. These developments are being spurred by an aroused public interest and an increasing amount of legislation.

It is important to note that there are substantial costs associated with equipment to remove particulates and gaseous pollutants from stack gases, and these costs must ultimately be borne by the consumer. In the case of the electric power industry, the costs of equipment to reduce air pollution necessarily increase power generation costs, and hence the kilowatt-hour cost to the consumer. The costs of this equipment can vary from $80 to $120 per kw of installed capacity, depending on the type and scope of equipment, and must be recognized as part of the price for maintaining a good atmospheric environment.

Use of stacks

Stacks are used successfully for dispersing gases and suspended particulate matter over a large area. Their heights have increased as unit sizes have increased. Stacks as high as 1200 ft are used, particularly in narrow valleys where it is desired to disperse gases beyond surrounding hills.

While stacks are effective in dispersing gases, in locations where there is a concentration of industry the atmosphere can become overloaded with the discharge from many stacks during periods of air stagnation. The effect is particularly objectionable on damp, foggy days when smog—a combination of smoke and fog—blankets the area. Thus, when the total discharge of pollutants reaches a certain amount, the stack alone may not constitute an adequate provision for the health and comfort of the community.

Ash removal and disposal

The problems of ash removal and disposal are significant principally in the case of solid fuels. The amount of ash in fuel oil is small and usually is a problem primarily inside the furnace and boiler setting (Chapter 15). Electrostatic precipitators have occasionally been used to

improve stack plume appearance.

With the early methods of burning coal on grates using natural draft, most of the coal ash remained on the grate and was ultimately discharged into a hopper for disposal. With more modern stokers, such as the spreader stoker (Chapter 11), part of the burning is accomplished in suspension and this results in a greater carry-over of particulate matter in the flue gas.

With pulverized-coal firing, all the burning is accomplished in suspension with the result that about 80 to 90% of the ash remains in the flue gases in the case of a dry-ash pulverized-coal-fired unit. This may be reduced to about 50% with a slag-tap unit with pulverized-coal firing.

With Cyclone-Furnace firing, the fly-ash loading in the flue gases is reduced to 20 to 30% of the ash in the coal. The problem of particulate carry-over in the flue gases is thus reduced by a factor of 3 or 4 for Cyclone-Furnace firing as compared with a dry-ash pulverized-coal-fired unit. This is important from the standpoint of the cost of equipment required to achieve a given par-

ticulate content in the stack gases (*see Ash Recovery and Dust Collectors, Chapter 10*).

Pending development of possible changes in cyclone firing or an economical or reliable flue gas clean-up system, Cyclone Furnaces are applied only to carefully selected applications. The high degree of turbulence and high combustion rates resulting in highly stable operation also results in flue gas whose makeup does not meet present U.S.A. environmental requirements.

Ash removal from the furnace

The nature of coal ash and the problems involved in handling it are discussed in detail in Chapter 15. Additional information is given in Chapters 9, 10 and 11.

Stoker-fired units and dry-ash pulverized-coal-fired units are designed so that the ash settles in hoppers from which it is removed for disposal. The slag-tap method for disposal of coal ash is discussed in Chapter 15 (*Design and Operation of Slag-Tap Units*). Some possible uses for this slag are as land fill, road-base material, granular material for roofing, aggregate for use in con-

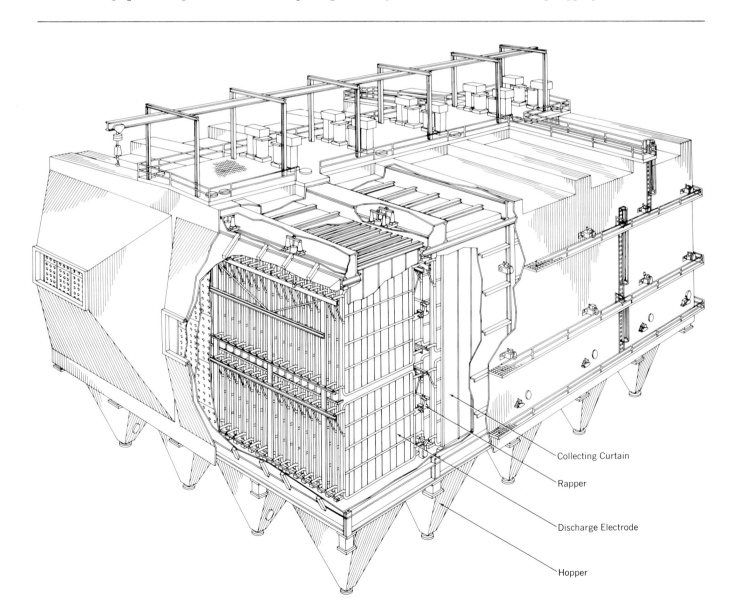

Collecting Curtain

Rapper

Discharge Electrode

Hopper

Fig. 1 Electrostatic precipitator — parallel plate type (B&W/Rothemuhle).

crete blocks and preformed concrete, asphalt mix material, cinders for icy roads, insulation, and grit for sandblasting. Most of these uses apply also to ash removed in dry form from stoker- and pulverized-coal-fired furnaces.

Particulate removal

To meet the objective of a clear stack, some form of particulate-removal equipment is now generally required to remove the fly ash from flue gases from units where fuels are burned in suspension. Several types of particulate-removal equipment are available. These may be classified as electrostatic precipitators, mechanical dust collectors, fabric filters and wet scrubbers. Fly ash removed by equipment of these types may be used for most of the applications listed for ash removed as slag.

Electrostatic precipitators. Electrostatic precipitators (Fig. 1) produce an electric charge on the particles to be collected and then propel the charged particles by electrostatic forces to the collecting curtains. The precipitator operation involves four basic steps:

1. An intense, high voltage electrical field is maintained between the discharge electrode and the collecting curtains.

2. The carrier gases are ionized by the intense, electrical field. These gas ions, in turn, charge the entrained particles.

3. The negatively charged particles, still in the presence of an electrostatic field, are attracted to the positively (grounded) charged collecting curtains.

4. The collected dust is discharged by rapping into storage hoppers.

The collection efficiency of the electrostatic precipitator is related to the time of particle exposure to the electrostatic field, the strength of the field, and the resistivity of the dust particle. An efficiency of 99% plus is obtained at a cost generally favorable in comparison with other types of equipment. Hence, as of 1970, a very high percentage of particulate-removal units installed in commercial boiler plants are electrostatic precipitators.

Mechanical collectors. The operation of mechanical collectors depends on exerting centrifugal force on the particles to be collected by introducing the dust-laden gas stream tangentially into the body of the collector. The particulate matter is thrown to the outside wall of the collector where it is removed. Mechanical collectors operate most effectively in the particle-size range above about 10 microns. Below 10 microns, the collection efficiency drops considerably below 90%. As efficiency requirements continue to increase, the use of mechanical collectors has declined.

Fabric filters. Fabric filters operate by trapping dust by impingement on the fine filters comprising the fabric. As the collection of dust continues, an accumulation of dust particles adheres to the fabric surface. The fabric filter obtains its maximum efficiency during this period of dust buildup. After a fixed operating period, the bags must be cleaned. Immediately after cleaning, the filtering efficiency is reduced until the buildup of collected dust takes place.

The fabric filter can be applied in any process area where dry collection is desired and where the temperature and humidity of the gases to be handled do not impose limitations. At efficiencies of 99% and less, the fabric filter is generally not competitive with the electrostatic precipitator for boiler application. However, for particulate matter, efficiencies above 99% can be achieved with fabric filters, and applications in congested areas may increase.

Wet scrubbers. Wet scrubbers remove dust from a gas stream by collecting it with a suitable liquid (*see Fig. 2*). A good wet scrubber is one that can effect the most intimate contact between the gas stream and liquid for the purpose of transferring the suspended particulate matter from the gas to the liquid. Collection efficiency, dust-particle size, and pressure drop are closely related in the operation of a wet scrubber. The required operating pressure drop varies inversely as the dust-particle size for a given collection efficiency; or, for a given dust-particle size, collection efficiency increases as operating pressure drop increases.

Unlike other particulate collection equipment, the wet scrubber employs a liquid stream to collect particulate matter. For this reason, it can usually perform additional process functions besides dust collection. Gas absorption, chemical reaction, and heat transfer are some of these. Simultaneous removal of dust and gaseous pollutants by use of a suitable scrubbing liquid can be accomplished with a wet scrubber (*see Sulfur Oxides*).

Control of pollutant gases

Even though all forms of gaseous pollutants have not been identified, oxides of sulfur and nitrogen have been recognized as being harmful.

Sulfur oxides

Sulfur oxides are produced in significant quantity by the combustion of most coals and fuel oils. The amount of sulfur oxides produced in gas-fired units is insignificant.

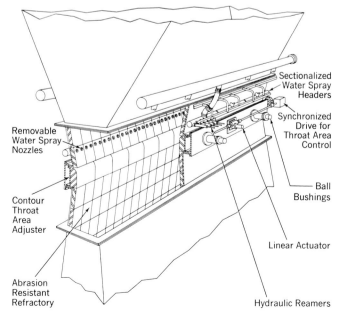

Fig. 2 Venturi-type wet scrubber.

However, the demand for natural gas for domestic fuel and as a feed stock for chemical manufacture makes it less available for steam generation.

Sulfur oxides can be controlled by removing sulfur from the fuel prior to its use, or by removing sulfur oxides from the combustion gases before they are released to the stack. Numerous regulations have been promulgated by federal, state, and local governmental agencies limiting emissions of sulfur oxides or fuel sulfur content. These regulations have required many plants to switch fuel supplies to an acceptably low sulfur content or provide flue gas desulfurization (FGD) equipment.

In the case of units designed to burn fuel oil, the reduction in fuel sulfur content has generally been obtained by purchasing low sulfur oil in lieu of installing FGD equipment. Some regulations have required fuel oils with a sulfur content of less than 0.3%.

In the case of coal, many plants have met environmental regulations by utilizing natural occurring low sulfur western source fuels mined in Wyoming, Montana and Utah. Others have achieved required emission levels by installing flue gas desulfurization systems. Some western states by imposing regulations that are more stringent than federal standards, have required installation of FGD systems at sites utilizing local natural occurring low sulfur coal.

For the past ten years a high level of research and development activity has gone into development of FGD processes. Generally, these processes are usually categorized as nonregenerable or regenerable process. The nonregenerable process produces a waste product that requires ponding or treatment to permit disposal in a land fill. Nonregenerable FGD processes are the best developed and most widely applied.

Most of these processes involve wet scrubbing of the combustion flue gas in a gas-liquid contactor using lime, limestone, alkaline fly ash with supplemental lime or limestone, sodium carbonate and dilute sulfuric acid as the scrubbing media. Performance for these systems can be as high as 90 to 95% SO_2 removal efficiency with combustion gases containing up to 5,000 ppm SO_2. These processes account for about 95% of FGD systems applied to utility and industrial application because of lower capital and operating costs as compared to the regenerable processes. A typical limestone system is shown in Fig. 3.

Regenerable processes. Regenerable FGD processes recover SO_2 from the combustion gases and convert it into marketable by-products such as sulfur, sulfuric acid and liquid SO_2 (Fig. 4). These systems generally have a higher initial cost and operating expense than the nonregenerable processes, and depend on credits from selling the by-product to partially offset the higher cost.

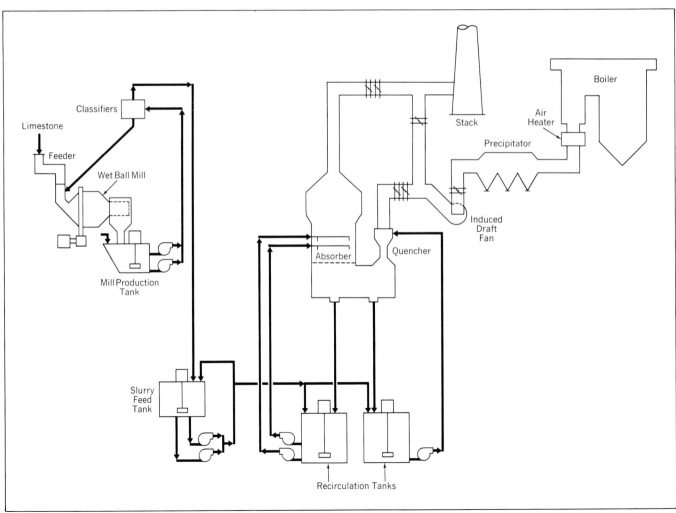

Fig. 3 Limestone wet-scrubbing system for flue gas desulfurization.

Some of these processes have been demonstrated in systems of over 100 Mw capacity. They include wet scrubbing systems such as the magnesium oxide, Wellman-Lord, and citric acid processes. A number of regenerable processes are of the dry sorbent type and do not require water quenching of the combustion gases. These processes utilize sorbent materials such as activated carbon, alumina impregnated with copper, and sodium carbonate. SO_2 removal efficiencies in excess of 90% are achievable with those systems.

Oxides of nitrogen

Oxides of nitrogen also contribute to air pollution and are a product of fossil fuel combustion. Unlike sulfur oxides, which are formed only from sulfur in the fuel, nitrogen oxides (NO_x) are formed from both fuel-bound nitrogen and nitrogen contained in the combustion air introduced into the furnace.

Conversion of fuel-bound nitrogen to NO_x applies mainly to coal and fuel oil since natural gas contains no nitrogen compounds. The emissions due to this mechanism are dependent on percent of nitrogen in the fuel, oxygen availability in the combustion zone, and the reactivity of the various nitrogen compounds contained in the fuel. The conversion of the nitrogen contained in the combustion air is highly temperature dependent. The formation of NO_x through this mechanism proceeds rapidly at combustion zone temperatures in excess of 3000F. Therefore, by maintaining combustion temperatures below 3000F, the NO_x emissions can be reduced by limiting the conversion of nitrogen in the combustion air to NO_x (thermal fixation).

Several methods are available for reducing nitric oxide emissions. The most effective of these is two stage (off-stoichiometric) combustion. With this method, initial combustion takes place in a fuel rich environment. The remaining air and any excess air are introduced in an area away from the initial combustion zone to complete combustion. This method reduces NO_x formation from both mechanisms described above. By reducing the oxygen availability in the combustion zone, the fuel-bound nitrogen will less likely be converted to NO_x. Rather, it will convert to N_2 and other stable nitrogen based compounds. Also, utilizing two staging prolongs combustion thus reducing the flame temperature. As stated above, the temperature dependent conversion of

atmospheric nitrogen will be lowered due to the reduced temperatures.

Another tool for NO_x reduction is low excess air operation. By firing with as low an excess air as possible to maintain unit performance and hold carbon losses to a minimum, the O_2 availability is decreased. Therefore, the amount of fuel bound nitrogen converted to NO_x will be reduced. Also, the amount of thermal NO_x formed due to nitrogen in the air is reduced due to lowered O_2 availability and reduced quantities of atmospheric nitrogen entering the combustion zone.

Finally, with oil and gas fired units, gas recirculation to the combustion zone is effective in reducing NO_x emissions. The introduction of gas recirculation into the combustion zone provides dilution of the combustion air thus prolonging combustion and reducing the flame temperature. As stated above, by reducing the flame temperature, the conversion of nitrogen contained in the combustion air is reduced. Since all NO_x from gas firing and about 50% of the NO_x from oil firing are attributed to thermally converted nitrogen, gas recirculation to the burners appears to be effective on overall NO_x reduction. With coal firing, however, the effect of gas recirculation on overall NO_x reduction is minimal.

The above methods provide the tools to meet current NO_x limits for fossil fired units. However, as the laws become more stringent, the use of other techniques such as removal of fuel nitrogen or removal of NO_x from flue gas may be required in conjunction with techniques described above.

The dual register burner. To meet current EPA NO_x limits, Babcock & Wilcox developed a burner designed to limit NO_x formation by limiting the combustion temperature through delayed air and fuel mixing. The dual register burner, as described in Chapter 9, limits the peak flame temperature by reducing the turbulence at the burner. This reduced turbulence provides for lower NO_x due to delayed mixing of fuel and air causing a much slower burning flame in the combustion zone. While maintaining stable, efficient operation, the burner has demonstrated NO_x reductions of up to 50% over previous high turbulence burner designs. Utilization of this burner in conjunction with low excess air operation (facilitated through use of a compartmented windbox system) and a more conservative design including lower input per burner and lower total furnace heat release rates provides the operational flexibility to meet or in some cases better the current EPA NO_x limits.

Air pollution legislation

In response to public demands for more stringent air pollution control, regulations are increasing, and pressures for cleaner air are being exerted at local, state and federal levels. The Clean Air Act of 1963 was the first major step toward more federal control. The purpose of this act was to improve, strengthen and accelerate programs for the prevention of air pollution. The Air Quality Act of 1967 provided greatly increased federal control. This act empowered the Secretary of Health, Education, and Welfare to impose federal regulations where states did not have adequate regulations, and to

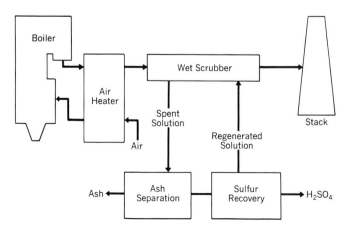

Fig. 4 Wet-scrubbing system with sulfur recovery.

seek immediate court injunctions where public health was in jeopardy. This act also provided for the:

1. Expansion and improvement of the research and development program for air pollution control.

2. Improved planning and controlling of programs on a regional basis.

3. Establishment of a Presidential Air Quality Advisory Board.

4. Registration of fuel activities.

5. A study of national emission standards and emissions from jet aircraft.

6. Comprehensive studies of the costs of controlling air pollution.

The most recent legislation was the Clean Air Act of 1970. This act incorporated provisions of the Clean Air Act of 1963, the Air Quality Act of 1967, amendments to the above acts, and the Clean Air Amendments of 1970. The major components of the law provided for:

1. Cooperative activities and uniform laws among the states.

2. Setting of national ambient air quality standards.

3. A plan of implementation, maintenance, and enforcement of the national standards in each state.

4. Standards of performance for new stationary sources.

5. Procedures for inspections, monitoring, and entry by state or federal authorities to insure that applicable standards of performance are being met.

As a result of the Clean Air Act of 1970, standards of performance for boilers have been set regarding particulates, oxides of sulfur, and oxides of nitrogen. Based on the act, the standards are subject to periodic review and can be revised based on the best current technology available.

Steam generation from nuclear energy

Section III

This section describes the application of the fundamentals of steam generation to the design of nuclear steam supply systems in which steam is generated by heat release from nuclear fuels.

These nuclear fuels are described in Chapter 19. The availability of uranium, the basic nuclear fuel, is discussed, and data on world and estimated U.S. reserves are given. The utilization of uranium in pressurized water reactors for commercial power generation is described with particular reference to uranium dioxide fuel contained in Zircaloy cladding tubes.

The various steps in the uranium-plutonium fuel cycle for water reactors, including milling, refining and conversion to uranium hexafluoride, enrichment in the uranium-235 isotope, conversion to uranium oxide, fabrication of fuel assemblies, spent fuel shipping, chemical reprocessing, and reconversion of uranyl nitrate to uranium hexafluoride, are discussed in detail. The costs of nuclear fuel based on the various elements of this fuel cycle are tabulated. An important element of these costs is the utilization of fissionable plutonium generated by conversion of uranium-238 during reactor operation. The properties, availability, utilization and handling of plutonium are treated. There is also a discussion of the requirements for the ownership and use of fissionable and fertile material.

The principles of nuclear fission are summarized in Chapter 20. Topics include fundamental particles and the structure of the atom, nuclides and isotopes, mass, mass defect, binding energy, radioactive isotopes, their exponential decay, and the alpha, beta and gamma radiations emitted. Various types of induced nuclear reactions are discussed, particularly the fission process, including the resulting fission fragments, and the neutrons and energy produced.

The means for producing a controlled nuclear chain reaction are discussed. The concept of cross section is described and the principles for calculating the critical mass of fissionable material required for a chain reaction are established. Also presented are the concept of reactivity, useful in control of the chain reaction, the use of neutron detectors to monitor the intensity of reaction, the function of a neutron source, and the buildup of fission product poisons that retard the chain reaction.

The basic principles of conversion of uranium-238 to plutonium in an operating reactor and the conversion of thorium-232 to fissionable uranium-233 are explained, and the concept of the "breeder" reactor is presented. Finally, a section is devoted to health physics, i.e., the science of radiation protection.

The design of nuclear steam supply systems for the production of steam is discussed in Chapter 21. This discussion, devoted principally to the pressurized-water reactor type, comprises consideration of materials, physics (including controls), heat removal, and structural integrity. Methods are included for determining the heat developed in the fission process and its distribution throughout the reactor core, as well as the coolant flow requirements for removal of heat from all parts of the reactor without distortion of the core or excessive coolant pressure drop. This includes means for calculating the neutron and heat fluxes as well as heat transfer and pressure drop under conditions of local boiling and, in some cases, net boiling of the coolant.

The design of a fuel assembly is described. The factors involved in reactor control and the requirements of a reactor control system are set forth. Also included are the reactor protection system and the necessary instrumentation.

The design of the reactor coolant system, including the reactor vessel, steam generators, reactor coolant pumps, pressurizer, piping, pressure relief system, auxiliary systems, and shielding are discussed. Provisions for handling the spent fuel are described. The means for containing a possible leak of radioactivity are discussed, including the reactor building and engineered safeguards systems.

Costs for generating electricity from a pressurized water reactor plant and the means for optimizing these costs are presented. Finally, this chapter contains a section concerning the licensing of construction and operation of nuclear plants.

Fuel loading, showing end view of fuel assemblies in place in reactor vessel.

Chapter 19

Nuclear fuels

The principal source of heat energy, other than the sun, has traditionally been the combustion of fossil fuels such as wood, coal, oil and gas. A new source of energy, popularly called "atomic" energy was dramatically demonstrated during World War II when the Manhattan Project in the U.S. developed the atomic bomb. The subsequent naval propulsion and civilian power programs have successfully harnessed the fission of the atomic nucleus as a practical source of heat. This source, properly called "nuclear" energy, converts by fission some of the matter in the nucleus of the atom into energy, in accordance with Einstein's mass-energy equation:

$$E = mc^2$$

where E is energy, m is mass and c is the velocity of light.

All practical applications of nuclear energy for the production of steam utilize the process of fission. The nucleus of a heavy atom splits into two principal fragments, each of which is the nucleus of a lighter atom. This is accompanied by the release of a very considerable amount of energy. In addition neutrons are released which can be used to fission additional atoms producing a "chain reaction," which is controlled to maintain a continuous production of heat (*see Chapter 20*).

Uranium

Uranium is the basic raw material of the nuclear power industry. It is a heavy, slightly radioactive chemical element of atomic number 92—the heaviest element that occurs in nature in more than trace quantities.

Chemically, uranium is a highly reactive metal with three principal valences, +3, +4 and +6. It has three crystalline phases and melts at 2070F. In the alpha phase, it is reasonably ductile and can be fabricated by standard metalworking techniques. Since small particles or chips of uranium are highly pyrophoric, machining operations and the storage of scrap require special precautions, such as use of coolant or an inert atmosphere.

Natural uranium is a mixture of three isotopes (*see Nuclides and Isotopes, Chapter 20*): uranium-234 (0.01%), uranium-235 (0.71%), and uranium-238 (99.28%). Uranium-234 is present in small amounts and is not significant. Uranium-235 is a fissionable isotope, and uranium-238 is generally known as a fertile isotope.

These three natural isotopes of uranium are radioactive and emit alpha particles. However, they have sufficiently long half lives so that only a minimum of precaution is required in handling natural uranium. Uranium is chemically toxic and must not be ingested. In areas where uranium is handled, the amount of uranium in the air must be kept below prescribed tolerances.

Uranium-235 is fissionable as a result of the absorption of a neutron by its nucleus. When one gram of uranium-235 is fissioned, the heat released is equivalent to approximately one megawatt-day (24,000 kwhr or 82,000,000 Btu). When one short ton of uranium-235 is fissioned, the heat released is equivalent to 22 billion kwhr or 75 thousand billion Btu, which is the quantity of heat contained in approximately three million tons of coal.

Uranium-235 can be fissioned by neutrons at various energy levels and a chain reaction can be maintained. It is a fissile material, which means that it can be fissioned by "slow" (low energy or thermal) neutrons.

Uranium-238 is not capable of sustaining a nuclear chain reaction but it is fissioned to some extent by high energy neutrons. When exposed to neutrons, as in a nuclear reactor, the uranium-238 nucleus, upon capture of a neutron, is ultimately transformed into plutonium-239, a fissile isotope of a new element. Plutonium-239 is capable of sustaining a chain reaction and, when fissioned, produces about the same amount of heat per gram as uranium-235. Because of this ability to be transmuted to a fissionable material, uranium-238 is known as a fertile material.

Uranium has become the basic raw material of the nuclear power industry because of its two principal isotopes, uranium-235 and uranium-238. The first is the only fissile material found in quantity in nature; the second is a fertile material from which fissile plutonium is produced. Since uranium-238 is 140 times as abundant as uranium-235, its ultimate potential as a source of power is very large.

Another fertile element, thorium, can be used for the production of power (see Thorium), but uranium is required for the conversion of thorium to a fissionable material.

Availability of uranium

Estimates of the composition of the earth's crust show uranium present to about 4 parts per million. Uranium is always found with radium and in much larger quantity. One common mineral is uraninite (uranium oxide). Pitchblende, in which uranium was first discovered, is a form of uraninite. Other important minerals are coffinite (uranium silicate), carnotite (potassium uranium vanadate), and tyuyamunite (calcium uranium vanadate). These minerals usually occur as small percentages of other materials so that the ore, as mined, contains only a small percentage of uranium. Considerably more uranium is available as a very small percentage of materials such as shale and phosphate rock.

Table 1 gives the U.S. Energy Research and Development Administration's 1975 estimate of world uranium reserves, exclusive of the communist countries. Reserves are included for only two categories.

In accordance with usual custom, uranium resources are expressed in terms of U_3O_8 content (or equivalent)

Table 1
Estimated foreign uranium resources (1975)
(Thousands of tons U_3O_8)

	$15/lb U_3O_8 Cutoff Point		$30/lb U_3O_8 Cutoff Point	
	Reasonably Assured Reserves	Estimated Additional Resources	Reasonably Assured Reserves	Estimated Additional Resources
Australia	360	100	390	80
S & SW Africa	260	10	340	40
Canada	190	420	240	550
Niger	50	30	70	40
France	50	30	80	70
Algeria	40	—	40	—
Gabon	30	10	—	—
Spain	10	10	130	140
Sweden	—	—	390	—
Argentina	10	20	20	50
Other*	60	30	100	120
Total	1,060	660	1,800	1,090

* Includes Central African Republic, Japan, Mexico, Portugal, Sweden, Turkey, Yugoslavia and Zaire.

Source, Foreign Resources and Production Capability, October, 1975, by John A. Patterson, Chief, Supply Evaluation Branch, ERDA.

Table 2
United States uranium resources as of January 1, 1976

Tons U_3O_8

$/lb U_3O_8 Cutoff Cost	Reserves	Potential		
		Probable	Possible	Speculative
$10	270,000	440,000	420,000	145,000
$10-15 Increment	160,000	215,000	255,000	145,000
$15	430,000	655,000	675,000	290,000
$15-30 Increment	210,000	405,000	595,000	300,000
$30	640,000	1,060,000	1,270,000	590,000
By-product 1976-2000*	140,000	—	—	—
	780,000	1,060,000	1,270,000	590,000

* Estimated by-product of phosphate and copper production.

Source, National Uranium Resource Evaluation, Preliminary Report, U.S. ERDA, June 1976.

in the ore. The term "reasonably assured" refers to demonstrated reserves; the "estimated additional" reserves are based on geological and exploration data.

In the U.S., most of the commercial-grade uranium ore is found in the western part of the country. The major producing areas are the Colorado Plateau, (northwestern New Mexico and adjacent portions of Colorado, Utah and Arizona), and central Wyoming. The U_3O_8 concentration is generally between 4 and 7 pounds per ton of ore, averaging about 5 pounds per ton. Some shallow deposits are mined by open-pit techniques, but underground mines supply most of the ore.

Nuclear fuel cost is a significant factor in the evaluation of nuclear versus fossil fuels in the electric power industry. It is therefore important that present and future uranium ore prices be carefully studied and estimated in the planning for future steam generating units. The rapid growth of the nuclear power industry has caused a corresponding increase in the demand for uranium.

Table 2 shows United States resources as of 1976. Further reserve additions are anticipated, but it is not clear that new low-cost uranium reserves will keep pace with the demand. As demand increases, the price of uranium can be affected by available milling capacity as well as mining costs.

Present designs of water reactors, which constitute nearly all of the reactors now in service and being sold in the U.S., are capable (in combination with current U.S. enrichment plant and chemical recovery facilities) of utilizing, over a period of years, approximately two-thirds of the uranium-235 available in natural uranium. They also utilize a substantial amount of uranium-238; however, the total amount of uranium-238 utilized in current commercial water reactors as a result of long-time operation is calculated to be less than 1% of the 238 isotope present in natural uranium. A small amount of uranium-238 is utilized by direct fissions caused by fast neutrons, and a larger amount by conversion to fissionable plutonium. Some of this plutonium fissions in the

fuel assemblies where it is generated. The rest is reclaimed for future use (*see Plutonium*).

It is expected that an advanced type of reactor, known as a "breeder," which produces more fissionable material than it consumes, will be able to utilize the greater part of uranium-238 by converting and "burning" it in the form of plutonium. This potential increase in utilization of uranium resources could postpone the necessity for using the higher priced ores and possibly, may make their use economical in the future. It is expected that breeder reactors will also be able to utilize the large stockpile of depleted uranium from the U.S. military programs and from the water reactors now operating and projected. Thus, breeder reactors should be generally adopted when they can be designed to operate dependably and produce power at competitive cost.

Large additional supplies of uranium from low-grade deposits are known to be available at prices above $30 per pound of U_3O_8. There is also a very large supply of uranium in the oceans, estimated at more than four billion tons.

Utilization of uranium

Unlike fossil fuels for steam generation which require a continuous feed of fuel for good combustion, nuclear fuel is utilized by a batch process. It is introduced into the nuclear furnace, or reactor, in the form of fabricated packages called "fuel assemblies." Fig. 1 illustrates typical fuel assemblies for water reactors where the heat developed by the nuclear fission chain reaction is removed by the water coolant. Views (a) and (b) in Fig. 1 illustrate fuel assemblies for pressurized water reactors used for power generation and ship propulsion respectively. These are assemblies of fuel rods, consisting of uranium oxide pellets contained in alloy cladding tubes. The term "cladding" does not imply deposition of one metal on another, but simply refers to the outer jacket of the nuclear fuel, which is used to prevent corrosion and the release of fission products to the coolant. For a large power reactor using fuel assemblies of this type, each assembly may be 14 ft or more in length and 8 in. square, or larger, in cross section. In pressurized water reactors, fuel rods must be designed to accommodate differential pressures of as much as 2500 psi that occur early in life as a result of system pressure external to the cladding tubes. These tubes must also contain the internal pressure from gaseous fission products that accumulate during the life of the fuel.

View (c) of Fig. 1 illustrates a fuel-assembly type used in research and test reactors. This assembly consists of metal plates, each plate being a uranium-aluminum alloy clad with aluminum.

The following requirements are basic to the utilization of fuel for the production of steam, whether the fuel is nuclear or fossil:

1. Control of heat release rate in the reactor or furnace.
2. Transfer of heat developed by the fuel into water for the production of steam.
3. Protection of the operators and control of the by-products of the reaction.
4. A design which results in good fuel economics.

Controlling the rate of heat release

When the nuclear fission process is applied to the production of steam, the production of heat is achieved by maintaining a controlled nuclear fission chain reaction (explained in Chapter 20). A certain minimum quantity of fissile material is required to initiate and sustain a chain reaction. This "critical mass" varies greatly, depending on the nature and amounts of other materials present and the geometry of the fuel arrangement.

It is necessary to provide a means of controlling the chain reaction and consequently the heat release rate in the reactor. Fortunately, it is practical to provide this control by means of neutron-absorbing rods which can be inserted into or removed from the system to maintain the desired heat release. Details of control systems are described in Chapters 20, 21, 23 and 35.

Since fissile material is consumed during the chain reaction, and since the reaction stops when the amount of fissile material falls below the critical mass, it is necessary to provide an excess over the critical mass of fissile material at least equal to the amount to be consumed during a scheduled operating period. It then becomes possible to operate a large commercial water reactor for periods of a year or longer without adding or rearranging fuel.

Removal of heat

In commercial reactors, the heat developed in the fuel is removed by the reactor coolant, which is usually water or gas. In a pressurized water reactor (PWR) the reactor coolant is maintained under pressure sufficiently high to prevent boiling, and the steam is generated in closed heat exchangers in which the reactor coolant transfers its heat through heat transfer surface to produce the steam. In boiling water reactors, the reactor coolant is allowed to boil, and the steam is produced in the reactor.

Protection

As in a conventional boiler, where a metallic barrier is placed between the combustion gas and the water and steam, it is necessary to have at least one metallic barrier in a nuclear reactor between the nuclear fuel and the steam. In the PWR, both the fuel cladding and the tubes in the steam generator are barriers which are provided to prevent the spread of radioactive material.

In the nuclear chain reaction, the mass of the fission products formed is much less than the waste products from fossil-fuel combustion releasing the same amount of energy. Most of these fission products are radioactive, and many are highly dangerous. Fortunately most of them are solids. Some of the fission products are gaseous, and the use of metallic cladding around the fuel serves to retain these fission gases as well as the solid fission products inside the fuel packages until they can be safely reprocessed.

Fuel handling

The batch process of replenishing nuclear fuel is favored due to the difficulty of removing fuel assemblies from the high-pressure reactor-coolant system with the reactor in operation. The removal or addition of a fuel assembly

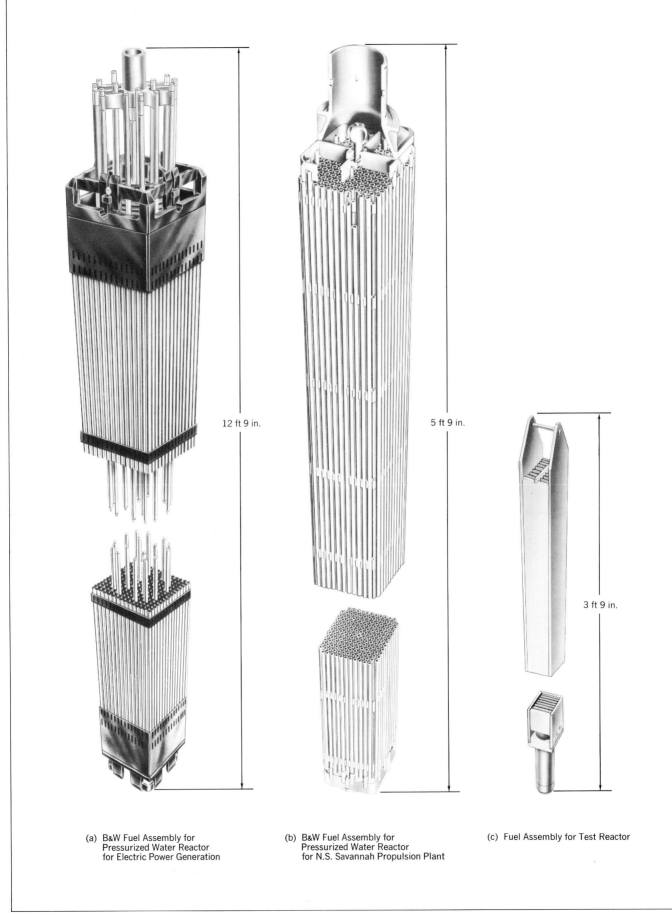

(a) B&W Fuel Assembly for
    Pressurized Water Reactor
    for Electric Power Generation

(b) B&W Fuel Assembly for
    Pressurized Water Reactor
    for N.S. Savannah Propulsion Plant

(c) Fuel Assembly for Test Reactor

12 ft 9 in.

5 ft 9 in.

3 ft 9 in.

Fig. 1 Fuel assemblies for water reactors.

during operation would involve difficult control problems because of the small number of fuel assemblies in these water reactors. Thus, it has proved more economical to place packages of uranium fuel (fuel assemblies) in the reactor, leaving them there until they are spent. They are then removed and transported to a central reprocessing plant where the fission products are separated and concentrated for safe storage. The uranium, plutonium and other useful heavy elements are reclaimed for further use. Loading and unloading is accomplished at intervals of about a year or longer, and with the reactor plant shut down. The amount of fuel which is removed and replaced at each shutdown varies from 25 to 100% of the total fuel assemblies.

In the large British and French gas-cooled reactors, a few spent fuel units are replaced at regular intervals while the reactor is in operation. This is possible because each unit contains only a small percentage of the total fuel in the reactor. The Canadian heavy-water-reactor designs are also adapted to fuel loading during reactor operation.

It is possible to design reactors for continuous replenishment of fuel by dissolving uranium fuel in a liquid which is circulated across heat transfer surfaces through which the heat is transferred to water or some other coolant. Such an arrangement can be adapted to the continuous removal of fission products. However, no competitive design of this type has been developed.

Chain-reaction considerations

There are many materials which, even in small quantities, are detrimental to the fission chain reaction, and it is necessary that all materials used in the reactor shall be of high purity.

The economic design of commercial water reactors requires uranium containing 2 to 4% of uranium-235, instead of the 0.71% which occurs in natural uranium. Increasing the uranium-235 content of uranium is known as "enrichment." The enrichment of uranium is accomplished by the "gaseous diffusion" process in plants owned by the U.S. government located at Oak Ridge, Tennessee; Paducah, Kentucky; and Portsmouth, Ohio. There are enrichment plants in the United Kingdom, France, Russia and, presumably, China.

Since the uranium must be in gaseous form for the enrichment process, the U_3O_8 is converted to uranium hexafluoride (UF_6), a solid which sublimes at low temperature. Since the conversion process is effective in the elimination of impurities, the major part of the chemical purification is accomplished at this time.

Fuel assemblies

In addition to the aluminum-alloy-plate and uranium-oxide-rod types of fuel assemblies shown in Fig. 1, a variety of fuel assemblies, having both geometric and chemical variations, has been developed for experimental work. These include uranium alloys, cermets, and ceramics. Some of these have been used successfully for long periods in power or plutonium production reactors.

The fuel assemblies used in some of the earlier gas-cooled reactors in the United Kingdom and France consisted of metallic uranium rods contained within a magnesium alloy can. Uranium-carbide and uranium-thorium-carbide fuel assemblies clad in graphite are being used in high-temperature gas-cooled reactors. Uranium carbide, uranium nitride, and a variety of alloys incorporating cermets are being considered for use in breeder reactors.

At the present time, however, the most important commercial fuel is uranium dioxide contained in metallic cladding tubes. In commercial water reactors the cladding is a zirconium alloy. Stainless steel cladding is used in advanced gas-cooled reactors in the United Kingdom and is projected for use in breeder reactors.

The most important operating requirements for a fuel assembly and its component units are:

1. Compatibility of the fuel assembly and its component units with the environment in the reactor.

2. Ability to accommodate high heat fluxes without melting or losing strength.

3. Ability to withstand "radiation" damage, thus permitting high fuel consumption (burnup).

The first of these requirements is fundamental to the successful operation of the reactor. Cladding of the fuel is usually necessary to provide compatibility with the coolant, particularly if water is the coolant. When the fuel is used in the form of oxide (UO_2), a sheath or cladding is required, not only from the standpoint of corrosion but primarily because the oxide lacks structural strength. It is also essential that the fuel be reasonably resistant to water corrosion if small breaches of the cladding should occur, and a small hole in the cladding must not result in swelling of the fuel material which could block the flow channel, causing overheating and burnout of the fuel assembly.

An important function of the cladding is to confine the fission products, including the gaseous ones, thereby greatly reducing the radioactivity in the coolant. Cladding also serves to contain radioactivity until it is released to suitable collection systems in the fuel reprocessing plant. Although it is possible to manufacture fuel assemblies so that all remain tight during the life of the reactor, reactor operation has proved that a limited amount of cladding failure is tolerable.

The second and third important operating requirements are major factors in the economics of the reactor fuel cycle. The capacity of a nuclear reactor is directly related to the second requirement, the ability to accommodate high heat fluxes. The third requirement, the ability to withstand radiation damage, limits the total amount of heat which can be generated in a fuel assembly during its lifetime.

Radiation damage

When an atom of uranium-235 fissions, the two principal fission fragments which are formed fly apart in essentially opposite directions with tremendous energy. Although these particles are infinitesimally small, they nevertheless are highly energetic and can knock other atoms out of their position in the lattice structure. They also introduce new chemical components into the composition and may produce a change in its material properties, such as lowering ductility and resistance to

distortion. This effect is much more damaging in some materials than in others. Metallic uranium is so susceptible to radiation damage that it is not used for fuel assemblies unless the accumulated heat release is low. Certain alloys, cermets and ceramics, including oxides, are more resistant to radiation damage.

Another source of radiation damage is high energy, or "fast" neutrons. This effect is important principally in fuel cladding and in structural materials rather than in the fuel itself, where the damage by the fission process is by far the dominant factor.

Gaseous fission products are also an important source of radiation damage. They cause swelling in metals and alloys. Properly fabricated oxide fuels can retain a surprisingly large amount of fission gases without appreciable swelling. Oxide fuels are clad in metal, usually tubing, to provide mechanical strength and protect the oxide against erosion by the coolant. Some gaseous fission products are ultimately released from the oxide and accumulate within the cladding. In current reactors, the cladding is strong enough to contain all these gaseous fission products, and the life of the fuel assembly may be limited by the amount of fission gas which can accumulate without swelling or bursting the cladding tube. In designs for some of the advanced reactor types, consideration is being given to the possibility of deliberately venting the fission gas from each fuel assembly into the coolant stream, or elsewhere, in order to prolong the life of the fuel assembly.

Uranium-dioxide fuel

For use in commercial water reactors for power production, the fuel assemblies which best meet the operating requirements have as their basic unit a fuel rod composed of uranium-dioxide pellets contained in zirconium-alloy (Zircaloy) cladding tubes. The properties of zirconium alloys are discussed in Chapter 29.

Table 3 lists some important physical properties of uranium dioxide. The melting point of uranium dioxide is 5144F. Its theoretical density at room temperature is 684 lb/cu ft. The uranium-dioxide pellets used as nuclear fuel range in density from 90 to 95% of theoretical, and in some cases higher. The average strength in compression for pellets of 95% density is 222,000 lb/sq in.

Table 3
Some physical properties of uranium dioxide

Temp, F	Thermal Conductivity* Btu/sq ft, hr, F/in.	Coefficient of Linear Expansion† (in./in. F) 10^{6}*	Specific Heat
300	48.6	5.67	0.056
1000	28.4	5.67	0.067
2000	18.7	5.73	0.072
3000	16.0	6.58	0.075
4000	16.6	7.42	0.081
5000	20.3	—	0.094

* Based on 95% density pellets.
† Between 70F and temperature shown.

Uranium-plutonium fuel cycle (water reactors)

A number of steps are required to extract uranium concentrate from the ore, prepare the uranium for use in a reactor and recover the useful materials left in the spent fuel. Fig. 2 shows the major steps involved in the fuel cycle for a pressurized water reactor of the type used for power production in the U.S. These steps include milling, refining and conversion to UF_6, enrichment, conversion to UO_2, fabrication of fuel assemblies, power generation, spent fuel shipping, chemical reprocessing, recycling or disposition of recovered materials, and storage of fission products.

Milling

The function of the uranium mill is to extract the uranium from the ore, which contains on the average about 5 pounds of uranium per ton. The ore is crushed and is then leached with an acid or alkaline reagent to dissolve the uranium which, in turn, is recovered from the solution by solvent extraction or ion exchange techniques. Excess water is removed by calcining (roasting). The resultant product, known in the industry as "yellowcake" is a crude uranium concentrate containing from 70 to 90% U_3O_8.

Refining and conversion to UF_6

For the purpose of enrichment, the uranium in yellowcake must be refined and converted into uranium hexafluoride (UF_6). Fig. 3 illustrates the process used by the Allied Chemical Corp., in which the essential steps are:

1. The U_3O_8 feed is reduced to raw UO_2 at 550 to 650C with hydrogen or dissociated ammonia in the first converter.

2. The raw UO_2 is converted to UF_4 at 450 to 650C with anhydrous hydrogen fluoride gas (HF) in the second converter.

3. The UF_4 is converted to crude UF_6 at 350 to 500C with elemental fluorine in the last converter.

The final step is fractional distillation for the removal of impurities, principally molybdenum and vanadium. The UF_6 product meets NRC's specifications for impurities allowable in uranium hexafluoride delivered for enrichment in the NRC's separation plants.

Enrichment

Prior to fabrication into fuel assemblies, the uranium must be enriched to the desired concentration of the fissionable isotope, uranium-235. This is accomplished in gaseous diffusion plants which are designed to separate isotopes by utilizing the principles of gas kinetics. In a mixture of two gases (uranium-238 hexafluoride and uranium-235 hexafluoride), molecules of the lighter gas ($^{235}UF_6$) travel faster and strike the walls of the containing vessels more frequently than do the molecules of the heavier gas ($^{238}UF_6$). If the wall of the vessel is provided with holes just large enough to permit passage of individual molecules without bulk flow of gas, the lighter molecules will diffuse through the holes faster, relative to their concentration, than the heavier molecules. The degree of separation attainable in this manner

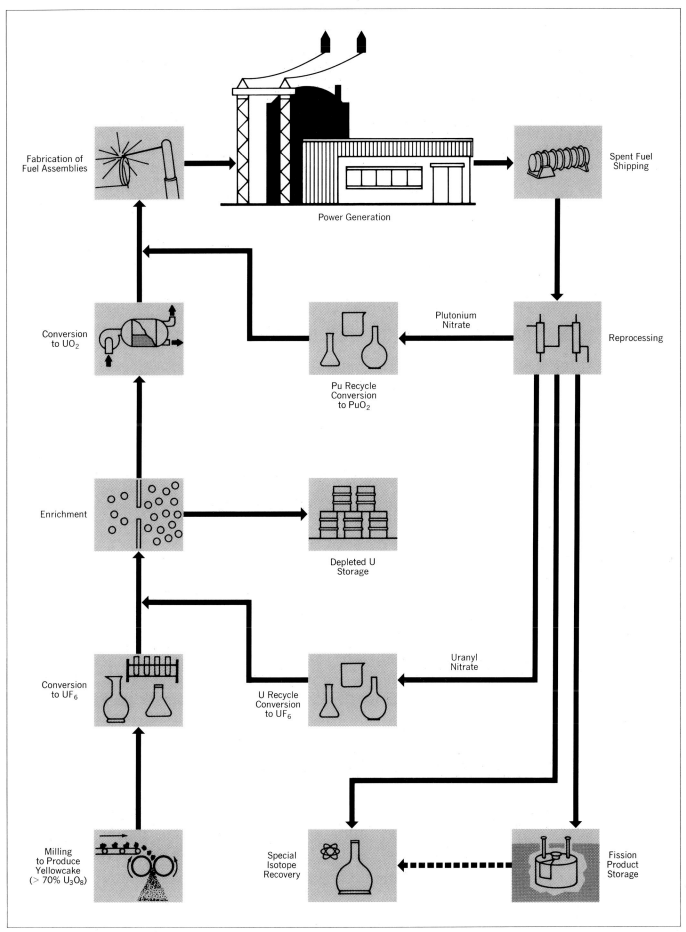

Fig. 2 Nuclear fuel cycle.

is very small, and the process must be repeated many times before a practical enrichment can be obtained. Thus, a gaseous diffusion plant consists of hundreds of stages connected in series in an arrangement known as a diffusion "cascade."

Each diffusion stage consists of a chamber divided into two zones by a finely porous, thin barrier. The gas mixture enters one zone, which is maintained at a higher pressure than the other. Conditions are adjusted so that part of the gas diffuses through the barrier into the lower pressure zone and then is directed to the next stage "up" the cascade. The remainder flows from the high pressure zone to the next stage "down" the cascade. The uranium-hexafluoride gas stream diffusing through the barrier is very slightly enriched in the uranium-235 isotope; the other stream is very slightly depleted in that isotope.

Fig. 4 illustrates the sequence of operations in the cascade. Stages are arranged in a counter-current cascade similar to a distillation column. In each stage, a pump compresses the gas from the pressure on the downstream side of the diffusion barrier to the pressure on the upstream side, and a cooler removes the heat of compression.

The natural uranium feed enters the cascade at an intermediate point. The gas becomes increasingly enriched as it progresses up the cascade. The enriched uranium product is withdrawn at some stage above the feed point, depending on the degree of enrichment desired. Depleted uranium (known as "tails") is withdrawn from the base of the cascade, and held in storage.

Conversion to UO_2

The first stage in the fabrication of fuel assemblies is the conversion of enriched UF_6 to UO_2. In a typical conversion process, the enriched UF_6 is first hydrolyzed to UO_2F_2; then it is reacted with ammonia to form ammonium diuranate (ADU). The ADU is calcined to UO_3 which is reduced to UO_2 with hydrogen at 800C.

Fabrication of fuel assemblies

The raw UO_2 is first reduced to the desired particle-size distribution by compaction, crushing, and screening. It is then pelletized at high pressure. The pellets are finally sintered at a high temperature in a reducing atmosphere and ground to proper diameter. They are then arranged in proper stack lengths and checked for uranium content. The proper stack length and weight is inserted into a thin-walled Zircaloy tube, having one end capped and welded. Helium is then introduced into the tube and the other end of the tube is capped and welded (see Fuel Assemblies for Nuclear Power, Chapter 31).

Fuel tubes are positioned into the desired array in a grid structure with an instrument tube and control rod guide tubes, and then the assembly is equipped with end fittings for handling and placement, and for guiding the coolant as it enters and leaves the assembly. Fig. 5 shows two fuel assemblies for a large power reactor, located vertically about 3 ft apart in a storage rack. Each assembly is almost 14 ft long and about 8¾-in. square in section. After quality control and dimensional checks, a fuel assembly is loaded into a special shipping container which protects it while in transit to the reactor site.

Spent fuel shipping

After their use in a reactor, the spent fuel assemblies are shipped to a fuel reprocessing plant for recovery of contained uranium and plutonium. When taken from the reactor, the spent fuel assemblies are extremely radioactive due to the fission products. They must be stored under water for several months to allow for some decay of radioactivity and then must be shipped to the fuel reprocessing plant in heavily shielded transfer casks.

Chemical reprocessing

The reprocessing procedure shown in Fig. 6 was developed by Nuclear Fuel Services, Inc., of West Valley, New

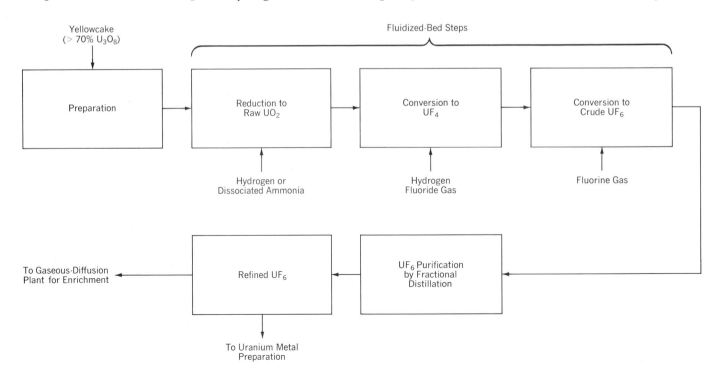

Fig. 3 Flowsheet for uranium refining and conversion to UF_6. (Based on Allied Chemical Corp. plant at Metropolis, Illinois.)

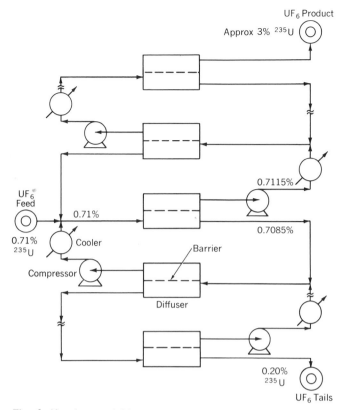

UF₆ Product

Approx 3% ²³⁵U

0.7115%

UF₆ Feed

0.71%

0.71% ²³⁵U

Cooler

Compressor

Barrier

0.7085%

Diffuser

0.20% ²³⁵U

UF₆ Tails

Fig. 4 Uranium-enriching cascade.

York. The fuel assemblies are first transferred from the storage pool to a mechanical processing cell where end-fitting hardware is removed and the fuel rods are sheared into small pieces. The pieces are collected in a canister which is placed in a dissolver where uranium, plutonium, and fission products are dissolved in nitric acid. The insoluble cladding materials (hulls) are monitored to establish completeness of dissolution of fuel values and buried in the plant's radioactive waste burial ground. The dissolvent solution undergoes solvent extraction by TBP, (a solution of tributyl phosphate in kerosine), in a pulse column to extract most of the contained uranium and plutonium from the aqueous solution which retains the fission products. The plutonium is then stripped from the TBP solvent stream, and the uranium stream subsequently stripped. Both aqueous streams are in turn purified to remove the remaining fission products.

The uranium product stream is concentrated by evaporation and subjected to a final decontamination by ion exchange with silica gel, resulting in a uranyl nitrate solution product. The plutonium product stream is subjected to an ion exchange treatment to effect both the concentration and further decontamination of the plutonium, yielding the final plutonium nitrate solution product which can be converted to PuO_2 for recycle, as indicated in Fig. 2.

Reconversion of uranyl nitrate to UF₆

A part of the uranium recovered from the reprocessing plant can be used again as reactor fuel by re-enrichment in a gaseous diffusion plant. To accomplish this the uranyl nitrate product from the reprocessing plant must first be reconverted to UF₆. This can be done by processes simi-

lar to those used in the initial conversion of natural uranium. Reconversion will cost more than initial conversion because the radioactivity in the recycled uranium will require more stringent health physics control (Chapter 20). Accountability is required since the uranium is enriched (*see Ownership and Regulation of Fissionable and Fertile Materials*). This is complicated by variations in the uranium-235 assay.

Fission product storage and special isotope recovery

The liquid waste containing the fission products is concentrated by evaporation, neutralized, and stored in underground liquid waste tanks. This waste contains special isotopes, e.g., neptunium-237, which are potentially valuable and can be recovered.

Fig. 5 Two nuclear fuel assemblies for a large power reactor.

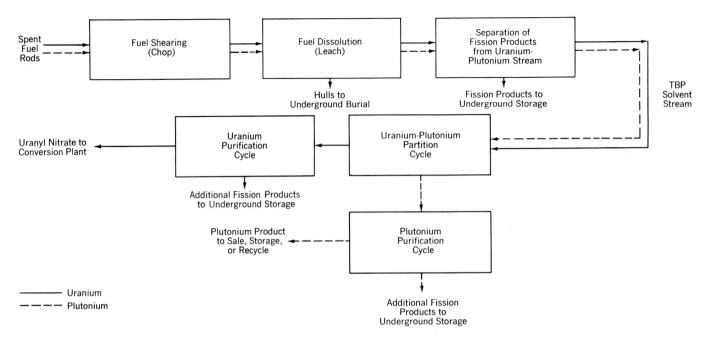

Fig. 6 Flowsheet for chemical reprocessing. *(Based on plant of Nuclear Fuel Services, Inc. at West Valley, New York.)*

Nuclear fuel costs

The costs involved in each stage of the fuel cycle must be established in order to determine the cost of nuclear fuel. Tables 4 and 5 illustrate the components of nuclear fuel cost for a pressurized water reactor utilizing enriched uranium.

The first column in Table 4 lists the cost for each of the steps in the fuel cycle in dollars per kilogram of total uranium in the fuel. The second column lists the fuel costs in terms of cents per million Btu. The third column lists the fuel costs in terms of mills per kwhr, based on a heat rate of 10,000 Btu per kwhr. Total costs include financing of the fuel inventory which raises the fuel component of the energy cost to about 5 mills/kwhr and the corresponding fuel cost equivalent to about 51 cents per million Btu. Both of these values are quite favorable in comparison with the fossil fuels available in most areas.

These costs were established for a pressurized water reactor capable of supplying steam for a turbine generator of approximately 1300 Mwe capacity; however, they are not influenced greatly by unit size. They are predicated on the assumption that a substantial credit will be realized by utilizing uranium and plutonium recovered from the spent fuel assemblies after reprocessing.

Table 5
Parameters used in establishing Table 4

Initial enrichment of uranium (uranium-235 content), %	3.18
Uranium-235 content in spent fuel, %	0.83
Final Pu content in spent fuel per kg U loaded, %	0.70
Final U content in spent fuel per kg U loaded, %	95.44
Energy output, Mw-days/kg U loaded	33.60
Yellowcake, $/lb U_3O_8	40.00
Conversion to UF_6, $/kg U	3.50
Enrichment, $/separative work unit	61.30
Cascade tails, %	0.20
Fabrication, $/kg U	110.00
Spent fuel shipping and recovery, $/kg U	200.00
Plutonium value, $/fissile gram	12.00
Financing rate (per year), %	15.00

Table 4
Nuclear fuel cost
Typical breakdown for 1285 Mwe pressurized water reactor utilizing enriched uranium-dioxide fuel

	$/kg U Loaded	Cents/ MBtu	Mills/ Kwhr	Percent- age
U_3O_8	615.5	22.3	2.23	43.9
Conversion	20.6	.7	.07	1.4
Enrichment	291.2	10.6	1.06	20.9
Fabrication	109.9	4.0	.40	7.9
Spent fuel shipping and recovery	192.8	7.0	.70	13.8
Spent uranium credit	(133.5)	(4.8)	(.48)	(9.5)
Plutonium credit	(81.9)	(3.0)	(.30)	(5.9)
Subtotal	1014.6	36.8	3.68	72.5
Financing	386.6	14.0	1.40	27.5
Total	1401.2	50.8	5.08	100.0

Net plant heat rate = 10,000 Btu/kwhr

Plutonium

Although trace quantities of plutonium exist in nature in certain uranium deposits, it was first discovered in 1941 as an artificial element produced by the bombardment of uranium with neutrons in a cyclotron, and plutonium for commercial use must be made by transmutation from uranium in nuclear reactors.

Plutonium is a radioactive heavy element with an atomic number of 94. It is classified as a metal but it does not have all the usual properties of a metal. Its electrical and thermal conductivity are low for a metal. It has a melting point of 640C and must be melted in vacuum or an inert atmosphere (helium or argon) because it is rather reactive chemically. It has complicated chemical properties with five valence states ranging from +2 to +6. It also has very complicated metallurgical properties, being the only element with six allotropes.

The 15 known isotopes of plutonium range in atomic weight from 232 to 246. All are radioactive, decaying through various sequences to form stable isotopes of elements, such as bismuth and lead. Plutonium-239 is the isotope of greatest importance because it is the most readily produced in operating reactors and it is fissile. It is superior to uranium-235 for use in fast breeder reactors. Plutonium generated in commercial power reactors contains substantial percentages of isotopes having mass numbers greater than 239, which considerably complicates its use with respect to handling, efficient utilization, and the calculation of the chain reaction.

An important element of the nuclear fuel cost is the credit received from the sale or future utilization of plutonium after its recovery from the spent fuel. The plutonium credit listed in Table 4 is realistic only if the plutonium is utilized for power production since, at present, there is no other commercial use for it which would yield a similar return. This credit amounts to a significant percentage of the cost of the nuclear fuel and can be of controlling influence in the economic evaluation of power supply sources.

Since the potential reserves of uranium-235 are limited, it is doubtful that nuclear fuels can remain competitive with fossil fuels beyond the 1980 decade without the development of means for the practical utilization of plutonium.

Availability of plutonium

Prior to the middle sixties, most of the world's plutonium was produced in special production reactors for military purposes, although substantial amounts had been made available for research use. This plutonium contained fewer higher isotopes than the plutonium produced in commercial reactors which is now becoming available. A considerable quantity of this commercial plutonium has been produced in the United Kingdom.

Plutonium is less effective than uranium-235 in water reactors. However, plutonium is superior in fast breeder reactors, where its value should be two or three times as high as in water reactors. Therefore, the value of plutonium in the seventies will depend largely on when the fast breeder reactor becomes commercial.

Utilization of plutonium

Although the technology of plutonium utilization is under intensive study and investigation, it presently appears that the best way to utilize plutonium in water reactors is in the form of plutonium oxide (PuO_2) mixed with uranium dioxide, as indicated in Fig. 2. Use of this type of fuel has been demonstrated in several test reactors; its use in fast breeder reactors is expected.

Handling of plutonium

If plutonium enters the body through cuts or abrasions, ingestion, or by inhalation, a considerable percentage tends to be absorbed in the bones where it can be retained. Plutonium emits alpha particles of rather high energy at a rate which results in serious damage to the blood-producing cells even when only small amounts are deposited in the bone. These properties make plutonium a highly toxic substance and the NRC has set a limit of 0.6 microgram as the total amount that can be accumulated in the bones of an adult.

To assure the safety of personnel, plutonium operations are normally handled in an essentially closed system, such as a "glovebox." In addition, "shielding" is required when certain isotopes, including plutonium-240 and plutonium-241, are present in appreciable quantity. A general discussion of radiation protection is given in the section *Health Physics* in Chapter 20.

Plutonium's chemical properties also increase the handling difficulties, for instance, metallic plutonium is pyrophoric, particularly in finely divided form. In spite of plutonium's unusually dangerous characteristics, people work safely with it routinely by careful observance of safety precautions.

Much time, effort and money are being expended on the development of fabrication methods for plutonium fuel. Although technical success is assured, the cost of fabrication will be greater than for uranium because of the difficulty of handling plutonium. The economics of the plutonium cycle is still being resolved.

Thorium

Although uranium is the basic raw material of the nuclear power industry, another enormous reserve of nuclear fuel is available in the form of thorium. Thorium contains no fissionable isotope like uranium-235, but is primarily a fertile material like uranium-238. The absorption of neutrons within a reactor converts thorium to uranium-233. This is another fissile isotope of uranium, but it does not occur in natural uranium.

"Reasonably assured" reserves of thorium, available as thorium oxide (ThO_2), are estimated at more than half a million tons. A large part of these resources occurs in the form of monazite sand, which is found in several locations, including India, Brazil and the United States. U.S. thorium reserves are estimated at about 100,000 tons of thorium oxide equivalent. Domestic reserves that are economically exploitable, including Lemhi Pass, Idaho and Montana, are large in relation to demand. Total thorium resources are believed to be much larger than the "reasonably assured" reserves.

Certain nations of the world are rich in thorium and poor in uranium. These nations, therefore, have considerable incentive to utilize thorium for the production of power. The technical feasibility of such utilization has been demonstrated.

However, the production of nuclear power throughout the world is proceeding primarily on the uranium-plutonium cycle rather than the thorium-uranium-233 cycle. The uranium-plutonium cycle currently has a cost advantage, and with ample present uranium reserves,

there is little incentive to develop the thorium cycle except in countries which are rich in thorium and lacking in uranium.

Ownership and regulation of fissionable and fertile materials

Since some of the materials which are used in producing power by nuclear fission are the same as those used in the production of nuclear weapons, Congress, shortly after World War II, passed a law, known as the McMahon Act, limiting to the U.S. government the ownership of fissionable material, including enriched uranium and plutonium, and requiring a license for the ownership of "source materials" after mining, including natural uranium and thorium.

The Atomic Energy Act of 1954 made fissionable materials available under lease from the government to private enterprise for use in research and development and in the production of power. A 1964 amendment, known as the "Private Ownership of Special Nuclear Materials Act," made it possible for qualified applicants to purchase from the then Atomic Energy Commission (AEC) and to own fissile as well as fertile material for specified purposes, including use in power reactors,

under license from the AEC. After December 31, 1970, the law prohibits further distribution of fissile material by the government for use in privately owned facilities, except by sale. Leased material must be transferred to private ownership by June 30, 1973.

Since essentially all the reactors being built or planned in the U.S. will utilize enriched uranium, and since the 1964 amendment does not provide for private ownership of enrichment facilities, the U.S. government has made provisions for enrichment of privately owned uranium in the government's facilities beginning January 1, 1969, in return for the payment of a fee by the owner of the material. This arrangement is known as "toll enrichment."

Regardless of the ownership of the fissionable material, the law provides that the government shall maintain careful records of the amount and location of all fissionable and fertile materials at all times. It is clearly of major importance that this be done on a worldwide basis, as well as within the U.S., to prevent the diversion of nuclear materials to non-peaceful purposes. The U.S. has been working for several years to reach international agreements for the inspection of nuclear facilities to preclude the possibility of such diversion.

Chapter 20

Principles of nuclear fission

The discovery of nuclear fission, credited to Otto Hahn, Lise Meitner and Fritz Strassman, was made possible through an accumulation of knowledge on the structure of matter beginning with Becquerel's 1896 detection of radioactivity. Experiments by these three led to the publication in 1939 of results showing that the nucleus of a uranium atom can be split into two parts by the absorption of a neutron. The immediate effect was a stimulated interest leading to further experiments in several countries. In the United States, the implications of nuclear fission were soon understood and a report was made to the President mentioning the possibilities of nuclear power and atomic explosives. This, in turn, led to the "Manhattan Project," the atomic bomb, and the subsequent development of nuclear power.

Current concepts of atomic structures and the equivalence of mass and energy expressed by Einstein's equation $E = mc^2$ have provided an adequate theoretical basis for the development of nuclear power systems.

Fundamental particles and structure of the atom

The postulated structure of the atom (Fig. 1) has a dense positively charged nucleus (10^{14}g/cc) made up of closely packed protons and neutrons. Each proton—the equivalent of a hydrogen atom nucleus—carries an elemental positive charge of electricity. Each neutron is an electrically neutral particle with a mass slightly greater than the proton. Because of their association with the nucleus of the atom, protons and neutrons are also referred to as nucleons. To complete the picture, each electron shown orbiting around the nucleus has a mass much less than either the proton or neutron but, like the proton, it is a charged particle. Experiments have shown that the electron charge (-4.8×10^{-10} esu)* is the fundamental unit of negative electricity.

Despite the minute size of the atom, there is a relatively great distance between the nucleus and the orbit-

* The electrostatic unit (esu) is the quantity of charge that is repelled with a force of 1 dyne by an equal charge 1 cm away.

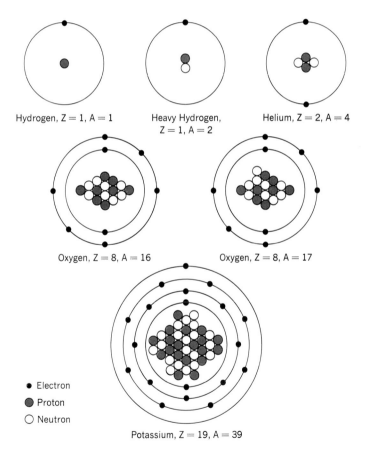

Hydrogen, Z = 1, A = 1

Heavy Hydrogen, Z = 1, A = 2

Helium, Z = 2, A = 4

Oxygen, Z = 8, A = 16

Oxygen, Z = 8, A = 17

● Electron

● Proton

○ Neutron

Potassium, Z = 19, A = 39

Fig. 1 Structure of the atom.

ing electrons. This distance, approximately 10^5 times the dimension of the nucleus, accounts for the ability of X rays and other radiation to "pass through" apparently dense materials.

Fig. 1 also indicates the relationship of the positively charged protons in the nucleus and the negatively charged electrons. In the un-ionized state, the number of

protons is balanced by an equal number of electrons. An atom becomes ionized by gaining or losing one or more electrons. A gain of electrons yields negative ions and a loss results in positive ions.

When an atom has more than two electrons, their orbits are located in a series of separate and distinct "shells," each capable of containing a specific number of electrons. In general, an inner shell fills to its maximum number of electrons before electrons begin to form in the next shell. The number of electrons in the outer shell determines certain chemical properties of the elements. The properties are similar for elements which have similar electron distributions in the outer shell regardless of the number of inner shells. This accounts for the repetition of chemical properties in the Periodic Table of the Elements.

Nuclides and isotopes

The atomic number, Z (number of protons in the nucleus), designates a chemical element. The total number of nucleons (protons plus neutrons) is denoted by A, the mass number. In the case of most chemical elements there are several types of atoms having different mass numbers, i.e., different numbers of neutrons in the nucleus but the same number of protons. Each different type of atom is called a nuclide and is identified when its atomic number Z and its mass number A are given. An isotope is one of two or more nuclides of the same chemical element.

Two isotopes of hydrogen and two isotopes of oxygen are shown diagrammatically in Fig. 1. An ordinary, or light, hydrogen atom contains one proton and no neutrons. Its atomic number Z and mass number A are 1. The heavy hydrogen, or deuterium, atom has one proton and one neutron; Z is 1 and A is 2.

Nuclides are usually identified by chemical name and mass number. Thus oxygen-16 and oxygen-17 (Fig. 1) have 16 and 17 nucleons respectively, although each has eight protons. When nuclides are described by chemical symbol, the atomic number is the left-hand subscript and the mass number the left-hand superscript. For example, symbols for the two isotopes of oxygen described above are $^{16}_{8}O$ and $^{17}_{8}O$.

Although either the atomic number or the chemical symbol could be used to identify the chemical element, use of the subscripts is sometimes useful in accounting for the total number of charges in an equation.

Mass

It is customary to list the mass of atoms and fundamental particles in atomic mass units (amu). This is a relative scale in which the nuclide $^{12}_{6}C$ (carbon-12) is assigned the exact mass of 12 amu.* One amu is the equivalent of approximately 1.66×10^{-24} grams, or the reciprocal of the presently accepted Avogadro number, 0.602252×10^{24} atoms per gram-atom. A gram-atom of an element is a quantity having a mass in grams numerically equal to the atomic weight of the element.

Table 1 lists the masses of the fundamental particles and the atoms of hydrogen, deuterium and helium in amu units.

* International Union of Chemists and Physicists, 1962.

Table 1
Masses of particles and light atoms

Isotope or Particle	Mass, amu
Electron	0.000549
Proton, $^{1}_{1}p$	1.007277
Neutron, $^{1}_{0}n$	1.008665
Hydrogen, $^{1}_{1}H$	1.007825
Deuterium, $^{2}_{1}H$	2.01410
Helium, $^{4}_{2}He$	4.00260

Mass defect

The mass of the hydrogen atom $^{1}_{1}H$ listed in Table 1 is almost but not quite equal to the sum of the masses of its individual particles, one proton and one electron. However, the mass of a deuterium atom $^{2}_{1}H$ is noticeably less than the sum of its constituents; one each of a neutron, proton and electron. Measurements show that the mass of a nuclide is always less than the sum of the masses of its protons, neutrons and electrons. This difference, the mass defect (MD), is customarily calculated in the following manner:

$$(1) \quad MD = Zm_h + (A - Z)m_n - m_e$$

where:

MD = mass defect, amu
Z = number of protons in the nucleus of the nuclide
m_h = mass of the hydrogen atom, amu
$A - Z$ = number of neutrons in the nucleus
m_n = mass of the neutron, amu
m_e = mass of the nuclide including its Z electrons, amu

Binding energy

Although most nuclei contain a plurality of protons with mutually repulsive positive charges, the nucleus remains tightly bound together and it takes considerable energy to cause disintegration. This energy, which is called binding energy, is equivalent to the mass defect.

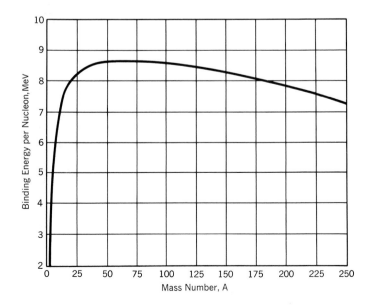

Fig. 2 Binding energy per nucleon vs. mass number.

From the equivalence of mass and energy one amu equals 931 million electron volts (MeV).* Hence

(2)   Binding Energy (MeV) $= [Zm_h + (A - Z)m_n - m_e] \times 931$

This represents the amount of radiant or heat energy released when an atom is formed from neutrons and hydrogen atoms. It also represents the energy which must be added to disintegrate a nucleus completely.

Dividing equation (2) by A, the number of nucleons in the nucleus, yields the binding energy per nucleon. This in turn can be plotted as a function of A, the mass number (Fig. 2). The result shows that the binding energy per nucleon reaches a maximum for mass numbers in the range of 40 to 80. On the rising portion of this curve, fusion of nucleons to atoms of higher mass number means increased binding energy per nucleon and therefore a greater mass defect and consequent release of energy. On the falling portion of this curve, the fission process results in nuclides of lesser mass numbers and greater binding energy per nucleon. Here again energy is released because of the increased mass defect.

Radioactivity and decay

Isotopes that occur in nature are stable in most chemical elements. However, a few are unstable—especially those of atomic number 84 and above. The unstable nuclides undergo spontaneous change at very definite rates by radioactive disintegration or radioactive decay. The decay is associated with emission from the nucleus of a charged alpha or beta particle, or of a gamma ray. Many nuclides decay into other unstable nuclides, resulting in a decay chain that continues until a stable isotope is formed.

Alpha particle

The alpha particle is the nucleus of a helium atom, ^4_2He, and is denoted by α or $^4_2\alpha$. It results from radioactive decay of unstable nuclides and, with very few exceptions, is observed only with heavy nuclides. Elements of atomic number 84 and above have no stable isotopes and generally emit alpha particles upon decay.

The alpha particle has a mass of 4.00150 amu and a positive charge of 2 units. It is highly ionizing and can be easily stopped by air or by very thin sheets of shielding material.

Beta particle

The beta particle (β or $^0_1\beta$) also results from radioactive decay and has the same mass and charge as an electron.

It is believed that the nucleus of an atom does not contain electrons and, in radioactive beta decay, the beta radiation arises from conversion of a neutron into a proton and beta particle; thus

$$\text{Neutron} \longrightarrow \text{proton} + \text{beta} + \text{energy}$$

In some instances a positive beta particle—called a positron—is produced from radioactive decay. This type of reaction is not significant in the functioning of a nuclear reactor.

---

* An electron volt is the energy gained by a particle of unit electrical charge when it passes, without resistance, through a potential difference of 1 volt.

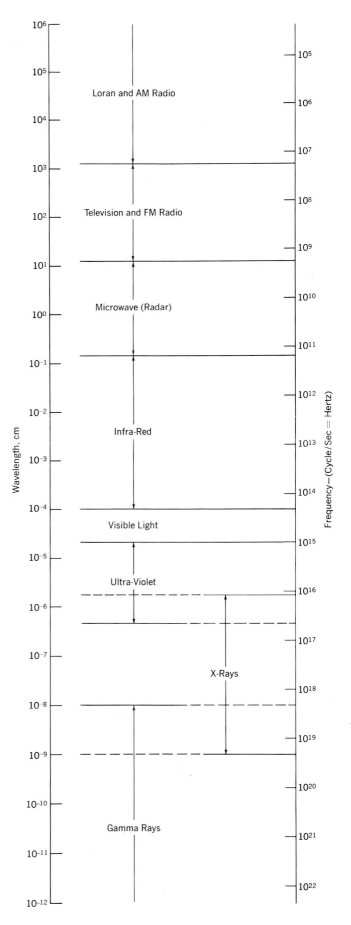

Fig. 3 Electromagnetic spectrum

$$\text{frequency in hertz} = \frac{3 \times 10^{10}}{\text{Wavelength in cm}}$$

Gamma ray

Gamma rays (γ or $_0^0\gamma$) are electromagnetic radiation resulting from a nuclear reaction. They behave like particles in nuclear reactions and are included among the fundamental particles. Although gamma rays have physical characteristics similar to X rays,* their energy is greater and wave length shorter (Fig. 3). The only other difference between the two rays is their origin.

Gamma rays have great penetrating power and can traverse enormous material thickness. The attenuation of gamma intensity through a thickness of material is described by the equation

$$(3) \qquad I(x) = I(0) B\, G\, e^{-\mu x}$$

where:

$I(x)$ = intensity at x
$I(0)$ = intensity before attenuation
x = thickness of material
μ = linear attenuation coefficient
B = buildup factor, to account for buildup by scattering, or secondary gamma emission on absorption of the original gamma ray
G = geometrical factor depending on the size and shape of the source and of the attenuating material.

The rate at which radioactive nuclides emit radiations is unaffected by temperature, pressure, or the presence of other elements that may dilute the radioactive substance. Each nucleus of a specific radioactive nuclide has the probability of decaying in a definite period of time. The rate of decay at any time, t, always remains proportional to the number of radioactive atoms existing at that particular instant. The decay is defined by

$$(4) \qquad N(t) = N(0)\, e^{-\lambda t}$$

where:

$N(t)$ = the number of atoms per cc at time t
$N(0)$ = the number of atoms per cc at time zero
λ = radioactive decay constant, the fraction of the total number of atoms which decays in unit time. (If t is in seconds, then λ = decay fraction per second.)

Decay is usually expressed in terms of a unit of time called radioactive half-life, $T_{\frac{1}{2}}$. This represents a measurable period of time—the period it takes for a quantity of radioactive material to decay to one-half of its original amount. The relationship between half-life and decay constant can be determined by substituting ($T_{\frac{1}{2}}$) for t and $N(0)/2$ for $N(t)$ in equation (4) and solving for λ. The result is

$$(5) \qquad \lambda = \frac{0.693}{T_{\frac{1}{2}}}$$

Thus the decay constants for radioactive isotopes are easily obtainable with the aid of listings of measured half-lives.

* The X ray is a quantum of electromagnetic energy resulting from a change in energy levels of the electrons surrounding the nucleus of an atom.

If $N(t)$ represents the number of radioactive atoms present at time t, then $\lambda N(t)$ becomes the number of radioactive nuclei that decay per unit of time at time t. Since a curie is 3.70×10^{10} disintegrations per second, $\lambda N(t)$ can be converted directly to curies, $\lambda N(t)/(3.70 \times 10^{10})$. If the energy of the ejected particle is known, the $N(t)$ also can be converted to dose rate by the application of proper conversion constants (*see Health Physics*). This means that atoms per cc, curies, and particles per unit time from a radioactive source are all proportional to $e^{-\lambda t}$. Fig. 4 shows on a relative scale how these measures of radioactivity decrease during several half-lives. This curve applies to all radioactive substances.

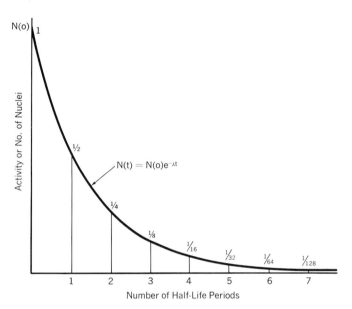

Fig. 4 Exponential decay of isotopes.

Sometimes it is difficult to distinguish between stable and radioactive nuclides. This is particularly true of the isotopes of uranium and other nuclides of high atomic number (Z greater than 84). In many cases, the half-lives of these nuclides represent such long periods of time (10^6 to 10^{10} years) that the nuclides can be considered stable for all practical purposes. In fact, they are generally referred to as the stable isotopes of the heavier chemical elements. Table 2 shows half-lives of some nuclides of high atomic number.

Table 2
Half-lives of heavy elements

Naturally Occurring Nuclides	Activity	Half-Life
Thorium-232	Alpha	1.39×10^{10} yr
Uranium-238	Alpha	4.51×10^{9} yr
Uranium-235	Alpha	7.13×10^{8} yr
Artificial Nuclides		
Thorium-233	Beta	22.1 min
Protactinium-233	Beta	27.4 days
Uranium-233	Alpha	1.62×10^{5} yr
Uranium-239	Beta	23.5 min
Neptunium-239	Beta	2.35 days
Plutonium-239	Alpha	2.44×10^{4} yr

Induced nuclear reactions

Under proper conditions all of the fundamental particles can be made to react with various nuclei. In this procedure the particle strikes or enters an atomic nucleus causing a transfiguration or change in structure of the nucleus and the release of a quantity of energy. Particles which activate these reactions include neutrons, deuterons†, alphas, betas, protons, electrons, and gammas. Many reactions result in the production of artificial radioactive nuclides. A total of about 800 artificial radioactive nuclides, including isotopes of most known chemical elements, have been produced in this manner.

Reactions of principal interest in the design of nuclear reactors are those that yield neutrons and those that absorb neutrons. The former are important because they include the fission process, the latter because of the loss of neutrons needed in the chain reaction and for the useful conversion of fertile to fissionable material.

The expression

$$(6) \qquad {}_{Z_1}^{A_1}X(P_1P_2){}_{Z_2}^{A_2}X$$

is generally used to denote a nuclear reaction and is the short form for

$$ {}_{Z_1}^{A_1}X + P_1 \rightarrow {}_{Z}^{A}X^* \rightarrow {}_{Z_2}^{A_2}X + P_2 $$

The X^* notation indicates formation of a compound nucleus which is generally unstable. Terms P_1 and P_2 represent incident and resultant particles respectively. The individual sum of the "Z's" (atomic numbers) and the sum of the "A's" (mass numbers) on the left side of the equation always equal, respectively, the sum of the "Z's" and the sum of the "A's" on the right side of the equation. (*See examples in Table 3*).

These nuclear reactions always conserve total mass-energy on the two sides of the equation in accordance with Einstein's equation for equivalence of mass and energy. However, there is usually an energy difference and a mass difference. A good statistical probability for the reaction exists when energy is released as a result of reaction. The more probable reactions generally can be initiated by lower energy particles. The less probable ones, those that require energy addition, can be initiated only by high energy particles.

Table 3 gives some typical induced nuclear reactions.

The fission process

Charged particles such as alphas, betas and protons do not have great penetration power in matter because the interaction with the existing electrical field within the atoms either slows or stops them. Collisions between charged particles require exceedingly high kinetic energy. Electrical fields, however, cannot deflect electrically neutral neutrons; hence they collide with nuclei of the material on a statistical basis. Because of this, the neutron is the most effective particle for inducing nuclear changes including fission.

Nuclear fission is the splitting of a nucleus into two or more separate nuclei accompanied by release of a large amount of energy. Many isotopes of the heavier elements are fissionable. The important one which occurs in nature is uranium-235. Other important artificial isotopes are plutonium-239 and uranium-233.

Fission occurs when the fissionable nucleus absorbs a neutron. In the case of uranium-235 the reaction is

$$(7) \qquad {}_{92}^{235}U + {}_0^1n \rightarrow {}_{92}^{236}U^*$$

$$ {}_{92}^{236}U^* \rightarrow {}_{Z_1}^{A_1}X + {}_{Z_2}^{A_2}Y + 2.43\,{}_0^1n + \text{Energy} $$

As previously noted, the asterisk in ${}_{92}^{236}U^*$ indicates an unstable nuclide. The value 2.43 applies to uranium-235 fission by a thermal neutron. X and Y represent the two principal fission fragments.

Table 3
Typical induced nuclear reactions

Short Form	Long Form
Alpha:	
${}_4^9\text{Be}(\alpha,n){}_6^{12}\text{C}$	${}_4^9\text{Be} + {}_2^4\alpha \rightarrow {}_6^{12}\text{C} + {}_0^1n$
${}_7^{14}\text{N}(\alpha,p){}_8^{17}\text{O}$	${}_7^{14}\text{N} + {}_2^4\alpha \rightarrow {}_9^{18}\text{F}^* \rightarrow {}_8^{17}\text{O} + {}_1^1p$
Deuteron:	
${}_{15}^{31}\text{P}(d,p){}_{15}^{32}\text{P}$	${}_{15}^{31}\text{P} + {}_1^2d \rightarrow {}_{16}^{33}\text{S}^* \rightarrow {}_{15}^{32}\text{P} + {}_1^1p$
${}_4^9\text{Be}(d,n){}_5^{10}\text{B}$	${}_4^9\text{Be} + {}_1^2d \rightarrow {}_5^{11}\text{B}^* \rightarrow {}_5^{10}\text{B} + {}_0^1n$
Gamma:	
${}_4^9\text{Be}(\gamma,n){}_4^8\text{Be}$	${}_4^9\text{Be} + {}_0^0\gamma \rightarrow {}_4^8\text{Be} + {}_0^1n$
${}_1^2\text{H}(\gamma,n){}_1^1\text{H}$	${}_1^2\text{H} + {}_0^0\gamma \rightarrow {}_1^2\text{H}^* \rightarrow {}_1^1\text{H} + {}_0^1n$
Neutron:	
${}_5^{10}\text{B}(n,\alpha){}_3^7\text{Li}$	${}_5^{10}\text{B} + {}_0^1n \rightarrow {}_5^{11}\text{B}^* \rightarrow {}_3^7\text{Li} + {}_2^4\alpha$
${}_{48}^{113}\text{Cd}(n,\gamma){}_{48}^{114}\text{Cd}$	${}_{48}^{113}\text{Cd} + {}_0^1n \rightarrow {}_{48}^{114}\text{Cd}^*$ $\rightarrow {}_{48}^{114}\text{Cd} + {}_0^0\gamma$
${}_1^1\text{H}(n,\gamma){}_1^2\text{H}$	${}_1^1\text{H} + {}_0^1n \rightarrow {}_1^2\text{H}^* \rightarrow {}_1^2\text{H} + {}_0^0\gamma$
${}_8^{16}\text{O}(n,p){}_7^{16}\text{N}$	${}_8^{16}\text{O} + {}_0^1n \rightarrow {}_8^{17}\text{O}^* \rightarrow {}_7^{16}\text{N} + {}_1^1p$
${}_{26}^{56}\text{Fe}(n,\gamma){}_{26}^{57}\text{Fe}$	${}_{26}^{56}\text{Fe} + {}_0^1n \rightarrow {}_{26}^{57}\text{Fe}^* \rightarrow {}_{26}^{57}\text{Fe} + {}_0^0\gamma$
Proton:	
${}_6^{12}\text{C}(p,\gamma){}_7^{13}\text{N}$	${}_6^{12}\text{C} + {}_1^1p \rightarrow {}_7^{13}\text{N}^* \rightarrow {}_7^{13}\text{N} + {}_0^0\gamma$
${}_4^9\text{Be}(p,d){}_4^8\text{Be}$	${}_4^9\text{Be} + {}_1^1p \rightarrow {}_5^{10}\text{B}^* \rightarrow {}_4^8\text{Be} + {}_1^2d$

† A particle equivalent to the nucleus of a deuterium atom (*see Table 1*). It consists of one proton plus one neutron and carries one positive charge.

* Indicates formation of a compound nucleus which is generally unstable.

The fission of any of the fissionable isotopes also produces gamma rays, neutrons, betas and other particles. The energy release per fission amounts to about 204 MeV for uranium-235 and is distributed as shown in Table 4. Release of approximately this amount of energy per fission can be predicted by examination of Fig. 2 or equation (2) for binding energy, bearing in mind that the principal fission products are those shown in Fig. 5a. Table 4 also includes data for plutonium-239 and plutonium-241.

Neutron production, neutrons per fission or neutrons per neutron absorbed in the fuel vary with the different fissionable isotopes and with the energy of the neutron producing the fission. Table 5 shows some values of ν, the neutrons produced per fission, and η, the neutrons produced by fission per neutron absorbed in fuel. Since some of the neutrons are absorbed without producing fission, η becomes a more meaningful quantity in reactor design than ν. The values in the table are for fission by thermal neutrons (2200 meters per sec neutron velocity).

Table 4
Energy produced in fission (MeV/fission)

	^{235}U	^{239}Pu	^{241}Pu
Instantaneous			
Kinetic Energy of Fission Fragments	169	175	177
Gamma Ray Energy	8	8	8
Kinetic Energy of Fission Neutrons	5	6	6
	182	189	191
Delayed			
β Particles from Fission Products	8	8	9
γ Rays from Fission Products	7	6	7
Neutron-Capture Gammas*	7	10	10
	22	24	26
Total	204	213	217

* Energy released depends on core composition.

Table 5
Neutrons from fission

Fuel	Neutrons per Fission, ν	Neutrons per Absorption, η
Uranium-233	2.51	2.28
Uranium-235	2.43	2.07
Natural uranium	2.43	1.34
Plutonium-239	2.90	2.10
Plutonium-241	3.06	2.24

It must be recognized that neutrons per fission as given in Table 5 represent only a statistical average. There are individual fission reactions that produce only one neutron, possibly none, or as high as five. This nonstatistical variation does not create a design problem. However, in the low start-up range of reactor instrumentation, peaks can be seen on the low range chart. These are caused by a nonstatistical distribution of the number of neutrons striking the detectors.

When a nucleus undergoes fission, the principal fission fragments may be any of a large number of nuclides. For a given type of nucleus, fissioned by neutrons of a specific

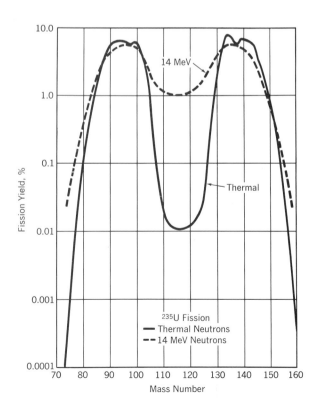

Fig. 5a Mass distribution of fission products from fission of uranium-235.

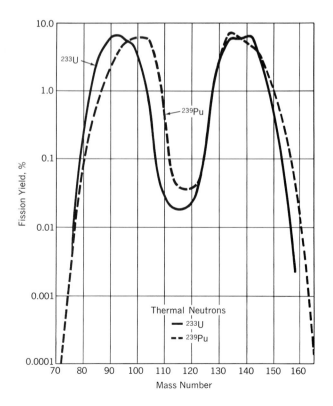

Fig. 5b Mass distribution of fission products from fission of uranium-233 and plutonium-239 by thermal neutrons.

energy, the statistical distribution of nuclides in the fission products is always the same. Distribution of fission products for three fissionable isotopes is shown in Figs. 5a and b. These are experimental curves based upon a representative statistical distribution of the fission products. In fission, as in any nuclear reaction, there is always conservation of total mass-energy.

Examination of Figs. 5a and b reveals that mass number of the fission products ranges from about 70 to 170 with two plateaus at approximately 95 and 135. All curves represent thermal energy neutrons except the 14 MeV curve for uranium-235 which is included to illustrate the effect of neutron energy.

Neutrons released from fission vary in initial energy over a wide range up to 15 MeV and above. The distribution of neutrons produced by fission as a function of energy has been determined from several experimental measurements, and typical results for uranium-235 and plutonium-239 are shown in Fig. 6. Based on these measurements, the average energy of fission neutrons is about 2 MeV; the most probable energy is about 0.8 MeV.

Nuclear chain reaction

To utilize fission as a continuous process for power production, it becomes necessary to initiate and maintain a fission chain reaction at a controlled constant level that can vary with demand. Obtaining a steady-state chain reaction requires availability of more than one neutron for each fission produced because non-fission reactions absorb some neutrons and others leak out of the reactor. The steady-state equation for neutron balance in a chain reaction or nuclear reactor is

Production = Absorption + Leakage.

Table 5 indicates that each fission of a uranium-235 atom by a thermal neutron makes available an average of 2.43 neutrons. However, only 2.07 neutrons are produced per thermal neutron absorbed in uranium-235 as indicated in Table 5. The other 0.36 neutrons are absorbed in non-fission ways. If natural uranium is used, the number of neutrons produced per thermal neutron absorbed is reduced to 1.34 because of the neutron absorption in uranium-238. Most of this absorption results in the ultimate production of fissionable plutonium-239. However, neutrons used in this manner are no longer available to help maintain the chain reaction.

Neutrons react not only with uranium, but also with the nuclei of most other elements. This is an important consideration because the core of a power reactor contains, in addition to uranium, structural elements and a coolant to remove the heat. Thus many materials which have high neutron absorption must be disqualified for structural use. Fortunately a few materials, such as aluminum and zirconium, have low neutron absorption. Steel and stainless steel can be used to a limited extent. The choice of coolants includes water, helium, carbon dioxide, and liquid sodium.

The low neutron fraction available with natural uranium makes it difficult to design a natural uranium reactor. It can be done, however, if all materials are of especially high purity. Minute quantities of certain high neutron absorbers, if present, would prevent the chain reaction. Nevertheless, all early reactors utilized natural uranium and many still operate—notably the large plutonium-producing reactors.

Critical size and mass

With a given mix of materials containing fissile* material, the leakage term in the steady-state equation decreases in importance as the size and mass of the material increases. Leakage depends on external surface, whereas production and absorption depend on volume. The ratio of external surface to volume decreases as size increases.

Thus a small mass of material may not sustain a chain reaction whereas a larger one often will. With a given mix and shape of materials containing fissile material, the minimum size that will sustain a chain reaction is known as the "critical size," and the mass of fissile material in this critical size is the "critical mass."

Control of the chain reaction

When less than one neutron per fission acts to produce new fissions, the chain reaction dies out. When more than one neutron per fission acts to produce new fissions, the chain reaction builds up. For operation at a constant power level a control must regulate the neutron population so that exactly one neutron per fission acts to produce new fissions.

More than 99 percent of neutrons produced in fission are "prompt" neutrons; that is, they are produced almost instantaneously. In certain types of reactors as many as ten million generations of prompt neutrons may be produced in a single second. It is easy to see that a slight excess of neutrons would cause the intensity of the chain reaction to increase very rapidly. The necessity for a positive and definite means for control is also clear.

Fortunately some of the neutrons (0.73% in the case of uranium-235) are released by the decay of fission products rather than directly from fission. The average half-life for these delayed neutrons from fissioning of uranium-235 is about thirteen seconds. This time is sufficient to provide a basis for safe control.

The chain reaction can be regulated by placing materials with high neutron absorption capability in the reactor and providing a means of varying their amounts. These materials, known as "poisons" because they tend to stop the chain reaction, include boron, cadium, hafnium and gadolinium. One or more of them usually goes into the reactor in the form of "control rods" that can be withdrawn to start up the reactor and reinserted to shut down. Safety considerations make it prudent to use more than the minimum calculated number of rods needed, all of which must be in place during initial assembly of the critical mass of fuel. To assure accurate control of power, at least one rod must be capable of fine regulation.

Fast and thermal reactors

The average energy of neutrons produced in fission is about two million electron volts (2 MeV). If a neutron is not absorbed by a nucleus, it loses its energy by elastic collisions with nuclei and particles until it reaches equilibrium with its surroundings. In this "thermal" state the

---

* Capable of undergoing fission by interaction with slow neutrons (see Uranium, Chapter 19).

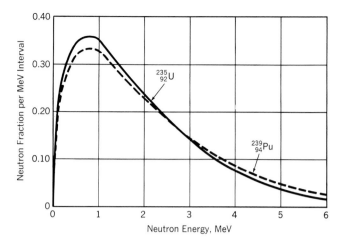

Fig. 6 Fission neutron energy distribution.

average neutron energy is about 0.025 electron volts (eV)—about one eighty-millionth part of its original energy.

It is possible to design for a chain reaction to occur predominantly with either "fast" (high energy) neutrons or "slow" (thermal energy) neutrons. In fast reactors the chain reaction is maintained primarily by fast neutrons. Thermal reactors are those in which the chain reaction occurs primarily from thermal neutrons. Today's commercial water reactors are thermal reactors.

It is not possible to maintain a chain reaction with fast neutrons by utilizing natural uranium. However, thermal neutrons cause uranium-235 to fission more readily than do fast neutrons and this makes it possible to produce a chain reaction from natural uranium in a thermal reactor. Since only natural uranium was available for the early reactors, thermal designs had to be used.

Because neutron velocity is proportional to the square root of neutron energy, thermal neutron velocity is 1/9000 of the fission neutron velocity. This lower neutron velocity increases the time between collisions in a thermal reactor and also increases the neutron lifetime compared to that in fast reactors. As a result some phases of control are easier to resolve with a thermal reactor even though normal control, depending on delayed neutrons, is similar for both fast and thermal reactors. All designs require provision for shutting down in case of prompt criticality (*see Reactivity*) and for the thermal reactor there would be more time available because of the longer neutron life. However, it should be added that experience and more sophisticated control devices make this factor less important today than it was for the first reactors.

Design of a thermal reactor requires incorporation in the core of a "moderator" (a material containing atoms of a light element such as hydrogen, deuterium, or carbon) to reduce the kinetic energy of the neutrons. Hydrogen is the ideal moderator because its nucleus is as light as a neutron and, therefore, it absorbs the energy of the neutron in a single direct collision. Hydrogen is normally used in the form of water. The heavier the atom the less energy it absorbs per collision, and the less the slowing down effect on the neutron. Carbon is about the heaviest atom that can be used practically as a moderator. Carbon has the additional advantage of absorbing

very few neutrons—even less than hydrogen. Other low weight atoms can be used, but they are less practical because of excess neutron absorption or high material cost. Since the helium nucleus absorbs essentially no neutrons, it would be an ideal moderator except that helium is a gas at reactor operating temperatures. In this state it would be impossible to provide the core with a sufficient number of atoms.

Sufficient amounts of a moderating material in a reactor automatically make it a thermal unit. For example, if water is used as a coolant, it is not possible to have a fast reactor. All thermal reactors necessarily contain some fast neutrons because only fast neutrons result from fission. The amount of moderator provided determines the degree of "thermalization"—or percentage of thermal neutrons in the reactor. Perhaps the greatest advantage of the thermal reactor is its compatibility with the water coolant. This has proved to be the most practical and economical coolant.

Fertile material such as uranium-238 can be used as a fuel by first converting it to plutonium in a reactor. The conversion of fertile materials to fissile material by neutron absorption is discussed in Chapter 19. Fast reactors and particularly fast breeder reactors accomplish this conversion most effectively (*see Chapter 21*). Liquid sodium, which has essentially no moderating effect, is the coolant most often considered for fast breeders. Use of helium and steam as coolants in fast breeders is also a possibility.

Other physical considerations in nuclear reactor design and operation

Cross section

The calculation of a chain reaction or the design of a nuclear reactor requires solution of the steady-state equation

(8)   Production = Absorption + Leakage

or its counterpart for transient conditions

(9)   Production − Absorption − Leakage = $\dfrac{\partial n}{\partial t}$

where $\dfrac{\partial n}{\partial t}$ is the variation of the neutron density with time.

Production, absorption, and leakage all depend heavily on interactions of neutrons with nuclei of the various materials in the reactor. Production depends primarily on those interactions with uranium-235 nuclei which result in fission. Absorption depends on interactions of neutrons with any nuclei in the core that result in absorption of neutrons with or without fission. Leakage depends on the scattering effect of collisions between neutrons, nuclei and other particles, with transport of neutrons toward the boundaries of the chain reacting system and ultimate escape from the system.

All these complex events depend upon neutron energy. Neutrons of various energies are present in all reactors; in thermal reactors neutron energy varies from the energy level of fast neutrons produced from fission to that of the thermal state. Neutrons of all energies produce fissions

and enter into absorption and scattering reactions, but the probability of any of these events occurring varies considerably with the neutron energy. Therefore, before calculating the behavior of a chain reaction and before designing a reactor, it is necessary to have basic physical information on the energy-dependent probabilities of possible reactions for all the nuclei in the core including those of the important impurities.

The probability of reaction between a neutron and a particular nuclide is expressed as the "cross section" for the particular reaction, and the chance of it occurring depends on the energy of the incident neutron. Nuclear cross sections may be referred to as:

1. The microscopic cross section, which has the dimensions of an area and is an intrinsic characteristic of the nuclei of the material.

2. The macroscopic cross section, which is a probability per centimeter of neutron path and takes into account the density of the material.

Symbol σ represents the microscopic cross section. In the case of a neutron approaching a fissionable atom it becomes possible to consider a total cross section σ_T in which

$$(10) \qquad \sigma_T = \sigma_c + \sigma_s + \sigma_f = \sigma_a + \sigma_s$$

where:

σ_c, known as the capture cross section, is a measure of the area presented for absorption without fission

σ_s is the equivalent area of the nucleus that will scatter or deflect the neutron

σ_f (present in only a few of the many nuclei) is the area that is presented for a neutron to strike and cause a fission to occur

σ_a, the absorption cross section, is the area presented for absorption with or without fission.

Experimental measurements determine microscopic cross sections for each element. Total cross section measurements are generally made by transmission techniques. For example, placing a material of known density and thickness in front of a neutron source permits measuring the intensity of neutrons at a particular energy on the incident and emergent sides of the material. The difference represents the loss or attenuation of neutrons by the material. The cross section required to obtain this attenuation is derived by calculation.

The program for measurement of cross sections has been carried out for many years in a large number of laboratories. Cross sections have been recorded by the Brookhaven National Laboratory, Upton, New York, and are available in BNL-325, "Neutron Cross Sections."

Brookhaven also maintains an "Evaluated Nuclear Data File" containing more detailed information. Besides providing a common basis for the nuclear industry, this file furnishes the reactor designer with the most recent and appropriate information about neutron reactions for those nuclides of interest in the reactor field. Several U.S. laboratories and industries (including Babcock & Wilcox) are participating in this effort to establish a central file on magnetic tape.

Isotopes of the same element can have very different cross sections. For example, the isotope xenon-134 has a microscopic cross section for neutron absorption of about 0.2 barn[*], yet xenon-135 has a cross section of 2.7×10^6 barns. Uranium-235 is fissionable at any energy, uranium-238 only at high energy.

Cross sections of some nuclides also contain abrupt peaks at certain energy bands (Fig. 7). These peaks, called resonances, have an important effect on nuclear reactor operation and control. Since a cross section is really a function of relative energy of the neutron and the nucleus, an effective change in the cross section results when the energies of the neutron and the nucleus increase or decrease as a result of temperature changes.

Where the curve of cross section versus energy is fairly smooth, the effect of a temperature change of the target nucleus is relatively small. However, it is large and important in the vicinity of a resonance. An increase in temperature results in increased vibration of the nucleus with a corresponding increase in the number of probable collisions between nucleus and neutron occurring at energies in the vicinity of the resonance. Therefore, an increase in the temperature of the nucleus results in an apparent broadening of the energy width of the resonance. This in turn results in a very effective increase in resonance neutron absorption, i.e., capture and fission. Conversely, a decrease in temperature of the nucleus results in narrowing the resonance width and decreasing resonance absorption. This effect, known as the Doppler effect, can be an important aid in reactor control.

Fig. 7 illustrates a typical cross section curve showing the neutron capture cross section of uranium-238 as a function of neutron energy. Below 10^2 eV the height of the resonance peaks is about 10^3 barns. Between 10^2 and 4×10^3 eV, the great number of resonances makes it impracticable to show the cross section as a curve, although the resonance parameter data are available for use on a computer. Between 4×10^3 and 10^5 eV the curve represents a statistical average of the measurements which have been made.

The macroscopic cross section has the dimensions cm^{-1} and can be obtained from

$$(11) \qquad \Sigma = \frac{N_o \rho}{M} \sigma$$

where:

Σ = macroscopic cross section, cm^{-1}
N_o = Avogadro's number, 0.602252×10^{24} atoms/ gram-atom
M = atomic weight, grams/ gram-atom
σ = microscopic cross section, sq cm/atom
ρ = density of the material, grams/cc

Determination of critical mass

While it is possible to obtain the critical mass by solution of the steady-state equation, it usually proves more convenient to utilize a quantity called the effective multiplication factor (k_{eff}). This is defined as the ratio of the neutron population in each generation to that in the preceding one. With a multiplication factor of less than one,

---

[*] One barn equals 10^{-24} sq cm.

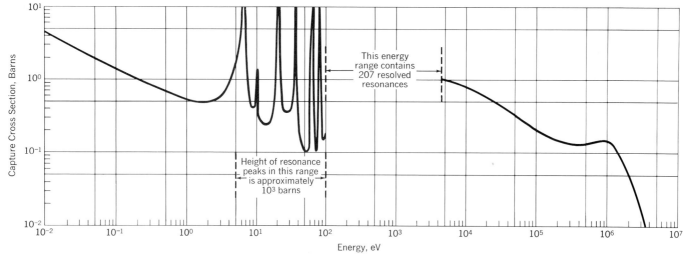

Fig. 7 Capture cross section of uranium-238.

the system is a decaying one and will never be self-sustaining. With a multiplication factor greater than one, a nuclear system reproduces more neutrons than it uses and becomes subject to an increasing chain reaction that must be controlled by some exterior method to avoid self-destruction. The steady-state condition of a nuclear system occurs when the effective multiplication factor, k_{eff}, exactly equals one. This corresponds to a constant power level.

For a thermal reactor the value of k_{eff} is obtained from the equation

$$(12) \qquad k_{eff} = f\eta\epsilon pL_tL_f$$

This is called the "six-factor" equation in which η represents the neutron production factor; f, ϵ and p account for the absorption of neutrons in various reactor materials, and L_t and L_f account for neutron leakage. These factors can be described briefly as follows:

Thermal utilization factor. The thermal utilization factor, f, is the ratio of the probability of a neutron being absorbed in the fuel to the probability that the neutron will be absorbed in any of the materials that make up the core.

$$(13) \qquad f = \frac{\Sigma_a(\text{fuel})}{\Sigma_a(\text{fuel}) + \Sigma_a(\text{other})}$$

where

Σ_a denotes macroscopic cross section for absorption.

Neutron production factor. η, the neutron production factor, equals the average number of neutrons produced per thermal neutron absorbed in the fuel (*see Table 5*).

ϵ factor. Factor ϵ represents a value greater than one and accounts for fast neutron fission in uranium-238. Its value would be one if there were no uranium-238 in the reactor. However, natural uranium reactors and current water-cooled power reactors contain large amounts of uranium-238 and ϵ is significant. This is so even though the probability for a fission reaction in uranium-238 is quite low.

Resonance escape probability. The resonance escape probability, p, is the fraction of neutrons that escape capture while slowing down to thermal energy. The term "resonance escape" refers particularly to uranium-238 because in the intermediate range of neutron energy there are several resonance peaks of absorption cross section for this isotope. These resonances are useful in the production of plutonium; however, to maintain criticality in a thermal reactor, sufficient neutrons must escape absorption in the resonance region.

Thermal nonleakage factor. The thermal nonleakage factor, L_t, is the fraction of thermal neutrons that do not leak from the system during thermal diffusion but remain to contribute to the chain reaction. It is also the probability that a thermal neutron will be retained and utilized within the system. This factor is expressed by the following equation

$$(14) \qquad L_t = \frac{1}{1 + L^2B^2}$$

where:

$L^2 = \frac{1}{6}$ of the mean square of the distance traveled by a neutron from the time it becomes a thermal neutron until it is lost to the system. "L" is known as the thermal diffusion length.

B^2 is a function of system geometry known as buckling because of a mathematical similarity to material buckling in structural design. Values of buckling are given in the following table

Table 6
Formulae for geometric buckling

Geometry	B^2	Symbols
Sphere	π^2/r^2	r = radius
Cylinder	$\pi^2/h^2 + 2.405^2/r^2$	h = height
Parallelepiped	$\pi^2\left(\dfrac{1}{a^2} + \dfrac{1}{b^2} + \dfrac{1}{c^2}\right)$	a, b, c = edges

Fast nonleakage factor. The fast nonleakage factor, L_f, refers to the leakage of fast neutrons. It represents the probability that a neutron will remain in the system and become thermal without leaking from the system at higher energy.

For the continuous slowing down model*

$$(15) \qquad L_f = \frac{1}{e^{\tau B^2}}$$

For the two-group model*

$$(16) \qquad L_f = \frac{1}{1 + \tau B^2}$$

where:

B^2 is buckling (Table 6)

τ, referred to as "Fermi Age," is an exact analog for fast neutrons of the quantity L^2 for thermal neutrons. It is $\frac{1}{6}$ of the mean square of the distance traveled by a neutron from the time of birth as a fast neutron until it reaches a thermal state.

A useful variant of the six-factor equation (12) in which the leakage terms have been eliminated is known as the four-factor equation,

$$(17) \qquad k_\infty = f\eta\epsilon p$$

where:

k_∞ = multiplication factor for a hypothetical infinite system.

Both the four-factor and six-factor equations can give a deceptively simple picture of a chain reacting system. To be accurate, such a system requires the simultaneous solution of the six-factor equation for a rather large number of energy levels. This must be done on a computer. On the other hand, an approximate solution for many chain reacting systems can be obtained by a single use of the six-factor equation (12) based on the concept of continuous slowing down of the neutrons. The condition of criticality is attained when $k_{eff} = 1.0$.

Setting $k_{eff} = 1$, and substituting for $f\eta\epsilon p$ its equivalent, k_∞ from equation (17), the six-factor formula (12) reduces to

$$(18) \qquad 1 = k_\infty L_t L_f$$

Replacing L_t by (14) and L_f by (15) for the continuous slowing down model, (18) becomes

$$(19) \qquad k_\infty = (1 + L^2 B^2)e^{\tau B^2}$$

More accurate results in calculating the effective multiplication factor for most thermal reactors can be obtained by using the two-group theory. In this approach the six-factor equation is solved simultaneously for two neutron energy groups — one thermal, the other fast, the latter including all energies above thermal. The actual solutions are customarily accomplished by the use of more general equations involving the Laplacian operator. However,

these solutions can be shown to be equivalent to that obtained with the equation

$$(20) \qquad k_\infty = (1 + L^2 B^2)(1 + \tau B^2)$$

Equation (20) also is obtained in a manner similar to (19) except that the two-group model is used for L_f instead of the continuous slowing down model.

Reactivity

The first step in operating a chain reacting system is to bring it to critical condition at essentially no thermal power. This is called operating at "zero power level." After making proper physical determinations at this low power, the reactor is gradually increased in power up to the operating level and maintained there for the desired period of time. The objective in each step of this procedure is to obtain and hold a constant value of $k_{eff} = 1.0$. In view of the changes that continually occur in a nuclear system, it is never possible to keep $k_{eff} = 1.0$ for more than a short period of time without adjustments to compensate for variations. Operating a reactor at any constant power level at an effective multiplication factor of unity corresponds to steering a ship on a compass course. It takes a continual effort, either automatic or manual, to hold the ship on the exact course.

If a reactor operates at a specific power level with $k_{eff} = 1.0$, and if anything changes to increase or decrease the multiplication factor, a reactivity change occurs. It may be a positive or negative change depending upon the direction of change in k_{eff}. Reactivity, represented by the symbol "ρ", is defined as the ratio of the excess of the effective multiplication factor to the effective multiplication factor.

$$\rho = \frac{k_{eff} - 1}{k_{eff}}$$

This is usually written

$$(21) \qquad \rho = \frac{\Delta k_{eff}}{k_{eff}}$$

The unit most commonly used to express reactivity is the dollar. It represents the amount of reactivity that is equal to the fraction of delayed neutrons. For uranium-235 fuel in a thermal reactor, one dollar equals approximately 0.007. When k_{eff} exceeds approximately 1.007 in such a reactor, it becomes critical on prompt neutrons and the control is considerably more difficult.

Neutron detectors

Operating a chain reacting system requires the use of neutron detectors to measure the level or intensity of the neutron radiation (neutron flux) which is a direct measure of the intensity of the chain reaction. Neutron detectors can be counter-type, which detect neutrons in terms of the individual ionizations produced; counters are most useful when neutron intensity is low. Another type of detector, more useful at high neutron flux, is the ionization chamber which measures the electrical current that flows when radiation ionizes gas in a chamber. At all power levels the neutron count should be read on at least two instruments operating in their design range (*see Instrumentation, Chapter 21*).

---

* The continuous slowing down model or one-group theory and the two-group model or two-group theory are different simplifications for obtaining approximate values of critical size and mass.

Neutron source

The start of the chain reaction is a critical phase of reactor operation. The mass of fuel in the core is much greater than the "critical mass" required to sustain a chain reaction. Control rods and neutron absorbers dissolved in the reactor coolant keep the core sub-critical when no power output is required.

When the core is to be brought to criticality, it is necessary to withdraw control rods and initiate the chain reaction. However, if the control rods are withdrawn before a measurable neutron flux is available, a reaction could be initiated by a stray neutron and build up to a high power level before the control rods could be reinserted to maintain the desired core output.

To control the rate of buildup of the reaction, it is necessary to have a neutron source present in the core for start-up. By having a neutron source available, it is possible to measure neutron flux before moving control rods. With the aid of such a source, a reactor can be started up safely at a much faster rate than is otherwise practicable.

Several types of neutron sources are available. One is a polonium-beryllium capsule. The radioactive isotope, polonium-210, emits alpha particles which react with the beryllium to produce neutrons (*see Table 3*).

Fission product poisons

Many fission products interact with neutrons, absorbing them so that they are not available to the chain reaction. As these fission products build up, they act as "poisons" to retard the chain reaction.

All long-lived fission product poisons except samarium build up as the core is operated, reaching a maximum effect at the end of core life. The effect of these relatively stable poisons is provided for in the design and operation of thermal reactors by assuming a buildup of poisons in the fuel at a rate of about 30 barns per fission.

A second group of fission products consists of xenon-135 and samarium-149, both of which have very high cross sections for absorption of thermal neutrons.

All initial products of fission are highly radioactive and decay rapidly to less active isotopes with somewhat longer half-lives. There are usually several isotopes in the chain before a stable end product is reached. The most significant such decay chain is the following:

$$(22) \qquad {}^{135}_{52}\text{Te} \xrightarrow[<1.0\text{m}]{\beta} {}^{135}_{53}\text{I} \xrightarrow[6.7\text{ hr}]{\beta} {}^{135}_{54}\text{Xe} \xrightarrow[9.2\text{ hr}]{\beta} {}^{135}_{55}\text{Cs}$$

$$\xrightarrow[2 \times 10^{6}\text{y}]{\beta} {}^{135}_{56}\text{Ba}$$

In this chain, tellurium-135 with a one minute half-life decays to iodine-135 with a 6.7 hr half-life and then to xenon-135. This xenon isotope, which fortunately has only a 9.2 hr half-life, has a cross section for thermal neutron absorption approximately 100,000 times as great as all the long-lived fission products together. Unfortunately, the nuclides of this chain occur abundantly as fission products; a predictable happening, since the mass number 135 occurs at a peak in the curves (Figs. 5a and b).

In a thermal reactor the xenon-135 absorbs an appreciable fraction of available neutrons as long as the reactor is operating. This changes some of the xenon-135 to xenon-136 (which has negligible neutron absorption). As a result, when a water reactor operates at constant power level, the xenon-135 builds up to its equilibrium value in 36 to 48 hours.

When reactor power lessens and, particularly, when the reactor shuts down, the iodine-135 formed at the original power level continues for a while to generate xenon-135 at a rate corresponding to the original power level. Thus the xenon-135 builds up rapidly after shutdown since fewer neutrons are available for conversion to xenon-136. The buildup reaches a peak 4 to 12 hours after shutdown and then slowly decays.

The neutron absorption capacity of xenon-135 depends on reactor design and may amount to as much as 2 percent in reactivity. To start up the reactor at any time during the cycle, an amount of fissionable material adequate to overcome the "maximum xenon" must be added to the critical mass of the fresh core in addition to that required by burnup and to overcome the stable fission product poisons.

Samarium-149, the second important poison produced in the reactor core during operation, is generated as follows:

$$(23) \qquad {}^{149}_{60}\text{Nd} \xrightarrow[1.7\text{ hr}]{\beta} {}^{149}_{61}\text{Pm} \xrightarrow[47\text{ hr}]{\beta} {}^{149}_{62}\text{Sm (stable)}$$

In the chain, neodymium-149 decays (1.7 hr half-life) into promethium-149, which in turn decays (47 hr half-life) into samarium-149. Although samarium-149 is a stable isotope it is destroyed so rapidly by high neutron absorption that it reaches an equilibrium value when the reactor operates at constant power. Typically samarium-149 equilibrium in a pressurized water reactor (about 1.2% in reactivity) is reached after 50 to 100 days. Buildup after shutdown is slower and less extensive than for ^{135}Xe. A typical example is an increase from 1.2% to about 1.33% in reactivity over a 12-day period following shutdown.

Decay after shutdown has little consequence for all other fission fragments because of their long lives and comparable capture cross sections between parent and daughter nuclides.

Conversion and breeding

This chapter and Chapter 19 refer to the conversion of fertile materials in the reactor to fissionable materials as a result of the absorption of neutrons. Most important of the conversion reactions is the capture of a neutron by a uranium-238 nucleus, resulting in the production of a nucleus of fissionable plutonium-239:

$$(24) \qquad {}^{238}_{92}\text{U} + {}^{1}_{0}n \rightarrow {}^{239}_{92}\text{U} + {}^{0}_{0}\gamma$$

$$ {}^{239}_{92}\text{U} \xrightarrow[23\text{m}]{\beta} {}^{239}_{93}\text{Np} \xrightarrow[2.3\text{d}]{\beta} {}^{239}_{94}\text{Pu}$$

The uranium-238 nucleus absorbs a neutron and becomes uranium-239, which decays with a half-life of 23

minutes, into neptunium-239. Again this nuclide, with a half-life of 2.3 days, is transmuted to plutonium-239 by beta decay. This is the nuclear process by which the most useful isotope of plutonium is formed.

There are other reactions in reactor operation which result in formation of different isotopes of plutonium. Some of these isotopes, including plutonium-241, are fissionable, and others, including plutonium-240, are converted to fissionable isotopes by neutron absorption. These isotopes cannot be separated economically from plutonium-239, and therefore must be taken into account when plutonium is used in a reactor.

If thorium is used as fertile material, the reaction for the formation of uranium-233 is as follows:

$$(25) \qquad {}^{232}_{90}\text{Th} + {}^{1}_{0}n \rightarrow {}^{233}_{90}\text{Th} + {}^{0}_{0}\gamma$$

$$ {}^{233}_{90}\text{Th} \xrightarrow[23\text{m}]{\beta} {}^{233}_{91}\text{Pa} \xrightarrow[27.4\text{d}]{\beta} {}^{233}_{92}\text{U}$$

Here the thorium-232 nucleus absorbs a neutron and is converted to thorium-233 which decays by beta emission to protactinium-233; this in turn emits a beta and decays to uranium-233. Currently, the production of uranium-233 is very small compared to plutonium production.

The U.S. ERDA operates large reactors at Savannah River for the production of plutonium by conversion from uranium-238. England, France and Russia also have plutonium production reactors. The large commercial pressurized water reactors in the United States operate on slightly enriched uranium fuel. These reactors convert uranium-238 to plutonium and produce about 50% as much plutonium as the uranium-235 consumed. A reactor is considered to be a converter when the amount of fissionable material produced (e.g. plutonium) is less than the amount of fissionable material consumed (e.g. uranium-235). A "breeder" reactor is one in which more fissionable material is produced than consumed.

"Breeding gain" and "doubling time" are important concepts in breeder reactor development. "Breeding ratio" equals the ratio of fissionable material produced to that consumed. Breeding gain equals breeding ratio less 1.0, or the excess of fissionable material produced over that required to fuel the reactor that produces it. Doubling time represents the reactor operating time required for excess fissionable material to equal the initial fuel loading.

By definition, a breeder reactor has a breeding ratio greater than 1.0. This means the value of η (neutrons produced per neutron absorbed in fissionable fuel—Table 5) must exceed 2.0 by some margin. One neutron is required to maintain the chain reaction, one or more for the breeding, and an additional fraction for parasitic* absorption and leakage.

It is not possible to make a breeder reactor with natural uranium fuel, since η is less than 2.0. Table 5 shows that η does not greatly exceed 2.0 with any common fissionable isotopes for fissions produced by thermal neutrons. Consequently, it becomes difficult and generally impracticable, to make a breeder with a thermal reactor, although some possibilities are still under exploration.

---

* Neutron absorption not leading to fission or other desired process.

Fortunately, at high neutron energies, η has a greater value than at thermal energies, particularly with plutonium-239. For this reason, and because the parasitic capture of neutrons is less than at thermal energy, fast reactors breed plutonium more effectively than thermal reactors. Fast reactors operate best with plutonium fuel. Work is currently in progress to develop breeder reactors to produce power and plutonium.

Health physics

Health physics, or radiological physics, can be defined as the science of radiation protection. The role of a health physicist in a nuclear plant is similar to that of a safety engineer in an industrial plant. Since the first nuclear reactor went critical on December 2, 1942, at the University of Chicago, the potential hazards of radiation have been given very careful attention, and health physics has been an integral part of public and private U.S. nuclear energy programs. As a direct result, U.S. nuclear energy programs have had an enviable safety record.

The health physicist concerns himself with alpha, beta, and gamma radiations in all areas of a nuclear facility, and with neutrons in the vicinity of an operating reactor.

Alpha particles are seldom harmful when the source is located outside the human body since ordinary clothing or even a single sheet of paper stops practically all of them. If emitted inside the body, however, alpha radiation can have serious consequences. It becomes important, therefore, to prevent the ingesting or inhalation of alpha-emitting nuclides. Particular care is required to keep the air in working spaces free of dust containing alpha emitters. Fabrication of alpha emitters such as plutonium or ${}^{233}\text{U}$ normally takes place inside a glovebox that remains under a slight negative pressure. The box discharges air effluent through a filter designed to prevent alpha-bearing dust from entering the working spaces and the atmosphere in general.

Beta rays penetrate up to an inch of wood or plastic material and travel several yards in air.

Gamma rays are essentially powerful X rays and penetrate deeply.

Shielding is required to protect personnel from gamma and the higher-energy beta radiation. In applications such as nuclear reactors, gamma radiation exists in very high concentrations and, to protect against it, concrete shielding must be several feet thick. Where lack of space prevents use of concrete, a lesser thickness of iron or lead can be used. Sometimes it is desirable for viewing purposes to store or handle gamma-emitting material under water. Water typically about 20 feet in depth makes a good shield.

The shielding that surrounds a nuclear reactor should moderate and absorb neutrons as well as protect against gamma radiation. For this purpose concrete containing a high volume of water is particularly effective. Fast neutrons escaping from the reactor are slowed down by the water moderator and absorbed by the heavier nuclei in the concrete. Usually a gamma ray is emitted in this process and there must be enough additional shielding to stop this secondary gamma radiation. Water also provides a good shield for research reactors operating at low power.

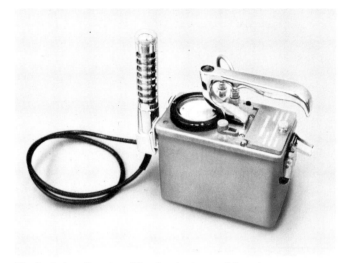

Fig. 8 Geiger Counter *(Eberline Instrument Corp.).*

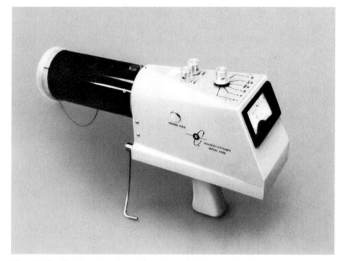

Fig. 9 Radiation Monitor *(Nuclear Chicago Corp.).*

An important quantity in Health Physics is the radiation dose. The term "dose" denotes the quantity of radiation absorbed in a specified mass of material. It is applied to radiation absorbed in the human body.

For gamma (or X-) radiation the unit of exposure is the "roentgen," which is defined as that radiation which in dry air at standard conditions of pressure and temperature produces ionization corresponding to 0.33×10^{-9} coulombs per cc. By definition, the roentgen's use extends only to measuring gamma (and X-) radiation, and only in air; therefore additional measuring units are needed.

For measuring absorbed dose, a unit called the "rad" is used. The rad measures the energy imparted to a specified mass of matter by ionizing radiation (1 rad = 100 ergs/g or 10^{-2} joules/kg). It can be used to measure all types of radiation, and has a value approximately equal to the roentgen in air.

Response of biological systems to radiation energy absorbed is different for different types of radiation, and is also influenced by other factors such as the distribution of internally deposited isotopes. For radiation protection purposes, a quantity termed "dose equivalent" is used. As defined in the International Committee on Radiation Units Report 19, July 1, 1971, the dose equivalent H, is the product of D, Q, and N, at the point of interest in tissue, where D is the absorbed dose, Q is the quality factor and N is the product of any other modifying factors.

$$H = DQN$$

The special unit of dose equivalent is the rem. When D is expressed in rads, H is in rems. The following should be noted:

a) This quantity is limited to radiation protection applications and may be used when H is in the region of, or below, the applicable maximum permissible dose equivalent. It should not be used for high level accidental exposures.

b) The dependence of Q upon L_x, the linear energy transfer, is specified by the International Commission on Radiological Protection and given in Note (e) of this definition. Further discussions are provided in the report of the Relative Biological Effectiveness Committee and ICRU Report 16.

c) In the usual case where D is delivered by particles having a range of L_x values

$$H = D\bar{Q}N$$

Where

$$\bar{Q} = \frac{1}{D} \int_0^\infty Q D_{Lx}\, dL_\infty$$

D_{Lx} denotes the differential distribution of D in L_x. In ICRU Report 16 $(1/D)D_{Lx}$ is denoted by $d_x(L)$.

d) N is the product of modifying factors such as those allowing for distribution of absorbed dose in space and time. At present this factor is assigned a value of 1 for external sources.

e) The dependence of the quality factor, Q, on L_x, is given in the following table:

L_x in water keV/μm	Q
3.5 or less	1
7.0	2
23	5
53	10
175	20

Since none of man's senses detects nuclear radiations, the health physicist has had to develop new instruments and techniques for measuring amounts of radiation. In general, three types of checks are required as follows:

1. Measurement of beta and gamma radiations by instruments such as the Geiger counter (Fig. 8) and "Cutie-Pie" (Fig. 9) provide instantaneous indications of the total level of beta and gamma.

All persons in areas where radiation may be encountered normally wear a film badge and/or pocket dosimeter. These instruments measure the amount of gamma (the film badge also measures the beta) radiation a person absorbs in terms of the total dose of radiation for a day, week, or month.

2. Keeping the concentration of alpha emitters in working spaces and in outgoing air below prescribed tolerances is sufficient to protect against alpha particles. Alpha counters monitor air content in working spaces on a regular schedule. Samples of dust accumulating in various areas of the room are monitored periodically for alpha radiation. Alpha counters are also used to monitor hands, shoes, and clothing of personnel leaving areas where exposure to alpha emitters could occur.

3. Protection against neutrons is provided, primarily, by the shielding around nuclear reactors. When a reactor first goes into service, neutron counters as well as gamma counters are used to make a careful survey of the surrounding area. Should leakage exist, the shielding is modified to prevent it. Thereafter, periodic checks are made for gamma and neutron leakage. In experimental installations, or where neutron surveys indicate the need for continuous surveillance, special film badges and neutron dosimeters may also be used.

NRC regulations (Title 10 of the Code of Federal Regulations, Part 20) require the operator of a nuclear power plant to control and monitor radiation exposure of plant employees and to protect the population in the vicinity of the plant. The latter requirement makes it necessary to perform analyses on the air, water, and vegetation around the plant. Also, all wastes leaving the plant must be analyzed to make sure that radioactive materials do not exceed maximum permissible concentration.

Records also must be kept of personnel exposure, test results, radioactive waste discharges, and other items bearing on personnel exposure or environmental contamination. Receipt and shipment of all radioactive materials must be carefully controlled. (*See Title 49, Code of Federal Regulations, Part 171-178, for complete requirements.*)

All employees who work with radioactive materials or who may be exposed to radiation must be indoctrinated to the extent necessary to enable them to protect themselves, other employees, and the general public in the performance of their duties.

Fig. 10 Health physicist surveying a drum, containing radioactive waste, as it is loaded into a shielded container for shipment. The shipping container, which is the property of Nuclear Engineering Company Inc. has the approval stamp of the Department of Transportation. The drum is being handled on a long boom to reduce radiation to the crane operator.

Control console for a large nuclear steam supply system in an electric generating station.

Chapter 21

Nuclear steam supply systems

The discovery of a practical method for the release of nuclear energy disclosed a new power source of tremendous importance. The device in which this energy is released is called a nuclear reactor, which is, in effect, a furnace that generates heat by the interaction of nuclear particles rather than by chemical reaction. At present the only nuclear reaction capable of sustained and large-scale production of heat is fission, or the splitting apart of a heavy nucleus upon absorption of a neutron.

A nuclear reactor is the apparatus in which fission can be initiated and maintained at a controlled rate in a self-supporting chain reaction. A reactor is principally composed of fissile material (fuel), such as uranium-235 or plutonium-239; a control system to initiate and control the fission chain reaction; a coolant to remove heat; and associated structural materials and shielding. In thermal reactors a moderator is required to slow down the speed of the neutrons.

Nuclear reactor types

Nuclear reactors are designed to accomplish one or more of the following objectives:

1. Production of steam for
   (a) Electric power generation
   (b) Ship propulsion
   (c) Supplying process steam
2. Production of plutonium or radioisotopes
3. Production of neutrons for research or testing
4. Experimental development of reactors

Reactors may be classified according to their application, or in several other ways as indicated in Table 1.

Reactors are classified as fast or thermal according to the energy of neutrons at the time they are captured by the fuel to induce fission (see *Fast and Thermal Reactors, Chapter 20*).

Reactors are classified as heterogeneous or homogeneous according to the physical condition of the fuel. Current commercial reactors are heterogeneous, in that the fuel is contained in packages and protected by cladding from contact with the reactor coolant or moderator (see *Utilization of Uranium, Chapter 19*). Homogeneous reactors, with the fuel dissolved or suspended in water or molten metals, have not proved successful commercially (see *Fuel Handling, Chapter 19*).

Reactors can also be classified according to the type of fuel used (Table 1). They can be classified as "burners," converters or breeders, depending on the amount of fissionable material generated by conversion from fertile material (see *Conversion and Breeding, Chapter 20*). They can also be classified by the fertile material used, or by the material used as coolant or moderator.

Table 1
Reactor design parameters

Neutron Energy
  Fast or thermal

Geometry
  Heterogeneous or homogeneous

Fuel
  Natural uranium, containing 0.7% uranium-235; uranium enriched in the 235-isotope to various percentages from slightly enriched (up to approximately 5%) to highly enriched (90% or higher); plutonium; plutonium and uranium; uranium-233

Fuel Regeneration
  No regeneration (burner), less than consumption (converter), or more than consumption (breeder)

Fertile Material
  Uranium-238, thorium, or none

Coolant
  Pressurized water, pressurized heavy water, boiling water, boiling heavy water, air, carbon dioxide, steam, helium, sodium, organic liquids, or molten salt

Moderator
  Water, heavy water, graphite, organic liquids, beryllium, or beryllium oxide

Power reactor types

Nearly all of the power reactors in the United States are water reactors, that is, the reactor coolant is ordinary water—not heavy water. There are two types of water reactors:

1. The pressurized water reactor (PWR) in which the reactor is cooled by water under considerable pressure so that the average enthalpy of the water leaving the reactor is less than the enthalpy at saturation temperature. With this type the high pressure water is conducted to heat exchangers and steam is produced on the low pressure side of the heat exchangers, which are usually known as steam generators.

2. The boiling water reactor (BWR) in which the coolant water is allowed to boil in the reactor; in this type, the steam is usually sent directly to a turbine for electric power generation.

In the United Kingdom and France, the commercial installations are gas-cooled graphite-moderated reactors, in which the heat generated in the fuel assemblies is removed by carbon dioxide and conveyed to the steam generators. Gas-cooled reactors are also being built in the U.S. utilizing helium coolant. Canada has commercial reactors of the heavy-water pressure-tube type, utilizing natural-uranium dioxide as fuel.

Commercial reactors are all of the converter type. They are fueled by uranium-235 either in the form of natural or enriched uranium. In the United Kingdom and France natural uranium has been generally used, although slightly enriched uranium will probably be more used in the future. In the U.S., slightly enriched uranium is generally used. With natural and slightly enriched uranium some plutonium is generated and this will be used as fuel in future cores. In some cases in the U.S. highly enriched uranium-235 has been used with thorium as fertile material and some uranium-233 has been generated.

Many other types of reactors have been proposed and built at least in developmental sizes. However, in the U.S. the water reactors have now achieved an excellent operating record with power costs that are favorable in many areas. They are expected to dominate the field in this country until breeder reactors are developed.

The United States Energy Research and Development Administration (ERDA) is actively supporting a program for the development of fast breeder reactors. These breeders will convert fertile to fissionable materials in greater proportion than the fissionable material is consumed. They may be cooled by liquid metal, steam, or gas, but the main program is currently directed towards fast breeder reactors cooled by liquid sodium. The United Kingdom, France, Germany, and Russia also have substantial programs directed toward development of liquid-sodium-cooled fast breeder reactors. This work should culminate near the end of the century in the development of economic fast breeders.

For marine applications, pressurized water reactors are being used. Since practicable breeder reactors must be too large in capacity for shipboard installation, it seems likely that the PWR type will dominate in the propulsion of ships for years to come.

Pressurized-water reactor system

Fig. 1 shows a simplified diagram of a PWR system for electric power generation. The left-hand loop or "primary loop" or "nuclear steam supply system" is the portion that utilizes the nuclear fuel to produce steam. The right-hand or "secondary loop" includes the turbine-generator, condenser, feed pump, and piping.

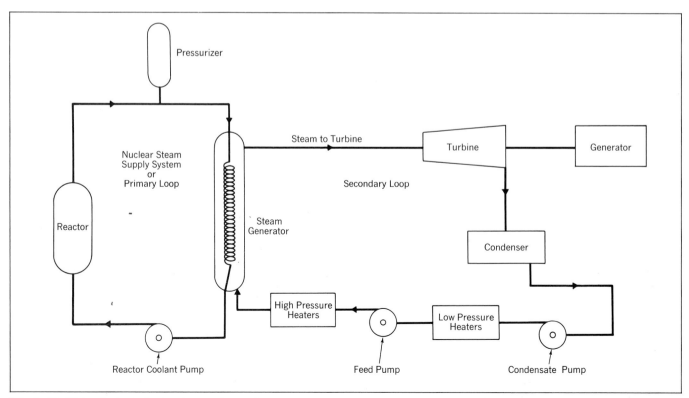

Fig. 1 Diagram of pressurized-water reactor system.

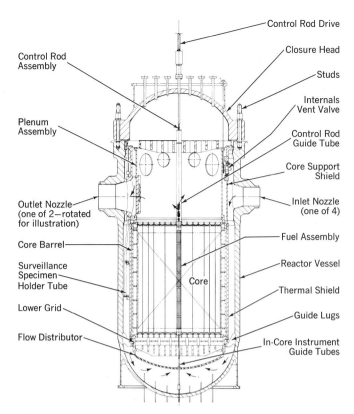

Fig. 2 Reactor vessel and internals—general arrangement.

The nuclear steam supply system is made up of five principal parts:

1. The nuclear reactor which consists of a pressure vessel containing the reactor core (including fuel assemblies and control rods). The chain reaction occurs in this core, producing heat that is removed by the pressurized-water coolant.

2. The steam generators where the water coolant from the reactor transfers its heat through tubes to generate the steam for the turbines.

3. Piping to deliver the water coolant to and from the reactor and the steam generators.

4. Pumps to circulate the water coolant.

5. A pressurizer to maintain the coolant water at a pressure high enough to prevent boiling, and to accommodate volume changes in the coolant.

Description of a pressurized water reactor

Fig. 2 is a vertical section of a modern pressurized water reactor for electric utility application. Its principal components are:

1. The reactor vessel which encloses the reactor core and makes it possible to contain the desired coolant pressure.

2. The core consisting of fuel assemblies and control rods. Fig. 3 shows a horizontal cross section through the core.

3. The thermal shields which absorb radiation emitted from the core, and reduce gamma and neutron energy absorption in the pressure vessel wall.

4. The flow path for the coolant water. The water enters (Fig. 2) through the inlet nozzles located above the midpoint of the vessel; flows sequentially downward in the annular space between pressure vessel and thermal shields; up through the core and upper plenum chamber; down around the inside of the reactor vessel (upper portion), then leaves through the outlet nozzles.

5. A number of control rods and drive lines. Only one control rod drive line is shown in Fig. 2. (A control rod drive line comprises the drive, guide tubes, and one control rod or control rod assembly.)

6. A bolted head at the top of the pressure vessel which is removable for replacement of the reactor core and internals.

7. Structural members including the core support shield, core barrel, and lower grid, which support the core and keep it in alignment.

Design of a pressurized water reactor

The heart of the reactor is the core where the chain reaction occurs in the nuclear fuel and the heat is removed by the coolant. The reactor, along with all other parts of the plant, must be capable of delivering the designed full-power output. This means that the coolant flow must remove the heat generated by the core without overheating at any point. The design must also accommodate starting up at a reasonable rate, instantaneous shutdowns, and the operator's requirements for rapid changes of load. Pressurized water reactors lend themselves readily to these requirements.

Safety considerations are very important with nuclear reactors. Because nuclear chain reactions are capable of substantial power transients if not inhibited by design, and because all nuclear chain reactions produce extremely dangerous radioactive fission products, it is necessary that consideration be given to safety throughout the design process. Therefore, major consideration is given in all phases of design to the safety measures that are required to prevent the escape of radiation to the environment under all conditions of operation, normal and abnormal.

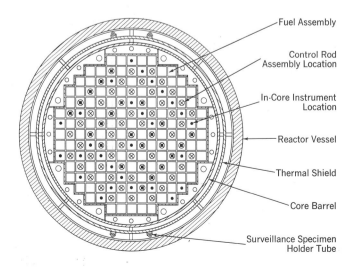

Fig. 3 Reactor vessel and internals—cross section.

The entire plant must be optimized for power cost, and because nuclear power reactors are generally operated at full output, the power cost is usually optimized for the full power condition.

In all aspects of reactor design the main considerations are materials, physics (including control), heat removal, and structural integrity.

Materials

The first fundamental is the availability of materials having the necessary properties and compatible with the service environment. Four materials make it possible to design a pressurized water reactor which can be utilized economically in the production of power:

1. The coolant water with its good heat transfer characteristics and its high heat transport capability possesses the additional attribute of reducing neutron energy and thereby enhancing neutron absorption in the fissionable and fertile material.

2. Uranium dioxide, a highly refractory material, which can be loaded easily into fuel rods, and withstands irradiation well.

3. Zircaloy (alloy of zirconium) which has adequate strength and is sufficiently resistant to interaction with water in a reactor environment up to temperatures of 650F so that it can be used for cladding tubes for reactor fuel rods. It also has the excellent advantage of a low neutron absorption.

4. Steel, the material used in the pressure vessel which contains the reactor. The pressure vessel is normally lined with stainless steel to minimize corrosion. Stainless steel is also used for thermal shielding, for reactor supports, and for core structure where zirconium alloys lack the required strength, or where the extra cost of zircaloy cannot be recovered by the improvement in neutron economy.

Experience to date in pressurized water reactors indicates that maximum economy is obtained by the utilization of uranium-dioxide fuel contained in zircaloy cladding tubes. Fig. 4 is a drawing of a typical fuel assembly. It is about 165 in. long and consists of 208 fuel rods with an active fuel length of 144 in. These fuel rods are mechanically joined in a 15 × 15 array to form a fuel assembly. The center position in the array is reserved for instrumentation. Another sixteen positions are provided with "guide tubes" for use as control rod locations. A number of these fuel assemblies are placed together in vertical position to form the reactor core. The coolant water flows vertically upward through each fuel assembly in a direction parallel to the fuel rods.

Physics

A basic consideration is that enough fissionable material be provided to sustain the chain reaction for the desired period of reactor operation. As the chain reaction proceeds, fissionable material is consumed more rapidly than new fissionable material is produced from fertile material. Also fission products accumulate, increasing parasitic neutron capture. Hence the amount of fissionable material required is not merely the critical mass (*see Chapter 20*) of the fresh core, but rather the critical mass required for the projected end-of-fuel-lifetime

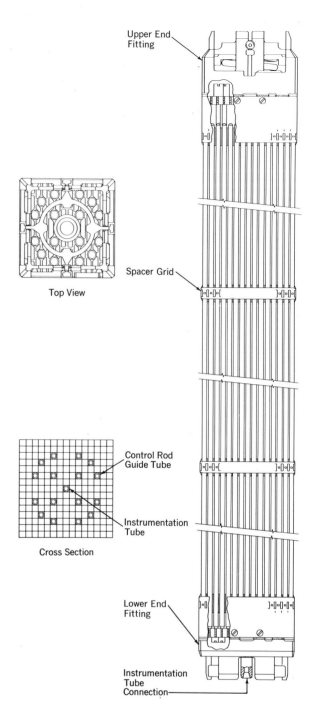

Fig. 4 Fuel assembly.

conditions plus the quantity of fissionable material to be consumed during the lifetime of the fuel.

Also basic is the presence of sufficient "poison" or neutron-absorbing material to control the chain reaction. Means must be provided to move this poison out of the reactor and in again as required to initiate, control, and shut down the chain reaction. The best known method is to contain the poison inside of rods, which are clad externally to provide strength and corrosion resistance to the coolant, and provided with a drive mechanism for controlled withdrawal and insertion.

Because control rods are expensive and distort the neutron density in the core, they are often supplemented by "soluble poison," usually boric acid, dissolved in the

coolant water. The concentration of boric acid is highest at the start of core operation when the greatest amount of fissionable material is present. This concentration is gradually reduced over the lifetime of the core as the fissionable material is depleted and the neutron-absorbing fission products build up. In some cases, fixed elements are used containing "burnable" poison in solid form, which is consumed as neutrons are absorbed. The consumption of burnable poison provides an increase in reactivity which at least partially offsets the reactivity loss from consumption of fuel and buildup of fission products. (*See also Reactor Control.*)

The heat developed in the whole reactor is a function of the number of fissions occurring. This, in turn, is a function of the neutron density in the core, once the design and quantity of fissionable material has been fixed. The reactor can be operated at any level provided means are available for removing the heat developed in all portions of the core. An important role of physics in design is to determine the distribution of neutrons throughout the core in order that all parts can be adequately cooled.

Heat generation is customarily calculated by the use of the quantity nv (neutron flux) where n is neutron density and v is neutron velocity. Heat generated in any part of a nuclear reactor is directly proportional to neutron flux and the concentration of fissionable material. In a uniformly loaded core, the heat generated in any part of the core is proportional to the local neutron flux. In general, the flux tends to peak at the center of the core, both axially and radially, and tends to approach zero at the boundary because of the leakage of neutrons out of the core.

A "reflector" is generally placed around the core to reduce neutron leakage from the reactor. The reflector contains a good scattering material, i.e., a material having a high probability of neutron collisions with the nuclei. This changes the direction of the neutrons and causes many of them to return to the reactor. Such a reflector, usually water in the case of the water reactors, improves the neutron flux distribution by increasing the flux at the core boundary. The utilization of the outer portions of the core is thus improved by increasing the heat generated in these areas.

Core flux distribution in a reactor core is obtained by spatial integrations of the criticality equations with consideration of control rods and any other discontinuities. Fig. 5 shows fast and thermal neutron flux distribution in a radial direction in a pressurized-water reactor core.

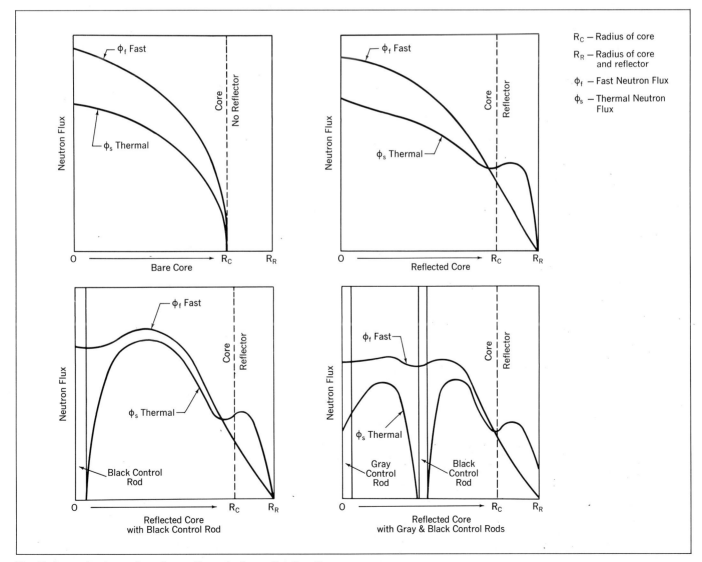

Fig. 5 Approximate neutron flux patterns in the radial direction.

The upper left-hand diagram shows the flux approaching zero at the boundary in a bare core, and the upper right-hand diagram shows the improvement effected by a water reflector.

The two lower diagrams in Fig. 5 show the effect of control rods on the radial flux distribution. The lower left-hand diagram shows a "black" control rod inserted at the center of the reactor. The term "black" implies that the control rod absorbs all thermal neutrons impinging upon it. Therefore, the thermal flux approaches zero at the boundary of the control rod but the fast flux is only slightly reduced. The lower right-hand figure shows a "gray" control rod, which absorbs only part of the thermal neutrons, in the center of the core and a black rod about half way between the center and the core boundary. When control rods in a water reactor are withdrawn, the effect is opposite to that shown in Fig. 5, i.e., the flux peaks at the edges of the control rod channels. This effect is minimized by reducing the width of the channels.

The flux pattern in the axial direction also tends to peak at the center, and approaches zero at the ends (usually top and bottom) of a bare core. The effect of a reflector is essentially the same at the end boundaries as at the radial boundary. Insertion of a control rod or rods reduces the flux over a portion of the core length (height), depending on how far the rods are inserted.

It has previously been necessary to verify physics calculations by a "critical" or "zero power" experiment conducted at atmospheric pressure and room temperature on a mockup of the proposed reactor core. These zero power experiments are used to verify the critical mass, or amount of fissionable material required, the "control rod worth," i.e., the value of the rods in controlling the reactor in terms of reactivity, and the distribution of the neutron flux throughout the core. The accuracy of nuclear physics calculations has now improved to the point where it is usually not necessary to conduct the zero power experiment for a water reactor in complete detail.

Heat removal

Since the maximum power level allowable in a reactor is determined by the rate at which heat can be removed, the design of the core is limited by heat transfer considerations. Transfer of heat from the fuel assemblies to the coolant is facilitated by increasing the fuel surface area and coolant velocity. These changes result in increased pumping power which in turn reduces system efficiency. The design must be an economic compromise between thermal, hydraulic, mechanical, and nuclear considerations.

Heat generation in a nuclear reactor is usually expressed in watts, kilowatts, or megawatts. Heat release rate in kilowatts in any element of volume of the core is obtained from the formula

$$(1) \qquad \text{Heat release rate} = \frac{\phi_s \Sigma_f V_c \, E_f K_f}{C}$$

where:

Heat release rate = kw

ϕ_s = thermal flux in the element of volume, neutrons/cm^2, sec

Σ_f = macroscopic fission cross section of the fissionable material in the core, cm^{-1}

V_c = volume element of the core, cm^3

E_f = energy produced per fission (204 MeV/fission for uranium-235)[*]

K_f = constant to cover fissions by fast neutrons = approximately 1.08 in commercial pressurized water reactors

C = conversion of MeV/sec to kilowatts = 6.25 $\times 10^{15}$ MeV/sec, kw

Overall heat release rate in the core is obtained by integration of the foregoing formulation.

It is important to know the temperature throughout all the fuel in the reactor in order that the core may be properly designed from the standpoints of stress and corrosion. Hence fuel and cladding-rod temperatures must be calculated at all significant points. To calculate the temperature at any point, the local heat flux, the mass velocity and temperature of the coolant water, and the dimensions and characteristics of the fuel and cladding must be known.

The local heat flux, q/S, is obtained by converting the local kw heat release rate from equation (1) to Btu/hr and dividing by the heating surface in the core element being considered.

$$(2) \qquad q/S = \frac{\text{heat release rate} \times 3412}{S}$$

where:

q/S = heat flux, Btu/sq ft, hr

S = heating surface, sq ft, contained in volume V_c used in determining heat release rate

Heat release rate = kw

3412 = conversion constant, Btu/kwhr

The bulk water temperature is obtained by integrating the heat input from the channel inlet to the point in question, and dividing by the flow rate of the water.

In regions of the core where there is no boiling, the temperature difference across the water film (Fig. 6) can be obtained by dividing heat flux by a conductance obtained from a correlation for turbulent flow inside tubes, such as equation (17), Chapter 4 or the Colburn equation: [†]

$$(3) \qquad \text{Nu} = 0.023 \, \text{Re}^{0.8} \, \text{Pr}^{1/3}$$

where:

Nu = Nusselt number

Re = Reynolds number

Pr = Prandtl number

More accurate conductance values are obtained by introducing into the general equation an empirical constant based on the actual configuration of the reactor flow channel.

---

[*] See Table 4, Chapter 20.

[†] Colburn, A. P., Trans. Am. Inst. Chemical Engineers 29, 174 (1933).

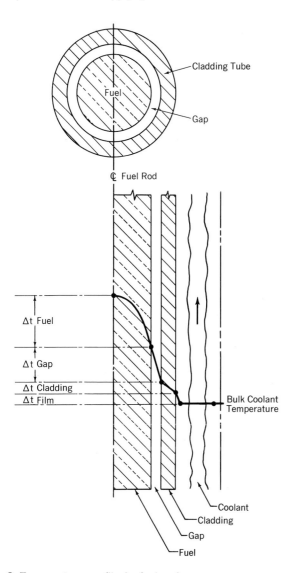

Fig. 6 Temperature profile in fuel rod.

In areas where local (subcooled) boiling is occurring, the wall temperature of the cladding tube is calculated from the Jens and Lottes formula: [*]

$$(4) \qquad t_w - t_{sat} = 60 \left(\frac{q}{10^6 S} \right)^{1/4} \Big/ e^{p/900}$$

where:

> t_w = tube temperature (cladding surface), F
> t_{sat} = saturation temperature, F
> q/S = heat flux, Btu/sq ft, hr
> p = pressure, psia

The temperature drop through the metal cladding (Fig. 6) is calculated on the basis of the known conductivity of the material used. The method for calculating the temperature difference between the center and the edge of the oxide fuel is similar. The most difficult item is the allowance to be made for the gap between the fuel and the cladding. This gap must be considered and is important with pellet fuel where it is customary

[*] W. H. Jens and P. A. Lottes, "Analysis of Heat Transfer Burnout, Pressure Drop and Density Data for High Pressure Water," ANL-4627, May 1951.

to provide clearance sufficient to permit pellet insertion into the cladding tubes with due allowances for the variations in tube and pellet diameter which must be accepted in practical manufacturing processes. Helium put into the fuel rods during fabrication improves the heat transfer across the gap. The release of fission product gases during burnup tends to reduce the conductivity across the gap. Fission product accumulation inside the fuel also decreases the conductivity of the fuel. As a result of both these effects fuel temperature tends to rise as burnup increases.

All portions of the reactor must operate without overheating. It is therefore necessary to know the distribution of neutron flux and to determine from it the heat generation in all channels and in all parts of each channel. It is not sufficient to consider each fuel assembly as a channel since there can be flux variations and flow variations across the section of a fuel assembly. A coolant channel is considered as the flow area between adjacent fuel rods or the flow area between fuel rods and a flow barrier or wall, as shown in Fig. 7.

Allowable heat flux cannot be calculated on the premise that average coolant flow exists in each channel. Variations in channel dimensions due to cladding-tube and fuel-assembly tolerances must be considered. Even with the best tolerances that can be obtained practically, the possible variations in channel area may have a substantial effect on coolant flow.

The possible reductions in flow due to reductions in the area of the channel are expressed in terms of hot channel factors. "Hot channel" factors are used to account for maldistribution caused by flow effects in the plenum chambers at the inlet and outlet to the core.

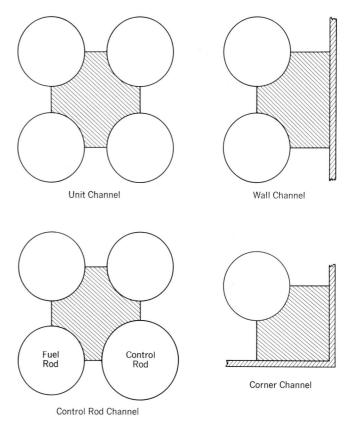

Fig. 7 Coolant channels.

Similar factors are also used to account for possible irregularities in amount or enrichment of fissionable material both locally and along entire fuel rod lengths. These factors can be combined effectively since either reduced flow or increased heat release give the effect of producing hotter conditions in the channel.

It is unlikely that the channel in the reactor, which has the highest heat input, will also have the lowest flow and the greatest excess of fissionable material. Hot channel factors are customarily applied on a statistical rather than an absolute basis. The performance of reactor cores to date has justified this procedure.

The reactor must be designed not only for satisfactory temperature conditions with steady state operation at the highest intended power, but consideration must also be given to transients which may occur for short periods of time before the controls act to shut the reactor down.

Another complicating factor is that the distribution of neutron flux and power generation usually varies during the lifetime of the core. Regions of high initial flux are depleted rapidly of fissionable material and accumulate more fission products early in core life. This shifts the peak power production toward other areas with less depletion and fewer fission products. Thus, a core must be designed for adequate heat removal from the hottest point or points at all times during its life.

The designer must make sure that temperatures of fuel and cladding are satisfactory over the full length of all fuel rods. Voids, caused by boiling in the coolant, must be kept within acceptable limits. These limits are determined by the effects of voids on the hydraulic stability of the flow and on the nuclear reactivity. A limited amount of boiling is permitted in pressurized water reactors under certain conditions but the designer must know how much this will be, under what conditions it will occur, and how it can be accommodated.

Heat transfer design limits. The design limits for the fuel assemblies are set by the melting point of the oxide fuel and the avoidance of burnout of the fuel cladding (*see Heat Transfer in Pressurized-Water Nuclear Reactors, Chapter 4*).

The melting point of UO_2 is about 5000F. Generally, fuel melting is not allowed even at the designed overpower, which is usually about 12% above the maximum continuous load. There are indications that some melting of fuel at the center of fuel rods may be allowable when more reactor operating experience is available.

Departure from nucleate boiling (DNB) with possible burnout of the fuel cladding will occur if the heat flux is too great for the coolant flow (*see Film Boiling, Chapter 1*). The critical heat flux from the standpoint of DNB can be determined by using the correlation described and referenced in *Heat Transfer in Pressurized-Water Nuclear Reactors*, Chapter 4.

The use of this correlation is illustrated by Fig. 8. The upper curve is the critical heat flux obtained from the correlation, with reductions for variations in the burnout data and the effect of hot channel factors due to flow variations and possible maldistribution of fissionable material. At any point "X" along the length of the heated channel, critical heat flux is not merely a function of the local heat flux, but actually of the history of the coolant

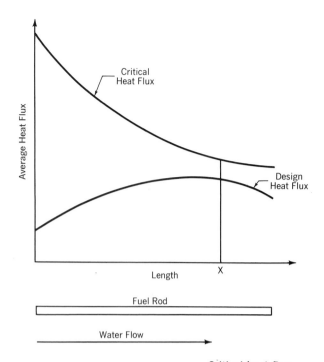

Fig. 8 DNB ratio = minimum value of $\frac{\text{Critical heat flux}}{\text{Design heat flux}}$.

from the channel inlet up to point "X." Both the critical and the design heat fluxes at each point are integrated average fluxes from the channel inlet to the point in question.

The ratio of the values given by these two curves is important in the design of the reactor from the standpoint of its safety from burnout. The minimum value of this ratio along the length of the channel is known as the DNB Ratio.

Pressure drop

The heat should be removed from the reactor without excessive coolant-flow pressure drop, thus keeping pumping head and power within acceptable limits.

The pressure drop of the coolant-water flow through the steam generators and piping can be calculated by standard formulas as given in Chapter 3. The problem is more complex in the reactor core which is designed for local boiling. A two-phase flow situation (bulk boiling) may exist in some channels under the overpower conditions that occur during transients.

Even in the single-phase part of the core channels, the effects of entrance and exit conditions, support grids, and other irregularities in the small passages are such that it is difficult to determine core pressure drop accurately by calculations. The pressure drop in a fuel assembly is usually verified experimentally before the fuel assemblies are fabricated.

The following formulas may be used for the heating region where there is only single-phase water:

for friction,

(5)
$$\Delta p_f = \frac{fL}{D_e} \frac{1}{\rho} \frac{G^2}{2g_c}$$

for acceleration (to account for change in kinetic energy of the fluid due to density changes),

(6)
$$\Delta p_a = \frac{G^2}{g_c}(v_2 - v_1)$$

for fluid head,

(7)
$$\Delta p_H = \rho(Z_2 - Z_1)\, g/g_c$$

The effect of contractions, expansions, and acceleration due to abrupt flow area change must also be considered.

Symbols in equations (5) to (7) are defined as follows:

Δp_f = pressure drop due to friction, lb/sq ft

Δp_a = pressure loss due to acceleration, lb/sq ft

Δp_H = fluid head expressed in lb/sq ft

f = friction factor (Moody) − Fig. 1, Chapter 3 (use average value over channel length)

G = mass velocity, lb/sq ft, sec

g_c = conversion constant, 32.17 ft lb mass/lb force, sec^2 (see equation 3, Chapter 2)

D_e = channel equivalent diameter, ft

μ = viscosity, lb mass/ft, sec for use in Fig. 1, Chapter 3 when G is expressed in lb/sq ft, sec

ϵ/d_e = relative roughness for use in Fig. 1, Chapter 3 (Fig. 2, Chapter 3)

ϵ = average height of roughness projections in in.

d_e = channel equivalent diameter, in.

L = channel length, ft

ρ = density, lb/cu ft (use average value over channel length)

g = acceleration of gravity, 32.17 ft/sec^2

v_1 = fluid specific volume at channel inlet, cu ft/lb

v_2 = fluid specific volume at channel outlet, cu ft/lb

Z_1 = height of channel inlet, ft

Z_2 = height of channel outlet, ft

To determine the point where local boiling begins, the temperature of the cladding tube is found by solving the modified Colburn convection equation for the all-water condition and the Jens and Lottes equation for wall temperature with local boiling.[*] Local boiling occurs when the wall temperature predicted by the modified Colburn equation is higher than the wall temperature for local boiling determined by the Jens and Lottes equation.

For the all-water condition, wall temperature is found from the bulk water temperature, equations (8) and (9), and the modified Colburn equation (10).

(8)
$$t_s = t_b + \Delta t_f$$

(9)
$$\Delta t_f = q/U$$

(10)
$$U = 0.030\,(k/D_e)\,\mathrm{Pr}^{1/3}\,\mathrm{Re}^{0.8}$$

where:

t_s = wall (cladding surface) temperature, F − modified Colburn equation

t_b = bulk temperature, F, of water below saturation

Δt_f = temperature differential across all-water film, F

q/S = heat flux, Btu/sq ft, hr

U = film conductance, Btu/sq ft, hr, F

k = thermal conductivity of water at bulk temperature, Btu/ft, hr, F

D_e = channel equivalent diameter, ft

Pr = Prandtl number, $\dfrac{c_p \mu}{k}$ (evaluated at bulk water temperature)

c_p = specific heat at constant pressure, Btu/lb

μ = viscosity, lb mass/ft, hr

Re = Reynolds number, $\dfrac{G D_e}{\mu}$ (evaluated at bulk water temperature)

For the local-boiling condition, wall temperature is determined from the saturation temperature corresponding to the coolant water pressure and from equation (11) and the Jens and Lottes equation (12).

(11)
$$t_w = t_{\mathrm{sat}} + \Delta t_{\mathrm{sat}}$$

(12)
$$\Delta t_{\mathrm{sat}} = 60 \left(\frac{q}{10^6 S}\right)^{1/4} \Big/ e^{p/900}$$

where:

t_w = wall (cladding surface) temperature, F − Jens & Lottes equation

t_{sat} = saturation temperature, F

Δt_{sat} = excess of wall temperature above saturation, F

p = water pressure, psia

For local boiling conditions:

1. Friction can be calculated by the formula used for the single-phase heating region with a modified friction factor (f_{LB}) to account for the effect of local boiling.

For pressures from 800 to 1850 psia, f_{LB} is defined by the equation[*]

(13)
$$\frac{f_{LB}}{f} = 1 + \left[\frac{t_b - t_{LB}}{t_{\mathrm{sat}} - t_{LB}}\right]\left[\left(\frac{f_{LB}}{f}\right)_{\mathrm{sat}} - 1\right]$$

where:

t_b = average bulk coolant temperature over the channel increment, F

t_{LB} = bulk coolant temperature at the initiation of local boiling as defined above, F

(14)
$$\left(\frac{f_{LB}}{f}\right)_{\mathrm{sat}} = \frac{\Delta p_{TPF}}{\Delta p_o}$$, which is the overall Martinelli-Nelson[†] multiplier evaluated at the operating core pressure and a steam quality of 4.2%.

2. Fluid head, acceleration, expansion and contraction are usually calculated by the formulas for the single-phase water heating region. While this neglect of local boiling is not precise, the error involved is inconsequential.

---

* Jens, W. H., and Lottes, P. A., "Analysis of Heat Transfer Burnout, Pressure Drop and Density Data for High Pressure Water," ANL-4627-May 1951.

* "Boiling Heat Transfer and Two-Phase Flow," L. S. Tong, Copyright © 1965 by John Wiley & Sons, Inc. Reprinted by permission.

† R. C. Martinelli and D. B. Nelson, "Prediction of Pressure Drop during Forced Circulation Boiling of Water," Trans. ASME August 1948, p. 695.

Conditions in certain channels during overpower transients and safety analyses require calculations of pressure drop in the two-phase-fluid (nucleate-boiling) region. The formulas used are basically the same as for the single-phase heating region except that allowances must be made for the reduced density due to steam bubbles. Corrections to account for the two-phase frictional pressure drop can be made by using the Martinelli-Nelson multiplier modified for the mass velocity corrections developed by the Bettis Atomic Power Laboratory (see *Reference 1, Pressure Loss in Two-Phase Flow, Chapter 3*). Several models available for predicting the void fraction used to determine density in the two-phase region, are suitable for use in a computer program.

A knowledge of the extent and location of boiling in a pressurized water reactor is important from the standpoint of coolant flow distribution. The formation of excessive quantities of steam in a channel can reduce water flow and produce burnout very quickly. The formation of steam bubbles also has an important effect on reactivity—fortunately, a corrective one.

Pressure drop information is used as a part of the computer design program. The pressure drop formulas are somewhat modified for adaptation to computer use.

Structural integrity

The design of the fuel assembly requires careful analysis from the standpoints of strength and fabricability. Fuel rod cladding tubes are designed to withstand the external pressure of the reactor coolant, which may be as high as 2750 psi. They must also contain the internal pressure of accumulated gaseous fission products, which may exceed 2000 psi toward the end of the life of the fuel. In addition, the effects of creep, erosion, corrosion, and neutron irradiation must be considered in cladding design.

Spacer grid assemblies are used to locate the fuel rods and form the basic array of the fuel assembly shown in Fig. 4. The spacer grid maintains the close tolerances between fuel rods that are required to distribute the reactor coolant for the adequate cooling of each fuel rod. Each spacer grid assembly is comprised of strips with shaped springs to contact the fuel rods. The strips are joined together in the form of an egg crate to make the spacer grid assembly. The spacer grids which form the horizontal structural integrity also hold the control rod guide tubes which provide the vertical structural integrity. The lower and upper end fittings are attached to the guide tubes to complete the fuel assembly structure.

Each of the control rod guide tubes is designed to contain and guide a control rod as it moves in and out of the reactor core. The control rods in each fuel assembly have a common drive located outside the pressure vessel. Each fuel assembly is carefully aligned with the pressure vessel to make sure that each control rod is aligned with its guide tube.

Each fuel assembly has a lower end fitting which provides a support base for the fuel rods while maintaining the maximum inlet flow area for the coolant. The lower end fitting rests on the lower grid plate as shown in Fig. 2. The upper end fitting, similar to the lower one, locates the upper end of the fuel assembly and provides a coupling with the handling equipment so that each fuel assembly can be inserted and removed.

The *Structural Design of a Nuclear Reactor Core* is discussed in Chapter 30. The economic penalty for distortion and failure of a fuel assembly is large and, therefore, it is essential that each new assembly design be tested before it is utilized in a reactor core. Thus, full-size assemblies are tested for vibration and distortion in water at the operating flow and temperature.

It also is necessary to know the effect of reactor conditions on the fuel. Operational data can be obtained through demonstration programs for new designs and post operation examinations of present designs. Additionally, test reactor programs can be used to obtain data that is applicable to operational performance. These data are utilized to verify performance and they provide a basis for predicting future performance.

The permissible lifetime of a fuel assembly is important in the economic evaluation of the core. This is generally expressed as burnup, which is defined as the thermal energy produced by the fuel and is expressed in megawatt-days divided by the weight of initially contained fissionable and fertile material (usually expressed in metric tons of metal). After a certain amount of burnup, the release of fission product gases in the fuel causes it to swell. The fuel assembly lifetime is limited by the amount of swelling which is tolerable (see also *Fuel Assemblies, Chapter 19*).

Reactor control

The design of any reactor must provide for a control system that is accurate and complete under all conditions of operation and shutdown. The requirement for operation at any constant power level is to maintain the effective multiplication factor (k_{eff}) at a value of unity (see *Reactivity, Chapter 20*). During transients the objective is to maintain the value of k_{eff} well under the prompt critical range. This is normally easy because of the fraction of delayed neutrons associated with fission.

In commercial pressurized water reactors, other important factors act to retard changes in power level. These factors provide a high degree of inherent stability and greatly facilitate control. Most significant of these are fuel Doppler coefficient, moderator temperature coefficient, and moderator void coefficient.

Fuel Doppler coefficient. As fuel temperature increases, uranium-238 has the property of absorbing increasing numbers of neutrons in certain intermediate (resonance) energy ranges. These are nonfission absorptions and act rapidly to retard the chain reaction by draining off the supply of neutrons which might be slowed down to the thermal level. Since this Doppler effect is temperature dependent (see *Cross Section, Chapter 20*), it can be expressed as a Doppler coefficient, which is a measure of the rate of change with temperature of the reactivity of a nuclear reactor resulting from the Doppler effect in fuel materials. Since fuel temperature is a function of the power level, this effect can also be expressed as a function of reactor power.

Moderator temperature coefficient. In a pressurized water reactor most of the fissions result from thermal neutrons. If the water temperature increases above operating temperature (e.g., because of a reduced load on the

secondary system), the water expands and reduces the number of hydrogen atoms in the core. As a result, the fast fission neutrons have fewer opportunities for collisions with hydrogen atoms and do not lose their energy so fast; thus the mean energy level of the neutrons rises and the chain reaction slows down.

The moderator temperature coefficient is defined as the change in reactivity initiated by a unit change in moderator temperature. Moderator temperature rises with a power increase, and this acts to retard the power increase. Boron, used as soluble poison, tends to counteract this effect because the water expands with temperature rise and removes boron from the core.

Moderator void coefficient. This coefficient is defined as the change in reactivity per unit volume change in the extent of voids in the moderator. In commercial pressurized water reactors the removal of water from the core or the production of voids in the water space greatly reduces the moderation of the neutrons and tends to shut the reactor down. Thus, the production of steam in the core has a strong effect on the chain reaction and must be provided for in a pressurized water reactor as well as a boiling water reactor. The inadvertent production of steam from an undesired overpower condition tends to retard the chain reaction. The use of boron as a soluble poison tends to counteract this effect.

Requirements of the reactor control system. A reactor control system must provide:

1. Sufficient excess reactivity to achieve the design power level with the required operating flexibility over the desired fuel cycle or lifetime.
2. Sufficient reactivity control (neutron absorbing capacity) to permit safe reactor operation and shutdown at all times during the core lifetime.

The most reactive condition of a PWR core occurs when it is loaded with fresh fuel and filled with water at a temperature between 100 and 200F. This condition determines the total neutron absorbing capacity required in the control materials. It must be sufficient to hold the reactor subcritical under the condition of maximum reactivity with an adequate allowance for a safety margin. The total absorbing capability can be supplied in the form of movable control rods plus soluble poison and fixed burnable poison.

For the instantaneous control of the reactor there must be enough neutron-absorbing capacity in movable control rods so that the reactor can be brought from a condition of no-load at operating temperature to full power and back again. Additional control rod capacity must be provided in case one rod fails to operate.

The neutron-absorbing material in the control rods can be hafnium, which is expensive; or boron in suitable chemical form contained inside a sheath of metal such as stainless steel; or silver-indium-cadmium clad with stainless steel. Control rods may be cruciform in cross section, with a web as large as ten inches from side to side.

In some modern pressurized water reactors, small diameter control rods are located throughout certain fuel assemblies as indicated in Fig. 4 (*see also Physics, and Optimization of a PWR Plant for Cost*). All control rods in one fuel assembly are driven by a common drive which may be hydraulic or, more frequently, electric-mechanical. Control-rod-drive mechanisms are usually located outside the pressure vessel but contained within the primary-coolant pressure system. Electric-mechanical drive motors are either "canned" (*see Control Rod Drive, Chapter 23*) or located outside the primary-coolant pressure system with a seal provided to prevent the escape of coolant.

The reactor is normally started up by manual actuation of the control rods but the control system is designed to function automatically when the reactor is operating throughout most of the load range (e.g., from 15 to 100% of full power).

Reactor protection system

This system monitors parameters automatically to prevent the reactor from entering an unsafe operating condition. It will trip (shut down) the reactor when power, reactor-outlet coolant temperature, or coolant pressure reach preset maximum limits. It will also trip the reactor when coolant pressure reaches a preset minimum value which is a function of coolant temperature. The reactor is also tripped by axial power imbalance, by ratios of neutron flux to reactor coolant flow that are too high for safe operation, or upon loss of power to the reactor protection system.

Instrumentation

The most important nuclear instruments are the neutron flux level meters, or neutron detectors. It is necessary for safety, control, and operating guidance to know the neutron flux accurately from the lowest levels encountered in start-up to the full power and transient overload range. No one type of detector will function adequately over this entire range, and several groups, each consisting of two or more instruments, are provided. There is overlap in the applicable ranges of the groups, and any level of flux is always read by at least two instruments operating in their region of accuracy.

A typical arrangement for measuring neutron flux level consists of eight channels of neutron information divided into three ranges of sensitivity—source range, intermediate range, and power range. The source range (10^{-1} to 10^4 *nv* approximately at the detectors) has two redundant channels originating in two high sensitivity proportional counters; the intermediate range (10^2 to 10^9 *nv* approximately) has two channels originating in electrically gamma-compensated ion chambers; and the power range (10^7 to 10^{10} *nv* or higher) has four channels, each originating in a long uncompensated ion chamber extending over the full core height. Each long chamber actually consists of multiple chambers, which are connected to give an integrated reading. These four power channels are located in four primary positions around the reactor core.

Additional neutron detectors, known as in-core instrumentation, are located at various points within the core to obtain the axial and radial flux distribution and to provide a history of power distributions and variations during power operating modes. In-core thermocouples to obtain coolant temperatures can be used for information on local reactor coolant temperatures.

Non-nuclear instrumentation to measure temperatures, pressures, flows, and water levels in the reactor coolant, steam and auxiliary systems, is also required.

Design of reactor coolant system

The components (Fig. 1) which make up the reactor coolant system (primary loop) are the reactor vessel, steam generators, reactor coolant pumps, pressurizer, and the interconnecting piping. Materials are selected for corrosion resistance in the coolant environment. Surfaces in contact with the coolant water are generally made of stainless steel or nickel-base alloy.

Reactor vessel

The reactor pressure vessel (Fig. 2) is constructed from carbon or low-alloy steel with an inner stainless-steel cladding about 1/8-in. thick. The upper head is removable for access and fuel handling. This head is held in place by high-tensile steel studs. Inlet and outlet nozzles are provided for connection to the coolant piping. Arrangement of the reactor core and structural supports inside the vessel is illustrated in Figs. 2 and 3.

Thermal shielding (Figs. 2 and 3) is placed inside the pressure vessel for absorption of radiation in order to minimize the effect on the pressure vessel metal. Nevertheless, fast neutrons may reach the pressure vessel wall in sufficient number to alter the ductility of the structural metal at low temperatures. The principal effect is to raise the nil ductility transition temperature below which the vessel must be operated at low stresses, i.e., the vessel must not be fully pressurized except at temperatures higher than the nil ductility transition temperature plus 60F. As an in-service check, samples of the pressure vessel material may be placed in the vessel to permit determination of material properties, such as tensile and impact strength after irradiation.

Steam generators

Another important component of the reactor coolant system is the steam generator. There are generally at least two steam generators, and these are usually of the vertical shell-and-tube type with the reactor coolant inside of the tubes. In recent designs the tubes are usually of nickel-iron-chromium alloy. Carbon steel is generally used for the pressure shell and tube sheets, with stainless steel or Inconel cladding on the coolant water side of tube sheets and the inlet and outlet plenum chambers.

Some of these vertical-tube steam generators are of U-tube design, having water entry and exit from the bottom. Others are of straight tube design with the coolant water flowing through tubes from the top downward and leaving at the bottom. The steam is formed on the outside of the tubes. Heat transfer on the steam side can be accomplished by natural circulation. A forced circulation once-through arrangement on the steam side makes possible a small amount of superheat. The design features of a unit of this type are described in Chapter 23, which also contains tabulations of the principal design parameters for units of two different sizes.

Reactor coolant pumps

These pumps circulate water in the primary loop (Fig. 1) through the reactor, steam generator, and associated piping, developing the requisite head to overcome fluid friction losses and to transport the heat from the reactor to the steam generators. The coolant temperature is raised only about 50F or less in the reactor, so that a large volume of water must be circulated to remove the heat generated. Table 1, Chapter 23, lists design parameters for two different units.

Reactor coolant pumps are of the centrifugal type. In earlier designs each pump was driven by an induction motor in which the motor rotor operates submerged in the reactor coolant water, with a membrane interposed between the rotor and stator providing hermetical sealing of the rotor-impeller assembly against leakage of the coolant. These were known as "canned pumps." In current large-size plants for electric power production, shaft-sealed pumps are generally used. Water may be injected at the seal to prevent outward leakage of the coolant as it becomes somewhat radioactive during operation.

Pressurizer

The pressurizer establishes and maintains the reactor coolant system pressure within the prescribed limits. It provides a steam surge chamber and a water reserve to accommodate reactor coolant density changes during operation. A typical pressurizer (Fig. 9) is a vertical, cylindrical vessel, with a bottom surge-line penetration connected to the reactor coolant piping. The pressurizer contains replaceable electric heaters in its lower section and a water spray nozzle in its upper section. The heaters

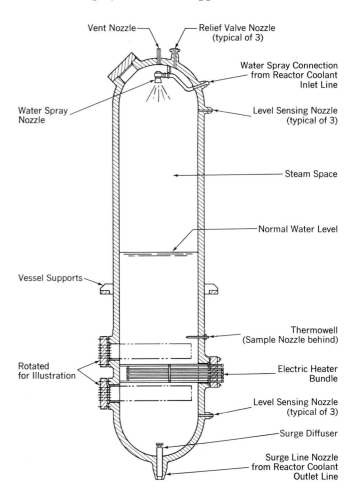

Fig. 9 Pressurizer.

and the spray act to maintain the steam and water at saturation temperature conditions corresponding to the desired coolant system pressure.

When the pressure in the reactor coolant system decreases, some of the water in the pressurizer flashes to steam to maintain pressure. The electric heaters are then actuated to restore the normal operating pressure. When pressure in the system increases, steam is condensed by a water spray from the reactor inlet lines, thus reducing pressure.

Water level is controlled automatically by varying the amount of water charged into and removed from the reactor coolant system. Multiple remote level indicators are provided.

Piping

The reactor coolant piping connects the components of the reactor coolant system as shown in Fig. 1. This piping is constructed of stainless steel or carbon steel clad internally with stainless. It is usually sized for a water velocity of 40 to 60 ft/sec to give a proper balance between the investment cost of piping and the operating cost of pumping power.

Pressure relief system

Relief valves must be provided in the reactor coolant system to protect against excess pressure. Since this system is radioactive, the relief valves are normally discharged into a "quench tank" inside the reactor building with cooling coils provided to condense the discharge.

Auxiliary systems

In addition to the main components of the nuclear steam supply system shown in Fig. 1, several auxiliary systems are required. These include:

Makeup and purification system
Chemical addition and sampling system
Decay-heat-removal system
Spent-fuel-cooling system
Waste-disposal system
Intermediate cooling system
Reactor-building-cooling system

Makeup and purification system. Impurities in the reactor coolant must be kept at a low level to minimize surface fouling and to assure maximum plant availability. This is usually accomplished by a makeup and purification system (Fig. 10). A portion of the water from the reactor coolant circuit is continuously removed through a letdown cooler, passed through a purification demineralizer to remove impurities other than boron, and introduced into a makeup surge tank from which it is returned to the reactor coolant system, as required, to maintain the pressurizer level. The capacity of the surge tank must accommodate changes in the volume of water resulting from load changes without discharge of the radioactive coolant.

In most PWR systems, low temperature water is injected continuously into seals (e.g., pumps) to prevent outward leakage of coolant. The water leaking into the reactor coolant at these seals is removed continuously through the makeup and purification system. The out-

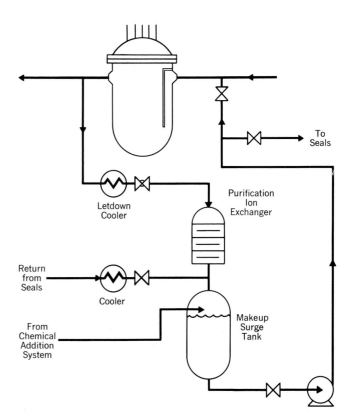

Fig. 10 Makeup and purification system.

leakage at the seals is returned to the makeup surge tank through separate coolers.

Major components of the makeup and purification system are preferably located outside the reactor building for access during plant operation.

Chemical addition and sampling system. Chemical addition and sampling operations are required to alter and monitor the concentration of various chemicals in the reactor coolant and auxiliary systems. The chemical addition and sampling system provides for the addition of boric acid for reactivity control, materials such as lithium hydroxide for pH control and hydrogen or hydrazine for oxygen control. The addition of chemicals is usually accomplished through the makeup surge tank (Fig. 10). This system may also be designed to add chemicals to the steam generator feedwater and condensate systems. Means are provided for taking samples from the reactor coolant system and steam generators.

Decay-heat-removal system. After shutdown of a reactor the radioactive fission product nuclides continue to decay exponentially (Fig. 4, Chapter 20). Considerable heat is thus generated by some of the shorter lived nuclides. Although this "decay heat" diminishes exponentially with time, its removal requires substantial cooling over an extended period. As long as the reactor coolant temperatures remain above a certain value (e.g., 250F) decay heat is conveyed through the reactor-coolant circulating system and removed through the steam generator. For lower reactor-coolant temperatures a supplementary means of cooling known as the decay-heat-removal system is provided. This system (Fig. 11) does not utilize the steam generator or coolant pumps, but is

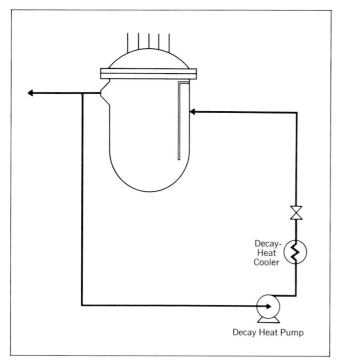

Decay-
Heat
Cooler

Decay Heat Pump

Fig. 11 Decay-heat-removal system.

designed to circulate water through the reactor and transfer the decay heat to the environment through a decay-heat cooler.

Spent-fuel-cooling system (Fig. 12). After the spent fuel assemblies are removed from the reactor and stored as described under *Fuel Handling,* they are cooled by the spent-fuel-cooling system, which circulates water from the fuel pool to a cooler for heat removal and to a filter and demineralizer to remove solids and minimize radioactivity in the pool water.

Waste-disposal system (Fig. 13). This system provides for the collection, storage, processing, and preparation for safe disposal of all plant wastes. Vessels and equipment containing potentially radioactive materials are shielded to protect operating personnel. All material released to rivers or the atmosphere is monitored. Ample storage capacity must be provided to hold up the release if the radioactivity approaches limits established by regulatory agencies. Solid wastes are shielded in approved concrete shipping containers for off-site disposal in licensed burial areas.

Intermediate cooling system (Fig. 14). During normal operation heat must be removed either continuously or intermittently from several components. These include the shielding external to the reactor vessel, the pump seal housings of the reactor coolant pumps, the quench-tank cooling coils and the letdown coolers. All of these heat loads are inside the reactor building and it is convenient to remove the heat through a common system known as the intermediate cooling system.

As a protection against possible radioactivity in this system, the intermediate cooling water is maintained in a closed circuit. The heat load is transferred through a closed "intermediate cooler" to service water, which can be released to the environment.

Reactor-building-cooling system. The heat loss from the reactor coolant system to the reactor building is sufficient to require a special cooling system to keep the building from overheating.

Shielding

The steel thermal shield (Figs. 2 and 3) inside the reactor pressure vessel protects the pressure vessel from excessive radiation. Since this vessel can withstand many orders-of-magnitude more radiation than the operating personnel, additional shielding outside of the pressure vessel must be provided to absorb neutrons and gamma radiation emanating from the core. This is usually accomplished by concrete several feet thick.

A typical arrangement of concrete shielding is shown in Figs. 2 and 3, Chapter 23. There is enough of this shielding around the reactor and reactor coolant system to permit limited access inside the reactor building during operation. The reactor building itself is a prestressed concrete structure with walls thick enough to shield adequately against radioactivity contained within it after a hypothetical rupture of the reactor coolant system.

A considerable amount of heat is generated by the absorption of gamma radiation in the shielding immediately around the reactor vessel. This usually requires water cooling, as noted under *Intermediate Cooling System.*

Fuel handling

Removal and replacement of fuel in a pressurized water reactor requires shutdown of the reactor and removal of the head. This is normally scheduled about once a year, and other plant maintenance is accomplished simultaneously. About one-third of the fuel assemblies are replaced each year, and the other two-thirds are relocated in the reactor to optimize the utilization of the fissionable material in each subassembly. The refueling operation is carefully planned to minimize the shutdown time required.

Spent fuel assemblies are normally removed vertically upward using a fuel-handling mechanism or a grapple tool suspended from a hoist. They are conveyed to storage through a water-filled canal, if provided, otherwise by using a shielded water-cooled cask. Underwater storage is provided in racks designed to prevent a chain reaction. There must also be provision for removing decay heat for a limited period (see *Spent-Fuel-Cooling System and Fig. 12*). When the decay heat has reached a low enough value, the spent fuel assemblies can be shipped to the fuel reprocessing plant in shielded casks specially designed to handle highly radioactive material.

Containment system

The large amount of water in an operating water reactor contains a considerable amount of short-lived radioactivity arising from activation of oxygen in the water itself. It may also contain radioactivity resulting from corrosion products or fuel assembly leakage or rupture. Therefore, a leak in the coolant water system could release radioactivity. Any such leakage must be confined, even to the extent of all the water in the system. A pressure-type vessel is usually provided to contain the

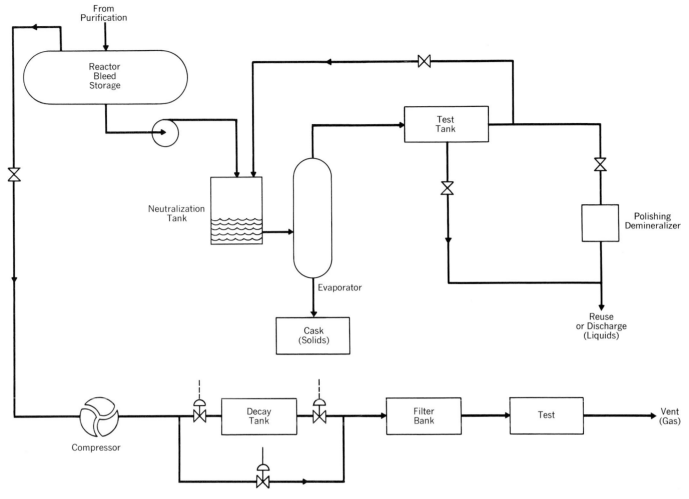

Fig. 13 Waste-disposal system.

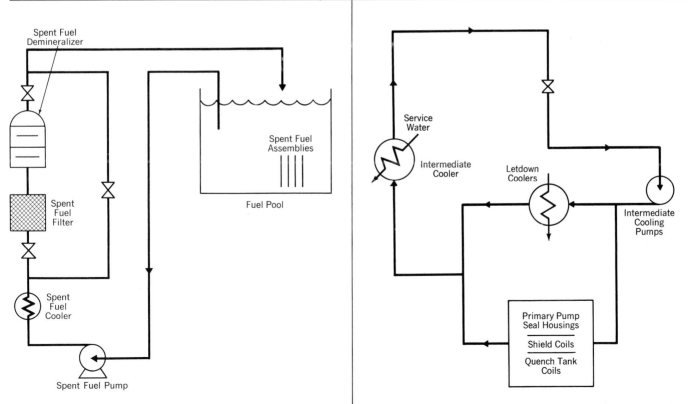

Fig. 12 Spent-fuel-cooling system.

Fig. 14 Intermediate cooling system.

energy and material that could be released by an accident. Engineered safeguards systems are also provided to limit the maximum value of the energy released by the accident.

Reactor building

For the early commercial water reactors and in some recent designs, the containment vessels are made of steel in the form of cylinders or spheres of 100 ft diameter or more and designed to withstand pressures up to 50 psi or more. Most modern containments for pressurized water reactors are concrete, with reinforcing steel used to provide tensile strength. They are called reactor buildings. The reinforcing steel can be placed in the concrete with no pre-stressing, in which case the building is called "reinforced." The building can be pre-stressed by applying tensile stress to the steel after the concrete is poured and set. This is called a "pre-stressed, post-tensioned" building. Both types are being used for current nuclear power plants (see also Reactor-Building-Cooling System).

The reactor building is also designed to withstand missiles from internal or external sources. Protection against internal missiles released by an accident is provided by internal concrete shielding placed around the reactor and reactor coolant system. Various reactor buildings have been designed to withstand the impact of a 35-ft long utility pole borne by a 150 mi/hr hurricane-force wind, an automobile traveling at 150 mi/hr, and a 4-in. by 12-in. by 12-ft wooden plank borne by tornado force winds striking end-on at 300 mi/hr.

The normally insignificant leakage from a reactor building would increase under the condition of leakage from the reactor coolant system which would release the coolant and its radioactivity into the reactor building. Therefore, precautions are required to minimize the leakage and maintain it within the NRC's prescribed standards. Since the greater part of the leakage is at the location of penetrations through the containment wall, particular care is required in designing the penetrations.

In some installations provision is made to collect the leakage through the metal vessel or liner, pass it through filters, and discharge it at the top of a stack where it can be further diluted by mixing with the surrounding air. With concrete shielding outside of a metal container, the space between can be used to collect the leakage; in the case of a concrete building, channels for collecting this leakage can be provided between the metal liner and the concrete. In some more recent designs, this provision is made only in the vicinity of penetrations.

In pressurized water reactors, as currently designed, there are four barriers between the fuel and the outside air:

1. The uranium oxide itself normally contains most of the fission products; even a large part of the gaseous products is retained within the fuel.

2. A second barrier is furnished by the fuel cladding.

3. The walls of the primary coolant system are the third barrier. (This barrier retains any leakage from the fuel assemblies within the reactor coolant.)

4. The reactor building is the fourth barrier.

Engineered safeguards systems

These systems are provided to limit the consequences of an accident involving a leak or break in the reactor coolant system. They include:

1. A system for isolation of the reactor building after rupture, including principally automatic closing of valves in all open lines piercing the reactor building.

2. Injection systems which introduce water into the reactor pressure vessel to cool the fuel assemblies and thereby prevent cladding rupture following a possible accident involving loss of coolant to the reactor. The injection water contains boron to inhibit the nuclear chain reaction.

3. Reactor-building-spray system (water or borated water) and cooling system to cool the building, thus reducing the pressure within it.

Cost of electric power from a nuclear plant

The year 1966 was a milestone year for the purchase of nuclear steam supply systems for the generation of electricity. In that year the kilowatt capacity of nuclear electric power purchased in the U.S. exceeded 40% of the total thermal capacity purchased.

By 1966 the cost of nuclear fuel reached a value somewhat lower than the mean cost of conventional fuels in the U.S. Since nuclear fuel costs are not greatly affected by plant size, nuclear power costs are more competitive with fossil fuels as plant sizes increase. Actually it was the rapid increase in the size of nuclear plants, in addition to improved technology, that resulted in the large increase in nuclear plant orders in the mid-sixties.

By 1976, the differential in cost had decreased, but fuel costs still favored nuclear fuel by an average of about 25%. The development of the economic nuclear fuel cycle for water reactors was an important factor in making nuclear power competitive (Chapter 19).

Another important factor is capital cost. The capital cost per kilowatt of a nuclear plant exceeds the cost of conventional power plants primarily because of the expensive safety, design and licensing requirements for a nuclear plant. These add equipment and additional time to both the engineering and construction schedules. The costs of these requirements do not increase proportionately with the size of the plant and become a lesser part of the total as size increases. Because of this and other factors, the capital cost of a nuclear plant per kw of capacity decreases more rapidly with plant size than does the cost of a fossil-fuel plant.

As of 1976 there is close cost competition between nuclear and conventional plants in most areas of the U.S. and this is spurring improvements both in nuclear and conventional plant designs.

The following can be considered as typical of the power costs expected from nuclear power plants ordered in 1976 by investor-owned electric power companies for operation in 1985 in the U.S.:

	mills/kwhr
Capital cost	24.2
Fuel cost	10.2
Operation and maintenance cost (including nuclear insurance)	2.0
Total	36.4

The figure for capital cost is based on a 1200 Mw (electric output) plant. It includes the nuclear steam supply system, the turbine and generating equipment, buildings, auxiliary equipment, escalation, interest during construction, land and other site costs. Plant location, plant use factor, rates for money, availability of cooling water, and other factors will significantly affect the capital cost. All costs are based on investor ownership of plants and fuel with corresponding rates to be used for capital. Power costs in government or municipally owned plants would be lower, reflecting the lower fixed charges on investment. Fuel cost evaluation is treated in *Nuclear Fuel Costs*, Chapter 19.

Optimization of a PWR plant for cost

The design of a pressurized water reactor plant for the generation of electricity requires that the entire system be optimized for cost within the framework of good practice and the safety features required by law. Investment and production (fuel, labor, maintenance, supplies) costs must be determined to give the most favorable overall cost for the electric energy produced by the plant. As indicated in the preceding section, the most significant elements of nuclear power cost are the capital (or investment) cost and the fuel cost. The design of the reactor core has a great influence on these costs; the principal parameters are:

1. Neutron economy, which determines the ratio of fuel generated by conversion to that burned. This is improved by minimizing the amount of "poison" or neutron-absorbing material in the core. In power reactors, this usually means the substitution of expensive zirconium alloy for the less costly but more neutron-absorbent stainless steel.

2. Size and dimensions of the reactor core. These affect both fuel cost and the cost of the reactor vessel.

3. Temperature rise of the coolant through the reactor, coolant flow, and pressure drop. These are interrelated in the cost of primary coolant piping, pumps, and the efficiency of the turbine room heat cycle.

4. Reactor coolant system pressure. Higher pressure requires heavier system equipment, but permits higher steam pressure and higher efficiency from the steam turbine cycle.

5. Flattening of the neutron flux throughout the reactor. In the early pressurized water reactors considerable ingenuity was required to design a reactor in which the maximum local neutron flux was less than four times the average. Reactor coolant flow must be provided in an amount sufficient to accommodate the heat released in the area of the highest neutron flux. Thus, a maximum-to-average flux ratio of 4 to 1 means that the reactor cooling system is operating at only 25% efficiency with respect to the reactor as a whole.

In the early pressurized water reactors the excess reactivity was held down at the start of core life by keeping a number of the control rods in the reactor. Portions of the reactor were thus blanketed by the rods. The large channels required for large control rods caused major power reductions in the vicinity of the rods when they were in the reactor, and large power increases occurred in the vicinity of the water-filled channels when the rods were withdrawn.

Present-day pressurized water reactors have achieved major improvements in flux distribution by utilizing soluble poison to take care of slow reactivity effects such as fuel burnup, fission product buildup, and the difference in reactivity between shutdown and operating temperatures. This reduces the functional requirement of the control rods to controlling the rapid reactivity changes which must be met during operations. The disadvantages of large control rods and large water channels are reduced by using a larger number of small control rods, several of which are operated as a group or cluster by a single control-rod-drive mechanism.

6. Fuel economy is increased by prolonging the life of the core up to an optimum point. For longer core life more excess fissionable material must be loaded at the start, thus increasing inventory costs. More poison must be provided to hold down the excess reactivity. This results in more neutron absorption in control poisons, and hence a reduced conversion ratio. The optimum design core life is determined when the value of the energy to be gained by additional core life is counterbalanced by the increased costs of fissionable material (uranium-235) and by reduction in credits from conversion (plutonium credits). (*See also Nuclear Fuel Costs, Chapter 19.*)

7. Fuel economy is usually improved by loading the fuel in batches which are shuffled from one part of the core to another. This tends to equalize the power generated by all fuel assemblies over their lifetime. Without shuffle, this would be difficult as the fuel assemblies near the periphery of the core are not utilized to their maximum capability. In order to shuffle the fuel the reactor must be shut down; this usually requires three to five weeks. A compromise must be made between using the fuel economically and minimizing plant downtime. A typical arrangement is to provide three batches of fuel at the start, shutting down once a year and removing one batch, shifting the other two batches to new locations, and installing a fresh batch.

Reactor licensing process

The Congress has vested in the Nuclear Regulatory Commission responsibility for the safety regulation of nuclear facilities with respect to radiation hazards. This control is accomplished by NRC standards, instructions, and licensing mechanisms to govern the use of nuclear material and nuclear facilities to minimize danger to health and property.

All nuclear reactors must be licensed by NRC. In the case of power reactors it is necessary initially to obtain a construction permit and, prior to operation, an operating license. Usually the Commission grants the operating license on a provisional basis. After a period of successful operation, a long-term operating license (up to 40 years) is issued. The reactor is always under the regulatory surveillance of the NRC.

In order to obtain a permit for construction of a nuclear facility, the applicant (who must be the pro-

spective operator) must file with NRC a formal application including a safety analysis of the proposed plant. This is reviewed formally by the NRC's regulatory staff. The staff submits questions to the applicant in writing concerning additional information which is needed, and also furnishes information and a preliminary analysis to the Advisory Committee on Reactor Safeguards (ACRS).* ACRS conducts an independent review and makes its report to the NRC staff.†

After the formal review, the ACRS report and the comprehensive NRC staff hazards evaluation are published and distributed to appropriate state, local and federal officials, and to the press and general public. A public hearing is scheduled and announced at least 30 days in advance by Federal Register and other publication, and letters to officials.

The public hearing, which is held before an Atomic Safety and Licensing Board, serves as a forum in which any controversy as to the safety of the proposed reactor can be adjudicated. The applicant must summarize the information in his application and must justify the grant-

---

* The Advisory Committee on Reactor Safeguards (ACRS) is a committee of experts appointed by the Nuclear Regulatory Commission. The law requires ACRS review of power reactor license applications from the standpoint of safety.

† If the applicant desires, before filing his formal application, he may have a preliminary informal site review by NRC regulatory staff and the ACRS.

ing of the construction permit on the basis of the provisions taken to protect public health and safety. The NRC staff summarizes its safety evaluation and conclusions, and its reasons why a permit should or should not be issued. Members of the public may present statements of their views, or if legally qualified, they may intervene and participate as parties to the hearing.

After the hearing, the Atomic Safety and Licensing Board reaches its decision. If there is no appeal, the Board's decision goes for review to the NRC Commissioners, who approve or may reverse the decision.

When the nuclear plant is completed, the operator of the plant must obtain an operating license. This procedure involves essentially the same review as for a construction permit. However, the review, including the safety analysis, is based on the actual plant.

The maximum power level at which the plant may be operated is specified in the operating license. A set of "technical specifications" defines other operating limitations that must be observed. NRC approval must be obtained before making any change which may affect the safety of the plant.

Reactor operators and their supervisors must obtain operators' licenses from NRC. These licenses are granted after comprehensive examinations requiring theoretical and practical knowledge of reactor technology, including the design and control of the particular reactor to be operated.

Applications of steam

A number of designs of steam generating units for various applications are described and illustrated in this section.

Chapter 22 deals with fossil-fuel equipment for the electric utilities. The principal factors involved in the selection of steam generating equipment are listed and examined. These include fuels, steam requirements, space and geographical considerations, power for driving auxiliaries, and guarantees. The B&W Radiant and Universal-Pressure boiler types for pulverized-coal, Cyclone-Furnace, natural-gas and oil firing are described. This chapter concludes by presenting procedures for the evaluation of equipment performance and characteristics in terms of justifiable expenditure. The use of these procedures is illustrated by examples.

Chapter 23 describes nuclear installations for electric utilities, and presents design data for units of two different sizes. Description of the units at Oconee Nuclear Station, Duke Power Company, includes the reactor building, reactor vessel and core, fuel and control rod assemblies, and control rod drives. Control and instrumentation characteristics are summarized, and a chart is presented, showing the variation of reactor-coolant and steam temperatures with load. The reactor coolant system, including the steam generators, reactor coolant pumps, pressurizer and piping, is described and illustrated, as are the provisions for fuel handling. Performance objectives, design limits, and some of the mechanical requirements for the reactor core and reactor internal components are discussed. The major design criteria for the reactor protection system are listed. The functions of the reactor building and engineered safeguards systems are outlined, and safety criteria and provisions are briefly discussed. Finally a summary is presented of the B&W nuclear steam supply system now being offered for electric utility service.

Chapter 24 describes marine installations both for fossil and nuclear fuels. Design considerations peculiar to marine service are discussed.

Three B&W boiler types for fossil-fuel applications are described and illustrated. A large portion of this chapter is devoted to the design of marine boilers, which differ from stationary units, particularly because of space requirements. This discussion includes oil burners; furnace design; boiler tube banks; superheaters, including the problems of oil-ash fouling and high-temperature corrosion; steam temperature control; reheaters; economizers; air heaters; boiler casing; boiler circulation; and steam separation.

The power plant for the Nuclear Merchant Ship *Savannah* is described briefly in the latter portion of Chapter 24, which also includes a brief summary of the construction and operation of this vessel. More recent designs for nuclear merchant ships, including the power plant for the German Nuclear Ship *Otto Hahn,* are also discussed.

Chapter 25 examines certain design requirements peculiar to industrial installations, including a wide size range, a wide range of pressure and temperature requirements, the supply of steam for more than one application, fluctuating loads and the use of waste fuels in many units. Package boilers are applicable to many industrial installations. Current B&W boiler types for industrial installations are presented and described. These are the Types FM, PFI and PFT Integral-Furnace boilers, and the two-drum Stirling boiler.

Chapter 26 describes the equipment used for the production of steam in the highly specialized chemical- and heat-recovery units in the paper industry. The principal features of the major pulping processes are summarized. The larger portion of the chapter is devoted to a description of a B&W recovery unit in which black liquor is dehydrated to form a char, the organic constituents are burned, and the heat is recovered in the production of steam. The inorganic constituents of the black liquor are recovered for reuse in the paper-making process. Several modifications of the sulfite process are also presented. The magnesium-base pulping and recovery process is described briefly and two designs of recovery boilers for use with this process are illustrated.

The utilization of industrial by-products as fuel for the production of steam is summarized in Chapter 27. These fuels include carbon monoxide from the petroleum industry, blast-furnace gas in the steel industry, pitch and tar from the distillation of petroleum and coal, bagasse from the milling of sugar cane, and wood refuse. The chapter includes a description of the oxygen-converter hood which burns the carbon monoxide from a basic-oxygen furnace for the production of steam, and provides a cleanup system to remove dust particles before the gases are discharged to the atmosphere. Other types of waste-heat boilers are also included.

In this central station in the Southeast, the large unit in the foreground, shown during construction, generates 8,000,000 lb of steam per hr in a Universal-Pressure boiler fired by coal in Cyclone Furnaces.

Chapter 22   Fossil-fuel boilers for electric utilities

Selection of steam generating equipment

Most of the electric power used in the U.S. is produced in steam plants using fossil fuels and high-speed turbines. These plants deliver a kilowatt-hour of electricity for 8500-9500 Btu supplied in the fuel. They utilize steam-driven turbine generators of 60 to 1300 Mw capacity supplied with steam from boilers generating half a million to approximately ten million pounds of steam per hr.

Each steam generating unit must satisfy the user's specific needs in the most economical manner. Achieving this requires close cooperation between the designer and the user's engineering staff or consultants.

Before the specifications for a steam generator can be written, the user or plant designer must conduct a cost evaluation of the entire electric generating plant. In areas where fossil-fuel costs are high, it may be necessary to evaluate both nuclear and fossil units to determine which best satisfies the user's needs. Methods for evaluating steam generating equipment for fossil fuel are discussed later in this chapter (*Evaluation of Equipment Performance and Characteristics*).

The cost of electricity from a steam plant has three principal elements: 1) capital equipment, 2) fuel, and 3) other operating and maintenance costs.

The capital cost survey must include the steam generator, steam turbine and electric generator, condenser, feedwater heaters and pumps, fuel handling facilities, buildings and real estate costs. The fuel cost survey must include the costs of the various fuels which may be used, and the probable changes in cost of these fuels during plant lifetime. There is a direct relation between plant efficiency and fuel used, and an important interrelation between plant efficiency and equipment cost.

Other important items are the location of the electric generating plant with respect to fuel supply and the areas where electricity is used. In some cases it is more economical to transport electricity than fuel, and some large steam generating stations are being built at the coal-mine mouth to generate electricity which is used

several hundred miles away. If the user is a member of a grid system, the probable requirements of other grid members may be an important factor. Anticipated costs of operation and maintenance must also be included in the evaluation.

Considerable time and effort are required to establish sufficiently accurate basic data with comprehensive consideration of engineering factors, judgment in planning for future expansion or changes, and evaluation of the tangibles and intangibles, so that the experience and craftsmanship of the boiler manufacturer and other suppliers can be applied to the full benefit of the plant designer and the owner. The user should, at the outset, decide who is to prepare this data. If he lacks personnel with the necessary qualifications, the services of consulting engineers should be utilized. A thorough discussion with the boiler manufacturer will provide many details which will aid the user in making correct decisions.

Before the equipment can be selected, the basis of operation and arrangement of the entire steam plant must be planned. Ultimately the available data must be translated into the form of equipment specifications so that the manufacturers of various components can provide apparatus in accordance with the user's requirements. After equipment selection, construction drawings must be prepared for the foundations, building, piping and walkways. The construction work must be coordinated utilizing modern schedule and control techniques for effective management and completion of erection.

Boiler designer's requirements

Most important to the boiler designer are the amount of steam required, the fuel to be used, and the steam conditions which are specified as a result of the user's cost evaluation. These steam conditions include temperature and pressure of the primary and reheat steam.

The boiler designer needs all data pertinent to steam generation to enable him to produce the most economical steam-generating equipment to satisfy the needs of the

user. This requires close cooperation between the boiler designer and the user's engineering staff or consultants.

The requirements and conditions that form the basis for the designer's selection of equipment can be outlined as follows:

1. Fuel(s)—sources presently available, analyses, costs, and future trends.

2. Steam requirements

   (a) Pressure and temperature—at points of use, at outlet of steam generating units, allowable temperature variations.

   (b) Rate of heat delivery (or steam flow)—to points of end use, to boiler house auxiliaries and feedwater heating, to blowdown, from outlet of steam generating unit, variations (minimum, average and maximum), and predictable future requirements.

3. Boiler feedwater—source and analysis, and temperature entering steam generating unit.

4. Space and geographical considerations—space limitations, relation of new equipment to existing boiler house equipment, environmental requirements and restrictions of local laws, earthquake and wind requirements, elevation above sea level, foundation conditions, climate, and accessibility for service and construction.

5. Kind and cost of energy for driving auxiliaries.

6. Operating personnel—experience level of workmen for operation and maintenance, and cost of labor.

7. Guarantees.

8. Evaluation basis—for unit efficiency, auxiliary power required, building volume, and various fixed charges.

With this information, the boiler designer is able to analyze the user's specific needs and coordinate the many components that make up a steam generator into the most economical design, by balancing first cost charges with long-term savings.

Design practice

The boiler designer usually works with standardized (pre-engineered) components. Detailed engineering of these components has been completed, hence shop fabrication is expedited and operating experience is proved. Examples of these are fuel burners, pulverizers, furnace sections, steam drums, and pressure parts. These components can be transformed readily into units of various capacities and dimensions. This results in lower costs, more rapid delivery schedules and improved availability of equipment in service.

There has been little standardization of complete unit designs for utility application primarily because of the distinctive nature of each user's conditions. The variables are not so much steam capacity, pressure and temperature as the types of fuels that are fired and the user's plans for utilizing the steam generating unit within his system. Variations of this type require changes in detail and overall arrangement of components. This, together with ever-changing costs of money, fuel, materials and labor, has made full unit standardization impracticable.

Fuels

For the dependable and economical generation of steam over the life of a plant, the equipment must be suitable for burning the fuel or fuels available at the particular site at a reasonable cost. The cost of delivered fuel is constantly changing because of fluctuations in price and freight rates, seasonal variations in availability of natural gas and temporary shortages of coal or fuel oil. Reliance on a single fuel is possible for some users with abundant and dependable local sources. Many utilities find it advantageous to plan for the use of more than one fuel because of cost fluctuation or to assure continuity of operation, should the normal supply be interrupted.

Because the cost of fuel(s) consumed throughout the life of a steam generating unit is such a significant part of the generating cost, a slight increase in unit efficiency can easily amount to savings worth many times the investment required to obtain this increased efficiency (see Evaluation of Equipment Performance and Characteristics). Thus, the plant designer should analyze the type of fuel or fuels he expects to burn, together with the present and anticipated future costs of fuels, and provide this information to the boiler manufacturer. This information will enable the boiler designer to incorporate features that will best meet the long-term requirements of the user.

The usual fuels burned in central stations are bituminous coal, lignite, natural gas and oil. Of these, bituminous coal is the most prevalent fuel used in steam production for power.

Coal. Coal is the most abundant and also the most complicated and troublesome of the major fuels. Its use involves storage and handling facilities, preparation before firing using crushers or pulverizers, ash disposal equipment, dust collectors, and sootblowers. The boiler stack discharge may be troublesome, depending on the equipment installed and local conditions.

There is a wide variation in the properties of coal and coal ash. The design of the steam-producing unit must be suitable for optimum performance in burning the particular coals available, with proper allowance for reasonable deviation should the design coals become unavailable. Coals with high-fusion temperatures are inherently suitable for burning, when pulverized, in dry-ash-removal hopper-bottom furnaces. Low-ash fusion coals, in crushed form, are burned economically and effectively in the Cyclone Furnace with slag-tap ash removal. In any particular instance, the final selection of burning method and boiler type is based on a combination of technical factors, economics and engineering judgment.

If coal is to be the fuel for a prospective installation, a tabulation should be prepared indicating the analyses of all the coals economically available. In addition, the plant designer should provide in his specifications the ash analysis of each coal. The ash composition has a marked effect on its slagging and fouling characteristics (see Chapter 15) and must be known for proper design of the furnace and heating surfaces.

The surveys which follow (pulverized-coal and Cyclone-Furnace firing) summarize the principal points affecting the choice of method and equipment when burn-

ing coal. Detailed descriptions of various types of fuel-preparation and burning equipment are given in Section II of this book.

Pulverized-coal firing. The size of pulverized-coal-fired boilers and turbine-generators has temporarily leveled off at 1300 megawatts. The equipment can be designed to burn practically any bituminous coal or lignite. Anthracite can be successfully burned in pulverized form, but fuel preparation and furnace and burner arrangements require special attention and additional expense.

The overall aspects of pulverized-coal firing, as applied to boiler units, are as follows (*see also Chapter 9*):

1. It is suitable for almost any coal mined in the United States.

2. It is economically suitable for a very wide range in boiler capacity.

3. It must have proper coal preparation equipment, including that required for the removal of moisture, and proper handling of the pulverized coal (direct firing and drying within the pulverizer preferred).

4. It requires hot air for combustion and for moisture removal (an air heater is required).

5. It provides for wide flexibility in operation and high thermal efficiency.

6. Proper means of handling the ash refuse (with either slag-tap or dry-ash removal) are required. This includes means for particulate removal from the flue gases.

For additional information on pulverized-coal firing, see Chapters 15 and 18.

Cyclone-Furnace firing. Cyclone-Furnace coal firing (*see Chapter 10*) is a parallel method to pulverized-coal firing but, in general, is used with low-ash-fusion coals. Burning crushed coal eliminates the initial and operating costs of pulverizing equipment. Cyclone-Furnace firing is currently suitable for boiler capacities ranging to more than 8,000,000 lb of steam per hr.

When selecting steam generating equipment with low-ash-fusion coal, the following should be considered with respect to Cyclone-Furnace firing as compared to pulverized-coal firing:

1. Reduced fly ash in stack gases results in a more compact arrangement and reduced flue-dust collection equipment costs.

2. Lower coal-preparation equipment cost and maintenance expenses for Cyclone-Furnace firing.

3. Reduction in furnace size.

4. Auxiliary power costs lower for low-grindability coals, but higher for high-grindability coals (*see Fig. 9, Chapter 10*).

Oil and gas are burned quite satisfactorily as secondary fuels in the Cyclone Furnace. In general, however, the Cyclone Furnace is advantageous when the primary fuel is a coal suitable for this type of firing.

Natural gas. Natural gas (Chapter 7) has the fewest design restrictions of the major fuels since it is clean and easy to burn. If only natural gas is burned, fuel storage facilities, ash hoppers, ash pits and ash-handling equipment are unnecessary. Sootblowers can be omitted and dust collectors are not needed. Control of heat input to the boiler furnace is simple. Heating surfaces can be arranged for optimum heat transfer and draft loss without consideration of ash deposits and erosion. The total enclosure volume is at a minimum, and the adaptability for outdoor service is increased.

Of all the major fuels, natural gas presents more of a potential hazard as a result of accumulation of gas from faulty valves or fittings or as a result of incorrect operation. Well trained operators plus modern detection and alarm systems minimize these hazards.

Fuel oil. Oil fuel (Chapter 7) has many of the desirable features of natural gas, including ease of handling and elimination of ash hoppers and ash pits. It does require fuel storage, heating and pumping facilities. Oils with high sulfur and vanadium content, when fired in a steam generating unit, can cause troublesome deposits on surfaces throughout the unit (Chapter 15). Care must be taken to minimize these deposits by arranging the heating surfaces for optimum cleaning by sootblowing equipment. Provision should be made for water washing furnace and all convection surfaces when the unit is shut down for maintenance. Air heater protection devices (a steam coil or hot water coil) should be installed to prevent condensation of gases and acid attack on the gas side of the air heater surfaces.

Steam requirements

Modern turbine generators are designed for nominal steam pressures from 1450 to 3500 psi at the turbine throttle with superheat and reheat temperatures from 950 to 1000F.

The steam temperature specified at the superheater outlet is taken as equal to the temperature required at the turbine plus 5F to compensate for the loss in temperature in the steam lines. For optimum performance and turbine maintenance, it is usually desirable that the steam temperature remain constant over a broad load range. Means for controlling superheat temperatures are required in utility practice. Steam temperature variation and control are discussed in Chapters 12 and 35.

The steam pressure at the superheater outlet is normally specified by the plant designer after evaluating the economics of pressure drop versus pipe sizing.

It is customary stationary-boiler practice in the U.S. to hold the main steam pressure constant for all loads, on the premise that this condition satisfies all pressure and quantity requirements of the steam-using equipment. Automatic combustion-control apparatus is accordingly designed to function on this basis.

Central station units, with a single boiler unit per turbine generator, utilize the reheat cycle because of the increased station thermal efficiency over the non-reheat cycle. The reheater, located within the boiler enclosure, receives steam exhausted from an intermediate pressure stage of the turbine. The steam temperature is raised to the initial turbine inlet temperature, and the steam is returned to the low-pressure section of the turbine.

The "double" reheat cycle, where steam is returned to the boiler twice for reheating and then delivered to low-pressure sections of the turbine, results in even higher station thermal efficiency than the single reheat cycle. However, the gain in plant efficiency must be weighed against the cost of additional piping systems and turbine and boiler equipment to accommodate the flow of low-pressure steam.

To determine the pressure, temperature and reheat cycle that results in the lowest total power cost throughout the life of a proposed steam power plant, it is necessary to balance levelized and capitalized fixed charges, fuel and other operating costs for the various alternatives. The plant designer should take advantage of the turbine and boiler manufacturers' experience which has been obtained from previous turbine-boiler cycle examinations, and apply this data to meet his individual conditions and requirements.

Rate of heat delivery (or steam flow)

It is necessary to select steam-producing equipment of sufficient capacity, range of output and responsiveness to insure prompt fulfillment of the turbine steam demands. The demand may be steady, as in base-loaded systems, or it may fluctuate widely and rapidly, as in cycling units. The steam-flow requirements should, therefore, be accurately established for peak flow, maximum continuous flow (usual steady maximum flow), minimum flow, and rate of change in flow. The peak load establishes the top capacity of the steam-producing equipment and all its auxiliaries.

The two principal methods of obtaining peak ratings in utility cycles are by operating at 5% overpressure at the turbine throttle and by removing one or more feedwater heaters from service. The method used is dependent on the steam turbine design parameters and limitations. For the condition of 5% overpressure at the superheater outlet, the steam generating equipment is designed to provide a steam flow 5% greater than the normal maximum continuous flow. Approximately 5% additional output from the turbine is obtained by passing this increased steam flow at higher pressure through the steam turbine.

The alternative method of obtaining peak ratings from the cycle is by removing feedwater heaters from service. Some of the steam normally bled to feedwater heaters from intermediate points on the turbine is continued through the turbine, thus increasing turbine output. This method results in higher than normal heat rates, while overpressure operation reduces heat rate.

Peak ratings are measured in terms of time. The time limits are generally a function of the metallurgical characteristics of high-temperature heating surface or fuel-and-ash characteristics and are described by the following terms:

1. Two-hour peak in 24 hours or 720 hr/yr.
2. Four-hour peak in 24 hours not to exceed 720 hr/yr.
3. Continuous peak not to exceed 30 days and not to exceed 720 hr/yr.

The above conditions could all apply to units firing oil or natural gas. However, only Item 1 above would apply to coal-fired units; peaks of longer duration would not be practicable because of the slagging, fouling and abrasive characteristics of coal ash.

The range from minimum to maximum output is a most important factor in selecting the firing equipment. To maintain ignition and smokeless combustion, the range from minimum to maximum output must also be considered in designing the furnace.

The required rate of change in steam flow (load) may materially affect the entire design of the steam-producing equipment. Within a specified load range, good response is easily obtained with well designed firing equipment for Cyclone-Furnace operation, pulverized coal, oil and gas. A multiplicity of burners (and pulverizers, where used) widens the available range, but if there is a frequent change in load, remote manual operation of cutting in and cutting out burners and pulverizers may be objectionable. It is, therefore, important that the designer, manufacturer and operator all understand what can be done by full-automatic firing and what is required beyond that.

To select equipment to produce steam at minimum total cost, it is also necessary to establish the probable "capacity factor"—the ratio of the average output to the rated output. The capacity factor serves as a basis for the exercise of judgment in establishing the value of incremental increases in the efficiency of steam generation. The first cost necessary to achieve high efficiency in a plant operating continuously at high output could not be justified for a plant operating as a peaking unit.

Boiler feedwater

Raw water from surface or subsurface sources invariably contains in solution some degree of troublesome scale-forming materials, free oxygen and sometimes acids. Since good water-conditioning is essential in the operation of any steam cycle, it is necessary to remove these impurities.

Dissolved oxygen will attack steel, and the rate of attack increases sharply with rise in temperature. High chemical concentrations in the boiler water and feedwater cause furnace tube deposition and also allow solids carry-over into the superheater and turbine, resulting in tube failures and turbine blade deposition or erosion.

As steam plant operating pressures have increased, the water treatment system has become more critical. This has led to the installation of more complete and refined water treatment facilities (Chapter 34).

The temperature of the feedwater entering an economizer should be high enough to prevent condensation and acid attack on the gas side of the tubes. Dew point and rate of corrosion vary with the sulfur content of the fuel and with the type of fuel-firing equipment.

Space and geographical considerations

Space limitations. New steam-producing equipment is sometimes installed in an existing building. Boilers are made in a variety of shapes, and a careful study of space conditions and possible arrangement of the equipment is necessary for best overall results. Space conditions sometimes have a direct bearing on the selection of the type of firing and number of steam generating units for

a given steam demand. The space occupied by an older boiler unit may be entirely suitable for a modern unit of high efficiency, with double the steam output or more.

Relation of new to existing equipment. New steam generating equipment is sometimes installed adjoining an existing steam plant, with the intent of using existing equipment, such as common structural columns, elevators and platform elevations for maintenance. The plant designer should consider these possible savings in plant cost and maintenance convenience, and provide drawings and design data to instruct the boiler designer of the need for compatibility of equipment.

Restrictions of local law and immediate neighborhood. Restrictions by local laws and the nature of the surrounding area affect the selection of equipment mainly due to stack discharges. Legislation increasingly limits the discharge of dust and particulate matter and objectionable gaseous constituents into the atmosphere. The plant designer must understand the local regulations applicable at the plant site. These regulations may necessitate increased stack height (not always permissible in the vicinity of airports—Chapter 17) and installation of equipment to remove fly ash from the stack gases. If the discharge of sulfur oxides is limited, this may dictate the use of more costly low-sulfur fuel (*see Chapter 18*).

Earthquake and wind requirements. In earthquake zones, the boiler-unit supporting structure must be braced in accordance with local laws and regulations. The design wind load on the vertical surfaces of the unit also varies with local experience and requirements (*see Design of a Structural Steel System, Chapter 30*).

Elevation above sea level. The site elevation materially affects draft loss, stack draft, fan sizing and resultant power requirements. It also affects the suction head of fuel pumps.

Climate as a factor. In many parts of the United States, particularly where the climate is mild year round, boilers are frequently installed outdoors to save building costs (Fig. 1). In areas where the climate is not favorable for complete outdoor installation, some savings are realized using semi-indoor construction where only the firing aisles are arranged with overhead protection. Construction varies from outdoor installations to totally enclosed installations. The plant designer should consider savings of this nature depending on climatic conditions at the plant site.

Power for driving auxiliaries

Modern practice in central stations generally calls for electric motor drives for rotating auxiliaries such as pumps, fans, pulverizers and crushers. The convenience and cost of the electrical drive substantiates this preference. Where variable speed may be desirable or where the steam generating unit is large (in excess of 500 Mw) a steam turbine is frequently chosen for an auxiliary drive, such as for feed pumps or forced draft fans. The combined nameplate rating of all auxiliaries in a modern plant may amount to 15% of the main-unit nameplate rating.

Guarantees

The plant designer must have some assurance that the judgment and decisions he makes concerning his selection of equipment are based on firm engineering data so that the steam plant will function in accordance with the user's needs. It is common practice to obtain guarantees from the various manufacturers confirming that expected performance data are applicable and true.

The boiler manufacturer is usually requested to provide the following guarantees, depending on the arrangement, type of fuel and type of boiler.

1. For one given load point and one fuel
   a) Efficiency
   b) Superheater steam temperature
   c) Reheater steam temperature
   d) Pressure drop
   e) Total air and gas resistance
   f) Solids in steam
2. Maximum capacity
3. Superheater and reheater control range
4. Pulverizer (where applicable)
   a) Fineness
   b) Power requirements

Fig. 1 Radiant boiler for oil and natural-gas firing—outdoor installation in the Southwest.

B&W boiler types for electric utility application

The selection of steam generating equipment requires a broad understanding of fuels, their preparation and combustion, and of heat transfer and fluid flow for steam-generating surfaces, superheaters, economizers and air heaters. Familiarity with various classes of steam generating units and their components is essential for an intelligent choice of equipment.

The brief descriptions of Radiant and Universal-Pressure boiler types which follow are intended to serve as an introduction to the types of steam generating units designed for the wide range of output and performance characteristics usually associated with electric utility practice.

Radiant boiler (RB)

The Radiant boiler derives its name from the fact that the heat absorption of a saturated surface is largely by radiant energy transfer. With its considerable range in output, the Radiant boiler is used in utility stations and larger industrial plants. Its components are pre-engineered with enough flexibility to adapt the design to various fuels and a broad range of steam conditions.

Range in capacity, steam output
About 300,000 lb/hr to an undetermined maximum exceeding 7,000,000 lb/hr.

Operating pressure
Subcritical, usually 1800 to 2400 psi throttle pressure with 5% overpressure.

Steam and reheat temperatures
As required, usually 1000F.

Fuel
Coal and lignite (Cyclone Furnace or pulverized fuel); oil; natural gas.

Operational control
Usually completely automatic, including feedwater flow, combustion and steam temperature.

Furnace
Water cooled; pressure or balanced-draft type.

Coal, oil and gas are burned singly or in combination. The furnace is completely water cooled and may be designed for either dry- or wet-ash removal. One or more division walls may be used, depending on the functional and economic requirements of the design. Superheater and reheater surfaces are pendant and/or horizontal. Steam-temperature control is by gas recirculation, excess air, or attemperation, separately or in combination. Gas tempering is used to control gas temperatures entering the superheater on the higher pressure Radiant-boiler units. Reheat-temperature control is accomplished by an attemperator located in the inlet piping to the reheater. Economizers and air heaters are required to obtain an efficiency commensurate with fuel costs. The physical size of the unit dictates field assembly, although many component parts are shop assembled.

Radiant boiler for pulverized coal (RBC)

The steam generating unit, shown in Fig. 2, is a pressure-fired Carolina-Type Radiant boiler. It is arranged with a water-cooled dry-bottom furnace, superheater, reheater, economizer and air heater components. The unit is designed to utilize coal, pulverized to a fineness of 70% or higher through a 200-mesh screen.

Fuel flow. Raw coal is discharged from the feeders to the pulverizers. The pulverized coal is transported by the primary air to the burners through a system of pressurized fuel and air piping.

Air and gas flow. Air from the forced draft fans is heated in the air heaters, then routed to the windbox, where it is distributed to the burners as secondary air and distributed to the primary-air system as hot primary air (*see Chapter 9*). A portion of the air from the forced draft fan is passed unheated, directly to the primary-air system as tempering primary air. The hot and tempering primary-air streams are mixed and directed to the primary-air fans to obtain the additional pressure required to route the air through the pulverizers and coal-air piping to the burners where combustion takes place.

Hot gas from the furnace passes successively across the secondary superheater and the pendant reheater located in the convection pass out of the high radiant-heat-transfer zone of the furnace. The gas turns downward and crosses the horizontal primary superheater and economizer, and passes to the air heaters.

Water and steam flow. Feedwater enters the bottom header of the economizer. The water passes upward through the economizer and discharges through the out-

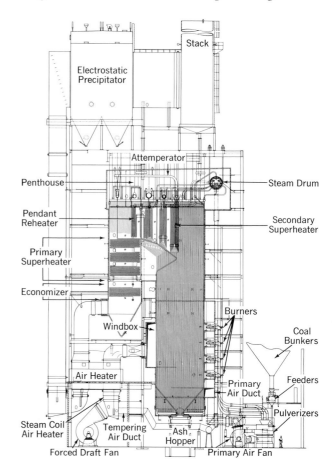

Fig. 2 Radiant boiler for pulverized coal.

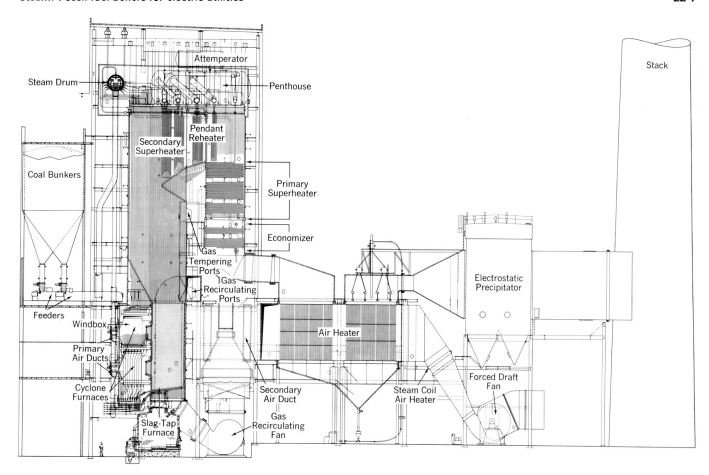

Fig. 3 Radiant boiler with Cyclone Furnaces.

let header into piping that conducts it to the steam drum. By means of natural circulation, the water flows down through downcomer pipes connecting supply distributor tubes to the lower furnace headers. From the furnace wall headers, the fluid rises through the furnace tubes to the upper headers. The flow then passes through riser tubes into the steam drum.

The water and steam mixture in the steam drum is separated by cyclone steam separators which provide essentially steam-free water in the downcomers. The steam is further purified by passing it through the primary and secondary steam scrubbers.

Steam from the steam drum passes through multiple connections to a header supplying the furnace roof tubes, then through other headers to the tubes located in the walls of the convection enclosure, and again through headers into the superheater.

Steam flow rises through the primary superheater and discharges through its outlet header and through connecting piping equipped with a spray attemperator. It then enters the secondary superheater by the inlet header, flowing through the superheater sections to the outlet header and a discharge pipe which terminates at a point outside of the penthouse.

Low pressure steam is introduced to the reheater inlet header and flows through the reheater tubes to the outlet.

Radiant boiler for Cyclone Furnace (RBC)

The steam generating unit, shown in Fig. 3, is a pressure-fired Carolina-Type Radiant boiler. It is arranged with a water-cooled slag-tap furnace, superheater, reheater, economizer, and air heater components, and fired with Cyclone Furnaces. It is designed to utilize coal of low ash-softening temperature crushed to minus $\frac{1}{4}''$ size.

Fuel flow. Crushed coal is discharged from the feeders to the Cyclone Furnaces with the amount of fuel determined by the rate of speed of the feeder.

Air and gas flow. Air from the forced draft fans is heated in the air heater and distributed to the Cyclone Furnaces. Hot gas from the furnace passes successively across the secondary superheater and the pendant reheater which are located in the convection pass out of the high radiant-heat-transfer zone of the furnace. The gas turns downward and crosses the horizontal primary superheater and economizer, and passes to the air heater.

Water and steam flow. Feedwater enters the bottom header of the economizer. The water passes upward through the economizer and discharges through the outlet header into piping which directs it to the steam drum. By means of natural circulation, the water flows down through downcomer pipes and connecting supply distributor tubes to the Cyclone Furnaces and furnace headers. The flow rises through the furnace tubes to the upper headers and through connecting riser tubes to the steam drum.

The water and steam mixture in the steam drum is separated by cyclone steam separators which provide essentially steam-free water for the downcomers. The

steam is further purified by passing it through the primary and secondary steam scrubbers.

Steam from the steam drum passes through multiple connections to a header supplying the furnace roof tubes, then through other headers to the tubes located in the walls of the convection enclosure, and again through headers into the superheater.

Steam flow rises through the primary superheater and discharges through its outlet header and through connecting piping equipped with a spray attemperator. It then enters the secondary superheater by the inlet header, flowing through the superheater sections to the outlet header and a discharge pipe which terminates at a point adjacent to the side of the penthouse.

Low pressure steam is introduced to the reheater inlet header and flows through the reheater tubes to the outlet.

Radiant boiler for natural gas and oil (RBE)

The steam generating unit, shown in Fig. 4, is a pressure-fired El-Paso-Type Radiant boiler unit. It is arranged with a water-cooled hopper-bottom furnace, superheater, reheater, economizer, and air heater components. The unit is designed to utilize natural gas and oil either separately or in combination.

Air and gas flow. Air from the forced draft fan is heated in the air heater and is distributed to the burner windbox. Hot gas from the furnace passes successively over the horizontal secondary superheater and reheater sections and one bank of the primary superheater. The gas then turns and flows downward and crosses the remainder of the primary superheater sections, the economizer sections, and thence out of the water-cooled enclosure to the air heater.

Water and steam flow. Feedwater enters the bottom header of the economizer. The water flows upward through the economizer and discharges through the outlet header into piping that directs it to the steam drum. By means of natural circulation, water flows downward through downcomer pipes, then through supply distributor tubes to the lower furnace headers. The flow then rises through the furnace tubes (which enclose the convection area) and thence to the upper headers and through connecting riser tubes into the steam drum.

The water and steam mixture in the steam drum is separated by cyclone steam separators which provide essentially steam-free water for the downcomers. The steam is further purified by passing through the primary and secondary steam scrubbers.

Steam from the steam drum passes through multiple connections at the rear of the convection enclosure into the primary superheater inlet header.

Steam flow rises through part of the primary superheater and, by means of connecting tubes, is directed into the remainder of the primary superheater in the first gas pass. The flow discharges through the primary-superheater outlet header into connecting piping equipped with a spray attemperator. The steam enters the secondary-superheater inlet header and flows through the secondary-superheater sections to the outlet header and a discharge pipe which terminates at a point outside of the casing at the front of the unit.

Low pressure steam, introduced to the reheater inlet header, flows through the reheater sections and out through the reheater outlet header to an outlet piping connection terminating outside the casing, also at the front of the unit.

Universal-Pressure boiler (UP)

The Universal-Pressure boiler, sometimes referred to as the Once-Through boiler, derives its name from the fact that it is applicable functionally at all commercial temperatures and pressures, subcritical and supercritical. Economically, it is applicable to the larger sizes, to the higher subcritical pressure range, and to the supercritical pressure range.

Range in capacity, steam output
   About 300,000 lb/hr to an undetermined maximum exceeding 10,000,000 lb/hr.

Operating pressure
   Subcritical, usually at 2400 psi throttle pressure, and supercritical at 3500 psi throttle pressure with 5% overpressure.

Steam and reheat temperatures
   As required, usually 1000F.
   Constant steam temperature can be maintained to one fourth load with any fuel.
   Constant reheat temperature can be maintained to 60% load with any fuel.

Fuel
   Coal and lignite (Cyclone Furnace or pulverized fuel); oil; natural gas.

Operational control
   Completely automatic, including pumping and firing-rate control and steam temperature control.

Furnace
   Water- and/or steam-cooled; pressure or balanced-draft type.

The principle of operation is that of the once-through or "Benson" cycle. The working fluid is pumped into the unit as liquid, passes sequentially through all the pressure-part heating surfaces, where it is converted to steam as it absorbs heat, and leaves as steam at the desired temperature. There is no recirculation of water within the unit and, for this reason, a drum is not required to separate water from steam.

Firing may be by oil, gas or coal, the last either in pulverized form or crushed for Cyclone-Furnace firing. The furnace is completely fluid cooled. It may be designed for balanced draft or pressure operation. Ash removal may be either dry or wet. Furnace division walls are used in the larger units to effect a reduction in building volume, building steel, and platforms. Reheaters for single or two-stage reheat may be incorporated in the design for the reheat cycle.

Fuel-pump speed and turbine throttle are used to control steam flow and steam pressure. Superheater steam temperature is controlled by the fuel firing rate. Gas tempering is used to control gas temperatures entering the superheater. Reheater steam temperature is con-

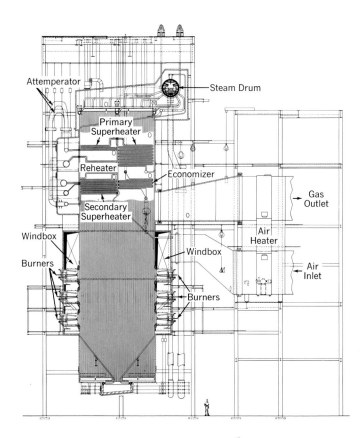

Fig. 4 Radiant boiler for natural gas and oil.

trolled by gas-recirculation, excess air, and attemperation, separately or in combination.

The Universal-Pressure boiler is designed to maintain a minimum flow inside the furnace circuits to prevent overheating of furnace tubes during all operating conditions. This flow must be established before start-up of the boiler. A bypass system, integral with the boiler, turbine, condensate and feedwater system, is provided so that the minimum design flow can be maintained through pressure parts which are exposed to high temperature combustion gases during the start-up operations and at other times when the required minimum flow exceeds the turbine steam demand (*see Chapter 34*).

The bypass system performs the following additional functions:

1. Reduces the pressure and temperature of the steam leaving the boiler during start-up to conditions suitable for the turbine, condenser and auxiliary equipment.

2. Provides means for recovering heat flowing to the bypass system, during start-up and low-load operation, utilizing the feedwater heaters.

3. Provides means for conditioning the water during start-up without delaying boiler and turbine warming operations.

4. Protects the high-temperature (secondary) superheater against shock from water during start-up.

5. Provides means for relieving excessive pressure in the system after a load trip.

Universal-Pressure boiler for pulverized coal (UPC)

The steam generating unit, shown in Fig. 5, is a pressure-fired Universal-Pressure boiler, comprising a water-cooled dry-bottom furnace, superheater, reheater, economizer, and air heater components. The unit is designed to utilize coal pulverized to a fineness of 70% or higher through a 200-mesh screen.

Fuel flow. Raw coal is discharged from the feeders to the pulverizers. The pulverizers can be located either at the front or sides of the unit. Pulverized coal is transported by the primary air to the burners through a system of pressurized fuel and air piping.

Air and gas flow. Air from the forced draft fans is heated in the air heaters, then routed to the windbox, where it is distributed to the burners as secondary air and to the primary-air system as hot primary air. A portion of the air from the forced draft fans is passed unheated, directly to the primary-air system as tempering primary air. The hot and tempering primary-air streams are mixed and directed to the primary-air fans to obtain the additional pressure required to route the air through the pulverizers and coal-air piping to the burners.

Hot gas from the furnace passes successively across the secondary superheater and the pendant reheater which are located in the convection pass out of the high radiant-heat-transfer zone of the furnace. The gas turns downward and crosses the horizontal primary superheater, reheater, and economizer, and passes to the air heaters.

Water and steam flow. Feedwater enters the bottom header of the economizer, and passes upward through

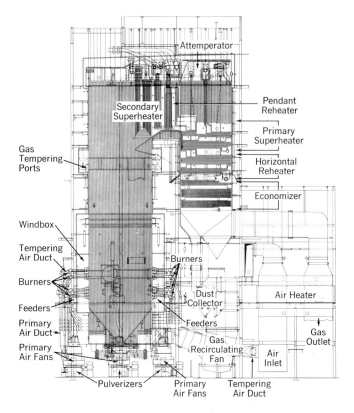

Fig. 5 Universal-Pressure boiler for pulverized coal.

the economizer to the outlet header. It is then distributed by a pipe system to the lower furnace area from which multiple connecting pipes are routed to the lower furnace headers.

From the furnace-wall headers the fluid is then passed upward through the furnace tubes. It is mixed en route to balance fluid conditions.

After discharging to the upper furnace wall headers, all fluid is routed through pipes to the front roof header, and then through the roof tubes to the rear roof headers where mixing again takes place. It is then passed through a pipe distribution system to the convection-enclosure lower headers, thence up through the wall tubes and the superheater screen. Pipes then convey the fluid to a common header and thence to the primary-superheater inlet header.

The fluid is collected and partially mixed before entering the primary superheater, then partially mixed again as it flows from the primary to the secondary superheater. Side-to-side crossover connections between primary and secondary superheaters reduce temperature unbalances.

Low pressure steam is introduced to the horizontal-reheater inlet header and flows through the tubes in the horizontal and pendant reheater sections to the outlet headers and return piping.

Universal-Pressure boiler for Cyclone Furnace (UPC)

The steam generating unit, shown in Fig. 6, is a pressure-fired Universal-Pressure boiler comprising a water-cooled slag-tap furnace, superheater, reheater, economizer and air heater, and fired with Cyclone Furnaces. The unit is designed to utilize coal with low ash-softening temperature crushed to minus $\frac{1}{4}''$ size.

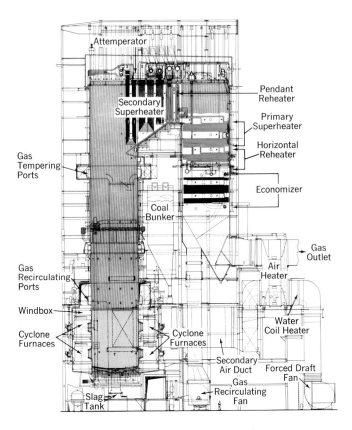

Fig. 6 Universal-Pressure boiler with Cyclone Furnaces.

Fuel flow. Crushed coal is discharged from the feeders to the Cyclone Furnaces, with the amount of fuel determined by the rate of speed of the feeder.

Air and gas flow. Air from the forced draft fans is heated in the air heaters and distributed to the Cyclone Furnaces. Hot gas from the furnace passes successively across the secondary superheater and pendant reheater which are located in the convection-pass out of the high radiant-heat-transfer zone of the furnace. The gas turns downward, crosses the horizontal primary superheater, reheater and economizer, and passes to the air heaters.

Water and steam flow. Feedwater is introduced to the bottom header of the economizer. It passes upward through the economizer to collecting headers, then goes through downcomer piping to the vicinity of the Cyclone Furnaces, where multiple pipe connections route the water to each cyclone. The cyclones, which are interconnected, discharge the water through multiple connections to a mixing bottle located under the furnace. Here the fluid from all the cyclones is mixed to eliminate unbalances in the fluid conditions. From this bottle, the fluid flows to the inlet headers of the floor circuit and side walls, and passes upward through the furnace wall tubes. It is mixed en route to balance fluid conditions.

From the upper furnace wall headers, the fluid is routed through pipes to the front roof header, then through the roof tubes to the rear roof headers where mixing again takes place. It passes through a pipe distribution system to the convection closure lower headers, and up through the wall tubes, discharging to the upper headers. Pipes then convey the fluid to a common header and then to the primary superheater inlet header.

The fluid is collected and partially mixed before entering the primary superheater and is partially mixed again as it flows from the primary to the secondary superheater. Side-to-side crossover connections between the primary and secondary superheaters reduce temperature unbalances. The secondary superheater discharges the steam to the main steam outlets.

Low pressure steam is introduced to the reheater inlet header and flows through the reheater tubes to outlets.

Universal-Pressure boiler for natural gas and oil (UPH)

The steam generating unit, shown in Fig. 7, is designed for natural-gas and oil firing either separately or in combination. The arrangement of this unit is similar to that of Fig. 5.

Evaluation of equipment performance and characteristics

Costs related to the performance and characteristics of equipment are a basic concern of the engineer and user. Equipment at an attractive initial cost, with high operating costs caused by low efficiency or other reasons, is frequently expensive over the period of its life. However, an increase in initial expenditure can be justified in the long run only if the improved performance is worth the extra expenditure. As a measure of justifiable expenditure, monetary values can be calculated for the performance and other characteristics of the equipment. These values are the basis for evaluations or cost comparisons.

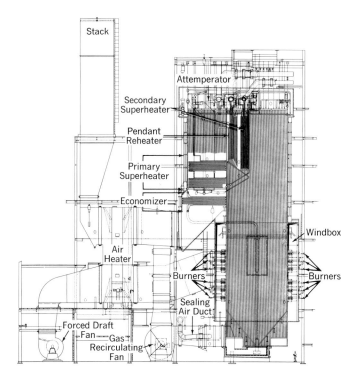

Fig. 7 Universal-Pressure boiler for natural gas and oil.

The principal items usually considered in the selection of boiler units and related equipment are:

1. Capital cost of equipment.

2. Efficiency (or net plant heat rate).

3. Auxiliary power (demand and operation)—forced draft fan, induced draft fan, gas recirculating fan, boiler feed pump, and circulating pump.

4. Building space.

5. Superheater and economizer pressure drop (can be accounted for in 3 above).

6. Reheater pressure drop.

7. Maintenance.

8. Availability.

9. Time span from start of project to commercial operation.

The last three factors are often considered in evaluation studies, but it is difficult to establish quantitative values for them.

Capital cost evaluations

To evaluate two or more alternates, it is first necessary to consider the capital or initial cost of equipment required to perform the task. The scope of equipment considered must be such as to produce comparable results for all alternates.

Evaluations are often made by considering the operating and demand charges for alternate schemes and capitalizing them by one of the two methods shown below. This capitalized difference between two alternates is the economically justified difference in first cost between the alternates.

Data needed for evaluation of operating costs

To make capital evaluations of two or more alternates for various conditions of operation, it is necessary to know:

1. Fuel cost per suitable unit, ¢/million Btu.

2. Net-plant-heat rate generated, Btu/kwhr.

3. Demand charge, usually $/installed kw.

Fuel cost. Fuel cost is the cost of fuel delivered to the point of use. This cost is used in evaluations of efficiency. It is also used in evaluations of power for the auxiliaries, when the power is produced within the plant.

Net-plant-heat rate (NPHR). The net-plant-heat rate of a power generating station is the fuel-heat input required to generate a kwhr and deliver the generated power to the transmission line leaving the station. This important quantity is inversely proportional to plant efficiency. In current central station practice net-plant-heat rates range from about 8860 Btu/kwhr for a 3500 psi cycle to 9000 Btu/kwhr for a 2400 psi cycle.

Demand charge. Demand charge represents the capitalized cost of any additional capacity in boilers, turbines, and generators necessary to generate the power required for the auxiliaries. The demand charge is not always used, but in many cases, especially in public utilities, its application is common practice.

Demand charges can be assessed on any motor-driven auxiliaries in service at full load. These will include fans, pumps, pulverizers and other auxiliaries. Demand charges on steam-turbine-driven equipment are more difficult to assess, since the use of low pressure steam for such drives can change the station heat rate and boiler steam flow.

Current demand charges for fossil-fuel-fired plants vary typically from $500/kw to $600/kw for coal firing.

Methods for evaluating operating costs

There are several approaches to the evaluation of operating costs. The capitalized cost method and the revenue requirements method are treated here and examples are given.

Capitalized cost method. This method assumes that the equipment being operated has an infinite lifetime and that the costs of operating the unit will continue indefinitely. It is a simpler evaluation procedure to use than the revenue requirements method described below, but is not as exact or flexible in accounting for future changes in such items as fuel and maintenance costs, which change during the life of the unit.

The dollar amount calculated using this method is the justifiable capital expense, i.e., the amount of money which can be spent to purchase the additional equipment which will give the operating advantage.

For example, if it is found that the capitalized cost of one in. of resistance (friction pressure loss for gas or air) for a given unit is $50,000, the expense of up to $50,000 in first cost for rearrangement of equipment to save one in. of resistance is justified.

Revenue requirements method. This method determines the minimum gross receipts which are required to make each alternate "pay its way." The alternate that requires the least receipts of "revenues" is the economic choice. It will permit profitable operation with the smallest revenues. This method takes into account the present worth of all future expenditures and costs.

The capital (first-cost) expenditure which is justified in order to put two alternates on an equal basis is less than the difference in future-revenue requirements. The future-revenue requirements are brought back to today's dollars by multiplying the expenditure of money in the future by the present worth factor for each year in which the money will be spent. By summing the present worth of the future revenue requirements, a total present worth in today's dollars is determined. To convert this sum into a justifiable capital expense, it must be "levelized," or converted to an equivalent equal annual cost. This is done by dividing the total present worth by the "uniform-annual-series present-worth factor" (which is 13.76 for a 30-year period and 6% interest rate, used in the examples below). A tabulation of present worth factors for 6% interest rate is shown in Table 1. Present worth factors for other interest rates and evaluation periods can be found in various engineering economics texts. After converting the total into an equal annual cost, the justifiable capital expenditure is determined by dividing the annual cost by the fixed charge rate. This will be illustrated by examples.

Table 1
6% Compound interest factors

Year	Single Payment Present Worth Factor	Uniform Annual Series Present Worth Factor	Year	Single Payment Present Worth Factor	Uniform Annual Series Present Worth Factor
1	0.9434	0.943	16	0.3936	10.106
2	0.8900	1.833	17	0.3717	10.477
3	0.8396	2.673	18	0.3503	10.828
4	0.7921	3.465	19	0.3305	11.158
5	0.7473	4.212	20	0.3318	11.470
6	0.7050	4.917	21	0.2942	11.764
7	0.6651	5.582	22	0.2775	12.042
8	0.6274	6.210	23	0.2618	12.303
9	0.5919	6.802	24	0.2470	12.550
10	0.5584	7.360	25	0.2330	12.783
11	0.5268	7.887	26	0.2198	13.003
12	0.4970	8.384	27	0.2074	13.211
13	0.4688	8.853	28	0.1956	13.406
14	0.4423	9.925	29	0.1846	13.591
15	0.4173	9.712	30	0.1741	13.765

General considerations. An evaluation calculation must take the future into account, since the cost of operating the equipment will continue throughout its life. Power-plant life is typically 30 years. In predicting the cost of operating a unit over 30 years, several factors must be considered:

1. Interest rate, or the cost of borrowing money. This is the rate the utility must pay to attract investment money. The interest rate affects the present-worth calculations; the higher the interest rate the less the value of a dollar spent in the future in terms of today's dollars.

2. Fixed charge rate, or the sum of the fixed costs of doing business. Fixed charges include all costs that are directly proportional to the investment initially made or the working capital necessary for its operation. These charges are independent of the extent to which the facilities, equipment or services are used. Interest, insurance, taxes, and depreciation are included in the category. Fixed charge rates vary between utilities, the range in 1970 being between 10 and 21%.

3. Unit capacity over its lifetime, taking into account the varying capacity with time. The unit will be operated at or near full load when new. As it gets older it will be operated at lower load more of the time, and the capacity factor will be lower.

4. Net-plant-heat rate. Varying with capacity, this rate is usually a minimum at full load, sometimes at about ¾ of full load. At lower capacities the net-plant-heat rate increases with resulting loss in plant efficiency.

5. Varying operating costs over the lifetime of the plant. For example, fuel costs may rise in the future.

These factors are used for evaluation in both the capitalized cost and the revenue requirements methods.

Examples

Three examples of the use of evaluation procedures are given. The first two examples use the revenue requirements method, and Example 3 uses the capitalized cost method.

Example 1

A) Problem: Determine the economic choice between a 2400 psi cycle and a 3500 psi cycle.

B) Given:

	Unit I	Unit II
1. Throttle pressure, psi	2400	3500
2. Temperature, SH/RH, F	1000/1000	1000/1000
3. Plant size, kw	600,000	600,000
4. Net-plant-heat rate, (NPHR), Btu/kwhr		
100% Load	9000	8860
80% Load	9000	8860
60% Load	9180	9040
35% Load	10,080	9920
5. Fuel cost, ¢/million Btu	25	25
6. Evaluation period, years	30	30
7. Interest rate, %	6	6
8. Maintenance costs	Same	Same
9. Availability	Same	Same
10. Operating costs (excluding fuel)	Same	Same
11. Fixed charge rate, %		
Interest	6.0	6.0
Taxes, insurance, debt return	5.5	5.5
Total, %	11.5	11.5

12. Plant capacity factors (Units I and II)

Years	1-10	11-20	21-30
100% Load	44%	23%	6%
80% Load	28	23	23
60% Load	13	34	34
35% Load	6	11	23
0% Load	9	9	14
	100%	100%	100%
Avg capacity factor for period	76.30%	65.65%	52.85%
Avg capacity factor for lifetime		64.93%	

C) Solution:

1. Cost of fuel consumed per yr − 2400 psi unit
(Hr/yr) × capacity factor × kw load × Btu/kwhr = Btu/yr
(Btu/yr) × (dollars/Btu) = \$/yr

  (a) Years 1-10

                                       Btu/yr

$$8760 \times .44 \times 1.00 \times 600,000 \times 9000 = 20,820 \times 10^9$$
$$8760 \times .28 \times .80 \times 600,000 \times 9000 = 10,600 \times 10^9$$
$$8760 \times .13 \times .60 \times 600,000 \times 9180 = 3,760 \times 10^9$$
$$8760 \times .06 \times .35 \times 600,000 \times 10,080 = 1,112 \times 10^9$$
$$\overline{36,292 \times 10^9}$$

$$36,292 \times 10^9 \times \$0.25/10^6 = \$9,066,000/\text{yr}$$

  (b) Years 11-20

$$8760 \times .23 \times 1.00 \times 600,000 \times 9000 = 10,880 \times 10^9$$
$$8760 \times .23 \times .80 \times 600,000 \times 9000 = 8,710 \times 10^9$$
$$8760 \times .34 \times .60 \times 600,000 \times 9180 = 9,840 \times 10^9$$
$$8760 \times .11 \times .35 \times 600,000 \times 10,080 = 2,040 \times 10^9$$
$$\overline{31,470 \times 10^9}$$

$$31,470 \times 10^9 \times \$0.25/10^6 = \$7,870,000/\text{yr}$$

  (c) Years 21-30

$$8760 \times .06 \times 1.00 \times 600,000 \times 9000 = 2,840 \times 10^9$$
$$8760 \times .23 \times .80 \times 600,000 \times 9000 = 8,700 \times 10^9$$
$$8760 \times .34 \times .60 \times 600,000 \times 9180 = 9,850 \times 10^9$$
$$8760 \times .23 \times .35 \times 600,000 \times 10,080 = 4,270 \times 10^9$$
$$\overline{25,660 \times 10^9}$$

$$25,660 \times 10^9 \times \$0.25/10^6 = \$6,415,000/\text{yr}$$

2. Present worth of fuel costs − 2400 psi unit
Fuel costs for period × Present worth factor for period (Table 1) = Present worth of fuel costs for period

  (a) Years 1-10
$$\$9,066,000/\text{yr} \times 7.36 = \$66,800,000$$

  (b) Years 11-20
$$\$7,870,000/\text{yr} \times (11.47 - 7.36) = \$32,300,000$$

  (c) Years 21-30
$$\$6,415,000/\text{yr} \,(13.76 - 11.47) = \$14,700,000$$
$$\overline{\$113,800,000}$$

3. Cost of fuel consumed per yr − 3500 psi unit
(Hr/yr) × capacity factor × kw load × Btu/kwhr = Btu/yr
(Btu/yr) × (dollars/Btu) = \$/yr

  (a) Years 1-10

                                       Btu/yr

$$8760 \times .44 \times 1.00 \times 600,000 \times 8860 = 20,500 \times 10^9$$
$$8760 \times .28 \times .80 \times 600,000 \times 8860 = 10,440 \times 10^9$$
$$8760 \times .13 \times .60 \times 600,000 \times 9040 = 3,700 \times 10^9$$
$$8760 \times .06 \times .35 \times 600,000 \times 9920 = 1,095 \times 10^9$$
$$\overline{35,735 \times 10^9}$$

$$35,735 \times 10^9 \times \$0.25/10^6 = \$8,940,000/\text{yr}$$

  (b) Years 11-20

$$8760 \times .23 \times 1.00 \times 600,000 \times 8860 = 10,710 \times 10^9$$
$$8760 \times .23 \times .80 \times 600,000 \times 8860 = 8,580 \times 10^9$$
$$8760 \times .34 \times .60 \times 600,000 \times 9040 = 9,690 \times 10^9$$
$$8760 \times .11 \times .35 \times 600,000 \times 9920 = 2,010 \times 10^9$$
$$\overline{30,990 \times 10^9}$$

$$30,990 \times 10^9 \times \$0.25/10^6 = \$7,750,000/\text{yr}$$

  (c) Years 21-30

$$8760 \times .06 \times 1.00 \times 600,000 \times 8860 = 2,795 \times 10^9$$
$$8760 \times .23 \times .80 \times 600,000 \times 8860 = 8,560 \times 10^9$$
$$8760 \times .34 \times .60 \times 600,000 \times 9040 = 9,700 \times 10^9$$
$$8760 \times .23 \times .35 \times 600,000 \times 9920 = 4,205 \times 10^9$$
$$\overline{25,260 \times 10^9}$$

$$25,260 \times 10^9 \times \$0.25/10^6 = \$6,320,000/\text{yr}$$

4. Present worth of fuel costs − 3500 psi unit

  (a) Years 1-10
$$\$8,940,000 \times 7.36 = \$65,800,000$$

  (b) Years 11-20
$$\$7,750,000 \times (11.47 - 7.36) = \$31,830,000$$

  (c) Years 21-30
$$\$6,320,000 \times (13.76 - 11.47) = \$14,480,000$$
$$\overline{\$112,110,000}$$

5. Saving in fuel costs − 3500 psi vs. 2400 psi
  Present worth of fuel costs

    2400 psi Unit −   \$113,800,000
    3500 psi Unit −   \$112,110,000
  Present worth of saving   \$ 1,690,000
  \$1,690,000 ÷ 600,000 kw = \$2.82/kw

6. Justifiable capital expenditure − 3500 psi vs. 2400 psi
Justifiable additional expenditure =
$$\frac{\text{Present worth of fuel cost saving}}{\text{Fixed charge rate} \times \text{Present worth factor}}$$
Present worth factor for 30 yrs at 6% interest = 13.76
Fixed charge rate = 11.5% = 0.115
Justifiable additional expenditure =
$$\frac{\$1,690,000}{0.115 \times 13.76} = \$1,068,000$$
Justifiable expenditure/kw =
  \$1,068,000 ÷ 600,000 kw = \$1.78/kw

D) Result:

1. In terms of today's worth, the 3500 psi cycle will save \$1,690,000 or \$2.82/kw in fuel costs over its life as compared with the 2400 psi cycle.

2. The saving will justify the expenditure of \$1,068,000 or \$1.78/kw more for the 3500 psi cycle than the 2400 psi cycle.

Example 2

A) Problem: Compare the use of gas recirculation and excess air for reheat-steam-temperature control.

B) Given:

1. Steam conditions, plant size, fuel cost, evaluation period, interest rate, fixed charge rate, maintenance, availability and plant load same as Unit II in Example 1. Net-plant-heat rate for gas recirculation same as Unit II in Example 1.

2. Boiler efficiency, %

	Gas Recirculation	Excess Air	Difference (Gas Recirculation as Base)
100% Load	85.51%	85.51%	—
80% Load	86.14%	85.45%	(−)0.69%
60% Load	86.41%	85.93%	(−)0.48%
35% Load	86.42%	86.06%	(−)0.36%

3. Additional auxiliary power — kw input to fan motors

	Gas Recirculation	Excess Air	Difference (Gas Recirculation as Base)
	Input to Gas Recirculating Fan	Additional Input to Forced Draft Fan	
100% Load	0	0	0
80% Load	800	400	(−)400
60% Load	1020	550	(−)470
35% Load	650	500	(−)150

4. Heat recovery factor for fans due to heat of compression
   = 30% or 0.30

5. Heat loss factor for fans $1.00 - 0.30 = 0.70$

C) Solution:

1. Difference in net-plant-heat rate for boiler efficiency,
   Btu/kwhr = $\triangle$NPHR =

   $$(-) \frac{\text{Difference in boiler efficiency} \times \text{Base NPHR}}{\text{Base boiler efficiency}}$$

	Gas Recirculation	Excess Air
100% Load	Base	0
80% Load	Base	$\frac{0.69 \times 8860}{86.14} = +71$
60% Load	Base	$\frac{0.48 \times 9040}{86.41} = +50$
35% Load	Base	$\frac{0.36 \times 9920}{86.42} = +41$

2. Difference in net-plant-heat rate for auxiliary power (accounting for heat recovery), Btu/kwhr.

   $$\triangle\text{NPHR} = \frac{\left(\begin{array}{c}\text{Difference in}\\\text{auxiliary power}\end{array}\right) \times \left(\begin{array}{c}\text{Heat loss}\\\text{factor}\end{array}\right) \times \left(\begin{array}{c}\text{Base}\\\text{NPHR}\end{array}\right)}{\text{Output}}$$

	Gas Recirculation	Excess Air
100% Load	Base	0
80% Load	Base	$\frac{-400 \times 0.7 \times 8860}{0.8 \times 600,000} = -5$
60% Load	Base	$\frac{-470 \times 0.7 \times 9040}{0.60 \times 600,000} = -8$
35% Load	Base	$\frac{-150 \times 0.7 \times 9920}{0.35 \times 600,000} = -5$

3. Net-plant-heat rates, Btu/kwhr

	Gas Recirculation	Excess Air
100% Load	8860	8860 = 8860
80% Load	8860	8860 + 71 − 5 = 8926
60% Load	9040	9040 + 50 − 8 = 9082
35% Load	9920	9920 + 41 − 5 = 9956

4. Present worth of fuel costs — Gas recirculation unit
   $112,110,000 (from Example 1, 3500 psi unit)

5. Cost of fuel consumed per yr — Excess air unit (see Example 1, 3500 psi unit)

   $$\frac{\text{Fuel consumed (Base)} \times \text{NPHR (Excess air)} \times \text{Fuel cost}}{\text{NPHR (Base)}}$$

(a) Years 1-10

Btu/yr
$20,500 \times 10^9 \times 8860/8860 = 20,500 \times 10^9$
$10,440 \times 10^9 \times 8926/8860 = 10,520 \times 10^9$
$3,700 \times 10^9 \times 9082/9040 = 3,720 \times 10^9$
$1,095 \times 10^9 \times 9956/9920 = \underline{1,100 \times 10^9}$
$\overline{35,840 \times 10^9}$

$35,840 \times 10^9 \times \$0.25/10^6 = \$8,960,000/\text{yr}$

(b) Years 11-20
$10,710 \times 10^9 \times 8860/8860 = 10,710 \times 10^9$
$8,580 \times 10^9 \times 8926/8860 = 8,650 \times 10^9$
$9,690 \times 10^9 \times 9082/9040 = 9,740 \times 10^9$
$2,010 \times 10^9 \times 9956/9920 = \underline{2,020 \times 10^9}$
$\overline{31,120 \times 10^9}$

$31,120 \times 10^9 \times \$0.25/10^6 = \$7,760,000/\text{yr}$

(c) Years 21-30
$2795 \times 10^6 \times 8860/8860 = 2,795 \times 10^9$
$8560 \times 10^6 \times 8926/8860 = 8,625 \times 10^9$
$9700 \times 10^6 \times 9082/9040 = 9,750 \times 10^9$
$4205 \times 10^6 \times 9956/9920 = \underline{4,220 \times 10^9}$
$\overline{25,380 \times 10^9}$

$25,380 \times 10^9 \times \$0.25/10^6 = \$6,350,000/\text{yr}$

6. Present worth of fuel costs — Excess air unit
   (a) Years 1-10
       $8,960,000 \times 7.36 =$ $65,950,000
   (b) Years 11-20
       $7,760,000 \times (11.47 - 7.36) =$ $31,900,000
   (c) Years 21-30
       $6,350,000 \times (13.76 - 11.47) = \$14,550,000$
       $\overline{\$112,400,000}$

7. Saving in fuel costs — Gas recirculation vs. Excess air
   Present worth of fuel costs
       Excess air unit — $112,400,000
       Gas recirculation unit — $112,110,000
   Present worth of saving — $ 290,000
   $290,000 ÷ 600,000 kw = $0.48/kw

8. Justifiable capital expenditure — Gas recirculation vs. Excess air

   Justifiable additional expenditure =
   $$\frac{\$290,000}{.115 \times 13.76} = \$183,000$$

   Justifiable expenditure/kw =
       $183,000 ÷ 600,000 kw = $0.30/kw

D) Result:
   1. The use of gas recirculation to maintain reheat steam temperature will save $290,000 or $0.48/kw over the life of the unit compared with the use of excess air.
   2. This saving will justify the expenditure of $0.30/kw for the gas recirculation system.

Essentially any auxiliary power usage, difference in boiler efficiency, or difference in net-plant-heat rate can be treated in the same manner as these examples. This method basically converts the differences between units into fuel costs. The fuel costs, which account for future load factor, cycle heat rates, and future fuel costs, are converted into present-day dollars using present-worth mathematics for the projected interest rate over the life of the unit. The justified capital expenditure can then be calculated.

Another approach to the solution of the two problems above is the capitalized cost method illustrated in Example 3.

Example 3

A) Problem: Compare the economics of 2400 vs. 3500 psi cycle.

B) Given: Same information as Example 1.

C) Solution:

   1. Avg NPHR — 2400 psi cycle — Btu/kwhr

100% Load	$(.44 + .23 + .06)$	$9000 = 6,570$
80% Load	$(.28 + .23 + .23)$	$9000 = 6,660$
60% Load	$(.13 + .34 + .34)$	$9180 = 7,440$
35% Load	$(.06 + .11 + .23)$	$10,080 = 4,040$
		$\overline{24,700}$

    Avg NPHR = $24,700/2.68^* = 9220$

    * This is the sum of all capacity factors in Item B12, Example 1, except the factors for zero load.

   2. Avg NPHR — 3500 psi cycle — Btu/kwhr

100% Load	$(.44 + .23 + .06)$	$8860 = 6,470$
80% Load	$(.28 + .23 + .23)$	$8860 = 6,560$
60% Load	$(.13 + .34 + .34)$	$9040 = 7,320$
35% Load	$(.06 + .11 + .23)$	$9920 = 3,970$
		$\overline{24,320}$

    Avg NPHR $= \dfrac{24,320}{2.68} = 9080$

   3. Capitalized value of heat rate difference

    Difference = $9220 - 9080 = 140$ Btu/kwhr

    Capitalized value =

$$\frac{\triangle NPHR \times \text{kwhr generation/yr} \times \text{Fuel cost}}{\text{Fixed charge rate}}$$

    kwhr generation/yr = Capacity factor $\times$ Capacity $\times$ hr/yr

Capitalized value =

$$\frac{140 \times .6493 \times 600,000 \times 8760 \times .25}{.115 \times 1,000,000} = \$1,038,000$$

$\$1,038,000 \div 600,000$ kw = $\$1.73$/kw

D) Result:

For these conditions the expenditure of up to $1.73/kw is economically justified for a 3500 psi plant vs. a 2400 psi plant. (Note that this is quite close to the $1.78/kw answer reached by the revenue requirements method in Example 1.)

The capitalized cost method of evaluation can be adapted to evaluate auxiliary power, boiler efficiency, or other operating costs by converting them to fuel cost.

Summary

Evaluations are necessary to compare alternates for complex, large capital expenditures like power plant equipment. Evaluations enable the comparisons to be made, putting various alternates on the same basis by accounting for the differences in first cost and operation of the full scope of equipment required to perform the function.

Evaluation procedures and factors vary from plant to plant, as many factors change with locale, e.g., type of fuel, fuel cost, and construction costs. Other factors, such as the components of the fixed charge rate, change with time as well as location. Thus each evaluation must be considered individually.

Oconee Nuclear Station, Duke Power Company.

Chapter 23   Nuclear installations for electric utilities

Nuclear power plants of the so-called second-generation are now in successful operation. In the United States these plants comprise water reactors of the pressurized-water or boiling-water types. Second-generation nuclear plants compete economically with fossil-fuel plants. Capital costs are generally higher and fuel costs lower with nuclear plants. Hence power costs from nuclear plants are generally more favorable in the larger sizes, where fuel cost represents a larger portion of the total cost (Chapters 19 and 21). Thus, the second-generation nuclear plants are comparable in size with the larger size fossil-fuel plants. In several of these nuclear plants, a single nuclear reactor supplies the heat to generate 10 to 12 million pounds of steam per hr and 800-1000 Mw of electricity. Single units to supply 1300 Mw of electricity are being built.

First-generation nuclear plants

Second-generation nuclear plants have evolved as the result of the successful operation of first-generation plants, such as the Consolidated Edison Company's Indian Point Station, Unit 1 (Fig. 1). In this unit, generating approximately 275 Mw of electricity, a pressurized water reactor supplies the heat for steam generation, and superheating is accomplished in an oil-fired superheater. Although this plant was not designed to generate power economically, the competitive cost of nuclear fuel has made it economical to operate, once the capital cost of the plant was incurred.

Second-generation nuclear units

At the beginning of 1977, thirty-four second-generation B&W units, each supplying steam to generate approximately 850 to 1300 Mw net of electricity, had been sold and twenty-six of these units were in the process of design, fabrication, installation, testing, or operation. Six of these second-generation units were in commercial

operation, and two others were in the process of power escalation testing.

Oconee Nuclear Station

The first of B&W's second-generation units is one of three built for the Oconee Nuclear Station of the Duke Power Company, located approximately eight miles northeast of Seneca, South Carolina, on new Lake Keowee. The chapter frontispiece shows the three units of this station. The nuclear steam supply system for each of these units was furnished by B&W. Each of these units has a net capacity of 886 Mw of electricity.

The three vertical cylindrical concrete buildings seen in the frontispiece are the reactor buildings for the

Fig. 1 Indian Point Station, Unit 1—Consolidated Edison Company of New York, Inc.—photographed in 1963.

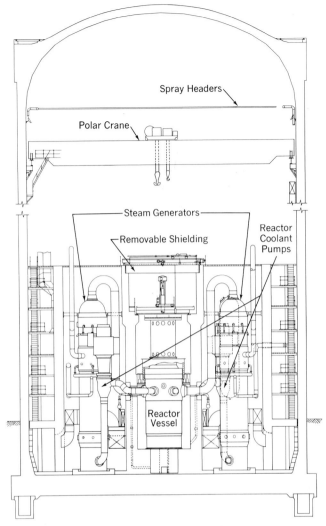

Fig. 2 Reactor building — sectional view, Oconee Nuclear Station.

The building encloses the pressurized water reactor, steam generators, reactor coolant loops and portions of the auxiliary and engineered safeguards systems.

The interior arrangement is designed to meet the requirements for all anticipated conditions of operation and maintenance, including new and spent fuel handling.

The building is designed to sustain all internal and external loading conditions which may reasonably be expected to occur during the life of the station. Due consideration has been given to all site factors and local environment as they relate to public health and safety.

Fig. 2 also shows the reactor vessel and the two vertical steam generators, each producing approximately 5,600,000 pounds of steam per hour at 910 psi pressure and 595F, corresponding to 60 degrees of superheat. The reactor vessel, steam generators, four coolant pumps and pressurizer are shown in Fig. 3 which is a plan section of the reactor building at the ground floor. The concrete shielding around the reactor vessel and the reactor coolant system are also shown in Fig. 3. Table 1 gives the important design parameters for the Oconee nuclear steam supply systems and for a 1300-Mw unit of more recent design, which is described on page 23-16.

Reactor vessel

Fig. 4 is a photograph of the reactor vessel inside the reactor building being placed in position between the two steam generators. Fig. 5 is a vertical section drawing of the reactor pressure vessel and its internals. As noted in Table 1, this vessel is constructed of low-alloy steel clad internally with stainless steel. It is designed for 2500 psi and 650F and will operate at 2185 psi. The cylindrical shell is 14-ft 3-in. ID and $8\frac{7}{16}$-in. thick. Outside diameter across nozzles is 20 ft 9 in. The internal height, including the closure head, is 37 ft 4 in., and the

three units. Each houses the nuclear steam supply system for one unit. Although some equipment is shared between units, each is operationally a complete and independent unit. The rectangular building at the right houses the turbine generators. The control room, auxiliary systems, and fuel handling facilities for Units 1 and 2 are located in a structure between reactor buildings 1 and 2. Corresponding equipment for Unit 3 is located separately. The following description, although generally applicable to all three units, applies specifically to Unit 1.

Fig. 2 is a vertical section of the reactor building. This building is a post-tensioned reinforced-concrete structure in the shape of a cylinder with a shallow domed roof and a flat foundation slab. The cylindrical portion is prestressed by a post-tensioning system consisting of horizontal and vertical tendons. The dome has a three-way post-tensioning system. The foundation slab is conventionally reinforced with high-strength reinforcing steel. The entire structure is lined with $\frac{1}{4}$-in. welded steel plate to provide vapor tightness.

Its approximate dimensions are: inside diameter, 116 ft; inside height, 208 ft; vertical wall thickness, $3\frac{3}{4}$ ft; dome thickness, $3\frac{1}{4}$ ft; and the foundation slab, $8\frac{1}{2}$ ft.

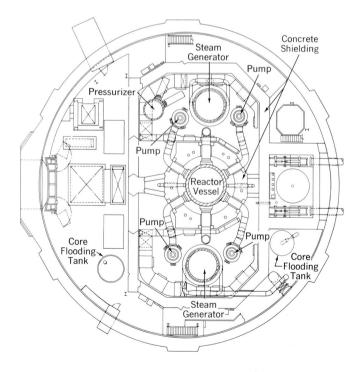

Fig. 3 Reactor building — ground floor plan, Oconee Nuclear Station.

Fig. 4 Reactor vessel being placed in position inside the reactor building.

overall height of vessel and closure head is 40 ft 9 in. The total dry weight of vessel and head is approximately 415 tons.

The vessel has six major nozzles for reactor coolant flow, 69 control rod drive nozzles mounted on the reactor vessel head, and two emergency injection system nozzles—all located above the core. Fifty-two in-core instrumentation nozzles are located on the lower head.

The removable closure head for the reactor vessel is held in place by sixty 6½-in. diameter high-tensile alloy steel studs (ASTM Specification A-540 Grade B-23). The nuts on these large studs or bolts are tightened by a hydraulic stud tensioner.

This tensioner is basically a hydraulic jack arranged to engage studs, elongate them to a desired loading and then allow the nuts to be tightened against the flange while the studs are thus loaded. By utilizing a stud tensioner, the tightening of the studs is accomplished in a fifth of the time formerly required with the traditional method of heating the studs.

The coolant water enters the vessel through four inlet nozzles located above the midpoint of the vessel, as indicated in Fig. 5. Water flows downward in the annular space between the pressure vessel and thermal shield, then up through the core and upper plenum chamber, down around the inside of the reactor vessel (upper portion) and out through two outlet nozzles, as shown in Fig. 5.

The core is supported by the core support shield and the core barrel which hang from the seal ledge near the closure head. The core barrel also provides some gamma attenuation to augment that provided by the thermal shield. Factors considered in the structural design of the core are discussed under the caption *Structural Design of a Nuclear Reactor Core* in Chapter 30.

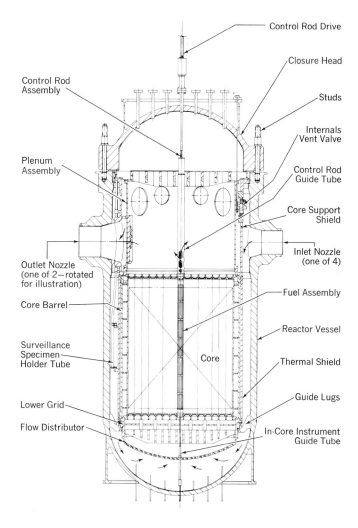

Fig. 5 Reactor vessel and internals — general arrangement.

Table 1 Design Parameters—Nuclear Steam Supply Systems

	Oconee Unit 1	1300-Mw Unit*
Reactor hydraulic and thermal design		
Rated heat output (core), Mw	2,568	3,760
Rated heat output (core), million Btu/hr	8,765	12,833
Design overpower, %	114	112
System pressure (nominal), psi	2,185	2,250
Power distribution		
Maximum/average power ratio, radial x local	1.78	1.55
Maximum/average power ratio, axial	1.70	1.67
Overall power ratio	3.03	2.65
Power generated in fuel and cladding, %	97.3	97.3
DNB ratio at rated conditions	2.0	1.81
Minimum DNB ratio at design overpower	1.55	1.40
Coolant flow		
Total flow rate, million lb/hr	131.3	158.2
Effective flow rate for heat transfer, million lb/hr	124.2	148.5
Effective flow area for heat transfer, sq ft	49.19	56.6
Average velocity along fuel rods, ft/sec	15.73	16.85
Coolant temperature, F		
Nominal inlet	554	568.6
Average rise in vessel	50	56.9
Average in vessel	579	597
Average film coefficient, Btu/sq ft, hr, F	5,000	5,000
Average film temperature difference, F	31	60
Heat transfer at 100% power		
Total heat transfer surface area, sq ft	49,734	63,991
Average heat flux, Btu/sq ft, hr	171,470	195,100
Maximum heat flux, Btu/sq ft, hr	534,440	517,640
Average thermal output, kw/ft	5.656	5.670
Maximum thermal output, kw/ft	17.63	15.04
Maximum clad surface temperature at nominal pressure, F	654	657
Fuel central temperature, F		
Maximum at 100% power at hot spot	4,250	4,040
Maximum at design overpower	4,650	4,400
Maximum thermal output, kw/ft at design overpower	20.1	16.85
Core mechanical design		
Fuel assemblies		
Number	177	205
Rod pitch, in.	0.568	0.503
Overall dimension, in. (side of square)	8.536	8.632
Total weight, lb	274,350	313,855
Number of spacer grids per assembly	8	8
Fuel assembly pitch spacing, in.	8.587	8.587
Fuel rods		
Number	36,816	54,120
Outside diameter, in.	0.430	0.379
Diametral gap, in.	0.007	0.008
Clad thickness, in. (Zircaloy-4)	0.0265	0.0235
Active fuel length, in.	144	143
Fuel pellets (UO_2 sintered)		
Density, % of theoretical		
First core	93.5	94.0
Subsequent cores	92.5	94.0
Diameter, in.	0.370	0.324
Length, in.	0.7	0.375

	Oconee Unit 1	1300-Mw Unit*
Control rod assemblies**		
Neutron absorber	5% Cd-15% In-80% Ag	Ag-In-Cd or boron carbide
Length of poison section, in.	134	134
Cladding material	304SS	304SS
Clad thickness, in.	0.021	0.019
Number of assemblies	61	64
Number of control rods per assembly	16	24
Axial-power-shaping rod assemblies		
Neutron absorber	5% Cd-15% In-80% Ag	Ag-In-Cd or boron carbide
Length of poison section, in.	36	36
Cladding material (poison section)	304SS	304SS
Clad thickness, in.	0.021	0.019
Number of assemblies	8	8
Number of control rods per assembly	16	24
Orifice rod assemblies		
Rod material	304SS	304SS
Number of orifice rods per assembly	16	24
Core structure		
Core barrel ID/OD, in.	141/145	156/161
Thermal shield, ID/OD, in.	147/151	
Nuclear design		
Structural characteristics		
Fuel weight (as UO_2), lb	207,486	233,850
Clad weight (active zone), lb	42,200	48,175
Core diameter, in. (equivalent)	128.9	138.7
Core height, in. (active fuel)	144	143
Reflector thickness and composition		
Top (water plus steel), in.	12	12
Bottom (water plus steel), in.	12	12
Side (water plus steel), in.	18	21.5
Metal/Water (unit cell—volume basis)	0.82	0.83
Fuel rods per fuel assembly	208	264
Performance characteristics		
Loading technique	3 region	modified checkboard
Fuel discharge burnup, Mwd/tonne of uranium		
First cycle average	9,600	16,864
Succeeding cycle average	9,700	11,243
Fuel enrichments, wt % ^{235}U		
Core average, first cycle	2.10	2.80
First reload	2.98	3.28
Core average, equilibrium cycle	3.06	3.18
Control characteristics		
Effective multiplication (beginning of life)		
Cold, no power, clean	1.248	1.333
Hot, no power, clean	1.198	1.286
Hot, rated power, Xe and Sm equilibrium	1.132	1.192
Control rod worth ($\triangle k/k$), %	10.9	8.1†
Boron concentrations		
To shut reactor down (k_{eff}=0.99) with all rods inserted (clean), cold/hot ppm	864/587	1178/910

*Approximate net electric power.

**The 1300-Mw unit has also 116 burnable poison rod assemblies, having 24 rods per assembly, each rod containing 126-in. length of $Al_2O_3 \cdot B_4C$ contained in Zircaloy-4 cladding tubes 0.032-in. thick.

†Burnable poison rods are worth an additional 5.1%.

Nuclear design (cont'd)

	Oconee Unit 1	1300-Mw Unit*
Boron concentrations (cont'd)		
Boron worth (hot), % ($\triangle$k/k)/ppm	1/85	1/105
Boron worth (cold), % ($\triangle$k/k)/ppm	1/64	1/79
Kinetic characteristics (range during life cycle)		
Moderator temperature coefficient, ($\triangle$k/k)/F	$+0.5 \times 10^{-4}$ to -3.0×10^{-4}	$+0.1 \times 10^{-4}$ to -3.0×10^{-4}
Moderator pressure coefficient, ($\triangle$k/k)/psi	-5.0×10^{-7} to $+3.0 \times 10^{-6}$	-0.5×10^{-7} to $+3.0 \times 10^{-6}$
Moderator void coefficient, ($\triangle$k/k)/% void	$+4.0 \times 10^{-4}$ to -1.6×10^{-3}	$+3.0 \times 10^{-4}$ to -3.0×10^{-3}
Doppler coefficient, ($\triangle$k/k)/F	-1.1×10^{-5} to -1.7×10^{-5}	-1.1×10^{-5} to -1.7×10^{-5}

Reactor coolant system

	Oconee Unit 1	1300-Mw Unit*
System heat output, Mw	2,584	3,780
System heat output, million Btu/hr	8,819	12,901
Operating pressure, psi	2,185	2,250
Reactor inlet temperature, F	554	568.6
Reactor outlet temperature, F	604	625.5
Number of loops	2	2
Design pressure, psi	2,500	2,500
Design temperature, F	650	670
Hydrostatic test pressure (cold), psi	3,125	3,125
Coolant volume, including pressurizer, cu ft	11,478	13,200
Total reactor flow, gpm	352,000	432,800

Reactor coolant system code requirements

	Oconee Unit 1	1300-Mw Unit*
Reactor vessel and closure head	ASME III	ASME III
Steam generator and pressurizer	ASME III	ASME III
Reactor coolant piping	ANSI B31.7	ASME III
Reactor coolant pump casing	ASME III**	ASME III

Reactor vessel

	Oconee Unit 1	1300-Mw Unit*
Base material	Low-alloy steel	
Cladding material	SS	SS and Inconel
Design pressure, psi	2,500	2,500
Design temperature, F	650	670
Operating pressure, psi	2,185	2,250
Inside diameter of shell, in.	171	182
Straight shell thickness, in.	8⁷⁄₁₆	9⅛
Minimum clad thickness, in.	⅛	⅛
Outside diameter across nozzles, ft-in.	20-9	23-4
Overall height of vessel and closure head (over control rod drive and instrument nozzles), ft-in.	40-8¾	42-2

Steam generators (see also Table 3)

	Oconee Unit 1	1300-Mw Unit*
Number of units	2	2
Type	Once-through	
Materials		
Tubes	Inconel	
Shell	Carbon-steel	Low-alloy steel
Hemispherical heads	Low-alloy steel, SS clad	
Tubesheets	Low-alloy steel, Inconel clad on reactor-coolant side†	
Tube side design pressure, psi	2,500	2,500
Tube side design temperature, F	650	670
Tube side design flow, million lb/hr	65.66	79.1

Steam generators (cont'd)

	Oconee Unit 1	1300-Mw Unit*
Shell side design pressure, psi	1,050	1,235
Shell side design temperature, F	600	631
Operating pressure, tube side, nominal, psi	2,185	2,250
Operating pressure, shell side, nominal, psi	910	1,060
Superheat at outlet at rated load, F	35	35
Hydrostatic test pressure (tube side cold), psi	3,125	3,125
Shell minimum thickness, in. (see Fig. 14)	4³⁄₁₆	5¾
Maximum outside diameter of straight shell, ft-in.	12-7¼	12-6½
Overall height (including supports), ft-in.	73-2½	77-6¼

Pressurizer

	Oconee Unit 1	1300-Mw Unit*
Material, shell and heads	Carbon-steel, SS clad	Low-alloy steel, SS clad
Design pressure, psi	2,500	2,500
Design temperature, F	670	670
Steam volume, cu ft	700	1,050
Water volume, cu ft	800	1,200
Electric heater capacity, kw	1,638	1,745
Shell minimum thickness, in.	6³⁄₁₆	5¹⁵⁄₁₆
Shell outside diameter, ft-in.	8-0⅜	9-11⅞
Overall height, ft-in.	44-11¾	41-4½

Reactor coolant pumps

	Oconee Unit 1	1300-Mw Unit*
Number of units	4	4
Type	Vertical, single-stage	
Design pressure, psi	2,500	2,500
Design temperature, F	650	670
Operating pressure, nominal, psi	2,185	2,250
Suction temperature, F	554	568.6
Design capacity, gpm	88,000	108,200
Total developed head, ft	350	370
Hydrostatic test pressure (cold), psi	4,100	3,340
Motor type (single speed)	a-c induction	Squirrel-cage induction
Motor rating (nameplate), hp	9,000	12,500

Reactor coolant piping

	Oconee Unit 1	1300-Mw Unit*
Material	Carbon steel, SS clad	
Hot leg (ID), in.	36	38
Cold leg (ID), in.	28	28

Engineered safeguards

	Oconee Unit 1	1300-Mw Unit*
Safety injection system		
Number of high pressure injection pumps	3	3
Number of low pressure injection pumps	2‡	2
Reactor building coolers		
Number of units	3	3
Rated capacity, each, million Btu/hr	80	140
Core flooding system		
Number of tanks	2	2
Total volume, each, cu ft	1,410	1,800
Reactor building spray		
Number of pumps	2	2

*Approximate net electric power.
**Not code stamped.
†1300-Mw unit lower tubesheet is Inconel-clad on both sides.
‡Plus one installed spare pump.

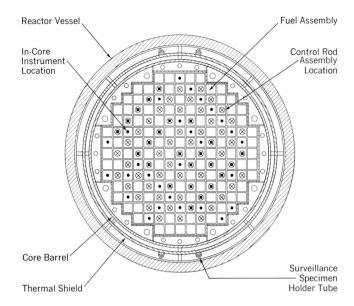

Fig. 6 Reactor vessel and internals — cross section.

[Labels in Fig. 6: Reactor Vessel; In-Core Instrument Location; Core Barrel; Thermal Shield; Fuel Assembly; Control Rod Assembly Location; Surveillance Specimen Holder Tube]

Reactor core

The reactor core inside the pressure vessel is shown in elevation section in Fig. 5 and in plan section in Fig. 6. Its irregular cross section is equivalent to a circle of about 10-ft 9-in. diameter, and the active fuel length is 12 ft. The core comprises 177 fuel assemblies, each about 8½-in. square in cross section, and composed of fuel rods located in a vertical position. Control rods are incorporated into some of the fuel assemblies.

The first core loading contains a total of 94.1 metric tons of UO_2, with an average of 2.10% by weight of enriched uranium-235. There is a buildup of fission product poisons in the fuel assemblies remaining in the core after the first cycle, so that an average enrichment of 3.06% is required for the equilibrium core. After equilibrium conditions are established, approximately one-third of the core is replaced every year. At the same time the other two-thirds of the fuel assemblies are relocated and a new third is added.

The core is designed for a steady-state heat release of 2568 Mw. This heat is removed by a flow of 131,320,000 lb/hr of coolant water entering the reactor vessel at 554F and leaving at 604F. The average coolant velocity in the core is 15.73 ft/sec.

The total heating surface in the core is 49,734 sq ft. The average heat flux is 171,470 Btu/sq ft, hr, and the maximum is 534,440 Btu/sq ft, hr. The coolant outlet temperature from the hot channel is 647F and the maximum clad surface temperature is 654F. Saturation temperature corresponding to coolant pressure (2185 psi) is 649F. The average fuel temperature is 1540F and the maximum fuel central temperature at the hot spot is 4250F, as compared to a melting point of 5144F for uranium dioxide.

The uranium requirement, the amount and disposition of the heating surface, and the provisions for control were determined in accordance with basic principles outlined in Chapter 21. Reactor output is regulated by the use of movable control rod assemblies and soluble boron dissolved in the coolant. Control of relatively fast reactivity effects, including Doppler, xenon, and moderator temperature effects, is accomplished by the control rods. The control response speed is designed to overcome these reactivity effects. Relatively slow reactivity effects, such as fuel burnup, fission product buildup, samarium buildup, and hot-to-cold moderator reactivity deficit, are controlled by soluble boron.

Fuel assemblies. Fig. 7 is a photograph of two fuel assemblies. Each assembly is the same as that shown in Fig. 4 of Chapter 21 and described in that chapter. Each fuel assembly contains 208 fuel rods consisting of uranium dioxide pellets contained in cold-worked Zircaloy-4 cladding tubes. The cladding is 0.430-in. OD and 0.0265-in. thick. Pellets are 0.370-in. diameter and 0.7-in. long. The gap between pellets and cladding is pressurized with helium to 360 psi initial pressure.

Each fuel assembly is fitted with an instrumentation tube at the center and with "guide tubes" to accommodate 16 control rods (Fig. 8). Each group of 16 control rods is coupled together to form a "control rod assembly" as shown in Fig. 9. At any particular time each of 69 fuel assemblies in the core contains such a control rod assembly. Since all fuel assemblies are identical and can be used anywhere in the core, the 108 fuel assemblies which do not contain a control rod assembly during a given core cycle have their guide tubes partially filled at the top by an "orifice rod assembly" to minimize bypassing of the coolant flow and thus aid in equalizing the coolant flow between fuel assemblies with control rods and those without them. Each orifice rod assembly

Fig. 7 Nuclear fuel assemblies.

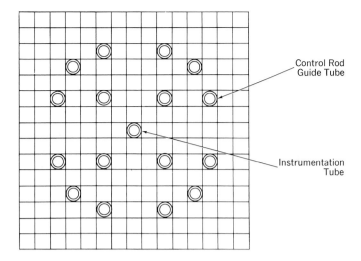

Fig. 8 Diagrammatic cross section of fuel assembly showing instrumentation-tube and control-rod-guide-tube locations.

is somewhat similar to a control rod assembly except that the orifice rods are short and contain no neutron poison.

Control rod assemblies. Each control rod assembly is made up of sixteen control rods attached to a single Type 304 stainless steel spider (Fig. 9). Each control rod consists of an absorber section of silver-indium-cadmium poison clad with cold-worked, Type 304 stainless steel tubing (0.440-in. OD and 0.021-in. thick) and Type 304 stainless steel upper and lower end pieces. The end pieces are welded to the cladding to form a water- and pressure-tight container for the poison. The control rods are loosely attached to the spider in order to permit maximum conformity with the channels provided by the guide tubes. The control rod assembly is inserted through the upper end fitting of the fuel assembly, each control rod being guided by an in-core guide tube. Guide tubes are also provided in the upper plenum assembly above the core so that full length guidance of the control rods is provided throughout the stroke. With the reactor assembled, the control rod assembly cannot be withdrawn far enough to cause disengagement of the control rods from these in-core guide tube assemblies.

Of the 69 assemblies, 61 are used to control reactor power level and are properly called shim safety rod or control rod assemblies (Table 1). The other 8, known as axial power shaping rods, contain a concentration of neutron poison in the lower quarter of the rod, and are used to improve the axial power distribution in the core.

Control rod drive. Each control rod assembly is driven by an individual control rod drive mechanism (Fig. 10), fabricated by the Diamond Power Specialty Corporation. These drives are of the roller nut type. Mounted on a nozzle on the reactor-vessel head, each drive provides for controlled withdrawal or insertion of a control rod assembly out of or into the reactor core to establish and hold the power level required.

For the control (shim safety) rod assemblies, the drive mechanism consists of a motor tube which houses a lead screw and its rotor assembly, and a buffer. The

top end of the motor tube is closed by a closure and vent assembly. An external motor stator surrounds the motor tube (a pressure housing) and position indication switches are arranged outside the motor tube extension.

The control rod drive output element is a nonrotating translating lead screw coupled to the control rod assembly. The screw is driven by separating anti-friction roller nut assemblies which are rotated magnetically by a motor stator located outside the pressure boundary. Current impressed on the stator causes the separating roller nut assembly halves to close and engage the lead screw. Mechanical springs disengage the roller nut halves from the screw in the absence of a current. For rapid insertion, the nut halves separate to release the screw and control rod, which move into the core by gravity. A hydraulic buffer assembly within the upper housing decelerates the moving control rod assembly to a low speed a short distance above the full-in position. The final deceleration energy is absorbed by the down-stop buffer spring. The control rod drive mechanism is a totally sealed unit with the roller nut assemblies magnetically driven by the stator coil through the motor tube pressure housing wall. The lead screw assembly is connected to the control rod assembly by a bayonet-type coupling. An anti-rotation device (torque taker) prevents rotation of the lead screw while the

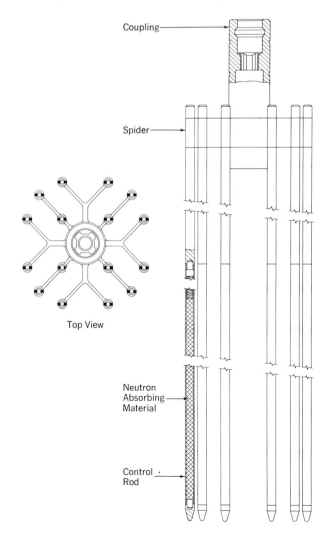

Fig. 9 Control rod assembly.

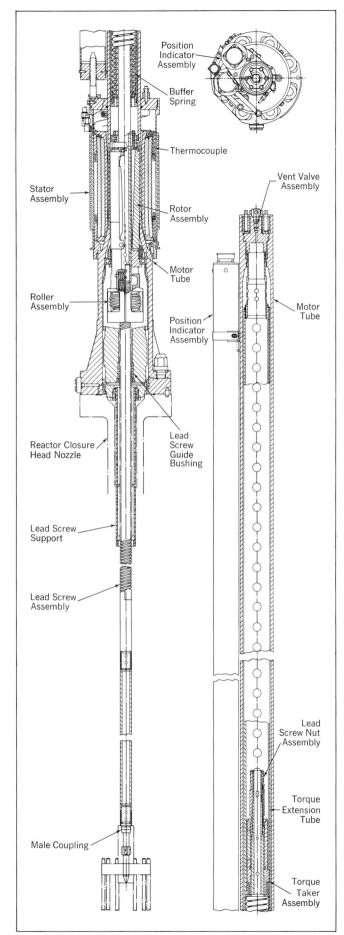

Fig. 10 Control rod drive — vertical section.

drive is in service. A closure and vent assembly is provided at the top of the motor tube housing to permit access to couple and release the lead screw assembly from the control rod. The top end of the lead screw assembly is guided by a buffer piston and its guide. Normal motion of the driver is accomplished by energizing the stator windings in sequence from a source of d-c power with silicon-controlled rectifiers, so that each drive operates as a stepping motor. Two of the six-phase stator-housing windings are energized to maintain the control rod position when the drive is in the holding mode. Shim safety rod drive design data are listed in Table 2.

Table 2
Control (shim safety) rod drive design data

Type	Roller nut drive
Quantity	61
Location	Top-mounted
Direction of trip	Down
Velocity of normal withdrawal and insertion, in./min	30
Maximum travel time for trip	
⅔ insertion, sec	1.40
¾ insertion, sec	1.50
Length of stroke, in.	139
Design pressure, psi	2,500
Design temperature, F	650
Approx weight of mechanism, lb	940

Axial-power-shaping rod drive. For actuating the partial-length rods, which maintain their set position during a reactor-trip of the shim safety drive, the control rod drive mechanism is modified so that the roller nut assembly will not disengage from the lead screw on a loss of power to the stator. Except for this modification, the shim drives and the axial power shaping rod drives are identical, although the latter have no trip function.

Reactor control and instrumentation. Equipment is provided to accomplish the requirements delineated in Chapter 21. The reactor control system incorporates measurement of neutron flux and reactor coolant temperatures, and means to actuate control rod assemblies to adjust reactor power to meet power demand and to maintain the average reactor coolant temperature constant over the range of load from 15 to 100%, as indicated in Fig. 11. As load increases above 15%, reactor inlet temperature decreases and outlet temperature increases linearly with load because the reactor coolant flow is maintained constant. Below 15% power, average coolant temperature is reduced, as shown in Fig. 11.

Constant average coolant temperature control results in a constant inventory of water in the reactor coolant system, thus eliminating the need to bleed or feed water in order to maintain a constant pressurizer level with changing load. Eliminating water-inventory control reduces the waste handling and soluble poison handling requirements for the operator. In addition, the extent of control rod action is reduced since it is not necessary to compensate for reactivity changes associated with coolant temperature changes or to provide added reactor

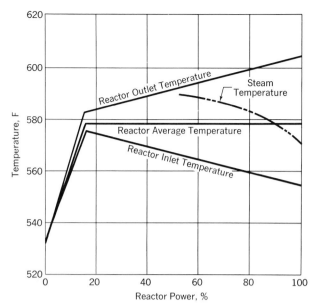

Fig. 11 Reactor coolant and steam temperatures versus reactor power.

power to change the stored energy of primary coolant and reactor components with load changes. The reactor is normally operated automatically above 15% load.

The steam generator outlet temperature as a function of load is superimposed on the reactor coolant temperatures in Fig. 11.

Additional information concerning design criteria of the control system is presented in this chapter under the captions *Performance Objectives* and *Design Limits*.

In-core instrumentation. This includes self-powered neutron detectors to measure the neutron flux in the core, and temperature detectors to measure the core outlet temperature. These detectors provide a history of the power distribution during power operating modes. The data obtained are useful in determining fuel burnup and in fuel management.

Reactor protection system. This system performs the functions listed in Chapter 21. It also contains circuitry which would cause the reactor to trip in case of a buildup of pressure in the reactor building. The major design criteria for the reactor protection system are listed later in this chapter.

Plant control system. The Integrated-Control systems for the Oconee nuclear units are described under the caption *Integrated-Control System for Nuclear Steam Plants* in Chapter 35. All control and protection systems were supplied by the Bailey Meter Company.

The control system (Fig. 12) provides automatic response to power demand signals which may originate either with the operator or directly from an automatic dispatch system. Following a change in load demand, the controls change turbine throttle position and alter feed flow to the steam generators to maintain a constant steam pressure at the turbine throttle. Simultaneously, the reactor control system moves to adjust reactor power and to maintain the average reactor coolant temperature described under *Reactor Control and Instrumentation*.

The control system, combined with the inherent sta-

bility and response characteristics of the reactor and steam generator, provides a unit capable of normal power transients of ± 10% step changes and ± 10% per min ramp changes over the range of 20 to 90% of full load. Under these conditions, the upset in steam pressure is less than 15 psi, and average coolant temperature upset is less than 5F.

When using the turbine bypass, the system can accommodate a drop in load of 40% of full load without automatic reactor shutdown or steam relief to the atmosphere. Under loss-of-load conditions, reactor operation is sustained to provide capability of restoring generating capacity in a matter of minutes.

Reactor coolant system

The reactor coolant system, consisting of two coolant loops interconnected at the reactor, is illustrated in Fig. 13 (arrangement plan) and in Fig. 2 (vertical section). Each of the two coolant loops contains a once-through steam generator and two coolant pumps, and one loop includes the pressurizer (Fig. 13).

Steam generators. Fig. 4 shows the two steam generators inside the reactor building. Each steam generator is a vertical, straight-tube-and-shell heat exchanger approximately 68 ft in height and 13 ft in diameter. The general arrangement for each is shown in Fig. 14.

Reactor coolant water enters the steam generator at the top, flows downward through the tubes and out at the bottom. The high pressure parts of the unit are the hemispherical heads, the tubesheets, and the straight tubes between the tubesheets. Tube material is Inconel Alloy 600, a nickel-iron-chromium alloy conforming to ASME Specification SB-163 (*see Inconel, Chapter 29*). Tube supports hold the tubes in a uniform pattern along their length. The unit is supported by a skirt attached to the bottom head.

Fig. 14 indicates the flow paths on the steam side of the unit. Feedwater enters at the side of the shell. It flows down through an annulus just inside the shell where it is brought to saturation temperature by mixing with steam. The saturated water enters the heating sur-

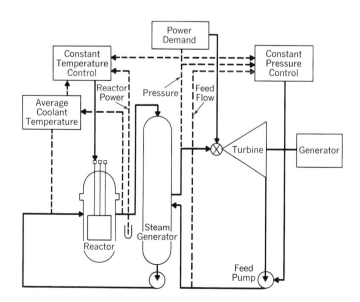

Fig. 12 Diagram of Integrated-Control system.

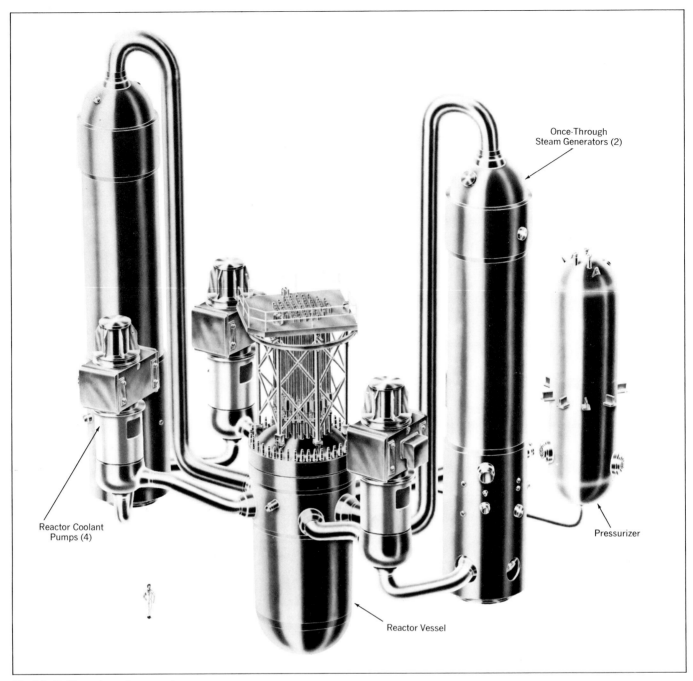

Fig. 13 B&W nuclear steam system.

face at the bottom and is converted to steam and super-heated in a single pass upward through the generator.

The shell, the outside of the tubes, and the tubesheets form the boundaries of the steam-producing section of the vessel. Within the shell, the tube bundle is surrounded by a shroud, which is in two overlapping sections with the upper section the larger of the two in diameter. The upper part of the annulus between the shell and baffle is the superheater outlet, while the lower part is the feedwater inlet-heating zone. Vents, drains, instrumentation nozzles, and inspection openings are provided on the shell side of the unit. The reactor coolant side has manways and inspection ports on both heads, and a drain nozzle for the bottom head. Venting of the reactor coolant side of the unit is accomplished by a vent connection on the reactor coolant inlet pipe to each unit.

Design data for each steam generator are tabulated in Table 3. Additional dimensional data are given in Fig. 14.

Superheated steam is produced at a constant pressure over the power range. Fig. 11 shows the steam generator outlet steam temperature as a function of load. At full power, the steam temperature of 595F provides approximately 60F of superheat. As load is reduced, steam temperature approaches the reactor outlet temperature, thus increasing superheat slightly. Below 15% load, temperature decreases to saturation at 900 psia at no-load.

Structurally, there are a number of factors related to both a pressurized-water nuclear steam supply system and the steam generator that permit the application of a

straight-tube, straight-shell design. The high heat transfer coefficients obtainable permit economic justification for the use of a secondary operating pressure and temperature sufficiently close to the primary average temperature so that a straight-tube design can be used.

Table 3
Nuclear steam generator design data

	Oconee Unit 1	1300-Mw Unit
Design pressure, reactor coolant, psi	2,500	2,500
Design pressure, steam, psi	1,050	1,235
Hydrotest pressure (tube side—cold), reactor coolant, psi	3,125	3,125
Design temperature, reactor coolant, F	650	670
Design temperature, steam, F	600	630
Reactor coolant flow, million lb/hr	65.66	79.1
Heat transferred, million Btu/hr	4,410	6,452
Steam conditions at full load, outlet nozzles		
Steam flow, million lb/hr	5.6	8.25
Steam temperature, F	570	587
Degrees of superheat, F	35	35
Steam pressure, psi	910	1,045
Feedwater temperature, F	455	465
Inside diameter of pressure shell, ft-in.	11-6	11-8
Inside height of pressure shell, ft-in.	66-0	65-7
Reactor coolant water volume, cu ft	2,030	2,025
Tubes		
Approximate number	15,530	16,000
Outside diameter, in.	0.625	0.625
Minimum thickness, in.	0.034	0.034

Fig. 15 is a plot of temperatures versus tube length showing the temperature differences between the shell and the tubes throughout the steam generator at full load. Control of the shell temperature is achieved by the use of a direct-contact feedwater heating zone that heats the feedwater to saturation and bathes the shell with a saturated steam mixture from feedwater inlet to the lower tubesheet. In the superheater section, the tube-wall temperature approaches the primary fluid temperature since the heat transfer coefficient of the primary water inside the tube is considerably higher than the coefficient of the steam film surrounding the tube.

With this once-through design, natural circulation flow is adequate to remove reactor decay heat without the use of reactor coolant pumps. Thus, even with a total loss of pumps, departure from nucleate boiling will not occur.

Reactor coolant pumps. Each of the two reactor coolant loops contains two vertical single-stage centrifugal-type pumps. The four pumps operating together are designed to deliver a water coolant flow of 131,320,000 lb/hr with an inlet pressure of 2185 psi and a head of 350 ft (113 psi). The pumps are designed for 2500 psi. All parts in contact with the reactor coolant are made of stainless steel.

The pump employs a controlled-leakage-seal assembly to restrict leakage along the pump shaft, as well as a secondary seal that directs the controlled leakage out of the pump, and a vapor seal which minimizes leakage of vapor from the pump into the containment atmosphere.

The reactor coolant pump motors are large, vertical, squirrel cage, induction machines. The motors have flywheels to increase the rotational inertia, thus prolonging pump coast-down and assuring a more gradual loss of main coolant flow to the core in the event pump power is lost. The motors are enclosed with air-to-water heat exchangers to provide a closed-circuit air flow through the motor. Instrumentation is provided to monitor motor cooling, bearing temperature, winding temperature, winding differential current, and speed.

Pressurizer. The general arrangement of the pressurizer is shown in Fig. 9, Chapter 21. The pressurizer, designed for 2500 psi and 670F, is a carbon steel vessel

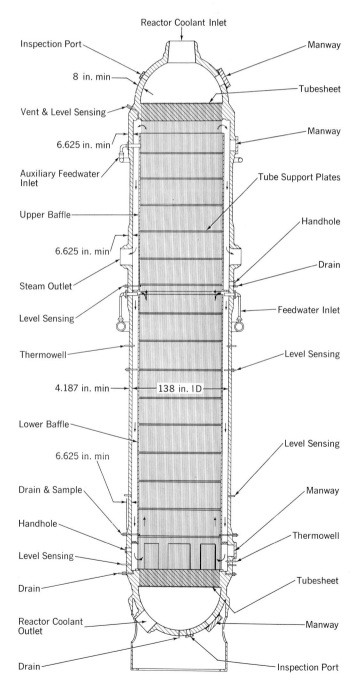

Fig. 14 Once-through steam generator.

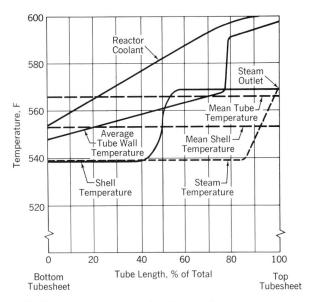

Fig. 15 Nuclear steam generator temperatures.

lined with 18% Cr - 8% Ni stainless steel. Its internal diameter is approximately 7 ft and internal height about 42 ft. The surge line at the bottom of the pressurizer is connected into the reactor outlet line in one of the coolant loops. The location of the pressurizer is shown in Fig. 13. The pressurizer vessel is protected from thermal shock by a thermal sleeve on the surge line and a distribution baffle located above the surge line entrance to the vessel.

The pressurizer functions as described in Chapter 21. Spray flow and heaters are controlled by a pressure controller. The water level is controlled by automatic regulation of the makeup to the reactor coolant system.

Piping. The reactor coolant piping is made of carbon steel clad internally with stainless steel. The general arrangement is shown in Figs. 2, 3 and 13. Each coolant loop has a single 36-in. ID line from the reactor outlet to the steam generator, and two 28-in. ID lines from the steam generator outlet to the reactor. One coolant pump is located in each of these 28-in. lines. In addition to the pressurizer-surge-line connection, the piping is equipped with welded connections for pressure taps, temperature elements, vents, drains, decay heat removal, and emergency high-pressure-injection water.

Pressure relieving devices. The reactor coolant system is protected against overpressure by control and protective circuits including the high pressure trip, and by the relief valves mounted on the pressurizer. The relief valves discharge into a quench tank located within the reactor building. The quench tank has a stored water supply, and condenses and collects the valve effluent. Since all sources of heat in the system, i.e., core, pressure heaters, and reactor coolant pumps are interconnected by the reactor coolant piping with no intervening isolation valves, the relief valves on the pressurizer protect the entire reactor coolant system from overpressure.

Auxiliary systems. These provide the functions described in Chapter 21. Most of the components of these systems are located within the auxiliary building.

Fuel handling

The fuel handling system is illustrated in Fig. 16. New and spent fuel assemblies are transferred between the reactor building and the fuel storage pool by dual transfer mechanisms. A fuel assembly is placed in horizontal position in the transfer mechanism prior to transfer, and is removed and up-ended after transfer. Within the reactor building, fuel is moved by means of two handling bridges. One of these transports fuel assemblies between the reactor core and the transfer mechanism. The other is free for use in rearranging fuel assemblies and control rods within the core.

The operator is responsible for fuel assembly accounting. Information on the replacement and relocation of fuel assemblies and control rods is supplied from a computer to the operator by a refueling panel mounted on each of the bridges in the reactor building. The bridge operator has control of bridge and tool movement.

Fuel assemblies are carried by a similar handling bridge in the fuel storage building, where they are stored in racks to await shipment. Crane facilities and building dimensions are sized for either a small two-assembly shipping cask or a large multiple-assembly cask.

Performance objectives

The reactor is designed to operate at a heat release of 2568 Mw (rated power) with design margins to accommodate transient operation and instrument error without damage to the core and without exceeding the pressure at the relief valve settings for the reactor coolant system.

The fuel rod cladding is designed to maintain its integrity for the anticipated core life. The effects of gas release, fuel dimensional changes, and corrosion- or irradiation-induced changes in the mechanical properties of the cladding are all considered in the fuel-assembly design.

Core reactivity is controlled by control rod assemblies and chemical poison dissolved in the coolant. Sufficient control rod worth is available to shut the reactor down with at least a 1% $\Delta k/k$ subcritical margin in the hot condition at any time during the life cycle with the most reactive control rod assembly stuck in the fully withdrawn position (*see Reactivity, Chapter 20*). Equipment is provided to add soluble poison to the reactor coolant to assure a similar shutdown capability when the reactor coolant is cooled to ambient temperature.

The reactivity worth of a control rod assembly and the rate at which reactivity can be added, are limited to insure that credible reactivity accidents cannot cause a transient capable of damaging the reactor coolant system or causing significant fuel failure.

The reactor coolant system is designed to contain and circulate reactor coolant at pressures and flows necessary to transfer the heat generated in the reactor core to the secondary fluid in the steam generators. In addition to serving as a heat transport medium, the coolant also serves as a neutron moderator and reflector, and as a solvent for the soluble poison (boric acid) utilized in chemical shim reactivity control.

As the coolant-energy and radioactive-material container, the reactor coolant system is designed to maintain its integrity under all operating conditions. While

performing this function, the system serves the safeguard objective of preventing the release to the reactor building of any fission products which escape the primary barrier (the core cladding).

Design limits

Nuclear limits. The core has been designed to the following nuclear limits:

1. The fuel is designed for a maximum burnup of 55,000 megawatt-days per metric ton of uranium (Mwd/tonne).

2. The power Doppler coefficient is negative.

3. The control system is capable of compensating for reactivity changes resulting from either a positive or a negative moderator coefficient.

4. A control system consisting of part-length axial-power-shaping rods is provided to allow the shaping of power axially in the core, thereby preventing any tendency towards axial instability resulting from a redistribution of xenon.

5. The core has sufficient excess reactivity to produce the design power level and lifetime without exceeding the control capacity or shutdown margin.

6. Controlled reactivity insertion rates are limited to a maximum value of 1.1×10^{-4} $\Delta k/k$ per sec for a single regulating control rod assembly group withdrawal, and 4.4×10^{-6} $\Delta k/k$ per sec for soluble boron removal.

7. Reactor control and maneuvering procedures will not produce peak-to-average power distributions greater than those listed in Table 1. The low reactivity worth of control rod assembly groups inserted during power operation limits power peaks to acceptable values.

Reactivity control limits. The control system and operating procedures will provide adequate control of the core reactivity and power distribution. The following control limits will be met:

1. Sufficient control is available to produce an adequate shutdown margin.

2. The shutdown margin will be maintained throughout core life with the control rod assembly of highest worth stuck out of the core.

3. The control rod assembly withdrawal rate limits the reactivity insertion rate to a maximum of 1.1×10^{-4} $\Delta k/k$ per sec for a single regulating group. Boron dilution is limited to a reactivity insertion rate of 4.4×10^{-6} $\Delta k/k$ per sec.

Thermal and hydraulic limits. The reactor core is designed to meet the following limiting thermal and hydraulic conditions:

1. There will be no central melting in the fuel at the design overpower (114%).

2. There is 99% confidence that at least 99.5% of the fuel rods (cladding tubes) are in no jeopardy of ex-

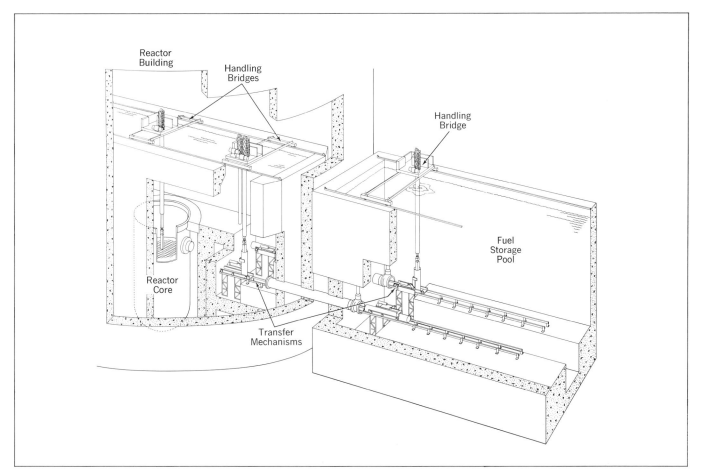

Fig. 16 Fuel handling system for a nuclear steam supply system.

periencing a departure from nucleate boiling (DNB) during continuous operation at the design overpower.

3. There is essentially 100% confidence that at least 99.96% of the fuel rods are in no jeopardy of experiencing DNB during continuous operation at rated power.

4. The generation of net steam in the hottest core channels is permissible, but steam voids will be low enough to prevent flow instabilities.

The design overpower is the highest credible reactor operating power permitted by the safety system. Normally, trip on overpower will occur at significantly lower power than the design overpower. Core rated power is 2568 Mw.

Mechanical requirements. The reactor internal components are designed to withstand the stresses resulting from start-up; steady-state operation with one or more reactor coolant pumps running; and shutdown conditions. No damage to the reactor internals will occur as a result of loss of pumping power.

Reactor internals are fabricated primarily from SA-240 (Type 304) material and designed within the allowable stress levels permitted by the ASME Code, Section III, for normal reactor operation and transients. Structural integrity of all core-support-assembly circumferential welds is assured by compliance with ASME Code, Sections III and IX, radiographic inspection acceptance standards, and welding qualification.

The fuel assemblies are designed to operate satisfactorily to the burnup values given in Table 1, and to retain adequate integrity at the end of life to permit safe removal from the core.

The assemblies are designed to operate safely during steady-state and transient conditions under the combined effects of flow-induced vibration, cladding strain caused by reactor pressure, fission gas pressure, fuel growth, and thermal strain. The cold-worked Zircaloy-4 cladding is designed to be free-standing. Fuel rod assemblies are held in place by mechanical spacers designed to maintain dimensional control of fuel rod spacing throughout the design life, without impairing cladding integrity.

The spacers are also designed to permit differential thermal expansion of the fuel rods without restraint that would cause distortion of the rods. The fuel-assembly upper-end fitting and the guide tube in the internals structure are both indexed to the grid plate above the fuel assemblies, thus assuring continuous alignment of the guide channels for the control rod assemblies. The control rod travel is designed so that the rods are always engaged in the fuel assembly guide tubes, thus assuring that control rod assemblies can always be inserted. The assembly structure is also designed to withstand handling and shipping loads.

Fig. 17 Reactor pressure vessel arriving at the plant site.

The control rod cladding is designed to the same criteria as the fuel cladding to the extent applicable. Adequate clearance is provided between the control rods and the guide tubes, which position them within the fuel assembly, so that control rod overheating is avoided and mechanical interference between the control rod and the guide tube does not occur. Overstressing of the control rod assembly components during a "trip" is prevented by providing adequate strength and minimizing the shock loads by snubbing. A trip is a quick shutdown of the reactor by dropping all control rods into the core.

Each control rod drive assembly is designed to prevent leakage of reactor coolant water. All pressure-containing components are designed to meet the requirements of the ASME Code, Section III.

Materials selected for the control rod drive assembly are capable of operating within the specified reactor environment for the life of the mechanism without deleterious effects. Adequate clearance is provided between stationary and moving parts of the control rod drive assemblies so that control rod assembly trip time to full insertion is not adversely affected by mechanical interference under any operating condition.

Structural integrity and adherence to allowable stress limits of the control rod drive and related parts during a trip are achieved by limiting the impact loads through snubbing.

Reactor protection system criteria

Major design criteria for the reactor protection system are as follows:

1. No single component failure shall prevent the protection system from fulfilling its protective functions when action is required. No single component failure shall initiate unnecessary protection system action, provided implementation does not conflict with the preceding criterion.

2. All protection system functions are implemented by redundant sensors, instrument strings, logic, and action devices which combine to form the protection channels.

3. Redundant protection channels and their associated elements are electrically independent and packaged to provide physical separation.

4. A loss of power in the protection system results in a trip of the affected channels.

5. Each protection system has manual actuating switches in the control room which are independent of the automatic-trip instrumentation. The switches and circuitry are simple, direct acting, and electrically connected close to the final actuating device.

6. The reactor protection system initiates a trip of the channel involved when modules, equipment, or sub-assemblies are removed.

7. Manual testing facilities are built into the protection system to make possible 1) preoperational testing to give assurance that the protection system can fulfill its required functions, and 2) on-line testing to prove operability and demonstrate reliability.

Reactor building

The reactor buildings shown in the frontispiece, and in Figs. 2 and 3, are designed to provide protection to the public from the consequences of a maximum hypothetical accident as defined in the safety analysis (see *Safety Criteria and Provisions*).

Each reactor building is designed to contain the energy and material released by a complete rupture of the largest reactor coolant pipe and to provide biological and missile shielding. Pressure and temperature subsequent to the accident are determined by the combined influence of engineered safeguards and the energy sources and heat sinks. The building is designed to be resistant to winds and earthquakes under post-accident conditions.

It is designed to withstand an internal pressure of 59 psi with a coincident temperature of 286F. Tests at the completion of construction demonstrated that the leakage is within the design tolerance.

Penetrations for process piping, instrumentation lines, ventilation ducts, and electrical lines are designed to withstand reactor-building design pressure and temperature as well as any forces due to differential expansion between piping systems and the structure. Similar criteria are used in the design of the equipment access opening and the personnel locks.

Engineered safeguards systems

Engineered safeguards systems, to limit the consequences of an accident, are provided to perform the functions described in Chapter 21. In the unlikely event of a serious loss-of-coolant accident these systems will function to isolate the reactor building, thus preventing uncontrolled leakage of reactor building contents to the atmosphere; to protect the fuel cladding; and to assure reactor building integrity by reducing the pressure within it.

To prevent uncontrolled leakage of reactor building contents to the atmosphere, an engineered safeguards system activates the closing of the reactor-building isolation valves upon detection of an abnormally high reactor-building pressure. It also starts one of the blowers to collect leakage from the reactor building, filter it, and discharge it through the station vent.

These blowers take suction in the penetration rooms located outside the reactor building. Experience has shown that building leakage is more likely to occur at penetrations. Therefore, essentially all penetrations have been located in groups with "penetration rooms" constructed around the points of penetration.

Two emergency injection systems and a core flooding system are provided to protect the fuel cladding. The high pressure injection is actuated when reactor coolant system pressure drops to 1500 psi, the low pressure injection at 500 psi. When so actuated, either system injects borated water into the reactor, protecting the fuel cladding by cooling and acting to stop a nuclear chain reaction by injecting poison in the form of boron.

The core flooding system provides two separate tanks containing borated water, each connected to a separate injection nozzle on the reactor vessel by a 14-in. line. The tanks are pressurized with nitrogen to provide the required injection force. This system provides for auto-

matic flooding of the core with borated water when the reactor coolant system pressure reaches approximately 600 psi. This is known as a "passive" system since it provides core flooding without the need of electrical power, automatic switching, or operator action.

To assure reactor building integrity, an engineered safeguards system automatically activates operation of the reactor-building cooling systems upon detection of an abnormally high reactor-building pressure. Reactor-building integrity is assured by two full-capacity independent systems—the reactor-building spray system and the reactor-building emergency coolers.

Each system is designed to provide sufficient heat removal capability to prevent exceeding the peak design pressure of the reactor building at any time following a loss-of-coolant accident. An initial heat removal capability of 240×10^6 Btu/hr is provided.

When the reactor building pressure reaches 4 psi, the engineered-safeguards instrumentation actuates the reactor-building emergency coolers into their post-accident operating mode. In this mode, the system consists of three units, each containing a fan and an emergency cooler. The reactor building atmosphere is circulated across a tubular heat exchanger, and a portion of the steam in the building air is condensed. The reactor-building emergency coolers would return the reactor building pressure to near atmospheric within 24 hours after an accident.

If the pressure in the reactor building reaches 10 psi, the second heat-reduction system, the reactor-building spray system, is automatically initiated and sprays 3000 gpm of borated water into the reactor building.

Separate equipment is used to perform each major function of the engineered safeguards system, and redundancy is provided for each. These systems are designed for maximum post-accident use of equipment serving normal functions. Electrical power for the engineered safeguards systems is supplied from emergency as well as normal power sources.

These systems are also designed with consideration of possible radioactivity conditions after an accident, to make sure that functioning and control of the systems would not be hampered. Systems are designed to be resistant to earthquakes, and equipment inside the reactor building is designed to operate under the accident environment of a steam-air mixture.

Safety criteria and provisions

The nuclear steam supply systems for the Oconee Nuclear Station are subject to the regulatory processes delineated under *Reactor Licensing Process, Chapter 21*, and licenses from the AEC (now NRC) were required for construction and operation.

As part of the regulatory process, a "safety analysis" report was prepared. This report discusses the pertinent characteristics of the plant site, the design and operating characteristics of the plant, and particularly, the means which are provided to control the leakage of radioactivity into the environment. Included is a careful analysis of effects and consequences of possible abnormalities which might occur during operation, together with means for mitigation of the consequences of these abnormalities where this might be needed.

Operating experience

The operating performance of B&W's second-generation units has equalled, or exceeded, expectations. The performance of the once-through steam generators has been especially noteworthy. At Oconee 1, the OTSGs produced steam with 60F of superheat at the normal 100% rated power of 2584 Mwt (2568 Mwt core power), as compared to a warranted minimum superheat of 35F and an expected superheat of 50F. The OTSG provides quick response to all normal changes in load, and good controllability during transients.

An inservice inspection of the OTSGs at Oconee 1 showed that the interior of the units was exceptionally clean, with no accumulation of sludge or deposits. Eddy-current examination of representative sampling of the tubes revealed no defects, and measured tube dimensions were within original manufacturing tolerances.

Nuclear steam system operating characteristics are as expected. The measured reactor coolant flow is approximately 108% of the minimum design value; thus providing additional core thermal margin, while not exceeding the maximum flow set by mechanical design limits.

Control rod worths and reactivity coefficients measured during start-up testing were well within the acceptance criteria. The response of the core to spatial xenon oscillations (*see Fission Product Poisons, Chapter 20*) is as predicted, and there is good agreement between the measured and calculated axial power distributions.

In order to assess the behavior of B&W fuel, the reactor coolant activity at Oconee 1 and other operating reactors has been closely monitored for fission products, the presence of which would indicate possible fuel leakage. Indications are that less than 0.05% of the fuel rods are leaking, which is well within operating tolerances.

Non-destructive examination of the fuel discharged from Oconee 1 during the first refueling showed the fuel in excellent condition after 310 effective full power days of operation. A destructive examination of the fuel is planned to further determine characteristics of the fuel in operation.

1300-Mw units

Units to supply the steam to generate approximately 1300 Mw net of electric power each are in the process of detailed design and fabrication by B&W, as of 1977. These units are similar to the Oconee units, although larger and approximately one-third greater in capacity. The type and the number of major components in each unit are the same. The reactor core of the 1300-Mw unit is made up of 205 fuel assemblies, as compared to the 177 fuel assemblies in the Oconee reactors. The 205 fuel assembly NSS is known as the BABCOCK-205.

Principal components of the BABCOCK-205 are disposed as shown in Fig. 13, which illustrates the general arrangement of B&W's more recent nuclear steam supply systems. Comparing Fig. 13 with Fig. 2 indicates that the principal difference in the two arrangements is the higher location of the nuclear steam generators with respect to the reactor vessel in Fig. 13.

The fuel assemblies in the BABCOCK-205 core have essentially the same overall dimensions as those in the

Oconee cores, but the fuel rods are smaller, thus allowing more fuel rods per assembly which, in turn, increases the power output per fuel assembly. Other factors which contribute to the greater power output per fuel assembly are improved design features, the use of heat transfer data derived from experimental programs completed since the Oconee design was established, and the knowledge gained from analyses of the operating performance data from Oconee and other units. Design improvements include flux flattening, accomplished by the use of burnable poisons, and more sophisticated fuel management (*see Optimization of a PWR Plant for Cost, Chapter 21*).

The important design characteristics for the BABCOCK-205 are listed in Tables 1 and 3.

The Bailey Meter Company is supplying the instruments and controls for each of these units as well as a data processing system. A Bailey digital computer system will monitor the performance of the nuclear steam supply system and perform other computing functions. Diamond Power is supplying the control rod drive system for each unit.

B&W nuclear steam supply system

Figure 13 illustrates the general arrangement of recent B&W pressurized-water nuclear steam supply systems which consist of a reactor vessel and internals, control rods and drives, pressurizer, and two reactor coolant loops, each with one steam generator and two reactor coolant pumps. These component units are shipped separately and assembled at the plant site.

These nuclear steam supply systems are applicable as steam producers for the generation of electric power, and in dual-purpose plants where substantial quantities of process steam are required in addition to power generation. They are available in sizes corresponding to electrical outputs of from 850 to 1300 Mw.

Reactor core

The reactor core, located in the reactor pressure vessel, comprises fuel assemblies containing fuel rods, control rods and instrumentation. Each fuel rod consists of uranium-dioxide pellets of low enrichment, contained in a Zircaloy cladding tube. The general arrangement of each fuel assembly is similar to that described for the units in the Oconee Nuclear Station. The neutron-absorbing material in the control rods is silver-indium-cadmium or boron carbide. Soluble poison is used in the reactor coolant at concentrations decreasing during core life, to compensate for fission product buildup. The soluble poison concentration is also varied in concert with control rod movement, to compensate for reactivity effects such as temperature defect and xenon poisoning.

In the fuel assemblies that do not require control rods, an orifice rod assembly is provided to restrict the bypass flow. Fuel assemblies that do not require control rods may accept lumped burnable poison rod assemblies when necessitated by fuel management requirements. Both types of assemblies are easily removed when shuffling fuel assemblies to positions requiring control rods.

Reactor coolant system

The reactor coolant system is designed to contain and circulate the reactor coolant at the pressures and flows necessary to transfer the heat generated in the reactor core to the secondary fluid in the once-through steam generators. In addition to serving as a heat transport medium, the coolant also serves as a neutron moderator and reflector and as a solvent for the soluble boron utilized in chemical shim reactivity control.

Coolant water enters the reactor vessel through four nozzles, two from each loop, located near the top flange of the vessel. The water flows downward between the thermal shield and the vessel wall, then upward through the core, removing the heat generated and transporting it to the steam generators. The reactor coolant is then returned to the reactor vessel by the coolant pumps.

The pressurized-water reactor vessel and reactor internals, shown in Fig. 5, contain and support the fuel and control rods, and provides means for directing the reactor coolant through the core.

Figure 19 shows the pertinent design features of B&W's once-through steam generator. In these steam generators, counterflow heat transfer is utilized to convert subcooled feedwater to dry superheated steam in a single pass through the steam generator.

Steam generator tubes are made of Inconel 600 and the pumps are of stainless steel. Other pressure parts of the reactor coolant system, including the reactor vessel, pressurizer, steam generators and piping, are made of

Fig. 18 Nuclear steam generator in position inside concrete shielding in process of construction.

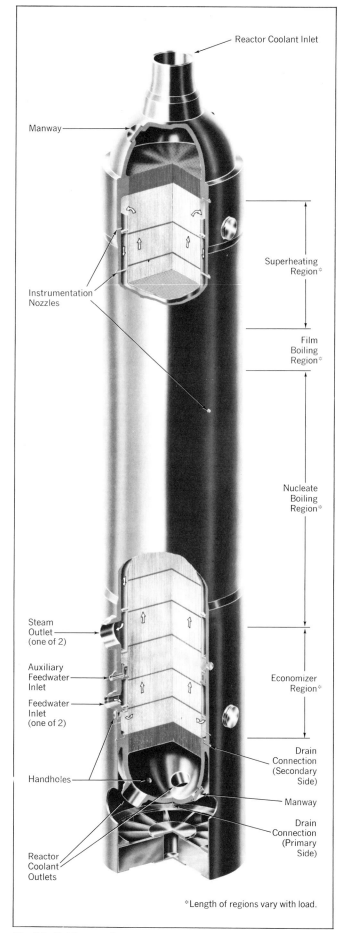

Fig. 19 B&W once-through steam generator.

carbon or low-alloy steel clad with stainless steel or Inconel on surfaces in contact with the coolant.

The pressurizer, shown in Fig. 20, is a vertical, cylindrical pressure vessel with hemispherical heads equipped with electrical heaters and spray nozzles for system pressure control. System controls maintain a constant water level in the pressurizer and the desired reactor coolant pressure during operation.

The reactor vessel is equipped with a removable flanged upper head, having a bolted joint sealed by two concentric gaskets, to provide access for refueling. The head is provided with the number of control rod nozzles required for the core. The control rod drive mechanisms are mounted on these nozzles by flanged connections. A motor tube, of the type shown in Fig. 10 forms a pressure boundary between the rotor and stator of the electric driving motor, thus eliminating the need for seals.

Auxiliary systems are provided to fill the reactor coolant system and to add makeup water, purify the reactor coolant water, provide chemicals for corrosion inhibition and reactor control, cool system components, remove residual heat when the reactor is shutdown, cool the spent fuel storage pool, sample reactor coolant water, provide for emergency core cooling, and vent and drain the reactor coolant system.

Emergency core cooling system

The emergency core cooling system is designed to supply abundant emergency core cooling water in the unlikely event of a break in the reactor coolant piping. The design covers all break sizes, up to and including the guillotine rupture of the largest (hot leg) pipe. The emergency core cooling system includes three subsystems:

1. The high-pressure injection system prevents uncovering of the core in the event of small coolant piping leaks at high pressure, and delays the uncovering of the core for intermediate sized leaks. This system normally operates for chemical and volume control as a part of the makeup and purification system.

2. The nitrogen-pressurized core flooding tank system automatically floods the core when the reactor coolant system pressure reaches approximately 600 psi. No external signal or power source is required for this operation.

3. The low-pressure injection system, cools the core when the reactor coolant pressure reaches 200 psi after a loss of cooling accident. This system normally operates for shutdown cooling as part of the decay heat removal system.

Instrumentation and control systems

Instrumentation and control systems are provided to monitor operating variables such as the neutron flux and the primary coolant pressures and temperatures, and to maintain these variables within prescribed operating ranges.

Reactor protection system

The reactor protection system monitors the parameters related to safe operation and trips the reactor to protect the reactor core against possible fuel rod cladding damage. It also assists in protecting against reactor coolant

system damage, caused by high system pressure, by limiting the energy input to the system during reactor trip action.

Trip setpoints are consistent with the safety limits that have been established from analyses of postulated transients. The setpoint for each input, which must initiate a trip of the system, has been established at a level that will ensure that control rods are inserted in sufficient time to protect the reactor core. Factors such as the rate at which the sensed variable can change, instrumentation and calibration inaccuracies, trip element trip times, circuit breaker trip times, and control rod travel times

have all been considered in establishing the margin between the trip setpoints and the safety limits that have been derived.

The reactor protection system is designed to meet the requirements of the IEEE "Criteria for Nuclear Power Plant Protection Systems" (IEEE No. 279). All equipment is subjected to qualification tests as required by that document.

Engineered safety features actuation system

The engineered safety features actuation system monitors variables to detect loss of the reactor coolant system's boundary integrity. Upon detection of "out-of-limit" conditions of these variables, the system initiates the emergency core cooling system, consisting of the high-pressure and low-pressure injection subsystems. The system also initiates the containment isolation and cooling systems and starts the emergency diesel generators. The reactor coolant and containment pressures have been selected to initiate safety features action.

Integrated-Control system

The Integrated-Control system provides the proper coordination of the reactor, steam generator feedwater control, and turbine under all operating conditions. Proper coordination produces the best possible load response to the unit load demand, while recognizing the capabilities and limitations of the reactor, the feedwater system, and the turbine. The Integrated-Control system maintains a constant average reactor coolant temperature over the load range between 15 and 100% rated power, and constant steam pressure at all rates of operation.

Nuclear instrumentation system

The nuclear instrumentation system is designed to supply the reactor operator with neutron information over the full operating range of the reactor, and to supply reactor power information to the reactor protection system and to the Integrated-Control system.

Non-nuclear instrumentation system

The non-nuclear instrumentation system provides the required input signals of process variables for the reactor protection, regulating, and auxiliary systems. It performs the required process control functions in response to these systems, and provides instrumentation for start-up, operation, and shutdown of the reactor under normal and emergency conditions.

In-core monitoring system

The in-core monitoring system provides neutron flux detectors to monitor core performance. In-core self-powered neutron detectors measure the neutron flux in the core to provide a record of power distribution and fuel burnup data to assist in fuel management. The plant computer provides normal system readout and a backup readout system is provided for selected detectors.

Fuel handling system

The reactor is refueled with equipment capable of handling the spent fuel under water from the time that it is removed from the core until it is placed in a cask

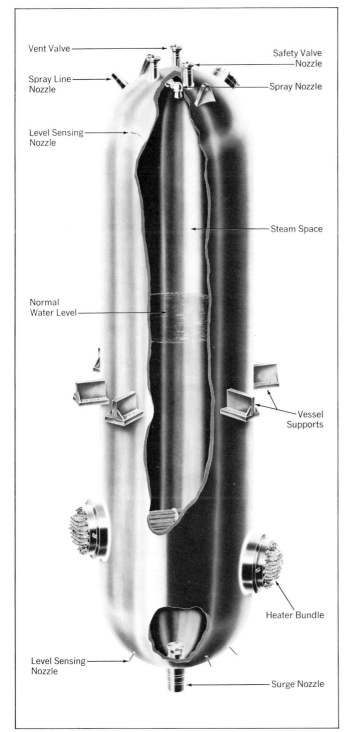

Fig. 20 Pressurizer.

for shipment from the site. Underwater transfer of spent fuel provides an optically transparent radiation shield, as well as a reliable source of coolant for the removal of decay heat. The use of borated water ensures subcritical condition during refueling.

The new fuel assemblies are stored dry in a separate, protected storage area. The center-to-center storage distance maintains a k_{eff} of less than 0.95, even if the area is flooded with nonborated water. After spent fuel has been removed from the reactor, it is transferred to and stored in the spent fuel storage pool. The pool and the spent fuel cooling system are sized to store and cool a full core of irradiated fuel assemblies plus one normal refueling batch. The spent fuel assemblies are stored in racks which provide a center-to-center fuel assembly spacing that ensures a k_{eff} of less than 0.95, even if the assemblies are immersed in unborated water.

Waste management systems

Waste management systems are designed to collect, process, store, reuse, or prepare for off-site shipment and final disposal of all plant wastes that contain, or could contain, radioactive material. The waste management system consists of three subsystems—the liquid, gaseous, and solid radioactive waste systems.

The liquid subsystem provides for the removal, concentration, storage, monitoring, and eventual safe shipment of radioactive contaminants produced by the several water systems of the reactor.

The gaseous subsystem provides for storing, sampling, and monitoring potentially radioactive gases produced during plant operations. The cover gases (nitrogen-rich sources) are stored and reused after the removal of hydrogen.

The solid subsystem provides for the collecting, storing, and packaging of the solid radioactive waste for shipping and storage offsite.

Other auxiliary systems

The component cooling system. This is a closed system that transfers heat from various components and systems in the primary plant, some of which may contain radioactive fluid, to the service water system. The system is charged with demineralized water treated to inhibit corrosion and to control pH. All drains and leakage are treated as radioactive waste and are, therefore, not discharged to the environment.

The makeup and purification system. This system regulates the boron concentration in the reactor coolant system, maintains the proper coolant inventory, removes fission and corrosion products, and supplies filtered water to the reactor coolant pump seals.

The decay heat removal system. In this system, decay heat and sensible heat are removed from the reactor coolant system and the core during the later stages of cooldown. The system also provides auxiliary spray to the pressurizer for complete depressurization, maintains the proper reactor coolant temperature during refueling, and provides a means for refilling and draining the refueling canal.

The chemical addition and boron recovery system. This system provides for the storage of reactor coolant bleed evaporator distillate, recovers boron from the reactor coolant for reuse, prepares, stores, and transfers lithium hydroxide for pH control and hydrazine for oxygen control, and stores and transfers concentrated boric acid to attain cold shutdown of the reactor.

The spent fuel cooling system. This system removes decay heat from the spent fuel stored in the spent fuel pool, and purifies the water in the spent fuel pool and the refueling canal.

The chemical sampling system. This system provides for the transfer of representative liquid and gaseous samples to the sampling sink for laboratory analysis.

Standardization

As of January, 1975, the BABCOCK-205 nuclear steam system was documented in a series of standard system descriptions and specifications, and a standard safety analysis report was being prepared. This documentation provides the base for B&W's standardization program, which is an important means of effecting economy in nuclear steam system design and manufacture. Standardization provides desirable commonality in analytical engineering and facilitates savings through identical component manufacture. Standardization also enhances confidence in plant reliability, simplifies operator training, shortens time requirements for start-up and testing, and increases confidence of licensing acceptability.

Chapter 24

Marine installations

Since the Industrial Revolution, the ingenuity of many inventors and engineers has been devoted to the application of steam boilers and engines to ship propulsion. At first steam was only a supplemental form of power used in dead-calm seas or in entering and leaving port, but continued experimentation with design and production techniques led to improvements which brought new economy and ultimately doomed the sailing vessel. Today the American Merchant Marine, faced with low-cost foreign-flag competition, must operate larger, more reliable, and more fully automated ships capable of high sustained speeds regardless of weather (Fig. 1). Modern marine steam-plant designs, by providing efficient and dependable power, make these ships possible today. In the future, steam generated from nuclear fuel will play an increasing role.

Marine boilers—fossil fuels

Marine boilers have evolved from units which were little more than closed containers holding water to the modern header-type and two-drum Integral-Furnace type boilers almost universally used today.

By World War II, most new merchant vessels were equipped with boilers operating at pressures of 450 to 600 psi and temperatures of 750 to 825F. Following the

Fig. 1 S.S. *American Astronaut*, United States Lines—a fully automated Lancer-Class containerliner.

war, greater emphasis was placed on speed and efficiency, and the tendency has been to increase steam pressure and temperature to provide more economical power. This was accomplished by using the two-drum Integral-Furnace type of boiler (Fig. 2).

The trend to higher steam temperatures, coupled with the firing of residual fuel oils with large amounts of slagging and corrosive constituents, resulted in design changes that provided better access to superheaters,

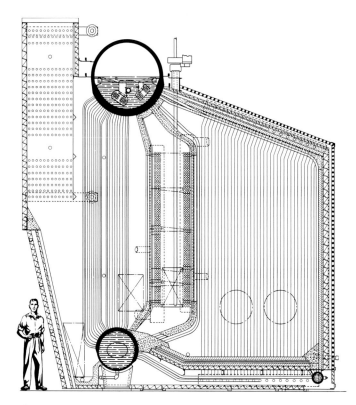

Fig. 2 Two-drum Integral-Furnace marine boiler.

thereby reducing the time required for cleaning and maintenance. B&W pioneered in providing an access cavity in the superheater bank and in using superheater tube supports that are replaceable without removing superheater tubes.

Even with these improvements, fouling of superheater surface frequently caused an excessive drop in steam temperature between cleanings. To overcome this, mass-action retractable sootblowers, previously used in the stationary boiler field, were installed beginning in 1952. Improvements in oil burning equipment also had beneficial effects. Later an additional cavity was added to increase accessibility to the superheater.

Modern merchant ships (Fig. 3) are designed for high boiler efficiencies to minimize fuel costs. Consequently, almost all installations have auxiliary heat exchangers, such as economizers and air heaters. In addition, the use of automatic feedwater controls and automatic combustion controls with wide-range steam-atomizing oil burners have permitted reductions in operating personnel with attendant reductions in cost.

General design considerations

Steam generating equipment for marine service is designed in accordance with the principles and considerations that apply to stationary units, with modifications to meet specific requirements for operation at sea.

Reliability is a primary requirement, since a ship at sea does not have the system reserve which backs up many stationary installations. Relatively simple steam cycles permit the use of equipment that is readily accessible for operation and maintenance in a limited space. Equipment must also be sufficiently rugged to absorb vibration and the forces resulting from rolling and pitching in heavy seas or shocks which may result from accidental causes such as groundings and collisions. In the case of naval vessels, the shock effects of the detonation of explosives must also be considered.

Fig. 3 Modern high-speed general-cargo ship.

Additional reliability is achieved through the careful selection of materials to withstand the high temperatures encountered in highly rated marine boilers and the corrosive atmosphere of the ocean environment in which they operate. High-strength materials provide light-weight construction with the desired ruggedness.

The ability to change power output rapidly over a wide range of loads and to operate for long periods at high rating is another important requirement. Maneuvering a ship into and out of docks or in restricted waters may require frequent changes of power with attendant fluctuations in boiler steam flow, oil flow, steam pressures and temperatures, and drum water levels. On the other hand, sustained high power outputs with high efficiency may be required on long passages by general-cargo and bulk-carrier vessels (Fig. 4). To satisfy these requirements, the marine boiler designer must consider: (1) the performance characteristics of oil burners and furnace to assure complete and smokeless combustion, (2) boiler circulation and steam-separator performance to provide dry steam, and (3) auxiliary heat exchangers, such as economizers and air heaters, to obtain the desired efficiency.

Merchant marine vessels are designed for maximum efficiency at this normal (or 100%) rating, while naval combatant vessels are usually designed for maximum efficiency at the cruising rate (about 35% of rated full power), since they operate at this power about 85% of their service life. In addition, naval boilers are capable of sustained operation at 120% of full-power rating without undue maintenance.

Boilers and related equipment for marine service are constructed in accordance with the rules and regulations established by several different authorities, including the U.S. Navy, the U.S. Coast Guard, the Maritime Administration of the Department of Commerce, the American Bureau of Shipping, and Lloyd's Register of Shipping. Boilers for non-self-propelled vessels may also have to conform to the *ASME Boiler and Pressure Vessel Code.* In addition to these general specifications, the design and construction of marine boilers must satisfy any special specifications of the owner and naval architect.

Many years of experience have established the general requirements for the main propulsion plant and auxiliary equipment. Operating experience has also established the requirements for such items as fuel input rates, steam flows and temperatures, pressure-part details, materials, and design arrangements as well as the operating procedures for satisfactory service.

The boilers of almost all ocean-going steam vessels built in the U.S. since World War I have been designed for oil firing. The few boilers installed for coal firing are larger and heavier than oil burning units of equivalent output. Larger furnaces are required to provide sufficient grate area and furnace volume, and hoppers must be arranged to handle fly ash.

The use of heavy residual fuel oils, with ash high in corrosive slag-forming constituents, has led to the establishment of minimum clearances required between oil burners and the adjacent furnace surfaces to assure complete combustion and avoid deterioration of refractory. Slagging oils also impose limitations on maximum metal temperatures of superheater tubes and supports to avoid vanadium corrosion at elevated temperatures. Also, the

Fig. 4 S.S. *Esso Gettysburg,* bulk oil carrier.

minimum temperatures of heat exchanger surface in economizers and air heaters must be limited to avoid sulfur corrosion at or below the dew point (Chapter 13). Ash and soot accumulations impose further limitations on tube spacings. However, if distillate fuels are used, these considerations become less important, and it is possible to decrease the overall size of the boiler provided other design criteria are not violated.

The limited space available for boilers in marine service makes it necessary to use small tubes and relatively high rates of heat input. Consequently good feedwater, with careful control of waterside chemistry in the boiler, is essential for most marine installations. Where it is impossible to provide these safeguards, it is necessary to design for a more conservative rating and operate the boiler accordingly.

Steam temperatures may be controlled through the inherent design characteristics of the superheater and also through the use of control devices, such as attemperators (desuperheaters) or gas bypass arrangements (*see Chapter 12*). Steam for auxiliary services, such as galley, space, and cargo heating, deck machinery, salt-water evaporators, and electric-generator-plant requirements, may be obtained from auxiliary surface-type desuperheaters installed in the steam or water drum or from spray- or bucket-types external to the boiler.

Although some smaller-capacity low-rating boilers still continue to operate with natural draft, most units are now fitted with forced draft fans to reduce size and weight. Insulated double casings, used in almost all current installations, prevent flue gas leakage into the fire-room and provide lower outer-casing temperatures and smaller radiation losses than those previously obtained with single-cased boilers.

B&W boiler types for marine application

A few of the outstanding characteristics of representative boiler types currently being installed in new ships are noted on following pages. In most instances, modifications of the basic design concepts can be readily made to satisfy the space or operating requirements of a particular vessel design.

Two-drum Integral-Furnace boiler, merchant type
Oil fired

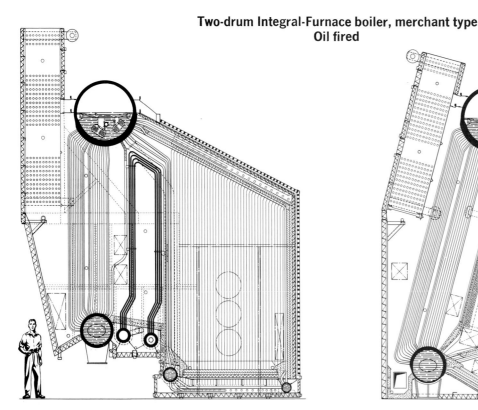

Fig. 5 Two-drum Integral-Furnace boiler with vertical super-heater.

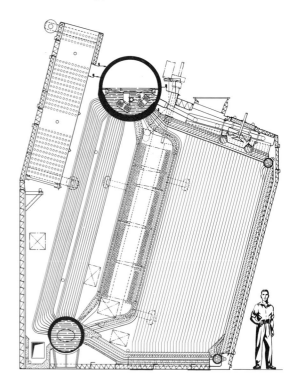

Fig. 6 Top-fired two-drum Integral-Furnace boiler with horizontal superheater.

General description

This Integral-Furnace boiler (Figs. 5 and 6) has a single gas pass and an insulated welded double casing for pressurized operation. The furnace is water cooled by closely spaced 2-in. OD tubes on the side, roof, front and rear walls. Recent designs have sloped, bare furnace-floor tubes with consequent reduction in exposed refractory. In designs with refractory floors, the floor tubes are usually buried in the floor to reduce refractory temperature and increase its life expectancy. Steam drum diameters range from 54 to 72 in. and water drums from 30 to 36 in.

An inclined or vertical boiler tube bank, composed of 2 to 4 rows of 2-in. OD screen tubes and 17 to 24 rows of 1¼-in. OD generating tubes, may be used, depending on space and performance considerations. The super-heater consists of either horizontal or vertical 1¼-in. OD tubes and has one or two access cavities to facilitate water-washing, cleaning, inspection, and maintenance of the superheater and boiler bank. A single cavity is normally provided when the fouling characteristics of Bunker C oil are average, and two cavities when fouling characteristics are more severe. The unit is generally equipped with steam-atomizing burners, retractable sootblowers and an air heater or an economizer.

Range in size, steam output
  To 280,000 lb/hr in no fixed increments

Design pressure
  100 to 1100 psi

Steam temperature
  Saturation to 1000F

Fuel
  Oil, light fractions to heavy residuals

Operational control
  Manual, or completely automatic, including feed-water flow, combustion and steam-temperature controls

Draft loss at maximum output
  From 15 to 30 in. of water total through all components

Dimensions outside setting
  Smallest, 7 ft 8 in. high × 5 ft 5 in. wide × 5 ft 6 in. deep
  Largest, 41 ft 6 in. high × 34 ft 3 in. wide × 24 ft 1 in. deep

Indicated field of application

1. Chiefly for propulsion power, although it is also used without a superheater for auxiliary or heating service in the smaller sizes.
2. Where space is at a premium and a compact light-weight design is needed.
3. Where feedwater is of good quality.

General comments. Designs of this type are suitable for vessels in which large power plants must be installed in a minimum of space and where weight saving is a vital consideration. Many possible variations in configuration permit application under difficult space conditions. Mass-action retractable sootblowers are recommended for the superheater zones.

Sectional-header boiler, merchant type
Oil and coal fired

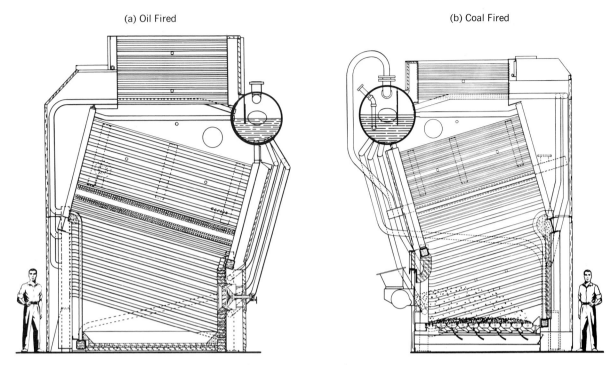

(a) Oil Fired   (b) Coal Fired

Fig. 7 Sectional header boiler.

General description

This type of boiler (Fig. 7), although no longer commercially available, has been in use for many years. Standard straight-tube units are from 7 to 35 sections in width, with 2-in. OD screen tubes ahead of the superheater arranged in clusters of 2 to 4 tubes, and clusters of nine $1\frac{1}{4}$-in. OD tubes in the boiler bank. Superheaters have $1\frac{1}{4}$-in. OD tubes arranged in 2 to 8 rows. Gas flow is upward through a single gas pass. Steam drums are normally 48-in. OD. Furnace side walls are cooled by inclined $3\frac{1}{4}$-in. tubes. Boilers are usually double cased to the top of the superheater and single cased above. Casing is all welded. For increased efficiency, air heaters or economizers may be included. Boilers may be installed with steam drums either athwartship or fore-and-aft, as space permits.

Range in size, steam output
To 150,000 lb/hr in no fixed increments

Operating pressure
100 to approx 550 psi

Steam temperature
Saturation to 910F

Fuel
Oil, light fraction to heavy residuals; coal, bituminous, spreader- or underfeed-stoker fired

Operational control
Manual, or completely automatic, including feedwater flow, combustion and steam-temperature controls

Draft loss at maximum output
From 10 to 15 in. of water total through all components

Dimensions outside setting
Smallest, 11 ft 11 in. high × 7 ft 10 in. wide × 12 ft 4 in. deep
Largest, 17 ft 10 in. high × 23 ft 10 in. wide × 18 ft 7 in. deep

Indicated field of application

1. Chiefly used for propulsion power and attendant requirements, but may be installed for auxiliary or heating service.
2. Particularly well suited for vessels equipped with steam reciprocating engines or those which operate with large percentages of makeup feedwater.

General comments. The header-type boiler has certain fundamental advantages over other types. The generating tubes are straight and of few sizes, which reduces the number of spares that must be carried. Each tube can be cleaned, inspected, and plugged easily and, if necessary, removed and replaced independently of any other without having to enter the drum. The time and cost of erecting and maintaining this unit are much less than required for a drum-type boiler. It is easy to check the condition of the equipment, since it is not necessary to enter the drum. However (as compared to the two-drum Integral-Furnace boiler) pressure, temperature and steam capacity are limited, and longer warm-up time is required. Thus application of the sectional-header boiler in modern power plants is limited.

Two-drum boiler, naval type

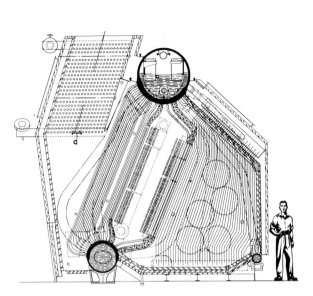
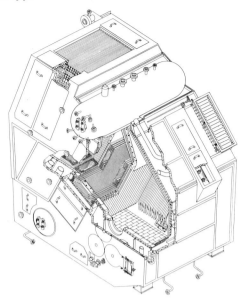

Fig. 8 Two-drum boiler, naval type.

General description

This Integral-Furnace type boiler (Fig. 8) is fitted with welded high-strength, low-weight stainless or low-alloy steel casings. Furnace roof, side and rear walls are water cooled by 2-in. OD close-spaced tubes. Front (burner) wall and floor are usually refractory, but some recent units have water-cooled front walls. Steam drum diameters range from 46 to 60 in. and water drums from 27 to 36 in. Two to four rows of 2-in. OD tubes form the superheater screen. The superheater has 1- or 1¼-in. OD tubes arranged in a maximum of 8 rows deep with provision for complete drainability. The boiler bank is usually inclined and has from 18 to 23 rows of 1-in. OD tubes. For maximum efficiency, the boiler is fitted with a stud-tube economizer and, in some cases, steam air heaters.

Range in size, steam output
    To 350,000 lb/hr in no fixed increments

Design pressure
    Up to 1400 psi

Steam temperature
    Saturation to 1000F

Fuel
    Navy special fuel oil (residual) and distillates

Operational control
    Manual to complete automatic, combustion and feedwater regulation

Draft loss at maximum output
    About 75 in. of water total through all components

Dimensions outside setting
    Smallest, 14 ft 2 in. high × 15 ft 1 in. wide × 10 ft 6 in. deep
    Largest, 21 ft 5 in. high × 18 ft 11 in. wide × 16 ft deep

Indicated field of application

1. Combatant naval vessels or special installations.

General comments. The nature of the construction and the rating at which these units operate limit their use to naval or high-speed naval auxiliary vessels requiring maximum power in minimum space. They are designed for maximum efficiency at cruising speed, and some attainable efficiency is sacrificed to develop high power-to-weight and power-to-boiler-volume ratios. The construction utilizes lightweight tubes, high-tensile drum plates, and other special features to minimize weight.

Marine boiler design

The techniques used in the design of marine boilers are similar to those applied to stationary units (Chapters 12, 13 and 14). However, the design of marine units is subject to constraints and requirements that are specific to marine plants. These include space conditions, fireroom configuration, list and trim, pitch and roll, and ship maneuverability.

Fuel characteristics can have considerable bearing on the design. Regardless of whether oil or coal is used, the chemical analysis and ash characteristics are particularly important and should be specified so that heat transfer surface can be arranged to minimize ash and slag deposition and corrosion.

The selection of a suitable boiler for a particular application starts by establishing the dimensions and arrangement of a furnace within which the desired fuel-burning equipment can be installed and the fuel burned efficiently, without exceeding allowable furnace heat absorption rates. This is particularly necessary for high-speed naval vessels, such as the frigate shown in Fig. 9.

The furnace arrangement and dimensions generally establish the overall size of the boiler tube bank. Hence the first step in designing a new boiler is to prepare a preliminary layout of a suitable furnace. To do this, the

amount of fuel to be fired is calculated based on the required steam pressure, temperature, capacity, feedwater temperature and efficiency. In the usual case, with oil fuel, it is then possible to estimate the type and number of burners to be used, the allowable pressure drop through the burners for good combustion conditions, the size and shape of the furnace, and the allowable furnace heat absorption rate.

Oil burners. The type and number of oil burners selected depend on the fuel rate and the allowable air resistance. The number is usually not less than two, so that at least one burner operates at all times, even when changing sprayer plates or cleaning atomizers of the idle burners. Many types of oil burners are available. The circular burner described in Chapter 7 was designed for stationary units and for burning pulverized coal and natural gas as well as oil. Marine burners are generally designed solely for oil burning, and three types are sufficient for most marine applications. The B&W Iowa, Saratoga, and Progress types (Fig. 10) are used in merchant and naval vessels to cover the range of oil rates up to 7000 lb of oil per burner per hr.

Most existing steamships use mechanical atomizers. However, extremely wide-range Racer steam atomizers have largely replaced this type in new construction and are being retrofitted in many older vessels. There is also

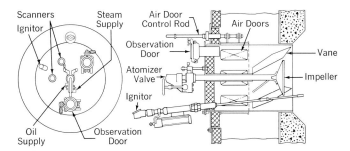

Fig. 10 B&W Progress-type oil burner with Racer steam atomizer.

a trend in the Navy to employ steam atomization in new vessels although most combatant vessels built since World War II are fitted with mechanical atomizers of the return-flow type. In this latter type, oil is supplied at 600 to 1000 psi and the amount of fuel fired is regulated by varying the return pressure.

To satisfy the demands imposed by automation and higher steam outputs, large capacity burners are used. The B&W Progress-type burner fitted with a Racer atomizer is employed where oil rates up to 7000 lb/hr per burner are required. The turn-down range is in excess of 20 to 1 to suit the requirements for fully automated installations.

Fig. 9 U.S.S. *Belknap,* DLG-26, a modern steam-powered naval vessel.

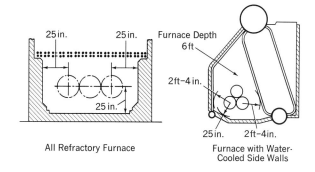

Fig. 11 Minimum burner clearances for two types of furnaces when burning Bunker C oil with maximum burner inputs of 3500 lb/hr.

When burning heavy residual fuel oil, certain minimum clearances are required around the burners to prevent flame impingement and carbon deposits (Fig. 11). In all boilers the burners should be conveniently located for ease of operation (see Fig. 2, Chapter 7). To assure adequate flame travel and complete combustion of the fuel, the furnace depth of both header and drum-type boilers is usually limited to a minimum of 6 ft, although both diesel and bunker oils have been burned successfully in furnaces 5 ft or less in depth.

With the minimum width and height fixed by the number of burners required and a selected minimum depth, the preliminary design of the furnace is set, provided the heat absorption rates and the temperatures of the gas leaving the furnace do not exceed acceptable values.

Furnace heat absorption. In the marine field the hourly heat release per cu ft of furnace volume is frequently used for comparing boilers, without regard to similarity of design. This ratio is not an important design criterion, and provides only an approximation of the time required for the products of combustion to pass through the furnace. However, it may be used to indicate the operating range for which the firing equipment is to maintain satisfactory combustion conditions. The availability of

suitable oil burners has permitted the installation (in naval vessels) of high-capacity lightweight boiler units with heat released at a rate of 200,000 Btu/cu ft of furnace volume at cruising conditions and over 1,000,000 at the maximum evaporative condition with satisfactory results. For merchant ships, arbitrary limits of 75,000 to 100,000 Btu/cu ft, hr at the normal rate of operation are commonly specified.

A more meaningful criterion of furnace design is the actual heat absorbed by the cold surfaces of the furnace, expressed as the heat absorbed per sq ft of radiant heat absorbing surface. The considerations enumerated under *Furnaces*, Chapter 4, also apply to the marine furnace, with particular emphasis on the determination of the furnace-exit-gas temperature to assure satisfactory superheater design and to establish the heat absorption by the furnace wall tubes for adequate circulation margins.

Marine boilers operate with higher heat-input rates per sq ft of boiler and superheater surfaces than stationary boilers designed for the same steam outputs. They have less heating surface and smaller overall dimensions. In terms of equation (1), Chapter 4, the general equation for heat flow ($q = US\Delta t$), the requisite heat transfer for a given surface, S, is obtained in a marine boiler by increasing the combined conductance, U, and the temperature difference, Δt. Flame temperatures more closely approach the adiabatic temperature, and furnace-exit-gas temperatures are considerably higher than those encountered in stationary boilers. Fig. 12 indicates the effect of excess air on furnace temperature. Comparison of Fig. 12b with Fig. 26, Chapter 4, indicates that the average marine heat absorption rates are usually considerably above those of stationary practice.

The effectiveness of the water-cooled surface in the furnace is determined by applying the factors shown in Fig. 23, Chapter 4, to the flat projected areas of the furnace walls and tube banks facing the furnace. Bare tangent tubes are used wherever possible in furnace water walls. Where tubes must be spaced to facilitate replacement, it is preferable to limit the width of the exposed refractory areas between tubes to one inch or

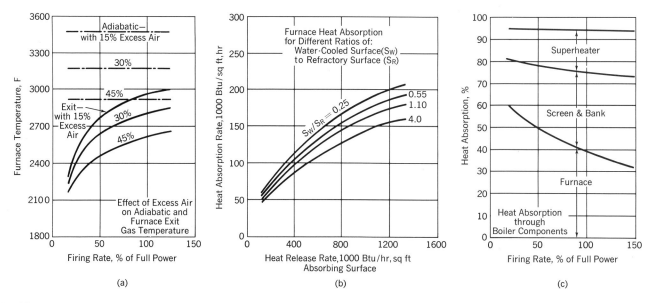

(a) (b) (c)

Fig. 12 General effect of excess air (a), ratio of heat-absorbing to refractory surface (b), and firing rate (c) on furnace heat absorption and temperature, based on 18,500 Btu per lb fuel oil.

less to avoid wastage resulting from sodium compounds in the oil ash. The effect of wall-tube spacing, or the ratio of water-cooled surface to refractory surface, on furnace heat absorption is shown in Fig. 12b. The heat absorption rate in the furnace increases with increased firing rate. However, furnace absorption as a percentage of the total boiler absorption decreases with increased firing rate as indicated in Fig. 12c.

Furnace tube temperatures. In all boiler tubes, and particularly in tubes exposed to the high heat absorption rates of marine furnaces, adequate circulation must be provided to avoid departure from nucleate boiling (DNB) as discussed in Chapters 1 and 4. This is generally accomplished by empirical methods based on tests and operating experience. Tube-wall thickness is usually set close to the minimum required for the pressure, because weight is a primary consideration and excess thickness increases external tube temperature. The heat transfer coefficient across the boiling water film in the furnace steam generating tubes may well be in excess of 20,000 Btu/sq ft, hr, F. However, in estimating tube temperature, a conservative value may be used, e.g., 2000 Btu/sq ft, hr, F, to obtain a somewhat higher estimated tube temperature, resulting in lower allowable stress in the tube metal, and thus a somewhat more conservative tube thickness.

Scale deposits on the waterside of boiler tubes are a long-recognized cause of tube failure. These deposits can be particularly serious in the furnace tubes of marine units because of the high heat absorption rates. Fig. 13 illustrates the serious consequences of a calcium sulfate scale deposit only 0.024-in. thick. In the upper section (Fig. 13), the clean tube operates with 500F water and steam inside and tube temperatures of 573 and 630F at inner and outer surfaces respectively, both representing good practice. In the lower section, with a 0.024-in. scale deposit on the inside of the tube, the low conductivity of the scale (10 Btu/sq ft, hr, F/in.) results in a 362F differential across the scale. Thus tube temperatures rise to 938 and 1004F at inner and outer tube surfaces respectively. The 1004F temperature exceeds the oxidation limit for steel, and oxidation and ultimate tube burnout will occur, even though boiler circulation may be adequate. Scale must be avoided by proper water conditioning (Chapter 34).

Boiler tube banks. The boiler tube bank, composed of multiple rows of tubes in which steam is generated, generally consists of a screen ahead of the superheater and a convection bank behind it. Both sections generate saturated steam but they are considered separately during the design stage, since the screen tubes, by virtue of their location, absorb considerably more heat than the main-bank tubes at a greater distance from the furnace. Consequently, to assure an adequate flow of water, the furnace-row tubes should be larger in diameter. For this reason, marine boilers are designed with two sizes of steam generating tubes. Generally, in both header- and drum-type boilers the diameters of screen tubes are 2 in. while those of the other generating tubes are 1 or 1¼ in. Circulation and the amount of heating surface required to obtain the desired gas temperature leaving the tube bank are the major factors in determining the tube size

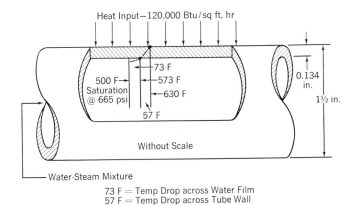

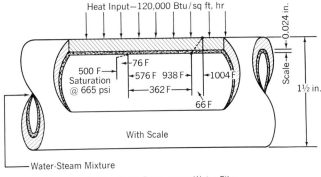

73 F = Temp Drop across Water Film
362 F = Temp Drop across Internal Scale
66 F = Temp Drop across Tube Wall

Assumed CaSO₄ Scale (0.024 in. thick)
Thermal Conductivity 10 Btu/sq ft, hr, F/in.

Maximum Tube Temp (1004 F) is above Allowable
Oxidation Temp Limit for SA-210 Carbon Steel

Fig. 13 Diagrams showing how very thin scale on inner surface of tube causes elevated tube-metal temperatures.

and the number of tube rows to be installed, although resistance to gas flow is also a factor.

In the design of the superheater screen, consideration must be given to the effect of tube spacing and the number of rows on the desired superheater outlet temperature and the maximum allowable superheater tube-metal temperatures. The screen must be designed so that the gas temperature entering the superheater and the radiant heat penetration from the furnace will provide the desired steam temperature with a superheater of reasonable size and arrangement. Fig. 14 shows the effect of radiant heat penetration on the performance of the superheater over the designed load range of the boiler.

The number of rows in the boiler bank is usually established by an analysis of the economic advantages of economizers and air heaters as compared with boiler surface. The proper proportions of boiler surface and additional heat-reclaiming surface beyond the boiler bank are based on the efficiency desired.

Superheaters. Superheaters of the convection type are generally used in marine boilers. While some radiant superheaters have been used, the difficulty of providing adequate cooling during fast start-ups and under maneuvering conditions has severely limited their application. In the convection superheater there is usually enough

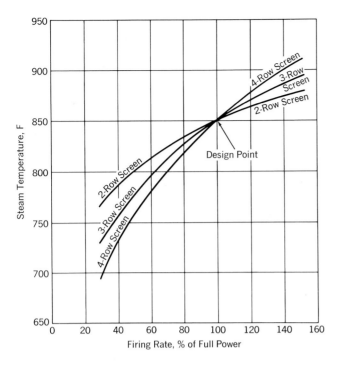

Fig. 14 Typical curves showing effect of superheater location and firing rate on superheat.

absorption by radiant heat penetration of the screen to give a flatter steam temperature characteristic than would be obtainable by convection alone. The characteristic steam temperature curves of radiant and convection superheaters are shown in Fig. 10, Chapter 12.

With a properly designed screen between the convection superheater and the furnace, it is possible to maintain a high temperature differential between the gas and the steam. The effect of this is to minimize the amount of heating surface necessary to obtain the desired steam temperature and to reduce the size and weight of the superheater and, consequently, the boiler unit as a whole. Superheater heating surface usually consists of U-shaped tubes connected into headers at each end, but continuous-tube superheaters are used in special designs.

Although a horizontal arrangement of superheater tubes is mandatory in header boilers, either a vertical or

a horizontal arrangement may be used in drum-type boilers. The horizontal arrangement can be vented, drained, and readily cleaned by mechanical or chemical means. However, complete draining and venting is possible only with the vessel on an even keel. Vertical superheaters have inverted loops and, though drainable at all times, cannot be vented. Typical superheater arrangements for a two-drum boiler are shown in Figs. 5 and 6.

Superheater surface is arranged in loops of in-line tubes (usually one to four loops), and the most commonly used tube size is 1¼-in. OD. Since the tubes are relatively short, adequate strength is available in the usual range of thicknesses to maintain proper alignment with a minimum of supports. The number of steam passes is selected to provide sufficient pressure drop to obtain proper steam distribution and to assure satisfactory tube-metal temperatures.

Good practice requires that maldistribution of gas and steam be kept to a minimum to maintain proper superheater tube temperatures. However, with various fuels and operating demands it is not possible to maintain the conditions necessary for perfect distribution. To provide a satisfactory margin when calculating steam and tube temperatures, the average gas-side heat transfer rate is increased and the steam-side rate is reduced. This allows for probable maldistribution of steam, which is a function of the tube-to-header pressure drop ratio. The resulting "upsets," as they are called, give the maximum calculated steam and tube-metal temperatures for tubes with less than average steam flow and more than average gas flow. Tube materials are selected on the basis of the calculated maximum mean wall temperature anticipated in each pass. Header materials are selected to withstand the maximum steam temperature to which they will be exposed in service.

For steam temperatures below 850F, tubes are usually expanded into headers. Above 850F rolled and seal-welded joints, or joints of the stub-welded type, are necessary for satisfactory service.

Use of stub-welded joints is limited to single- or double-loop superheaters because of the space required for welding. Where dissimilar metals are used for tubes and headers, the tubes must be "safe-ended" at the place of manufacture with a short length of tubing, compatible with the header material, which is welded to the superheater tubes under closely controlled procedures.

In addition to being supported by the headers, superheater tubes may also be supported at one or more points by alloy castings dovetailed into brackets welded to water-cooled support tubes. Fig. 15 shows two widely used types that permit rapid replacement should high temperature oil-ash corrosion be experienced. With these designs the superheater tubes can be replaced without removing the supports.

In two-drum boilers, superheaters of the inverted-loop vertical type have their headers beneath the superheater, whereas the headers of the horizontal design are at the front or the rear of the boiler, depending on the tube-renewal space available in the fireroom. In header boilers, superheater headers must be located at the boiler side, with tube-renewal space provided on the opposite side of the unit.

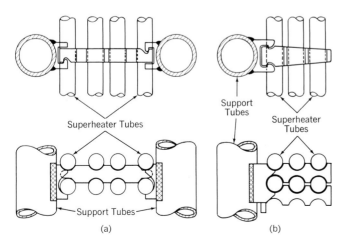

Fig. 15 Two widely used types of tube supports for horizontal marine superheaters.

Superheater fouling and high-temperature corrosion.
The use of higher steam temperatures and the nature of
the residual fuel oils burned following World War II
resulted in rapid fouling of superheater surfaces and corrosion and wastage of superheater supports. The heavy
ash deposits came from burning oils with 0.05 to 0.20%
or more ash by weight. The most significant constituents
of the ash are vanadium, sodium, and sulfur. While the
exact mechanism of deposit formation is questionable,
experience indicates that heavy deposits occur with a
combination of high gas and heat-receiving-surface temperatures. This is evidenced by the fact that the heaviest
ash accumulations occur on the furnace side of a superheater, where the gas temperatures are relatively high
while less ash forms at the back side, where the gas
temperatures are much lower.

Additional evidence is that the gas temperature entering the superheater screen may be nearly 500F higher
than the gas temperature entering the superheater, but
with a screen surface temperature about 400F lower than
that of the superheater, little, if any, ash is deposited.
For further discussion of high-temperature corrosion
in oil-fired boilers, see *Oil-Ash Corrosion, Chapter 15.*

Steam temperature control. In the marine power plant,
just as in the stationary power plant, accurate control of
steam temperature is often desirable. The trend toward
fast high-powered ships, operating with improved cycle
efficiencies, has resulted in higher steam temperatures
and greater changes in rating between the full-power
(normal design conditions) and the maximum rates of
operation. In most cases steam temperature controls are
used to assure that the allowable metal temperatures of
the main steam piping and the main turbine or engine
are not exceeded. Close control of the maximum steam
temperature permits the use of less expensive alloys in
the superheater and piping. Several methods are used for
superheat control, as described in Chapter 12. One or
more methods may be used to alter the characteristic
steam temperature curve of a particular unit design.

Gas bypassing has formerly been widely used, chiefly
in two-furnace boiler designs in which regulation of the
firing rates in each of the furnaces provides control of
the steam temperature over a wide range of load by
changing the superheater absorption. By varying the oil
firing rate in the "superheater" furnace, the quantity and
temperature of the gases flowing across the superheater
are controlled to obtain the desired steam temperature.
At the same time, the firing rate in the "saturated" furnace, which contains no superheater surface, is adjusted
to hold the desired steam pressure. This method is also
employed as a means of controlling reheater outlet temperature (*see Reheaters*) on some recent designs.

In most modern two-drum or header-type boilers,
steam temperature is controlled, where required, through
the use of a drum-type surface attemperator or "desuperheater." With this type of control, all of the gas passes
over the superheater, but a portion of the steam is passed
through the attemperator, which is a steam-to-water heat
exchanger submerged in boiler water in the steam or
water drum. Fig. 16 indicates two piping arrangements
for control attemperators.

Auxiliary desuperheaters. Steam for auxiliary use, such
as fire, feed, and ballast pumps, electric generators, cargo
heating, and tank cleaning may be required at a lower
temperature than that delivered by the superheater to
the main engine. To satisfy these demands, auxiliary desuperheaters are used, often in conjunction with pressure-
reducing stations. These desuperheaters may be:

1. The internal-surface type submerged in the steam or
   water drum in the manner of a control desuperheater.
2. The external spray type which has a significantly
   higher capacity, but requires large quantities of pure
   water for cooling.

Selection is dependent on the quantity of steam required
and the availability of water of adequate purity for the
spray type.

Reheaters. The use of steam reheat in a marine plant
is more attractive as the speed and power requirements
of the ship increase. Although its use reduces the simplicity of the boiler design and increases the first cost of the
plant, fuel savings in high-horsepower high-utilization
plants can be significant. Design considerations are similar to those for superheaters but must be augmented by
the requirements to protect the reheater from overheating during periods when there is no steam flow to
the reheater during maneuvering, running astern or at a
stop bell.

Economizers and air heaters. Economizers or air heaters, and in some instances both, are required if a high
boiler efficiency is to be obtained. The temperature of
flue gas leaving the boiler bank at full power (the design
rate) is a function of the saturation temperature corresponding to the drum pressure at which the unit is operat-

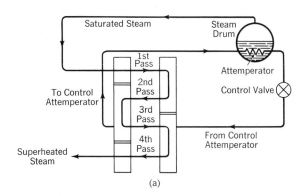

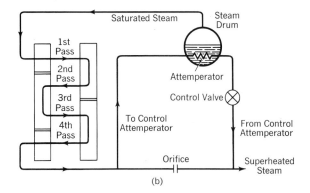

Fig. 16 Internal attemperators, (a) interpass control, (b) after-
pass control.

ing. Space, weight, and economic considerations usually result in a boiler bank sized to reduce the exit-gas temperature to within 50 to 100F of the saturation temperature. Gas temperatures in the range of 550 to 650F leaving the boiler bank are typical of merchant units. To reduce this temperature sufficiently to obtain acceptable efficiency, economizers and/or air heaters may be added. The choice of which to use depends on the design of the power plant and the desired performance characteristics of the unit.

Where the design includes a deaerating feedwater heater and a single stage of feed heating to supply water at 240 to 280F, an economizer can be used, either alone or in conjunction with a steam air heater, to provide reasonably high boiler efficiency. In this range of feed temperature an economizer can be economically designed to reduce the products of combustion to within 40F of the inlet water temperature at the normal rating. Thus, with 280F feedwater a boiler efficiency of 88.0% can be obtained with an economizer alone and about 88.3% if a steam air heater is added.

When the feedwater temperature to the economizer is higher, the efficiency is limited, since the temperature of the gas leaving the economizer cannot be lower than the inlet feedwater temperature. Consequently, when additional stages of regenerative feed heating (turbine bleeding) are used, the inlet feedwater may be at a temperature of 300 to 450F, and it may not be economical to use an economizer unless it is followed by an air heater.

Cycle efficiency is increased approximately 1% for each 100F rise in feedwater temperature through regenerative feed heating. An air heater is particularly attractive because it contributes additional efficiency even when the maximum practical amount of regenerative feedwater heating is used. At normal operating rates and an inlet air temperature of 100F, exit-gas temperatures of 300 to 320F are readily obtained, corresponding to 88.5 to 88.0% efficiency. Air temperatures leaving air heaters are normally in the range of 300 to 450F.

Economizers. Two general types of economizers, the bare-tube and extended-surface types, are used in marine service. Both are non-steaming and are almost always arranged for counterflow of water and flue gas to obtain the best possible heat transfer characteristics. The bare-tube type is used where high feedwater temperature makes the application of both an economizer and air heater desirable. These economizers are designed to reduce the gas temperature about 100F, with the remainder of the required temperature drop obtained with an air heater. The second and more usual type employs extended surface to reduce the size of the economizer. There are many types of extended surface, including cast-iron or aluminum gill rings, spiral fins and small metal studs welded to the tubes. B&W has chosen the latter for its marine economizers because the shape and size of the stud in conjunction with the method of attachment eliminates soot-collecting crevices where corrosion usually starts.

Extended-surface economizers are usually constructed of 1½-in. OD tubes formed into continuous loops. This construction requires only two headers. Tube-to-header joints are welded, or expanded and seal-welded, to

eliminate seat leakage. There is a definite trend toward the elimination of handhole fittings, except those required for inspection, by externally welding the tubes in sockets or to stubs on the headers. A typical arrangement of an extended-surface economizer with studded tubes is shown in Fig. 17.

Fig. 17 Extended-surface stud-tube economizer.

When used alone, economizers are generally designed to reduce gas temperatures by 200 to 300F, with a corresponding increase in the water temperature of 70 to 100F. If the inlet water temperature is 280F, the exit water temperature normally will range from 350 to 365F, far enough below saturation temperature at a pressure of 600 psi to prevent steaming.

In designing an economizer, the possibility of sulfuric acid corrosion of the economizer tubes must be considered (*see External Corrosion, Chapter 13*). The tube-metal temperature of bare-tube economizers is essentially the same as that of the water within the tube. This is also true for the tube metal of extended-surface elements, but the tip temperature of the studs or the gills is considerably higher.

In order to eliminate gas-side corrosion of carbon steel economizer tubes, B&W recommends that feed temperature be kept above 246F when burning Navy Special Fuel Oil (NSFO) and above 270F when burning Bunker C. Where these temperatures are not obtainable, the use of a corrosion-resistant alloy tube is advised. The use of cast iron is not recommended as the corrosion resistance of cast iron is less than that of plain steel, and any improvement in tube life with cast iron cladding is only due to its greater mass. The mass, of course, is not desirable from the naval architect's point of view as it adds weight high in the fireroom.

A bypass line is usually provided for operation of the boiler with the economizer out of service. During such operation, it is necessary to fire more fuel to maintain the required evaporative rating because of the decreased efficiency. This increases the steam temperature and requires either more attemperation or a reduction in rating to prevent overheating of superheater tubes or

turbine. Normally there is no danger of metal oxidation in the economizer during bypass operation, since the gas temperatures entering the economizer are usually less than 850F.

When economizers are included in the design, deaerating feed heaters should be installed to remove all traces of oxygen from the feedwater and prevent internal corrosion of tubes and headers (see *Internal Corrosion, Chapter 13*).

All marine economizers are designed to be drainable and ventable. This, coupled with the wide acceptance of chemical cleaning for internal surfaces of boilers and superheaters has made it possible to eliminate the cleanout fittings formerly required. Elimination of these fittings and the use of all-welded continuous-tube designs with a minimum number of handhole fittings has effectively reduced maintenance costs and provided increased reliability.

Air heaters (gas-to-air). The tubular air heater is usually the least expensive form of heat-recovery equipment that can be used in a marine plant. Unlike the economizer, the gas-to-air heater is not designed for boiler pressure, and can be relatively simple in design and light in construction. In addition to the tubular air heater, rotary regenerative air heaters are available and provide higher efficiencies. Because of their size and weight, regenerative air heaters must be installed in the uptake opening over the boilers, with suitable connecting ductwork.

Tubular air heaters in marine service usually have the tubes placed horizontally with air passing through them and hot gases over the outside. They are supported on boiler structural members and are integral with the boiler casings. Air heaters of the vertical type, in which gas passes up through the tubes and air crosses the outside, are seldom used in marine practice because of their large space requirement.

In-line tube patterns increase sootblower effectiveness and facilitate water-washing. This more than offsets the slight advantage in heat transfer of staggered arrangements. Tube diameter is usually 1½ or 2 in., selection depending on draft-loss and heat-transfer requirements.

Corrosion of tubes and tube sheets may occur if metal temperatures fall below the dew point of sulfur trioxide (SO_3)-bearing flue gas. Even small quantities of sulfur in the fuel can produce troublesome deposits and sulfuric acid of sufficient strength to attack the steel.

Air heater corrosion can be reduced or practically eliminated by several means (see *Corrosion Control, Chapter 13*). Initially, the basic design should be selected so that, even with probable air and gas maldistribution, metal temperatures are as high as practicable. If the fuel is expected to have a high sulfur content, a material more resistant than steel should be selected. Low-alloy copper-bearing steels, originally developed for high strength under atmospheric corrosion conditions, have been found to outlast ordinary steels by a factor of 2½ to 1, although the initial cost is somewhat greater. Increasing tube-wall thickness also provides longer life with slightly higher costs, weight, and fan requirements.

Another factor to be considered in reducing corrosion is the air flow pattern entering the tubes. Because of

turbulence, the local heat transfer rates at tube inlets may actually be greater than the average. This results in low tube temperature and tube failure in the area adjacent to the tube sheet. To avoid such failure, inserts are installed in the inlet ends of the tubes to provide air spaces, which reduce heat transfer in the critical zone and raise tube-metal temperature to safer values. Insulation applied to the tube sheet reduces conduction of heat from the tube ends and helps maintain satisfactory metal temperatures of both the tubes and the tube sheet.

A bypass damper may be used on the air side to control tube temperatures and minimize corrosion either during low-load operation or when low ambient air temperatures are encountered. During such periods the dampers are manipulated to bypass enough air to maintain tube temperatures at a satisfactory level.

Tube-metal temperatures can be increased by recirculating a part of the hot air leaving the air heater to the entering air pass to raise the inlet air temperature. However, the space required for suitable air ducts and the increased fan power needed make this method generally unsuitable for marine service.

For a given exit-gas temperature, metal temperatures are somewhat higher with a regenerative air heater than with a recuperative type. Conversely, for a given satisfactory metal temperature, a lower exit-gas temperature and a higher unit efficiency can be obtained with a regenerative-type air heater. Units of this type are being used increasingly in marine service, in cases where fuel saving is sufficient to justify the higher cost of the regenerative air heater. This is particularly true with the larger horsepower plants.

Boiler casing. As defined in Chapter 16, the term *boiler setting* comprises the walls that form the boiler and furnace enclosure. In marine service these walls, together with those surrounding the economizer and air heater, are normally made gastight by using metal casing. Hence the term *casing* is generally used for the walls surrounding a marine unit.

To provide a comfortable fireroom, an outer-casing temperature of 130F is usually specified and is achieved through the use of suitable insulation and casing arrangements in conjunction with adequate fireroom ventilation. A typical double-casing arrangement of furnace refractory and insulation at both boiler bank and uptake areas is shown in Fig. 18. The arrangement shown in Fig. 19 is employed on welded membrane-wall construction. In

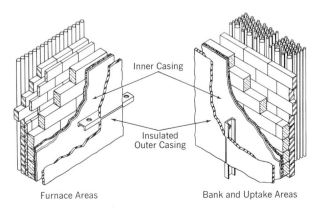

Inner Casing

Insulated Outer Casing

Furnace Areas   Bank and Uptake Areas

Fig. 18 Casing constructions.

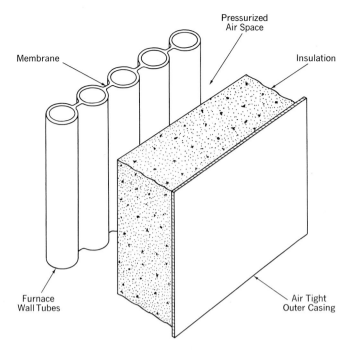

Fig. 19 Typical section through furnace wall (membrane design).

both cases the space between the inner and outer casing is pressurized with air at or near the forced draft fan discharge pressure, to prevent leakage of combustion gases into the fireroom and to help maintain the desired outer casing temperature.

Circulation and steam separation. Satisfactory circulation characteristics and efficient steam separation are of prime importance in the successful operation of any boiler. These factors take on increased importance in a marine boiler rolling and pitching in a seaway or undergoing rapid load changes. In analyzing circulation, the procedures outlined in Chapter 3 are applied to the design at the maximum anticipated rate of evaporation.

Generally, steam drum diameters range from 54 to 72 in. for merchant vessels and from 46 to 60 in. for naval units. The drum must accommodate the desired number of tube rows and provide sufficient space for steam separation, feedwater introduction, distribution and treatment, and water-level fluctuations caused by sudden load variations.

Marine steam-drum baffling is usually simple in construction and arrangement. Most header-type boilers achieve primary steam separation by gravity behind a vertical baffle (Fig. 20a) or an inclined baffle (Fig. 20b) sized to maintain steam velocities below the critical velocity at which steam entrains water particles. A V-type baffle using a triple layer of perforated steel plates is used in moderately rated drum-type boilers. With relatively small clearances between the plates it is installed (Fig. 20c) just below the normal water level to break up steam-and-water jets issuing from the riser circuits. In more highly rated two-drum boilers the duplex compartment baffle (Fig. 20d) is more effective, since it separates the high-steam-by-volume mixture leaving furnace and screen circuits from the low-steam-by-volume discharge of the boiler bank.

Horizontal cyclone steam separators (Fig. 21) are now standard for all propulsion boilers, both merchant and naval. Cyclones are the most positive means of steam separation and the horizontal arrangement provides more free area at the water level, thereby helping to minimize shrink and swell during maneuvering operations. Cyclones also provide a greater density of the water in the steam drum resulting in less carry-under of steam in the downcomers. This assists boiler circulation by providing maximum density difference between downcomers and risers.

In header-type boilers (Fig. 22) each bank section consists of a downtake and an uptake header joined by boiler generating tubes. Water is supplied from the steam drum to each downtake header by tube nipples. A horizontal header, or mud drum, connects the lower ends of the downtake headers to equalize flow and to provide a place for the accumulation and subsequent removal of solids. External downcomers and risers connect the steam drum with the side-wall supply and uptake headers, respectively. Downcomers from the steam drum also supply water to the lower header of the rear furnace-water-wall tubes. The steam-water mixture from these tubes is discharged into the boiler bank uptake headers. Horizontal circulator tubes connect the uptake headers with the steam drum and convey the steam-water mixtures of the rear wall and the boiler bank to the drum.

Drum-type boilers are generally rated conservatively and do not require external downcomers, since adequate circulation can be maintained by the rear rows of boiler-bank tubes, where the gas temperature is about 850F or less. At low rates the first several rows of tubes act as risers, and the remaining tubes serve as downcomers. As the firing rate increases, the high-temperature gas zone

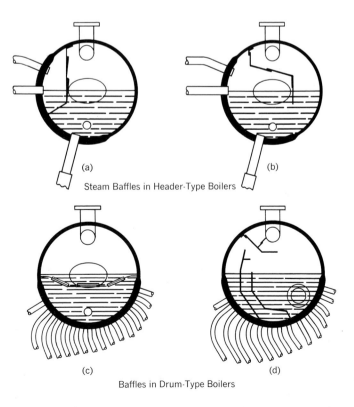

Fig. 20 Several arrangements of steam-drum baffling in header- and drum-type marine boilers.

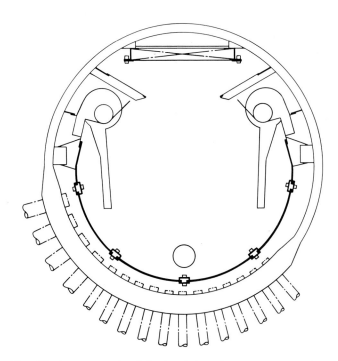

Fig. 21 Arrangement of horizontal cyclone separators in a marine boiler drum.

moves deeper into the tube bank, and the number of tubes acting as risers increases, with a corresponding decrease in the number of downcomer tubes. Excessive firing rates and rates beyond those contemplated in the design can reduce the number of downcomers below the minimum requirements. For highly rated units it is necessary to install unheated downcomers to supplement the number of bank tubes acting as downcomers. Circulation is benefited by interposing a convection superheater in the boiler bank, since the heat absorbed by the superheater reduces the temperature of the gas flowing over the boiler tubes beyond it and more boiler tubes act as downcomers over a wide operating range.

In most drum-type boilers, furnace water-wall supply headers receive water from the water drum through supply tubes located below the furnace floor These tubes are spaced along the lengths of the water-wall headers to assure even distribution of water to the high-duty furnace tubes and provide cooling for the furnace floor refractory. Naval and other high-rated designs have external downcomer tubes from the steam drum to the lower wall header, since the supply of water from the boiler bank only would be inadequate.

Furnace side-wall tubes discharge directly into the steam drum since the tubes are arranged to form the furnace roof. Rear water-wall tubes either terminate in a header connected to the steam drum by riser tubes or go directly into the steam drum. Similar arrangements are used where front water walls are installed.

External downcomers between steam and water drums are required in conservatively rated drum-type boilers only in those circuits where the boiler tubes cannot perform this function.

Review of boiler components. Upon completion of the preliminary design phase, the estimated performance of all boiler components must be reviewed and correlated

by the designer. It is at this time, while assessing the performance of the various components, that it may be possible to reduce the size and weight of a particular design or to increase its reliability and efficiency by making suitable adjustments. Final design details can then be developed to assure optimum performance.

To produce the best possible design for each installation, the designer must be free, within the limitations imposed by the intended service, to apply his knowledge and accumulated experience. The task of developing satisfactory and economical boiler units is facilitated when the ship owner, his naval architect, and the boiler designer have a complete and mutual understanding of all the problems involved.

Nuclear applications

Nuclear Merchant Ship *Savannah*

A nuclear merchant ship was first proposed by President Eisenhower in 1955 as evidence of this country's interest in promoting the peaceful uses of atomic energy. In 1956 Congress authorized the program and provided funds for the design and construction of a vessel, subsequently named the Nuclear Ship (N.S.) *Savannah*. The President directed the Atomic Energy Commission (AEC) and the Maritime Administration (MARAD) to proceed with design and construction, and the project was placed under the direction of the AEC-MARAD Joint Group.

The major objectives were to demonstrate the peaceful use of nuclear energy and resolve the problems of commercial marine reactor operation, including port entry. Requirements for the nuclear plant included a conservative design with a long core life, use of commercially available materials and equipment wherever practicable, and safe operation of the ship.

B&W contracted to supply the nuclear propulsion plant and auxiliaries for the N.S. *Savannah* and to train the engineering and deck officers of the operating crew. The N.S. *Savannah* (Fig. 23) is a single-screw, geared-turbine vessel, 595 ft long, with a beam of 78 ft, design draft 29 ft 6 in., and a displacement of 21,990 tons. The ship has a design speed of 22 knots at 22,000 shaft horsepower, accommodations for 60 passengers and 652,000 cu ft of space for general cargo.

Fig. 22 Compact arrangement of header boilers in a typical fireroom.

Fig. 23 Nuclear Ship *Savannah.*

Power plant design. The reactor is of the pressurized water type. The flow diagram of the power plant is shown in Fig. 24. The reactor coolant water delivers heat through two main coolant loops to generate steam in two steam generators. This steam expands through the main turbines to the condenser, where pumps return the condensate to the steam generators. There are two 1500-kw turbine-generators to provide auxiliary power for all propulsive and ship services. A low-pressure heat exchanger furnishes a maximum of 7500 lb/hr of steam at 110 psi for hotel and heating services. An oil-fired package boiler, capable of supplying 7500 lb/hr of steam at 150 psi, is used when reactor steam is not available.

Emergency take-home power is provided by a 750-hp electric motor which can be coupled to the main gearing. Two 750-kw diesel generators, designed to start auto-

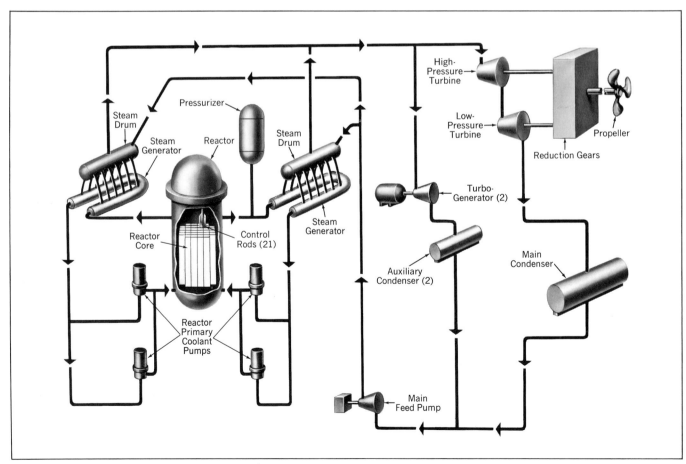

Fig. 24 Flow diagram of N.S. *Savannah* propulsion system.

matically if the turbine generators fail, provide power for the take-home motor and other essential electrical loads.

Pertinent design data for the power plant are given in Table 1.

Table 1
N.S. *Savannah*
Summary of power plant design characteristics

Load	Normal	Maximum Shaft Power
Shaft power, shp	20,000	22,000
Propeller speed, rpm	107	110
Turbine inlet pressure, psi	445	430
Condenser vacuum, in. Hg	28.5	28.5
Feedwater temperature, F	348	340
Total steam generation, lb/hr	246,000	266,000
Total electric load, kw	2,170	2,400
Total reactor power, Mw	64.7	70.0
Reactor coolant data:		
Pressure in reactor, psi	1,735	1,735
System pressure drop, psi	61	61
Mean temperature in reactor, F	508	508
Flow, lb/hr	9,400,000	9,400,000

The reactor is fueled by 7100 kilograms of uranium enriched to an average of 4.4% of uranium-235. Uranium oxide in the form of pellets is contained in stainless steel tubes. Each of the 32 fuel assemblies (Fig. 2, Chapter 19) contains 164 tubes. Individual stainless steel boxes surround each assembly, direct the coolant flow through the fuel assemblies, and form channels in which the control rods move.

The reactor is controlled by rods of cruciform section made of stainless steel plates containing boron clad in stainless steel sheets. The rods are actuated by top-mounted electromechanical-hydraulic drives. Zircaloy-2 followers, fastened to the bottom of the absorbing rods, fill the rod channels in the core as the rods are lifted.

The entire primary system is enclosed in a steel containment shell (Fig. 25) which supports the primary and a portion of the secondary shielding. The secondary or biological shielding reduces the radiation in crew and passenger spaces to acceptable levels.

The operation and control of the entire power plant is centered in an air-conditioned control room within the engine room (Fig. 26). The major equipment consists of a main control console, the main electrical switchboard, the nuclear instrumentation and safety system, the radiation monitoring system, and auxiliary instrumentation.

The nuclear instrumentation and safety system includes instruments for measuring the neutron flux at different power levels, and monitors to initiate reactor shutdown upon receipt of signals indicating an unsafe condition.

The radiation monitoring system provides information for personnel protection against possible radiation hazards, functional radiation data from the plant, and information on the radioactivity levels of the gaseous waste effluent and ventilating system intake air. The inherent self-regulating characteristics of a low-enriched uranium-oxide pressurized water reactor, coupled with the centralized instrumentation and control systems of the N.S. *Savannah*, permit rapid power transients and maneuvering rates. The reactor power plant was designed to increase load from 20 to 85% in ten seconds and decrease power from 100 to 20% in three seconds.

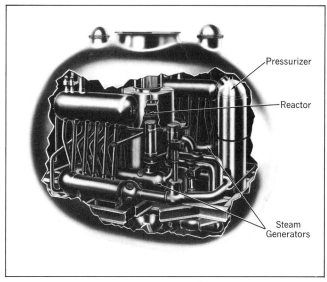

Fig. 25 Model of nuclear steam supply system of N.S. *Savannah*.

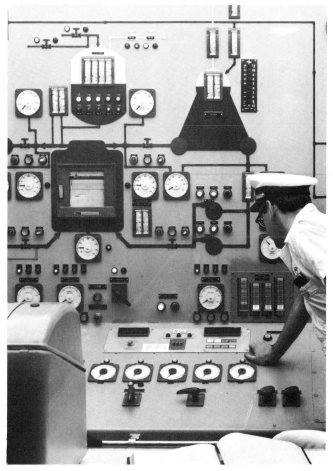

Fig. 26 N.S. *Savannah* control console.

The refueling equipment for the N.S. *Savannah* was designed and built by B&W. Fig. 27 shows the shielded fuel transfer cask on the rotary manipulator. The cask contains an integral fail-safe hoisting mechanism. Controls permit the operator to spray-cool the fuel assembly during transit from the reactor to the cask and then to fill the cask with water for transport. With an extension piece added to increase its length, the same cask is used for removal of control rods.

A similar, but larger, cask is used to remove the reactor internals. Extended to its full size, this cask can accommodate the upper flow baffle. The shield portion is designed to telescope, thus doubling the shield thickness to permit removal of the smaller, but more radioactive, upper-grid-plate assembly. An internal-hoist and tool-column assembly facilitates the handling of vessel internals.

Construction and operation. The keel of the N.S. *Savannah* was laid in May, 1958 and the ship was launched in July, 1959. In May, 1962 the ship was delivered to the operating agent, and the initial port visitation voyage began in August. Three years later, after visiting a number of domestic and foreign ports, the N.S. *Savannah* began operation in regular commercial service, transporting cargo between U.S. East Coast and European North Atlantic and Mediterranean ports, and later to ports in Eastern Asia.

The *Savannah* traveled approximately 330,000 nautical miles and developed 15,000 full power hours using her first core with no relocation of fuel. At Galveston (August–November 1968) four of the original 32 fuel assemblies were replaced and some of the remaining 28 were relocated to different positions in the core. With

Fig. 28 The German Nuclear Ship *Otto Hahn*. (*Courtesy of Gesellschaft für Kernenergieverwertung in Schiffbau und Schiffahrt mbH.*)

this rearrangement the *Savannah* was capable of continuing normal commercial operation for another 2½ years without further manipulation of fuel. By late 1970, the *Savannah* had traveled more than 450,000 miles, visited 32 different domestic ports in 20 states, 45 different foreign ports in 27 countries, and been visited by more than 1,500,000 people.

The operation of the N.S. *Savannah* provided technology for development of economical nuclear ships, and established standards for the design of the ship and reactor, operating practices, manning, port entry and operation, and safety of the crew and the general public.

Improved designs for merchant ships

Since building the N.S. *Savannah*, B&W has developed an improved nuclear marine plant design known as the CNSG (Consolidated Nuclear Steam Generator) with the objective of obtaining economic nuclear propulsion systems for merchant ships.

This design incorporates the reactor and steam generator into a single pressure vessel, thus achieving a compact arrangement and eliminating some of the auxiliary equipment. Other features include a once-through steam generator, self-pressurization, and wet containment. The first design to be developed based on these principles was the CNSG I design in 1962.

This CNSG design, revised slightly and including a dry-containment arrangement, was incorporated in the nuclear plant of the German Nuclear Ship *Otto Hahn*, Fig. 28. This ship is a single-screw geared-turbine ore carrier 565 ft long, with a beam of 77 ft, a draft of 30 ft, deadweight of about 15,000 tons, and a design speed of 16 knots at 10,000 shaft horsepower.

The nuclear plant for this ship was designed and constructed by the German-Babcock Interatom consortium with the assistance of The Babcock & Wilcox Company. A diagrammatic cross section of the pressure vessel is shown in Fig. 29. Pertinent design data for the power plant at normal load are given in Table 2.

Fig. 27 Shielded fuel-transfer cask on rotary manipulator.

Table 2
German Nuclear Ship *Otto Hahn*
Summary of power plant design data

Shaft horsepower	10,000
Total steam generated, lb/hr	141,000
Superheater outlet pressure, psia	440
Superheater outlet temperature, F	523
Feedwater temperature, F	365
Reactor power, Mw	38
Reactor coolant data:	
Pressure in reactor, psi	918
Core temperature in reactor, F	523
Flow, lb/hr	5,280,000

Steam from the reactor system expands through the main turbine to the condenser where the condensate is pumped back to the steam generator. There are two 450-kw turbine-generators supplying auxiliary power for propulsive and ship services. Emergency take-home power is provided by two auxiliary water tube boilers that can propel the ship at about 10 knots. There is a diesel generator of 450-kw capacity and an emergency diesel generator of 260 kw. Initial criticality was first attained August 26, 1968. Following dockside testing, the first sea trial was conducted October 11, 1968. After successfully completing a series of research and training

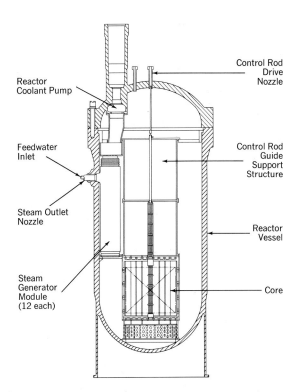

Fig. 30 The Consolidated Nuclear Steam Generator design (CNSG IVA) surrounds the core with steam generators located within the pressure vessel. Visible in the upper part of the figure are coolant pumps and control rod drives. A pressure suppression region inside the shielding surrounds the reactor vessel.

trips, the *Otto Hahn* started commercial service in February 1970 with a trip to Morocco. Since that time, besides a number of regular trips to Morocco, the *Otto Hahn* has visited Iran, Senegal, Togo, Mauritania, Tunisia, Argentina and Holland. Further port entry permissions have been issued by Ghana, Sierra Leone, Colombia, Venezuela and Peru.

Since the CNSG I, work has continued on the design of nuclear plants with improved economic characteristics. The CNSG IVA, shown in Fig. 30, incorporates a number of features designed to improve performance and reduce weight, space, and cost for a given output. Among these features are:

1. Use of control rod assemblies and elimination of follower rods.
2. Lowering of the core in the vessel, permitting reduction in vessel height and water inventory.
3. Placement of pumps in the head of the vessel instead of at the side, permitting a reduction in size and weight of the containment and shielding.
4. Electrically heated separate steam pressurizers.
5. Vapor suppression containment.
6. Steel and water around entire reactor containment.
7. Use of lumped burnable poison in core design to attain high core burnup and attractive fuel economics.
8. Use of modular "once-through" steam generators derived from B&W central station practice.

Reactors with these desirable features may be used in the future on high-powered vessels capable of high sustained speeds.

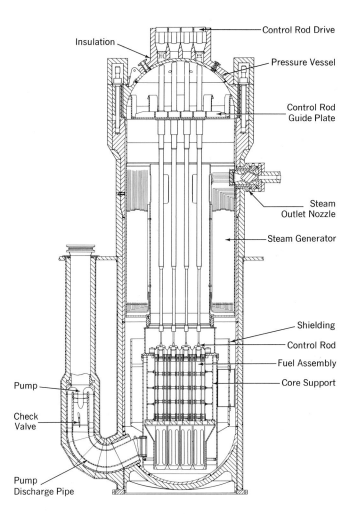

Fig. 29 Pressure vessel of the *Otto Hahn*—diagrammatic cross section. (*Courtesy of Gesellschaft für Kernenergieverwertung in Schiffbau und Schiffahrt mbH.*)

PFI-type Integral-Furnace boiler installed in an industrial plant.

Chapter 25

Industrial installations

The principles governing the selection of boilers and related equipment for industrial installation are, for the most part, similar to those discussed in Chapter 22 for electric utility service. Proper selection of equipment can be accomplished only in the framework of a sound cost evaluation. This requires a working knowledge and understanding of the performance of the different components of the steam generating unit under various conditions, including the significance of the many different arrangements of heat-absorbing surfaces, the characteristics of different fuels which may be available, methods of fuel burning, and the handling of refuse. The principles for evaluating the performance and characteristics of industrial steam generating units are similar to those described under *Evaluation of Equipment Performance and Characteristics* in Chapter 22.

To provide the designer with proper information, the user must establish his present and, as far as possible, his future conditions and requirements. The requirements and conditions that form the basis for the designer's selection of equipment are repeated from Chapter 22 for ready reference:

1. Fuel(s)—sources presently available, analyses, costs and future trends.
2. Steam requirements
   (a) Pressure and temperature—at points of use, at outlet of steam generating units, allowable temperature variations.
   (b) Rate of heat delivery (or steam flow)—to points of end use, to boiler house auxiliaries and feedwater heating, to blowdown, from outlet of steam generating unit, variations (minimum, average and maximum), and predictable future requirements.
3. Boiler feedwater—source and analysis, and temperature entering steam generating unit.
4. Space and geographical considerations—space limitations, relation of new equipment to existing boiler house equipment, environmental requirements and restrictions of local laws, earthquake and wind requirements, elevation above sea level, foundation conditions, climate, and accessibility for service and construction.
5. Kind and cost of energy for driving auxiliaries.
6. Operating personnel—experience level of workmen for operation and maintenance, and cost of labor.
7. Guarantees.
8. Evaluation basis—for unit efficiency, auxiliary power required, building volume, and various fixed charges.

With this information, the boiler designer is able to analyze the user's specific needs and coordinate the many components that make up a steam generator into the most economical design, by balancing first cost charges with long term savings.

In the case of most industrial installations, the requirements for steam generating units differ in several important respects from those of the units purchased by the electric utilities. For the most part these differences result in the use of boilers of different design in industrial applications. The principal differences are:

1. Industrial units cover a wide size range with many units small enough to permit shop fabrication and shipment as package boilers. At the upper end of the range, single industrial units generate as much as 1,200,000 lb/hr of steam in some cases.
2. Pressure and temperature requirements also vary over a wide range—from as low as 2 psi and 215F (saturated) for heating to 1800 psi and 1000F for a large turbine generator.
3. Industrial units often supply steam for more than one application. For some applications steam demand may be cyclic or fluctuating, thus complicating unit operation and control of the boiler.
4. Many industrial units use waste fuels generated by the process or plant which they serve.

Design practice

Most of the discussion under *Selection of Steam Generating Equipment* in Chapter 22 is applicable to industrial installations. However, certain additional factors which are applicable in industrial units should be noted.

Fuels

Bituminous coals, natural gas and fuel oil are the leading fuels for industrial installations. Other natural fuels include lignite, anthracite coal and peat. By-product and waste fuels are available in many industrial installations, and they are burned unless there is a more profitable use for them. These include wood refuse, bagasse, digester liquor, blast-furnace gas, coke, petroleum coke, refining gas, and carbon monoxide waste gas.

Coal. Factors to consider in the selection of pulverized-coal firing are listed in Chapter 22. The effects of coal ash on boiler design and operation are described in Chapter 15.

Pulverized-coal firing, described in Chapter 9, is applicable to almost any bituminous coal, lignite, or anthracite, although anthracite requires special arrangements and additional expense. There is no recognized upper limit of size for pulverized-coal-fired units. There is a practical lower limit at a steam output of about 200,000 lb/hr. This is set by the disproportionately high incremental costs of pulverizers and other auxiliaries for smaller units.

Stokers. For many small industrial units, stokers still constitute the most practical method of firing coal. In spite of lower efficiency, stoker firing is the most economical method of firing where capacity is less than 100,000 lb/hr of steam. In some larger units stokers may be chosen for their greater firing range, capability of burning a wide range of solid fuels, and lower power requirements. Almost any coal can be burned successfully on some type of stoker. Chapter 11 describes the different types of stokers, their operating characteristics, and field of application.

The spreader stoker is the most generally used in the capacity range from 75,000 to 400,000 lb of steam per hr, because it responds rapidly to load swings and can burn a wide variety of fuels, although anthracite and coking coals are not suitable. Two types of ash-removal equipment are used with this stoker, the dumping grate and the moving grate. The former requires more manual labor; the latter has the advantage of lower carbon loss.

With the spreader stoker there is a carry-over of coarse fly-ash and carbon particles through the boiler and to the stack. It is therefore necessary in most locations to install a fly-ash or dust collector with the added operating cost of higher induced-draft-fan power. To reduce thermal loss, the collected ash is continuously reinjected into the furnace to burn out any remaining carbon. In selecting a boiler unit for spreader-stoker firing, care must be taken in the arrangement of tubes, supports, baffles, and other components to avoid coarse-particle erosion or sandblast action. Boilers with straight-through gas flow are desirable for these conditions (*see B&W Boiler Types for Industrial Application*).

Underfeed stokers of the single (and double) retort, horizontal-type are used in small units up to a capacity of about 30,000 lb of steam per hr. They operate best with "free-burning" coal that does not tend to coke. Their main disadvantage is the labor required to remove ash when burning coal with a low-ash fusion temperature (ash-softening temperature on a reducing basis) below 2200-2300F, which tends to clinker.

The water-cooled vibrating-grate type of stoker, introduced into the U.S. in the middle fifties, is suitable for burning a wide range of bituminous and lignite coals. It has found increasing acceptance, particularly in the intermediate size range, because of its simplicity, low fly-ash carry-over, and very low maintenance.

Chain- and traveling-grate stokers can burn a wide variety of fuels, and have minimum fly-ash carry-over. They are particularly effective in burning low-volatile fuel.

The temperature of preheated air for all types of stokers is limited to about 350F, because of increased maintenance at higher temperatures. This condition tends to curtail the overall thermal efficiency of the unit without an economizer.

Natural gas and fuel oil. The burning of these fuels is described in Chapter 7, and their application to electric utility boilers is discussed in Chapter 22. Natural gas and fuel oil are generally excellent fuels for industrial boilers. Problems encountered with certain types of fuel-oil ash are discussed in Chapter 15.

Blast-furnace gas. Blast-furnace gas, a by-product of blast-furnace operation, is usually the principal fuel for steam generation at steel mills. Its storage is impractical because of the low heat value per unit volume (75-90 Btu per cu ft), and it is either burned immediately or wasted to the atmosphere. Since the supply varies with cycles of blast-furnace operation, either oil, pulverized coal, or coke is commonly used as a supplementary fuel. When the auxiliary fuels are used, it is desirable to water-cool the furnace and thus avoid excessive maintenance. Hot air should be used for combustion to maintain ignition of the blast-furnace gas in the water-cooled furnace.

In most modern plants using blast-furnace gas, precipitators or water-washing equipment are installed to eliminate iron ore dust, lime and coke particles, which, if carried over, tend to deposit on the heating surfaces, where they are difficult to remove during operation. In addition, a high dust loading in the entering blast-furnace gas requires a boiler designed for low gas velocities to minimize erosion. Firing clean blast-furnace gas with a dust loading of 0.05 grains per cu ft or less provides the advantages of lower capital investment for the steam generating unit and reducing particulate discharge from the stack.

When a shift is made to the auxiliary fuel in a unit burning blast-furnace gas, there is a drop in superheated steam temperature because of the lower gas mass flow. Some type of steam temperature control is therefore necessary when constant steam temperature is desired, as with most turbines operating at 825F or higher (*see also Chapter 27*).

By-product and waste fuels. Severe air and water pollution restrictions coupled with large steam requirements make it economical and practical to burn the waste by-products of industry in modern boilers for disposal and

steam generation. The use of these materials, including gaseous, liquid and solid by-products for steam generation is discussed in Chapter 27. Gaseous fuels include particularly carbon monoxide, or rather the carbon-monoxide-rich gases produced in a fluid-catalytic cracking unit in the petroleum industry. Solid-waste fuels include bagasse and wood refuse.

Firing of the "black-liquor" by-product in the paper industry is discussed in Chapter 26. Black liquor is used as fuel for steam generation as part of a process which recovers process chemicals as well as heat.

Steam requirements

To assure prompt fulfillment of all steam demands, i.e., the delivery of heat to all points of use at the required rates, it is necessary to select steam-producing equipment of sufficient capacity, range of output, and responsiveness. The demand may be steady, as in most space-heating systems, or it may fluctuate widely and rapidly, as in a heavy-forging plant. Many steam-heating processes, as in the initial heating of a liquid batch, require high peak flows of short duration. Rapidly changing rates of steam flow are usually required for a steel-rolling mill in generating electric power, which fluctuates with the load on the rolls. The steam-flow requirements should, therefore, be accurately established for:

Peak flow
Maximum continuous flow (usual steady maximum flow)
Minimum flow
Rate of change in flow

The peak load will, of course, establish the top capacity for the steam-producing equipment and all of its auxiliaries. For widely fluctuating loads it is advisable to establish the 15-minute peak. In most systems, peaks of shorter duration can be met by the "storage" of heat.

The discussion under *Rate of Heat Delivery* in Chapter 22 is directly applicable to industrial installations, except that the magnitude and duration of load cycles and peak loads vary with each industrial application.

Steam for process and heating. The pressure of saturated steam (no superheat) used for process heating is such that the corresponding condensing steam temperature is somewhat above the required temperature of the materials to be heated. Generally superheat is of no value for this kind of service and is often undesirable because of its interference with temperature control. Reclaiming or devulcanizing rubber, where the rubber in a caustic solution is heated to 400F by condensing saturated steam at 250 psi (407F) in the jacket of the devulcanizer, is a typical example of process heating with steam.

Pressures of saturated steam for comfort heating of buildings range from 2 psi to as high as 80 psi in the case of "space heaters." It is seldom economical to distribute steam through long lines at pressures below 150 psi because of piping costs. Furthermore, the usual requirements for steam within the boiler house for sootblowers, feed pumps, and other auxiliaries make it desirable to operate boilers at a minimum of 125 psi. Consequently few steam plants of any size are operated at pressures below 125 psi. If the pressure required at points of use is lower, it is common practice to use pressure-reducing

stations at or near these locations. The central steam-heating systems in New York, Rochester, Pittsburgh, Cleveland, and Detroit are examples of this practice.

The pressure required at the outlet of steam-producing equipment for heating service usually ranges from 125 to 250 psi, and superheat is not required. For this service, boiler manufacturers have generally standardized on a pressure of 250 psi for small water-tube boilers.

It is customary American stationary-boiler practice to hold the main steam-line pressure practically constant for all loads, on the premise that this condition satisfies all pressure and quantity requirements of the steam-using equipment. Automatic combustion-control apparatus is accordingly designed to function on this basis.

Combination heating and power service. Some manufacturing operations, as in paper and textile mills, in the production of chemicals, and in processing rubber, require mechanical or electrical power as well as steam for process heating. For such applications (Fig. 1), studies are made of the relative merits and costs of 1) a plant where the power is purchased and steam is generated to supply the heating requirements only, and 2) a plant where steam is generated to supply both the power and the heating loads. A sound appraisal of the relative merits of the two alternatives requires a knowledge of the steam and power requirements, ability to correlate these requirements, economic studies, and good judgment. The following general summary may be of assistance.

1. The basic economic advantage in generating steam to supply both power and heating requirements is from the utilization of a much larger portion of the heat supplied in the fuel, by reduction or elimination of the loss to the circulating water in a condensing plant. This loss can be as much as 60% of the heat supplied

Fig. 1 Two-drum Stirling boiler for process steam and power generation—pulverized coal with supplementary bark firing.

in the fuel, even in a modern central station (*see Multipurpose Steam Power Plants, Chapter 2*).

2. Despite this fundamental thermodynamic advantage, it is usually more economical to buy power when it is available at reasonable rates from a dependable source, except where:

   (a) Waste fuels and waste heat, such as bagasse, blast-furnace gas, sawdust or hogged wood, and hot gases, are available at low cost from the plant process.

   (b) The steam-heating and power demands are reasonably parallel and relatively large, i.e., 50,000 lb of steam per hr or more.

3. Variations in process-heat and power demands usually do not coincide. However, if the process-steam requirement is always the larger, the exhaust steam from a straight back-pressure machine can be supplemented with a pressure-reducing and desuperheating system. Where this is not the case, two possible alternatives are available:

   (a) Use of an extraction condensing machine.

   (b) Generation of a part of the power in a straight back-pressure machine and purchase of the remainder of the requirement.

As an example of a by-product power installation under favorable conditions, the cost of power generated in a plant of 10,000-kw capacity with 12% fixed charges and fuel cost of 30¢ per million Btu will be in the neighborhood of 4 to 5 mills per kwhr.

The selection of steam pressure and temperature for by-product power plants requires study. Approximate steam conditions at the turbine or engine may range from 150 psi and 500F in one type of factory application to 1800 psi and 900F in other applications.

Power generation. Steam engines and steam turbines are the alternative prime movers available for the generation of mechanical or electrical power. Except for small isolated installations, the high-speed turbine predominates because of its compactness, efficiency, and low-cost features. However, since mechanical power in large amounts is seldom required locally, it is usually more economical to buy it as electrical energy from a central station. The present-day central stations can easily deliver a kwhr for each 9000-10,000 Btu supplied in fuel. The economy of the central station is evident when this heat rate is compared with a heat rate of 50,000 Btu, or more, per kwhr required for a 100-kw noncondensing engine or turbine-driven generator set. Consequently, the bulk of the mechanical and electrical power used in this country today, for stationary service, is produced by relatively large steam-driven turbine generators—from 10,000 to 1,300,000 kw in size. For such installations the highest pressures, superheats, reheats, and vacuums are all used to obtain maximum economy.

To determine the pressure and temperature that give the lowest total power cost throughout the life of a proposed industrial steam power plant, it is necessary to balance plant investment, fixed charges, fuel, and other operating costs for the various alternatives. The optimum may be steam at 400 psi and 700F, as for a 500-kw unit, or 1500 psi and 1000F with reheat for the largest units.

The variation of superheat temperature with load, and means for controlling this variation are discussed in Chapter 12. Some steam temperature control is generally provided where electric generator capacity exceeds 30,000 kw. In steel-mill installations, where alternate firing with blast-furnace gas, oil, coal or coke breeze tends to produce widely different steam temperatures for a given steam flow, superheat temperature control is particularly attractive.

Other design requirements

Space limitations, stack discharges (Chapter 18), boiler feedwater (Chapter 34), earthquake and wind requirements, and the effect of elevation and climate, including use of outdoor installations, are discussed in Chapter 22.

Relation of new to existing equipment. If the pertinent facts are established and studied, existing equipment can frequently be used for a new steam-producing unit. For instance, in a natural-draft plant, if there is an existing stack of sufficient area to accommodate the additional load, the unit selected should have a draft loss less than the available draft, to save the expense of a new stack. Where superheaters are used and the new boiler is to be connected to the old steam main, the steam pressure drop through the new superheater should be about the same as through the old superheaters, since all boiler drum safety valves (as required by most state laws) are set to relieve at the same pressure. Modern coal pulverizers and direct firing may be necessary to relieve the older overloaded equipment, so that needed steam-generating capacity can be installed without addition to buildings. If the new boiler unit is to be erected on existing piling and the conditions limit the allowable column loading, the unit can frequently be designed for column-loading distribution to match the existing footings and thus save expensive foundation work.

Draft loss in various boiler types. Draft loss through a boiler unit depends on many factors. Among these are: type of fuel, excess air, manner of gas flow in gas passes, and arrangement of convection surface of boiler, superheater, economizer, and air heater. In each case, the draft loss to be expected must be calculated for the final arrangement of the complete unit. Hence, specific draft loss data cannot be given in descriptive outlines of boiler types. With the usual operating conditions the smaller boilers have a draft loss in the range from less than 1.0 to about 4.0 in. of water, depending on type and size. The larger higher-duty units operate with higher drafts.

Power for driving auxiliaries. Power is required for driving feed pumps, fans, stokers, and pulverizers. Feedwater heating is required for all steam plants. It is common practice in industrial process-heating plants to use sufficient steam-driven auxiliaries to provide enough exhaust steam for the feedwater heater and to use motor drives for the other auxiliaries. There are instances, however, where the demand for low-pressure exhaust steam is great enough so that all the auxiliaries can be economically steam driven and thus often avoid the expense of purchased power. Sometimes both motor and turbine drives are provided for each auxiliary—particularly appropriate for "cold" start-up.

Fig. 2 Shop-assembled type FM Integral-Furnace boiler during shipment.

Boiler-water concentration. The maximum allowable boiler-water concentration (total solids in boiler water, ABMA recommended values) in relation to the pressure at the outlet of a steam generating unit (applicable to the boiler types in the following descriptive outlines) is given in Table 1.

Table 1
Limits for solids content of boiler water in drum boilers, ppm

Pressure at Outlet of Steam Generating Unit, psi	Total Solids	Total Alkalinity	Suspended Solids
0 to 300	3500	700	300
301 to 450	3000	600	250
451 to 600	2500	500	150
601 to 750	2000	400	100
751 to 900	1500	300	60
901 to 1000	1250	250	40
1001 to 1500	1000	200	20
1501 to 2000	750	150	10

B&W boiler types for industrial application

The selection of steam-generating equipment requires a broad understanding of fuels, their preparation and combustion, and of heat transfer and fluid flow for steam-generating surfaces, superheaters, economizers and air heaters. Familiarity with various classes of steam generating units and their components is essential for an intelligent choice of equipment.

By coordinating the various components— boilers, furnaces, fuel burners, fans and controls—the boiler manufacturers have produced a broad series of standardized and economical steam generating units (up to 550,000 lb of steam per hour) burning oil or natural gas. Up to 200,000 lb of steam per hour, most units can be shipped as a package by rail or truck (Fig. 2). When such ship-

ment is not possible, the larger units (200,000 to 550,000 lb of steam per hour) can be shipped as a package by barge or selected ocean vessels. The maximum utilization of building space (whether existing or new) is generally accomplished by installing modern high-capacity package boilers.

Beyond the shop-assembled boiler limits, units are designed to reflect 1) the user's individual requirements and conditions for pressure, temperature, capacity, and fuel, and 2) the incidence of continual improvement as a result of the constant search for better overall economy and design. These units are standardized in modularized sections and are shipped in large shop-assembled sections consistent with shipping clearance requirements.

Where natural gas or oil is available, even at a higher fuel cost than other fuels, use of a package boiler, such as the FM-type, should be considered since some or all of the following advantages are available compared to field-erected units:

1. Minimum capital investment
2. Minimum space required
3. Minimum operator attention
4. Fully automatic controls
5. Multiple units, providing flexibility
6. Minimum delivery time
7. Indoor or outdoor installation
8. Minimum foundation requirements
9. Arrangement versatility
10. Minimum number of burners
11. Proven reliability

The brief descriptions of the several boiler types that follow are intended to serve as an introduction to the types of steam generating units that are designed to meet the wide range of output and performance characteristics required for industrial application.

Type FM Integral-Furnace Boiler

Indicated field of application

1. In the economical production of steam for heating, process, or power within the output and specifications noted above, using oil and gas fuel singly or in combination.
2. Where a boiler is needed quickly for either outdoor or housed location.
3. Where the boiler operators may be called upon for additional duties.
4. Where space is at a premium and a compact unit, including all auxiliaries, is needed.
5. Where removal of the boiler to another location may be contemplated (applicable in low- and intermediate-capacity sizes).

Low-capacity FM Boilers

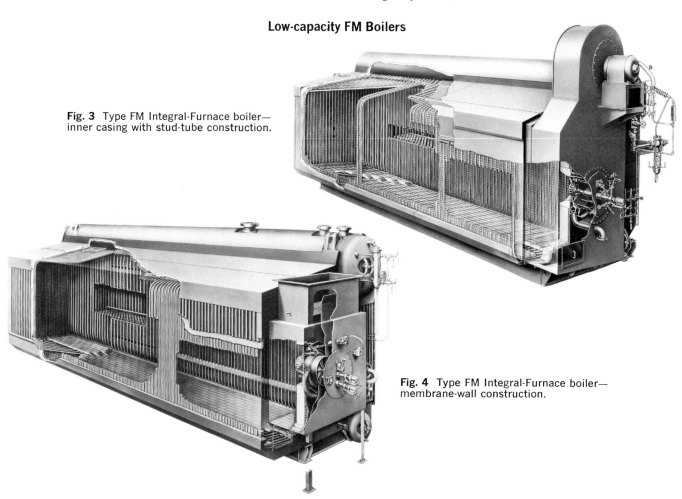

Fig. 3 Type FM Integral-Furnace boiler—inner casing with stud-tube construction.

Fig. 4 Type FM Integral-Furnace boiler—membrane-wall construction.

General description

Standard bent-tube unit arranged with gastight furnace and boiler for pressurized operation with water-cooled furnace. The gas flow is horizontal through the entire unit.

Range in Size, Steam Output
   10,000 to 180,000 lb/hr.

Operating Pressure
   Up to approximately 925 psi.

Steam Temperature
   Saturation to 825F.

Fuel
   Oil and gas, singly or in combination.

Operational Control
   Manual to complete-automatic combustion and feedwater regulation.

Furnace
   Water-cooled; pressure type.
   Welded casing (10,000 to 75,000 lb/hr capacity).
   Membrane wall with partial welded casing (75,000 to 180,000 lb/hr capacity).

Dimensions Outside Setting, Approximate
   Smallest, 10 ft wide × 12½ ft high × 8 ft front to rear.
   Largest, 12 ft wide × 15½ ft high × 29 ft front to rear.

General comments. These units are normally shop assembled to be shipped as a complete package by rail or by barge. The shippable package includes boiler, furnace, windbox and burners, and an integral forced draft fan for units up to 75,000 lb/hr capacity. Above the 75,000 lb/hr unit, the forced draft fan and connecting duct are shipped separately. Many units are arranged with air heater or economizer. These are shipped as shop-assembled components, when possible.

Intermediate-capacity FM Boilers

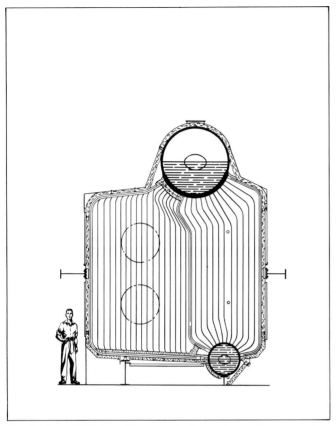

Fig. 5 Type FM Integral-Furnace boiler—intermediate capacity.

General description

Standard bent-tube unit arranged with a gastight furnace and boiler for pressurized operation with water-cooled furnace. The gas flow is horizontal through the entire unit.

Range in Size, Steam Output
    160,000 to 200,000 lb/hr.
Operating Pressure
    Up to approximately 925 psi.
Steam Temperature
    Saturation to 825F.
Fuel
    Oil and gas, singly or in combination.
Operational Control
    Manual to complete-automatic combustion and feedwater regulation.
Furnace
    Water-cooled; pressure type.
    Membrane wall with partial welded casing.
Dimensions Outside Setting, Approximate
    12½ ft wide × 18 ft high × 36 ft front to rear.

General comments. These units are shipped as either complete packages including boiler, furnace, windbox and burners, or in standardized modules if rail clearances do not permit a package shipment or if barge facilities are not available. Many units are arranged with an air heater or an economizer.

High-capacity FM Boilers

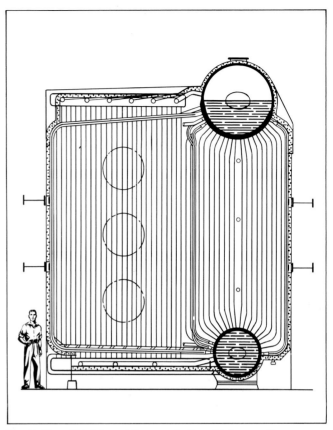

Fig. 6 Type FM Integral-Furnace boiler—high capacity.

General description

Standard bent-tube unit arranged with gastight furnace and boiler for pressurized operation. The gas flow is horizontal through the entire unit.

Range in Size, Steam Output
    200,000 to 550,000 lb/hr.
Operating Pressure
    Up to approximately 1500 psi.
Steam Temperature
    Saturation to 1000F.
Fuel
    Oil and gas, singly or in combination.
Operational Control
    Manual to complete-automatic combustion and feedwater regulation.
Furnace
    Water-cooled; pressure type.
    Membrane-wall construction.
Dimensions Outside Setting, Approximate
    Smallest, 20½ ft wide × 23 ft high × 39½ ft front to rear.
    Largest, 34 ft wide × 38 ft high × 45 ft front to rear.

General comments. The high-capacity FM boilers can only be shipped as a complete package if barge or ocean vessel facilities are available. These units are normally supplied with an air heater or economizer.

Type PFI Integral-Furnace Boiler

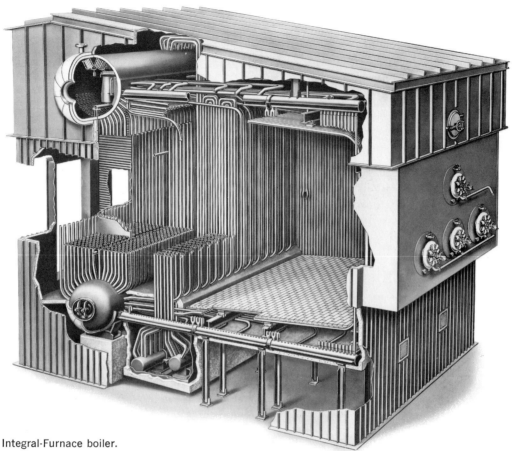

Fig. 7 Type PFI Integral-Furnace boiler.

General description

Standard bent-tube, bottom-supported, two-drum unit arranged with gastight membrane furnace and bare-tube boiler for pressurized or induced draft operation, with completely water-cooled furnace and drum cyclones. Maximum shop subassembly facilitates field erection. The unit is designed in 3 heights, and in several widths for each height. Superheated units are equipped with an inverted-loop, fully drainable superheater. Gas flow is horizontal throughout the unit with multiple passes in the boiler bank. The unit is designed with integral gas and air ducts.

Range in Size, Steam Output
    80,000 to 700,000 lb/hr.

Operating Pressure
    Up to approximately 975 psi.

Steam Temperature
    Saturation temperature to approximately 900F.

Fuel
    Oil and gas, in combination or singly.
    Waste fuels such as CO gas, turbine exhaust gas, blast-furnace gas or liquid fuels.

Operational Control
    Manual to complete-automatic combustion and feedwater regulation.

Furnace
    Membrane-wall construction; pressure or suction type.

Dimensions Outside Setting, Approximate
    Smallest, 11 ft wide × 30 ft high × 27 ft front to rear.
    Largest, 37 ft wide × 41 ft high × 35 ft front to rear.

Indicated field of application

1. In the production of steam for heating, power, or process, within the output and specifications noted above with oil, gas, or waste-fuel firing.

2. For either outdoor or housed locations; bottom supports for minimum space requirements; reinforced concrete or steel foundations.

3. Where economic conditions require high efficiency, sustained operation, and a minimum of attention and maintenance.

General comments. The PFI Integral-Furnace boiler is used for applications covering the aforementioned steam conditions and waste-gas firing. The completely water-cooled furnace provides a gastight unit suitable for pressurized or induced draft operation. The unit is specifically designed to operate at high ratings for maximum steam output with a minimum of available space. Superheaters are completely drainable and arranged with wide tube spacing to provide a relatively constant steam temperature over a wide load range. Air heaters or economizers are normally provided.

Type PFT Integral-Furnace Boiler

Fig. 8 Type PFT Integral-Furnace boiler.

General description

Standard bent-tube, bottom-supported, two-drum unit arranged with gastight membrane furnace and bare-tube boiler for pressurized or induced draft operation, with completely water-cooled furnace and drum cyclones. Maximum shop subassembly facilitates field erection. The unit is designed with one height with several widths and furnace depths. Superheated units are equipped with an inverted-loop, fully drainable superheater. Gas flow is vertical through the superheater and boiler bank sections. The unit is designed with integral gas and air ducts.

Range in Size, Steam Output
    400,000 to 1,100,000 lb/hr.
Operating Pressure
    Up to approximately 1500 psi.
Steam Temperature
    Saturation temperature to approximately 950F.
Fuel
    Oil and gas, in combination or singly.
    Waste fuels such as turbine exhaust gas or liquid fuels.
Operational Control
    Manual to complete-automatic combustion and feedwater regulation.

Furnace
    Membrane-wall construction; pressure or suction type.
Dimensions Outside Setting, Approximate
    Smallest, 15 ft wide × 53 ft high × 46 ft front to rear.
    Largest, 37 ft wide × 53 ft high × 56 ft front to rear.

Indicated field of application

1. In the production of steam for heating, power or process, within the output and specifications noted above with oil, gas or waste-fuel firing.
2. For either outdoor, or housed locations; bottom supports for minimum space requirements; reinforced concrete or steel foundations.
3. Where economic conditions require high efficiency, sustained operation, and a minimum of attention and maintenance.

General comments. The PFT Integral-Furnace boiler is used for high pressure and capacity under conditions beyond the limits of the PFI boiler. Like the PFI boiler, the PFT boiler has a gastight, water-cooled furnace and a completely drainable superheater with tubes widely spaced, and is normally supplied with an air heater or economizer.

Two-Drum Stirling Boiler

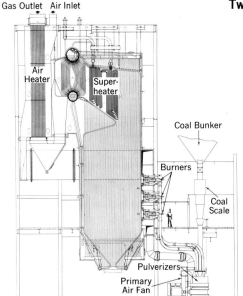

Fig. 9 Two-drum Stirling boiler for pulverized coal.

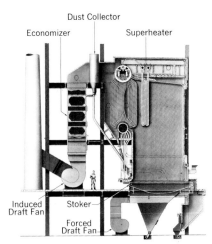

Fig. 10 Two-drum Stirling boiler (Type SS) for spreader-stoker firing.

General description

Bent-tube boiler, partly standard, usually steel cased, with one 42-in. to 72-in. upper drum vertically above one 24-in. to 54-in. lower drum. The steam drum is fitted with cyclone separators. The unit is field assembled and is top supported. It may be built with or without a superheater.

The boiler generating tubes may be $2\frac{1}{2}$ in., $2\frac{3}{4}$ in., or $3\frac{1}{4}$ in., and are frequently swaged at ends to reduce the required thickness of drum plate. Tubes of $2\frac{1}{2}$ and $2\frac{3}{4}$ in. swaged to 2 in. at ends are side-spaced at $3\frac{9}{16}$ in. on centers. Tubes of $3\frac{1}{4}$ in. swaged to 2 in. at ends are side-spaced $4\frac{1}{2}$ in. on centers. The furnace is of membrane-wall construction, $2\frac{1}{2}$ in. tubes on 3 in. centers.

When the ash is abrasive and for conditions requiring low draft loss, the gas flows from front to rear in a single pass. Furnace width varies in 1-ft increments. There are several standard dimensions of furnace depth and between upper and lower drum centers.

Range in Size, Steam Output
    To 1,200,000 lb/hr (and higher, special).

Operating Pressure
    Up to approximately 1500 psi.

Steam Temperature
    Saturation to 1000F.

Draft Loss at Maximum Output
    From 1 to 8 in. of water or more.

Fuel
    Coal, pulverized, or stoker fired; oil and gas, singly or in combination, as regular or supplemental fuel; also waste-heat sources.

Operational Control
    Manual, or automatic in varying degree.

Furnace
    Water-cooled; pressure or nonpressure type.

Dimensions Outside Setting, Approximate
    Smallest, 12 ft wide × 60 ft high × 25 ft deep.
    Largest, 40 ft wide × 130 ft high × 30 ft deep.

Indicated field of application

1. In the production of steam for heating, process, or power needs within the output and specifications noted above, using any of the fuels listed.

2. Where coal ash is particularly abrasive with stoker and sometimes pulverized-coal firing.

3. Where fuel ash-fusion characteristics require a water-cooled furnace.

4. Where simplicity of change to accommodate another fuel and method of firing is essential because of a possible future fuel source.

General comments. The range in steam output of the two-drum Stirling boiler is greater than for any of the other units considered in this series. Because of its range in output and its ready adaptability for burning most fuels, this unit is now widely used. It is particularly suitable for steam production with spreader-stoker firing up to the limit of output possible in using a stoker, about 400,000 lb of steam per hr. In this application, the single-pass gas flow (no turns) helps to prevent concentration of abrasive particles and consequent tube damage.

All tubes can be entered from the two drums for inspection and cleaning.

Where the additional cost is warranted to maintain a constant steam temperature at reduced loads, the superheater is designed for temperature control by an attemperator of either the submerged-surface type installed in the lower drum or the spray type.

Hopper bottoms are usually fitted for pulverized-coal firing. In the larger units, additional furnace surface is frequently provided by an intermediate or furnace division wall.

An economizer or an air heater, or both, may be installed if justified by fuel saving and performance.

Chapter 26

Chemical and heat recovery in the paper industry

Steam and its companion, electric power, are two of the basic "raw materials" necessary for the manufacture of pulp and paper. Every type of pulp or paper manufactured requires large quantities of steam for power and process.

Among the major industries, pulp and paper is rated first in power used per ton of product, second in total power generated, and third in total power consumed. In 1976, this industry in the United States alone used more than 67 billion kwhr of electricity, of which 35 billion kwhr was generated internally. Between 1967 and 1975, B&W installed steam generating capacity in excess of 36,000,000 lb per hr in the paper and allied industries.

The past and predicted production of this industry and the annual per capita consumption of paper and paperboard products in the U.S.A. are shown in Fig. 1. In 1976, 597 pounds of paper and paperboard were consumed per capita in the United States. About 70% of this was derived from wood-pulp production, the remainder coming from imports and reclaimed waste paper. For this production, steam requirements varied within wide limits, from a minimum of 5,000 lb per ton to a maximum of 20,000 lb per ton, depending on the production operations in the mill.

The following tabulation (compiled by *Pulp and Paper*) shows the consumption of paper in pounds per capita during 1975 in the leading paper-consuming countries of the world.

United States	524	New Zealand	271
Sweden	430	Japan	257
Canada	350	Australia	253
Finland	299	Federal Republic	
Norway	298	of Germany	248
Denmark	295	Switzerland	242
Netherlands	273		

It was not until the middle of the nineteenth century that wood was used as a raw material in making paper by the major basic pulping processes—groundwood, alkaline pulping, and acid pulping. The first groundwood mill and the first chemical wood-pulp mills for both the alkaline and acid processes were started between 1852 and 1874.

In the past 100 years, great technical progress has been made in the manufacture of pulp and paper products. The range of wood species used as raw material has required many technical modifications to the several processes. Refinements have been made in the techniques of forestry, logging, barking and chipping the logs, digesting and washing the pulp, supplementary purification of the pulp for chemical use, bleaching, and shipping.

A large share of the steam and power consumed by this industry is generated from the combustion of waste fuels. The collection, combustion and recovery of heat and chemical value from these waste fuels, and the demands of air and stream pollution control present many interesting and unique problems for the engineer.

Electric power requirements in the making of pulp and paper have increased disproportionately to the process steam requirement. This factor, coupled with steadily rising fuel costs, has led to higher pressures and temperatures and high efficiencies in boilers for pulp and paper mills. The increased value of steam has produced a demand for more reliable and efficient heat- and chemical-recovery units. Whereas steam was formerly

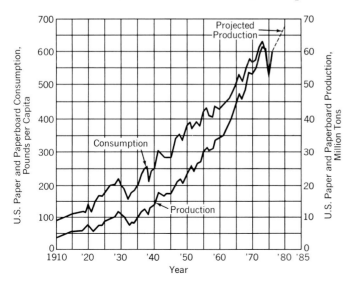

Fig. 1 Production and consumption of paper and paperboard products in the United States.

regarded as a by-product of chemical recovery, today the heat value of liquor solids is a reliable source of steam for power generation and process.

Boilers to supply the heavy steam demands of this industry and satisfy the balance of process steam and power when fired by the usual primary fuels (coal, oil, gas, wood refuse, or bark) are of conventional design (*see Chapters 25 and 27*). However, a large proportion of the steam required for the pulp mills is produced in the highly specialized chemical- and heat-recovery units operated at a steam pressure and temperature required by the steam-power balance.

Major pulping processes

Total pulp production in the U.S. is divided between three principal processes, approximately as follows: the kraft process–78%, the sulfite process–21%, and the soda process–1%.

Two of these, the "kraft" (or sulfate) and the soda process, are alkaline pulping processes deriving their names from the use of sodium sulfate and sodium carbonate, (soda ash), respectively, as makeup chemical. Reclamation of chemicals and the production of steam from waste liquor are well established in the kraft and soda processes.

The soda process accounts for less than 1% of alkaline pulp production, and its importance is now largely historic. The discussion of alkaline pulping and application of a recovery unit will, therefore, be confined to the sulfate process. The recovery equipment for the soda process is quite similar, and differences in detail for the soda process are delineated.

Kraft pulping and recovery process

Pulping process

The process flow diagram (Fig. 2) shows the relationship and importance of the recovery unit in the chemical and heat balances of a typical pulp and paper mill. Following the flow diagram: the logs entering the mill are first debarked (1), reduced to chips (2), and then charged into a digester (3) where they are cooked under pressure in a steam-heated aqueous digestion solution of sodium hydroxide and sodium sulfide, known as "white liquor" or "cooking liquor." In the cooking operation, the lignin binder, which holds together the cellulose fibers of the wood, is dissolved.

After cooking, the cellulose fibers, now called "pulp" or "brown stock," are separated from the spent cooking liquor in the pulp washers (4). The pulp may then go through several fiber refining and bleaching processes and finally to the paper machine. The spent cooking liquor containing the lignin dissolved from the wood is called "black liquor." As the dilute or "weak" black liquor (15-18% dissolved solids) comes from the washers, it is first concentrated in a multiple-effect evaporator (5) by the use of steam.

The concentrated or "strong" black liquor then passes to the recovery unit (6, 7 and 8). It is further concentrated to "heavy" black liquor in a direct-contact evaporator (6) using the sensible heat of the flue gas. Alternatively, concentrating can be completed in the multiple-effect evaporator and the contact evaporator not included in the process. The concentrated black liquor then goes to the mix tank (7) where sodium sulfate (salt cake) is mixed with the liquor to make up the chemical

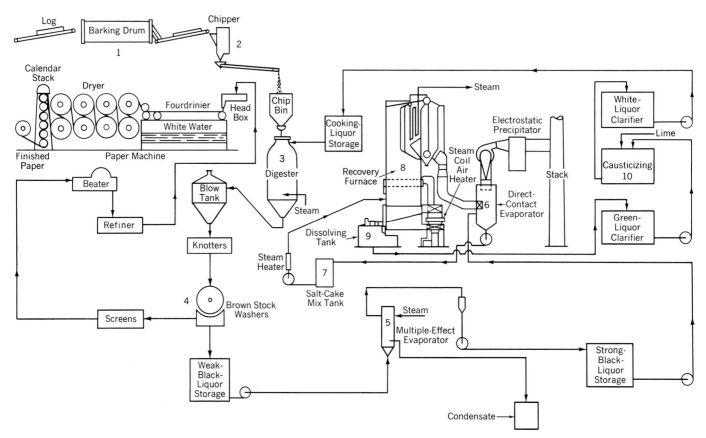

Fig. 2 Process flow diagram of a typical kraft pulp and paper mill.

losses in the system. Chemical ash recovered from the boiler hoppers and from the fume collector following the direct-contact evaporator is also returned to the liquor cycle. The "heavy" black liquor with its salt-cake burden is heated to lower its viscosity and is then pumped to the recovery furnace (8). In the furnace, the heavy black liquor is sprayed on the walls for dehydration prior to final combustion of the dried char on the hearth.

Chemical and heat recovery process

The essential function of the recovery unit is the reduction in the furnace of the sodium sulfate content of the black liquor to sodium sulfide.

In the recovery furnace, heat obtained from the combustion of the organic liquor constituents dissolved from the wood is recovered in production of steam, and the inorganic sodium constituents in the liquor are recovered as molten smelt.

The smelt, composed largely of sodium carbonate, Na_2CO_3, and sodium sulfide, Na_2S, is tapped from the furnace and dissolved in water in the dissolving tank (9) to form "green liquor." The green liquor is then subjected to a causticizing treatment (10) with slaked lime, $Ca(OH)_2$, to convert the sodium carbonate to sodium hydroxide. In this step, the sodium sulfide remains unchanged. The liquor, now known as "white liquor," is then ready for reuse as cooking liquor in the digester. Calcium carbonate sludge from the causticizing operation is calcined in a lime kiln, with loss of CO_2, to yield calcium oxide, which is hydrolyzed and reused in causticizing green liquor to white liquor.

Rated capacity of a recovery unit

The capacity of a pulp mill is based on the tons of pulp produced per 24-hr day. The object of a recovery unit is to reclaim the chemicals for reuse and to generate steam by burning the liquor residue from pulp production. The capacity of a recovery unit, within the limitations noted above, should be based on its ability to burn completely, in 24 hours, the dry solids contained in the liquor recovered from the pulp produced in 24 hours. Since the proper measure of the capacity of a recovery unit is the heat input to the furnace, B&W has established as a unit of capacity a heat input of 19,800,000 Btu in 24 hours. This unit, known as the B&W-Btu ton, corresponds to the heat input from 3000 lb of solids (approximately equivalent to one ton of pulp produced) having a heating value of 6600 Btu/lb of solids. These are fair averages for the liquor from a ton of kraft pulp.

The nominal size of a B&W recovery unit for the conditions at a particular mill, where the solids contained in the liquor from an average ton of pulp and the heating value per lb of solids differ from the standard values used in the unit of capacity, will be greater or less in B&W-Btu tons. The nominal size of a recovery unit for a particular mill will, therefore, be:

$$\text{Nominal size} = \frac{ABC}{19,800,000}, \text{ in B\&W-Btu tons}$$

where:

A = solids recovered, lb/ton of pulp
B = heating value of solids, Btu/lb
C = pulp output of mill, tons/24 hr

Thus, for a mill producing 600 tons of pulp per 24 hr, where the cook yields 3400 lb of solids in the liquor from a ton of pulp at a heating value of 6700 Btu per lb of solids, the nominal size of the recovery unit will be:

$$3400 \times 6700 \times 600/19,800,000 = 690 \text{ B\&W-Btu tons.}$$

Characteristics of a B&W recovery unit

Kraft recovery furnace

The functions, objectives, and requirements of the kraft recovery furnace are as follows (Fig. 3):

1. Black liquor is dehydrated to form a char bed in the furnace bottom, and organic constituents are burned.

2. Ash (inorganic constituents), resulting from the incineration of the char, is exposed to active reducing conditions to convert its sodium sulfate and other sodium-sulfur-oxygen compounds to sodium sulfide.

3. Air is distributed between the furnace hearth and upper furnace to provide a controlled reducing atmosphere in the lower furnace zone for chemical operation and an oxidizing atmosphere in the upper furnace to complete combustion.

4. Char-bed and furnace temperatures in the hearth should be kept as low as practicable to minimize the loss of sodium in the combustion gases from the furnace through "boiling off" or volatilization of sodium salts and also to minimize fouling of heat-absorbing surfaces.

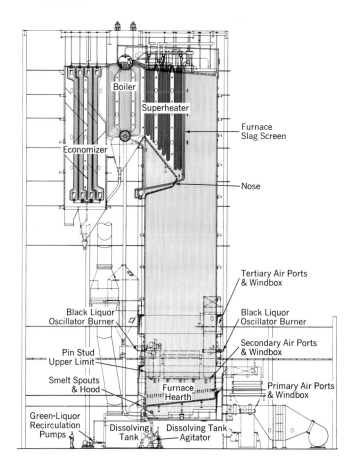

Fig. 3 Modern kraft recovery unit.

5. Furnace gas velocities should be kept as low as practicable (700-1000 fpm is a good range) in the hearth and liquor-spray zone to minimize loss of sodium through mechanical entrainment and attendant fouling of heat-absorbing surfaces.

6. Turbulent mixing of air and combustibles in the upper furnace completes burning of volatile hydrogen sulfide and organic sulfur compounds that can constitute odorous discharge from the kraft furnace.

7. Ash is recovered as molten smelt with as little contamination as possible.

8. The furnace hearth provides positive smelt drainage and discharge to the smelt spout in recognition of the incompatibility of smelt and water. The minimum of smelt inventory is present in the furnace to react (violently) with water inadvertently admitted; under certain conditions and proportions, smelt and water can react with explosive force.

9. The furnace floor is tight to contain the molten smelt and insure against smelt leaks.

10. The furnace design in the hearth, where a reducing atmosphere is maintained, provides protection of wall and floor tubes against wastage from sulfide compound corrosion and smelt erosion.

11. The furnace walls are constructed to preclude infiltration of ambient air into the furnace through the walls, or leakage of gas from the furnace to the ambient, or penetration of sodium-ash compounds to the outside of the furnace walls.

12. The furnace must have adequate radiant-heat-absorbing surface in water-cooled walls and a widely spaced slag-screen to reduce the temperature of the gas and entrained low fusion-temperature ash below the "sticky" or "tacky" stage before entering closely spaced tube sections of absorbing surfaces.

The modern recovery unit illustrated in Fig. 3 incorporates a furnace designed to provide these features, and the aims of the design have been achieved to a high degree. The important components of this recovery unit design are discussed in the following sections.

Oscillator and spray nozzle. The black liquor is sprayed on the walls of the furnace to be prepared for combustion and reduction; it is dehydrated on the walls and then falls to the hearth char bed below. Oscillator burners, Fig. 4, located in the center of the front and rear walls, emit from the spray nozzle, Fig. 5, a flat, or sheet, spray of coarse droplets. The nozzles are continuously both rotated and oscillated to cover a wide band on all walls above the hearth. The degree of movement is adjustable to cover a greater or smaller area of wall surface as required to compensate for variation in the solids concentration of the atomized liquor and the consequent residence time that is needed for dehydration.

The temperature and pressure of atomized liquor are important to kraft recovery furnace operation. Minimizing both temperature and pressure generally creates a larger particle of atomized liquor. This maximizes the amount of liquor sprayed on the wall to minimize in-flight drying of liquor particles and mechanical entrainment of sodium chemicals in the combustion gases passing to heat absorbing surfaces. A liquor temperature of approximately 220F and pressure of about 30 psig generally give the most satisfactory operation, with variation in actual operation as may be required to satisfy the characteristics of individual liquors.

A unit having a capacity from 500 to 1000 tons utilizes the two spray nozzles in the front and rear walls; whereas, smaller capacity recovery units have a single oscillating burner in the center of the front wall distributing liquor on the side and rear walls. Units larger than 1000 tons have four oscillating burners, one in the center of each of the four walls. Considerable variation in the quantity of liquor introduced through a nozzle location is accomplished by varying nozzle sizes.

Combustion air to furnace. Combustion air is admitted to the furnace through three sets of air ports to optimize combustion control and reduction. Zones of air entry are designated from the hearth or bottom of the furnace upward (Fig. 3) as primary, secondary, and tertiary. The primary air ports extend around the four walls of the furnace at the sides of the char bed at an elevation 36 in. above the hearth. The secondary air ports at a nominal 8 ft above the floor are just over the char bed. Tertiary air ports are located in two opposite walls above the upper limit of the spray zone.

The primary air ports admit about 50% of the total air required at a low static pressure for low velocities and minimum penetration of the bed. The controlled reducing atmosphere at the hearth burns dehydrated char falling from the walls to effect maximum reduction of sodium sulfate to sulfide in the smelt.

The remaining air required is admitted at the secondary and tertiary air zones. High-pressure air entering through large secondary ports completely penetrates across the furnace and assures mixing of the air with the volatile gases rising from the char bed. Combustion at the secondary air level creates a high-temperature zone below the liquor spray for drying the liquor on the furnace walls. Secondary air also effec-

Fig. 4 Black-liquor oscillator burner.

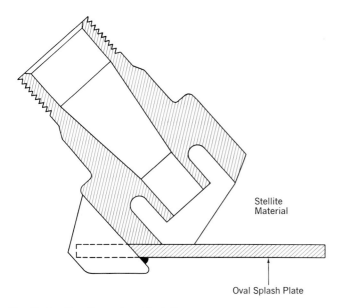

Fig. 5 Section through a black-liquor spray nozzle.

Stellite Material

Oval Splash Plate

tively limits the height of the char bed by providing heat and turbulence across the top of the bed.

Further turbulence is created by the admission of the tertiary air to assure complete combustion of any unburned gases rising from the secondary zone and any volatiles escaping from the sprayed liquor during its flight across the furnace. Tertiary air mass penetration also provides a uniform gas temperature entering heat-absorbing surfaces.

Air is admitted at a temperature of 300F in the large majority of recovery units. However, liquors of high inorganic content and low heating value and liquors with a high silicon-oxide content, such as that resulting from pulping bamboo and grasses, may require an increased air temperature to provide stable combustion.

Combustion air is preheated in an extended-surface coil heater using low-pressure steam. In using this steam, the preheated air becomes an additional source of heat input to the system, resulting in the generation of a correspondingly greater quantity of high-pressure steam. An alternate method of air preheating is to burn natural gas in the air duct, where the fuel cost and plant heat balance are favorable.

Floor and wall construction of furnace. The lower half of the furnace, Fig. 3, is operated as a chemical retort. Partial combustion of the char in a reducing atmosphere at the surface of the porous bed in the furnace releases carbon monoxide and incandescent carbon which act as reducing agents to convert the sulfate in the smelt to sulfide. The heat evolved melts the inorganic sodium compounds of the smelt. The molten smelt filters through the char bed to the sloped furnace floor, or hearth, and drains to spouts, from which smelt flows into the dissolving tank.

To withstand the erosive and penetrating characteristics of the smelt, furnace walls and floor are constructed to assure tightness. The surface of the floor and wall tubes must also be protected against the corrosive potential of the smelt in the reducing atmosphere of the hearth. Chrome refractory, cooled and

retained by pin studs on the water-cooled tubes, prevents molten smelt from contacting the tube metal. Refractory and stud construction is used for the floor and walls in the retort zone to about 2½ ft above the secondary air ports (Fig. 6). The length of the studs and thickness of refractory are limited to that which can be effectively cooled. A positive membrane barrier at the centerline of the tube prevents penetration beyond that point.

Furnace wall tubes above the pin-stud zone are bare, with membrane closing the space between tubes (*see* Fig. 2, Chapter 16). The construction provides a gastight, fully water-cooled metallic surface, forming a barrier to furnace combustion products and air infiltration. It is upon this surface, below the tertiary air ports, that the liquor from the oscillator burners is deposited.

The modern recovery unit (Fig. 3), including furnace, superheater, boiler and economizer, is suspended from overhead steel. The wall tubes of the furnace, boiler, and economizer support the block insulation and lagging so that the total assembly moves with the tubes as they expand, eliminating the need for differential expansion seals. Furnace buckstays are attached directly to the tubes and expand with the walls. Buckstays fitted completely around the furnace and boiler at several elevations are joined together at the corners to provide structural stability. The complete assembly of wall tubes, refractory, insulation, buckstays, and casing is free to expand independently of the supporting steel.

Upper furnace and slag screen. The arrangement of upper furnace, nose, and furnace slag screen shown in Fig. 3, is most important in the performance of a recovery unit. Combustion is completed in the tertiary-air port zone, as a result of distributed air admission and turbulence. The water-cooled furnace walls and volume above this zone provide the necessary surface

Fig. 6 Furnace pin-stud and refractory construction.

and retention time to cool the gas to a temperature satisfactory for sootblower removal of chemical ash from convection surfaces.

The furnace nose baffle serves two important functions, necessitating an engineered application of length and angle. First, the nose baffle shields most of the superheater from the radiant heat of the active burning zone of the furnace, the high-temperature steam loops at the rear of the superheater being completely protected. Secondly, penetration of the nose into the furnace distributes the gas to enter the furnace screen and superheater at a uniform temperature and velocity. An eddy above and behind the tip of the nose causes the gas to recirculate in the superheater tube bank, preventing hot gas from bypassing superheater surfaces.

Convection heating surfaces

In the recovery unit shown in Fig. 3, the flue gases leaving the furnace are cooled by the furnace slag screen. The extent of screen surface is determined by the quantity of heat which must be absorbed in the superheater. Where a large superheater for high steam temperature is used, the screen must be small.

The superheater is arranged for parallel flow of gas and steam. Saturated steam enters the front tubes of the superheater in contact with the hot gas and flows through successive loops, so that the final tube with the hottest steam is in contact with the cooler gas. There is a dual advantage with this arrangement: first, cooling of the gas is most rapid at the front of the superheater, where the need for cooling of the ash is greatest; second, the parallel-flow arrangement results in a lower average tube metal temperature at both the high-steam-temperature and high-gas-temperature end of the superheater. Careful coordination of alloys for superheater tubes permits final steam temperatures up to 950F.

The boiler section is of single-pass design without gas baffling, thus providing maximum cleanability of boiler surfaces (Chapter 12). For recovery units of 275 tons capacity and less, it is necessary to apply a multiple-pass boiler surface arrangement, with gas baffling arranged to provide generous flow areas at the gas turns where crossflow occurs.

The economizer, when used, is the vertical bare-tube type, generally baffled to establish crossflow of gases (Chapter 13). The economizer design is subject to a practical limitation because of the sulfur content in the products of combustion from kraft black liquor. To prevent rapid corrosion and failure as a result of condensation and formation of dilute sulfurous acid, the metal temperature of ordinary steel in contact with the gas must not be below the dew point of the gas. This means that the temperature of the feedwater to the economizer should be above the dew point temperature of the gas. To minimize external corrosion, experience in recovery unit operation indicates that feed temperature must not be less than 275F (see External Corrosion, Chapter 13).

Sootblowing

The buildup of chemical ash on recovery-unit heat-transfer surfaces is related to design and operation. Entrainment of ash in gases ascending the furnace is affected by gas velocity, air distribution, and liquor properties. Care

is taken in the design of all recovery-unit heating surfaces to assure that such surfaces are arranged for sootblower cleaning. Cavities are left at optimum locations in superheater, boiler, and economizer banks to provide for insertion of sootblowers. Gas temperatures are calculated to make certain that velocities and particular tube patterns are compatible with good cleaning characteristics. Steam sootblowers are universally used in modern recovery unit installations. Sootblowers are arranged for automatic sequential operation, controlled from the main recovery unit panel board.

When a modern recovery unit is operated at or near its rated capacity, no hand lancing is required to keep the gas passages open. As load is increased on a unit, however, mechanical entrainment of ash and volatilization of sodium compounds increase and invariably lead to cleaning problems. In addition to excessive quantities of ash in the flue gas, velocities and temperatures at all points in the unit are increased, and ash deposits become more difficult to remove.

Direct-contact evaporator

In the direct-contact evaporator (Fig. 2) the liquor and flue gas are brought into intimate physical contact, and there is a mass transfer of water vapor from the liquor to the gas across the liquor-gas interface. While there is a decrease in the temperature of the gas in the evaporator, the enthalpy of the gas and evaporated water leaving is nearly the same as the enthalpy of the gas entering the evaporator. Any difference may be accounted for by radiation loss from, and air leakage into, the evaporator, plus the sensible heat given up or absorbed by the liquor.

The design of the direct-contact evaporator requires that adequate liquor surface be provided for the desired heat and mass transfer. If liquor is splashed or sprayed on hot metal, the quantity must be sufficient for continuous washing. The liquor must be agitated to prevent local over-concentration. A further reason for continuous agitation or movement of the liquor is that sludge tends to precipitate because of acidification by absorption of CO_2 and SO_2, which decreases solubility of the dissolved solids.

The direct-contact evaporator used in the recovery unit is of the cyclone (Fig. 7), cascade, or venturi type.

When black liquor char is burned in the furnace, sodium chemicals are entrained in the gas stream as a finely dispersed fume. Fume reclaimed by heating surface is cyclically dislodged by sootblowers and re-entrained in gases passing to the direct-contact evaporator. Some of this fume is reclaimed by deposition on the wetted surfaces of the evaporator. The remainder passes from the unit. Although some of these particles are as large as 10 microns, collection of the fume from flue gas must generally be considered in terms of sub-micron size. The quantity of sodium, largely as sodium sulfate, carried out of the unit in the flue gas depends on the service conditions and care in operation. Over a period of time, the sodium in the flue gas at the boiler outlet averages 2.6 grains per standard cu ft of dry gas (32F, 1 atm). The equivalent of approximately 210 lb of sodium sulfate per ton of pulp would represent a costly chemical loss and a nuisance as an air pollutant if not collected. Alkaline pulping mills collect this fume from the flue gas with either electrostatic precipitators or venturi scrubbers.

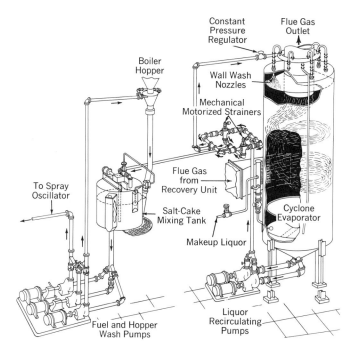

Fig. 7 Cyclone evaporator.

The first equipment successfully used to collect the fume was the electrostatic precipitator (*see Chapter 18*). Many installations of this type are now in use, operating with collection efficiencies between 95 and 99.8%. The electrostatic precipitator is used in combination with either a cyclone or cascade evaporator operating at an exit-gas temperature of 300-325F. Care is taken to maintain the gas temperature entering the precipitator at or above this range as, otherwise, local cold spots result in condensation, fouling, and rapid corrosion. The fume can also be collected by a venturi evaporator-scrubber.

Cyclone evaporator

The cyclone evaporator (Fig. 7) is a vertical cylindrical vessel with a conical bottom. The flue gas is admitted through a tangential inlet near the bottom. It flows in a whirling helical path to the top and leaves the cylinder through a concentric reentrant outlet. Black liquor is sprayed across the gas inlet to obtain contact of liquor with gas. The liquor droplets mix intimately with the high-velocity gas and are then thrown by centrifugal force to the cylinder wall. Recirculated liquor flowing down the wall of the cylinder carries the droplets and any dust or fume thrown from the gas to the conical bottom out through the drain and into an integral sump tank. Sufficient liquor from the sump tank is recirculated to the nozzles at the top of the evaporator to keep the interior wall continuously wet, preventing ash accumulation or localized drying on this surface.

Cascade evaporator

In the modern cascade evaporator, spaced tubular elements arranged horizontally are supported between two circular side plates to form a wheel that is partially submerged in a bath of hot liquor contained in the lower portion of the evaporator housing. Slow speed rotation turns the wetted tubes into the gas stream; as the tubes

rise above the liquor bath, the surface coated with black liquor contacts the gas stream flowing through the wheel above the liquor level. The number and arrangement of the wheels to provide the amount of total contact surface required, depends on the weight and temperature of the gas, and the weight of water that must be evaporated from the liquor.

The liquor is constantly agitated by the paddle-wheel action of the rotating tubular elements. External flow channels provide for return circulation of the liquor as it is moved to one end of the bath by the rotation of the wheel. Each wheel is driven by a constant-speed motor through a centrifugal clutch, gear reducer, and chain drive. The concentrated liquor is withdrawn through a flow box mounted at the side of the evaporator.

Venturi evaporator-scrubber

The venturi evaporator-scrubber is a device that collects the fume from the waste gas and also provides contact of the gases with the black liquor for concentration by evaporation. This scrubber depends on the collision of fume particles with liquid droplets. In practice, the gas is accelerated in a venturi section, and liquid is admitted through steam-atomizing nozzles at the throat in a plane normal to the flow of the gas. The liquid is finely atomized by the steam and high-velocity gas, and intimate mixing results. The fume or dust particles collide with and adhere to the liquid droplets. The mixture of gas and liquid droplets then goes to a cyclone separator where the droplets with their fume particles are centrifugally removed from the gas stream and drain to the integral sump.

In this application, the liquor is concentrated by cooling the gas to about 180F. The liquor is recirculated from the cyclone-separator sump to the venturi throat nozzles at a concentration of 60-70% solids. Liquor is fed from this system to the furnace for firing, as with the direct-contact evaporators previously described, and makeup liquor from the multiple-effect evaporators is added to the system to compensate for the liquor fired.

The venturi scrubber is a simple piece of equipment, easy to operate and control. Fume collection efficiencies of 90% are continuously maintained. A recovery unit equipped with a venturi scrubber achieves a higher thermal efficiency since its terminal gas temperature is about 120F lower than that permissible with an electrostatic precipitator.

Smelter recovery unit

The "smelter" type of recovery unit, designed for economical burning of small quantities of black liquor, is shown in Fig. 8. This type of unit is unconventional in appearance, consisting of a water-cooled furnace and not including the usual boiler section and other heat traps. Operation of the furnace and air admission is as previously described for the conventional recovery unit. The flue gas leaving the furnace is tempered by air or, in many cases, water, and passes directly to a venturi evaporator-scrubber. An alternate arrangement would be the use of a cyclone evaporator or cascade evaporator with an electrostatic precipitator. This unit sacrifices some steam flow in favor of lowering first costs, reduces operating labor, and eliminates the problem of cleaning heating surfaces.

Flue gases at 900-1000F enter the venturi or cyclone

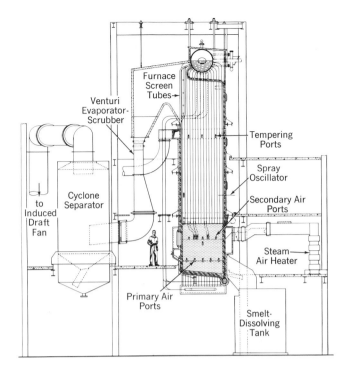

Venturi
Evaporator-
Scrubber

Furnace
Screen
Tubes→

Tempering
Ports

Spray
Oscillator

Secondary Air
Ports

Cyclone
Separator

to
Induced
Draft
Fan

Steam
Air Heater

Primary Air
Ports

Smelt-
Dissolving
Tank

Fig. 8 "Smelter" type of recovery unit.

evaporator to evaporate liquor from an initial concentration of 28-30% solids to a burning concentration of about 60% solids. The unit is well suited to the sodium-base neutral-sulfite semi-chemical recovery system because this application has a relatively small amount of heat in the waste liquor. The smelter may also be applied to small kraft installations.

Auxiliaries for recovery unit

Successful operation of a recovery unit depends to a large extent on the performance of its auxiliaries. All the smaller components must be designed and selected with the same care and attention to reliability and continuity of service as the main components. The auxiliaries, preferably and usually supplied as a part of the recovery unit, are:

Auxiliary oil or gas burners. These burners, used for preheating at start-up and in case of unstable furnace conditions, are designed for quick and easy operation. They are provided with safety devices for flame-failure protection and are interlocked for maximum safety.

Meters and controls. Automatic controls are provided for boiler water level, furnace draft, direct-contact evaporator liquor level, black-liquor firing temperature, and the combustion air flows. Flue gas is continually analyzed by an oxygen-combustibles analyzer. Instruments are provided for recording steam flow, total air flow, primary air flow, tertiary air flow, boiler water level, gas temperatures at various points in the system, air preheat temperature, steam temperature, and black liquor flow. Gages indicate draft losses through the different sections of the recovery unit, primary air pressure, secondary air pressure, tertiary air pressure, furnace draft, induced-draft fan suction, and steam pressure.

Fans. Because of the possible imbalance of the rotor caused by deposits from fume-laden gas, the design and selection of the induced draft fan are particularly important. Speed must be conservative, and straight or nearly straight blades are preferable. A variable-speed drive is used in the form of a steam turbine (if the mill steam balance warrants) or hydraulic coupling.

Smelt dissolving tank. This tank should be of heavy construction and should be equipped for good agitation. One or more side-entering agitators are generally used. The dissolving tank must be vented with a vertical stack of sufficient size to carry off the vapor formed in the tank. Green liquor is recirculated to shatter-nozzles to disperse the stream of molten smelt before it enters the liquor in the tank. Steam jets are also provided to help break up the stream of molten smelt and to reduce the noise resulting from the chilling of the hot smelt by the cooler liquor.

Mixing tank and salt-cake feeder. Careful attention to detail is required in the design of this tank and feeder, so that makeup salt cake may be fed at a regular rate and may be well mixed with the black liquor. The mixing tank includes a mechanically scraped screen to assure that all material which passes to the fuel pumps is small enough to pass readily through the burner nozzle.

Pumps for moving the liquor. Pumps are important components of the recovery unit. All liquors encountered in the recovery cycle are to some extent corrosive. As concentrations increase above 65% solids, black liquor becomes rapidly more viscous; and, after salt cake is added at the mixing tank, it also becomes highly abrasive. Centrifugal pumps of special design are used in this service, and due attention must be given to suction heads and liquor concentrations and temperatures.

Black-liquor piping and heaters. Piping, fittings, and heaters must be designed to withstand corrosion and abrasion. Piping sizes must represent a compromise between pressure drops with highly viscous fluids and a tendency for sludge to precipitate when liquor velocities are low. Black-liquor heaters are generally of the direct steam-injection type since scaling on surface heaters renders them ineffective, thereby requiring standby or spare heaters.

Optimum heat balance

Multiple-effect evaporation is the most efficient way to remove moisture from the liquor. The thermal efficiency of the recovery unit is to a large degree determined from the solids content of the liquor leaving the multiple-effect evaporator and, to a lesser but significant degree, by the temperature of the flue gas leaving the recovery unit.

The conventional approach to cool the gases leaving the boiler bank at 700-850F is to utilize all or part of the heat to concentrate liquor in the direct-contact evaporator. Liquor is concentrated to 45-50% solids in the multiple-effect evaporator and further concentrated in the direct-contact evaporator to achieve a liquor concentration of 60-70% solids for firing in the furnace. The final concentration is limited by the ability to pump the viscous liquor.

Recovery-unit design to utilize the heat in the flue gas between an exit temperature from the boiler bank and the optimum temperature leaving the direct-contact evaporator (300-325F for cyclone and cascade evaporators and 180F for a venturi scrubber) is in practice approached by determining the heat required for direct-contact evaporation of black liquor from the multiple-effect evaporator to the optimum concentration for firing. The contact-evaporation heat requirement establishes the required temperature entering the direct-contact evaporator. The difference between this temperature and the exit-gas temperature from the boiler bank determines the heat absorption requirement of the economizer.

The design of a recovery unit does not require a direct-contact evaporator. The total required evaporation of water from the liquor to a firing solids content of 60-64% can be accomplished in the multiple-effect evaporator so as to increase the thermal efficiency of the recovery unit and generate additional steam. In such a design the total heat absorbed in the cooling of flue gases is used to generate steam. The practical limitation of minimum feedwater temperature at 275F governs the optimum final gas temperature (360-400F) and the extent of economizer surface. A feedwater temperature at 275-300F permits most efficient use of economizer surface at a minimum cost.

The arrangement to preheat combustion air is flexible, depending on the steam and power balance for the specific installation. Fig. 9 illustrates a system in which water is recirculated from the economizer outlet to an extended-surface air heater, which preheats the air to 300F. An alternate approach is to utilize low pressure steam for air preheating with the total heat absorbed by the economizer feedwater going into high pressure steam production. In conventional units with direct-contact evaporators, heat is inefficiently used in evaporating water from the liquor being concentrated. The evaporation can be handled more efficiently in multiple-effect evaporators to increase the system net steam.

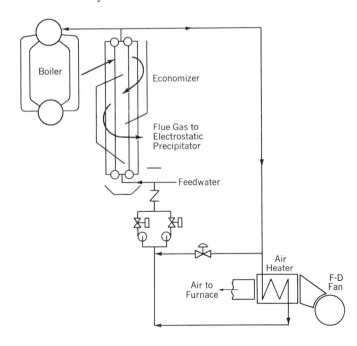

Fig. 9 Economizer-circulation water-air-heater system.

The recovery unit and air pollution

The black liquor recovery unit in a kraft mill has traditionally been malodorous. This odor is largely a consequence of:

1. passing the flue gases from the boiler through a direct-contact evaporator for direct preheating of unoxidized black liquor, and

2. boiler operation with insufficient combustion air.

Elimination of the direct-contact evaporator in the recovery boiler design removes a prime source of odor. The boiler itself is not a source of malodorous emission if liquor is burned with sufficient air and turbulence to complete combustion.

Where a contact evaporator is used, odor can be reduced by oxidation of sulfur compounds in the liquor before entering. The oxidation operation stabilizes sulfide compounds to preclude their reaction in the evaporator with flue gas and consequent release of volatile odor compounds. Oxidation as a means of control has had limited application in the industry. Oxidation can effectively reduce but does not eliminate discharge of malodorous gas compounds from the direct-contact evaporator.

Burning of black liquor in the reducing atmosphere of the furnace hearth produces malodorous combustible gases. The hydrogen sulfide and methylated sulfur compounds evolving from the hearth must be converted by burning at a relatively high temperature in an oxidizing atmosphere. Combustion is completed in the upper furnace by the thorough mixing of additional air admitted at secondary and tertiary locations. Where burning of black liquor is accomplished with sufficient air for complete combustion, the gases leaving the boiler and economizer heat-transfer surface are essentially free of hydrogen sulfide, methyl mercaptan, and methyl sulfides. Gases discharged from a recovery boiler can be controlled to less than 1 ppm of hydrogen sulfide and no detectable malodorous organic compounds. Operation of a 900-ton/day recovery unit with complete combustion of odorous compounds in the gas in the furnace and evolution of odorous compounds from unoxidized liquor in the direct-contact cyclone evaporator are summarized as follows:

Recovery-unit odor distribution gas analysis
(Volume basis)

	Leaving Boiler (Entering Evaporator)	After Evaporator
O_2, %	1.1	
Combustibles, %	0	
H_2S, ppm	0.1	86.5
CH_3SH, ppm	0	3.4
$(CH_3)_2S$ and $(CH_3)_2S_2$, ppm	0	1

The data emphasize the contribution to air pollution of a contact evaporator handling unoxidized liquor and the improvement in pollutant emission that can be realized with elimination of the direct-contact evaporator.

Performance of a recovery unit

Calculation of the recovery unit performance to determine a material and heat balance is approached by defining boundaries of a recovery unit schematically illustrated in Fig. 10 to include a chemical recovery boiler with cyclone evaporator and related equipment. Material and energy leave and enter the unit boundaries and do not accumulate within. Therefore, the material and heat balances used to determine overall thermal performance of the recovery unit require only identification of material and energy flows entering and leaving the system.

The boundary is established such that calculation of recovery unit performance always has as a basis the gross heating value and analysis of strong black liquor discharged from the multiple-effect evaporator for feed to the recovery unit. By considering recovery-unit performance in this way, the material and heat balance can be calculated independently of the many recycle streams within the system, e.g., ash collected in the direct-contact evaporator and electrostatic precipitator.

The heat of combustion and sensible heat of the material streams entering the recovery unit are utilized to produce steam at a designed temperature and pressure. The energy not effectively utilized in this manner is a heat loss. The overall heat balance for a kraft recovery unit is approached by first calculating the total heat input in the streams of material entering the system. The heat losses are then calculated and subtracted from the total heat input to obtain the heat that can be effectively utilized for steam production.

The total heat input to the recovery unit consists of:

1. The gross heating value of the strong liquor solids.
2. The sensible heat in the strong liquor to the direct-contact evaporator or, in a design without a contact evaporator, to the furnace.
3. The heat added in the liquor heater.
4. The sensible heat in the air for combustion. For a unit with a steam heater, the sensible heat is at the air temperature leaving the heater. Where heat in the combustion gases is used to heat air, as in a unit with tubular air heater or circulation-water air-heater system similar to Fig. 9, performance calculations are based on air temperature leaving the forced draft fan.
5. Gross heating value and sensible heat of other streams such as sulfur that may be introduced into the recovery unit.

The recovery unit losses consist of the sensible heat in material streams leaving the unit and the endothermic heat of chemical reaction. Also included are the radiation loss, unaccounted-for losses, and the manufacturer's margin. Such losses would be:

1. Sensible heat in the flue gases discharged to the atmosphere from the unit.
2. Heat of evaporation of water produced from the hydrogen in the liquor solids.
3. Heat to evaporate water in the semi-concentrated liquor to the unit.
4. Heat to evaporate water added as steam in the direct liquor heater.
5. Sensible heat in the molten smelt leaving the furnace.
6. Endothermic heat of reduction of salt-cake makeup.
7. Heat-of-reaction correction for the difference in the heat of formation of the furnace combustion products and the bomb calorimeter products.
8. Radiation loss.
9. Unaccounted for losses and manufacturer's margin.

An elemental analysis of strong black liquor provides the engineer with the means of determining chemical and thermal performance of a unit. The elemental analysis provides a distribution of chemical elements in the black liquor solids, e.g., carbon, hydrogen, sulfur, sodium, and oxygen. The elemental analysis permits calculation of the actual heat available to the furnace from the calorific heating value obtained for the residual liquor in a laboratory bomb calorimeter. This is necessary as the combustion products in a recovery furnace operating in a reducing atmosphere are different from those in the bomb calorimeter, where combustion is carried out under pressure with an excess of oxidant. A portion of the heat in the bomb calorimeter is actually not available in the recovery furnace, and the gross heating value determined in the bomb calorimeter must be adjusted to reflect furnace products of combustion using a heat-of-reaction correction. This makes it possible to obtain a calculated performance that predicts the actual material and thermal performance of a recovery unit.

It is not necessary to know the actual form of the chemical compounds present in residual black liquor. It does not matter whether the sulfur is in the form of elemental sulfur, sulfates or sulfide; whether carbon is in the form of carbonate or organic carbon; or whether the inorganic chemicals are combined with the lignin. The only facts that must be known are the elemental chemical analysis

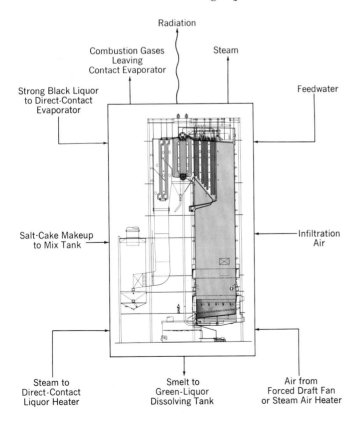

Fig. 10 Streams entering and leaving recovery unit.

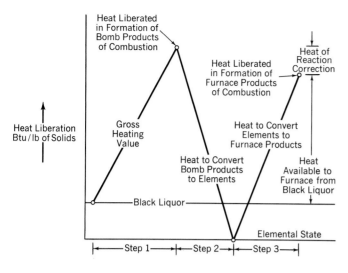

Fig. 11 Determination of black liquor heat-of-reaction correction.

and the chemical compounds in the products of combustion for both the bomb calorimeter and the furnace.

The heat-of-reaction correction is calculated as the difference between the standard heat of formation of the bomb products and the heat of formation of the furnace products. Application of the heats of formation to determine a reaction correction is illustrated diagrammatically in Fig. 11 for kraft liquor.

Step 1. This is the gross heating value of the residual liquor sample determined in the bomb calorimeter. If the furnace products of combustion were the same as those in the calorimeter, this would be the heat available to the furnace from the liquor.

Step 2. From the quantitative analysis of the compounds produced by combustion in the bomb, the heat required to convert these products to their elemental state can be calculated from the standard heats of formation of the compounds from their elements.

Step 3. Similarly, from the quantity of each chemical compound present in the products of combustion in the furnace, the heat effect accompanying the formation of the actual furnace products from the elemental state can be calculated.

The difference between the calculated heat of formation of the bomb products, Step 2, and the calculated heat of formation of the furnace products, Step 3, is the heat-of-reaction correction. This correction is used in the calculation procedure of recovery unit performance as a reduction in the heat available for steam production.

Soda-process recovery unit

With few exceptions, the requirements and features of the kraft recovery unit, as described above, apply to the soda recovery unit. Since sulfur is not present in the soda process, there is no reduction of sulfur in the recovery unit furnace and the heat-of-reaction correction is zero. The makeup chemical is sodium carbonate, Na_2CO_3

(soda ash), added to the recovered green liquor rather than to the black liquor ahead of the furnace (as in the kraft process). Consequently, the salt-cake feeder and mixing tank are not required. The dust and fume collected from the boiler hoppers and the fume collector are in the form of soda ash, and can be added directly to the green liquor after the furnace rather than to the black liquor before burning.

In the furnace the soda liquor does not form a suitable reactive char for burning in a bed; and it is, therefore, finely atomized and sprayed into the furnace by multiple steam-atomizing soda-liquor burners. The fine spray dehydrates in flight, and combustion takes place largely in suspension. Combustion air is admitted through primary and secondary ports around the furnace periphery, and the hottest part of the furnace is just above the hearth. The ash, sodium carbonate, collects in molten form on the hearth and is tapped through the smelt spout or spouts.

Sulfite process

Pulp produced by the sulfite processes is divided into two broad categories—chemical and semi-chemical. Semi-chemical pulp is differentiated from chemical pulp in that the former requires mechanical fiberizing of the wood chips after cooking. Chemical pulp is largely manufactured by the acid sulfite and bisulfite processes, which differ from the alkaline processes in that an acid liquor is used for the cooking of wood chips. The acid sulfite process is characterized by an initial pH at 25C of 1 to 2 for the cooking liquor, and the bisulfite process operates with a pH of 2 to 6. Cooking liquor used in a neutral sulfite process for manufacture of semi-chemical pulps has an initial pH in the 6 to 10 range. Spent sulfite liquor, separated from chemical and semi-chemical pulp and containing the residual cooking chemicals and dissolved constituents of the wood, is evaporated, burned, and the chemical recovered in a system particular to each base.

Sulfite process pulp mills normally utilize one of four basic chemicals for digestion of wood chips to derive a large spectrum of pulp products. The bases are sodium, ammonium, calcium, and magnesium. The principal difference in burning the sulfite waste liquor of the four bases is in the physical properties of the base and the products of combustion.

Sodium

Incineration of sodium liquor yields the base as a mixture of sodium compounds requiring processing in a relatively complex secondary chemical system in order to reconstitute the base in the form suitable for reuse in the pulping cycle. The sodium-base liquor may be burned alone or in combination with kraft black liquor in a recovery unit of the kraft type. The base chemical is recovered as a smelt of sodium sulfide with some sodium carbonate, which would be suitable makeup chemical for an associated or nearby kraft mill. The approach of combining the sulfite liquor with kraft liquor, referred to as "cross recovery," is common to a number of pulp mill operations and has the advantage of providing chemical recovery without the complex secondary recovery operation. The proportion of sulfite liquor in cross recovery is generally estab-

lished equivalent to replacing the salt-cake makeup requirement of the kraft mill cycle.

Ammonium

Ammonium-base liquor is the ideal liquor fuel in producing an ash-free combustion product, and burning can be accomplished in a simple recovery system. The ammonia in ammonium-base liquor decomposes on burning to nitrogen and hydrogen, the latter oxidizing to water vapor and thereby destroying the base. Sulfur dioxide produced in combustion can be absorbed in a secondary system to yield cooking acid for pulping. Concentrated spent ammonium-sulfite liquor is burned in a water-cooled furnace enclosure faced with refractory. The combustion products, including recoverable sulfur dioxide, are discharged from the furnace and cooled in passing over heat-transfer surface to generate steam for power and process. A small quantity of ash results from noncombustible solids and is separated in a mechanical collector for disposal. The sulfur dioxide reacts in an absorption system with anhydrous or aqueous ammonium makeup chemical to produce ammonium bisulfite acid. In a neutral sulfite semi-chemical plant, the absorption system produces cooking liquor consisting essentially of ammonium sulfite.

Calcium

Calcium-base liquor can be and, to a limited extent, is concentrated and burned in especially designed furnaces. The basic concept of furnace and boiler design applicable to combustion of magnesium-base liquors can also be applied for calcium. When calcium-base spent liquor is burned, the calcium is present as calcium oxide and sulfate entrained in the flue gas as finely divided fly ash. This ash is separated from the combustion gases in mechanical and electrostatic precipitators for disposal. The large content of calcium sulfate makes it generally uneconomical to reuse the ash in acid preparation.

Magnesium

With the magnesium base, a simple system is available for recovery of heat and total chemical. This is possible because of the chemical and physical properties of the base. The spent liquor is burned at elevated temperatures in a controlled oxidizing atmosphere, and then the base is recovered in the reusable form of an active magnesium-oxide ash. The oxide can be readily recombined in a simple secondary system with sulfur dioxide produced in the combustion, thus reconstituting the cooking acid for pulping.

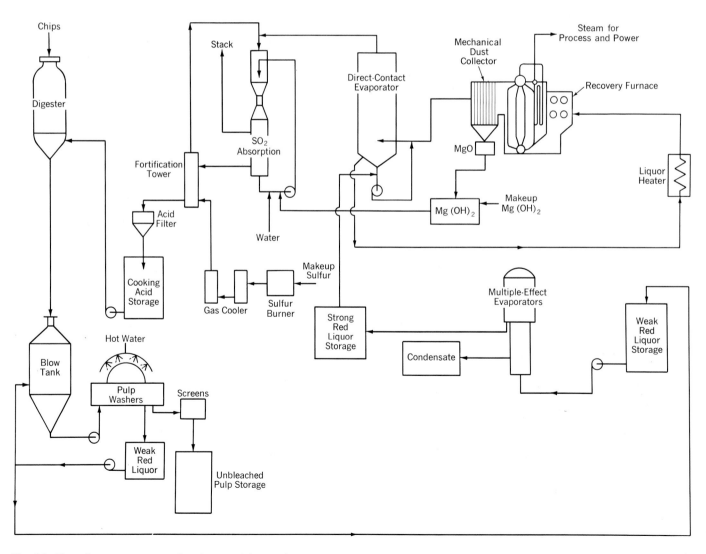

Fig. 12 Flow diagram of magnesium-base pulping and recovery process.

Magnesium-base pulping and recovery process

Industrial interest in the improved pulp from a wide variety of wood species has stimulated the development of advanced pulping techniques using magnesium base. Four basic pulping techniques can be utilized in a magnesium-base mill, depending on the pulp products desired. These pulping procedures, by which pulps with a wide spectrum of characteristics can be produced, are magnesium acid sulfite, Magnefite*, two-stage Magnefite, and two-stage acid sulfite. The basic magnesium recovery system is congruous with each of these pulping processes.

To establish the relation of the recovery system to the process, a flow diagram (Fig. 12) describes the cyclic processing of chemicals in a typical mill to produce unbleached pulp. With the digester as an initial point of reference, the pulp and spent sulfite liquor are discharged into a blow tank from which the digester contents, diluted with additional weak liquor, are pumped to stage washers. The first-stage washer filtrate, having 13 to 15% solids, enters the weak red-liquor storage tank. The liquor is concentrated in the multiple-effect evaporator and transferred to the strong liquor tank at the concentration required for operation of the recovery system. Liquor is further concentrated in a direct-contact evaporator before being fed to the recovery furnace for burning; alternatively, the direct-contact evaporator can be eliminated and all the concentration accomplished in the multiple-effect evaporators. The as-fired liquor concentration may vary between 55 and 65%, depending on the system design. The liquor is fired at about 230F and, where necessary, this temperature is obtained using an indirect steam heater.

The heavy liquor is burned in a furnace that has burners located in opposite sidewalls. The combustion products of the sulfur and magnesium in the liquor are discharged from the furnace in the gas stream as sulfur dioxide and solid particles of magnesium-oxide ash. Gases are cooled in passing over heat-transfer surface to generate steam for process and power. The major portion of the magnesium oxide is removed from the gas stream in a mechanical collector and then slaked to magnesium hydroxide. The sulfur dioxide is recovered by reaction with the magnesium hydroxide to produce a magnesium bisulfite acid in an absorption system. This acid is passed through a fortification or bisulfiting system and fortified with makeup sulfur dioxide. The finished cooking acid is filtered and placed in storage for reuse in the digester.

Burning magnesium-sulfite liquor

Two designs of recovery boilers can be selected for a recovery system depending on the specific requirements of an installation. Fig. 13 shows a bottom-supported boiler design typical of the majority of magnesia recovery systems that have been placed in operation. The bottom-supported furnace is a firebrick chamber of suspended arch and air-cooled wall design, having burners evenly divided between the opposed side walls. This design is generally limited to capacities of less than 750,000 lb per day of dry liquor solids to the furnace. The design is further limited by the amount of auxiliary gas or fuel oil firing at 15% of total heat input.

* Registered trademark—Howard Smith Paper Mills, Ltd.

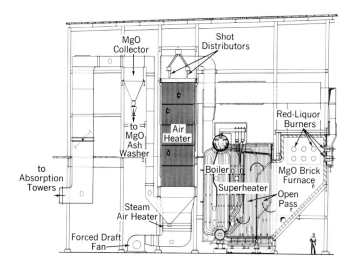

Fig. 13 B&W magnesium-base chemical- and heat-recovery unit.

Fig. 14 illustrates a design that has been developed to eliminate the brickwork furnace and provide for auxiliary fuel capacity in the red-liquor burners. This design is a recovery unit incorporating a water-cooled furnace where the absorption in the combustion zone is minimized by applying refractory over studded tubes which, in turn, cool the refractory. Burners are arranged in opposite walls of the combustion chamber, and gases discharged from the chamber pass through a water-cooled secondary furnace prior to entering the superheater and boiler bank.

In general, 55% solids is considered the minimum for brickwork furnaces and 60% the minimum for the new design furnace of water-cooled enclosure with refractory

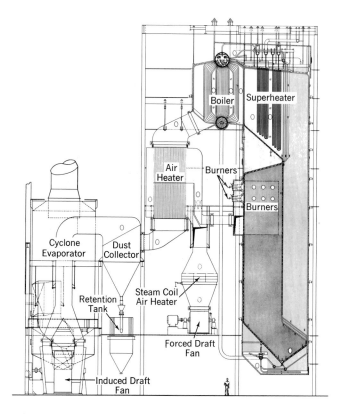

Fig. 14 B&W water-cooled-furnace magnesium-base recovery unit.

lining. Small liquor particles are injected into the furnace through steam-atomizing sulfite-liquor atomizers. The opposed burners provide a highly turbulent condition in a combustion chamber maintained at elevated temperatures by the refractory lining. A combination of temperature, turbulence, and time provides for complete combustion of the spent liquor. An oxidizing atmosphere is maintained by introduction of a controlled quantity of air slightly in excess of that required for theoretical combustion.

Combustion must be complete to produce a magnesium-oxide ash that is essentially carbon free. Ash will have a carbon content of less than 0.1% by weight when produced in a properly operated furnace having a furnace-exit-gas temperature in excess of about 2400F. Combustion air at a temperature of about 700F is supplied through the burner windbox.

Sulfur-dioxide absorption

Absorption of the nominal 1% by volume of sulfur dioxide in the furnace flue gases in a secondary recovery system is carried out by contacting the combustion gases with recirculated acid containing magnesium sulfite absorbent. A constant level of magnesium sulfite is maintained by feeding magnesium-hydroxide slurry to the recirculated acid sprayed into the gas stream. The magnesium sulfite contacted with the gas stream absorbs sulfur dioxide to form magnesium bisulfite acid. A secondary recovery system incorporating three venturi absorbers arranged in series is shown in Fig. 15. Each venturi dis-

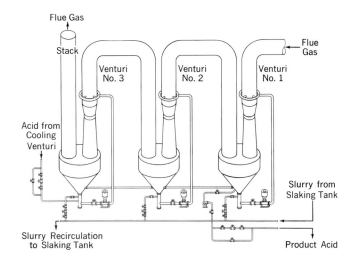

Fig. 15 Sulfur-dioxide absorption system.

charges into a collection tank for separation of recirculated acid from the gas stream. Acid is recirculated from the collection tank and sprayed into the gas stream above the venturi throat with acid introduced co-current to the flow of gas. If each venturi is considered as a stage of absorption, the stage-wise flow of gas and acid is countercurrent.

A three-stage venturi absorption system can operate to produce any desired acid strength at a high efficiency of sulfur-dioxide recovery—about 98%.

Chapter 27

Industrial by-products utilization

The progressive increase in the cost of fuel has fostered technical progress in the utilization of waste energy, including specialized designs and applications of boilers. Many industries have their specific problems with waste-product recovery. For example, the oil industry has a tremendous source of energy in the gas discharged from the catalytic regenerators; steel mills have their blast-furnace gas; the sugar industry has its cane refuse; the wood-and-pulp industry has sawdust, hogged fuel, bark, and process liquors (*see Chapter 26*) as wastes. All these waste products or residuals can be burned as fuels for the generation of steam. In addition, there are industries or processes that have large quantities of high-temperature gases from which the sensible heat may be abstracted for steam generation. Such gases are produced in copper reverberatory furnaces; annealing, forge and billet-heating furnaces; open-hearth and basic-oxygen furnaces; and fired kilns of many types.

Gaseous by-product fuels

Carbon monoxide

In the petroleum industry, the efficient operation of a fluid-catalytic-cracking unit produces gases rich in carbon monoxide. To reclaim the thermal energy represented by these gases, the fluid-catalytic-cracking unit can be designed to include a "CO" boiler that uses the CO as fuel to generate steam for use in the process.

For refineries generating large quantities of CO, field erected boilers such as the Integral-Furnace boiler (Chapter 25) are used. There are also many smaller refineries that have cracking units in the general range of 12,000 bbl per day or less which produce from 75,000 lb/hr to 175,000 lb/hr of CO gas. CO boilers for this capacity are small enough to be shop assembled in many cases. A shop-assembled boiler modified for CO firing is shown in Fig. 1. CO gas is admitted through ports in the side and front walls to promote mixing and rapid combustion. The burners for firing supplementary fuel are located in a refractory front wall and fire into a horizontal furnace.

The maximum steam requirements of the cracking unit may occur at normal full-load operation or during start-up of the cracking unit, depending on the plant steam cycle. The supply of CO is normally not sufficient to generate the maximum amount of steam required; hence supplementary fuel is needed.

Supplementary fuel is also required to raise the temperature of the CO gases to the ignition point and to assure complete burning of the combustibles in the CO-gas stream. The following design criteria have been established:

1. The basic firing rate should produce a temperature of 1800F in the furnace, to provide safe and stable combustion of the fuels.

2. Air is supplied by the forced draft fan to provide 2% oxygen leaving the unit when burning CO gases and supplementary fuel.

3. Supplementary firing equipment is provided capable of raising the temperature of the CO gases to 1450F which is the temperature needed for ignition of the combustibles in the CO gases.

Because of the possible variations in the combustible and oxygen content of the CO gases, in the sensible heat of the CO gases, and in the amount of supplementary firing, it is impractical to set up a fuel-air relationship as done for conventionally fired units. Consequently it is necessary to determine directly the amount of excess oxygen leaving the unit. This may be determined intermittently by an Orsat, or continuously by an oxygen recorder or combination oxygen-combustible recorder.

Water-seal tanks are installed to act as shutoff valves in the large gas lines so that the CO gases from the regenerator may be passed through the boiler or sent directly to the stack. This permits independent operation of the CO boiler without interfering with the operation of the regenerator. Water-seal tanks are preferred to mechanical shutoff dampers because of the high gas temperature, the size of the CO ducts, and the necessity for leak-proof construction.

The operation of the CO boiler is coordinated with that of the catalytic cracker. Normally, the boiler will be required to supply steam for the operation of the catalytic cracking unit and will be started using supplemen-

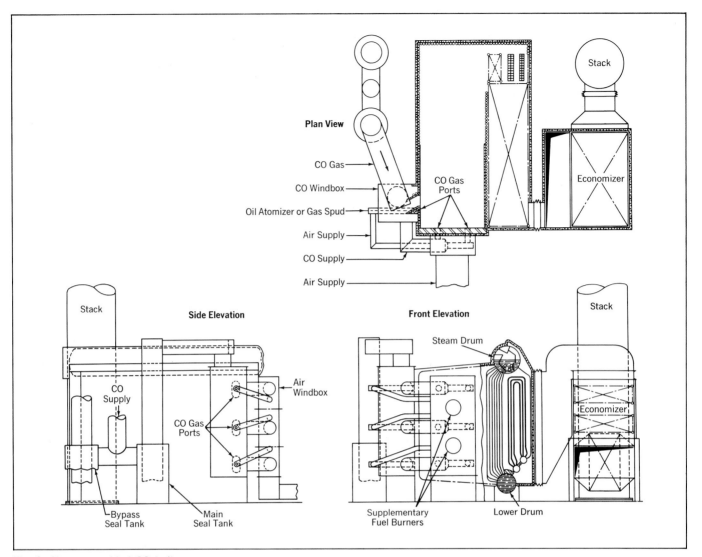

Fig. 1 Shop-assembled CO boiler.

tary fuel. The CO boiler should always be started using only the supplementary-fuel burners and bypassing the gases from the regenerator to the atmosphere. CO gases should not be introduced into the boiler until it is brought up to temperature because these gases usually are at or below 1000F and consequently tend to cool the furnace. They ignite quite readily and burn with a non-luminous flame. As the CO is introduced to the boiler, it is necessary to reduce the supplementary fuel and the combustion air. This readjustment in the air requirement is determined from the oxygen-recorder reading.

Since there are only slight variations in the operation of the catalytic cracking unit, the CO boiler is normally base loaded. It handles all the gases from the regenerator regardless of the CO_2/CO ratio. A change in this ratio merely affects the quantity of supplementary fuel necessary to maintain the required furnace temperature of 1800F. This temperature provides a reasonable operating margin for possible variation in the operation of the regenerator or the boiler. Stable operation can be maintained at a furnace temperature as low as 1500F, but the margin above the ignition temperature of the CO gas is considerably reduced.

The economics of the CO boiler depends on the amount of available heat in the regenerator exhaust compared with an equivalent amount of heat from an alternate fuel. The heat from the CO gases is calculated by taking the sensible heat above an assumed boiler stack temperature plus all the heat from the combustibles. The additional steam generated in the CO boiler by the supplementary fuel is comparable with the steam generated in a conventional power boiler. Normally, the supplementary-fuel requirement will account for $\frac{1}{4}$ to $\frac{1}{3}$ of the output, when the temperature of the entering CO gas is maintained at 1000F.

Blast-furnace gas

A gas containing about 25% by volume of CO is generated in the blast furnaces of steel mills and is used principally as fuel for the generation of steam and the reheating of blast air for the furnace (Chapter 5).

Although this gas can be burned as discharged from the blast furnace, its high dust loading (5 to 7 grains/cu ft) would cause plugging of burner ports and excessive fouling of heat-absorbing surfaces. It is desirable, therefore, to reduce the amount of entrained dust through washing, followed by electrostatic precipitation. Washing alone is not satisfactory, since washing does

not remove all the solids. Those that remain mix with the entrained water and form a mud which adheres firmly to hot surfaces and is very difficult to remove.

Several times a day the charge of iron, coke, and chemicals in a blast furnace arches over. The collapsing of this arch is known as a furnace "slip." A slip causes a surge in gas pressure throughout the system which, although momentary, can extinguish the flames from the burners. Consequently, provision for immediate reignition is made in the design of blast-furnace-gas-fired boilers, in order to prevent serious explosions of furnace gas. Modern boiler units use little or no refractory in order to minimize maintenance, and continuous-burning pilots are used to reestablish ignition after a slip. These pilots burn coke-oven gas, natural gas, or fuel oil.

Liquid by-product fuels

Pitch and tar

The liquid and semiliquid residues from the distillation of petroleum and coal are known as pitch and tar. Most of these residues are suitable for use as boiler fuels. Some handle as easily and burn as readily as does kerosine, whereas others give considerable trouble. To determine whether a particular pitch or tar might be a suitable fuel for a given installation, the following items are important:

Moisture. If the fuel contains moisture, it must be well emulsified to avoid reaching the burner in slugs. If there is a brief break in the continuous flow of fuel to the burners, the fires will be extinguished. Upon reestablishing the fuel flow, a furnace explosion might occur if there is any delay in reigniting the burners. Consequently, a slug of water in the fuel supply can be disastrous if it extinguishes the flame briefly. Tars and pitches containing as much as 35% moisture may be burned in properly designed units.

Flash and fire points. Flash point is defined as the lowest temperature at which, under specified conditions, a liquid fuel will vaporize sufficiently to flash into momentary flame when ignited. Fire point is the lowest temperature at which, under given conditions, a liquid fuel will vaporize to an extent to burn continuously when ignited. Many liquid fuels are blends of two or more different liquids. One of these might have low flash and fire points, whereas the other might have high flash and fire points. Such a fuel usually burns with a bright flame at the burner, where the low-flash-point constituents are burning off; but beyond, where the components with the higher flash and fire points are burning, the flame is a dark yellow. Actually, if there is too little turbulence at the burner or if the burning products are quenched by passing too quickly from the active combustion zone, combustion is incomplete, and high unburned combustible loss results. Consequently, while the flash temperature is useful for determining the possible hazard involved in storing the fuel, the fire point determines its suitability for firing in a boiler. Fuels with fire points as high as 600F can be burned in properly designed equipment.

Viscosity. Practically all tars and pitches are burned in the same manner as fuel oil. They are reduced to a foglike dispersion in an atomizer located in a burner and then vaporized and burned. To produce the fine particles, the viscosity of the fuel must be correct—not over 180 Saybolt Universal Seconds (SUS) for most atomizers, although if favored by the burner-furnace arrangement, viscosities as high as 1000 SUS may be used.

Suspended matter. Many of these fuels contain suspended matter. If they are delivered to the burners in this condition, there will be:

1. Abnormal fouling of the atomizers, requiring frequent cleaning.
2. Excessive rate of wear of burner parts.
3. Deposition of unburned carbon throughout the unit or objectionable stack emission.

Such fuels should therefore be passed through strainers before they are fed to the burners.

Compatibility. When some of these fuels come into contact with ordinary fuel oil, they combine to form liver-like substances. If this happens in tanks or piping, trouble results. The mixture cannot be pumped from the tanks, and plugging of the piping often requires complete dismantling for cleaning. Burner operation, too, is erratic and spasmodic. Therefore, before mixing large quantities of tar or pitch with fuel oil, laboratory tests should be made at both storage and pumping temperatures to determine the compatibility of the fuels.

Solid by-product fuels

Bagasse

Bagasse is the refuse from the milling of sugar cane. It consists of matted cellulose fibers and fine particles, the percentage of each varying with the process. A shredder with revolving knives cuts the cane which then passes through sets of grooved rolls, each set comprising a mill having finer grooves than the preceding one. The end product has a higher percentage of fines and short fibers.

A typical analysis of bagasse is given in Table 29, Chapter 5. Bagasse generally contains about 50% moisture and has a heat content of 3600 to 4200 Btu/lb as fired. It is used chiefly as a fuel to generate steam and power for the plant. Other by-product uses are for making cellulose, for paper and paperboard manufacture and for furfural production.

As a fuel for the production of steam, bagasse has been burned in several types of furnaces, the earliest being a Dutch oven with flat grates. One of the popular furnaces burned the bagasse in a pile on a refractory hearth. Air was admitted to the pile around its circumference through tuyeres. However, this arrangement resulted in high maintenance costs because of excessive radiation and cleaning difficulties. To overcome these problems the Ward furnace was designed (Fig. 2).

The Ward furnace has been very successfully used under sugar-mill boilers. It is easy to operate and maintain. Bagasse is gravity fed through chutes to the individual cells, where it burns from the surface of the pile

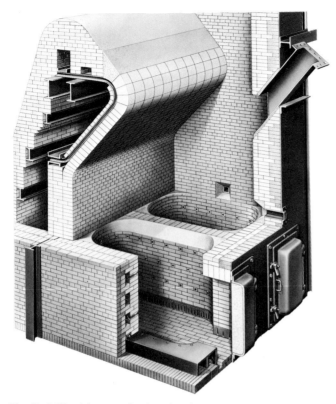

Fig. 2 A Ward furnace for burning bagasse.

with approximately 85% of the air which is injected into the sides of the pile adjacent to the hearth. This results in local incomplete combustion, but there is sufficient heat released to dry the raw fuel partially. Additional drying is accomplished by radiant heat reflected from the hot refractory to the cells. Combustion is completed in the secondary furnace above the arch. Ward furnaces are now equipped with dumping hearths, which permit the ashes to be removed while the unit is in operation.

Raw-sugar mills process enough bagasse to meet all their steam requirements and, in some cases, an excess. Sugar mills that also refine the product usually generate from 80 to 90% of their steam requirements with bagasse, the remainder with supplementary fuel oil. Because of the high moisture content of the gas, the weight of the gaseous combustion products from bagasse is about twice that from oil and one and one-half times that from coal. This high gas weight causes a high draft loss and requires either extremely high stacks or large fans to obtain the required steam capacity from the boilers. The low draft-loss Stirling boiler, shown in Fig. 3, was designed to alleviate these conditions.

Mechanical harvesting of sugar cane increases the amount of dirt in the bagasse to as much as 5 to 10%. To overcome the resultant slagging tendency of the ash, water cooling is incorporated in the arch and secondary furnace.

The vertical tube bank facilitates cleaning, and the special baffle arrangement usually permits natural draft operation to the required peak capacity at thermal efficiencies in the order of 57%. In sugar mills with refineries, a higher efficiency is necessary to reduce the amount of supplementary oil required. A thermal efficiency of 65% may be obtained by the addition of an

air heater and an induced draft fan.

In recent years bagasse has been burned on stokers of the spreader type. This method of burning, however, requires bagasse with a high percentage of fines, a moisture content not over 50%, and more experienced operating personnel. Because of such limitations, the Ward furnace is considered the most reliable, flexible, and simplest method of burning bagasse.

Wood refuse

The burning of wood as a fuel for steam generation is generally confined to those industries or operations where wood refuse is available. In average sawmill practice nearly half the total weight of a log appears as refuse — sawdust, chips, slabs, and bark. The pulp and paper, furniture, and plywood industries are typical operations where such refuse appears in appreciable quantities.

All woods have substantially the same chemical analysis on the dry basis, but may vary considerably in density and moisture content. Analyses of several kinds of wood are given in Table 32, Chapter 5.

Wood refuse available as a fuel may consist of slabs, logs, bark strips, sawdust and shavings. Furnaces for burning wood refuse are usually designed to handle chip-size material, in which case it becomes necessary to pass the large pieces through a hogger or chipper. Use of chip size permits uniform continuous feeding, a more rapid burning of the small particles, and a more complete coverage of the grate. To obtain useful heat from the combustion of this type of fuel, the moisture content should not exceed 60 to 65%.

Wood-burning furnaces are not usually troubled with severe slagging conditions unless the wood is burned in combination with other fuels or unless the refuse comes from salt-water-borne logs. Ashes from two fuels often combine to form an ash of lower melting temperature than that of either ash taken separately. In some parts of the country, provision must be made for the removal of large amounts of sand and dirt which are dragged in with the logs. Such foreign material entrained in the combustion gases would cause the erosion of such surfaces as tubes, baffles, flues and fans.

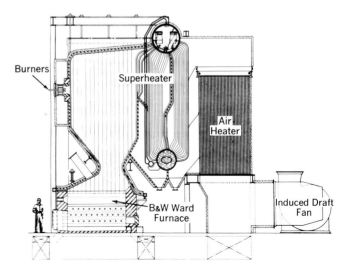

Fig. 3 A two-drum Stirling boiler with air heater and water-cooled Ward furnace.

Grates for wood-burning furnaces may be air-cooled or water-cooled, or a combination of the two. They should have about 30% free air space. For ash removal, grates may be of the rake-out, dumping or moving type.

To design an efficient wood-burning furnace, the following steps in the combustion process must be considered: (1) drying, which proceeds rapidly on the surface but requires time to reach interior parts of large pieces, (2) distillation and burning of volatile matter, and (3) burning of fixed carbon. The temperature in the furnace must remain above the kindling point (between 750 and 1000F). Furnace temperature depends on the calorific value and the moisture content of the fuel, the weight of air flowing through the fuel bed, and the heat loss from flame and fuel bed by radiation. Furnaces designed for the burning of wood refuse are of two characteristic types—pile and thin-bed.

Pile burning. The Dutch oven, or extension type of furnace with a flat grate, is the earliest design of furnace for burning wood refuse in a pile. The hogged fuel is fed through the extension roof, forming a conical pile on the grate. Most of the air for combustion enters through the grate around the edge of the pile and sweeps over the fuel, so that most of the burning takes place on the surface of the pile.

The fuel supply cannot be closely regulated with this method of firing, and excess air at the boiler outlet is between 30 and 40%. Combustion rates of 125 lb per hr per sq ft of grate area (approximately 600,000 Btu/sq ft, hr) have been attained with wood having 45% moisture (as fired), using cold air. With hot air (300 to 350F), the burning rate can be increased 25%. Above 45% moisture the combustion rate decreases rapidly. Ash is removed by rake-out or by dumping grates.

A large two-drum single-pass boiler unit, with a pile-burning furnace is illustrated in Fig. 4. In addition to auxiliary burners, the unit is provided with a water-cooled grate consisting of sloped-floor tubes covered with cast-iron grate blocks. The tubes are spaced so that undergrate air can be admitted through holes in the grate blocks. Ash-rake-out doors are provided in the front wall. Overfire air ports to promote turbulence and combustion are located in the side walls of the furnace. Hogged refuse is fed into the furnace by mechanical feeders or by air-swept gravity chutes. Char carry-over from the furnace is collected in the mechanical dust collector, passed through a sand classifier to remove entrained sand, and reinjected pneumatically into the furnace. This unit is capable of burning hogged fuel having 60 to 65% moisture at a rate of 285 lb per hr per sq ft of grate (approximately 1,000,000 Btu/sq ft, hr) with 30% excess air at the boiler outlet. Ash is raked out every third day.

Thin-bed burning. Fig. 5 illustrates a two-drum single-pass boiler equipped with a traveling-grate spreader stoker similar to that used for coal firing. Introduction of the wood refuse well above the grate permits the smaller particles to dry out and burn in

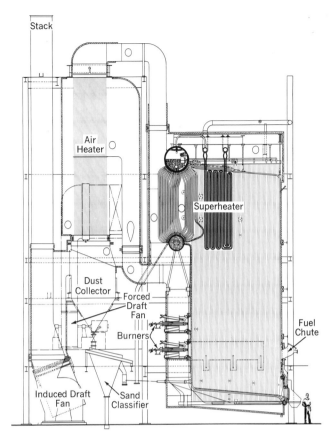

Fig. 4 Two-drum Stirling boiler with furnace arranged for pile burning of wood.

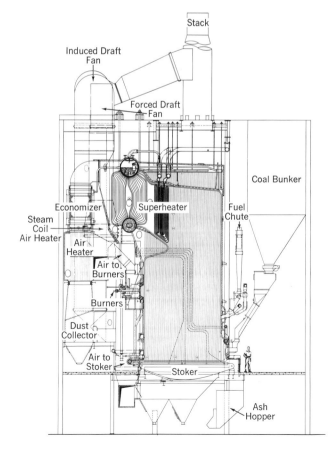

Fig. 5 Two-drum Stirling boiler for suspension and thin-bed burning of wood.

suspension, while the remainder of the fuel continues in flight to the grate, where combustion is completed.

Preheated combustion air is introduced under the grate. Air temperature depends on the moisture content of the fuel, but usually does not exceed 400F to prevent overheating of the grate parts.

This type of unit is designed to burn large quantities of wood refuse solely, in combination with supplementary fuel, or to operate at full capacity with oil, gas or coal firing. Char collected in the boiler bank and mechanical dust collector is reinjected pneumatically through the rear furnace wall just above the grate.

With preheated air, units of this design can burn wood refuse containing 45 to 50% moisture at rates of 1,000,000 Btu per hr per sq ft of grate area with 35 to 45% excess air. Boiler capacity ranges from 200,000 to 500,000 lb of steam per hr.

Waste heat

Utilization of the heat in the exhaust gases from industrial process furnaces becomes more important as fuel costs increase. Boiler equipment, properly designed to absorb the heat in what was formerly waste gas, often will generate all the steam required to power the process. Where the waste gases carry some of the process material in suspension, suitable hoppers associated with the boiler equipment will collect a portion of the material, and the cooled gases leaving the boiler may be passed through precipitators for a major recovery of the remainder. Many types of boilers are necessary to meet the wide range of requirements in this field. Their design depends on the chemical nature of the gases, their temperature, pressure, quantity and dust loading.

Heat transfer from waste gases

The rate of heat transfer from the gas to the boiler water depends on the temperature and specific heat of the gases, their velocity and direction of flow over the absorbing surfaces, and the surface cleanliness (see Chapters 4 and 15). To obtain the proper velocity of the gases over the surfaces, sufficient draft must be provided, either by a stack or a fan, to overcome the losses caused by the flow of gases through the unit, with adequate allowance for normal fouling of the heating surfaces. Temperatures of many process gases are relatively low, as shown in Table 1. The radiation component in heat transfer is low with consequent tendency in the design of many waste-heat boilers to use higher gas velocities than prevail on fuel-fired units. However, high velocities with dust-laden gases must be avoided to prevent abrasion of tubes. This is particularly critical where changes in direction of gas flow occur.

Diagrams A and B, Fig. 6, give an approximate measure of the convection heating surface required for usual conditions in waste-heat boiler practice. A water-cooled "vestibule" or furnace is a feature of many modern waste-heat boiler units. The vestibule provides cooling of the gases to the temperature necessary for prevention of slagging before they enter the convection surface. The approximate amount of surface required for this purpose is given in diagram C of Fig. 6.

Table 1
Temperature of waste-heat gases

Source of Gas	Temp, F
Ammonia oxidation process	1350-1475
Annealing furnace	1100-2000
Cement kiln (dry process)	1150-1500
Cement kiln (wet process)	800-1100
Copper reverberatory furnace	2000-2500
Diesel engine exhaust	1000-1200
Forge and billet-heating furnaces	1700-2200
Gas turbine exhaust	850-900
Garbage incinerator	1550-2000
Open-hearth steel furnace, air blown	1000-1300
Open-hearth steel furnace, oxygen blown	1300-2100
Basic-oxygen furnace	3000-3500
Petroleum refinery	1000-1100
Sulfur ore processing	1600-1900
Zinc-fuming furnace	1800-2000

Basic-oxygen furnace

The basic-oxygen process for steelmaking is described in Chapter 28. Arrangement of the major equipment components is illustrated in Fig. 5, Chapter 28.

Unlike older steelmaking furnaces, the basic-oxygen furnace (BOF), Fig. 7, is blown with pure oxygen through a retractable water-cooled lance mounted vertically above the furnace. After each charge of molten iron, scrap steel and fluxing material is loaded into the furnace, the oxygen lance is lowered into position above the charged material and a blowing period of 15 to 20 minutes commences. During the blowing time the oxygen starts a chemical reaction which brings the charge up to temperature by burning out the silicon and phosphorus impurities and by reducing the carbon content, as required for high grade steel. Large amounts of carbon monoxide gas, at 3000 to 3500F, are released in this conversion process. The gas is collected in a water-cooled hood and burned with air introduced at the mouth of the hood. The products of combustion are subsequently cooled by the addition of excess air, by the injection of spray water or by water-cooling of the hood. Combinations of these cooling methods may be used. The flue gas is finally delivered to a cleanup system for electrostatic or wet-scrubber removal of dust particles before discharge to the atmosphere. The service demands are such that the life of furnace linings is only a few weeks. Consequently, two or three furnaces, with sequential operation and relining, are usually installed for continuous steel production.

Oxygen-converter hood

The high temperature (3000–3500F) of the gases discharged from the basic-oxygen furnace and their high carbon-monoxide content (about 70% by volume) make them ideal for burning in the hood (Fig. 8). While there are basic similarities to usual boiler service there are

significant differences, particularly the carry-over of iron-bearing slag from the BOF and the short, intermittent, operating periods. Accordingly the criteria established for good hood design include:

1. Adequate structural strength. This is a rugged type of service where equipment is roughly handled.
2. The hood surface in contact with the furnace gases must be smooth to shed more readily the skulls or slag that is heavy with iron.
3. There should be a minimum of crevices, cracks, sharp corners, and openings in the fore part of the hood which would permit anchorage of the slag.
4. Positive and uniform water cooling of all surfaces exposed to the furnace gases. There should be a minimum of temperature differences between any and all water circuits—no eddy currents or uncooled corners.

Fig. 7 Basic-oxygen furnace.

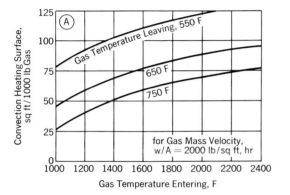

Conditions for Diagrams A and B
Tubes 2½ in. OD in-line
Tube Spacing, $l_\perp$ and $l_\parallel = 5$ in.
Sat. Temperature, $t'_s = 450$ F
Draft Loss, 0.2 in. to 0.4 in. water

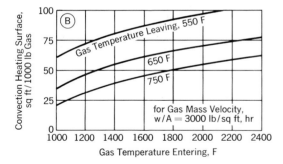

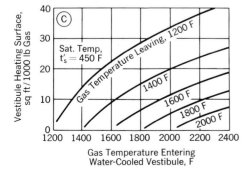

Fig. 6 Approximate surface required in convection tube bank and vestibule for various entering and leaving waste-gas temperatures.

5. The hood water walls should be cooled with treated and deaerated water to prevent internal deposits of hard scale or oxygen corrosion. Good water is necessary because of the high rate of heat absorption.
6. Water circulation should be maintained at a high rate through the entire cycle. Recirculation makes possible high flow rates without excessive makeup.
7. The hood cooling system should be suitable for pressurizing to permit the generation of steam or high-temperature water in keeping with industrial boiler practice.

The membrane wall for oxygen-furnace hoods ideally meets these design criteria. The membrane wall can be formed into a variety of hood configurations to suit the plant layout. The hood may be a long flue type to transport the gases to an evaporation or quench chamber, or it may be a bonnet type that collects the gases and immediately discharges them into a spark box where the temperature is sufficiently reduced with spray water for use in the gas cleanup system. Selection and arrangement of the auxiliary equipment may well provide other general arrangements with equally good results. The method of reducing the gas temperature with spray water and the selection of a wet scrubber cleanup system or an electrostatic precipitator affect the geometry of the hood. Fig. 8 illustrates a hood and quencher arrangement for a wet-scrubber gas cleanup system.

The hood with water-cooled membrane walls may be applied to the oxygen-converter process in the following alternative ways:

1. It may be operated as a boiler at pressures from 100 to 1500 psi to generate steam for general plant use.

2. It may generate steam which is condensed in a closed system with the heat dissipated by an air-cooled heat exchanger.

3. Water in a closed system may be heated in the membrane walls of the hood and the heat dissipated by an air-cooled heat exchanger.

Steam-generator hood

The oxygen-converter hood, when equipped with a steam drum, boiler circulation pumps, boiler mountings, and controls is an effective steam generator during the oxygen-blowing portion of the converter cycle. Steam generation is limited to the time of the oxygen-blowing period because of the intermittent or cyclic operation of the oxygen steelmaking process. The rate of steam generation varies from zero to a maximum and back to zero during the oxygen-blowing period, and is normally about 20 minutes for a complete cycle of 40 to 45 minutes. This cyclic operation, coupled with the outage time for relining the converter vessel every few weeks, limits the steam production of a single hood to 12 to 15% of the life of the lining.

The steam, during its period of generation, may be discharged directly into the plant steam mains. The cyclic type of operation, combined with short-period high rates of generation, imposes widely fluctuating load swings with which the steam system must cope. The effect of load swings can be reduced by operating the hood boiler unit at a higher pressure and discharging the steam into an accumulator. Heat is thus stored in water at saturation temperature by the rising accumulator pressure. When the steam-production rate in the hood boiler drops, the heat stored in the high-temperature water of the accumulator is released to produce steam at the lower pressure of the plant mains.

Steam-pressurized-hood closed-circuit system

There are BOF plants which cannot presently utilize the potential steam production of hood boilers. However, if use of the steam can be anticipated, the units can be arranged for closed-circuit operation as illustrated in Fig. 9. The closed-circuit system assures an ample supply of good boiler water without the need for an elaborate treating plant. A portion of the heat absorbed during the blowing period raises system pressure to 250-450 psi. Any excess of heat is discharged to the atmosphere through the air-cooled condenser operating under system pressure. The condensate collected is returned to the hot well and from there to the hood drum, completing the cycle.

The air-cooled condenser of the closed pressurized circuit is physically small because of the high temperature difference (about 350F degrees) between condensing steam and cooling air. The power required for dissipating the heat is small when compared to the pump power for an equivalent system using cooling water as the condensing medium. The power required for water circulation is also small. Makeup is limited to the wastage that occurs at pump packings and valve stems, plus blowdown.

This closed-circuit system can be readily altered to supply plant steam. All that is necessary is to tap into the steam line from the hood. Steam can be taken from the hood drum and the load on the air-cooled condenser is reduced by the amount of steam thus withdrawn.

Steam-pressurized, high-temperature water, closed-circuit system

Some steel mills find it advantageous to forego recovery of heat absorbed by the hoods. For these plants the steam-pressurized, high-temperature water, closed-circuit system is preferred. This installation is simpler to control and is less costly than the equivalent closed-circuit steam generating system.

The steam-pressurized, high-temperature water system serves the same purpose as the closed-circuit steam system. The only real difference is that saturated-temperature water is generated in the hood and discharged to the system's steam-pressurized expansion tank. The saturation-temperature water from the expansion tank is pumped through the air-cooled heat exchanger to lower its temperature and to return it to the hood completing the circuit. With this system, the high-temperature water is pressurized to a value of 250 to 450 psi by controlling the air flow over the heat exchanger.

Other types of waste-heat boilers

The design of a boiler for a particular application depends on many factors, most of which vary not only from process to process but also within an industry. The cost of equipment, auxiliary power and maintenance

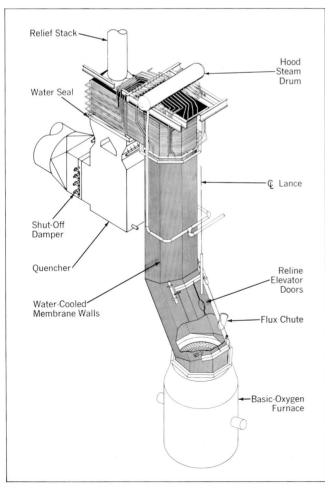

Fig. 8 Hood arrangement for wet scrubber.

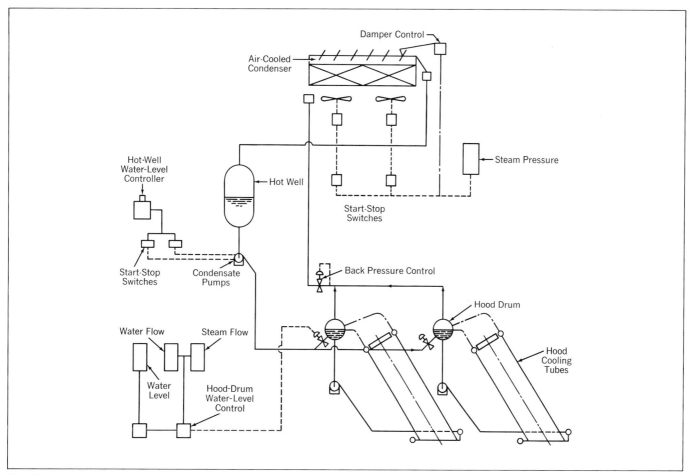

Fig. 9 Steam generating hood with air-cooled condenser.

must be compared with the dollar value of the savings expected. The design of the boiler itself is subject, to a degree, to the cost of power at the plant. A small unit with closely spaced tubes will cost less but will require more fan power, because of high draft loss, than a larger, more expensive unit with lower draft loss. However, if power costs are low, the small unit may be justified. Other factors to be considered are the available space, locations for the proper flue connections, the corrosive nature of the gases, the effect of dust loading on erosion, and whether the process operates under pressure or suction.

If the gases carry dust, attention must be given to tube spacing and provisions for the removal of dust dislodged from the heating surfaces. The tubes must be spaced reasonably close for good heat transfer and yet must be far enough apart to prevent bridging of deposits. Quite often the boiler is arranged for wide tube spacing where the gases are hottest, with spacing reduced where the gases are cooler.

Sometimes the deposits that are carried into the boiler from the process can be removed by mechanical cleaners, whereas the nature of the deposits from other processes may call for periodic manual lancing to keep the boiler passes open. In either case, suitable hoppers should be provided to collect the deposits removed from the tubes.

Gases from oil- or gas-fired process furnaces are relatively clean and, therefore, can be used in units with close tube spacing (one in. clear spacing) with little likelihood of bridging and plugging.

Waste-heat boilers for open hearths

Oxygen blowing of the open hearth, in preference to air, greatly increases the production rate and materially reduces the cost of steel. Therefore, most open-hearth furnaces of recent design are being changed to the oxygen-blown process.

The new process of oxygen blowing greatly increases the steel-producing rate, but also increases the dust discharge. In addition, the gas is discharged at higher temperature, possibly as high as 2100F. The combination of increased dust carry-over, higher gas temperature, and, in many cases, an increased total gas flow makes it desirable to replace the gas-tube boiler formerly used with a water-tube unit of higher capacity. Furthermore, because of the increase in dust carry-over, the new boiler is usually arranged with a new precipitator.

As a result of the increase in both gas weight and temperature, the steam output is materially increased. For many installations it is desirable to maintain the steam flow, during furnace charging and maintenance periods, by firing an auxiliary fuel, which requires a boiler furnace for its combustion. Thus, the waste-heat boiler for oxygen-blown open hearths is a versatile unit that takes into account the space available, the amount of waste gas, steam capacity, cleanability, and supplementary-fuel firing. The steam capacity for a single unit

serving a single open hearth may be as high as 150,000 lb/hr, Fig. 10.

Three-drum waste-heat boiler

A simple three-drum waste-heat boiler, designed to operate with dust-laden gases, is illustrated in Fig. 11. This type of waste-heat boiler is particularly well suited for use with waste gases of high solids content (up to 10 grains/cu ft) from cement kilns. Maximum precipitation of solids is assured by the horizontal flow of the gases through the vertical tube banks and by the effective arrangement of baffles. With this tube arrangement, hand lancing is possible from both sides of the unit. Every space in the full width of the boiler can be lanced. Hand lancing can also be done through the roof and above the lower drums, making all absorbing surfaces accessible with a short hand lance.

With gases of high solids content it is frequently possible to reduce the amount of hand lancing by the use of long retractable sootblowers. These are located at one, or sometimes two, elevations along the depth of tube banks at gaps provided by the omission of a single row of tubes.

To maintain optimum conditions of heat transfer without changing the direction of gas flow, the tubes in the rear sections of the boiler are closely spaced. Gas by-passing below the tube bank is prevented by steel baffles and sectioned hoppers. Dust buildup is practically avoided as baffles, both in the boiler and hoppers are vertically positioned smooth steel plates.

Circulation in this boiler is very simple, with the boiler tubes in the hot-gas end acting as risers and the tubes in the cooler-gas zones acting as downcomers or supply tubes. The boiler has a relatively long drum in which steam separation takes place without the use of baffles. The steam is collected in a dry pipe located in the quiet, cool-gas end of the drum. Feedwater is thoroughly mixed with the boiler water rising into the steam drum.

Expansion and contraction of the drums and tubes have no effect on the steel casing, firebrick, or insulation; hence, the most common source of brickwork trouble is eliminated, and air infiltration is reduced to a

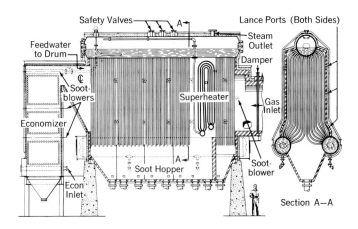

Fig. 11 Three-drum bent-tube waste-heat boiler fitted with lance ports and sootblowers.

minimum. All pressure parts rest on supports located below the lower drums.

The location of the superheater can be varied to secure the degree of superheat required. To increase heat absorption further, an economizer can be installed in the flue leaving the boiler. The economizer is arranged for downward flow of gases to aid in the collection of solids.

Solids collected in the hoppers under the boiler and economizer can be readily removed while the boiler is in service. In a single boiler behind a cement kiln, from 20 to 40 tons of cement dust may be recovered each day from these hoppers. Table 2 lists some performance data for the three-drum boiler illustrated in Fig. 11.

Table 2
Performance of three-drum unit (Fig. 11) fired by waste gas from a cement kiln

Boiler heating surface, sq ft	12,000
Superheater surface, sq ft	523
Steam flow, lb/hr	43,000
Flue gas entering boiler, lb/hr	150,000
Gas temperature entering boiler, F	1,500
Gas temperature leaving boiler, F	438
Gas temperature leaving economizer, F	320
Steam pressure at superheater outlet, psi	200
Steam temperature at superheater outlet, F	480
Feedwater temperature entering economizer, F	212
Draft loss, boiler, superheater, and economizer, in. water	9.6

Waste-heat boilers for special conditions

Other types of waste-heat boilers to recover the heat from waste gases or fluids from industrial processes including ore-refining for copper, lead and zinc have been designed for special conditions of space, temperature, pressure and draft. When all of the requirements are known, waste-heat-recovery boilers can be designed to accommodate almost any set of conditions.

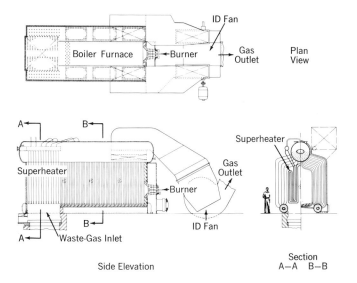

Fig. 10 Waste-heat boiler for oxygen-blown open-hearth furnace.

Metallurgy and structural design

Section V

This section deals with the metals and alloys that constitute the pressure parts and supports of steam generating units. These materials are primarily carbon and low-alloy steels. Stainless steels and chromium-nickel-iron alloys have important applications in fossil-fuel and nuclear units, and zirconium alloys are used for fuel cladding in nuclear reactors.

Chapter 28 discusses the basic metallurgy of iron and steel and the metallurgical requirements for the selection of materials for steam generating units. It discusses the ores of iron and the manufacture of pig iron and iron castings. The basic-oxygen, open-hearth and electric-furnace processes for the manufacture of steel are depicted. The casting of steel ingots is examined, and the differences in steel types—killed, semikilled, rimmed, and capped—are summarized.

This chapter contains information on the atomic structure of iron and the physical metallurgy of steel. The latter includes phase changes, critical points and transformation in steel. An equilibrium diagram is presented, showing phase solubility limits of carbon in iron. Microscopic examination provides an index to the prior fabrication and mechanical properties of metals and alloys. Characteristic steel structures are portrayed with photomicrographs. The specific effects of various alloying elements are catalogued, and the effects of heat treatment are described. The chapter concludes with a discussion of the mechanical working of steel, including forging, rolling and the production of plates.

Chapter 29 deals primarily with the mechanical properties of steels. The chapter begins with a description of tensile, hardness, and impact tests. This is followed by a discussion of high temperature properties, with emphasis on creep and creep-rupture. The methods used to obtain creep data are described and the test equipment illustrated. Factors affecting creep are delineated; these include alloying elements, grain size, heat treatment, surface stability and the method of manufacture. Creep stress values for carbon, chrome-molybdenum and 18-8 alloy steels at various temperatures are tabulated.

Steels used in boiler construction are discussed in Chapter 29. Chemical and tensile requirements of carbon and low-alloy plate steels, and maximum allowable stress values at various temperatures are presented. ASME specifications and the maximum metal temperatures recommended by B&W for several tube steels are tabulated, and the allowable stress values for these steels at various temperatures are given. Corresponding information for pipe materials is also provided.

Materials used in pressurized-water nuclear steam supply systems are discussed in the latter part of Chapter 29. Some physical and mechanical properties of zirconium alloys and Inconel Alloy 600 are included.

Steam generating equipment comprises pressure parts ranging from small diameter tubing to pressure vessels that may weigh 700 tons or more. A large fossil-fuel boiler may extend about 300 ft above the ground, requiring steel support structure comparable to a building 30 stories high. To assure reliability, a thorough design analysis of all pressure parts and support structure is required. To illustrate the range of the requirements, Chapter 30 discusses design in three areas.

The first of these is the stress analysis of pressure vessels, pertinent to both nuclear and fossil-fuel units. The methods used for stress analysis, subject to applicable pressure vessel construction codes, are outlined. The difference between primary and secondary stresses, including thermal stresses, is defined and evaluated. Design procedures for avoiding fatigue damage are presented, and the problem of increased stress around an opening in a vessel is examined.

The second area considered is the structural design of a top-supported fossil-fuel steam generator for electric utility service. The discussion covers wind and seismic loads, top support steel, platform arrangements, column rows and stress calculation for member sizes.

The third design area examined is the structural design of a nuclear reactor core.

Ladle / entering vacuum degassing chamber. In this installation in a B&W steel mill, steel in a ladle car enters a straight-through degassing chamber through one door, is degassed, and emerges through the other. When the car moves into the chamber, induction coils are connected to provide stirring action. Chamber doors close and steam ejectors evacuate the air and degas the steel while the steel is stirred. Pressure is brought up to atmospheric and the exit door opens onto the teeming floor where the metal is teemed from the ladle into ingots.

Chapter 28

Metallurgy of iron and steel

Metallurgy deals with the extraction of metals from ores and with the combination, treatment and processing of metals into useful engineering materials. As an art, metallurgy has been of great importance to the progress of civilization for at least 6,000 years, beginning with the production of the first metal during the Bronze Age. As a science, metallurgy is less than a century old.

Progress in metallurgy has been rapid since 1920, particularly since World War II. Technological developments in industry are closely related to advances in metallurgical science. This relationship is basic in the boiler industry. Whether for fossil or nuclear fuels, modern steam generating units with high economy and reliability would not be practicable without these advances in the theory and application of metallurgy.

Main fields of metallurgy

Metallurgy is divided into two main fields: ferrous, which covers iron and iron base alloys; and nonferrous, covering metals and alloys other than iron or iron-base. Metallurgy may also be divided into the fields of (1) process or chemical metallurgy, and (2) physical and mechanical metallurgy. Process metallurgy includes the numerous mining and refining processes, such as reduction of ores, refining of metals and the manufacture of metals and alloys. Physical metallurgy is devoted to studying the constitution and structure of metals and alloys, including the factors and processes that control physical and mechanical properties.

The principal pressure parts of a power boiler—drums, headers and tubes—are made from ferrous alloys. The same is true for most of the other parts of the boiler and its closely related auxiliaries, such as coal pulverizers, fuel conveying systems, sootblowers, steam piping, economizers and air heaters. Nonferrous metals are used only to a minor extent in boiler installations; in auxiliary equipment, such as water heaters and deaerators in the condensing system beyond the turbines; and in valves and instrumentation. The advent of nuclear power has required more extensive use of nonferrous metals; however, ferrous metals comprise the bulk of materials used in a nuclear steam supply system,

including the pressure parts of pressure vessels and piping for reactor coolant and steam.

This chapter presents the fundamental metallurgical concepts and practices, and outlines the metallurgical requirements for the selection of materials for the construction of steam generating units.

Ores of iron

Iron was first known in ancient civilization, probably 5,000 years ago. Nevertheless, its great usefulness was not fully realized until the characteristics of the metal itself and its effects when combined with alloying elements were established by the application of the science of metallurgy.

Although iron is one of the most common of metals, metallic iron is very rarely found in nature. It usually occurs in the form of mineral oxides (Fe_2O_3 or Fe_3O_4), and as such it comprises about 6% of the earth's crust. The principal ores of iron, in order of abundance and importance in this country are: hematite (Fe_2O_3), magnetite (Fe_3O_4), limonite ($2Fe_2O_3 \cdot 3H_2O$), and siderite ($FeCO_3$).

Reserves of high-grade iron ores in the United States have been depleted so rapidly that lower-grade ores and imported ores are being smelted in increasing amounts. The iron minerals in the lower-grade ores are concentrated to yield a product of greater iron content for smelting. The beneficiation of taconite is one example of the concentration (usually by magnetic methods) of the iron minerals in large deposits of low-grade ores in the Lake Superior region.

Foreign ores are smelted in blast furnaces in some areas of the U.S., generally at sites accessible to seagoing vessels, where transportation costs make the operation economical. Substantial amounts of iron ore from Brazil, Canada, Liberia and Venezuela are smelted in American furnaces. Minor quantities of ore are derived from other foreign sources. Much of the iron ore consumed in this country at the present time is the red oxide of iron, hematite. It is found chiefly in the Lake Superior region, in the states of Minnesota, Michigan and Wisconsin. In much of this region, the ore is economically extracted by

open pit mining. Some subsurface mining is also performed. The black oxide (magnetite) will be used in increasing quantities as red ore (hematite) supplies continue to be depleted.

Iron ores are classified on the basis of their metallic iron content and the percentage of undesirable impurities, known as "gangue." Ores may be shipped as-mined or subjected to concentration processes, known as "beneficiation," prior to shipment. More recently, even relatively high-grade ores are beneficiated somewhat. This reduces the amount of unusable gangue which adds unnecessarily to the cost of transportation. Beneficiation of ores includes drying to reduce the water content, roasting to reduce the sulfur content and washing to remove some of the gangue materials. A relatively new process, pelletizing, directly refines ore to produce pre-reduced pellets with high iron content. The iron ore, either as-mined or beneficiated, is shipped by rail and boat to blast furnaces, where it is smelted.

Manufacture of iron

The first step in the production of iron and steel is the reduction of the ore with coke and limestone in the blast furnace. In this process, "reduction" is the removal of the oxygen from the ore, leaving a mixture of iron and carbon and small amounts of other elements as impurities. The coke is the reducing element and source of heat. The limestone ($CaCO_3$) is a flux which promotes fusion. In the molten state, it also combines with impurities of the ore and floats to the top of the metal where it can be removed as slag.

A blast furnace is a vertical steel shell structure 100 ft or more in height. It is lined from top to bottom with refractory brick. Carbon block linings have been used in some furnaces. The principal components of the blast furnace plant are illustrated in Fig. 1. Its product is pig iron, an impure form of iron containing about 4% carbon and varying amounts of silicon, manganese, phosphorus and sulfur.

Pig iron cast from the blast furnace may be used directly as hot metal in certain steelmaking processes. It may also be taken to pig-casting machines and cast into standard-size pigs. Sometimes it is taken to a mixer, where iron from several blast furnaces is mixed to produce more uniform or average analyses.

Cast iron

Liquid pig iron cast from the blast furnace is sometimes used directly for metal castings. More often, however, the iron is remelted in a cupola, air furnace, or electric furnace, to adjust its composition before it is used for castings. Pig iron that has been so remelted is known as cast iron, a general term applicable to a group of iron-carbon alloys containing carbon in excess of 2% (usually less than 4.5%) and appreciable amounts of silicon. Compared with steel, cast iron is decidedly inferior in malleability, strength, toughness, and ductility. On the other hand, cast iron has better fluidity, can be cast satisfactorily into complicated shapes, and is less costly than steel. The most important types of cast iron are the white and the gray cast irons.

White cast iron

White cast iron is so known because of the silvery luster of its fracture. The structure of this material is illustrated in Fig. 2. In this alloy, the carbon is present in combined form as iron carbide (Fe_3C), known metallographically as "cementite." This carbide is chiefly responsible for the hardness, brittleness, and poor machinability of white cast iron. These remarks also apply to chilled iron, which differs from white cast iron only in the method of manufacture. Chilled iron is cast against metal chills that cause rapid cooling at the adjacent areas, thus promoting the formation of cementite. Consequently, a white or mottled structure is obtained, which is characterized by high resistance to wear and abrasion. Elverite, a type of chilled-iron casting developed by B&W for use in pulverizers, cement and clinker grinders, and in other wear-resistant parts, has long been noted for its uniformity and high quality.

Malleable cast iron is white cast iron that has been heat-treated to change its combined carbon (cementite) into free or "temper" carbon (nodules of graphite). The iron becomes malleable because in this condition the carbon no longer forms planes of weakness.

Gray cast iron

Gray iron is by far the most widely used of cast metals. In this alloy (Fig. 3), the carbon is predominantly in the free state, in the form of graphite flakes that form a multitude of notches and discontinuities in the iron matrix. The appearance of the fracture of this iron is "gray" since the graphite flakes are exposed. The strength of gray iron depends on the size of the graphite crystals and the amount of cementite formed together with the graphite. The strength of the iron increases as the graphite crystal size decreases and the amount of cementite increases. Gray cast iron is easily machinable because the graphite carbon acts as a lubricant for the cutting tool and also provides discontinuities which break the chips as they are formed. Modern gray iron having a wide range of tensile strength, from 20,000 to 90,000 psi, can be made by suitable alloying with nickel, chromium, molybdenum, vanadium and copper. Mechanical properties of several engineering grades (ASTM classes) of gray cast iron are given in Table 1.

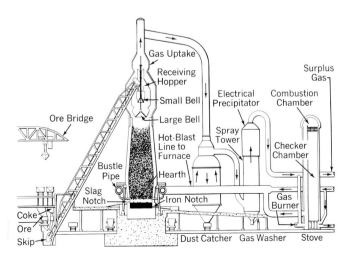

Fig. 1 Schematic outline—external features of a blast furnace and its components.

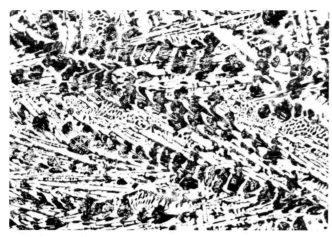

Fig. 2 White cast iron—typical microstructure (250x) reduced about ⅔. Note carbide "Fe_3C" (light areas) and tertiary eutectic "Steadite" (mottled areas).

Fig. 3 Gray cast iron—typical microstructure (50x) reduced about ⅔. Note graphic flakes (dark areas).

Ductile cast iron

Another member of the cast iron family is the so-called "ductile cast iron." It is a high-carbon magnesium-treated ferrous product containing graphite in the form of spheroids or impacted particles. Ductile cast iron is similar to gray cast iron in melting point, fluidity and machinability, but possesses superior mechanical properties. This alloy is especially suited for pressure castings. By special procedures (casting against a chill) it is possible to obtain a carbide-containing abrasion-resistant surface with an interior of good ductility.

Cast iron was used to a considerable extent in early steam boilers for both tubes and headers. This material is no longer used in the pressure parts of modern power boilers but is utilized in related equipment, such as stoker parts and the housings and grinding rings of coal

pulverizers. Fig. 4 shows a gray-iron pulverizer housing which is being inspected in the shop after machining.

Manufacture of steel

Steel may be simply defined as an alloy of iron and carbon which contains not over 2.0% carbon and is cast in an initially malleable mass. This is by no means a complete definition of steel, but for all practical purposes it is adequate. Since the early 1920's, a great variety of steels has been developed for widespread use. All of these steels are basically iron-carbon alloys, but they differ appreciably in carbon content and, in many instances, also in the amount of other alloying elements present. In this way several classes of steels have been produced, with a wide range of physical characteristics and mechanical properties suitable for the specific requirements

Table 1
General engineering grades of gray iron—mechanical and physical properties

Class	30	35	40	45	50	60	70	80
Tensile strength, psi (min)	30,000	35,000	40,000	45,000	50,000	60,000	70,000	80,000
Compressive strength, psi	105,000	115,000	125,000	135,000	150,000	175,000	200,000	225,000
Torsional strength, psi	40,000	45,000	54,000	60,000	67,000	76,000	85,000	90,000
Modulus of elasticity°, psi × 10⁻⁶	14	15	16	17	18	19	20	21
Torsional modulus, psi × 10⁻⁶	—	—	5.5	6.6	7.0	8.0	8.1	—
Impact strength, Izod AB (1.2-in. diam unnotched), ft-lb	23	25	31	36	65	75	120+	120+
Brinell hardness	180	200	220	240	240	260	280	300
Endurance limit, psi:								
Smooth	15,500	17,500	19,500	21,500	25,500	27,500	29,500	31,500
Notched	(13,500)	(15,500)	17,500	(19,500)	21,500	23,500	25,500	27,500
Damping capacity	Excellent	Excellent	Excellent	Good	Good	Good	Fair	Fair
Machinability	Excellent	Excellent	Excellent	Good	Good	Fair	Fair	Fair
Wear resistance	Fair	Fair	Good	Good	Excellent	Excellent	Excellent	Excellent
Pressure tightness	Fair	Fair	Good	Good	Excellent	Excellent	Excellent	Excellent
Specific gravity:								
g per cm³	7.02	7.13	7.25	7.37	7.43	7.48	7.51	7.54
lb per cu in.	0.254	0.258	0.262	0.267	0.269	0.270	0.272	0.273
Thermal coefficient of linear expansion: (in. per in., F) × 10⁻⁹ (50-200 F)	6.5-6.7	—	6.6-6.8	6.4-6.4	—	—	—	—
(50-500 F)	6.9-7.2	—	7.1-7.3	6.8-7.0	—	—	—	—
(50-800 F)	7.4-7.6	—	7.4-7.6	7.0-7.2	—	—	—	—
Magnetic properties	Mag	Mag	Mag	Mag	Mag	Mag	Mag	Mag
Pattern shrinkage, in. per ft	⅒-⅛	⅛	⅛	⅛	⅛	⅛-³⁄₁₆	⅛-³⁄₁₆	⅛-³⁄₁₆
Coef of friction (against steel)	—	—	—	(0.19)	(0.195)	(0.20)	—	—

° At 25% of tensile strength.

Note: Values in parentheses estimated.

Fig. 4 Inspecting finish-machined gray-iron pulverizer housing.

of many different industrial applications.

Most modern processes in the manufacture of steel start with pig iron. Pig iron is transformed into steel by the oxidation of the impurities with air, oxygen, or iron oxide, since the impurities have greater affinity for oxygen than does iron.

Pig iron may be refined by oxidation alone ("acid" process) or by oxidation in conjunction with a strong basic slag ("basic" process). Carbon, silicon, and manganese are removed by both processes, but phosphorus and some of the sulfur in the pig iron can be removed only in the basic process. Phosphorus stays persistently with the iron if the slag is strongly acidic (high in silica), and therefore is not removed. However, if in addition to oxidizing conditions, there is also an abundance of a basic constituent (such as calcium or magnesium) in the slag, then the latter will hold the phosphorus as phosphate in combination and prevent it from being again reduced and seized by the metallic iron. The removal of sulfur is similarly facilitated by reducing conditions and basic slag.

The principal methods of manufacturing steel for subsequent rolling or forging are: the basic-oxygen process, basic open-hearth process, and basic electric-furnace process. Steel for castings can be made by the foregoing methods and also by the acid electric and acid open-hearth methods.

The furnace charge is steel scrap and pig iron in both the basic-oxygen and basic open-hearth processes and selected steel scrap in the electric-furnace process. Pre-reduced iron pellets may also be used in these processes as part of the charge. Each of these processes requires raw materials of particular composition. The resultant product is therefore somewhat different in chemical analysis and physical characteristics.

Vacuum treatment of liquid steels was brought about by the need, particularly in the forging industry, for steels of a quality level not consistently attainable by the various air-melting processes.

Basic-oxygen process

Experiments in steelmaking begun during 1941 in Germany culminated in the commercial production of basic-oxygen steel at Linz and Donawitz, Austria, during the early 1950's and later in Canada, the United States and other countries. Since that time, many modifications of the process have been developed.

In the United States, the basic-oxygen process operates in a basic-lined cylindrical furnace with a solid bottom and an open top, Fig. 5 (*see also Basic-Oxygen Furnace, Chapter 27*). These furnaces are usually rated at 150 to 300 tons capacity. The furnace is tilted to receive the charge which usually consists of 30% cold scrap and the balance hot metal. The furnace is returned to the upright position and an oxygen lance is lowered into the opening at the top to start the melting cycle. At the completion of the oxygen blow period, a sample is removed from the vessel and submitted for chemical analysis. The analytical procedures employed are the most modern available and the time for determining the chemistry of a "heat" is usually 3-5 minutes. On receipt of the analysis, the chemistry is adjusted to specification and the heat is tapped. The quality of the steel produced in the basic-oxygen furnace is considered the equivalent of that produced in the basic open-hearth. The normal production time for carbon steel and low-alloy steel heats by this process is about 40 minutes.

The high production rates attainable by the basic-oxygen process have resulted in a major shift from the basic open-hearth for large tonnage items. Recent data indicate that major producers are successfully replacing basic open-hearth melting facilities of 10-12 furnaces with basic-oxygen facilities having only 2 or 3 furnaces.

Open-hearth process

In the 1950's, the greatest tonnage of steel in this country was produced by the basic open-hearth process. However, this process has lost its lead position since the advent of the basic-oxygen process. Production rates are higher with the basic-oxygen process and quality is considered equivalent. Hence the basic open-hearth process may be completely replaced within several years.

The basic open-hearth process is carried out in a large regenerative furnace lined with basic refractories, especially magnesite or dolomite (Fig. 6). These furnaces vary in size up to 550 tons capacity. A typical charge would consist of 30-50% cold scrap and the remainder hot metal. One of the major improvements to the basic open-hearth process has been the introduction of oxygen roof lances resulting in a 25-50% reduction in the time required for a heat.

Various types of alloy steel are also produced by the open-hearth process. These include 1) carbon-molybdenum steel for boiler plate, superheater tubes and piping, and 2) low chromium-molybdenum tube steels (1.5% maximum chromium). It is usually preferable, however, to make the chromium-containing tube grades by the electric-furnace process.

Electric-furnace process

Most high-grade alloy steels are manufactured in the electric furnace. For these alloys, the electric-furnace process offers the following important advantages:

1. Ability to control bath temperature within close limits.
2. Maintenance of oxidizing, reducing or neutral conditions in the furnace at will. This permits the addition of alloying elements to the bath with assurance of complete deoxidation in the furnace.

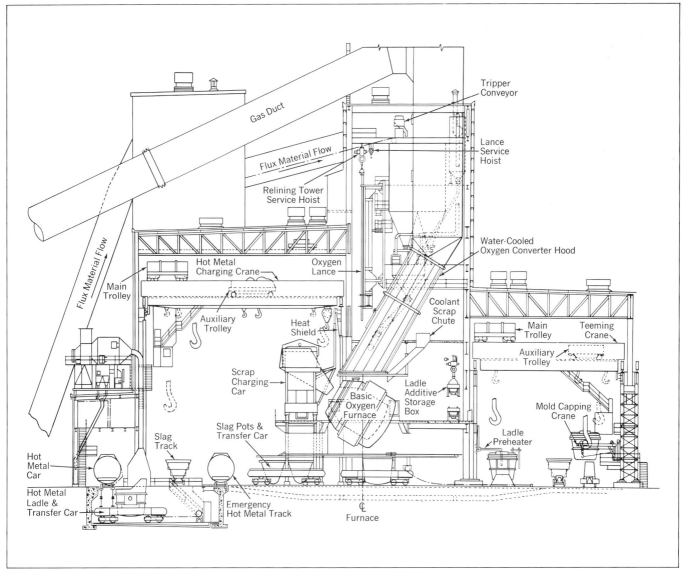

Fig. 5 Basic-oxygen-furnace steel-manufacturing plant.

3. The bath is not subject to contamination by the heat source.

4. Sulfur, solid nonmetallic impurities, and occluded gases are significantly reduced.

The higher temperature generated in the electric furnace increases the fluidity of the metal, permits rapid reaction in removing sulfur and phosphorus, and permits recovery of oxidizable alloying elements from the slag. The control of quality and composition is, therefore, better than in either the basic-oxygen or basic open-hearth process, but the cost is somewhat higher. An electric-furnace heat ranges from 5 to 250 tons in size as compared with 150 to 300 tons in the basic-oxygen process or 150 to 550 tons in the basic open-hearth process.

Steels of intermediate chromium-molybdenum composition, such as those used for superheaters, are generally made in the electric furnace. The basic electric-furnace process is used for production of stainless, high alloy and tool steels. Fig. 7 shows a sectional view of an electric-arc furnace used to produce high quality steels. The acid process is used essentially for castings and other special applications in the steel foundries.

Vacuum degassing

Vacuum treatment of liquid steel was investigated as early as 1886 by Aitken, who received a number of patents on vacuum metallurgy. In the early stages of development, there were problems associated with the inability of pumping systems to handle the large volume of gases evolved. Rapid strides were made in vacuum engineering in the 1940's, and pumping systems were developed to handle the large throughputs of gas at low pressures with efficient degassing. This breakthrough in the design of vacuum pumping systems led to the production-scale ladle-degassing (16 ton) program at the Enakievsk plant in Russia in the early 1950's. At this time a vacuum-stream degassing program was initiated at the Bochumer Verein Company in Germany. The significance of the results is reflected by the number of vacuum degassing plants (more than 200) placed in operation since 1954.

The objective of vacuum degassing has changed somewhat with development. In the early stages the elimination of hydrogen from forging ingots was the sole purpose of the operation. After the problems associated with

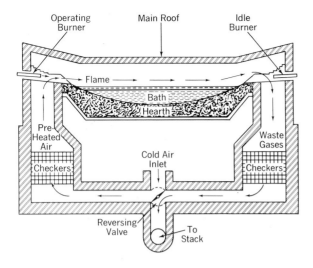

Fig. 6 Diagrammatic cross section, open-hearth furnace.

hydrogen embrittlement were solved, attention was focused on new techniques for the production of cleaner steel by the removal of oxygen from the liquid melt. The carbon and oxygen dissolved in the liquid steel, react at low pressure to form carbon monoxide which is continuously withdrawn by the vacuum pumping system.

In the design of degassing equipment each steelmaker was desirous of making any equipment modifications that would improve a particular plant's level of steel quality and best suit that plant's product mix. Consequently, there are many types of commercial vacuum-degassing systems in operation today, classifiable in the following three main groups:

1) *Ladle-degassing process.* At the completion of the tap the ladle of steel is placed in a chamber which is rapidly evacuated (*see chapter frontispiece*). The boiling action induced in the steel by the evolution of gas is often adequate to degas the bulk of the steel in the ladle. Degassing efficiency can be increased by an inert purge-gas, such as argon, or by induction-stirring. The practice at B&W is to use induction-stirring not only to improve the degassing efficiency but also to assure complete mixing of any alloy additions made during the degassing cycle.

2) *Stream-degassing process.* There are many variations of this process in use today. The two most popular appear to be the ladle-to-ladle and the ladle-to-mold systems. In the ladle-to-ladle system, the tapping ladle with metal from the furnace is positioned over a vacuum chamber containing the teeming ladle.* The metal from the tapping ladle is poured through vacuum into the teeming ladle. The deoxidation and dehydrogenation occurs as the pouring stream fans out into many droplets of metal. In the ladle-to-mold process (Fig. 8) steel is poured from the tapping ladle into a mold located in a vacuum chamber.

3) *Vacuum-lift degassing process.* In this process (Fig. 9) the steel is drawn from the tapping ladle into an evacuated refractory lined vessel. After treatment the

---

* Pouring molten metal from a ladle into ingot molds is known as "teeming". The teeming ladle is used for this purpose.

steel is returned to the vessel. The degassing cycle consists of a series of these lifts. This cycle may be carried out in a single-leg unit, the Dortmund-Hörder (D-H) process, or in a unit employing two legs, the Ruhrstahl-Heraeus (R-H) process, which uses argon in conjunction with the vacuum system. The D-H process is illustrated in Fig. 9.

Extensive changes in the techniques and equipment for vacuum treatment of steel can be expected in the years ahead as steelmakers strive to improve product quality further.

Other melting practices

Other melting practices are in commercial use throughout the steel industry. The most common practices are associated with a remelting of the product from one of the more common melting processes. The two most common practices are:

a) *Vacuum arc remelting.* This is electric arc remelting in vacuum. The electrode is the "charge" and is consumed during the process. The arcing takes place under vacuum in a water-cooled mold.

A vacuum is first created in the furnace. Power is then turned on, and an arc is struck between the electrode and a starting block that is placed in the mold before the operation begins. Heat from the arc progressively melts the end of the electrode. Melted metal is transferred across the arc and deposited in a shallow pool of molten metal on the top surface of the ingot being built up in the mold. Solidification of the melted metal takes place almost immediately. The rate of descent of the electrode is automatically controlled to maintain the proper distance to maintain the arc between the end of the electrode and the top of the ingot as the end of the electrode is "consumed" or melted away.

The resulting product is very low in dissolved gas content. The presence of solid nonmetallic inclusions is minimized, particularly those that form in normal melting as a result of reactions with atmospheric gases.

b) *Electroslag remelting.* In this process, electrical resistance between a consumable electrode and a slag

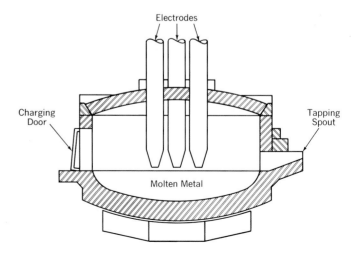

Fig. 7 Diagrammatic cross section, electric furnace. Molten metal is tapped into a ladle by tilting the furnace.

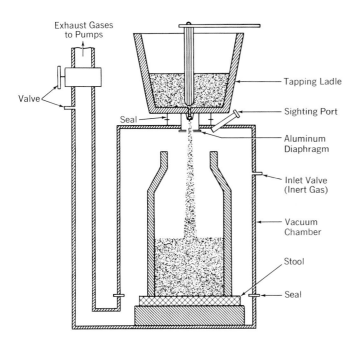

Fig 8 Arrangement for vacuum casting using stream degassing.

blanket provide the energy for remelting. The electrode is the "charge" and solidification takes place in a water-cooled mold.

The process is started by placing a quantity of prepared refining slag on the mold baseplate and then striking an arc between the electrode and baseplate to form a pool of molten slag. The electrode remains immersed in the slag which is electrically conductive. Electrical-resistance heating of the slag increases its temperature until droplets of molten metal form and fall from the electrode through the slag to form a pool in the mold. As melting proceeds, the molten pool progressively solidifies but retains a molten depth equal to roughly one-half the diameter of the mold.

The resulting product has a reduced dissolved gas content. The cleanliness of the steel is much improved and center porosity and segregation in the ingot are very minimal.

It will be noted that the above processes remelt material previously produced by some other practice. In general, the electrode composition in these processes is generally near the desired composition of the remelted product. Practically, the processes refine the material to a high quality product.

Quality alloy steel for tubes—B&W practice

The rotary-piercing and the extrusion processes, employed in the manufacture of seamless tubing and pipe, are perhaps the most rigorous hot-forming operations in the entire metalworking industry. They require the highest quality steel, not only to withstand these rigorous forming operations, but also to obtain a satisfactory product suitable for the severe conditions encountered in high temperature service.

A wide range of ferrous alloys are melted in electric-arc furnaces, from plain low-carbon steel to 25% chromium-20% nickel stainless alloy. In addition, some

nonferrous alloys such as nominal 76% nickel, 15% chromium, 9% iron alloy are manufactured. All alloy and stainless steels are made under rigid technical control. In double-slag practice, the slag is drawn off twice during the heat. After the first removal of slag, fresh fluxing reagents are added, the heat is continued, and the newly formed slag is drawn off before tapping. Standard melt practices are established for each grade to assure quality level consistent with application requirements. This is important in providing uniform piercing qualities and performance in service. The electric-furnace melt for high-quality alloy tube steel calls for thorough deoxidation of the melt regardless of composition.

Alloying elements are added under the second or finishing slag which is formed after the completion of the oxidizing period. Samples of the molten steel are taken from the bath and poured into test ingots. These are rapidly analyzed in the laboratory by chemical methods and spectrography. The results of the analyses are quickly reported to the melter and guide him in making the necessary alloy additions to the bath to bring the steel to the specified composition. To assure high quality, two or more samples are necessary in the course of making the steel heat.

The steel ingot

Molten metal tapped from the steelmaking furnaces is teemed from ladles into metal molds and allowed to solidify as an ingot preparatory to blooming and rolling.

All steel used in the production of wrought-steel products, such as plate, tubing, and bars for boilers or any other uses, is cast into ingot molds of suitable size and shape. Proper ingot practice is essential to assure a good quality product, free from surface breaks, internal defects, or harmful segregation.

Ingots are cast in many sizes and shapes, established by the research and experience of the steel producer. The cross section of most ingots approximates a square or rectangle with round corners but may be fluted to give additional hot strength and avoid corner cracks. The greatest dimension is always vertical, and all ingots are tapered. The exact cross section and vertical height are selected for the job at hand. Steel of the rimmed and semikilled types (*see Fig. 10*) is usually cast in ingots with big end down, while killed steel is commonly cast

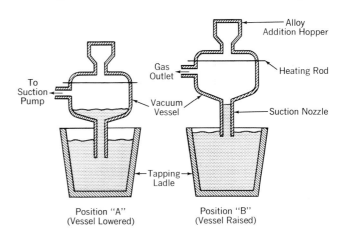

Fig. 9 D-H process for degassing.

in ingots with a sink head or "hot top," and with big end up. This procedure is employed in the latter case in order to feed molten metal into the so-called "pipe" which forms during cooling and thus confine the pipe to the hot top (*see Killed Steel*). This portion of the ingot is later sheared or cropped from the body of the ingot, which is sound metal. A bottom crop also is taken so that only sound metal remains in that area of the ingot.

All steels, regardless of type, are subject to certain internal variations from natural phenomena which occur as the steel solidifies in the mold. The character and magnitude of such variations and their effects depend on the size of the ingots and may be generalized as follows:

"Primary pipe" in the upper portion of the ingot is caused by shrinkage of the metal in passing from the liquid to the solid state during solidification. Rolling at a welding heat will not close the cavity because the surface has been oxidized. The pipe end of the ingot, consequently, must be cut off and discarded. Under certain conditions, a shrinkage cavity known as "secondary pipe" is formed below but is not connected with the primary pipe. Secondary pipe is usually associated with the evolution and entrapment of gases in the ingot during solidification. It can be avoided by proper ingot mold design combined with appropriate steelmaking practices.

Another phenomenon associated with rate of solidification is segregation, or nonuniformity in chemical composition within the ingot. Certain portions of the solidified metal contain either more or less of the elements originally contained in the liquid steel. Segregation in varying degree is found in all types of steel ingots. The amount of segregation depends chiefly on the type and composition of the steel, the teeming temperature, the ingot size and the inherent segregating characteristics of the individual elements of the steel. These phenomena have been widely studied and controlled by proper practices, and discard, and recognition of the intended end use of the product.

Special heating cycles

Special heating cycles are maintained for ingots of alloy steel, particularly for the hardenable grades to prevent thermal shock or stress-cracking. Each alloy has a certain thermal cycle which must be followed in the proper heating of ingots for blooming and bar-mill rolling. All surface defects are removed from blooms before bar rolling. This conditioning is an important operation to remove such surface defects as checks and slivers. The conditioning is effected by scarfing, grinding or machining. Superficial scale and loose foreign matter are removed by the scale-breaking action of rolling. Bars of stainless grades for tube manufacture are turned in the round form before being sent to the tube plant.

To make a satisfactory seamless tube by the rotary piercing process a billet must be free of injurious surface or center porosity and harmful surface defects and must not exhibit any undue segregation. It must have good ductility over a broad range of high temperature to permit piercing of hollows of commercial length. Adequate allowance should be made for temperature buildup from friction during deformation in piercing.

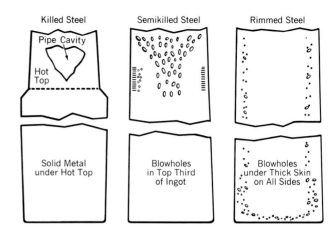

Fig. 10 Schematic sections of ingots—three types of steel.

Steel types

In most steelmaking processes, the charge is first heated to an approximate temperature. During this heating, oxygen is introduced to refine the charge. This oxygen combines with carbon to form a gas. If the oxygen introduced for this reaction is not removed or combined, prior to or during casting, by the addition of silicon, aluminum, or some other deoxidizing agent, the gaseous products continue to evolve during solidification of the metal in the mold. Control of the amount of gas evolved during solidification determines the type of steel. If no gas is evolved and the liquid lies quietly in the mold, it is known as killed steel. With increasing degrees of gas evolution the products are known as semikilled steel and rimmed steel. Typical locations of blowholes in rimmed and semikilled steels, and pipe in killed steels are indicated in Fig. 10. The efficiency of several of the common deoxidizers in molten steel at 2900F (1600C) is shown in Fig. 11.

Killed steel

Steel of the killed type is deoxidized almost completely, so there is essentially no evolution of gas during pouring and solidification. Consequently, a primary shrinkage cavity, known as pipe, forms during solidification, and this affected part of the ingot is discarded. Killed steel is usually cast in big-end-up ingot molds with hot top to minimize the size of the shrinkage cavity by supplying it with liquid metal.

Although killed steel has a more uniform composition than any of the other types, there are some variations in composition from surface to center and from bottom to top. Practically all compositions of steel can be killed, if sufficient deoxidizing agents are added to inhibit gas formation. Most alloy steels and most carbon steels containing more than 0.25% carbon are of the killed type. Such steels usually contain 0.10% silicon minimum. For certain uses, however, some steels are killed almost entirely with aluminum. B&W seamless-steel boiler tubes are made exclusively of killed steel.

Semikilled steel

Semikilled steel has a variable degree of uniformity in composition. This type of steel is only partially deoxidized with silicon, aluminum, or both, to allow the

evolution of sufficient gas to offset the shrinkage accompanying solidification. Since pipe cavities are minimized, semikilled steel is usually cast in big-end-down molds without hot tops. Most semikilled steels contain between 0.15% and 0.25% carbon, and about 0.05% silicon.

Rimmed steel

In rimmed steel there is a marked difference in composition across the section and from top to bottom of the ingot. The outer rim is ductile, and the amounts of carbon, phosphorous, sulfur, and nonmetallic inclusions in this rim are lower than the average composition of the whole ingot, while the amount of these constituents in the inner portion or core is higher than the average in the ingot as a whole. A marked evolution of gas during solidification of the outer rim is responsible for the typical structure of rimmed steel. When solidification begins, concentration of certain elements in the liquid core of the ingot increases, and at the core there is some additional segregation toward the upper and central portions.

Rimmed steels normally contain less than 0.25% carbon, 0.60% manganese, and 0.01% silicon. Satisfactory rimmed steels do not retain any significant percentages of highly oxidizable elements such as aluminum, titanium, or silicon. Aside from the closing and welding of gas voids (blowholes), the structural pattern of the rimmed-steel ingot persists through the rolling process to the final product. Rimmed steel, which costs less to make than either killed or semikilled steel, is widely used as structural plate. It is used also in strip form for electric-resistance-welded tubing. The rimmed surface is particularly suitable for welding by that process.

Capped steel

The characteristics of capped steel and rimmed steel are similar, but capped steel represents an intermediate step between rimmed and semikilled steels. A deoxidizer may

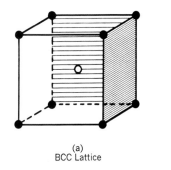 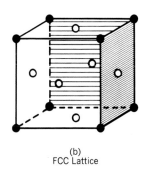

(a)
BCC Lattice

(b)
FCC Lattice

Fig. 12 Space-lattice diagrams of crystalline structure (iron) showing arrangement of atoms in (a) body-centered cubic and in (b) face-centered cubic.

be added when the ingot is cast to effect a controlled rimming action. Capped steel is generally cast in bottle-top molds, big-end-down, and using a heavy metal cap. Capped steel generally has a somewhat thinner rim, and the segregation in the upper central portion of the ingot is less than in rimmed steel. This method is not ordinarily used for steel containing more than 0.15% carbon.

Atomic structure of iron

Pure iron at room temperature is highly ductile and is nearly comparable to copper in hardness. It is strongly magnetic (ferromagnetic). In this respect it differs from all other elements—although nickel and cobalt are magnetic to a milder degree.

Like all other metals, iron is crystalline in structure. Crystalline bodies may be considered as composed of atoms placed at the points of a space lattice (*see Fig. 12*). The smallest component unit of this lattice is known as a unit cell and is characterized by a regularity of structure. A crystal is composed of these unit cells, piled upon one another like bricks, and reproducing at their corners the points of the lattice. Different crystals have different types of space lattice. Analysis by X-ray diffraction shows that iron, on solidification from the molten state, crystallizes in the cubic space lattice.

Iron may exist in one of two forms of cubic space lattice, body-centered (BCC) or face-centered (FCC), Fig. 12. These lattice types are differentiated by the manner in which the atoms are arranged. The body-centered cubic form has an atom at each corner and one at the center of the cell. The face-centered cubic form has an atom at each corner and one in the center of each of the six faces.

At room temperature, iron is composed of a body-centered cubic lattice (*see Fig. 13*). In this form it is known as "alpha iron" or "alpha ferrite," and it is soft, ductile, and magnetic. When heated above about 1415F, alpha iron loses its magnetism but retains its body-centered crystalline structure. This structure changes to face-centered cubic at about 1670F at which temperature alpha iron is transformed to "gamma iron" and remains nonmagnetic. As temperature rises further, another phase change occurs at 2570F, when "delta iron" is formed. The latter is identical in crystal structure (body-centered) with that of the low-temperature alpha iron. It is stable to the melting point. There are no known phase changes in the liquid form (above about 2800F).

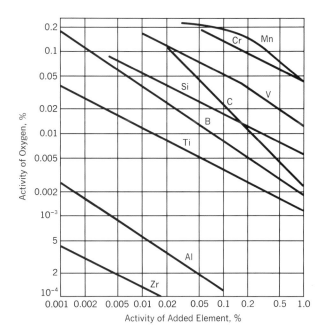

Fig. 11 Comparison of deoxidizing powers at 1600C. (*Source, "Electric Furnace Steelmaking," Vol. II, The Metallurgical Society of AIME.*)

On cooling very slowly from the liquid state, the structural rearrangements described occur again, but in reverse order.

The modifications of atomic structure which occur in iron during heating to and cooling from the melting point are called "allotropic" changes. The temperatures at which these changes take place are known as "transformation points" or "critical points." The range of temperature covered by the transformation points is called the "critical range."

Physical metallurgy of steel

The foregoing pertains to pure iron, which is difficult to obtain, is correspondingly expensive and, in any case, does not have suitable characteristics for construction purposes. However, iron alloyed with carbon and other elements such as manganese, silicon, phosphorus, and sulfur becomes steel, which is an economic material of construction. Since carbon in combination with iron is most effective in producing desirable characteristics, it has been brought under careful regulation in the manufacture of steel. Some effects of carbon in iron are illustrated graphically in the equilibrium diagram, Fig. 14.

Phase changes in steel

This diagram (Fig. 14) indicates the phase changes in iron-carbon mixtures at various temperatures. No reference is made to the time it takes, after the temperature is changed, for these phase transformations to reach the point of equilibrium shown. The addition of carbon (up

to 4.3%) to iron lowers the melting point. At the higher temperatures, solid and liquid coexist, as might be expected. The delta iron range is restricted and finally is eliminated as a single phase in the presence of 0.1% carbon. Some delta iron persists up to about 0.5% carbon, but in combination with other phases. Below the delta iron region, gamma iron absorbs carbon up to composition limits along line S-E, the limiting solubility (solid-solution solubility). When gamma iron contains, in solution, measurable amounts of any second constituent, such as carbon, it is known as "austenite." The temperature at which austenite exists by itself decreases as the carbon increases, along G-S to the so-called "eutectoid point" (0.80% carbon, 1333F). Then the temperature increases, along S-E, as the carbon increases, since the austenite is unable to absorb additional carbon except at higher temperatures.

Critical points in steel

In Fig. 14 the critical points in steel lie along A_1 corresponding to line P-S at 1333F, and along A_3 corresponding to line G-S at temperatures varying with composition. As they occur in heating and cooling, these critical points are again subdivided as Ac_1 and Ac_3 (heating), and Ar_1 and Ar_3 (cooling), respectively. These designations have no place in an equilibrium diagram since they are related to time, another variable, the effect of which is shown later. Below the temperature of 1333F, carbon is relatively insoluble in the "ferrite," as alpha iron is called when rendered impure by the

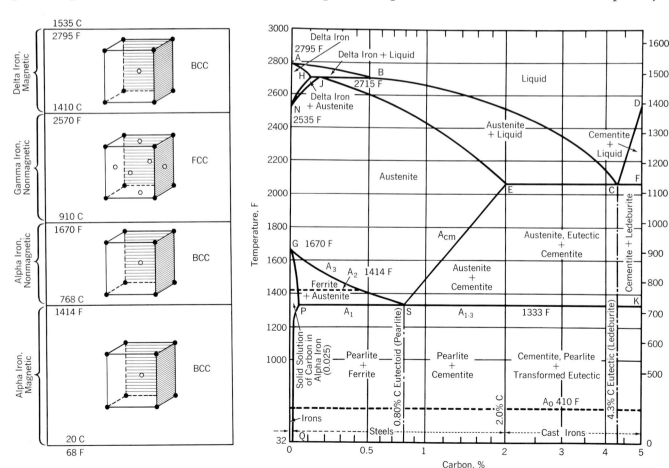

Fig. 13 Allotropic transformations in pure iron.　　Fig. 14 Equilibrium diagram showng phase solubility limits, carbon in iron.

addition of other elements. The relative solubility of carbon in ferrite and austenite may be judged by comparing lines Q-P and S-E. This difference in solubility of carbon in the one as compared with the solubility in the other is the crux of practically all steel heat treating.

The data in Fig. 14 show the end points of the possible transformation which are approached, but never attained, short of an infinite time. Processes in steel fabrication, however, may involve periods of time from seconds (spot welding) to several days (heat treating large vessels). To evaluate the impact of these processes on an internal transformation of the steel, it is necessary to know the effect of time. A typical isothermal transformation is illustrated in Fig. 15.

Transformation in steel

The diagram of Fig. 15, which covers a specific composition of steel, indicates the time required for the progress of transformation from austenite to other constituents at the various temperature levels. As an example, a hypoeutectoid* steel is heated to a temperature (about 1600F) where it becomes completely austenitic. It is then quickly transferred to and held in a furnace or bath at 700F. From Fig. 14 it is evident that, eventually, ferrite and carbides should exist at this temperature, but Fig. 15 indicates how long this reaction takes. By projecting the time intervals during the transformation, as indicated in the lower portion of Fig. 15, to the top portion of the diagram, it will be noted that the austenite continues to exist for three seconds before anything happens. It then starts to transform and at about 100 seconds the transformation is 50% complete. At 700 seconds the austenite is entirely replaced by an agglomerate of fine carbides and ferrite.

The symbols used in Fig. 15 are: A for austenite, F for ferrite, and C for carbide. At temperatures below about 600F (the M_s line) austenite transforms to "martensite," a specialized form of ferrite and the hardest constituent of heat-treated steels. The "nose" of the left curve in Fig. 15 at about 900F, is of prime significance. The transformation at this temperature is very rapid. Also, if this steel is to be quenched to form martensite (for maximum hardness), it must pass through the temperature range about 900F very rapidly to prevent the transformation of some of the austenite to pearlite ($F + C$), which is much softer.

Alloying elements

The effect of alloying elements on steel is indicated by the changes in the equilibrium diagram resulting from their addition to iron. Chromium first lowers the melting point of iron and then raises it as the alloy becomes leaner in iron. On the addition of chromium, the region of austenite (*G-S-E-J-N* in Fig. 14) is diminished, and the austenite phase is eliminated when the proportion of chromium reaches 13%. The addition of carbon (making a three-component system) changes these values considerably. At about 45% chromium and below about 1500F, pure nonmagnetic compound known as "sigma phase" occurs, which renders this alloy brittle. Small

---

* A steel containing less than 0.80% carbon. With 0.80% carbon it is known as eutectoid steel, and with more than 0.80% carbon it is known as hypereutectoid steel.

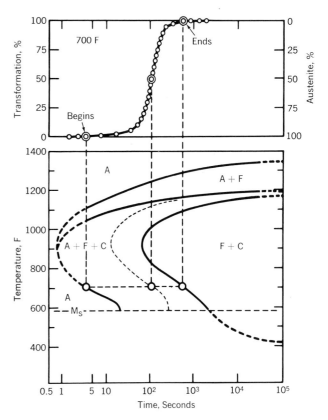

Fig. 15 Typical isothermal transformation. Time required in a specific steel at 700F taken as an example.

fractions of sigma phase can occur in the ferrite of alloys with as low as 15% chromium.

Nickel acts to widen the region of austenite, so iron alloys containing more than 25% nickel are practically austenitic at all temperatures. The action of all other alloying elements can be classed as (a) like chromium (ferrite formers), (b) like nickel (austenite formers), or (c) to form compounds.

The foregoing paragraphs have considered only iron-carbon mixtures which are alloyed with one other element. Practically, however, steels contain iron which is alloyed with many elements. Usually, one, two or more of the elements are added in appreciable amounts, while the other elements are present in smaller, almost residual percentages. Frequently an experienced metallurgist can forecast a steel's performance by inspecting its chemical analysis.

When alloying elements act in concert, there is sometimes radical departure from the behavior which might be predicted from a diagram such as Fig. 15. For instance, an alloy which contains 18% chromium, 10% nickel, balance iron and residual elements, can be austenitic at room temperature and below. Also, the behavior during practical heat treatment cannot necessarily be predicted precisely by an equilibrium diagram because of the difference in cooling and heating rates.

Microscopic examination

A microscope is traditionally the tool of the metallurgist for exploring changes in steel from alloy additions and thermal treatment. The surface of the sample is ground flat and then polished to a mirrorlike finish. When the

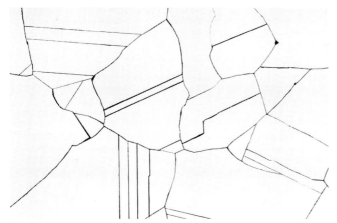

Fig. 16 Austenite, typical microstructure (500x) reduced about ⅔.

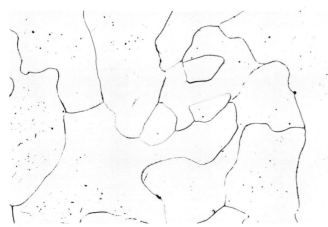

Fig. 17 Ferrite, typical microstructure (1000x) reduced about ⅔.

sample is placed under the microscope, the metal reflects light back to the eyepiece. Any discontinuities, which absorb some of the light, appear dark. Customarily, the samples are etched in acid or other solutions to bring out the characteristic appearance of: austenite, Fig. 16; ferrite, Fig. 17; pearlite, Fig. 18; or hard martensite in quenched steel, Fig. 19.

To the metallurgist, the structures shown in these photomicrographs are clear indices to the prior fabrication and to the mechanical properties. For good quality, foreign matter in steel should be reduced to a minimum. The characteristic appearances of the photomicrographs mentioned above may be defined as follows:

Austenite. A solid solution of carbon in gamma iron, containing a maximum of about 2.0% carbon at 2090F and about 0.80% carbon at 1333F. It exists in ordinary steels only at elevated temperatures, but it is also found at ordinary temperatures in some stainless steels (18 Cr-8 Ni type). This structure has high ductility and high impact strength, which it retains down to minus 320F.

Ferrite. A commercially pure alpha iron containing a small amount of carbon (0.04-0.05%) in solid solution. This phase is soft, ductile, and relatively weak. Below about 40F the impact strength is materially reduced. The tensile strength of commercially pure ferrite is about 40,000 psi, the elongation is about 40%, and the hardness is from 90 to 95 Brinell.

Pearlite. A mixture, in lamellar form, of iron carbide (cementite) in ferrite, which occurs on slow cooling above the nose of the left curve in Fig. 15. This condition is obtained by annealing or normalizing and generally represents an optimum high strength while retaining ductility and some machinability.

Cementite. Iron carbide, Fe_3C (cementite), a compound containing 6.67% carbon, is very hard (about 650 Brinell) and is extremely brittle. The ordinary occurrence of cementite is in slowly cooled hypereutectoid steels (carbon content greater than 0.80%). Cementite also appears as part of several steel structures, one of which is pearlite. The form of its appearance depends on the heat treatment which the steel has received.

Bainite. A hard structure which is a mixture of ferrite and cementite. It forms by the transformation of austenite just above the M_s temperature in many steels of low alloy content. It has higher strength than either ferrite or pearlite, but is not quite as hard as martensite. In some of its forms, bainite appears quite similar to martensite.

Martensite. A very hard constituent formed by the decomposition of austenite below M_s temperature (*see Fig. 15 and Transformation in Steel*). The M_s temperature varies with steel composition.

Specific effect of alloying elements

Steel alloys are the chief structural materials of modern engineering because of their wide range in properties to suit almost any specific application. These properties are affected directly not only by the characteristics and the amounts of the elements which, either alone or in combination, enter into the composition of the steel but also by their reaction as constituents under various conditions of temperature, fabrication and use. For example, chromium increases resistance to corrosion and scaling; molybdenum increases creep strength at elevated temperatures; and nickel (in adequate amounts) renders the steel austenitic. The specific effects of the most important elements found in steel are as follows:

Carbon. Carbon is not generally regarded as an "alloying" element because steel would not be steel without

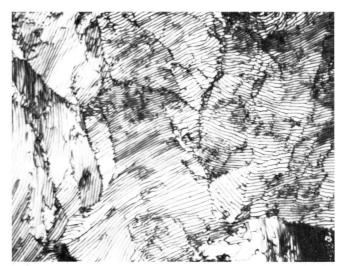

Fig. 18 Lamellar pearlite in 0.80% carbon steel (500x).

Fig. 19 Martensite, typical microstructure in quenched steel (500x) reduced about ⅔.

carbon. Nevertheless, it is appropriate in a discussion of alloying elements to note the specific effects of carbon on the properties of steel.

In general, an increase in carbon content produces higher ultimate strength and hardness but lowers ductility and toughness of steel alloys. The curves in Fig. 20 indicate the general effect of carbon on the mechanical properties of hot-rolled carbon steel. Carbon also increases air-hardening tendencies and weld hardness, especially in the presence of chromium. In low-alloy steel for high-temperature applications, the carbon content is usually restricted to a maximum of about 0.15% in order to assure optimum ductility for welding, expanding, and bending operations. To minimize intergranular corrosion caused by carbide precipitation, the carbon content of austenitic (18-8 type) alloys is limited in commercial specifications to a maximum of 0.08%, or even less, i.e., 0.03% in the extremely low-carbon grades used in certain corrosion-resistant applications.

No generalization is warranted regarding the effect of carbon on the long-time high-temperature (creep) properties of low- and high-alloy steels. In plain carbon steels in the normalized condition, the resistance to creep at temperatures below 825F appears to increase with carbon content up to 0.4% carbon; at higher temperatures there is but little variation of creep properties with carbon content.

An increase in carbon content lessens the thermal and electrical conductivities of steel and increases its hardness on quenching (*see Fig. 21*).

Phosphorus. High phosphorus content has an undesirable effect on the properties of carbon steel—notably on its resistance to shock and ductility when the steel is cold-worked. This embrittling effect, generally referred to as "cold-shortness," results from the tendency of phosphorus to enlarge the grain size and cause segregation. The harmful effect of phosphorus increases as the carbon content increases.

Phosphorus is effective in improving the machinability of free-cutting steels. This is related to its embrittling effect causing breakage of the chips on machining. In open-hearth (carbon) steels, phosphorus is limited to a maximum of 0.04%. In alloy steels intended for boiler applications, the permissible phosphorus content is still less. Its presence is objectionable for welding. Phosphorus is used as an alloying element (up to 0.15%) in

proprietary low-alloy high-strength steels, where increased yield strength and resistance to atmospheric corrosion are primary requirements. In certain acids, however, high phosphorus may increase the corrosion rate.

Silicon. Silicon contributes greatly to the production of sound steel because of its deoxidizing and degasifying properties. When added in amounts up to 2.5%, the ultimate strength of the steel is increased without loss in ductility. Silicon in excess of 2.5% causes brittleness, and amounts higher than 5% make the steel nonmalleable.

Resistance to oxidation and surface stability of steel are increased by the addition of silicon. These desirable effects partially compensate for the tendency of silicon to lower the creep properties of steel. Silicon increases the electrical resistivity of steel and decreases hysteresis losses. Silicon steels are, therefore, widely used in electrical apparatus.

Manganese. Manganese is an excellent deoxidizer and sulfur neutralizer, and improves the mechanical properties of steel, notably the ratio of yield strength to tensile strength at normal temperatures. As an alloying element, manganese serves as an inexpensive means of preventing "red shortness" (brittleness, now more commonly known as "hot shortness"). It improves rolling properties, hardenability, and resistance to wear. However, manganese increases the crack sensitivity of weldments, particularly with steels of higher carbon content.

Unlike silicon, manganese benefits the creep properties of steel. It does not appear to have any specific influence on the resistance to oxidation or corrosion of steel.

Chromium. This element is the essential constituent of stainless steel. Chromium raises the yield strength, ultimate strength, hardness and toughness of steel at room temperature. It also contributes somewhat to the strength of steel at high temperatures.

Resistance of the steel to wear or abrasion and increase in cutting ability are two of the outstanding effects of the addition of chromium. A steady improvement is noted in resistance to atmospheric corrosion and to attack by many reagents when the chromium content

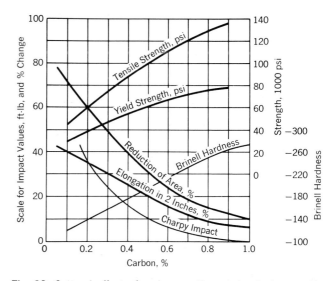

Fig. 20 General effect of carbon on the mechanical properties of hot-rolled carbon steel.

of steel is increased above 12%. The chemical properties of the steel, however, are affected by the carbon content; and, generally, the higher the chromium and the lower the carbon, the more resistant the alloy will be to certain types of corrosion. Chromium is instrumental in increasing the resistance to oxidation at elevated temperatures. Addition of sufficient chromium will prevent graphitization during long-time high-temperature service. Chromium is, consequently, of prime importance in steels intended for high temperature service.

The addition of 1% or more of chromium may cause appreciable air-hardening in the steel. Up to about 13.5% Cr, air-hardening is a direct function of chromium and carbon content. Low-carbon alloy steels containing over 12% Cr tend to become nonhardening, but the impact strength is reduced and the ductility is poor. Chromium lessens both thermal and electrical conductivities.

Nickel. Increased toughness is the principal benefit when nickel is added to steel, particularly in an amount over 1%. Improved resistance to corrosion by some media is attained with nickel contents over 5%. Nickel dissolves in the iron matrix in all proportions and, therefore, raises the ultimate strength without impairing the ductility of the steel. Nickel is particularly effective in increasing the impact properties—especially at low temperature. It is a useful element in carburizing steels and for improvement of core properties in steels for roller bearings.

Probably the most important use of nickel as an alloying element is in combination with chromium in amounts of 8% Ni or more. By the addition of nickel, the high-chromium-iron-carbon alloys become austenitic in character. The various combinations of these two elements produce alloys (18-8 type) with properties which cannot be obtained with equivalent amounts of any of the elements alone. Such steels are resistant not only to corrosion by the atmosphere and other sources but also to oxidation at high temperatures. In addition, they offer greatly enhanced creep strength. It should be remembered, though, that resistance to oxidation and corrosion is controlled mainly by the chromium content, rather than the nickel content.

Nickel has only a slight beneficial effect on creep properties of low-alloy ferritic steels. It reduces the coefficient of thermal expansion and diminishes the electrical conductivity of steel.

Molybdenum. Addition of molybdenum to steel increases its strength, elastic limit, resistance to wear, impact qualities, and hardenability. Molybdenum contributes to high temperature strength and "red-hardness" of steel, that is, the ability of a steel to be heated to a visible degree without materially lowering the hardness. It also increases the resistance to softening on tempering and restrains grain growth. Molybdenum makes chromium steels less susceptible to temper embrittlement.

An important use of molybdenum is the improvement of corrosion resistance in stainless steels of the 18-8 type. It enhances the inherent corrosion resistance of these steels in reducing chemical media. Also it increases their passivity under mildly oxidizing conditions. Experience indicates that under certain conditions molybdenum

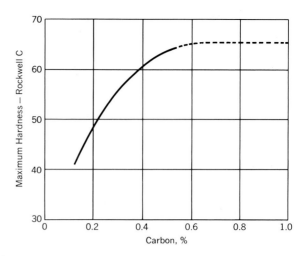

Fig. 21 Approximate maximum hardness attainable in steel with increase in carbon.

effectively reduces the susceptibility of stainless steels to pitting. Molybdenum is the most effective single alloying addition that increases the high-temperature creep strength of steel.

Tungsten (Wolfram). Tungsten is similar in behavior to molybdenum. However, of the two, molybdenum appears to be the more effective in increasing strength for a given cost. Tungsten is an important element in high-speed cutting and cemented-carbide tools.

Vanadium. Vanadium is, to some extent, a degasifying and deoxidizing agent, but is seldom used in that capacity because of high cost. It is applied chiefly as an alloying element in steel to increase strength, toughness and hardness. It is essentially a carbide-forming element which stabilizes the structure especially at high temperatures. Vanadium minimizes grain-growth tendencies, thus permitting much higher heat-treating temperatures. It also intensifies the individual properties of other elements in alloy steels. Small additions of vanadium (0.1 to 0.5%) accompanied by proper heat treatment, give steels containing 0.5 to 1.0% molybdenum pronounced improvement in high temperature creep properties. Vanadium improves the cutting properties of tool steels.

Aluminum. Aluminum is an important minor constituent of low-alloy steels. It is an efficient deoxidizer and is almost universally used in the production of killed steel. When added to steel in appreciable quantities, aluminum forms tightly adhering refractory oxide scales and thus increases resistance to scaling. It is difficult, however, to add appreciable amounts of this element to steel without producing undesirable effects. It is generally agreed that an excessive quantity of aluminum has a detrimental effect on creep properties, particularly in plain-carbon steel. This is attributable to its grain-refining effect and, what is even more serious, to its acceleration of spheroidization and graphitization of the carbide phase.

In the amounts customarily added, aluminum does not increase resistance to ordinary forms of corrosion. Actually, because of its avidity for oxygen, steels of high aluminum content generally contain numerous alumina inclusions. These inclusions tend to produce pitting

corrosion under conditions favorable for corrosive attack. Aluminum, however, increases resistance to oxidation when applied to steel as a surface coating, as in the calorizing process.

Titanium and Columbium (Niobium). These are potent carbide-forming elements. Titanium is also a good deoxidizer and denitrider. These elements are most effective in the chromium-nickel austenitic alloys (18-8 type) where they react more readily with carbon than does chromium. This allows the chromium to remain in solid solution and in the concentrations necessary to maintain the "stainlessness" (corrosion resistance) of the steel. Titanium and columbium (or columbium plus tantalum) are sometimes used to reduce air-hardening tendencies and to increase resistance to oxidation in steel containing up to 14% Cr. These elements seem to have a beneficial effect on the long-time high-temperature properties of chromium-nickel stainless steels. Both columbium and titanium have been used in some of the "super alloys" to improve high-temperature properties.

Copper. Addition of copper in small amounts improves the resistance of steel to atmospheric corrosion and lowers the rate of attack in reducing acids. Copper is not resistant to sulfur compounds at elevated temperatures. Consequently, it is not ordinarily used in low alloy steels intended for high temperature service where sulfur is a major component of the environment, as in combustion gases. Copper is added (up to 1%) in low-alloy constructional steels to improve yield strength and resistance to atmospheric corrosion. Its presence in some of the high-alloy steels increases resistance to corrosion by sulfuric acid. Copper, in amounts between 2.0 and 4.0%, also has been added to certain complex high-alloy austenitic steels, in conjunction with molybdenum, titanium and columbium, to cause precipitation hardening, thereby improving the creep-rupture properties.

Heat-treating practices

The properties of steel can be altered through modification of its microstructure by heat treatment. Various heat treatments may be used to meet specific requirements as to hardness and ductility, to improve machinability, to refine grain structure, to remove internal stresses, or to obtain high strength levels and impact properties. The heat treatments commonly employed—annealing, normalizing, spheroidizing, hardening (quenching), and tempering—are briefly described in the following:

Annealing. This is a general term applied to two distinctly different heat treatments more properly described as full anneal and "process" anneal.

In full annealing, the steel is heated at a predetermined rate to about 100F above the upper limit (locus of A_3, Fig. 14) of the critical range; it is held there for a suitable length of time, and then allowed to cool at a controlled rate in the furnace. The microstructure of fully annealed hypoeutectoid steel (containing less than 0.80% carbon) consists of ferrite and pearlite. A full anneal refines grain structure and provides a relatively soft, ductile material free of internal stresses.

The process anneal, sometimes referred to as stress-relieving, is carried out at temperatures below the criti-

cal range, usually between 950 and 1300F. The process anneal is used to improve the ductility and decrease residual stresses in work-hardened steel and, in some cases, is employed to obtain certain desired tensile and impact properties.

Normalizing. This heat treatment is, in effect, a special annealing process, except that the steel is allowed to cool in air from temperatures above the critical. Normalizing is sometimes used as a homogenization procedure, and the absolute assurance of eliminating any prior history of the material. Normalizing relieves the internal stresses caused by previous working and, while it produces sufficient softness and ductility for many purposes, yet it leaves the steel harder and with higher tensile strength than after full annealing. For the purpose of removing cooling stresses, normalizing is often followed by tempering (see Tempering).

Spheroidizing. The usual purpose of spheroidizing (another type of annealing) is to soften the steel sufficiently, and improve its machinability. Heating fine pearlite for a long time just below the lower critical temperature of the steel, followed by very slow cooling, will cause spheroidization—an agglomeration of the iron carbide (Fe_3C), which eventually becomes rounded and assumes the globular or spheroidal shape shown in Fig. 22. The properties of this product are similar to those of coarser pearlite. This treatment is most commonly applied to the higher carbon (above 0.45% C) and hypereutectoid steels.

Hardening (Quenching). When steels of the higher-carbon grades are heated to produce austenite and then cooled rapidly (quenched), the austenite transforms into the constituent "martensite" (see Fig. 19). Martensite is formed at temperatures below about 400F, depending on the carbon content and the type and amount of alloying elements in the steel. It is the hardest form of heat-treated steels and has high strength and resistance to abrasion. Martensitic steels have poor impact strength and are difficult, if not impossible, to machine.

Tempering. Normalizing some air-hardening steels and liquid-quenching treatments impart the desired degree of hardness to the steel but also make it brittle. The object of tempering, a secondary treatment, is to remove some of that brittleness by allowing certain transforma-

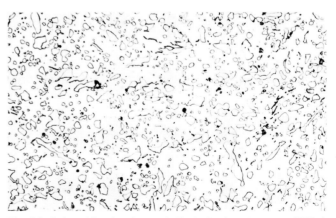

Fig. 22 Spheroidization in steel. Typical microstructure (750x) reduced about ¾. The Fe₃C has been almost completely agglomerated.

tions to proceed in hardened steel. It involves heating to a predetermined temperature, always below the critical, followed by any desired rate of cooling. Some of the hardness of the steel is lost by tempering, but its toughness is increased, and stresses set up by quenching are eliminated. The higher the tempering temperature the softer and tougher the steel will become. Some steels may become embrittled on slowly cooling from certain tempering temperatures. Steels so affected are said to be "temper-brittle." To overcome this difficulty, steels of that type are cooled rapidly (quenched) from the tempering temperature.

Mechanical working of steel

Metals may be shaped directly by casting or formed by mechanical working, which also imparts desirable properties. Metals may be worked either hot or cold. The initial working of the metal, as in forging, pressing, rolling and piercing, is almost always a hot operation, while subsequent working, as in drawing, forming, and stamping, is usually a cold operation. Any mechanical work applied to the metal below its recrystallization temperature is cold work. Mechanical work performed above the recrystallization temperature of steel is hot work, and the simultaneous annealing which occurs at that temperature prevents stress- and work-hardening. For satisfactory plasticity, hot work is usually performed above the transformation temperature (A_3, Fig. 14), which varies with the composition of the steel.

The temperature at which steel is mechanically worked has a profound effect on its properties. Cold work increases the hardness, tensile strength, and yield point, but its indices of ductility—elongation and reduction of area—are decreased. The extent of the work-hardening, with progressive elongation of the grains in the direction of working, depends on the amount of cold work and on the material. If the work-hardening caused by the necessary shaping operation becomes excessive, further work will cause fracture. For this reason the metal must be given some sort of heat-treatment to restore its ductility.

Hot-working improves the quality of the steel by closing blowholes in the ingot, thus increasing its homogeneity and soundness. The crystal structure is refined (reduced in size), which increases the ductility and toughness of the metal. Hot work does not harden the steel during the deformation process. It is a rapid and comparatively inexpensive method of production for tolerable dimensional accuracy and surface appearance. Because the forces involved in hot working steel are substantially less than those necessary for cold working, less power is required in forming by this method.

There is a great variety of steelworking equipment for shaping and forming steel products used in industry. The following deals briefly with the working of steel into plate, strip, tubing, headers, and other parts for boiler construction.

Methods of hot-working

Forging. Forging is the working of metal by intermittent or continuous application of force. A forging hammer works the metal by successive blows, while in a forging press the pressure is applied slowly, and the steel is thoroughly kneaded in every direction.

Steam hammers used in boiler works are of the open-die type, but much forging of steel products is done in closed dies by drop forging. Hydraulic or steam-hydraulic presses are used to make large forgings. Nozzles, drum heads, saddles, and other boiler parts are usually formed on presses (*see Chapter 31*) using suitably shaped dies.

At the B&W Tubular Products division, ingots are hot-worked into blooms of rectangular cross section, which are reheated and rolled into rounds for the manufacture of seamless tubing. When extra sectional thickness is required in a tubular element, the tube is upset in mechanical forging presses. Forging operations are also used to manufacture elbows, certain tees and other fittings used in boiler systems. The elbows are made by pushing a hot tube section over a tapered curved mandrel or "horn." The mandrel has the desired shape so as to achieve a uniform tube-to-elbow deformation during this operation.

Rolling. An expeditious method of reducing steel to shape is by rolling, and much the greater part of steel tonnage is so worked. The cast or forged metal in the form of ingot, slab, bar or billet is first brought to the proper temperature throughout and is then passed through rolls which revolve in opposite directions. The flow of metal is continuous and almost entirely in a longitudinal direction. The cross-sectional area is reduced, the internal structure is refined by reduction in grain size and change in shape (compared with cast or unworked metal), and the metal is shaped to the desired form.

Production of plates. Plate steels are very important in boiler construction. The drum shell, drum ends (heads), certain drum internals, and certain structural supports are made from plate.

Plates are made from ingots of rectangular shape by using a slabbing mill, which performs the same function as a blooming mill but permits rolling the wider sections desired in the initial operation for the production of plates, sheet, and strip. After conditioning and reheating, the rough slabs are rolled to finished plates on either a sheared-plate mill or a Universal mill. Some extremely heavy plates may be rolled directly from the ingot. Sheared plate is rolled between straight horizontal rolls only and must be trimmed to the finished size on all edges. Universal-mill plates are rolled between horizontal rolls and vertical rolls and are trimmed on the ends only. Mills of various designs are used for rolling plates.

For sheared-mill plates it is customary to roll the ingots or slabs in both directions (cross-rolling) to give uniform physical properties whether the test sample is taken parallel or transverse to the greatest dimension. On the Universal mill, plates are rolled in one direction only, the vertical rolls producing a straight, fairly parallel mill edge. The product of such a mill cannot be expected to have uniform properties in both directions. This metallurgical practice is important in the judicious selection of suitable quality plate material for various parts of the boiler. Drum plate, for instance, must be of higher quality and uniformity than plate used solely for structural purposes.

Chapter 29   Properties of structural materials

Mechanical properties of steel

Steel is the basic material in the construction of pressure parts for fossil-fuel steam-generating units and nuclear steam supply systems. Steels of different properties are used, each especially suited for one or more specific purposes. Each steel must have properties suitable for manufacturing as well as for long service life. Steels within each grade must be consistent in their properties, and tests must be run on each batch of material to prove its consistency.

Specifications standardizing all the conditions relating to the test piece and the method of testing have been formulated by the American Society for Testing and Materials and other authorities. By conforming to these specifications, it is possible to assure obtaining certain minimum mechanical properties that determine the acceptability of a steel for a particular use.

Tensile test

The tensile test, a gradually applied undirectional pull, determines the maximum nominal load that a material can withstand before actually breaking.

The relationship between stress (load per unit area) and the corresponding strain (deformation) in the test piece is illustrated in the stress-strain diagrams (a) and (b) of Fig. 1. The metal begins to stretch as soon as the load is applied, and during the period of the metal's elastic behavior the strain is directly proportional to the stress (Hooke's Law, elongation is proportional to load ÷ area). Consequently, if the stress is released at

any point along O-A (in either diagram, Fig. 1), the test coupon will return to its initial dimensions. However, if the stress is increased beyond the value A, the metal will no longer continue to be perfectly elastic (there will be a permanent elongation), and the linear relationship (proportionality) between stress and strain ceases. The value A is known as the proportional limit of the material, and in this elementary discussion it may be considered practically the same as the elastic limit, which may be defined as the maximum unit stress that can be developed just before permanent elongation occurs. The exact location of these limits involves laborious techniques and requires extremely sensitive measuring devices.

The unit stress at which a ductile material suddenly continues to elongate without further increase in load is known as its yield point (YP). Since the true yield point for most metals is indefinite and, in common with the proportional and elastic limits, is difficult to determine with accuracy, these terms are being supplanted by "yield strength." Yield strength (YS), which can be readily determined, is the unit stress at which the permanent elongation of the metal reaches an arbitrarily specified value, usually 0.1, 0.2, or 0.5% of the gage length of the test piece.

If the loading is continued after the point of yield strength has been reached, a test piece of homogeneous composition and uniform cross section will be elongated uniformly over its length, with a corresponding reduction in area. Eventually a constriction or "necking down" will occur (in ductile material), usually in the region of the middle third of the test piece (Fig. 2). In other materials the necking down may not be localized but may occur as a more or less uniform reduction in area along the full gage length to the instant of rupture. In all cases with ductile materials, however, an appreciable increase in elongation occurs over the portion of reduced area. The elongation before the specimen finally breaks increases with the ductility of the steel. The maximum applied load, in lb required to pull the specimen apart, divided by the area, in sq in. of the original cross section, is a value known as the ultimate or tensile strength (TS).

Ductility of the metal is determined by measuring the increase in length (total elongation) and the final area at

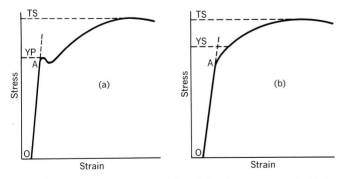

Fig. 1 Stress-strain diagram, (a) mild carbon steel, (b) high-tensile steel and nonferrous metals.

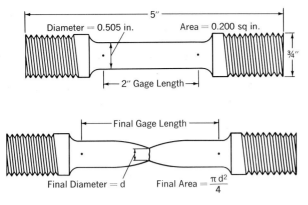

Fig. 2 Tensile-test specimen before and after testing (ASTM standard).

the plane of rupture after the specimen has broken. Ductility values are expressed as the percent change of the original length and/or area. In general the strength of a metal decreases as the ductility increases. Conversely, very strong metals are likely to be hard and brittle, i.e., lacking in ductility. To suit the requirements of an intended application, steels are mechanically worked or heat treated to develop varying combinations of these properties.

Hardness test

Hardness may be defined as resistance to indentation under static or dynamic loads and also as resistance to scratch, abrasion, cutting, or drilling. To the metallurgist, the property of hardness is of considerable significance in its indication of other important characteristics of the metal: heat treatment, machinability, wear resistance, and fabrication.

Hardness is usually determined by using the Rockwell, Brinell, or Vickers (diamond pyramid) hardness testers, all of which measure resistance to indentation under static loads. A hardened steel ball, a spheroconical diamond, or a diamond pyramid is impressed into the material to be tested for hardness. The pressure is applied under a definite load and for a specified time. For the Rockwell machine, the hardness is read directly on a dial gage. Using the Brinell and Vickers machines, the diameter and diagonals respectively of the impressions, measured by means of a microscope, are converted to hardness numbers by reference to tables. Hardness can also be determined by a scleroscope test in which the loss in kinetic energy of a falling metal weight, absorbed by indentation upon impact on the metal being tested, is indicated by the height of rebound.

In special cases where it is desired to determine the hardness of microscopic constituents of steel, such as ferrite, pearlite, sigma and delta phases, a microhardness tester (the Tukon machine) is used. In this test operation, which is completely automatic, the indentation is made by applying either a Knoop or a diamond-pyramid indenter under a definite load and for a specified time. The diagonals of either type indentation are measured by means of a microscope, and the readings are converted to hardness numbers (Knoop or Vickers, depending on the type of indenter used) by reference to tables.

The approximate relationship between the several hardness scales is given in Fig. 3.

Impact test

Notched-bar impact tests are also important in the field of mechanical testing. These tests determine how well a material is actually able to equalize concentrated stresses, and they are sometimes taken as a measure of "toughness," a term difficult to define otherwise.

The two types of impact testing machines widely used are the Charpy and the Izod. In the Charpy test the specimen is a simple horizontal beam supported at both ends, while in the Izod test the specimen is treated as a cantilever beam. Standard impact bars for both tests are illustrated diagrammatically by Fig. 4. In both tests the bars are struck by a single blow of a swinging pendulum. The energy absorbed by the specimen is related to the height of rebound and can be read directly in ft-lb on a calibrated dial or scale.

Other tests

Deformation tests are also made to determine the ductility of steel. These include cupping, bending, flattening, and flare tests. They furnish visual evidence of the ductility of the tube material.

High temperature properties of steel

Tensile- or yield-strength data determined at normal temperatures cannot be used as a guide to the mechanical properties of metals at higher temperatures. Even

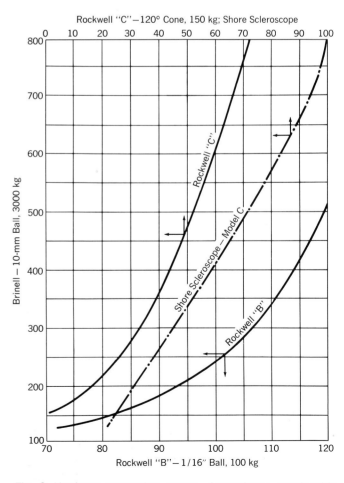

Fig. 3 Hardness-conversion curves. Approximate relationship between Brinell, Rockwell C, Rockwell B, and Shore Sclero-scope testing systems.

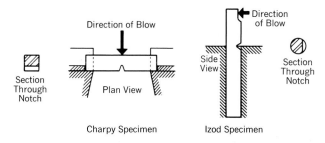

Fig. 4 Method of striking Charpy and Izod notched-bar impact specimens.

though such tests are made at the higher temperatures, the data are inadequate for designing equipment for long-time service at these temperatures. This is true because continued application of load produces a very slow continuous deformation, which may be significant and measurable over a period of time and may eventually lead to fracture, depending on the stress and temperatures involved. This slow deformation of continuously stressed metal, with time a very important factor, is called "creep."

The importance of this phenomenon is now widely recognized, and extensive studies of creep characteristics (including the creep-rupture time) at operating temperatures have been and continue to be made on metals and alloys, both by manufacturers and users of metal. The creep and creep-rupture test data now available provide the basis for a much more rational approach to the design of high-temperature equipment than was possible using only the data from short-time high-temperature tensile tests. Thus, for temperatures exceeding about 700F, the maximum allowable working stresses for ferrous materials in power boilers set by ASME are based on long-time creep and creep-rupture (stress-rupture) tests (*see Creep Test and Creep-Rupture Test*).

The *ASME Boiler and Pressure Vessel Code*, Section I, Power Boilers, has established the maximum allowable stress values for pressure parts to be no higher than the lowest of:

1. One-quarter of the minimum specified tensile strength.
2. One-quarter of the tensile strength at temperature as reported by test data.
3. $62\frac{1}{2}\%$ of the specified minimum yield strength at room temperature.
4. $62\frac{1}{2}\%$ of the yield strength at temperature as reported by test data.
5. A conservative average of the stress to give a creep rate of 0.01% in 1000 hours (1% in 100,000 hours) as reported by test data.
6. 67% of the average or 80% of the minimum stress to produce rupture in 100,000 hours as reported by test data.

Tensile strength

Although the design of high-temperature equipment generally requires use of creep and creep-rupture test data, the short-time tensile test does indicate the strength properties of metals up to the creep range of the material. This test also provides information on ductility characteristics helpful in fabrication.

The procedure used in conducting high-temperature tensile tests should conform to the requirements of ASTM Specification E21. In this test, an electric-resistance furnace maintains the standard tensile specimen (*see Fig. 2*) at the selected constant temperature during application of the load. A constant-loading pull at a rate not exceeding 0.05 in./min is applied, because rapid rates of loading may produce inordinately high ultimate strength values. The tests are usually made on normalized or fully annealed material, corresponding to its prospective service condition.

The ultimate strength of plain-carbon steel and a number of alloy steels (Croloys), as determined by short-time tensile tests over a temperature range from 100F to 1300-1500F, is shown in Fig. 5. In general, the results of these tests indicate that strength decreases with increase in temperature, although there is a region for the austenitic Croloys between 400 and 900F where strength is fairly constant. An exception to the general rule is the increase in strength over that at room temperature of plain-carbon steel (with corresponding decrease in ductility) over the temperature range from 100 to 600F. A similar increase occurs with certain low-alloy steels. The temperature zone between 400 and 700F is often called the "blue-brittle" range, because of the bluish oxide film that forms on steel in this temperature range. As the temperature is increased beyond 600-750F, the strength of the carbon and some of the alloy steels falls off from that at room temperature with a corresponding increase in ductility.

Creep test

It has long been known that certain nonmetallic materials, such as glass, undergo slow and continuous de-

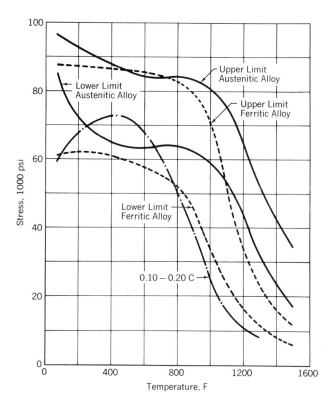

Fig. 5 Tensile strength of various steels at temperatures to 1500F.

formation with time when subjected to stress. The concept of creep in metallic materials, however, did not attract serious attention until the early 1920's. Results of several investigations at that time demonstrated that rupture of a metallic material could occur when it is subjected to a stress at elevated temperatures for a sufficiently long time, even though the load applied is considerably lower than that necessary to cause fracture in the short-time tensile test at the same temperature. Although there are still many gaps in the theory of metallic creep, the creep characteristics established since 1930 for many metals and alloys have proved of great practical value in indicating the fitness of these materials for continuous service under stress at elevated temperatures. This information has also been useful in the development of better alloys for such service.

The earliest investigations of creep in the U.S. were sponsored by B&W in 1926. Many steels now used successfully in power-generating units and in the petroleum-refining and chemical industries were tested and proved in the course of these investigations, using the best equipment available at the time. Extensive studies of the creep and creep-rupture characteristics of metals have been in progress for a number of years at B&W's Alliance Research Center. The laboratory shown in Fig. 6 is equipped with modern creep and creep-rupture testing facilities.

The general method of creep testing is defined by ASTM Specification E150. A test piece, maintained at constant temperature, is subjected to a fixed static tensile load. The deformation of the test sample is accurately measured at regular intervals during the test (*see Fig. 7*). The duration of the test may range from 1000 to

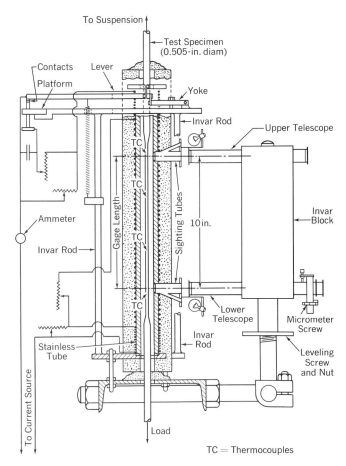

Fig. 7 Creep-test station showing specimen, heating element, and telescopes for observing elongation.

Fig. 6 Creep and creep-rupture laboratory at B&W's Alliance Research Center.

Table 1
Creep stress for ferrous tube materials
for high-temperature service, pounds per square inch

Temp, F	Material					
	SA-210 A1		SA-213 T22		SA-213 TP304H	
	1% per 10,000 hr	1% per 100,000 hr	1% per 10,000 hr	1% per 100,000 hr	1% per 10,000 hr	1% per 100,000 hr
800	21,400	13,840				
850	14,600	9,100				
900	9,900	5,980				
950	6,700	3,900				
1,000	4,550	2,580	13,000	8,000	25,500	17,900
1,050			10,200	6,300	20,500	14,000
1,100			8,000	5,000	16,500	11,100
1,150			5,000	3,700	13,300	8,900
1,200			3,150	2,700	10,800	7,200
1,250					8,700	5,700
1,300					7,000	4,500
1,350					5,700	3,600
1,400					4,600	2,900
1,450					3,700	2,300
1,500					2,950	1,800

Chemical Composition—%			
	SA-210 A1	SA-213 T22	SA-213 TP304H
C	0.27 max	0.15 max	0.04 to 0.10
Mn	0.93 max	0.30 to 0.60	2.00 max
P	0.048 max	0.030 max	0.040 max
S	0.058 max	0.030 max	0.030 max
Si	0.10 min	0.050 max	0.75 max
Cr		1.90 to 2.60	18.0 to 20.0
Mo		0.87 to 1.13	
Ni			8.0 to 11.0

The creep-stress data in this table are reproduced, by permission, from Metals Properties Council reports ASTM DS-11S1, DS-6S2, and DS-5S2.

10,000 hr, or even longer. A diagrammatic plot of the observed length of the specimen against elapsed time is usually of the form illustrated in Fig. 8.

The curve representing creep is divided into three stages. It begins after the initial extension (O-A), which is simply the measure of deformation of the specimen caused by the loading. The magnitude of this initial extension depends on test conditions, varying with load and temperature, and normally increasing with increases in temperature and load. The first stage of creep (A-B), referred to as "primary creep," is characterized by a decreasing rate of deformation during the period. The second stage of creep (B-C), referred to as "secondary creep," is usually characterized by extremely small variations in rate of deformation; hence this period is essentially one of constant rate of creep. The third stage of creep (C-D), referred to as "tertiary creep," is characterized by an accelerating rate of deformation leading to fracture. The important thing to the engineer is that these stages of creep always occur to greater or lesser degree.

In this country, to simplify the practical application of creep data it is customary to establish two values of stress in lb per sq in. (for a material at a temperature) that will produce two corresponding rates of creep (elongation): one of 0.1% per 1000 hr and the other of 0.01% per 1000 hr, or, as usually expressed: 1.0% per 10,000 hr and 100,000 hr, respectively. Table 1 presents creep-test data for ferrous tube materials of three different compositions.

For any specified temperature, several creep tests must be run under different loads (*see typical curves, Fig. 9*). The creep rate during the period of secondary creep is determined from these curves and is plotted against the stress. When these data are plotted to logarithmic scales, the points for each specimen usually lie on a line with a slight curvature. The minimum creep-rate for any stress level of interest can be obtained from this graph, and the curve can also be extrapolated to obtain creep-rates for stresses beyond those for which data are obtained. Fig. 10 presents such creep-rate curves for Croloy 2¼ at 1000, 1100 and 1200F.

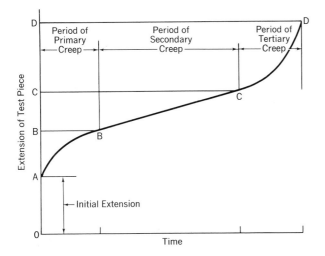

Fig. 8 Typical creep-test (diagrammatic) specimen held at constant load and temperature.

The shape of the creep curve depends on the chemical composition and microstructure of the metal as well as the applied load and test temperature. The creep behavior of steel is influenced also by various metallurgical factors which are detailed below. Tests of long duration provide the most reliable data, both as to the accuracy of the observation and the attainment of structural equilibrium of the metal.

Creep-rupture test

This test, formerly called the stress-rupture test, is essentially an overload creep test continued to actual rupture of the specimen. The more descriptive names "creep-to-rupture" and "creep-rupture" are now more frequently used for this test.

In this context creep-rupture strength is the stress (initial load/initial area) at which rupture occurs in some specified time in an air atmosphere in the temperature range in which creep takes place. The time for rupture at any temperature is a function of the applied load. Since the concept of this test was first formulated in 1937 and 1938, it has rapidly gained favor as a necessary supplement to the regular creep test in evaluating the load-carrying ability of metals at elevated temperatures.

Generally, the equipment employed in making the rupture test is the same as that used for the creep test. However, while the elongation of a specimen during a creep test usually varies from 5 to 250 microinches per day, the elongation during a rupture test may be 100 times greater, or even more. Consequently, different instruments for measuring the elongation of the specimen are required. A logarithmic-scale plot of stress versus time for fracture of specimens generally takes the form of the curves shown for Croloy 2¼ in Fig. 11.

In general, rapid rates of elongation indicate a transgranular (ductile) fracture, and slow rates of elongation indicate an intergranular (brittle) fracture. As a rule, surface oxidation is present when the fracture is transgranular, while visible intercrystalline oxidation may or may not be present when the fracture is intergranular. Because of the discontinuities produced by the presence of intercrystalline oxides, the time to rupture at a given

temperature-load relationship may be appreciably reduced. In Fig. 11, the trend of the data band at 1200F is much steeper than the bands for lower temperatures. This is to be expected because 1200F is above the usual temperature limits for Croloy 2¼ for maximum resistance to oxidation. Thus excessive scaling occurs in the long-time rupture tests conducted at 1200F.

The duration of the rupture test of a single specimen may be a few hours to 10,000 hr or longer. A complete creep-rupture test program for a given steel actually consists of a series of tests at constant temperature with each specimen loaded at a different level. The time for rupture of each specimen is noted. It is customary in the report of test data to give the stress for fracture in 100, 1000, 10,000 and 100,000 hr (*see Fig. 12*). Since tests are not normally conducted for more than 10,000 hr, the values for fracture times longer than this are determined by extrapolation. At B&W's Alliance Research Center, it is customary to load the specimens so that one or more at each temperature will run for at least 5000 hr, and usually for 10,000 hr or more. The longer testing times give greater assurance that the material has reached structural equilibrium, and also materially improve the accuracy of extrapolating the rupture strength for longer times.

In recent years an increasing amount of effort has been devoted to evaluating creep-rupture properties by parameter methods with the objective of discovering a correlation between short- and long-time tests. These studies are valuable because elevated-temperature tests which simulate actual operating times are time-consuming and costly. The relationship most widely used for evaluating creep-rupture properties is the Larson-Miller curve which assumes that all creep-rupture test points for a given material fall on a single curve according to the formula $T(20 + \log_{10}t) = $ constant, where T is the absolute

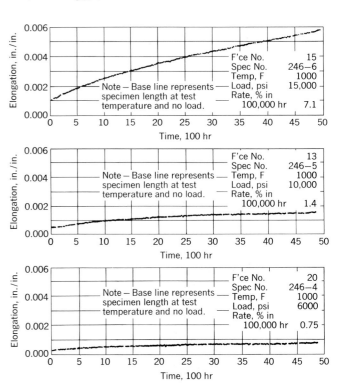

Fig. 9 Typical time-elongation curves for Croloy 2¼ tested for three loads at 1000F.

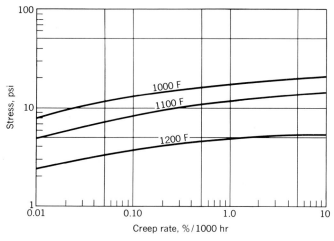

Fig. 10 Creep-rate curves for Croloy 2¼.

Some factors affecting creep

Creep of metals is a sensitive property and may be profoundly affected by a variety of metallurgical factors. Variations can occur because of differences in heat treatment, grain size, microstructure, or chemical composition of the test specimens. Other differences are attributable to such factors as fluctuations in temperature, rate of loading, and relative accuracy of measurement during the test. Thus it is practically impossible to duplicate test conditions precisely. In addition to variables in test conditions, there are inherent differences between different heats of steel, leading to a scatter of data.

Composition

It is generally recognized that the most direct way to improve the creep properties of a metal is by adding alloying elements. Carbide-forming elements, such as molybdenum, tungsten, and, to a lesser degree, chromium and vanadium effectively enhance the creep resistance of steels. Increased carbon content is beneficial up to a temperature range of approximately 900–1000F; above this range, however, variations in carbon content in most wrought steels appear to have little influence. Manganese and small additions of silicon have some effect in improving the resistance to creep at the lower temperatures. Aluminum, used as a deoxidizer in plain-carbon steel or

temperature, t is the rupture-time in hours. The value of 20 was determined as a constant most suitable for all materials. This formula is assumed to hold true regardless of the temperature at which the tests are conducted. The curve generated by applying this formula is actually a superposition of rupture curves at different temperatures. The temperature-time relationship performs the function of modifying the times to failure so that all the various curves fall on a single line. There are some limitations to the use of this approach. It is recognized that a relationship does not hold true if any major phase changes occur during the life of a material. Other changes in the structural stability of a steel might not be accounted for in the formula and this could lead to erroneous conclusions. In short, the expression, $T (20 + \log_{10} t)$ = constant, cannot account for all of the possible incongruities of an alloy. However, such studies are continuing in an effort to increase our knowledge of the elevated temperature properties of steels.

In addition to the normal creep-rupture tests where specimens are stressed uniaxially, tests are also being conducted on tubular specimens. These tests are conducted by maintaining a tubular section at a selected temperature and applying an internal pressure to supply the desired stress. Their purpose is to provide a more meaningful correlation of the results obtained by conventional creep-rupture tests with performance expected from tubular sections. This testing is part of B&W's continuing effort to study the creep-rupture properties of steels used in elevated temperature service.

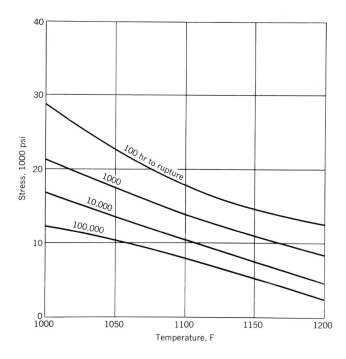

Fig. 12 Average stress for rupture for Croloy 2¼.

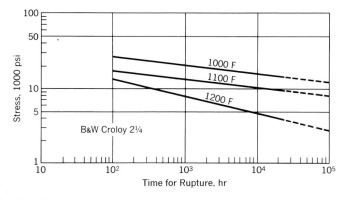

Fig. 11 Typical creep-rupture curves.

as an intentional addition in alloy steels, greatly reduces creep strength at high temperatures. Nickel additions are beneficial when used in sufficient amounts to produce an austenitic structure, which is more creep resistant than ferrite. At the higher temperatures, austenitic stainless steels (18 Cr-8 Ni type) and certain special alloys have creep properties much superior to low- or high-alloy ferritic steels.

Grain size

At the higher temperatures, experimental evidence strongly indicates that coarse-grained materials usually exhibit greater resistance to creep than fine-grained materials. Conversely, at the lower temperatures, fine-grain structures appear to be slightly superior. However, there are many exceptions to this rule, and no satisfactory explanation has been advanced to account for the specific effect of grain structure on the creep behavior of metals.

Heat treatment

The creep characteristics of metals are affected by heat treatment, which controls grain size and the stability of structure. When a metal is exposed to elevated temperatures for a long period of time, there is a tendency, under the stress and heat to which it is subjected, for the initial structure to attain a more stable state. For instance, lamellar pearlite may revert during service to the more stable spheroidized structure, which, in turn, brings about rapid deterioration in the creep strength of steel. After prolonged heating in the 900 to 1200F range, the carbide phase in plain-carbon and carbon-molybdenum steels may ultimately change to graphite, which, when highly localized, is believed to account for certain failures noted in service. Therefore, the selection of the best type of heat treatment for a particular high-temperature application should be based largely on the degree of stability that it would impart to the structure initially and also throughout the service life of the steel at elevated temperatures.

In general, experience has shown that, for service above approximately 950F, annealing (or normalizing) is the most suitable treatment. Age-hardenable alloys, intended for service in which creep resistance is required, are usually subjected to a dual heat treatment. In the initial heat treatment, the precipitating phase is brought into solution; the final heat treatment is to assure stability of the precipitated phase at the service temperature.

There is considerable interest at present in the use of steels with mechanical properties enhanced by heat treatment. Such steels are used for large pressure vessels designed to operate at stress levels higher than those allowable with normal steels. In these steels the higher strength is obtained by quenching and tempering. The maximum temperature for application of these vessels is approximately 850F. A large effort is being made at this time to define the creep-rupture properties of quenched and tempered steels.

Surface stability

Creep strength may be seriously impaired by surface reactions at elevated temperatures. By reduction in effective cross section from progressive oxidation or corrosion of the metal, the unit load is increased, and the rate of creep is accelerated. Under certain conditions, highly concentrated stresses may greatly accelerate and localize the mechanism of oxidation.

Surface stability may be enhanced by alloying additions of silicon, aluminum, chromium or nickel. Surface oxidation may also be decreased by applying protective coatings to the metal.

Method of manufacture

Minor variations in method of manufacture have markedly modified the creep behavior of steel. In general, investigations indicate that steel melted in the electric furnace is somewhat superior to open-hearth steel. This is probably because controls are more rigid and, therefore, variations encountered in deoxidation practice are generally less in the electric furnace. It is also recognized that killed steel is more creep resistant than rimmed or similar nondeoxidized steel. However, deoxidation of itself does not assure superior long-time high-temperature properties. For example, at 850F, steels deoxidized only with silicon and having a coarse grain structure are much more resistant to creep than steels deoxidized with large amounts of aluminum and of fine grain size. The detrimental effect of aluminum results from its acceleration of spheroidization and graphitization of the carbide phase. Both of these characteristics tend to lower creep resistance at elevated temperatures, while a coarse grain size and stability of structure tend to increase resistance to creep.

Steels used in boiler construction

A considerable variety of both carbon and alloy steels is used in boiler construction.

Plate steels

Since steam drums normally operate at approximately saturated steam temperature, the significant mechanical properties of steel for steam drums are the tensile and yield strengths rather than the creep strength. For special requirements and higher temperatures, there are certain advantages in going to higher-tensile-strength carbon-steel plate or to alloy-steel plate. Above 650F, reduction in working stresses is mandatory for carbon steels and some grades of alloy plate, while certain other alloy plate materials may be used for temperatures to 750F without reduction in working stress. A typical example is illustrated in Table 2, which lists several approved drum plate materials and the maximum allowable stress values in accordance with the *ASME Boiler and Pressure Vessel Code*, Section I, Power Boilers, December 31, 1975 addenda. Chemical and physical properties of these plates are given in the Code, Section II, Material Specifications.

Firebox quality plate is used for any part of a boiler subjected to pressure and exposed to the fire or products of combustion. For parts of the boiler subject to pressure and not exposed to fire or to products of combustion such as manway covers and drum heads, firebox or flange quality plate is used. For stationary boilers, B&W mainly uses thoroughly deoxidized (killed) carbon steel plate to SA-515 Grade 70 specifications. However, for certain service conditions such as to reduce plate thickness required for high pressure vessels to facilitate fabrication, for saving weight in marine work or because of design requirements, other grades of higher tensile steels including alloy-steel plate, such as manganese-molybdenum steel SA-302 Grade B, may be used.

The chemical composition and physical properties of several plate grades of carbon and low-alloy steels, approved by the ASME for the construction of boiler pres-

Table 2
Plate steels—maximum allowable stress values for ferrous materials, pounds per square inch

Spec Number	Grade	Nominal Composition	Spec Min Tensile	Notes	For metal temperatures, F, not exceeding							
					650	700	750	800	850	900	950	1000
Carbon steel												
SA-285 A	—		45,000	(1)	11,250	10,900	9,700	8,300	*6,600*	*5,000*	—	—
SA-285 B	—		50,000	(1)	12,500	12,100	11,000	9,400	*7,300*	*5,000*	—	—
SA-285 C	—		55,000	(1)	13,750	13,250	12,050	10,200	*7,800*	*5,000*	—	—
SA-515 55	C-Si		55,000	(1)	13,750	13,250	12,050	10,200	*7,800*	*5,000*	*3,000*	*1,500*
SA-515 60	C-Si		60,000	(1)	15,000	14,350	12,950	10,800	*7,800*	*5,000*	*3,000*	*1,500*
SA-515 65	C-Si		65,000	(1)	16,250	15,500	13,850	11,400	*7,800*	*5,000*	*3,000*	*1,500*
SA-515 70	C-Si		70,000	(1)	17,500	16,600	14,750	12,000	*7,800*	*5,000*	*3,000*	*1,500*
Low-alloy steel												
SA-302 A	Mn-½ Mo		75,000	(2)	18,750	18,750	18,300	17,700	16,800	*13,700*	*8,200*	*4,800*
SA-302 B	Mn-½ Mo		80,000	(2)	20,000	20,000	19,600	18,800	17,900	*13,700*	*8,200*	*4,800*

Notes: (1) Upon prolonged exposure to temperatures above about 800 F, the carbide phase of carbon steel may be converted to graphite.

(2) Upon prolonged exposure to temperatures above about 875 F, the carbide phase of carbon-molybdenum steel may be converted to graphite.

(3) Stress values shown in italics are permissible but use of these materials at these temperatures is not current practice under, *ASME Boiler and Pressure Vessel Code*, Section I.

Chemical Requirements

SA-285

Element	Grade B %
Carbon, max..................	0.22
Manganese, max..............	0.90
Phosphorus, max..............	0.035
Sulfur, max....................	0.045
Copper,* when copper steel is specified:	
Ladle analysis...............	0.20-0.35
Check analysis..............	0.18-0.37

*When specified, the maximum incidental copper content shall be 0.25%.

SA-515

Element	Grade 55 %	Grade 70 %
Carbon, max:		
1 in. and under..	0.20	0.31
Over 1 to 2 in., incl..............	0.22	0.33
Over 2 to 4 in., incl..............	0.24	0.35
Over 4 to 8 in., incl..............	0.26	0.35
Over 8 to 12 in., incl..............	0.28	0.35
Manganese, max...	0.90	0.90
Phosphorus, max..	0.035	0.035
Sulfur, max.........	0.04	0.04
Silicon:		
Ladle analysis....	0.15 to 0.30	0.15 to 0.30
Check analysis...	0.13 to 0.33	0.13 to 0.33

SA-302

Element	Grade B %
Carbon, max:	
For plates 1 in. and under in thickness............	0.20
For plates over 1 to 2 in., incl, in thickness.......	0.23
For plates over 2 in. in thickness.............	0.25
Manganese:	
Ladle analysis.............	1.15 to 1.50
Check analysis............	1.10 to 1.55
Phosphorus, max...........	0.035
Sulfur, max.................	0.040
Silicon:	
Ladle analysis.............	0.15 to 0.30
Check analysis............	0.13 to 0.32
Molybdenum:	
Ladle analysis.............	0.45 to 0.60
Check analysis............	0.41 to 0.64
Nickel:	
Ladle analysis.............	—
Check analysis............	—

Tensile Requirements

SA-285

	Grade B
Tensile strength,† psi..........	50,000 to 60,000
Yield point, min, psi...........	27,000
Elongation in 8 in. (203 mm), min, %†....................	25
Elongation in 2 in. (50.8 mm), min, %.....................	28

†See ASME code for additional limitations.

SA-515

	Grade 55	Grade 70
Tensile strength, psi..............	55,000 to 65,000	70,000 to 85,000
Yield point, min, psi..............	30,000	38,000
Elongation in 8 in., min, %.........	23	17
Elongation in 2 in., min, %.........	27	21

SA-302

	Grade B
Tensile strength, psi........	80,000 to 100,000
Yield point, min, psi.........	50,000
Elongation in 8 in., min, %..	15†
Elongation in 2 in., min, %..	18†

sure parts are also given in Table 2. Typical microstructures of three plate steels are shown in Fig. 13.

Tube steels

Boiler, furnace-water-wall, and economizer heating surfaces are generally made of hot-rolled low-carbon seamless or electric-resistance-welded steel tubes, although small-diameter tubes or special sizes may be cold drawn and annealed. Seamless tubes are supplied for high-pressure units requiring a wall thickness beyond the welded tube limits.

Medium-carbon steel (0.35% C max) finds considerable application for boiler and furnace-wall tubes, since

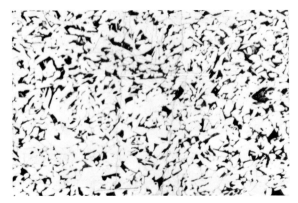

A. SA-285 Grade B

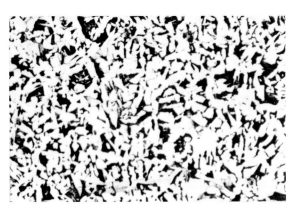

B. SA-515 Grade 70

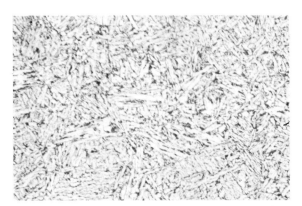

C. SA-302 Grade B

Fig. 13 Typical structures of plate steels (100x). White matrix, ferrite; dark areas, pearlite; with carbide phase appearing in mottled areas (Widmanstatten pattern) in B and C. Steel shown in A used principally in nonpressure parts. Steels shown in B and C used in pressure parts.

this grade will permit higher stress levels than low-carbon steel in the 540-685F saturation-temperature region usually encountered. The mechanical strength properties are also superior to low-carbon steel, and therefore lighter-wall tubes may be used for equivalent design conditions.

The highest metal temperatures of pressure parts in the steam generating unit occur in the superheater and reheater. Consequently, these tubes are made of material having superior high-temperature properties and resistance to oxidation. Carbon steel is a suitable and economical material to about 850-950F metal temperature, depending on pressure. Above this range, alloy steels are required because of the low oxidation resistance and the low allowable stresses of carbon steel. Usually two or more alloys are used in the construction of the superheater. The lower alloy, such as carbon-molybdenum steel, is used toward the inlet section, while the so-called low and intermediate chromium-alloy steels are used toward the outlet, where the steam and metal temperatures are increasing. Stainless steel tubes are required in the hottest sections of the superheater to meet the operating conditions of modern high-pressure (1800-4000 psi) high-temperature (1000-1050F) central station boilers.

The B&W Croloy steels. For many years B&W has been active in the development of tubing alloys for high-temperature applications. A considerable number of the presently accepted ASME standard steels for superheater practice were developed originally by B&W. These steels with the designation "Croloy," meaning chromium-containing alloy, are available in a graded series of intermediate Cr-Mo alloys and also in stainless Cr or Cr-Ni grades.

The intermediate Croloy steels (up to and including Croloy 9) are complex chromium steels with varying contents of molybdenum. These alloy steels are magnetic and have normal thermal transformations. They may be considered "ferritic" steels in that their microstructure, in the annealed state, is composed mainly of ferrite (alpha iron) and carbides. In general, the behavior of these alloys is somewhat similar to that of high-carbon steel, although they are more ductile for a given strength because of the absence of the equivalent amount of carbide. Heating to or above their transformation temperature, required for forming and after welding, makes these alloys so susceptible to air-hardening that an annealing or stress-relieving (tempering) treatment is necessary to restore toughness and ductility following these operations. Addition of carbon-forming (stabilizing) elements, such as titanium and niobium tends to restrict air-hardening of the Croloys on heat treating at temperatures up to 1700F. Gradual hardening takes place above these temperatures.

Stainless Croloys are low-carbon chromium-nickel steels containing above 16% Cr with sufficient nickel to provide an austenitic structure at all temperatures. Moderate amounts of other elements, such as molybdenum, niobium, niobium plus tantalum, titanium, and silicon, may be added for special purposes. Austenitic Croloys are normally nonmagnetic but may become slightly magnetic when cold worked. These steels do not undergo transformations in the usual sense and therefore

cannot be hardened by heat treatment. They can be hardened and strengthened materially, however, by cold working. Included in the austenitic group of stainless Croloys are the widely known 18-8 type steels (18% Cr and 8% Ni).

Ferritic stainless Croloys, usually referred to as "high-chromium irons" or "straight-chromium steels," are iron-chromium alloys containing chromium in excess of 11.5%. Compared with austenitic (chromium-nickel) Croloys, these steels are ferromagnetic, possess less ductility, are notch sensitive, and are subject to excessive grain growth on welding or other treatment at high temperatures. Despite these features which tend to curtail their utility to some degree, the high-chromium irons occupy an important place in industry in both corrosion- and heat-resisting applications. The 12%, 18% and 27% chromium steels are representative of the ferritic group of stainless Croloys.

Applications of tube steels. The Croloy steels in widest use for superheater tubing in boiler service are Croloy ½, Croloy 1¼, Croloy 2¼, and Croloy 9. The most widely used stainless steels of the austenitic 18-8 types are TP 304 H and the titanium-stabilized TP 321 H. Table 3 lists the tube materials used for heat-absorbing surfaces in fossil-fuel units. This table also gives the ASME material specifications and the maximum allowable metal temperatures recommended by B&W. These temperature limits apply to the surface in contact with the flue gas and are based solely on the resistance-to-oxidation characteristics of the metal.

Table 3
Ferrous tube material specifications and maximum allowable metal temperatures

Material	ASME Specification	Max Allowable Metal Temp, F[1]
Carbon steel	SA-192	950
Carbon steel	SA-210 Grade A1	950
Carbon steel	SA-210 Grade C	950
Carbon steel, (ERW)	SA-178 Grade A	850
Carbon steel, (ERW)	SA-178 Grade C	950
Carbon moly	SA-209 Grade T1a	975
Croloy ½	SA-213 Grade T2	1025[2]
Croloy 1¼	SA-213 Grade T11	1050
Croloy 2	SA-213 Grade T3b	1100
Croloy 2¼	SA-213 Grade T22	1125
Croloy 5	SA-213 Grade T5	1150
Croloy 9	SA-213 Grade T9	1200[3]
Croloy 304H	SA-213 Grade TP-304H	1400[3]
Croloy 321H	SA-213 Grade TP-321H	1400[3]

[1] Metal temperature of side in contact with flue gas.

[2] The mean wall temperature for selecting tube thickness shall not exceed 1000 F.

[3] For oil fired units temperature of side in contact with flue gas must not exceed 1150 F.

The maximum allowable stress values to be used for calculating tube wall thickness at a given temperature for the materials listed in Table 3 can be found in Table 4. These values are in accordance with the *ASME Boiler and Pressure Vessel Code*, Section I, Power Boilers, December 31, 1975 addenda. Chemical and physical properties can be found in Section II of the *ASME Boiler and Pressure Vessel Code*.

Creep strength in the intermediate-alloy steels is not proportional to chromium content and is somewhat better in those of lowest chromium content. Therefore it becomes necessary in choosing the optimum composition, to consider both strength properties and resistance to oxidation at the anticipated metal temperatures.

The selection of an appropriate and economical material for construction of the superheater is dependent on a number of factors. Because of the temperature drop through the steam film immediately adjacent to the inside surface, the metal of the superheater tube will usually be from 50 to 150F hotter than the steam in the tube.

Dry steam is delivered to the superheater from the boiler at saturation temperatures ranging up to 675F or more, depending on the pressure at which the boiler is designed to operate. As the steam passes through the tubes, it may be superheated to a final temperature of 1000F or higher. Carbon steels are reasonably resistant to scaling in steam and in combustion atmospheres up to about 1000F but, under high stress, may suffer accelerated oxidation at somewhat lower temperatures. This attack generally takes the form of intergranular penetrations which reduce the effective wall thickness of the tube, and thus increase the unit stress and act as stress-concentration centers. Carbon-steel tubing in the superheater is therefore restricted to moderate temperatures and pressures.

To assure the long life required for satisfactory superheater design, the metal used must meet the following primary requirements at the anticipated operating temperature:

1. Resistance to corrosion by steam.

2. Resistance to corrosion by flue gas.

3. Resistance to creep.

4. Resistance to creep-rupture.

To establish an adequate margin of safety and length of service life, these characteristics of the metal must be given due consideration in design. Economy dictates that the lowest alloy with properties suitable to the conditions should be used, stepping up from carbon steel to carbon-molybdenum steel and to the lower-chromium alloy steels as temperatures increase. For metal temperatures approaching 1125F, the lower-alloy steels up to and including 2¼% chromium are usually adequate. Chromium-molybdenum steel (9% Cr) and the stainless steels are used at higher temperatures, where conditions require either an increase in resistance to oxidation or higher load-carrying characteristics, or both.

Steam piping

The steam leads, or piping connecting the boiler and turbine, are highly important components of the power

Table 4
Tube materials—maximum allowable stress values for ferrous materials, pounds per square inch
(Values are per code case 1508-1 for ASME Section 1, Power Boilers)

Spec Number	Grade	Nominal Composition	Spec Min Tensile	Notes	For metal temperatures, F, not exceeding															
					-20 to 100	300	400	-20 to 400	500	600	650	700	800	900	1000	1100	1200	1300	1400	1500
Seamless carbon steel																				
SA-192	—	—	(47,000)	(1)(6)	—	—	—	11,750	11,750	11,750	11,750	11,500	9,000	*5,000*	*1,500*	—	—	—	—	—
SA-210	A-1	—	60,000	(1)	—	—	—	15,000	15,000	15,000	15,000	14,350	10,800	*5,000*	*1,500*	—	—	—	—	—
SA-210	C	—	70,000	—	17,500	17,500	17,500		17,500	17,500	17,500	16,600	12,000	*5,000*	*1,500*	—	—	—	—	—
Seamless alloy steel																				
SA-209	T1a	C-½ Mo	60,000	(2)				15,000	15,000	15,000	15,000	15,000	14,900	13,700	4,800	—	—	—	—	—
SA-213	T5	5 Cr-½ Mo	60,000	—				15,000	14,500	14,000	13,700	13,400	12,800	10,350	5,600	3,050	1,300	—	—	—
SA-213	T9	9 Cr-1 Mo	60,000	—				15,000	14,500	14,000	13,700	13,400	12,800	12,000	8,500	3,300	1,500	—	—	—
SA-213	T11	1¼ Cr-½ Mo	60,000	—				15,000	15,000	15,000	15,000	15,000	15,000	13,100	6,550	3,000	*1,200*	—	—	—
SA-213	T3b	2 Cr-½ Mo	60,000	—				15,000	15,000	15,000	15,000	15,000	14,700	12,500	6,200	2,750	1,200	—	—	—
SA-213	T22	2¼ Cr-1 Mo	60,000	—				15,000	15,000	15,000	15,000	15,000	15,000	13,100	7,800	4,200	2,000	—	—	—
SA-213	TP304H	18Cr-8Ni	75,000	(4)	18,750	16,600	16,150		15,900	15,900	15,900	15,900	15,150	14,650	13,750	9,750	6,050	3,700	2,300	1,400
SA-213	TP304H	18Cr-8Ni	75,000	—	18,750	14,050	12,950		12,150	11,400	11,250	11,050	10,550	10,150	9,750	8,850	6,050	3,700	2,300	1,400
SA-213	TP321H	18Cr-10Ni-Ti	75,000	(4)	18,750	17,300	17,100		17,100	16,350	16,050	15,800	15,450	15,250	14,000	9,050	5,350	3,150	1,850	1,100
SA-213	TP321H	18Cr-10Ni-Ti	75,000	—	18,750	14,150	12,900		12,000	11,350	11,150	10,950	10,750	10,600	10,450	8,800	5,350	3,150	1,850	1,100
Seamless low-alloy steel																				
SA-213	T2	½ Cr-½ Mo	60,000	—	15,000	15,000	15,000		15,000	15,000	15,000	15,000	14,400	12,500	6,250	—	—	—	—	—
Electric-resistance-welded carbon steel																				
SA-178	A	—	(47,000)	(1)(3)(5)(6)	—	—	—	11,750	11,750	11,750	11,750	11,500	7,650	*4,250*	*1,300*	—	—	—	—	—
SA-178	C	—	60,000	(1)(3)(5)	—	—	—	15,000	15,000	15,000	15,000	14,350	9,200	*4,250*	*1,300*	—	—	—	—	—

General notes:

(a) Stress values shown in italics are permissible but use of these materials at these temperatures is not current practice under, *ASME Boiler and Pressure Vessel Code*, Section I.

(b) The stress values in this table may be interpolated to determine values for intermediate temperatures.

Notes:

(1) Upon prolonged exposure to temperatures above about 800 F, the carbide phase of carbon steel may be converted to graphite.

(2) Upon prolonged exposure to temperatures above about 875 F, the carbide phase of carbon-molybdenum steel may be converted to graphite.

(3) Only killed steel shall be used above 850 F.

(4) Due to relatively low yield strength of these materials, these higher stress values were established at temperatures where the short time tensile properties govern to permit the use of these alloys where slightly greater deformation is acceptable. The stress values in this range exceed 62½% but do not exceed 90% of the yield strength at temperature. Use of these stresses may result in dimensional changes due to permanent strain. These stress values are not recommended for the flanges of gasketed joints or other applications where slight amounts of distortion can cause leakage or malfunction.

(5) Above 700 F these stress values include a joint efficiency factor of 0.85. When material to this specification is used for pipe, multiply the stress values up to and including 700 F by a factor of 0.85. When material to this specification is used for boilers, water wall, superheater and economizer tubes, that are enclosed within a setting, the stress values above 700 F up to and including 850 F may be divided by a factor of 0.85.

(6) Tensile value in parentheses is expected minimum.

plant. Such piping should be properly designed and erected to accommodate thermal expansion and absorb vibratory stresses, and it should be so supported that it does not produce imposed stress on the boiler proper. While some mechanical joints are still used, it is now common practice to weld most of the joints between the boiler and the turbine. Carbon-steel piping is used for moderate pressures and for steam temperatures up to 800F.

Carbon-steel pipe has shown a tendency to graphitization in the region of the welds at temperatures over 800F, and it has been safe and prudent to restrict its use in this service to a temperature limit of this value.* Consequently, at these higher temperatures carbon-molybdenum steel has been commonly used for steam piping in many central stations. Long-time service, however, indicates that piping of this material also graphitizes, with a chain-like formation in the heat-affected area of welds and random formations in the body of the pipe proper. This phenomenon, the effect of which has made it necessary to reweld and replace a considerable amount of piping in the power industry, has been widely investigated. It has been found that the rate and extent of graphitization in piping materials are affected to some degree by steel-manufacturing practice. While it appears that graphitization is more liable to occur in materials which have received a considerable amount of aluminum during deoxidation, recent investigations indicate that, at somewhat longer time, it will also occur (at 900 to 950F) in coarse-grain normal steel in which little or no aluminum has been used.

For greater resistance to graphitization under prolonged usage, the current trend in steam-piping materials is to use chromium-molybdenum steels. Steels of 0.5% Cr-0.5% Mo and 1% Cr-0.5% Mo are now commonly used in the range between 850 and about 1000F with a somewhat higher chromium content preferable in the range of 950 to 1050F. Steel of 1¼% Cr-0.5% Mo has been used to some extent. In several recently designed plants, steels of 2¼% Cr-1% Mo, and 3% Cr-0.9% Mo have been used for steam piping.

Steam piping of extreme wall thickness is made by pierce-and-draw forging or by boring solid forgings. Where moderate wall thickness is required, piping of seamless type is made by the rotary piercing process. Precise practices in welding, hot bending, and heat treating are required in fabricating air-hardening alloys containing chromium, and metallurgical control is a predominant factor in securing the results desired. The steels presently used for steam piping and the corresponding maximum metal temperatures used by B&W are listed in Table 5. The maximum allowable stress values to be used for calculating ASME piping wall thickness at a given temperature are listed in Table 6. These values are in accordance with the *ASME Boiler and Pressure Vessel Code*, Section I, Power Boilers, December 31, 1975 addenda. The chemical and physical properties can be found in Section II of the *ASME Boiler and Pressure Vessel Code*.

---

* Graphitization has been detected in carbon-steel tubes in small amounts, but the experience has been that no failures have occurred, and consequently carbon steel is used for tubing at somewhat higher temperatures than in the case of piping (*see Tube Steels*).

Table 5
Pipe material specifications and maximum allowable metal temperatures

Metal or Alloy	ASME Specification Number	Grade	Max Allowable Metal Temp, F
Carbon steel	SA-106	B	800
Carbon steel	SA-106	C	800
Carbon steel	SA-266	II	800
Croloy ½	SA-335	P2	950
Croloy 1	SA-335	P12	1000
Croloy 1¼	SA-335	P11	1035
Croloy 2¼	SA-335	P22	1100
Croloy 5	SA-335	P5	1150
Croloy 9	SA-335	P9	1200
Croloy 304H	SA-376	TP304H	1500
Croloy 304H	SA-430	FP304H	1500
Croloy 316H	SA-376	TP316H	1500
Croloy 316H	SA-430	FP316H	1500

Forgings, castings, bolts and studs

A variety of parts for attachments, fittings, valves and flanges may be made from carbon- or alloy-steel forgings and castings. While many of these parts are joined integrally to drums, water feed lines, steam lines and other parts, by welding, there are also certain attachments which are joined with studs or bolts. The material for bolts and studs must have high mechanical strength, and it is usually conditioned by normalizing and tempering or quenching and tempering. The tempering temperature is at least 100F higher than the operating temperature in service. Furthermore, the material must be creep-resistant to minimize the relaxation in service, which would gradually loosen the fastening and necessitate retightening. Considerable study has been devoted to the subject of stresses and relaxation in bolts and studs, and a variety of bolting steels, suitable for various temperature levels and stresses, has been developed and is now in common use.

Heat-resistant alloys

High-alloy heat-resistant materials must be used for certain boiler parts that are exposed to high temperature and cannot be water cooled. These parts are made from alloys of the oxidation-resistant, relatively high-strength, chromium-nickel-iron type, many of them cast to shape as metallic baffles, supports, and hanger fittings. Oil burner impellers, sootblower clamps, and hangers are also made of heat-resisting alloy steels.

Deterioration of these parts may occur through conversion of the surface layers to oxides, sulfides and sulfates, and in this condition they are referred to as burnt or oxidized. Experience indicates that steels containing 25% Cr-12% Ni or 25% Cr-20% Ni give reasonably good service life, depending on the location of the part in the flue gas stream and on the characteristics of the fuel. Temperatures to which these metal parts are exposed may range from 1000 to 2800F.

Life may be shortened if these steels are exposed to flue gases from fuel oil containing vanadium compounds.

Table 6
Pipe materials—maximum allowable stress values for ferrous materials, pounds per square inch
(Values are per code case 1508-1 for ASME Section 1, Power Boilers)

Spec Number	Grade	Nominal Composition	Spec Min Tensile	Notes	−20 to 100	300	400	−20 to 400	500	600	650	700	800	900	1000	1100	1200	1300	1400	1500
Seamless carbon steel																				
SA-106	B	—	60,000	(1)	—	—	—	15,000	15,000	15,000	15,000	14,350	10,800	*5,000*	*1,500*	—	—	—	—	—
SA-106	C	—	70,000	—	—	—	—	17,500	17,500	17,500	17,500	16,600	12,000	—	—	—	—	—	—	—
Seamless alloy steel																				
SA-335	P2	½ Cr-½ Mo	55,000	—	—	—	—	13,750	13,750	13,750	13,750	13,750	13,450	12,500	6,250	—	—	—	—	—
SA-335	P5	5 Cr-½ Mo	60,000	—	—	—	—	15,000	14,500	14,000	13,700	13,400	12,800	10,350	5,600	3,050	1,300	—	—	—
SA-335	P11	1¼ Cr-½ Mo	60,000	—	—	—	—	15,000	15,000	15,000	15,000	15,000	15,000	13,100	6,550	3,000	*1,200*	—	—	—
SA-335	P12	1 Cr-½ Mo	60,000	—	—	—	—	15,000	15,000	15,000	15,000	15,000	14,750	13,100	6,550	2,800	*1,000*	—	—	—
SA-335	P9	9 Cr-1 Mo	60,000	—	—	—	—	15,000	14,500	14,000	13,700	13,400	12,800	12,000	8,500	3,300	1,500	—	—	—
SA-335	P22	2¼ Cr-1 Mo	60,000	—	—	—	—	15,000	15,000	15,000	15,000	15,000	15,000	13,100	7,800	4,200	2,000	—	—	—
SA-376	TP304H	18Cr-8Ni	75,000	(2)	18,750	16,600	16,150		15,900	15,900	15,900	15,900	15,150	14,650	13,750	9,750	6,050	3,700	2,300	1,400
SA-376	TP304H	18Cr-8Ni	75,000	—	18,750	14,050	12,950		12,150	11,400	11,250	11,050	10,550	10,150	9,750	8,850	6,050	3,700	2,300	1,400
SA-376	TP316H	16Cr-12Ni-2Mo	75,000	(2)	18,750	18,350	18,050		17,950	17,000	16,650	16,300	15,850	15,550	15,300	12,400	7,400	4,100	2,250	1,250
SA-376	TP316H	16Cr-12Ni-2Mo	75,000	—	18,750	14,600	13,350		12,450	11,800	11,550	11,300	11,000	10,800	10,600	10,300	7,400	4,100	2,250	1,250
Forged and bored austenitic steel																				
SA-430	FP304H	18Cr-8Ni	70,000	(2)	17,500	15,500	15,050		14,800	14,800	14,800	14,800	14,600	14,150	13,350	9,750	6,050	3,700	2,300	1,400
SA-430	FP304H	18Cr-8Ni	70,000	—	17,500	14,050	12,950		12,150	11,400	11,250	11,050	10,550	10,150	9,750	8,850	6,050	3,700	2,300	1,400
SA-430	FP316H	16Cr-12Ni-2Mo	70,000	(2)	17,500	17,100	16,800		16,800	16,800	16,650	16,300	15,850	15,550	14,950	12,400	7,400	4,100	2,250	1,250
SA-430	FP316H	16Cr-12Ni-2Mo	70,000	—	17,500	14,600	13,350		12,450	11,800	11,550	11,300	11,000	10,800	10,600	10,300	7,400	4,100	2,250	1,250
Carbon steel forgings																				
SA-266	II	—	70,000	(1)	—	—	—	17,500	17,500	17,500	17,500	16,600	12,000	*5,000*	*1,500*	—	—	—	—	—

For metal temperatures, F, not exceeding

General Notes:
(a) Stress values shown in italics are permissible but use of these materials at these temperatures is not current practice under, *ASME Boiler and Pressure Vessel Code.* Section I.
(b) The stress values in this table may be interpolated to determine values for intermediate temperatures.

Notes:
(1) Upon prolonged exposure to temperatures above about 800 F, the carbide phase of carbon steel may be converted to graphite.
(2) Due to relatively low yield strength of these materials, these higher stress values were established at temperatures where the short time tensile properties govern to permit the use of these alloys where slightly greater deformation is acceptable. The stress values in this range exceed 62½% but do not exceed 90% of the yield strength at temperature. Use of these stresses may result in dimensional changes due to permanent strain. These stress values are not recommended for the flanges of gasketed joints or other applications where slight amounts of distortion can cause leakage or malfunction.

Sulfur compounds formed from combustion of high sulfur fuels are also detrimental and act to reduce life. These may react in the presence of vanadium and cause greatly accelerated rates of attack, especially when the temperature of the metal part exceeds 1200F. Combinations of sodium, sulfur and vanadium compounds are reported to melt as low as 1050F. Such deposits are extremely corrosive when molten because of their slagging action. In these circumstances, 50% Cr-50% Ni or 60% Cr-40% Ni castings are used to resist corrosion.

Grades of steel in boiler construction

The grades of steel used in boiler construction for tubes, piping, plates, forgings, and castings are listed in Section I of the *ASME Boiler and Pressure Vessel Code*, and the chemical and physical properties are listed in Section II of this code. Other steels in the form of plate, bars or structural shapes, used for nonpressure parts of boilers or for supports, are of usually accepted commercial standards. Arc-welding electrode materials for various material combinations are given in Table 1, Chapter 31.

Materials for nuclear steam supply systems

As in the fossil-fuel units, steel is the basic material in the construction of pressure parts for nuclear steam supply systems. In the primary loop of a pressurized-water reactor system (Fig. 1, Chapter 21), the material in contact with the reactor coolant is usually stainless steel. Heavy pressure vessels and thick piping are generally made of low-alloy steel with stainless steel cladding or lining. Piping one in. or less in thickness and most of the supports and other structure inside of the reactor vessel are customarily made of stainless steel because of its corrosion resistance.

The stress analysis of pressure vessels is discussed in Chapter 30. Nuclear vessels are designed in accordance with the *ASME Boiler and Pressure Vessel Code*, Section III, Nuclear Power Plant Components. Piping internal to the nuclear steam supply system, including the reactor-coolant piping, is also designed in accordance with Section III. The code lists approved materials, together with strength values and the stresses allowable at various temperatures. In the case of clad vessels and piping, no credit is taken for the cladding in determining the minimum wall thickness of the pressure parts.

The economic success of a pressurized water reactor depends also on another important material—Zircaloy. This is a name used for alloys of zirconium, particularly Zircaloy-2 and Zircaloy-4. These alloys have low neutron absorption plus adequate strength and resistance to corrosion in the environment of the reactor coolant water, and thus are used for cladding tubes for nuclear fuel rods.

Inconel, a nickel-iron-chromium alloy, is also an important material, which is generally used for the tubes in steam generators of pressurized-water reactor systems.

Zirconium alloys

Zirconium alloys have been developed as structural materials for the nuclear industry, because they have a desirable combination of nuclear, physical and mechanical properties for use in thermal nuclear reactors. Nu-

clear-grade zirconium is expensive. Hence, the use of zirconium alloys is usually limited to the active region of the nuclear core, where low neutron absorption, characteristic of zirconium, is of greatest benefit.

The two most important of these alloys, Zircaloy-2 (Zr-2) and Zircaloy-4 (Zr-4), differ slightly in alloy content. The small nickel content of Zr-2 is replaced by iron in Zr-4 (Table 7). This small change reduces the hydrogen absorption rate during service in high temperature water (reactor coolant) and, consequently, Zircaloy-4 is the alloy generally used for fuel-rod cladding in pressurized water reactors (Chapters 21 and 23). Physical and mechanical properties of Zircaloy-2 and Zircaloy-4 are nearly identical.

Table 7
Alloying elements in Zircaloy-2 and -4*

| Element | Percent by Weight | |
	Zr-2	Zr-4
Tin	1.45	1.45
Iron	0.14	0.21
Chromium	0.10	0.10
Nickel	0.05	nil.
Zirconium	Balance	Balance

*Nominal values from ASTM-B-353

Physical properties. Table 8 lists some important physical properties of Zircaloy-4. Its density is 412 lb/ft³ (0.24 lb/in.³). The coefficient of thermal expansion to 600F is 3.43×10^{-6}/F. Because of Zircaloy's relatively low thermal expansion and its low modulus of elasticity—approximately 11×10^6 psi at 600F—a given thermal gradient produces less thermal stress in Zircaloy than in other structural materials.

Several temperature indices are of interest to the designer. Zircaloy undergoes a phase change in the region 1440 to 1750F, resulting in a density change. At temperatures somewhat below this range, the exothermic reaction rate in water becomes significant. The melting point is 3353F. These factors are of interest in evaluating the consequences of hypothetical accidents for safeguards analyses. The practical upper limit for operation

Table 8
Some physical properties of Zircaloy-4

Temp, F	Density lb/ft³	Thermal Conductivity Btu/sq ft, hr, F/in.	Coefficient of Linear Expansion† (in./in. F) 10⁶	Specific Heat	Modulus of Elasticity in Tension (Static Value) psi/10⁶
70	412	98		0.070	14
200		101	3.24	0.073	13
400		107	3.33	0.077	12
600		113	3.43	0.081	11
800		120	3.53	0.085	9
1000		131	3.62	0.086	7
1200		142	3.72	0.086	6

†Between 70F and temperature shown.

of Zircaloy is 700 to 800F, based on creep rates and the short-time strength and corrosion characteristics of the material.

Mechanical properties. The strength of Zircaloy-4 is dependent on a number of factors, which are often interdependent. Zirconium is an anistropic material, i.e., it exhibits different properties in different directions. The method of fabricating the material influences the texture, or the orientation of the crystal structure, and hence the anistropy of the finished product. Zircaloy cannot be strengthened by heat treatment. Yield strength is increased by cold working. The ultimate strength and yield strength of Zircaloy-4 in the cold-worked and annealed conditions are plotted in Fig. 14.

The data available on the creep rates of Zircaloy are sufficient to establish that creep is not limiting in the design of fuel-rod cladding for water reactors, particularly since the service requirement for a fuel rod (approximately 3 years) is short compared to normal pressure-part service.

Ductility. The ductility of Zircaloy varies over a wide range from about 1½% elongation to about 80%. It is influenced by temperature, cold work, fabrication methods, anistropy, hydrogen concentration, and hydride platelet orientation. Allowable permanent strain is limited to 1% for design purposes. The ductility of as-received material is typically 10 to 30% depending on the degree of cold work.

Fatigue. Fatigue data for the entire range of temperature and loading conditions expected in service are limited. However, the data are adequate to demonstrate that fatigue is not normally limiting in the design of water-reactor fuel rods.

Effects of irradiation exposure. In its use as cladding for nuclear fuel, Zircaloy is exposed to a substantial flux of fast- or high-energy neutrons. Over a period of time this results in changes in the properties of the material (*see Structural Integrity, Chapter 21*), which the designer must take into account.

Fast-neutron irradiation generally increases ultimate strength and lowers ductility. The yield strength of tubing can be either increased or decreased, depending on the temperature during irradiation. At irradiation temperatures above 650F, the strengthening effect of irradiation is concurrently annealed along with a similar relief of cold-work strengthening so that the strength of the material is reduced. Creep rates also may be increased or decreased, depending on the interrelated effects of temperature, the energy spectrum of neutron flux, the fluence (accumulated neutron flux), stress, and the degree of cold work. Fast-neutron irradiation also affects fatigue strength.

Corrosion. Zircaloy-4 forms a protective oxide film which effectively inhibits corrosion in the water coolant of a nuclear reactor. The film is sufficiently thin and adherent at reactor operating conditions so that no special allowance is required for metal loss. When Zircaloy is oxidized in water, a portion of the hydrogen released is absorbed by the base metal. Hydrogen concentrations in excess of the solubility limit at room temperature can cause a loss of ductility. Zirconium hydride precipitates are formed as platelets, and the orientation of the platelets causes a greater loss of ductility normal to the direction of the platelets. Primarily for this reason, tubing is now made by tube-reducing methods called "rocking" in preference to drawing. In tube reducing, the diameter and wall thickness are reduced primarily by radial compressive force whereas other methods act on the tube with a combination of axial tensile and radial compressive forces. In rocked tubing the hydrides precipitate primarily in a circumferential direction and have a minimal effect on longitudinal and transverse ductility.

Corrosion rates of Zircaloy and other reactor materials are dependent on water chemistry. For this reason, the chemistry of the reactor coolant is closely controlled.

Inconel

Steam generator tubes for pressurized-water reactor systems transfer the heat from the reactor coolant on one side to generate steam on the other. While 18-8 stainless steels are well suited to the reactor coolant environment, they are subject to some corrosion on the steam side. The search for a material compatible with the environment on both sides of these steam generator tubes has resulted in the choice of seamless cold-drawn tubes of nickel-iron-chromium alloy conforming to ASME Specification SB-163. Commercial Inconel Alloy 600 tubing is generally used. This material has the additional advantage of a lower coefficient of thermal expansion, resulting in less differential expansion between tubes and the low-alloy shell as compared to 18-8.

The chemical composition of this material is given in Table 9; cobalt is usually specified as 0.20% maximum. Tensile and yield properties are given in Table 10, and creep properties in Table 11. Table 12 lists some important physical properties. The source of Tables 9 to 12 is the bulletin *Inconel Alloy 600*, Huntington Alloy Products Division, The International Nickel Company, Inc., 1969.

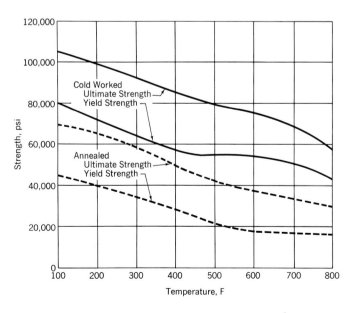

Fig. 14 Mechanical strength of Zircaloy-4 in the cold-worked and annealed conditions.

Table 9
Inconel Alloy 600—limiting chemical composition, %

Nickel (plus cobalt)	72.0 min	Carbon	0.15 max
Chromium	14.0-17.0	Copper	0.5 max
Iron	6.0-10.0	Silicon	0.5 max
Manganese	1.0 max	Sulfur	0.015 max

Table 10
Tensile properties of cold-drawn, as-drawn Inconel Alloy 600 bar

Strain rate 0.005 inch/inch to yield strength, then 0.05 inch/inch

Temp F	Tensile Strength psi	Yield Strength 0.2% Offset psi	Elongation %
85	128,500	120,500	14.5
200	124,500	118,000	13.0
400	120,500	—	—
500	119,500	113,000	12.5
600	118,000	113,000	13.0
700	118,000	111,000	14.0
800	117,500	109,500	14.0
900	113,500	103,000	17.0
1000	110,500	100,000	14.0
1100	105,000	93,500	13.0
1200	92,500	81,500	20.0
1300	68,500	61,000	43.0

Table 11
Creep properties of cold-drawn, annealed* Inconel Alloy 600

Temp F	Stress, psi for a Secondary Creep Rate of:	
	1% per 10,000 hr	1% per 100,000 hr
800	40,000	30,000
900	28,000	18,000
1000	12,500	6,100
1100	6,800	3,400
1200	—	2,200
1300	—	1,400
1400	—	970
1500	—	660
1600	880	450
1700	—	—
1800	560	340
1900	—	—
2000	270	160
2100	170	100

*3 hours at 1750F—air cooled.

Table 12
Other properties of Inconel Alloy 600

Temp F	Density lb/ft³	Thermal Conductivity Btu/sq ft, hr, F/in.	Coefficient of Linear Expansion† (in./in. F) 10⁶	Specific Heat	Modulus of Elasticity in Tension (Dynamic Value) psi/10⁶
70	525.3	103	—	0.106	29.9
200		109	7.4	0.111	29.4
400		121	7.7	0.116	28.4
600		133	7.9	0.121	27.6
800		145	8.1	0.126	26.6
1000		158	8.4	0.132	25.6
1200		172	8.6	0.140	24.5

†Between 70F and temperature shown.

Top support steel of a large steam boiler unit in an electric power generating station.

Chapter 30   Stress analysis and structural design

Stress analysis of vessels

Equipment used in the power, chemical, petroleum and cryogenic fields often involves the use of large steel vessels. These vessels can be shop-fabricated up to about 32 ft in diameter, 125 ft long, 16 in. thick, and a weight of 1000 tons. Still larger vessels can be fabricated in the field. These vessels may require tons of structural steel for their support. In steam generating units, the large vessels usually operate at internal pressures of 1000-3000 psi and at the saturation temperature of steam. They must be designed to be safe and reliable.

Maximum reliability can be assured only on the basis of a thorough stress analysis of the entire structure. Consequently, considerable attention is given to the design and stress analysis of vessels used for steam drums, nuclear reactors, heat exchangers and pressurizers. In this analysis the basic approach is to account for all unknown factors such as extent of local yielding and stress redistribution, and inexact solutions, by using allowable working stresses below those at which the material will fail.

This "factor of safety" approach is illustrated by the triangle of knowledge shown in Fig. 1. At the top of the triangle, full utilization of material requires complete knowledge; at present this is an ideal rather than a practical goal. However knowledge continues to increase with recognition and understanding of more of the factors affecting behavior. As greater knowledge decreases the latitude for error, it is possible to decrease the factor of safety. Accordingly, the potential properties of materials applied in the design analysis can be more fully utilized with confidence. Of particular impetus to this supply of knowledge has been the nuclear steam plant and the necessity of using the best in design principles to permit the safe adoption of this new source of power.

Probably no development in the history of engineering has had as much effort expended on it in such a short time as the application of nuclear energy to commercial power through the development of nuclear power plants. As a consequence, considerable attention has been focused on the design of vessels for reactors (Fig. 2), steam generators, and pressurizers. This is appropriate because pressure vessels are the main components of these systems—the ones on which their operational in-

tegrity and safety depend. The unique design problems of these vessels are:

1. Potential hazard to people and property because of the radioactive materials they contain.
2. Limited availability for inspection and maintenance because of the difficulties imposed by radioactivity.
3. Thermal stresses due to the temperature transients associated with thick-wall vessels where heavy flanges and nozzles are slow to thermal response. This is complicated by heat generated within the wall of the vessel through the absorption of gamma rays emitted by the nuclear core.
4. Long-term changes in mechanical properties of the material resulting from fast-neutron irradiation. The effect is to raise the yield point of the material at a sacrifice of its ductility.

The design of pressure vessels for large nuclear steam supply systems requires the use of sophisticated design principles. Indeed the adoption of nuclear power has initiated much of our present vessel design and material knowledge. This involves the solution of mathematical

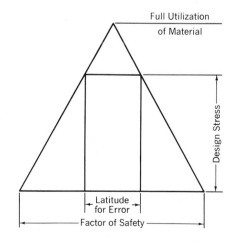

Fig. 1 Triangle of knowledge. (*From "Pressure Vessel Design—Nuclear and Chemical Applications" by John F. Harvey. Copyright © 1963 by Litton Educational Publishing Inc. Reprinted by permission of Van Nostrand Reinhold Company.*)

equations based on a theory of elasticity including regions of discontinuities, nozzle openings and supports. Solutions of these equations became practical for the first time when the digital computer came into general usage in the mid-fifties.

Pressure vessel construction codes adopted by state, federal and municipal jurisdictional authorities play an important part in establishing safety requirements and, accordingly, vessel construction features. The most widely used of these is the ASME "Boiler and Pressure Vessel Code" published by The American Society of Mechanical Engineers, including:

Section I, *Power Boilers*
Section III, *Nuclear Power Plant Components*
Section VIII, *Pressure Vessels*

These codes give excellent guidance and basic requirements. The purpose of the following brief discussion of the stress analysis of pressure vessels is to introduce the bases and formulas on which these codes are founded.

Methods of stress analysis

Stress analysis can be performed by analytical or experimental methods. The analytical method involves a rigorous mathematical solution based on the theory of elasticity and plasticity, and is the most direct and inexpensive approach when the problem adapts itself to such a solution. The formulas given in this chapter are the result of analytical stress analysis. When the problem is too complex to be expressed in continuous mathematical form or is beyond analytical solution, experimental methods must be employed.

The most widely used experimental technique is photoelasticity. This consists of measuring optically the princi-

Fig. 2 Head for nuclear reactor vessel.

Fig. 3 Photoelastic stress pattern.

pal stress differences in isotropic transparent material models which become double refractive when polarized light is passed through the model, Fig. 3. (*See also* Fig. 25, *Introduction to Steam.*) In two-dimensional models this method gives the average stress throughout the thickness. In three-dimensional models, by using newly developed "freeze" techniques, the stress variation throughout the thickness can be determined. Normally, these models are relatively small in size; however, this method has been extended to permit analyses of large actual structures. This is accomplished by bonding thin sheets of photoelastic plastic to the part to be analyzed. The surface strains of the part are transferred to the plastic coating and measurements made by reflected light.

The photoelastic method is expedient, accurate and economical, and particularly useful in analyzing complicated shapes, such as the perforated plate subject to an equal biaxial stress field shown in Fig. 3. It readily gives an overall visual picture of the shearing stress concentrations and indicates where design modifications are warranted.

Primary pressure stresses in vessels

Pressure vessels commonly have the form of spheres, cylinders, ellipsoids, tori or composites of these. When thickness is small in comparison with other dimensions, vessels are referred to as membranes and the associated stresses resulting from the contained pressure are called membrane stresses. Membrane stresses are average tension or compression stresses acting over the thickness of the vessel wall and are considered to act tangentially to its surface. The stresses resulting from pressure in boiler drums, accumulators, or chemical or nuclear reactors are primary stresses since they remain as long as the pressure is applied.

The basic equation for the longitudinal stress, σ_1, and hoop stress, σ_2, in a vessel of thickness, h, longitudinal radius, r_1, hoop radius, r_2, and subject to a pressure, p, is (Fig. 4):

$$(1) \qquad \frac{\sigma_1}{r_1} + \frac{\sigma_2}{r_2} = \frac{p}{h}$$

From this equation, and the equilibrium of the total pressure load with the longitudinal forces acting on a transverse section of the vessel, the stresses in the commonly used vessels of revolution can be found.

1. Cylindrical vessel

In this case $r_1 = \infty$, $r_2 = r$, and

(2) $$\sigma_1 = \frac{pr}{2h}$$

(3) $$\sigma_2 = \frac{pr}{h}$$

2. Spherical vessel

In this case $r_1 = r_2 = r$, and

(4) $$\sigma_1 = \frac{pr}{2h}$$

(5) $$\sigma_2 = \frac{pr}{2h}$$

3. Conical vessel

In this case $r_1 = \infty$, $r_2 = r/\cos\alpha$ where α is half the cone apex angle, and

(6) $$\sigma_1 = \frac{pr}{2h\cos\alpha}$$

(7) $$\sigma_2 = \frac{pr}{h\cos\alpha}$$

4. Ellipsoidal vessel

In this case the radius varies with each position on the ellipsoid, whose major axis is "a" and minor axis "b", and the stresses are given by

(8) $$\sigma_1 = \frac{pr_2}{2h}$$

(9) $$\sigma_2 = \frac{p}{h}\left(r_2 - \frac{r_2^2}{2r_1}\right)$$

At the equator the longitudinal stress is the same as the longitudinal stress in a cylinder, namely:

(10) $$\sigma_1 = \frac{pr}{2h}$$

and the hoop stress is

(11) $$\sigma_2 = \frac{pa}{h}\left(1 - \frac{a^2}{2b^2}\right)$$

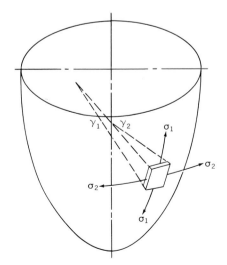

Fig. 4 Membrane stress in vessels. *(From "Pressure Vessel Design—Nuclear and Chemical Applications" by John F. Harvey. Copyright © 1963 by Litton Educational Publishing Inc. Reprinted by permission of Van Nostrand Reinhold Company.)*

When the ratio of major to minor axis is 2:1 the hoop stress is the same as that in a cylinder of the same mating diameter, but the stress is a compressive one rather than tension. The hoop stress rises rapidly when the ratio of major to minor axis goes above 2:1 and, since this stress is compressive, buckling instability becomes a major concern. For this reason ellipsoidal heads of 2:1 ratio are recognized as a standard, and greater ratios are seldom employed.

5. Torus

In this case (Fig. 5) the radius of the bend centerline is R_o; θ is the angular hoop location from this centerline; and

(12) $$\sigma_1 = \frac{pr}{2h}$$

(13) $$\sigma_2 = \frac{pr}{2h}\left(\frac{2R_o + r\sin\theta}{R_o + r\sin\theta}\right)$$

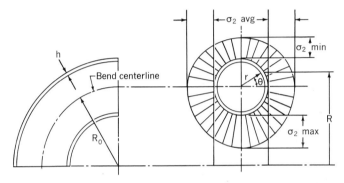

Fig. 5 Variation in hoop stress in a bend. *(From "Pressure Vessel Design—Nuclear and Chemical Applications" by John F. Harvey. Copyright © 1963 by Litton Educational Publishing Inc. Reprinted by permission of Van Nostrand Reinhold Company.)*

The longitudinal stress remains uniform around the circumference and is the same as for a straight cylinder. The hoop stress, however, varies for different points in the cross section of the torus. At the bend centerline it is the same as in a straight cylinder. At the outside of the bend it is less than this and a minimum value. At the inside of the bend, or crotch, the value is more than this and a maximum value. These stresses are dependent on the sharpness of the bend and become particularly high when the bend radius is very small. In pipe bending operations the natural redistribution of metal which occurs during the bending operation, namely, thinning at the outside and thickening at the crotch, is a compensating factor of the same order as the acting stress for the bend radii customarily used.

The torus shape, or part of it, is one of the most useful and widely used shapes in vessel construction. Curved cylinder manifolds, U-shaped heat exchangers, and pipe bends are examples.

Secondary stresses in vessels

Secondary stresses are those developed by the constraint of adjacent parts. They are confined to local areas or portions of the vessel thickness. The basic characteristic of a secondary stress is that it is self-limiting. Local yielding or minor distortion can satisfy the condition causing the stress to occur. Examples of secondary stresses in pres-

sure vessels are the thermal stress produced by radial thermal gradients through the thickness of a heat exchanger tube, and the discontinuity stresses at the junction of a cylindrical vessel and its closure head resulting from the differential growth or displacement of these parts under pressure. Although these secondary stresses do not affect the static bursting strength of the vessel, they are none the less important in establishing the fatigue life of the vessel. Accordingly, it is the practice in vessel design, and applicable construction code requirements, to permit higher allowable stresses for secondary stresses than for primary stresses, and to limit these on a fatigue evaluation.

Thermal stresses. Thermal stresses result from restricting the natural expansion or contraction of a member due to a temperature change, Δt. If the material is restricted in one direction only, the stress developed is

$$(14) \qquad \sigma = \pm E\alpha\Delta t$$

where E is the modulus of elasticity and α is the coefficient of thermal expansion. If the member is restricted from expanding or contracting in two directions, as is the usual case in pressure vessels, the resulting stress is

$$(15) \qquad \sigma = \pm \frac{E\alpha\Delta t}{1 - \mu}$$

where μ is Poisson's ratio.

These values of thermal stress are for full restraint, and hence are the maximum that can be created. When the temperature varies within a member the natural growth of one fiber is influenced by the differential growth of adjacent fibers. The result is that fibers at high temperatures are compressed and those at lesser temperatures are stretched. The general equations for the radial, tangential and axial thermal stresses in a cylindrical vessel subject to a radial thermal gradient are

$$(16) \qquad \sigma_r = \frac{\alpha E}{(1 - \mu)r^2}\left[\frac{r^2 - a^2}{b^2 - a^2}\int_a^b trdr - \int_a^r trdr\right]$$

$$(17) \qquad \sigma_t = \frac{\alpha E}{(1 - \mu)r^2}\left[\frac{r^2 + a^2}{b^2 - a^2}\int_a^b trdr + \int_a^r trdr - tr^2\right]$$

$$(18) \qquad \sigma_z = \frac{\alpha E}{(1 - \mu)}\left[\frac{2}{b^2 - a^2}\int_a^b trdr - t\right]$$

where:

   a = inside radius
   b = outside radius
   r = radius at any location
   E = modulus of elasticity
   t = temperature
   μ = Poisson's ratio

An important example of thermal stress occurs in a cylindrical vessel when heat is flowing through the sides under steady-state conditions. The maximum thermal stress for this case, where a is the inside radius and b is the outside radius, is

$$(19) \qquad \sigma_{t_a} = \frac{\alpha E t_a}{2(1 - \mu)\log_e\left(\frac{b}{a}\right)}\left[1 - \frac{2b^2}{b^2 - a^2}\log_e\left(\frac{b}{a}\right)\right]$$

$$(20) \qquad \sigma_{t_b} = \frac{\alpha E t_a}{2(1 - \mu)\log_e\left(\frac{b}{a}\right)}\left[1 - \frac{2a^2}{b^2 - a^2}\log_e\left(\frac{b}{a}\right)\right]$$

For relatively thin tubes this can be simplified to

$$(21) \qquad \sigma_{t_a} = -\frac{\alpha E\Delta t}{2(1 - \mu)}$$

$$(22) \qquad \sigma_{t_b} = \frac{\alpha E\Delta t}{2(1 - \mu)}$$

from which it is seen that the maximum stress is one half of that for full restraint of the member, i.e., the multiplier of the full restraint thermal stress equation (15) is ½ for this case.

A thermal gradient of different shape results from gamma ray attenuation in the walls of nuclear reactor vessels where the highest temperature occurs within the thickness. In all cases, the maximum thermal stress can be expressed as a fraction K ranging between ½ and 1.0 of the total restraint stress

$$(23) \qquad \sigma = \frac{K E\alpha\Delta t}{1 - \mu}$$

Thermal dimensional changes. When vessels incorporate moving parts such as the rotating elements of turbines, or the axial moving control rods in nuclear reactors, large deflections or distortions can produce essential failure by rendering the structure inoperative even though the associated stresses are relatively low. For instance, a linear thermal gradient through the thickness of an unrestrained flat plate produces no stress, but the plate will assume a spherical shape and may not perform its intended function because of the change in shape and curvature.

Discontinuity stresses. Discontinuity stresses are those that result from the differential growth or displacement, δ, of adjacent parts of a vessel under the action of pressure. The differential growth can result from a variation in vessel thickness, or a change in geometric shape. This is illustrated by the juncture of a cylindrical shell and hemispherical head of equal thickness which, as free bodies, grow different amounts, Fig. 6. The redundant forces, P_0, and moments, M_0, at the juncture of these parts cause local bending to take place to preserve continuity of the vessel wall. The additional stresses set up at these locations are called discontinuity stresses. They reach a maximum in the region of the discontinuity, but attenuate rapidly with distance from it in accordance with the theory of beams on an elastic foundation. Hence, these

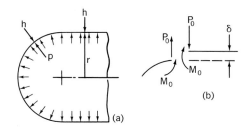

Fig. 6 Discontinuity stresses. (*From "Pressure Vessel Design—Nuclear and Chemical Applications" by John F. Harvey. Copyright © 1963 by Litton Educational Publishing Inc. Reprinted by permission of Van Nostrand Reinhold Company.*)

stresses are both self-limiting and are also confined to local areas or portions of the vessel.

Theory of failure

In order to determine allowable working stresses for stress conditions which occur in complicated practical designs, several strength theories of failure have been developed. Their purpose is to predict when failure will occur, assuming that the material behavior in a simple tension test is known, and that failure is considered to be either yielding or rupture. The oldest and simplest theory is the "maximum stress" theory. It considers the maximum stress as the criterion for strength. This means that yielding starts in a stressed body when the maximum stress reaches the yield point of the material in simple tension.

$$(24) \qquad \sigma = \sigma_{y.p.}$$

This is the failure theory upon which many codes, such as the ASME Code for *Power Boilers*, are based.

Another theory of failure that predicts both static and fatigue failures more accurately is the "maximum shear-stress" theory. It assumes that yielding begins when the maximum shear stress in the stressed body becomes equal to the maximum shear stress at the yield point in a simple tension test. Noting that the maximum shear stress, τ, is equal to half the difference of the maximum and minimum principal stresses, and further that the maximum shear stress in a tension test is half the normal stress, the condition for yielding becomes

$$(25) \qquad \tau = \frac{\sigma_{max} - \sigma_{min}}{2} = \frac{\sigma_{y.p.}}{2}$$

$$(26) \qquad 2\tau = \sigma_{max} - \sigma_{min} = \sigma_{y.p.}$$

This is twice the shear stress and is called "stress intensity."

In a vessel the minimum stress is the radial stress or the pressure itself; hence, the two theories of failure are essentially the same for low pressures. However, when the pressure is high, the maximum shear stress theory of failure is more applicable. This is the failure theory on which the ASME Code for *Nuclear Components* is based.

Stress significance

The significance of a stress depends not only on its magnitude but also on:

1. The type and nature of the applied loading, and the resulting stress distribution. For instance, is the applied loading mechanical or thermal, of a steady-state or transient nature, and is the resulting stress pattern uniform or does it have high peaks?

2. The ductile and plastic properties of the material. For instance, are the material properties such that internal yielding or readjustment of strain can reduce the effect of local stress concentrations?

Steady-state conditions. Under the action of a steady-state stress the type of failure is one of gross distortion and leakage at fittings prior to actual fracture of the vessel. The basic method of coping with this type of failure is to apply a suitable factor of safety to the material

properties and limit the applied primary membrane stress to this value. This is the present method employed by all codes, including those of ASME, each of which employs a factor of safety consistent with the sophistication of the associated quality assurance, manufacturing control and design analysis requirements. The two predominant material properties controlling this type of failure are tensile strength, which establishes the bursting pressure, and yield strength which establishes the pressure at which gross distortion occurs. Local stress concentrations are secondary stresses and are of no concern with the ductile materials used in pressure vessel construction since these peak stresses are relieved by local yielding.

Transient conditions. On the other hand, when the stress is a repetitive one, such as occurs during testing and transient operation, all stresses become significant and contribute in establishing the "fatigue life" of the vessel, even though the material is a ductile one. Vessels must have nozzles, supports, and flanges for practical functional purposes. These features embody abrupt changes in cross section and introduce irregularities in the immediate adjacent stress pattern which are called local stresses or stress concentrations. Accordingly, construction details give rise to stress concentrations, which in turn essentially establish the fatigue life of a vessel. The fundamental approach in reducing stress concentrations is gradual accommodation of structural changes in geometry. This means:

1) the use of tapers at the juncture of courses of different thickness,
2) the use of large fillets at the crotch of nozzles and lugs,
3) generous rounding of inside corners of nozzles,
4) careful profiling and contouring of added reinforcement material,
5) the use of full penetration weldments.

Fatigue life is evaluated by comparing the amplitude of the alternating stress intensity with that established from design fatigue curves (σ-N curves) experimentally established for the material. A typical σ-N design curve for carbon steel is shown in Fig. 7 and can be expressed by the equation

$$(27) \qquad \sigma_a = \frac{E}{4\sqrt{N}} \log_e \frac{100}{100 - RA} + 0.35 TS$$

where:

σ_a = allowable value of alternating stress intensity amplitude, psi
E = modulus of elasticity at temperature
N = number of cycles
RA = reduction in area, percent
TS = tensile strength, psi

The two controlling material parameters are tensile strength, and reduction in area. Tensile strength is controlling in the high-cycle-fatigue region, while reduction in area is controlling in low-cycle fatigue. The usual division between low- and high-cycle fatigue is taken as 200,000 cycles. Pressure vessels fall in the low-cycle-fatigue range; hence, the importance of the reduction-in-area material property since it is controlling in this

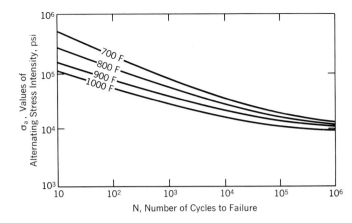

Fig. 7 Design fatigue curve.

range. The lower strength materials, with their greater ductility, show better behavior in low-cycle fatigue than do higher strength materials.

Cumulative fatigue damage. Practical operating service conditions subject many vessels to the random occurrence of a number of cycles of stress of different magnitudes. One method of appraising the damage from repetitive stress to a vessel is the criterion that the cumulative damage from fatigue will occur when the summation of the increments of damage at the various stress levels exceeds unity, i.e.

$$(28) \qquad \sum \frac{n}{N} = 1$$

where n = number of cycles at stress, σ, and N = number of cycles to failure at the same stress, σ. The ratio n/N is called the cycle ratio since it represents the fraction of the total life which is expended by the cycles that occur at a particular stress value. The value "N" is determined from σ-N curves for the material. If the sum of these cycle ratios is less than unity, the vessel is presumed safe. This is particularly important in designing an economic and safe structure which experiences only a relatively few cycles at a high stress level and the major number at a relatively low stress level. As an example, a vessel subjected to 500 cycles at a stress of 55,000 psi,

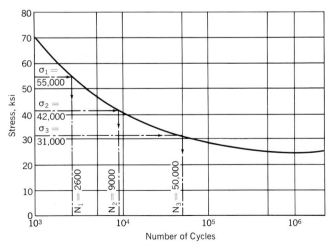

Fig. 8 Fatigue evaluation. (*From "Pressure Vessel Design— Nuclear and Chemical Applications" by John F. Harvey. Copyright © 1963 by Litton Educational Publishing Inc. Reprinted by permission of Van Nostrand Reinhold Company.*)

2000 cycles at 42,000 psi, and 10,000 cycles at 31,000 psi, and fabricated of material with allowable fatigue strength properties given in the σ-N curve of Fig. 8, would be considered safe fatigue-wise because the sum of the cycle ratios is less than unity.

$$(29) \qquad \sum \frac{n}{N} = \frac{500}{2,600} + \frac{2,000}{9,000} + \frac{10,000}{50,000} = 0.61$$

Construction features

The most important single consideration in designing for long life is to obtain the lowest feasible value of stresses throughout the entire vessel. Practical operating requirements necessitate construction features such as openings, lifting lugs and support skirts, which can become "weak links" by introducing abnormal stresses. Accordingly, minimizing stress concentrations associated with these by gradual transitions in geometric shape is the key factor in designing vessels for long life in transient operation.

Openings. Openings are the most prevalent construction feature on a vessel, Fig. 9. They are usually round because this shape is readily fabricated. They are required in pressure vessels for the practical introduction of the operating media and for maintenance accessibility.

Fig. 9 Boiler steam drum.

However, when an opening is placed in a vessel, the stresses increase in a region confined to the edge of the opening, and this can become an area of weakness. These local peak stresses are called stress concentrations, K_t, and are expressed as a multiplier of the normal stress that would occur in the vessel without the opening. For instance, a stress concentration factor of 3.0 exists for an unreinforced circular hole under uniaxial tension such as would exist in a hydraulic ram cylinder. In the cylindrical portion of a pressure vessel, e.g., a steam drum, in which a biaxial stress state exists such that the circumferential stress is twice the longitudinal stress, the stress concentration factor is 2.5. In the case of the same hole in a spherical vessel, in which circumferential and longitudinal biaxial stresses are equal, the stress concentration factor is reduced to 2.0.

One method of reducing the stress at an opening is to thicken the entire vessel and thereby decrease the mem-

brane stress to which the stress concentration multiplier is applied. This is not always a practical or economical solution. An alternative is to reinforce the opening with additional material to compensate for the high local stress at the edge of the hole. Analytical and experimental studies of unreinforced and reinforced openings have shown that the high local peak stress is substantially confined to a distance from the edge of the opening equal to the radius of the opening, and that it is sensitive to the geometric shape of the compensation material with the maximum stress located at the inside and outside corners of added material, such as the material added to the nozzle in Fig. 10. The two basic rules for the reinforcement of openings are:

1. Replace the cross-sectional area of the material removed by the opening with an equal amount of reinforcement material placed immediately adjacent to the opening.

2. Dispose the reinforcement in profile and contour so as to accomplish a gradual transition and not introduce an overriding stress concentration in itself. This means adding equal amounts to the inside and outside of the vessel wall to obtain a "balanced" arrangement, Fig. 11a. When restrictions, such as the removal of internals, require that the reinforcement be all on the outside of the vessel wall, generous tapers, fillets and rounded edges are used, as in Figs. 11b and c.

Virtually all failures result from fatigue in an area of high localized stress. Hence safe pressure vessel construction is accomplished by eliminating or minimizing high local stresses.

Structural design

Fossil-fuel steam generators

The primary responsibility of the structural designer is to translate the structural requirements of modern steam generators into design arrangements. Knowledge of the properties of materials is utilized together with approved analytical methods to create an economical design that will assure structural and mechanical adequacy of supporting systems. The type of structure is greatly influenced by the size, design and location of the steam generator, and the design specifications.

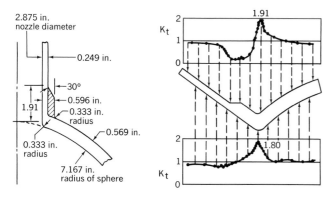

Fig. 10 Variation in stress concentration, K_t, about a circular reinforced nozzle in a sphere subject to internal pressure. *(From "Pressure Vessel Design—Nuclear and Chemical Applications" by John F. Harvey. Copyright © 1963 by Litton Educational Publishing Inc. Reprinted by permission of Van Nostrand Reinhold Company.)*

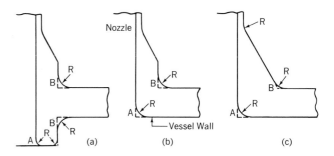

Fig. 11 Details of nozzle reinforcement to reduce stress concentration. *(From "Pressure Vessel Design—Nuclear and Chemical Applications" by John F. Harvey. Copyright © 1963 by Litton Educational Publishing Inc. Reprinted by permission of Van Nostrand Reinhold Company.)*

Bottom support is usually more economical for the smaller-size fossil-fuel steam generators, and is standard for shop-assembled units. Problems arising from expansion and temperature differentials make it more economical to support the larger units from the top.

Fossil-fuel boilers for utilities and the larger industrial boilers, including recovery units for pulp and paper mills, are top supported. The remainder of this chapter (except for the section *Structural Design of a Nuclear Reactor Core*) deals with the structural design of a top-supported fossil-fuel steam generator for an electric utility.

The location of the unit has an important effect on the design of a steam-generator supporting structure. It establishes seismic conditions and wind loads, and the site yields information on the soil bearing capabilites for foundations. Climatic conditions are also important in determining whether indoor or outdoor construction is to be used.

To the extent practicable, indoor units utilize the building columns as well as the boiler columns for vertical support. Lateral support is furnished by vertical bracing and horizontal trusses. Outdoor units may be partially enclosed, as well as partially roofed, or completely exposed to the weather.

Sources of design information. Once the site location is known and the special job specifications available, the arrangement and details of the steam generator steel can be established. This includes choice of end connections, i.e., whether they are welded, riveted, or bolted. The selection of field-erected connections need not be the same as that used for shop-fabricated connections. In fact, it is general practice to weld one end of the connection to the structural member in the shop, and use bolts to complete the assembly in the field.

There are a number of codes, standards and specifications available to aid in structural design. Those most frequently used are:

1. The *American Standard Building Code Requirements for Minimum Design Loads in Buildings and Other Structures*, published by the American National Standards Institute, Inc., lists design loads for a great number of materials and provides information on snow and seismic loads for all areas of the U.S.

2. The *Uniform Building Code*, published by the International Conference of Building Officials, is a helpful

tool for the development of better and safer building constructions.

3. The *Manual of Steel Construction*, published by the American Institute of Steel Construction (AISC) contains design details as well as information on fabrication and erection of structural steel for buildings.

These documents aid the designer in carrying out the complex design problems of steam-generator supporting structures. It should be noted that such structures are very large, in many cases exceeding 250 feet in height, and involve the design, fabrication and erection of several thousand tons of structural steel.

Design of a structural steel system. The steam-generator supporting structure is a highly irregular and indeterminate system, made up of rolled and built-up structural-steel members. It must carry the weight of the steam generator and associated equipment and withstand wind and seismic loads. The two latter are dynamic forces and it is standard practice to resolve these loads into equivalent static design forces. The governing loading condition, either wind- or earthquake-loading, is then applied as a design load for the analysis of the structure, since wind and earthquake loads are not considered to occur simultaneously.

The wind load on the vertical surface of a boiler is usually given in customer's design specifications or can be taken from local building codes. It varies from 25 lb/sq ft (corresponding to a wind velocity of approximately 100 mi/hr) up to 50 lb/sq ft (and more) for some shore-line areas that experience hurricanes.

The equivalent static seismic force, applied laterally, is usually stated as a function of gravity, "g", or weight. It is expressed by:

$$(30) \qquad F = CW$$

Where F is the horizontal force, C is a coefficient and W is the total dead load at or above the elevation under investigation. The value of the coefficient, C, is a function of the zone of seismic probability in which the structure is located and the type of structure. The value of this coefficient normally ranges from 0.05 to 0.20 (for fossil-fuel units). For units that are not enclosed, both the seismic loads due to the dead load of the boiler and wind loads are transferred via boiler ties into the structure and then through the bracing system down into the foundations. For enclosed units, earthquake ties are required. However, the transfer of wind loads to the columns and thence, through the vertical bracing system, into the foundation takes place directly through girts supporting the siding.

Loads from wind and earthquake must be distributed and the governing (maximum) condition is then combined with the statical forces for proper sizing of members. In one case, wind load plus live and dead load determine the member size in a system and, in another area of the same system, the combination of earthquake load plus live and dead load may govern member size.

Top support steel. The loads of the various steam generator components are carried by hanger rods to the top steel. This top-steel arrangement from which the boiler is suspended and allowed to expand downward is a grid composed of rolled shapes and built-up girders. The layout of the top steel will greatly affect the load distribution into the columns, and thus will influence pier loads. Built-up girders 22 feet deep, over 110 feet in length and weighing 165 tons have been used to support the top grid steel.

Platform arrangements. Platforms are located where required for access to permit operation and maintenance of the steam generator and associated equipment. Frequently platforms are made into horizontal trusses and provide lateral support for those boiler columns that cannot be stabilized by vertical bracing. These horizontal trusses also serve as a means of transferring lateral wind and earthquake forces through ties to the vertical bracing system.

Column rows. Vertical bracing between columns is arranged to clear walkways and boiler accessories, such as sootblowers, and to provide maximum accessibility. The bracing system provides support for the boiler structure against wind and earthquake forces, as well as unbalanced internal (pressure) forces. Side-sway (lateral deflection) must be limited as excessive side-sway could damage steam piping, auxiliary equipment, flue and duct work, the boiler or the supporting structure itself.

Stress calculation for member sizes. As many as 5000 to 7000 structural steel members are needed to make a steam-generator supporting structure. Before the introduction of the computer, all these structural steel members had to be sized by "longhand" procedures. Load distribution in a bracing system had to be performed under simple assumptions, disregarding secondary effects, and side-sway calculations were very time-consuming. With the use of computers, information on the behavior of the structure, which was not previously available, can be obtained.

Repetitive calculations are performed on the computer, thereby allowing the engineer to optimize the system economically. Various computer programs are presently available to the structural steel designer. These are:

1. Frame analysis and design program
2. Hewlett-Packard programmable calculator
3. Girder design program
4. Connection design and structural steel detailing program

Frame analysis program. Given a plane structure composed of straight uniform members of a predetermined size, and the loads imposed on this structure, a typical computer program will:

a) Calculate and print the displacements at every joint.

b) Calculate and print pier loads.

c) Calculate and print the end reactions for every member.

d) Determine if the given size is acceptable for every member, and either search in a steel table for a lighter section or a suitable section.

The load distribution is based on the following:

a) Member equation. The equation relating the end reactions of a straight member to its end displacements may be indicated as:

$$(31) \quad \begin{bmatrix} f_1 \\ f_2 \end{bmatrix} = \begin{bmatrix} y_{11} & y_{12} \\ y_{21} & y_{22} \end{bmatrix} \begin{bmatrix} d_1 \\ d_2 \end{bmatrix} + \begin{bmatrix} g_1 \\ g_2 \end{bmatrix}$$

where:

f_1 = true reactions at end "1" = F_{x1}, F_{y1}, M_1

d_1 = displacement at end "1" = θ_1

g_1 = fixed end reactions at end "1" caused by loads applied to the member

f_2, d_2 and g_2 = true reactions, displacement and fixed end reactions at end "2"

y_{11}, y_{12}, y_{21} and y_{22} = stiffness matrices

b) Equation of structure. Given the equation for every member in a structure, it is possible to construct a set of simultaneous linear equations which express the unknown joint displacements as a function of known loads applied to the structure. This is accomplished by combining the member equations for all members connected to each joint in such a way that the "equilibrium" and "compatibility" equations for all joints are satisfied. The equilibrium equations for the joints simply state that each joint must be in equilibrium under the forces and moments exerted on it by members connected to it together with an external load acting on the joint.

The compatibility equations indicate that continuity at the joints must be preserved; that is, all members meeting at each joint must (if they are rigidly connected to it) have the same displacements and rotations.

c) Member end reactions. Once the displacements for every joint are known, the member end reactions may be found by substituting into the member equations.

At the completion of the analysis portion of the program, the computed values for end reactions and maximum interior moment for each member for each of the stress conditions have been stored in the computer.

Each member in the structure is now checked by the computer independently of other members as follows:

a) Determine what stresses exist in the member for the beam size which was specified as input data.

b) Select from a steel table a lighter beam (if the input beam was satisfactory but understressed) or a suitable size (if the input beam was not satisfactory, i.e., overstressed). In other words, the computer selects the most economical size.

c) If the lightest suitable section was a column section reinforced with cover plates attached to the flanges of the column, attempt to find a suitable rolled section using high-strength steel.

A beam size is satisfactory only if it meets stress requirements for all stress conditions (based on the *AISC Manual of Steel Construction*) and also meets certain other specified requirements, such as maximum and minimum depth specifications.

Hewlett-Packard programmable calculator. With the advent of the programmable calculators, many previously tedious calculations have been minimized or eliminated. Several programs such as beam stress check, shear and moment calculations for both simply supported members and multi-span continuous members, beam deflections, earthquake redistribution, column base plate design and other related programs have been developed to aid the structural engineers.

Girder design program. Given the span and loading condition of a simply supported plate girder, bending moments and shear forces at all cross-sections can be determined by static analysis. Based on the most critical actions, an initial profile is obtained. The cross-section of an I-shape plate girder is a function of web height, web thickness, flange width, and flange thickness. To maximize the section modulus and minimize the area, different profiles are obtained by increasing the web height. After comparing various trial sections, a section with minimum area is adopted. After getting such a section, flange cuts, if any, are determined and a stress check is made. If any standard requirements are not satisfied, the program, if possible, automatically changes appropriate dimensions and rechecks the results.

Connection design program. Given a plane structure composed of straight uniform members of a predetermined size (column rows and platform arrangements), and given the loads imposed on these members (including member end reactions), a computer program will design all AISC standard connections and several types of special connections.

The connection can be designed as completely bolted, completely welded or a combination of welding and bolting. If bolted connections are used, the connection can be designed as friction or bearing-type.

The program furnishes computer printed version of transmittal and input information, tabulation of member details, steel detail index, material listing, procurement material order listing, purchase order listing, stock allocation inventory entry cards, summary of drawings, steel detail bolt list, shop order pages for members detailed by computer, steel detailing index, hole pattern data sheets, and hole pattern data sheet index.

Structural design of a nuclear reactor core

In nuclear power plants particular consideration is required for the structural design of the nuclear fuel assemblies and control rods constituting the reactor core, and the fixed structure required for core support. This structure, together with the thermal shielding, is usually referred to as the reactor vessel internals.

The general arrangement of the pressure vessel, core, and internals is shown in Figs. 2 and 3, Chapter 21, for a large nuclear reactor for an electric utility. A fuel assembly for this reactor is shown in Fig. 4, Chapter 21. The basic structure of the fuel assembly is described under the heading *Structural Integrity* in Chapter 21.

In addition to normal design criteria, a nuclear plant must meet other criteria arising from the need to prevent release of radioactivity from the plant under conditions of abnormal operation or natural disaster, such as an earthquake, at the plant site. (*See also Safety Criteria*

and Provisions, Chapter 23.) In the process of licensing a nuclear plant to operate, the Nuclear Regulatory Commission gives careful consideration to plant design and its conformity with design criteria of this type.

In the structural design of the core and reactor vessel internals, it is necessary to consider the consequences of buckling, low-cycle fatigue, thermal stresses, flow-induced vibration and seismic forces. Consideration must also be given to changes in the structural material properties caused by irradiation.

Fuel assemblies are designed to minimize fretting and wear of clad (caused by flow-induced vibration). Also, plastic strain of the fuel clad is conservatively limited to one percent. The static stress analysis of the composite structure, which constitutes a fuel assembly, involves a special approach. Classical beam equations do not apply since the coupled-tube structure of the fuel assembly cannot transfer shear. In the case of the fuel assembly shown in Fig. 4, Chapter 21, the theoretical model used is based on the coupling effect of individual tubes between spacer grids. This theoretical model was verified by a test program, and a special digital computer code was written and used to complete the analysis.

The lower grid assembly, Fig. 2, Chapter 21, is an example of an unusual structure that must accommodate not only the nuclear core load, but also the imposed seismic forces. This grid is composed of tapered beams intersecting in rectangular patterns. The resulting equal displacements at the beam intersections give rise to a group of simultaneous equations which are then solved for unknown joint forces.

Dynamic loading of the core and reactor internals results from flow-induced vibration, and postulated earthquakes and loss-of-coolant accidents. Analyses of these conditions are based on the solution of basic equations of motion. The mathematical models used to determine dynamic stresses and deflections employ lumped masses connected by flexible elements. Because of interdependent or coupling effects, a complete dynamic model for seismic analysis of the core includes the reactor building and foundation, reactor vessel, steam generator, primary piping, reactor internals, control rod drives, and fuel assemblies. An accurate analysis of the structures for earthquake input is difficult because of the random nature of the excitation forces and non-linearity introduced by impacts. At present, considerable research and development effort is devoted to structural dynamics to represent more accurately the behavior of components during postulated earthquake conditions and loss-of-coolant accidents.

Manufacturing and construction

The benefits of good design are incorporated into a dependable product by using proven materials and manufacturing procedures, maintaining careful quality control during fabrication, and by proper assembly and installation of each unit at the user's plant. Chapter 31 describes the fabrication of steam generating equipment as this is done in B&W's shops, and Chapter 32 describes the additional work performed at the plant site to achieve the completed installation.

Chapter 31 begins with the description of welding processes. Arc welding processes include manual shielded-metal-arc welding with coated electrodes, automatic submerged-arc, gas-shielded tungsten-arc, gas-shielded metal-arc, flux core, and electroslag welding. Gas welding and pressure welding are also considered. This is followed by a discussion of preheating, and postweld heat treatment. A table is included listing recommended electrode materials for the arc welding of carbon- and alloy-steel tubes and combinations. Preheating and postweld heat-treatment requirements are also tabulated.

This is followed by a brief discussion of tooling with several illustrations, including a vertical boring mill with digital readout for tool location, and a deep-hole drilling machine for tape-controlled drilling of thousands of small holes through thick tubesheets.

Quality assurance and quality control procedures are established to make sure that pressure parts are fabricated in accordance with applicable codes and specifications. Welding is performed by personnel qualified in accordance with a specific procedure. Nondestructive testing procedures are used to control the quality of base materials and weldments. These are radiography (using X or gamma rays), ultrasonics, magnetic-particle testing and liquid-penetrant testing.

Processes used in the manufacture of fossil-fuel equipment are described and illustrated. The first is drum fabrication, including the forming and welding of shells, the forming and attachment of drumheads and nozzles, stress relief, nondestructive testing, and the installation of internal parts. Also depicted are the fabrication of headers, the shop assembly of wall panels and platens for convection banks, and the manufacture of fuel-preparation and -burning equipment.

Production of the large pressure vessels required for nuclear power generation is depicted in some detail through the various stages of manufacture. The fabrication of a nuclear steam generator from its component parts is described and illustrated. Also included is the production of uranium oxide fuel rods and the insertion of these rods into spacer grids to produce fuel assemblies for nuclear power.

The manufacture of tubing, both seamless and welded, is described in the latter part of the chapter. The usual process for making seamless tubes comprises heating, piercing, rolling, reeling, sizing, and cold drawing. The Ugine-Sejournet hot-extrusion process is also included. The production of electric-resistance-welded tubes is described by steps, including preparation of incoming strip, folding into open-tube form, resistance welding, sizing, heat treatment, straightening, and cutting. Quality control requirements and inspection and testing procedures are summarized.

Chapter 32 begins with a discussion of planning and coordination for the erection of steam generating equipment at the plant site. The treatment covers time and cost estimates, erection schedule, selection of tools and equipment, and preparations at the jobsite, including provisions for handling and storage of materials and equipment.

For a large top-supported fossil-fuel unit, erection begins with steel supports. This is followed by location of the steam drum, top headers, interconnecting tubes and piping, wall panels, superheater, reheater, economizer and air-heater surfaces, fuel-burning equipment, fans, flues and ducts.

In the case of a large nuclear steam supply system, at least three large pressure components must be moved to the jobsite and lifted into position. Large pumps and heavy-wall piping must also be installed. Inside the reactor vessel, the reactor internals must be assembled to close tolerances to accommodate the fuel assemblies and control rods. Installation also includes control rod drives, fuel-handling equipment and several auxiliary systems involving piping as well as control and instrumentation equipment.

Field erection work, like shop fabrication, must be performed in accordance with applicable codes. Code and inspection requirements are discussed in Chapter 32. Field welding processes and the nondestructive testing of weldments are summarized. The necessity for internal cleanliness of pressure parts is treated. The procedure for conducting the hydrostatic test of the pressure parts is described. The chapter concludes with a summary of work required for nonpressure parts and auxiliaries, and the final preoperation inspection.

Reactor vessel (without closure head) for a B&W nuclear steam supply system being loaded on a barge for shipment from Mount Vernon Works.

Chapter 31

Manufacturing

For many years, steam generating equipment built by reliable manufacturers in accordance with accepted codes, and properly operated, has been recognized as dependable and safe. In addition, during the last thirty years, there has been significant improvement in the quality of the materials employed, in the control of fabrication processes, and in the methods used for inspection. Perhaps the greatest achievement of the boiler industry during the last thirty years has been this improvement in the quality of its product accomplished through better methods of inspection and quality control.

This improvement in quality has necessarily been achieved concurrently with rapid expansion in the size of steam generating units. The majority of units, particularly in the larger industrial and utility applications, are specially designed to meet the user's requirements. Most of the pieces, subassemblies, and assemblies that make up the complete unit must be individually designed and shown on separate shop drawings. Thus, only a small segment of the manufacturing procedure could be classified as a quantity-production operation.

Fabrication of the pressure and nonpressure parts and of the auxiliary equipment for modern units involves a great variety of skills and unique manufacturing methods and requires facilities for almost every metalworking and metal-forming process. Welding is employed in the manufacture of almost every component produced by Babcock & Wilcox. It is especially important in the construction of boiler drums and pressure vessels. Its development has facilitated fabrication of vessels of large size and great functional capability.

Welding

Basically, welding consists of heating the surfaces of two pieces of metal above their melting temperatures at the point where a joint is to be made. It is usually necessary to add "filler metal" to the molten weld puddle to fill the cavity. After the weld cools and solidifies, a metallurgical bond is formed between the joined surfaces.

Arc welding processes

The most common welding processes used in the manufacture of pressure vessels, headers and piping utilize an electric arc as the source of heat. A special welding machine is generally used to transform high-voltage low-amperage primary power to low-voltage high-amperage power suitable for arc welding. Alternatively, motor-generator sets are often used in the field. Peak arc temperatures are near 10,000F. Since most metals melt at 2500-2750F, the electric arc adequately and efficiently supplies the concentrated heat source necessary to cause local melting of large work surfaces.

If the surfaces to be joined are more than $\frac{3}{16}$-in. thick, it is necessary to bevel the edges to permit the addition of filler metal to the weld groove. The method of adding filler metal varies with the welding process and is discussed with each process.

Manual shielded-metal-arc welding with coated electrodes. The original metal-arc-welding process was introduced near the end of the nineteenth century. In this process an arc is produced between a consumable metallic electrode and the workpiece. The heat energy of the arc melts not only the metallic electrode but also the surface of the work in contact with the arc. At first, when bare electrodes (unshielded arc) were used, the weld metal lacked ductility and was porous because of high oxygen and nitrogen content.

In the late twenties, flux coatings were developed for metallic electrodes. To produce weld metal essentially free from oxides and nitrides, the welding wire is covered with fluxing ingredients and combustible materials. In this way the molten metal is shielded from the surrounding air during the period of heat transfer through the arc, and undesirable oxides are cleansed or fluxed from the weld puddle.

Specific electrodes have been developed to enable the deposition of weld metal in a variety of positions and under various conditions. These coated electrodes have been classified by the American Welding Society primarily according to usability and the type of deposit produced. An important factor in this classification is the type of coating applied to the weld wire, which has an important bearing on the quality of the weld produced.

For instance, high-cellulose type electrodes (such as the E-7010 electrodes, Table 1) were formerly used to meet X-ray quality specifications for all welding of pressure-containing components. With coatings of this type, the soundness of the weld metal depends primarily on the protective hydrogen-gas shielding afforded by the

combustion of the cellulose. Although now largely replaced by "low-hydrogen" electrodes, high-cellulose electrodes are employed for applications such as seal welding on economizer tube-to-header joints in the field, where it is difficult to maintain the degree of cleanliness required for use of the low-hydrogen electrodes.

Electrodes having the designation E-7015 or E-8015, for use with d-c reverse polarity (i.e., with the workpiece negative, electrode positive) and E-7016 or E-8016 for use with direct or alternating current are known as low-hydrogen electrodes. They were developed during World War II to eliminate the cracking problems encountered when military armor plate was welded with the hydrogen-producing electrodes used up to that time. The low-hydrogen electrodes have a coating that contains lime. During welding, carbon-dioxide gas is liberated, shielding the molten puddle from contamination. This type of electrode offers the highest degree of protection against cracking and produces the cleanest weld-metal attainable with manual metal-arc welding. Low-hydrogen electrodes having the designation E-7015 or E-8015 (Table 1) are used with d-c reverse polarity. E-7016 and E-8016 types are low-hydrogen electrodes for use with direct or alternating current.

Many boiler components are made of steels containing various amounts of alloying elements, from small amounts of chromium and molybdenum up to the highly alloyed stainless steels and Inconel. For the welding of these alloy steels, there are electrodes available that will deposit weld metal of essentially the same composition as the parent metal. Electrodes suitable for welding the various Croloy steels are listed in Table 1. Coatings on these alloy-steel electrodes are the lime type.

Automatic submerged-arc welding. The manual arc process described above uses an open arc, with slag-producing flux from the coating of electrodes deposited simultaneously with the weld metal of the rod. In the submerged-arc process, a bare filler wire, usually $\frac{1}{8}$-in. diameter, is continuously fed from a large coil, through a welding head and into the weld area. As before, an electric arc is maintained between the filler wire and the base metal resulting in the melting and subsequent fusion of both metals to form a weld. However, with the submerged-arc process, a layer of granular flux about 1-in. deep is separately deposited just ahead of the welding arc. In effect, the welding arc is submerged under this blanket of protective flux, a portion of which is melted by the heat of the arc.

The electric-current value permissible with a given size electrode is a function of the weight of flux used per pound of rod. The amount of flux that can be economically applied to a coated manual metal-arc welding electrode by an extrusion process is limited. A greater amount of flux can be used with the submerged-arc method. The outstanding advantage of submerged-arc welding over open-arc welding is that greater electric-current values are practicable. For instance, with $\frac{1}{4}$-in. diameter wire, current values range to 1500 amperes in the submerged-arc method, as compared with about 400 amperes for a coated rod. Current values in excess of 2000 amperes may be used successfully in submerged-arc welding with larger wire, e.g., $\frac{5}{16}$-in. and $\frac{3}{8}$-in. diameter. The amount of molten flux in the submerged-arc method is roughly 1 to $1\frac{1}{2}$ times the weight of the molten metal, while in the open-arc method the flux seldom exceeds 25% of the weight of core wire.

Table 1
Recommended arc welding electrodes for various material combinations

Base Material	Carbon Steel	Carbon-Mo	Croloy $\frac{1}{2}$	Croloy 1 & $1\frac{1}{4}$	Croloy 2	Croloy $2\frac{1}{4}$ & 3M	Croloy 5	Croloy 7 & 9M	Type 304 Stainless Steel	Type 321 Stainless Steel
Carbon Steel	E7010A1 E7015A1	E7010A1 E7015A1	E7010A1 E7015A1	E7010A1 E7015A1	E7010A1 E7015A1	E7010A1 E7015A1	E7010A1 E7015A1	E7010A1 E7015A1	ENiCrFe3	ENiCrFe3
Carbon-Mo		E7010A1 E7015A1	E7010A1 E7015A1	E7010A1 E7015A1	E7010A1 E7015A1	E7010A1 E7015A1	E7010A1 E7015A1	E7010A1 E7015A1	ENiCrFe3	ENiCrFe3
Croloy $\frac{1}{2}$			E8015B2L	E8015B2L	E8015B2L	E8015B2L	E8015B2L	E8015B2L	ENiCrFe3	ENiCrFe3
Croloy 1 & $1\frac{1}{4}$				E8015B2L	E8015B2L	E8015B2L	E8015B2L	E8015B2L	ENiCrFe3	ENiCrFe3
Croloy 2					E9015B3L	E9015B3L	E9015B3L	E9015B3L	ENiCrFe3	ENiCrFe3
Croloy $2\frac{1}{4}$ & 3M						E9015B3L	E9015B3L	E9015B3L	ENiCrFe3	ENiCrFe3
Croloy 5							E502-15	E502-15	ENiCrFe3	ENiCrFe3
Croloy 7 & 9M								E505-15	ENiCrFe3	ENiCrFe3
Type 304 Stainless Steel									E308-15 E308-16	E308-15 E308-16
Type 321 Stainless Steel										E16-8-2-15

Note to Table 1:
    The ASME Materials Specification for each electrode is given below:

SFA 5.5 Type E7010A1 (carbon steel)	SFA 5.4 Type E308-15 (stainless steel)	SFA 5.11 Type ENiCrFe3
Type E7015A1 (carbon steel)	Type E308-16 (stainless steel)	(Inconel 182)
Type E8015B2L (Croloy 1A)	Type E16-8-2-15 (stainless steel)	
Type E9015B3L (Croloy 2$\frac{1}{4}$A)	Type E502-15 (Croloy 5A)	
	Type E505-15 (Croloy 9A)	

In production, plates up to 2 inches thick may be welded in two passes by the submerged-arc-welding method. These welds are clean, sound, free from defects, and have excellent mechanical properties. The submerged arc is used successfully for multipass welding of plate as thick as 15 inches.

Gas-shielded tungsten-arc welding. This type of welding utilizes an electric arc which is maintained between a nonconsumable tungsten electrode and the workpiece. Shielding gas, normally pure argon, is introduced through a hollow cylinder which surrounds the tungsten. This gas cools the electrode and protects it and the molten puddle from contamination by the atmosphere. The process can be manual with a hand-held torch or the entire operation can be automated. Filler metal from 0.035-in. to 0.125-in. diameter is manually or automatically added to the molten-weld pool.

This welding process has many applications. It is particularly useful for making high quality welds in small diameter tubing where it is difficult to manipulate the longer coated electrodes used with the manual metal-arc-welding process. Since no slag is produced, gas-shielded tungsten-arc welding is used for making the root pass where high-quality full-penetration welds are required and where it is not possible to gain access to the back of the joint. The "root pass" of a weld is defined as the first layer of weld used to join the component parts.

Gas-shielded metal-arc welding. Gas shielded metal arc has been used by B&W since 1965 as a replacement for manual metal-arc welding in many applications. This semiautomatic method provides a greater rate of weld-metal deposition than the manual metal-arc method, yet does not require the extensive setup times often needed for automatic submerged-arc welding.

An electric arc is maintained between a coil of filler metal and the base material. The heat of the arc melts both the base material and the filler metal, which is continuously fed into the joint. The smaller ($\frac{1}{16}$-in. diameter) wire can be used with the weld groove in any position except overhead, but the larger diameter electrodes can be used only when the welding groove is in a horizontal plane.

Argon, carbon dioxide, or mixtures of the two gases are introduced through the same gun that feeds the welding wire. These gases prevent contamination of the molten-weld puddle by the oxygen and nitrogen in the atmosphere.

Gas-shielded metal-arc welding is used primarily with solid wire in a semiautomatic process 1) to join thin carbon-steel materials, 2) to make groove welds with Inconel-filler metal, and 3) to deposit overlay cladding with Inconel-filler metal.

With solid wire the electric arc can be of the short-circuiting, pulsed-power or spray type. Each type provides a different amount of heat for melting the filler metal and the base material. The short-circuiting arc is especially good for welding carbon-steel sheet or plate less than $\frac{1}{4}$-in. thick, in any position and for the first pass in pipe welds. Pulsed power is used for welding heavier carbon-steel material, for overlay of steel with Inconel, and to join Inconel material in any thickness.

Spray arc is used to overlay steel with Inconel at higher deposition rates than with pulsed power.

The filler metal may also be a cored wire called flux-cored electrode—a thin, low carbon-steel sheath which surrounds a core of packed powdery materials. These core materials contribute alloying elements to the weld, protective slag for the surface of the molten pool, and deoxidizing minerals that help to cleanse the weld metal.

Shielding gases are the same for solid and flux-cored electrodes. They shield the weld puddle to prevent oxidation by the atmosphere. Chemistry of the deposit depends solely on the filler material selected.

Electroslag welding. Electroslag welding is a welding process used to make full thickness welds in one pass, with the welding groove in a vertical plane. The weld filler-metal is fed into the groove continuously through a layer of slag formed by melted flux. The passage of welding current through the flux generates the heat required to melt the flux and keep it molten. Since a large pool of flux and molten filler metal exists throughout the welding operation, it is necessary to keep this pool within the confines of the welding groove by means of a water-cooled dam on each side of the groove. After welding is started at the bottom of the component, with respect to its position on the shop floor, welding proceeds in a vertically upward direction. To accommodate this, the welding equipment, including the sliding dams, is mounted on a vertical column adjacent to the part being welded. Automatic feed devices cause the welding equipment to move at the proper rate to keep pace with the deposit of weld metal. When the top of the part being welded is reached, the weld is completed.

Electroslag welding has an advantage of speed over other processes, with deposition rates of 80 to 100 lb/hr, compared to about 12 lb/hr for single-wire submerged-arc welding. It has an additional advantage of producing a defect-free deposit because the large molten pool of weld metal stays fluid long enough to allow defect-causing solids and gases to float out of the weld metal into the slag pool. However, as deposited, this kind of weld has the disadvantage of a coarse-grained structure, like that of a casting. Before such welds can be used in a pressure vessel, it is generally necessary to refine the grain of the weld and heat-affected zone. This is usually accomplished by "normalizing," which involves heating the entire component to the austenitizing temperature, approximately 1600F, and then cooling in still air to ambient temperature. In addition to normalizing, other heat treatments, such as water quenching from the austenitizing temperature, tempering and stress-relief, may be necessary, depending on the mechanical properties desired for the weld and heat-affected zone. The cost of heat treatment is such that electroslag welding is generally not used unless the base metal of the component must be heat-treated for some reason such as to enhance tensile or impact strength. Under this condition, the weld receives heat treatment without additional cost and the electroslag welding process can be justified economically.

Gas welding

Oxyacetylene gas welding, another fusion-welding process, finds relatively little application in boiler construc-

tion. This process is slow in comparison with metal-arc welding, particularly for materials over $\frac{1}{8}$-in. thick. However, there are some applications such as butt joints in light-gage tubing, where gas welding is used to advantage. In boiler construction, gas welding is generally limited to the plain carbon steels.

Electrogas welding

Electrogas welding is a continuous casting process used to weld vertical joints. The parts to be welded can be in a butt or "T" configuration. The weld is cast between water-cooled shoes that move vertically as the joint is filled. One or more consumable electrodes are melted in a gas cover of argon or argon plus carbon dioxide. The electrode is oscillated to distribute the heat and metal uniformly through the joint, which is typically 0.8 to 4.0 inches in thickness.

Typical applications are tanks, ships, and tall structural members one to 20 feet high in various steel and aluminum alloys.

Electron beam welding

Electron beam welding is a process where coalescence is produced by the heat obtained from a concentrated beam composed primarily of high velocity electrons impinging upon the surfaces to be joined. An electron gun generates, collimates, and directs the beam of electrons at the location being welded. The weld progresses by moving the electron beam with respect to the part being welded. This process is typically performed in a vacuum which provides a pure and inert environment, free from contamination, but which limits the use of the process to components which can physically fit into the vacuum enclosure. In comparison with conventional arc welding processes, welds are made with low energy input and at high power density. These features produce welds that have a minimum amount of distortion, have a minimum change in mechanical properties, can be very deep with respect to their width, can be made in a single pass, can be made on a variety of materials, including refractory and reactive metals. The process is easily and accurately controlled, and is sometimes used for its accessibility to weld joints. Welds made by this process are usually made with square butt joint preparations without filler metal additions. Mechanical properties of electron beam welds are usually equivalent or superior to those of the parent metals.

Pressure welding

In pressure welding, the surfaces to be joined are heated to high temperatures and welded by applying pressure. No filler metal is added to the joint. Solid phase welding of this type is exemplified by the "blacksmith" weld. Resistance butt-welding of superheater and economizer tubing and the studding of various tubes fall into this category. Seam-, spot-, projection- and flash-welding methods are all in this category but seldom used in the manufacture of boiler components. The source and heat energy for pressure welding surfaces may be electrical, oxyacetylene, forge or any other that is convenient.

The attachment of parts, such as studs and bolts, to a tube or plate, may be considered as a special case of pressure welding. Here a small amount of molten metal is produced between the stud and the surface of the tube

---

Table 2
General welding practices

A. Preheat

Base Material	Minimum Preheat Requirement
1. Carbon Steel	200F for material which has both a maximum carbon content in excess of 0.30% and a thickness at the joint in excess of 1 in.; 60F for materials not meeting above criteria.
2. Carbon-Molybdenum Croloy $\frac{1}{2}$	200F for material which has either a specified minimum tensile strength in excess of 70,000 psi or a thickness at the joint in excess of $\frac{5}{8}$ in.; 60F for materials not meeting above criteria.
3. Croloy 1, 1$\frac{1}{4}$, 2	250F for material which has either a specified minimum tensile strength in excess of 60,000 psi or a thickness at the joint in excess of $\frac{1}{2}$ in.; 60F for materials not meeting above criteria.
4. Croloy 2$\frac{1}{4}$, 3M	300F for all thicknesses.
5. Croloy 5, 7, 9	300F for joints of $\frac{1}{2}$-in. thickness or less; 400F for joints in excess of $\frac{1}{2}$-in. thickness.
6. Stainless Steel	(300 series) 60F for all thicknesses.

B. Postweld Heat Treatment

Base Material	Temperature	Notes
1. Carbon Steel	1100-1150F	1
2. Carbon-Molybdenum, Croloy $\frac{1}{2}$	1100-1150F	2
3. Croloy 1, 1$\frac{1}{4}$, 2	1325-1375F	3
4. Croloy 2$\frac{1}{4}$, 3M	1325-1375F	4
5. Croloy 5, 7, 9	1325-1375F	–
6. Stainless Steel	—	5

Notes:

1. Postweld heat treatment of carbon steel materials is not required for circumferential welds in pipes or tubes having a nominal wall thickness of $\frac{3}{4}$ in. or less at the joint.

2. Postweld heat treatment of carbon-molybdenum or Croloy $\frac{1}{2}$ materials is not required for circumferential welds in pipes or tubes having both a nominal wall thickness of $\frac{1}{2}$ in. or less and a specified maximum carbon content of not more than 0.25%.

3. Postweld heat treatment of Croloy 1 thru Croloy 2 materials is not required for circumferential welds in pipes or tubes meeting all of the following conditions:
   a. A maximum nominal outside diameter of 4 in.
   b. A maximum thickness of $\frac{1}{2}$ in.
   c. A maximum specified carbon content of not more than 0.15%.
   d. A minimum preheat of 250F.

4. Postweld heat treatment of Croloy 2$\frac{1}{4}$ or Croloy 3M materials is not required for circumferential welds in pipes or tubes meeting all of the following conditions:
   a. A maximum nominal outside diameter of 4 in.
   b. A maximum thickness of $\frac{1}{2}$ in.
   c. A maximum specified carbon content of not more than 0.15%.
   d. A minimum preheat of 300F.

5. Postweld heat treatment for stainless steel materials is neither required nor prohibited. Whether the weldment requires postweld heat treatment depends on the service intended and should be established accordingly. Where required, the recommended heat treatment may be either:
   a. A solution quench from within the range of 1900-2050F, or
   b. A stabilizing treatment consisting of heating to 1600-1650F followed by air cooling.

or plate by electric-resistance heating of the two parts at their point of contact. The stud is then forcibly projected against the workpiece. In this operation, control of timing, current values, and push-up force are important. Most of the molten metal is ejected from the weld area and the actual joint is really a plane of fusion between the stud and mating surface.

Preheating and postweld heat treatment

Preheating the parts to be welded effectively counteracts high stresses in deposited weld-metal and eliminates the tendency for some low-alloy steels to crack after welding. The proper preheat temperature depends mainly on the chemical composition and the thickness of the material to be welded, and to a lesser extent on the welding method selected.

Preheating reduces the hardness in the weld area by reducing the quenching effect of the base metal on the comparatively small volume of material which is heated to high temperature during welding. Depending on the type and thickness of material, a preheat of 150 to 400F uniformly applied to the weld area prior to the start of welding will usually be sufficient. Less preheat is required when welding with the low-hydrogen (lime-based) electrodes than with the cellulose-based electrodes, because the hydrogen shielding gas produced by the cellulose coating diffuses into the heat-affected zone of the base material. This can cause cracking in some materials, unless higher preheat temperatures are employed to facilitate escape of hydrogen from the weld.

A weld in 3-in. thick austenitic material, such as 304, 316 or Inconel, requires no preheat since it is not hardenable by quenching. However, a joint in 2¼ Cr-1Mo tubing of any thickness requires a minimum of 300F preheat. A carbon steel tube, 4-in. OD by ⅜-in. wall thickness, requires no preheat, but a 6-in. thick drum plate of similar material would be heated to more than 200F prior to and during welding.

Postweld heat treatment of weldments is a function of the complexity of the structure and of the composition and thickness of the materials joined. The *ASME Boiler and Pressure Vessel Code* gives rules defining the temperatures and conditions for postweld heat treatment of pressure-vessel components.

Postweld heat treatment has several purposes. The primary purposes of the heat treatment are 1) to reduce hard zones in the weld area of carbon and low-alloy steels, 2) to relieve residual stresses caused by welding, 3) to enhance the corrosion resistance of some materials, and 4) to reduce distortion during subsequent machining by removal of local concentration of peak residual stress. The temperature required to accomplish these purposes varies with the material and its application.

Welded joints are heat treated after welding, when necessary to develop adequate material properties. Exceptions are those in plain carbon steel ¾-in. or less in thickness, and carbon-molybdenum-steel tubing or piping ½-in. or less in wall thickness. Croloy steels of the low-chromium air-hardening grades and most of the high-alloy steels are heat treated after welding except tubes and pipes that comply with all details of the following specification: outside diameter, 4 in. or less; thickness, ½ in. or less; chromium, 3% or less; carbon,

0.15% or less. The postweld heat treatment temperatures may vary from 1100 to 1375F for carbon, carbon-molybdenum and Croloy steels, to 2050F for some of the Cr-Ni austenitic steels.

Table 1 lists recommended materials for welding electrodes for arc welding of carbon, carbon-molybdenum, ferritic and austenitic materials and their combinations. Requirements for preheating and postweld heat treatment are listed in Table 2.

Tooling

There are more than 2,000 machine tools in the shops of B&W's Power Generation Group. These include practically every type of standard machine equipment. In addition to these standard tools, there are many specially designed machines. Fig. 1 shows a machine for boring holes through a forging in a "skewed" pattern to close tolerance on size and location. The tool position in each of five systems is observed by means of a readout.

Fig. 2 shows the arrangement of a process identified as "Electrical Discharge Machining (EDM)." Here, an electrode is used to remove metal, as distinguished from a cutting tool. Instead of cutting or peeling the metal, as in Fig. 3, removal is achieved by erosion, caused by an electric current between the electrode and workpiece. In this way the machining of intricate shapes can be handled simply by properly shaping the electrode as shown in Fig. 2.

Increase in size of pressure vessels has made necessary similar growth in machine tools. For example, the vertical boring mill shown in Fig. 4 will accommodate a part 16 ft in diameter and 16 ft high. Such equipment is now commonly provided with digital readout to facilitate fast, accurate readings of tool location.

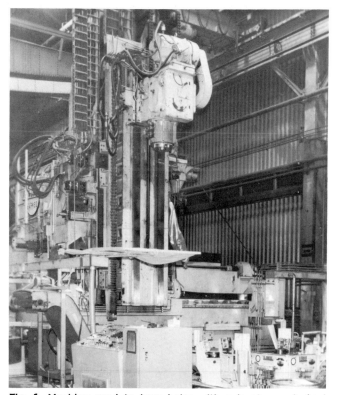

Fig. 1 Machine used to bore holes with axis at any desired angle to surface of workpiece.

Fig. 2 Electrode (right) and workpiece resulting from Electrical Discharge Machining.

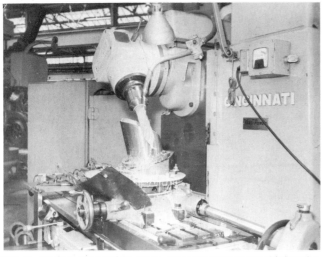

Fig. 3 Equipment used to make by conventional machining the part shown in Fig. 2 made by EDM.

Fig. 4 14-ft vertical boring mill equipped with digital readout for tool location.

The drilling of many thousands of small diameter holes through thick forgings is required for heat exchanger tubesheets. Fig. 5 shows the application of a deep-hole drilling machine to a 24-in. thick part having over 15,000 holes of ⅝-in. diameter. Numerical control is used to control positioning and cutting speed of the drills which are hollow to allow entry of coolant under high pressure.

An improvement over conventional drilling using drill jigs is represented in Fig. 6, showing a numerically controlled drill press. In this application work is performed in accordance with instructions programmed on a perforated tape. Speed and accuracy are achieved with this equipment.

Fig. 7 shows the application of a box-type fixture, with coordinate plates, to the precision boring of holes in a forging. Also shown is the use of "satellite" or "portable" tooling to drive the boring bar. This idea was developed to relieve the load on horizontal boring mills normally used for such work.

Quality assurance and quality control

Each division of B&W has a quality assurance group to establish planned and systematic patterns of all actions necessary to provide adequate confidence that the products conform to technical requirements. In addition each manufacturing facility of B&W has a quality control group to ensure that all products are made in accordance with applicable codes and specifications.

The *ASME Boiler and Pressure Vessel Code* published by The American Society of Mechanical Engineers provides a set of rules for the safe construction of boilers and other pressure vessels (*see Stress Analysis of Vessels, Chapter 30*). In most of the states of the U.S., these rules are a part of the state law and are enforced as such. The ASME Code is written by members of industry, users of boilers and pressure vessels, and members of inspection agencies. As such, it is well balanced from the standpoint of safety and practicality. Section I of the code, Power Boilers, requires that the fabricator of a power boiler have fabrication procedures, as well as design and material selection, monitored by an inspector. This inspector is usually employed by an insurance agency, and is licensed by the National Board of Boiler and Pressure Vessel Inspectors. In fabricating shops that produce a large volume of parts, this inspector is a full time resident. Therefore, he is on hand to check drawings, review materials certification, inspect welds, review radiographs, witness hydrostatic tests, and monitor general workmanship achieved by the fabricator. At the completion of a job, if he is satisfied that the parts comply with all aspects of the ASME Code, he signifies this by signing a Code Data Sheet.

All pressure-part welding performed on power boilers and pressure vessels must be performed by personnel qualified by the fabricator and in accordance with a procedure qualified by the fabricator. The variables that are involved in these qualifications include type of material, thickness of material, type of filler metal, position of welding, and factors related to preheat and postheat. In combination, these variables make necessary a large number of procedure qualifications. The number of per-

Fig. 5 24-in. thick tubesheet for nuclear power steam generator with tube holes drilled by tape-controlled gun drill.

sonnel qualifications depends on the number of men involved in fabrication. When this is measured in the thousands, it is necessary to have a facility that can quickly produce both qualified procedures and qualified personnel. For this purpose, B&W maintains welding schools where trained instructors handle this qualification work.

Nondestructive examination

One way to control the quality of base materials and weldments is by means of nondestructive examination. There are four basic methods used in the pressure vessel industry: radiography, ultrasonics, magnetic-particle, and liquid-penetrant. The first two are used for volumetric examination, and the latter two are useful for surface examination.

Radiography. Radiography has been used by B&W as the primary control of weld quality since the earliest application of welding in 1929. Starting with a single X-ray machine rated at 200 kilovolts, B&W has increased its capability to 52 radiographic units. The largest X-ray machine is the 12.8 million volt linear accelerator shown in Fig. 8. These machines are supplemented by gamma-ray equipment, using the radioisotope iridium-192 for activity from 10 to 100 curies, and cobalt-60 for activity from 10 to 2500 curies.

X-ray machines and radioisotopes have specific application based on the mobility of the part to be examined or the availability of an X-ray facility. The X-ray units can be used to advantage in shops where fixed position equipment is applicable. For field use or when the component to be examined is not readily moved, there are advantages in the use of the portable radioisotopes. Remote control equipment, now available, contributes greatly to the safe handling of these radioactive sources.

Radiography, with either X-ray machines or gamma-ray producing isotopes, consists of arranging the source of rays on one side of the weld to be examined, with a suitable film on the other side. The rays, X or gamma, pass through the weld and expose the film. If there are no flaws in the weld, the film is uniformly exposed. If there is a flaw, the rays will pass through it more readily than through the base metal. Therefore, the particular area of the film in the path of such rays will become darker than the surrounding area. The location and geometry of the flaw is thereby established.

In order to assure that the rays properly penetrate the object being examined, a small metal plaque or "penetrameter," containing three holes, is placed on the object in such a manner as to cause an image to form on the film. The thickness of this penetrameter and the size of the holes in the penetrameter are specified in applicable regulatory documents, such as the ASME Code. When the methods used are technically correct, an image of the holes in the penetrameter will appear on the film. From this, it can be concluded that an image of flaws of equal size, or larger, would also appear on the film. The ASME Code specifies acceptance standards with respect to the size of defects that might occur in the welds, such as slag and porosity. The code also describes the kinds of welds in pressure vessels that must be radiographed. B&W not only complies with the code requirements for radiography but also uses this form of nondestructive examination to control the quality of welds for applications other than those made mandatory by ASME.

The greatest advantage of radiography over other nondestructive methods is that a permanent record is made on film for each inspection. These films are retained for a minimum of 10 years or as required by the contract.

Ultrasonics. The fundamentals of examining plate and forgings by the use of ultrasonics have been known for 30 years, and production use of this method has now gained wide acceptance.

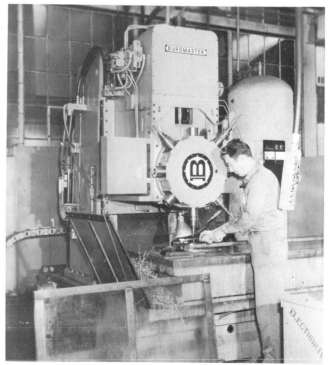

Fig. 6 Tape-controlled drill press.

Fig. 7 Box-type boring fixture and portable boring bars used for finish boring in place of horizontal boring mill.

Ultrasonic examination (Fig. 9) can be applied to almost all material used in the pressure vessel industry. In general, any size or thickness of such material can be examined. The principle involved in generating the sound required to penetrate the material involves a natural phenomenon of certain materials, called "piezoelectric materials." When these materials are pulsed by electrical means, they respond by vibrating mechanically, thereby causing sound. These same materials, upon receiving sound vibrations, have the ability to transform sound into electrical pulses. The sound can be generated in frequencies ranging from 200 kilohertz (kilocycles/sec) to 25 megahertz. In the pressure vessel industry, the useful range is from 1 to 5 megahertz.

In ultrasonic examination, electrical pulses are directed from an oscillator to a "transducer" that is applied to the material being examined. Good contact is achieved between transducer and material through a liquid "couplant." The transducer contains a crystal of piezoelectric material, and high frequency sound is generated and directed into the material being examined. If a flaw is encountered by the sound beam and, if the geometry involved is proper, some of the sound will reflect from the flaw back to the transducer. This returning sound generates an electrical impulse which, through proper circuitry, is changed into a visual display on an oscilloscope screen. The entire surface of a plate or forging can be traced with the transducer, thus making an examination of the entire volume of material. Technicians, by observing the oscilloscope, identify the size and location of any flaws that might exist. Acceptance standards for ultrasonic examination are given in the ASME Code.

B&W not only complies with code requirements for ultrasonic examination, but also uses this method of nondestructive examination to control the quality of materials and welds in some cases where this is not required by ASME.

Ultrasonic examination has the important advantage that base material of any practical thickness can be examined quickly, in place, with relatively inexpensive equipment, either in the manufacturing plant or at a jobsite.

Magnetic-particle examination. Fabrication procedures within B&W involve wide usage of magnetic particle examination. This kind of test is limited to magnetic materials and may involve the dry method, with either alternating or direct current, or the wet method using either normal light or ultra-violet light for inspection. All such procedures involve the generation of a magnetic field in the part under examination. A flaw in the material, on the surface, or slightly subsurface, causes an interruption of this field and, hence, makes itself discernible by the accumulation of magnetic particles. The specific method of magnetic-particle testing employed depends largely on the size, shape, and surface condition of the part to be examined.

Magnetic-particle examination provides an inexpensive method of determining the surface, and near-surface condition of magnetic materials. It can be employed in position, in shop or field, with personnel that can be trained readily.

Liquid-penetrant examination. Liquid-penetrant examination can be applied to either magnetic or nonmagnetic materials, for examination of the surface only. While there are variations in procedures to adapt them to specific applications, all employ the principle of using a dye, usually red, to coat the surface. This is followed by removal of the dye from the surface, leaving it only in small openings, if any exist on the surface. While this small amount of dye may not be seen with the unaided eye, it is brought to attention by the application of a white developer. Fabrication procedures in B&W's shops employ liquid-penetrant examination of welds or base metals of nonmagnetic material such as stainless steel or Inconel. Liquid-penetrant testing can be performed in position, in shop or field, with inexpensive, portable equipment, and personnel can be trained readily for this operation.

Fig. 8 12.8 MeV linear accelerator used for radiography of nuclear reactor vessel course.

Fig. 9 Ultrasonic examination of plate used for nuclear power reactor vessel shell course.

Quality control of fossil-fuel equipment

A quality control system for fossil-fuel equipment is maintained throughout the manufacturing operation. One important step is receipt inspection of material to assure that it conforms to the purchase orders and appropriate codes. For fossil-fuel boilers, ASME Code Sections I, II, V and IX are the governing documents.

Besides specifying the requirements related to welding, the ASME Code also describes requirements for stress-relief of pressure parts and mandatory nondestructive examination such as radiography.

In addition to the examinations stipulated by ASME, B&W performs nondestructive examination in certain areas where the code is silent. For example, all butt welds in panel-wall tubes for Universal-Pressure boilers are examined by means of a fluoroscope. A percentage of welds of tube-stubs to headers is examined by the magnetic-particle method. Radiography is used to examine a percentage of butt welds in superheater, reheater, and economizer sections; all such sections are hydrostatically tested in the shops.

Internal cleanliness of pressure parts is an important part of quality control, particularly in the very large boilers made for electric utilities. The operations of sandblasting, searching with sponges and steel balls, and coating with rust-preventive water-soluble liquids are typical mandatory check points in B&W's quality system.

A final inspection completes the quality control program. This usually consists of determining as-built dimensions and verifying that all required nondestructive examination has been accomplished. A final inspection of car loading is made to assure safe delivery of components to the jobsite.

Quality assurance for nuclear equipment

Quality assurance for nuclear equipment begins with a study of job specifications and a written set of "process sheets" detailing the plan for fabrication. This plan makes certain that every operation is performed in the correct sequence, and that all applicable tests are performed and recorded. Starting with supplier examinations and surveillance, the history of all material is recorded and its location in the vessel identified. As parts are finished and become ready for assembly, the process records are examined to make sure that all operations that must be performed before the parts are joined have actually been completed. Nondestructive examinations involving radiographic, magnetic-particle, liquid-penetrant, and ultrasonic methods are performed and recorded. This work requires trained operators who are qualified by formal examinations. Quality-control records are maintained to verify that all welding, preheating and postheating are performed in accordance with approved procedures and by qualified personnel. Frequent audits are made to confirm that personnel are following instructions given in process sheets and quality control specifications.

Section III, Nuclear Power Plant Components, of the *ASME Boiler and Pressure Vessel Code* describes welding, heat treating and testing programs for nuclear items. This section also describes the requirements of the quality assurance system that the manufacturer of such components must have. Further, the ASME requires that a manufacturer's facility and quality assurance system must satisfy an audit team representing ASME before a code stamp for nuclear items is granted.

The U.S. Nuclear Regulatory Commission has also published documents that establish requirements for the nuclear items used in nuclear plants. B&W complies with these requirements.

Fabrication of fossil-fuel equipment

Drum fabrication

Fig. 10 shows a large steam drum for a utility boiler ready for shipment after shop fabrication. In this case, the drum is made up of four cylindrical sections or courses, and two hemispherically shaped heads. The many large stubs and nozzles along the length of the drum are connections to flow circuits for the steam generating and steam superheating surfaces of the boiler unit. Large nozzles along the bottom of the drum and the push-outs shown on the hemispherical head are connections from the drum to the downcomers, through which the water is carried to supply the various circuits in the generating system.

Fabrication of a drum of this type begins with the pressing of flat plate into half cylinders or the rolling of plate into full cylindrical shells. Fig. 11 shows one of the larger presses used for this purpose, and Fig. 12 a close-up of the pressing operation in the early stages. A plate-rolling operation in a set of vertical rolls is shown in Fig. 13. When short courses must be used because of material dimensions or heat-treatment requirements, the plate is rolled into a cylindrical course. For large drums, the normal procedure is to press plate into half-cylinders in lengths up to 42 ft and to form a course by welding two half-cylinders together longitudinally. The desired

Fig. 10 Steam drum for an electric utility boiler. This drum is 98 ft long and weighs 382 tons.

Fig. 11 Large hydraulic press for forming heavy plate into half cylinders for pressure vessels.

Fig. 12 Template checking the contour of a drum plate being formed into a half cylinder.

drum length is obtained by circumferentially joining courses as required. Longitudinal and circumferential seams in drums are made by the automatic submerged-arc-welding process.

Drumheads are formed from flat plate by hot-pressing with suitable forming dies. This operation is shown during its initial stages in Fig. 14. Drumheads are attached to the completed cylinder by circumferential welds.

Automatic techniques are used for the greater part of the welding of a boiler drum. Fig. 15 shows a double-submerged-arc welding machine in operation on a longitudinal seam (see Welding). The filler metal, in wire form, is continuously fed to the arc area, which is completely covered by a granular flux to exclude air from the weld metal area. During the operation, the electrode carriage moves along the seam from one end to the other. Many passes may be required, depending on the plate thickness, the material specifications, and the form of the welding groove.

For submerged-arc circumferential welds, the drum is mounted on a turning device and rotated while the welding head and the flux-applying equipment are stationary. Prior to and throughout all welding operations, a preheat is applied to the weld area to avoid detrimental stress conditions and metallurgical transformations. For some applications this preheat is maintained after welding until the vessel is stress relieved.

In recent years advances in engineering designs and the development of high-strength high-temperature alloys have required new welding techniques. What was formerly considered sound welding may be unsatisfactory for current applications. Old procedures had to be discarded and new ones developed, especially for welding stainless steels and high-nickel alloys. Thus today the use of the inert-gas-shielded tungsten-arc welding process (TIG) is often specified for welding the root pass where the job requires full root penetration and a uniform inside surface contour that will not interfere with fluid flow.

Nozzles and stubs are formed by hot forging from a solid billet. Larger connections may be integral with the heads, formed from rolled plate, or made from pierced-and-drawn pipe (page 31-13) as are those shown along the bottom of the drum in Fig. 10. Attachments to the drum are made by hand welding with the manual shielded-metal-arc process using coated electrodes, by automatic welding with the submerged-arc process, or by semiautomatic welding with the gas-shielded metal-arc method. This latter method was introduced about 1965 and has been substituted for the slower manual metal-arc welding process in many applications. In the gas-shielded method, a continuous coil of filler wire is fed through a hand-held gun which is directed at the joint to be welded. Slag-producing ingredients and

alloying elements are contained inside a tubular sheath. Gas is introduced to shield the molten puddle from contamination by the atmosphere.

This process has almost the same weld-deposition rate as the submerged-arc process sometimes used for nozzle welding; its advantage lies in the portability of the equipment, the much lower setup time that is required, and the decreased time span that can be realized by putting several welders to work on the same job.

Other techniques that will contribute significantly to the quality of the welded joint and appreciably increase the deposition rate of weld metal are continuously being developed.

Every drum fabricated must be subjected to a postweld heat treatment after all welding on the drum has been completed, and in some cases several heat treatments are required during the course of construction of

the drum. In instances where the application requires high impact strength, formed heavy plate is quenched in water to cool it rapidly from 1600 to 600F through the transformation range. This heat treatment is followed by normal stress-relief, which consists of heating to 1150F, holding for one hour per inch of thickness, and furnace cooling to 600F.

Every inch of every longitudinal and circumferential weld in a drum, and numerous other welds, must be subjected to radiographic examination. For this purpose extensive X-ray equipment (Fig. 16) of a wide range of power, from portable machines rated at 400,000 electron volts to the 12.8 MeV linear accelerator shown in Fig. 8, is provided. Supplementing the X-ray equipment are radioactive isotopes, such as cobalt-60, used in various capsule sizes up to 2500 curies. Other forms of nondestructive examination comprise liquid-penetrant methods

Fig. 13 Checking the contour of a cylindrical section (course) rolled from heavy plate.

Fig. 14 Hot-forming a drumhead from heavy plate in a hydraulic press.

Fig. 15 Welding longitudinal drum seam with double submerged-arc machine.

Fig. 16 Registering 2 million volt X-ray machine on circumferential seam of drum for radiographic examination of weld. Film cassette is positioned on inner surface.

for locating fine surface defects, and magnetic-particle methods for finding defects on or just slightly below the surface of the material. Reflectoscopic examination utilizing ultrasonic vibrations has been adopted as standard testing procedure on all heavy plate for pressure vessels.

Throughout the fabrication process of any pressure vessel, all work is conducted under the strictest surveillance of the company's quality assurance and quality control departments to assure compliance with the ASME Code, company standards, governmental standards, and users' requirements. All materials used for pressure parts are certified as to specifications by wet chemical analysis and spectroscopy as well as mechanical tests for tensile, bending, and impact strengths.

After all welding of pressure parts has been completed and found satisfactory, the vessel is ready for the finishing operations, which include installation of minor attachments and of the internals. Fig. 17 shows the internal baffling arrangement for a large steam drum partially preassembled on the shop floor. This structure later will be knocked down and reassembled inside the steam drum for shipment with the drum.

Headers as terminal pressure vessels

Headers are used extensively in modern steam boilers as a means for joining two or more boiler circuits. Headers are of smaller diameter (under about 24 in. ID) than drums and can be fabricated from seamless tubing, pipe, or hollow forgings. Access to their interior is through handholes, whereas drums have manholes for ingress and egress of individuals. Fig. 18 shows a superheater header nearing completion of fabrication.

Many straight or bent tubes (stubs) and tee connections have been shop welded to the 20-in. OD, 4½-in. thick, 50-ft long superheater header shown in Fig. 19. All welds to pressure vessels are completed in the shop so that postweld heat treatment of welds can be done quickly and economically under controlled conditions.

Complete facilities are available for the piercing and

Fig. 18 A large superheater header of low-alloy steel in the final stage of fabrication.

Fig. 19 Bent tubes (stubs) and tee connections (opposite side) shop-attached to a large superheater header.

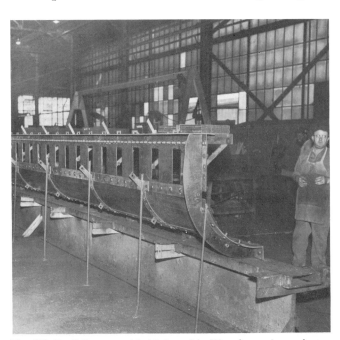

Fig. 17 Partially assembled internal baffling for a steam drum.

Fig. 20 Cupped forging leaving piercer pot of vertical press, ready for drawing into pipe stock.

drawing of large-diameter heavy-wall pipe stock. This equipment consists of an 8500-ton press (Fig. 20) for initial piercing of the ingots, a 1200-ton drawbench (Fig. 21) for reducing outside diameters and wall thicknesses and extending the lengths of the pieces, a multiplicity of engine lathes for machining the outside and inside diameters of the produced pieces, and numerous types of special test equipment for checking and controlling the quality of the finished products.

Fabrication of a large header (Fig. 18) begins with circumferentially welding the required pieces of pierced-and-drawn hollow-forging stock by the automatic submerged-arc method to obtain the desired length. The ends of the header stock are then spun hot until closed, as shown in Fig. 22. To assure absolute tightness after spinning, the center portion of the closure is drilled out and replaced by a fusion-welded steel plug. For the larger headers, when the outside diameter exceeds the capacity of this spinning machine, the ends of the headers are closed by welding a forged hemispherical head made in an operation similar to that previously described for drumheads (Fig. 14).

Completion of the header includes drilling and machining of tube and nozzle holes, fitting and welding the nozzles, stubs and other attachments by manual and semiautomatic methods, heat treating, cleaning, and finishing operations, all conducted under strict quality control. Figs. 23 and 24 depict some of these operations.

While the majority of headers today are circular in cross section, there are some applications where square headers are suitable. The fabrication process for these is similar to that described above, except that, prior to closing the ends, the header stock is changed to a square cross section by passing it at forging temperature through a set of rolls.

Tubes as heat absorbing surface

Tubes, in an almost endless variety of arrangements, serve as the heat-absorbing surface and provide flow circuits in today's steam generating units. Tubes range

Fig. 22 Header end closed by hot spinning.

Fig. 23 Fusion welding nozzle connections to a large header.

Fig. 21 Drawbench converts 26,000-lb pierced ingot into long hollow forging.

Fig. 24 Shop assembly of two connecting headers.

Fig. 25 Membrane wall assembly of steam generating surface.

Fig. 26 Section of membrane wall panel.

Fig. 27 Welding head for welding membrane bar to panel wall tubes.

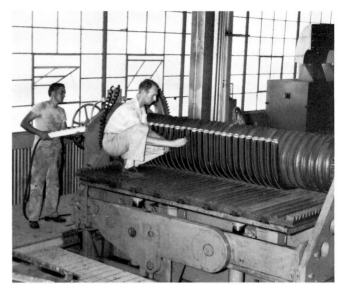

Fig. 28 Bending a membrane wall panel between special multiple dies.

Fig. 29 Pendant superheater platens ready for finishing operations.

Fig. 30 Automatic butt-welding machine for making continuous tube platens. Note newly made weld and other welds in completed portion.

from 1- to 6⅝-in. diameter and may be plain or fitted with studs for extended surface, as in the case of some furnace-wall tubes. (*See also Tube Manufacturing.*)

For the larger units, past practice was to fabricate and ship each wall tube as an individual item. This required a piece-by-piece field assembly during erection. Today, wall panels are generally assembled in the shop to expedite field erection. The latest design of panel walls is a "membrane" construction of furnace and setting walls. This construction is shown for the major part of the pre-assembled wall section, Fig. 25, where the space between wall tubes, from the top header down to the bottom, is closed with a metal filler piece continuously welded on both sides to the adjacent tubes. The result is a gas-tight metal wall surrounding the enclosed volume. A close-up view of a section of a membrane wall panel is shown in Fig. 26.

This design eliminates the need for a pressure-tight casing, and reduces the cost of field erection. Walls of this type can be assembled on a table in sections up to 10 ft wide and 90 ft long. The membrane is then welded to the tubes by the submerged-arc process, with a traveling head feeding a number of electrodes simultaneously. The machine for this operation is shown in Fig. 27.

Wall panels may be bent to required radius and degree after assembly of panels, using a multiple die encompassing as many as 60 tubes. Fig. 28 shows a membrane wall panel being bent in special multiple dies.

While wall-type surface is used to some extent for superheating purposes, most convection superheaters use continuous tube sections. A typical section of the pendant type is illustrated in Fig. 29. Convection superheater platens are made from relatively short lengths of straight tubes which are first bent and then welded together to give the desired configuration. All of the bends are formed cold except the inside hairpin bend, which must be made hot.

Close return bends are made by first upsetting a section of straight tube to increase its wall thickness at the location for the bend and then hot bending and sizing to the desired dimension. The prepared ends of the resulting "canes" are joined by an automatic butt-welder to form the section. In addition to forming the weld, this machine also heat treats the weld (*see Fig. 30*).

To complete the platen, supporting lugs are fitted and welded into position, a hydrostatic test at 1½ times the design pressure is applied, and the section ends are milled to exact lengths and beveled for field assembly. Sections are then painted and prepared for shipment.

Structural steel and casings

As many as 11,000 tons of structural steel may be required for the support of a modern central station boiler designed to furnish steam to a 1300-Mw electric generator. Most of the structural material required is readily available in standard mill shapes. However, in some cases, the horizontal members that directly support the heavy loads must be fabricated from plate and standard shape material.

In modern units, water- or steam-cooled tubes constitute the basic structure of the enclosure in high-temperature areas of the setting. Nevertheless most boiler units contain non-water-cooled or cased enclosures. These include hopper and penthouse casings, windbox, and tem-

Fig. 31 Cyclone Furnaces in the process of assembly.

pering gas plenum. See Chapter 16, especially the section captioned *Fabrication and Assembly.*

Fuel-burning equipment

Babcock & Wilcox manufactures a great variety of fuel-burning equipment for all types of fuel, including oil, gas, coal, combinations of these standard fuels, and many special fuels. This is one of the principal areas where standardization of product has been possible to a large extent, and manufacturing techniques in some cases approach those of mass production industries. One example is the manufacture of Cyclone Furnaces. Fig. 31 shows a number of these furnaces in the process of assembly on the shop floor.

Cyclone barrels range from 5 to 10 ft in diameter and are composed of tubes bent to a semicircular shape joined to form a cylinder. Since large quantities of duplicate tubes are required to form a cyclone, jigs, fixtures, and power operated equipment are used to minimize the human effort for these repetitive operations.

Cyclone Furnaces are completely shop assembled in erection frames that permit stress relief of the finished product. This enables close quality control to assure that ASME Code and company standards are met. Before shipment to the jobsite, plastic refractory is applied to the stud tubes on the inside of the furnace barrel while the outside is covered with a protective skin casing.

The B&W coal pulverizer is another well-standardized product. Fig. 32 shows a partially assembled coal pulverizer on the shop floor.

The outer casing or housing of this pulverizer is a steel weldment formed from rolled plate and other standard shapes. The base of this machine is a large gray-iron casting manufactured in the B&W foundry. Within this base, the main spiral bevel gear and its driving pinion are mounted. During operation, these parts are completely flooded with lubricating oil. The need to keep this oil clean dictates close manufacturing tolerances. The seal between the driving and grinding parts must prevent coal dust from entering the lubrication zone. The grinding rings are cast of wear-resistant alloy. Chill blocks, inserted in the mold at the grinding surface of the ring, cause the rapid cooling necessary to develop the required wear-resistant quality. Pulverizer balls are of wear-resistant alloy cast iron.

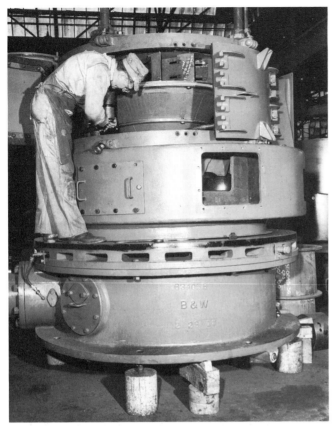

Fig. 32 B&W pulverizer nearing completion of shop assembly.

Fig. 33 Pinch rolls used to form cylindrical courses.

Fig. 34 Electroslag welding of nuclear vessel components.

Fig. 35 Reactor vessel components shown outside the heat-treating furnace.

There are many operations in the production of a pulverizer. Some parts require machining, such as the seals and gearing described above. Others, too hard for machining, such as the grinding rings of a pulverizer, must be ground to the finished dimensions. Pressing, rolling, welding, bending, shearing, and drilling are examples of additional operations required. Each pulverizer fabricated is shop assembled and run-in prior to shipment.

Fabrication of nuclear equipment

Manufacture of components for nuclear steam supply systems is accomplished by methods similar to those used for fossil-fuel equipment. Manufacturing requirements are more exacting because of the nature of the nuclear industry, including the need for close manufacturing tolerances in many instances and more rigorous requirements by customers, code authorities, and the Nuclear Regulatory Commission. The large size of components, particularly for the nuclear power industry, has led to the use of new equipment and new fabrication methods.

Reactor vessels for nuclear power

Many of the pressure vessels required for nuclear power generation are so large that they cannot be shipped by rail and, therefore, are shipped via waterways. For this reason a fabricating facility was established on the Ohio River at Mount Vernon, Indiana. Vessels up to about 32 ft diameter, 125 ft long, and a weight of 1000 tons can be manufactured in this plant.

Each reactor vessel is made up of cylindrical sections called "shell courses" and two hemispherically shaped heads. Welded to the courses are appropriate nozzles to provide connections for the various pipes that are required to connect one component with another.

Heavy ring forgings may be used as shell courses for fabricating the cylindrical vessel sections. Alternatively these courses may be fabricated from flat plate.

Fabrication of courses from plate. After receipt at the plant, the flat plate is ultrasonically examined as shown in Fig. 9. This inspection supplements quality control at the vendor's plant as stipulated in the purchase order.

Fabrication begins with the forming of the plate. For the thicker vessels, plates are heated and then rolled into cylindrical segments or complete cylinders as dictated by the size of the finished vessel. Fig. 33 shows the equipment used for this operation.

Programmed controls automatically regulate the heating rate, temperature and atmosphere in the furnace and provide a permanent record of each heating cycle. Proximity of the furnace and rolls reduces scaling and cooling. The rolls are pinch-type, making it unnecessary to press the plate ends to form the desired curvature.

Where plates are formed hot, they may be joined by submerged-arc or electroslag welding to complete the shell course (Fig. 34). The weld is started at one end of the vertically arranged course and proceeds upward, the full thickness weld being made in one pass.

The use of electroslag welding requires heating to approximately 1600F, followed by quenching below 600F and then tempering to provide the required mechanical properties of tensile strength and impact strength (*see Electroslag Welding*). Figs. 35 and 36 show the furnace, handling equipment and quench pit.

Fig. 36 Water quenching of reactor vessel course.

Fig. 37 Nuclear components in shot blasting facility.

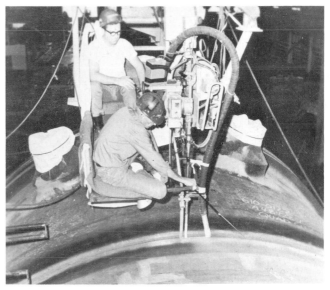

Fig. 38 Submerged-arc welding of circumferential seam in reactor vessel.

Fig. 39 Longitudinal seam welding of torus section for hemispherical head.

Fig. 40 Six-wire submerged-arc welding of stainless steel cladding to inside surface of nuclear component.

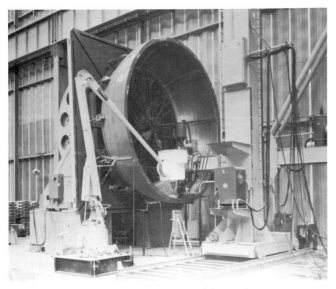

Fig. 41 Cladding of hemispherical head for nuclear power reactor vessel.

Upon completion of heat treatment, sample pieces from the component are tested to determine their mechanical properties. If specifications are met, the component is approved for assembly to other parts of the vessel. If the desired properties are not achieved, other cycles of heat treatment are used until the part is acceptable. It is then cleaned of scale by shot blasting as shown in Fig. 37.

Courses joined by circle seam welding. When shell courses are fabricated from flat plate, they are approved for assembly to other courses, after their acceptability has been established as described above.

When heavy ring forgings are used, the material is inspected by ultrasonic and magnetic-particle techniques at an early stage in fabrication. The forgings are quenched and tempered, then turned and bored to correct dimensions.

The required vessel length is obtained by joining courses together by welding "circle" seams by the submerged-arc method. The parts to be joined are rotated by means of "drum turners" under a fixed welding head, as shown in Fig. 38. During welding, the parts are held at the preheat temperature dictated by material chemistry and thickness. After welding, stress-relief is accomplished by heating slowly to a temperature in the range of 1100 to 1350F (depending on the material), holding for a period of one hr per in. of thickness, then cooling slowly in the furnace to 600F.

Fabrication of hemispherical heads. Each reactor vessel requires two hemispherical heads, one fixed by welding to the cylindrical portion of the shell, and the other as the bolted closure. These are made from flat plate by hot pressing to form ring or "orange peel" type segments. The segments are then heat treated by quenching, tempering and stress relieving, as described for cylindrical shell courses (*see Fabrication of Courses from Plate*). Mechanical properties are determined from test pieces cut from each of the segments. After all segments have been approved, they are joined by submerged-arc welding as shown in Fig. 39.

Cladding. All components made of ferritic material are clad on the inside with austenitic stainless steel (or Inconel) to provide resistance against corrosion by the reactor coolant. Figs. 40 and 41 show a vessel course and a head being clad with stainless steel using the six-wire submerged-arc cladding system developed specifically for this purpose. Under normal conditions a deposit rate of about 80 pounds per hr can be achieved. This provides a layer of $3/16$-in. minimum thickness that is suitable for nondestructive examination with a minimum of surface preparation. Chemistry of the deposit is determined by chips taken for analysis. The bond between cladding and base metal is measured by ultrasonics and surface integrity is determined with liquid penetrant.

Nozzles. After completion of a cylindrical course, nozzles are installed, utilizing one of a number of welding processes, as best suits the particular application. The larger nozzles, which may be 48-in. OD, are welded by submerged arc through the full thickness of the vessel wall (Fig. 42). Where two such nozzles are on opposite ends of a vessel diameter, both can be welded simulta-

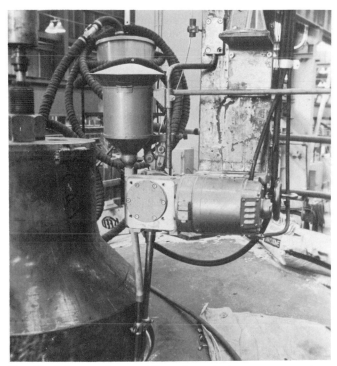

Fig. 42 Submerged-arc welding of nozzle to reactor vessel.

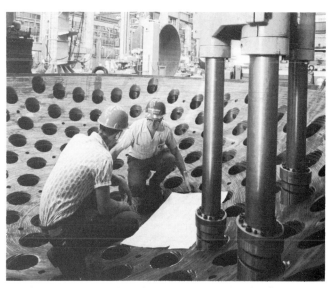

Fig. 43 Weld preparations for reactor vessel head being machined with portable equipment.

Fig. 44 30-ft diameter vertical boring mill used to machine bolting ring forging.

Fig. 45 Machining center used to machine closure head for pressurized-water reactor vessel.

neously, i.e., one can be welded from the outside of the vessel while the other is welded from the inside.

Smaller stub-nozzle connections for control rods are welded to the inside of hemispherical heads using an integral backing ring. Fig. 43 shows a portable machine for preparing holes for this welding operation.

Throughout the fabrication process of nuclear pressure vessels, all pressure-part welding is examined by radiography. X-ray equipment is used in some cases while radioactive isotopes such as cobalt-60 are used in others, the choice depending on the thickness and configuration of the weld (*see also Radiography*). Fig. 8 shows a 12.8 MeV linear accelerator being used for the examination of nozzle welds in a vessel course. Exposure time for a 14-in. thick steel shell is about 3 minutes.

Bolting rings. A closure head is connected to a reactor vessel by means of bolts and a gasketed joint. The two bolting rings for each vessel are made from forgings that are welded to the vessel and head respectively. These are machined, clad on the gasket surface, and welded to their mating parts. Vertical boring mills with a capacity for parts up to 30-ft diameter are used for machining bolting rings and other vessel parts. One such machine and a bolting ring are shown in Fig. 44.

Machining center—a new concept. The large size of nuclear components makes it difficult to transfer work repeatedly to specialized-purpose machine tools. For this reason, a "machining center" was developed and built at the Mount Vernon, Indiana, works (Fig. 45). This center permits the performance of a number of varied operations, some of them simultaneously, without moving the work.

Hydrostatic test. A pit for the hydrostatic testing of large pressure vessels is illustrated in Fig. 46. This arrangement minimizes the required head room for the

Fig. 46 Arrangement of machining center and hydrotest pit.

installation of equipment inside the vessel, and allows adequate staging for outside access.

Shipment. The dock and cranes shown in the frontispiece are designed for handling and loading the heaviest vessels. The two cranes, each rated at 500 tons, work in tandem to move vessels from the shop to the barge with one lift.

Steam generators for nuclear power

The manufacture of nuclear steam generators will be discussed with reference to the once-through design described under *Steam Generators* in Chapter 23. Fig. 47 shows a simplified cross section of this design. The important pieces from which this steam generator is assembled are the cylindrical shell, hemispherical heads, tubesheets, tubes, broached-plate tube supports, shrouds, and nozzles. These various pieces are fabricated in different locations and brought together in one bay of the shop for assembly.

Cylindrical shell. The shell courses used to fabricate the cylindrical portion of the vessel are made from plate formed in the pinch rolls shown in Fig. 33, by a process similar to that described under *Fabrication of Courses from Plate.* However, the plates are generally not as thick as those for reactor vessels; so the forming is done cold. This makes it possible to complete the cylinder by submerged-arc welding, eliminating the special heat treating and quenching required with electroslag welding. Only a few parts of the steam generator vessels are thick enough to require hot forming. Shell courses are assembled to form a continuous cylindrical section, including a boiler section and a superheater section, as shown in Fig. 47.

The broached tube-support plates, illustrated in Fig. 48, are fabricated from plate by drilling cylindrical holes and then broaching each hole at three areas 120 degrees apart to form openings for steam and water flow. The shrouds are fabricated from steel plates rolled into cylindrical form, with the longitudinal seams welded by submerged-arc welding.

The tube-support plates are then installed in the upper and lower shrouds. After moving the plates to the

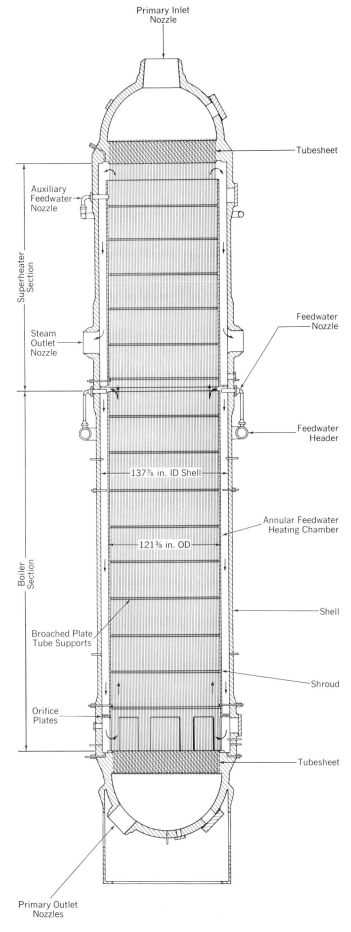

Fig. 47 Cross section of nuclear once-through steam generator.

correct location in the length of the shroud, the plates are adjusted to the proper radial location by installing wedges between the plate and the shroud. The wedges are then welded to the support plates but remain free from the shroud. Spacers between support plates keep them properly spaced lengthwise in the shroud.

After the upper and lower shroud sections and tube-support ring assemblies are completed, they are installed in the steam generator shell. Then the tubesheets are welded to the shell and the shroud sections are secured to the vessel by bolting to the lower tubesheet and welding to the shroud support ring.

Tubesheets. The upper and lower tubesheets (Fig. 47) are fabricated from heavy forgings by machining to dimensions, and then drilling the holes with a tape-controlled gun drill as shown in Fig. 5.

After fabrication of the cylindrical section, the tubesheets are welded to it by submerged-arc welding. The unit is then cleaned and inspected, preparatory to inserting the tubes (*see Fig. 49*).

Installation of tubes. The tubes are then installed in the assembly. Each tube hole is cleaned just prior to insertion of a tube. The tubes are adjusted to length at one end and tack-rolled, i.e., expanded sufficiently to hold them in place for welding. After the tubes are trimmed to the right length at the second end, the assembly is heated on a differential basis and the tubes are tack-rolled at the second end while they are held at a temperature higher than the shell. As a result, the tubes are under slight tension after cooling.

The tubesheet is again cleaned after the expanding operation. It is heated and maintained above ambient temperature to eliminate moisture or condensation at the tubesheet face and weld area. The tubes are then welded to the tubesheets with automatic tungsten-inert-gas (TIG) welding. During this period, quality control measures are rigidly enforced. These include the inspection of welding samples from each operator and each machine on a scheduled basis. Each sample is inspected with liquid penetrant, then sectioned and inspected metallographically.

After completion of welding, a visual examination is conducted by comparing each weld to a workmanship sample. All welds not meeting the requirements are removed by machining and rewelded by the TIG process. This is followed by liquid-penetrant examination of the entire tubesheet. No indications of defects are permitted on the weld or adjacent to the weld at the line of fusion. In addition, a helium leak test is conducted to a sensitivity of 1×10^{-3} cc of helium at 100 psi.

Final steps. The final step in fabrication is welding the hemispherical heads to the ends of the assembly. These heads have previously been fabricated (Fig. 50) by the method described under *Fabrication of Hemispherical Heads* and clad internally as described under *Cladding.*

When the work load permits, the fabrication of these steam generators can be accomplished by scheduling which resembles assembly-line operation. The parts of several steam generators move progressively in the shop for the various operations. As many as 10 steam generators may be located in the assembly area at one time.

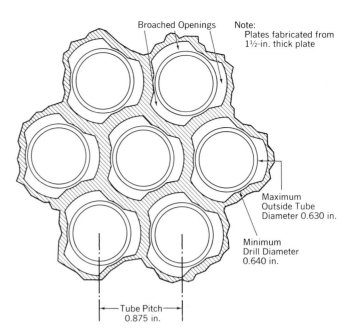

Fig. 48 Broached tube-support plates.

Fig. 49 Steam generator for nuclear power, ready for installation of tubes.

Fig. 50 Hemispherical head mounted on welding positioner being welded for application to nuclear power steam generator shown in Fig. 49.

Fig. 51 Stress-relieved steam generator for nuclear service emerging from furnace.

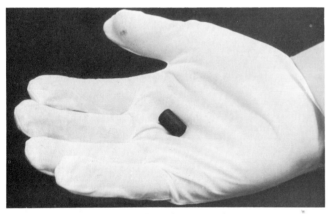

Fig. 52 Uranium-dioxide pellet of low enrichment.

After all welding is completed, the steam generators are heat treated in an electrically heated stress-relieving furnace. After this operation (Fig. 51), both secondary and primary sides of the generators are hydrostatically tested. If any tube-to-tubesheet leaks are found, they are repaired by TIG welding, and the vessel is retested. B&W's acceptance standard requires no leakage after several cycles of pressure are applied to the primary and secondary sides.

After the hydrostatic test and removal of test water, the secondary side of the generator is evacuated and filled with argon with a very low moisture content to eliminate condensation inside the vessel prior to installation. After this, the various openings in the secondary side are sealed for shipment. The primary side of the generator is cleaned, dried, and sealed with containers of desiccant inside to keep this side of the vessel dry.

While these operations are in progress, all accessible pressure-boundary welds are examined by the magnetic-particle method to assure acceptability of these welds after the final postweld heat treatment and hydrostatic tests. In addition, radiographs are made of the welds between the tubesheets and the primary heads of the generators. This is required by the ASME Code because these particular welds were not previously examined by radiography "after a postweld heat treatment." Similarly, the welds between the tubesheets and the cylindrical portion of the generator require radiography or ultrasonic testing at this time because they have not previously been examined "after a postweld heat treatment." Since it is extremely difficult to radiograph these particular welds after the tubes are in place, the code permits ultrasonic testing.

Other steam-generator welds that require radiography are examined after a postweld heat treatment during the fabrication span before the tubes are installed and, therefore, do not require radiography after the final postweld heat treatment.

When all nondestructive examinations have been completed, the vessel is loaded on special cars, painted, and shipped.

Pressurizers for nuclear power

Pressurizers are, in fact, pressure vessels, and are manufactured by methods similar to those described for reactor vessels and the vessels of steam generators. Additionally each pressurizer is fitted with special penetrations for installation of the electrical heaters.

The heaters are the direct-immersion type, sheathed in stainless steel or Inconel, and assembled in bundles. Each of the two or three bundles is field assembled through penetrations in the vessel wall, and sealed by means of a gasketed closure. An electrical connection is then made to the end of each heater using a special fitting which provides insulation from the steam and water.

Piping for nuclear power

Piping for conducting primary fluid from the reactor vessel to the steam generator and back is made from hollow forgings clad on the inside surface with stainless-steel-weld overlay. Elbows are made by pressing plate, previously clad by explosive cladding.

The fabrication of nuclear piping is governed by controls similar to those previously described for steam generators and pressurizers. The piping is shop assembled in maximum shippable lengths, with assembly to other components accomplished at the jobsite (Chapter 32).

Fuel assemblies for nuclear power

The nuclear fuel for light water reactors consists of uranium dioxide pellets contained in Zircaloy tubes (Chapter 19). The uranium dioxide (UO_2) is slightly enriched in the Uranium-235 isotope.

The oxide powder is first prepared from uranium hexafluoride (UF_6) which is supplied by the ERDA enrichment facility. Cylindrical pellets of UO_2 (Fig. 52) are pressed from the powder and sintered under a reducing atmosphere at about 3050F to a density of about 643 lb/cu ft (10.3 grams/cc)—94% of theoretical density. The pellets are inspected and tested for uniformity of dimensions and density. Samples are removed for destructive testing to verify chemical composition and level of impurities. Pellets meeting the specified requirements are weighed and arranged into unit lengths required for a single fuel rod.

A unit or "stack" of pellets is placed in a loading device with tubular spacers and end springs positioned

at each end. The tubular spacers protect the springs from overheating during service while the springs maintain the fuel column intact during shipment and keep the pellets in the desired axial location during operation.

After the column length is adjusted to meet specifications, the fuel is inserted in the Zircaloy tube. An end cap is then inserted and the loaded rod transferred to the welding station.

Welding of end caps into the tube is accomplished using a tungsten-inert gas process. Precautions are required to insure against contamination of the welding chamber atmosphere, because traces of impurities in the chamber can result in defective welds. The first end weld is made and inspected before the fuel tubes are accepted for fuel loading. The fuel is loaded into the tubes, and the second end cap is welded. The second end weld accomplishes the complete enclosure of fuel in the fuel rod except for a pressurization and drying penetration. After fuel drying, pressurization to a specified pressure is accomplished using helium as the pressurizing medium. The pressurizing penetration is then welded. Inspections and tests of the final end cap weld are performed which are equivalent to those for the first end cap weld. Periodically, during fabrication, specimen welds are prepared for sectioning and metallographic examination for sub-surface defects and verification of weld penetrations.

Inspection of individual fuel rods consists of dimensional measurements and visual examinations for surface flaws. After the rods pass inspection, they are cleaned and inserted into spacer grids to make up the fuel assembly (Fig. 53).

Components of the assembly other than the fuel rods include 1) tubes that act as guides for the control rods, and 2) a central tube to accommodate in-core instrumentation. The guide-tubes also are structural members connecting the upper and lower end fittings. The guide-tubes have threaded ends that project up and down through the end fittings. Fasteners are threaded onto the guide-tubes and welded to the end fittings to insure against their becoming disengaged during service. The instrument tube is held between the end fittings and is mechanically attached to the lower end fitting. Spacer grids, another component of the fuel assembly, are fabricated from strips of an age-hardenable nickel-based alloy. The grids are assembled in the fashion of an egg crate, and are welded at each intersection to increase the rigidity of the structure. The assembled grids are heat treated to increase strength and stabilize their dimensions. Final inspection of the grids assures compliance with cell dimensions, intercell spacing, and weld integrity.

End fittings are made from stainless-steel precision castings which are welded together and machined to final dimensions. The end fittings are attached to the end spacer grids with welded mechanical fasteners.

Final inspection of the completed assembly is conducted in both horizontal and vertical attitudes. This includes dimensional measurements and tests to assure straightness and compatibility with the control components. After final acceptance, the assemblies are encased in protective wrappings and placed in special shipping containers for transportation to the power station.

Tube manufacturing

Many thousand feet of steel and alloy tubes of suitable size, shape, and material are required for a large steam generating unit. These tubes are used for steam generating surfaces including furnace walls and floors, and in superheaters, reheaters, economizers, and air heaters. Headers also might be classed as tubes, since the process of manufacture is similar, but the size range (9¾ to 24 in.) is beyond that ordinarily associated with tubes.

There are two general types of tubes manufactured by B&W—seamless and welded. Each has its proper application as dictated by users' specifications or technical details related to diameter, wall thickness, and chemistry (*see also Quality Alloy Steel for Tubes—B&W Practice, Chapter 28*).

Seamless tubes

Seamless tubes, defined as tubes without weld or seam, are made by piercing from solid rounds of carbon or alloy steels. Most of the steel for B&W seamless tubes is produced by B&W in electric furnaces (Fig. 54). This steelmaking process is carefully monitored and controlled at every step and produces steel quality consistent with application requirements.

Tubes for boiler application are furnished either hot finished or cold-drawn, depending on size, tolerance and finish desired. Metallurgically, the two are similar; the

Fig. 53 Installation of nuclear fuel rods in a fuel assembly.

Fig. 54 Tapping steel from a B&W electric-arc furnace.

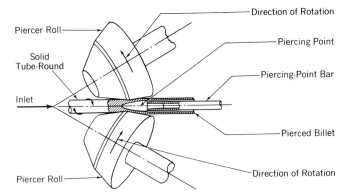

Fig. 55 Piercing operation (diagrammatic) in B&W's cone-type piercing mills.

difference is mainly in surface finish and the permissible tolerance in dimensions. To obtain a smooth, even surface and close tolerances, stainless steel tubing is generally finished by cold-drawing only. This process also permits control of grain size in final heat treatment which is important in high temperature application of austenitic stainless steels. The production of seamless tubes requires special tools, careful control of heating, and exactness in procedure.

Centering and heating. So that the piercer point may be accurately centered in relation to the piercing rolls, the hot-rolled conditioned tube-round or machine-turned round (if of stainless steel) is provided with a concentric "starting hole." This shallow hole may be produced by a centering machine that drills the cold tube-round prior to heating, or by a punch which indents the end of the hot round just prior to piercing. In some of the stainless steels a small diameter hole may be drilled through the entire length of the billet to ease the load in the piercing mill and to preserve the piercer point.

The round, which may range in length from about 40 to 144 in. and from $2\frac{1}{4}$- to $8\frac{3}{4}$-in. diameter, is then heated in a rotary-hearth furnace.

Piercing. Piercing is done in machines especially designed for the purpose. The round is gripped between the surfaces of two revolving rolls that rotate in the same direction. Each roll is directly driven by its own motor. By the rapid rotation and kneading action of the rolls, set at the proper angle, the round, somewhat reduced in diameter, moves forward helically over the piercing point held firmly in position. The piercing operation is illustrated diagrammatically in Fig. 55. After piercing, the bar is withdrawn from the inside of the tube and the rough pierced hollow may be reheated in a suitable furnace to the correct temperature for rolling.

Rolling. The function of the rolling mill is to lengthen the tube and reduce the wall thickness to the approximate dimensions required. A ram forces the tube into the grooves of the rolls, the rotation of which carries it forward over a plug and bar, working the metal between the grooved surfaces of the rolls and the plug as illustrated in Fig. 56. Two to six passes with change of plugs may be required in rolling stainless steel tubes. To make the wall uniform and to avoid ribs or overfills, the tube is turned 90 degrees after each pass through the mill.

Reeling and sizing. After rolling, the tube is in a semi-finished condition, i.e., of required wall thickness and approximate diameter but with a relatively rough surface. Directly after rolling and while the tube is still hot, it is conveyed to a reeling machine illustrated in Fig. 57 where it is forced helically over a smooth mandrel, or "reeler plug," supported by a thrust bar on the outlet side of the mill. In rolling over this plug, light overfills and scratches are removed and the tube is smoothed and burnished. The tube is also rounded and expanded a little in diameter, but the wall thickness remains approximately constant, or, depending on the pressure applied, is slightly reduced. After reeling, the tube is taken to a sizing mill.

The function of the sizing mill is to hot-size the tube to its proper diameter. Its main elements are several sets of roll stands with single-grooved rolls set in tandem. Following the sizing operation, the tube is annealed or otherwise heat treated, if required, and then straightened, cut to length, hydrostatically tested and submitted for final inspection. Appropriate samples are secured for tensile, hardness and deformation tests, and the length, gage and diameter of the tubes are measured.

Cold-drawing. Tubes requiring finer finish, closer dimensional tolerances, or smaller sizes than can be obtained by the hot-finish process are cold-drawn. The cold-drawing process is used after the tube is brought close to the desired size by hot finishing.

The cold-drawing is done on a drawbench fitted at its center with a heavy steel holder for the die through which the tube is drawn. The arrangement of the drawbench, tube die, and mandrel is shown diagrammatically

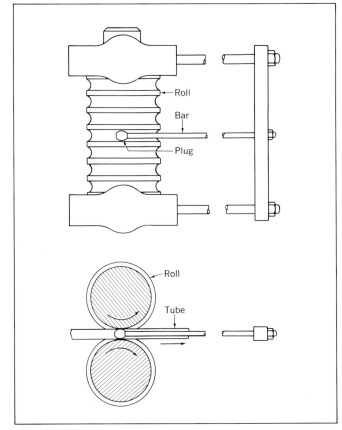

Fig. 56 Rolling operation (diagrammatic) in tube-rolling mill.

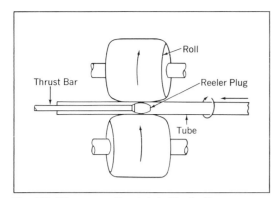

Fig. 57 Diagrammatic sketch illustrating reeling operation.

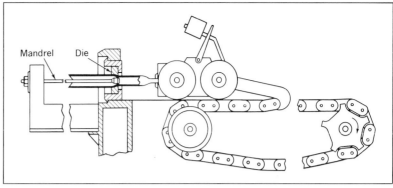

Fig. 58 Drawbench for producing close-tolerance fine-surface-finish cold-drawn tubes.

in Fig. 58. Tubes may be cold-drawn one or more times to obtain desired dimensions. They are usually pickled and lubricated before each cold-drawing operation. In most cases annealing is also required.

After cold-drawing, tubes are given appropriate heat treatment according to specific analysis and specification. Tubes are then descaled, straightened (Fig. 59), cut to length, tested and examined as required by the American Society for Testing and Materials (ASTM) and other applicable specifications.

Tubing can be made with special shapes such as square, rectangular or airfoil design. It can also be made with helical ribs on the inside or longitudinal ribs on the outside. Such tubes are generally shaped on the hot mill or by extrusion, in each case followed by cold finishing.

Extrusion process for seamless tubes

The Ugine-Sejournet hot-extrusion process is used for the manufacture of certain sizes and types of tubes, especially those made from "refractory" alloys that are difficult to pierce in a rotary piercing operation. A hollow billet, with glass lubrication, is confined in a container between the ram of a press and the extrusion die. A mandrel extending from the ram passes through the billet and the die. As the ram moves forward, the metal is squeezed out between the die and the mandrel.

With present facilities it is possible to produce, by extrusion, tube hollows ranging in size from $1\frac{1}{2}$- to $5\frac{3}{4}$-in. outside diameter and from 0.160 to 1.000-in. wall thickness. Extrusion product lengths vary from 20 ft for heavy wall products to 60 ft for those having lighter wall. After the hot-extrusion process is finished, cold-drawing is used to bring the product to the desired size.

Tubing for nuclear units. Zirconium alloys, particularly Zircaloy-4, are used in tubular form for fuel cladding in nuclear reactors for power production. Inconel Alloy 600, a nickel-iron-chromium alloy, is used for tubes in nuclear steam generators. Tubes of these alloy materials are produced by extrusion followed by cold finishing. Application of these tubes is described in Chapters 21 and 23. Material properties are discussed in Chapter 29.

Electric-resistance-welded (ERW) tubes

Electric-resistance-welded steel tubing is made by forming flat strip into tubular shape and welding the edges together in an electric-resistance-welding machine. A mill used for the continuous production of electric-

resistance-welded tubing is shown in Fig. 60.

ERW carbon-steel tubing, rather than seamless tubing, is widely used in stationary and marine boilers. It offers smoother surfaces, more uniform wall thickness, and less eccentricity. Because of softness and uniformity, welded tubes are easily installed. ERW tubing is commonly produced in sizes from $\frac{3}{4}$- to $4\frac{1}{2}$-in. diameter and to minimum wall thicknesses from 0.028 to 0.220 in.

Pressure tubing produced by electric-resistance welding is mainly of carbon steel, and both rimmed- and killed-steel strip are used. Rimmed steel is used extensively in the lower carbon grades because of its excellent welding characteristics. However, if the additional cost is justified and killed steel is required by the specifications, it poses no problem in the manufacture of ERW tubes.

Hot-rolled strip, in coils, is used for most of the tubing produced by this method. The first operation consists of running the strip through a scale breaker under tension onto a re-coiler. After re-coiling, following the scale-breaking operation, the coil is backspun to open the individual wraps. The coil is then pickled, rinsed and conveyed to the cold-rolling and sizing mill.

Cold-rolling is applied to the hot-rolled strip to smooth its surface and to obtain a uniform dimensional accuracy.

Fig. 59 Straightening operation for finished tubes.

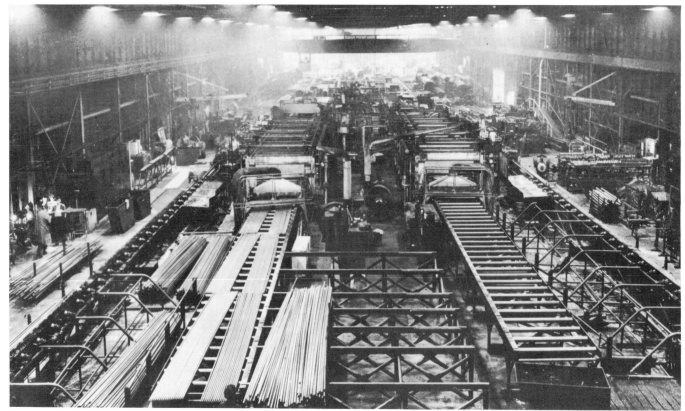

Fig. 60 B&W electric-resistance-welded-tube mill for continuous tube-length production.

Control of the thickness is obtained by the use of a beta-ray gage using strontium 90 as the radioactive source.

After cold-rolling, the strip is re-coiled and the coil is fed into a leveler for flattening. The ends are then cut square and butt welded to the ends of the preceding and following coils to form an "endless" strip. Width and thickness within close limits are essential for welding of acceptable quality. Freshly slit or shaved edges are used to eliminate rust and assure strong, sound welds.

The strip is folded into an open-tube form in a forming mill preparatory to welding. In the resistance welder, high frequency current (450,000 cycles per sec) is fed into the surface of the strip through silver-tungsten-carbide sliding contacts, positioned on both sides of the seam just before the edges are brought together. The inside flashes (or upsets) formed during welding are trimmed to a specified height, and the outside flashes are cut off. These operations are continuous as the tubing emerges from the welding mill.

Next, the tubing is accurately sized and straightened in a three-pass mill. As it emerges from the sizing mill, it is cut to required lengths. All transverse welds at coil ends are cut out. The tubes are then normalized in a controlled-atmosphere furnace to produce a uniform metallurgical structure throughout. During this heat treatment the tubes receive a rust-retardant oxide finish.

The tubes, emerging from the normalizing furnace, are conveyed through rotary straighteners (Fig. 59) to the cutoff machines where each tube is cut to the required length. Coupons cut from the ends of tubes are tested mechanically, according to specifications. One coupon is flattened with the weld at the flattened edge; another coupon is expanded; and, if required, a third coupon is crushed longitudinally. To pass the acceptance test, coupons must not crack or split in the tube metal or open at the weld.

After normalizing, the tubes may be cold-drawn to produce intermediate sizes or smaller diameters.

Quality and metallurgical control. Steel used in the manufacture of pressure tubing either seamless or welded, is carefully inspected to verify that the material is of the desired quality. In process control, checks are made as required to assure product quality.

Immersed ultrasonic testing is used to inspect the weld of electric-resistance-welded tubing. Imperfections in the weld cause deviations in the normal pattern, alerting mill operators to the possibility of unacceptable material. Nondestructive testing is also employed in the production of seamless tubing to supplement routine inspection where necessary to assure product quality.

For most applications, tubes are inspected and tested in accordance with ASTM (American Society for Testing and Materials) specifications. In many cases it is also necessary to meet other specifications including those of the American Association of Railroads, the American Bureau of Shipping, The American Society of Mechanical Engineers (ASME), United States Coast Guard Marine Inspection, United States Navy, and other responsible authorities.

All pressure tubes are subjected to either a hydrostatic pressure test or a nondestructive electric test of their entire length and periphery. Final inspection includes, for example, measurement of dimensions, visual examination and, in the case of welded tubing, a check of bead-trim height.

Chapter 32

Construction

A few boiler types are small enough to permit shipment completely assembled. Some marine and industrial boilers of moderate capacity are in this class. They usually weigh less than 100 tons and can be loaded on a single freight car. Larger industrial and central station boilers are shipped to the jobsites in various stages of fabrication and subassembly. A central station boiler, with its associated heat-transfer equipment and auxiliaries, may weigh more than 12,000 tons, requiring 500 railroad cars to ship the material to the site over a period of several months. A nuclear steam supply system is shipped to the jobsite in the form of shop-fabricated components. Some individual components weigh 400 to 600 tons and are large enough to make overland shipment a special operation.

The field assembly of a high-capacity steam generating unit, whether fossil-fuel or nuclear, requires efficient, well-engineered, well-organized erection methods to permit installation of the equipment within a reasonable time and at minimum cost without sacrifice of quality. The cost of erecting a steam generating unit such as shown in Fig. 1, represents a sizable part of the total investment.

Sound field assembly is essential for correct functional performance. For this reason, the construction organization must apply techniques that will complement the designer's skill and the fabricator's craftsmanship. Boiler components must be on the jobsite at the right time with the necessary tools, equipment, manpower and supervision for assembly.

Planning and coordination with the use of modern management and control techniques are essential for the efficient erection of a steam generating unit. The construction organization must be experienced in estimating, planning, quality control, cost analysis, labor relations, tool and equipment design, technical services and finance. Direct liaison should be maintained with the engineering and manufacturing departments, making field assembly a continuation of shop fabrication with its high standards of quality control.

Accurate estimates are needed to determine the duration and cost of erection, to permit planning of all phases of the job, and for sales pricing purposes. Schedules must coordinate shop fabrication with field erection in such a manner that an orderly sequence of installation is maintained with a minimum time span. Design details should be reviewed as they are developed to avoid difficult assembly operations. In order to have adequate tools, equipment and facilities available on the job when needed, preparation should be made well in advance of material shipments.

Time and cost estimates

There is no fixed relationship between boiler capacity in pounds of steam per hour and cost of field assembly. The fuels to be burned determine the furnace shape and vol-

Fig. 1 Construction of a central station boiler for a large electric-generating unit.

ume, with consequent variations in size and weight of component parts. Higher pressures result in greater tonnage of materials. Higher temperatures require more field welds in alloy tubes and pipes. Design improvements and additions for increased efficiency affect installation costs. Coal-fired boilers, with sootblowers and ash- and slag-removal devices cost more to build than oil- or gas-fired units of similar capacity.

A breakdown of weights and quantities of components must be available to estimate the field-erection cost of a steam generating unit. The basic quantities are multiplied by standard man-hour units compiled from reports on similar boilers erected in the past. Man-hour units on a tonnage basis are used for structural supports, drums, headers, tubes, casing, superheaters, economizers, and air heaters. Man-hour units on other bases are applied to operations like welding, stress-relieving, and tube expanding. The sum of the various unit totals equals the man-hours of productive labor required. A further sum, usually estimated as a percentage of the standard productive man-hours, must be added for general operations, supervision, field equipment, maintenance, and cleanup. The standard estimate must be adjusted for expected labor performance on the project by factors pertaining to the construction schedule, including site conditions, availability of skilled labor, and local labor practices and productivity. The resulting total estimated man-hours are multiplied by field-labor rates, with additions for fringe benefits, subsistence payments, insurance, taxes, and other overheads, to obtain dollar costs. Field-labor rates vary so widely and change so rapidly that it is preferable to use man-hour requirements rather than dollars in comparative studies of erection costs.

While there is no definite relationship between steam capacity in pounds per hour and the cost of field assembly of boilers, there is an approximate relation between the kilowatt capacity of large electric-generating units and the standard man-hours required for the erection of the boilers serving it. This approximate relationship holds even though the boilers may be of different types, reheat or nonreheat, and designed for different temperatures and pressures. Standard field-erection requirements for coal-fired boilers vary from ¾ to 1¼

man-hours per kilowatt capacity; for gas-fired boilers from ½ to ¾. These requirements do not include allowances for structural supports, dust collectors, ash-removal equipment, and power piping, and must be adjusted for expected performance at a given site.

The elapsed time needed to erect a complete steam generating unit is largely a function of man-hours. There is a limit, however, for any given size of unit, to the number of men that can be used during any given stage of erection. If more than the optimum number are employed, the lack of adequate places for them to work results in excessive costs. Fig. 2 shows the number of weeks required for various man-hour expenditures on single fossil-fuel boiler units and the maximum number of men that can be employed efficiently at peak operations. Fig. 3 shows a manpower graph for a job of 1,000,000 man-hours employing 263 men at the peak of construction. These schedules are based on single-shift operation with a 40-hr week. The erection period can be reduced by multiple shifts or overtime. These procedures increase total erection costs because of inefficiency and higher wage scales.

Erection schedule

A construction schedule based on specific unit design, contract requirements, jobsite conditions, and manpower availability is prepared immediately after sale of the boiler or nuclear steam supply system. Such a schedule serves not only to establish a sequence for the actual construction work, equipment requirements, and manpower needs, but it defines the shop fabrication and shipping sequences necessary to optimize overall fabrication and erection time spans. This schedule shows, in considerable detail, when each component will be needed at the site. The projected sequence of erection steps must make allowance for the expected manufacturing time, the shipping characteristics, the accessibility of the site, and the time available to complete the assembly. Certain general sequences are mandatory because of size, location within the structure, and method of support of the parts. The erection schedule, with additional information from the engineering, purchasing, and fabricating departments, is incorporated in a production schedule. This schedule must be distributed within the customer's organization in order to coordinate erection of the steam generating unit with other plant construction work.

Review of design details

The early design drawings are reviewed by construction personnel with representatives of engineering, manufacturing, and shipping departments for overall coordination. For fossil-fuel units, the dimensions of shop-assembled components, such as furnace-wall panels, burner casings, and duct work, are limited by allowable clearances required for railroad or truck shipment. Shop assembly reduces field work and, when supplemented by ground assembly at the jobsite, leads to lowest construction costs. Design details are reviewed to assure the best shop- and field-assembly combinations. Preliminary plans for hoisting heavy members determine the lifting-lug and hanger requirements. Within the limits of practical eco-

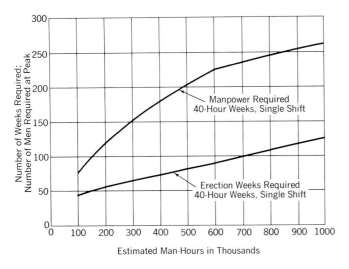

Fig. 2 Graph showing number of weeks and number of men required for boiler erection related to total man-hours.

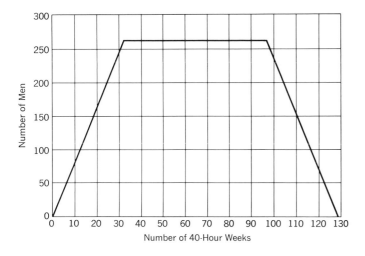

Fig. 3 Manpower graph for unit requiring 1,000,000 man-hours for erection.

nomics, these attachments are generally made in the shop. Otherwise, advance information is obtained to provide them as part of the construction equipment for the job. During the design review, the locations of field welds in tubes, pipes, and other pressure parts are determined. Such joints must be few in number, consistent with size limitations, and so located as to leave clearance for welding and stress-relieving operations.

For nuclear units a similar review is made. In general, a maximum of fabrication is accomplished in the shop to minimize field installation costs. Hence, there are fewer, but larger and heavier components.

Selection of tools and equipment

Many types of power equipment are needed for unloading, hauling, and positioning the heavy assembled sections and components of modern boilers and nuclear steam supply systems. The amount of material that can be handled manually is almost negligible. The manpower for welding and stress relieving operations during various stages of construction may run as high as 25 to 50% of the total project requirements. Equipment for this work must be available when needed. Construction buildings, trucks or flatcars for moving material, hundreds of hand tools, and much additional hardware are necessary for general construction work. Determination of the specific pieces of equipment to be furnished to a particular job is influenced by the unit design, project schedule, site conditions, location and layout of storage area and extent of ground assembly of major components. The initial selection of equipment is subject to a continuous review and changes are made as the job requirements change.

A modern construction organization must have a substantial inventory or availability of crawler cranes, truck and hydraulic cranes, derricks, hoisting engines, tractors, trucks, trailers, loaders, backhoes, bulldozers, welding equipment, air compressors and other tools and equipment required for construction. To supplement standard equipment, it is necessary to design and manufacture special tools and devices for unique construction application. These include large capacity lifting towers and frames and special machining, boring and refacing tools.

Preparations at the jobsite

Before starting shipment, the details of storage, handling and erection must be thoroughly reviewed with the customer and others responsible for the construction of the total project. Provisions must be made for:

1. Adequate storage space near the site, varying from a few hundred square feet to several acres, depending on the size of the boiler. The storage area should be served by railroad tracks with one or more spurs leading to the erection site. Roadways must be provided for material arriving by trucks and for access by mobile cranes.

2. A specific area designated for ground assembly of major components.

3. Material flow paths from the storage and ground assembly areas to the erection site. An uninterrupted flow of material into several areas of the erection site is essential for meeting the tight schedules that normally apply.

4. Access into the building, which will house the steam generating unit, such as hatchways in the roof and large doors in the walls at ground level. Structural members may have to be removed or left out to provide the necessary access for large components.

5. A field office, tool and material rooms, and change rooms for the workmen.

6. Services such as electricity, compressed air, construction and drinking water, sanitary facilities and first aid facilities.

7. Stairways and walkways installed in time to permit safe access and working conditions.

8. Derricks or other lifting equipment on the roof for raising material (*see Fig. 4*).

9. Construction elevators for the larger units that may be over 200 ft high.

Fig. 4 Stiff-leg derrick located on roof of building for handling boiler material.

Fig. 5 Boiler unit components in field storage convenient for assembly at boiler site.

Some boiler installations are outdoors with no permanent roof, or with the erection of the permanent roof scheduled late in the project. In such cases, a decision must be reached concerning the weather protection to be furnished by each contractor on the job.

Drawings indicating size and location of equipment anchor bolts, conduits, openings and the loads to be carried are supplied by the equipment manufacturers. All foundations must be completed and checked for compliance with specifications before erection is started to avoid subsequent delays, interferences and corrective work.

Material handling and storage

One feature that distinguishes a successful construction project is an efficient material handling operation. When shipments from manufacturing plants arrive at the job, a crew and the necessary equipment must be on hand to unload them. The proper placing of parts and equipment in storage is essential. Most of the material is stored outdoors with sufficient blocking to protect it from dirt and water. Welding electrodes, instruments, mechanical items such as motors and bearings, and parts for bin storage are kept indoors. All material must be protected against damage from the elements. During storage, material should be periodically examined for evidence of internal and external corrosion, and necessary corrective measures taken.

The storage yard is divided into numbered plots. Records are maintained to indicate the location of the various parts stored. A numbering system is also used for inside bin storage. Fig. 5 shows a typical material storage yard.

Contents of freight cars and trucks are checked against material lists. A material inventory must be made before work is started to disclose any shortages. Shortages must be eliminated to prevent costly interruption of any phase of the work. Planning is greatly simplified if all material is at the jobsite before erection is started. This is not normally practicable, so material arrival is usually scheduled to satisfy assembly sequences and to provide work areas for the largest possible working force.

Derricks, cranes, hoists, welding equipment and other tools are delivered with the early shipments of material and continually supplemented as the field organization expands and as assembly operations develop.

Erection procedure for a fossil-fuel unit

The large size of steam generating units for central stations makes them more complex to build than is the case with smaller industrial units. The following discussion is primarily concerned with the assembly of the larger units but many of the basic procedures apply to all sizes.

Considerable planning precedes the actual start of field operations to assemble a unit. From its earliest inception as a customer's inquiry, preliminary evaluations are made of the site characteristics, climatic conditions, equipment requirements, usable facilities and manpower availability. As the engineering phase progresses, erection planning meetings are conducted to formalize assembly sequences and establish a field operations schedule.

Structural supports

Most large units are top supported, as the units shown in Figs. 6 and 7. Erection of the steel supports is consequently the first step in building the unit. This is done by conventional methods, using cranes and derricks, as shown in Fig. 1. Some structural members may be omitted temporarily to allow access for drums, tube assemblies, and other large pieces. The omission of these members must not jeopardize the stability of the structure. Stairways and walkways are completed to the fullest possible extent to provide safe access to all parts of the unit.

Since many of the structural members govern the location of boiler and auxiliary components, supporting

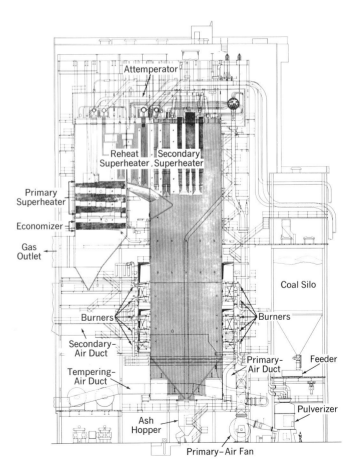

Fig. 6 Side view of Radiant boiler.

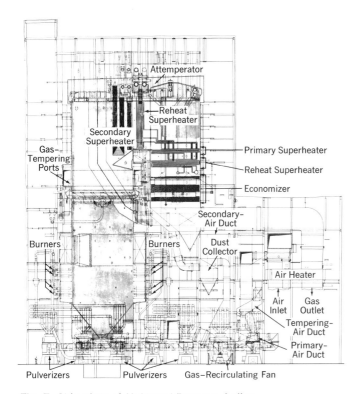

Fig. 7 Side view of Universal-Pressure boiler.

steel must be aligned with established building center-lines. After the structure has been aligned and plumbed, the members are rigidly connected with high-tensile bolts or welding prior to supporting any loads from the structure.

Assembly of pressure-containing components

If the unit includes a steam drum, it will be located near the top of the unit and should be positioned before any other components are placed in the boiler cavity. Likewise top headers, interconnecting tubes and pipes are placed while unrestricted space is available to hoist them.

It is of prime importance that field assembly of the extensive water-cooled surface, which encloses the boiler, start as soon as site conditions permit. A major percentage of the wall tubes are shop assembled into large membrane panels. These panels are either erected as received or, if site conditions permit, assembled on the ground into large wall sections complete with tie bars, buckstays, insulation and casing (*see* Fig. 8). The membrane between adjacent panels is welded and the tube ends either welded to header stubs or to the adjacent panel tube end. As a quality control measure, the tube butt welds are radiographed on small tubes to verify alignment and integrity of the welded joint.

Superheater, reheater, and economizer surfaces are installed in the order dictated by the design features of the particular units. During the same period, work proceeds on the installation of the air heaters, fuel-burning equipment, fans, flues, and ducts. As appropriate areas become available the sootblowers, control equipment, and other auxiliary items are installed.

Drums. Drums for the largest boilers may exceed 400 tons in weight and 100 ft in length, and may be located more than 200 ft above the ground. To clear building steel, the drum is usually raised out of level by as much as 60 degrees. Capacity and safety of the drum rigging is of primary importance in the selection of the proper equipment and methods.

Fig. 9 shows a typical drum-lifting arrangement using lugs which were shop-welded to the drum. Attachment pieces for the top of tackle blocks are located on temporary steel members above the boiler structure. The tackle blocks should be of special design to permit simple linkage connections at both top-support and drum attachment. The capacity of the hoisting engine and the sizes of tackle blocks and wire rope are determined with ample factors of safety.

When the drum is in final position, it is supported from top structural steel by means of U-bolts that permit linear movement of the drum with temperature variations. Fig. 10 shows a typical drum and structural support arrangement. The drum is used as a major anchor point for other boiler components and, for this reason, accurate location is important. The structural members, platforms, and stairways that were omitted for drum clearance are then installed to complete the structure.

Downcomers. Large pipe downcomers connecting the drum with lower furnace headers or, in the case of Universal-Pressure boilers, large pipes connecting upper and lower headers are erected as access permits. These pipes are shipped in the longest possible lengths to avoid costly field welds. Large downcomers are often placed in the boiler well while steel is being erected and are moved to final location when convenient. Otherwise, down-

Fig. 8 Raising furnace-wall section into position. Buckstays and other parts were attached during ground assembly.

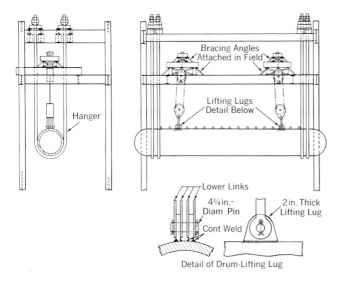

Fig. 9 Schematic arrangement of lifting lugs and tackle for hoisting heavy drums (30 tons and over).

comers must be shipped in shorter lengths and sufficient steel omitted to allow clearance for erection.

Tube connections. Tubes may be attached to drums or headers by welding, expanding or a combination of both. Welded connections may be made by joining the tube directly to the header, as in the case of membrane wall panels or by welding the tube to a stub (short length of tube) that is attached to the drum or header in the shop. This type of construction is used for the majority of tube connections.

In some applications, however, tube expanding is a practical method of tube connection. Tube expanding or tube rolling is a process of cold working the end of a tube into contact with the metal of the drum or header containing tube holes or seats. When a tube is expanded, the outside diameter, inside diameter and length increase and the wall thickness decreases (*see Fig. 11*). The increase in length, called extrusion, occurs in both directions from some section X-X. The residual radial pressure between the tube and tube seat resulting from a properly expanded tube will provide a pressure tight joint of great strength and stability as shown in Figs. 12a and 12b.

A typical roller expander is shown in Fig. 13. This tool contains rolls set at a slight angle to the body of the expander causing the tapered mandrel to feed inward when it is rotated in a clockwise direction. As the mandrel feeds inwards, the rolls develop the internal force which expands the tube.

The expanded joint presents a simple and economical way of fastening tubes into low-pressure boilers. Under axial loading, the expanded joint is almost as strong as the tube itself. However, for conditions of widely fluctuating temperatures and bending loads, the expanded joint must be seal welded (Fig. 14) or replaced by a shop-attached tube stub (*see Fig. 15*).

Generally, tubes above a 1500-psi range are either expanded and seal welded or attached to shop-attached stubs. Selection of the type of tube-end connection to be used is dictated by design, assembly, and operating characteristics.

Erection of a nuclear steam supply system

Construction activities in the nuclear power field require the latest construction techniques and the most intensive methods of quality control. The field installation of a nuclear steam system demands the use of efficient, well-organized and well-engineered erection methods, to install a quality product within the scheduled time and at the lowest cost.

Experienced and qualified erection personnel are necessary to assure planning and coordination of the project. The nature of the installation and contruction schedules results in a large number of simultaneous activities being performed within a confined area. Restricted construction openings necessitate careful planning of access for major components. Detailed scheduling is essential to assure that an adequate supply of tools and equipment

Fig. 10 Radiant-boiler steam drum located in position with arrangement for top support.

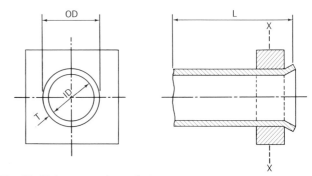

Fig. 11 Tube expansion effects.

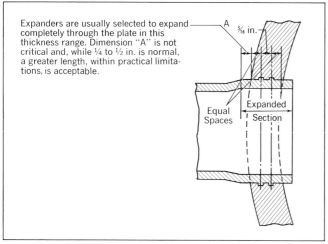

Fig. 12a Sketch showing arrangement of tube, tube seat, and length of expanded section of tube for thinner plate thicknesses.

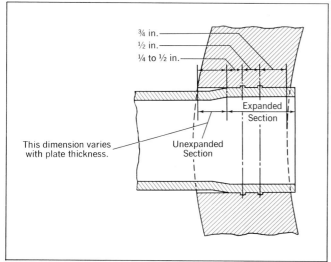

Fig. 12b Sketch showing arrangement of tube, tube seat, and length of expanded section of tube for heavier plate thicknesses.

are available at the project. Extensive warehouse facilities and careful inventory methods are dictated by strict storage specifications.

The principal construction activities involved in the installation of a nuclear steam supply system encompass the following: heavy hauling and rigging; erecting and welding large heavy-wall pipe; assembly and installation of close-tolerance reactor-vessel internals, closure head, control rods and drives; erection of fuel-handling equipment; and installation of control and protection systems.

The major pressure components, weighing from 400 to 600 tons, are moved by barge, railroad, or highway to the jobsite. Because of the remote and inaccessible location of many jobsites, a combination of two or three of these hauling methods is often required. In order to meet highway standards for wheel and axle loading, special multi-wheeled or tracked vehicles are used to transport heavy components over the highways (Fig. 16). Load and size restrictions require a careful analysis of the proposed route to facilitate safe and prompt delivery to the project. In addition, new segments of improved highway, shoring of existing bridges, construction

of temporary bridges or fills, and relocation of overhead utilities are often necessary.

The large components are moved into the containment building and upended into a vertical position by one of several methods, which may be dictated by building design and orientation (*see Fig. 4, Chapter 23*). This final moving and upending may be accomplished by means of railroad dollies or tracked transporters.

Lifting these components may be performed by using a large derrick, a framed structure supporting a large bridge crane or various methods utilizing the reactor building crane. Generally, the same lifting mechanism is used to install smaller vessels, such as the pressurizer, and the core flooding tanks.

The B&W reactor coolant system includes four large electrically driven pumps that are connected to the steam generators and reactor vessel by large heavy-wall piping. Welding, postweld heat treatment and nondestructive examination are required in the installation of the piping subassemblies.

The reactor internal components, including the core support assembly, are assembled on a specially constructed stand with matching reference points for simulated alignment of the core with the vessel and the head. Because of the close tolerances to be maintained, an exacting standard of precision is required in the fabrication and assembly of the internals and in the erection of the system. The head must be precisely fitted to the flange of the vessel to meet the alignment tolerances between the control rods and the core.

The fuel handling equipment consists of fuel transfer bridges in the reactor building and fuel pool, fuel transfer carriage, fuel rotators, storage stands, containers and miscellaneous tools. The erection of this equipment involves assembly, alignment, and leveling of structural components and installation and testing of mechanical equipment.

Several auxiliary systems are listed and described under the heading by that name in Chapter 21. These systems are made up of mechanical equipment with interconnecting piping. The erection procedures required are those normally associated with the installation of pumps, coolers, filters, tanks, process piping, control valves, and sampling equipment.

In addition to the auxiliary systems just named, the

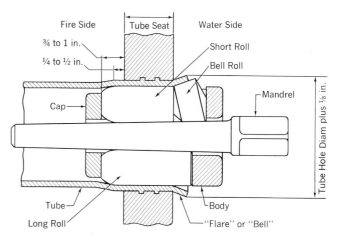

Fig. 13 Position of expander and mandrel after tube is expanded and flared.

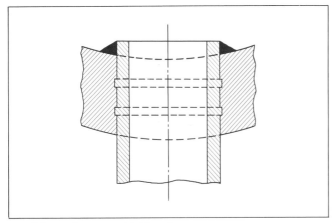

Fig. 14 Inside seal weld (drum).

entire plant is dependent on numerous systems that serve both the nuclear portion of the plant and the turbine-generator equipment. These systems include provisions for cooling and service water, water treatment, compressed air, heating and ventilation, vents and drains.

Nuclear instrumentation and engineered safeguards systems (Chapter 21) comprise a substantial amount of control and instrumentation equipment. The engineered safeguards systems also include high and low pressure piping. Installation procedures for the controls, instruments, piping, and mechanical equipment are basically the same as those employed in erecting similar equipment in fossil-fuel plants.

Throughout the course of installation, equipment and work areas must be maintained in clean condition. As each area and component of work is completed and tested, the vessel, piping and equipment are thoroughly cleaned and inspected. These areas are then closed off by temporary closures in order to maintain the clean condition.

Prior to starting the installation, detailed procedures and methods are formulated and approved. Thereafter, all work and testing is performed in accordance with the procedure covering that item of work. The work and methods are inspected by quality control personnel.

An acceptable method of record keeping is established prior to commencement of the job. The filing procedure guarantees that the latest approved drawings and pro-

Fig. 15 Superheater headers showing shop-welded stubs.

cedures are being employed. It also assures that the records of installation and testing may be easily audited by all inspection agencies.

In order to assure that the constant inspection and required testing are performed, a quality assurance group audits the erection procedures and inspection methods. The personnel performing quality assurance activities are independent from the jobsite construction staff. The quality assurance functions are intended to assure that structures and components essential to safety and performance are installed, constructed, and tested in conformance with contract requirements and applicable codes.

Codes and inspections

Codes

Steam generating units built by B&W comply with applicable codes. Fossil-fuel boilers for stationary application conform to the requirements of the *ASME Boiler and Pressure Vessel Code*, Section I, Power Boilers. Nuclear steam supply systems for stationary application, comply with the *ASME Boiler and Pressure Vessel Code*, Section III, Nuclear Power Plant Components.

One of the requirements of both Section I and Section III of the ASME Code is that organizations responsible for field assembly of boilers (Section I) or field installation of nuclear power plant components (Section III) must be in possession of a valid ASME Certification of Authorization and the proper code symbol stamp. Organizations applying for a code symbol stamp must meet certain prerequisites including having an established and documented quality assurance program and having a current contract with an authorized inspection agency.

During the construction phase of a nuclear power plant, inspections are also performed by the United States Nuclear Regulatory Commission (USNRC) as part of the licensing requirement. It is necessary for the organization performing the installation of nuclear power plant components to have a quality assurance program in accordance with USNRC requirements.

Repairs to boilers and pressure vessels that have been in service are performed in accordance with the *National Board Inspection Code* which includes rules for repairs by welding. This code requires that the organization responsible for the repair be in possession of a valid Certificate of Authorization and a repair symbol stamp or be otherwise authorized by the appropriate jurisdiction to perform repair work.

The field assembly of a boiler or the field installation of nuclear power plant components must be inspected by an authorized inspector, as defined in the ASME Code, in order to meet code requirements. The frequency of inspections is determined by mutual agreement between the assembler (or installer) and the inspector, although the inspector may look at any phase of field work he desires. The purpose of the inspection is to assure that the assembler (or installer) is complying with the requirements of the code and his own quality assurance program.

The inspector is required to witness the pressure test of the completed unit and usually signs the appropriate data report forms at that time.

Fig. 16 Transporting a reactor vessel at a nuclear power plant construction site.

Field welding

The welds that are made in the erection of a steam generating unit can be divided into two categories—those for joining of pressure parts and attachments to pressure parts and those for joining nonpressure parts.

Welds that are made to pressure parts must conform to the requirements of applicable codes. The codes establish the minimum requirements for thermal treatment, nondestructive examination, and qualification of procedures and personnel. These requirements form the basis of quality control procedures which govern every aspect of field erection.

Welds that are made to nonpressure parts such as flues, ducts, casing, hoppers and structural steel must conform to the requirements of engineering detail drawings with respect to size and location. The minimum requirements for thermal treatment, inspection, and qualification of procedures and personnel are defined by quality control procedures. In general, these specifications agree with the American Welding Society structural code.

Welding processes

The majority of field welding is accomplished by the manual shielded metal-arc- and gas-shielded tungsten-arc-welding processes (*see Welding, Chapter 31*).

Both processes are versatile and may be used with a wide variety of filler metals, welding positions and other welding conditions.

Types of welds

Butt welds. Tubes and pipes are usually shipped with the ends machined for butt welding and covered with a protective cap. Field preparation is limited to cleaning. The weld groove preparation shown in Fig. 17 is a B&W standard. It is suitable for welding with or without a backing ring. The tapered backing ring is machined to fit

accurately into the tube end, providing a welded joint with a smooth internal surface.

Socket welds. Socket welds of the type shown in Fig. 18a are used to join small valves and fittings. They provide a simple connection that is easily aligned and welded. This fillet-type weld provides a fluid seal and mechanical strength for the joint.

Seal welds. Seal welds are used to make mechanical joints fluid tight (Fig. 18b). The strength of the connection is developed by the expanded joint, pipe threads or by the configuration, as in the case of handhole fittings. The throat dimension of a seal weld is limited to $\frac{3}{8}$ in. maximum, and postweld heat treatment is not required.

Welding qualifications

The requirements for qualification of welders and procedures are outlined in Section IX of the ASME Code. A welder qualification test will verify that the welder can deposit sound weld metal in a given position, following an established procedure. A competent welder can make the test welds in one or two days that will qualify him for the majority of welding on the boiler. The test welds are generally welded and tested at the jobsite. If the results of the tests are satisfactory, a certificate of welder qualification is issued for each test completed.

A procedure qualification test establishes that designated materials can be welded by following a specific technique. The code requires that each manufacturer or contractor set up his own procedure specifications and make tests to qualify these procedures.

Thermal treatment

The reasons for preheating and postweld heat treatment are discussed in Chapter 31.

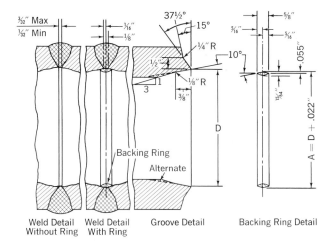

Fig. 17 Weld groove preparation.

Preheating. The "preheat temperature" is defined as the temperature that the base metal must attain in the welding area immediately before welding operations are performed. The ASME Code prescribes minimum preheat temperatures for each base material. Preheating may be accomplished through the use of flame torches or electric resistance elements.

Postweld heat treatment. The ASME Code describes the limitations of diameter, thickness and material of welds that must be subjected to postweld heat treatment. In addition, it describes the minimum temperature and holding times for each material.

Equipment. Electrical resistance heaters are the most widely used form of equipment for preheating and postweld heat-treatment operations. This type of equipment is designed to operate on conventional manual metal-arc-welding power supplies. It offers the advantages of ease in application, long life, and ease in temperature control. The three most common types of heaters are: 1) nichrome wire encased in ceramic beads, 2) flexible heating elements, and 3) special "finger-elements." The selection of a particular type of equipment depends on the base material size (diameter and thickness) and other factors. In preheating and postweld heat-treatment operations, temperatures are monitored with temperature-indicating crayons or attached thermocouples. The thermocouples are connected to potentiometers or strip-chart recorders.

Nondestructive examination

Techniques for the examination of materials, including weldments are discussed under *Nondestructive Examination* in Chapter 31.

Radiography is the most widely used method in the field assembly of steam generating units. Other methods, such as magnetic particle, liquid penetrant, ultrasonic and eddy current are used, but to a lesser degree.

The ASME Code defines the requirements for nondestructive examination including personnel qualifications, procedure qualifications, type of method to be employed, size (diameter, thickness) of welds to be examined and appropriate acceptance criteria.

Handhole and manhole fittings

Handholes and manholes are provided in boiler components for access to tubes that must be expanded or welded during erection and for subsequent inspection, maintenance, cleaning and repairs. Gasketed handhole fittings are used in headers designed for pressures and temperatures up to and including 1200 psi and 850F (Fig. 19). For higher pressures and temperatures, a welded cup-type closure is used (Fig. 20).

When gasketed fittings are installed, it is important to have all surfaces clean and free of burrs. The studs, nuts, and washers should be lubricated with a mixture of graphite and kerosine. Handhole fittings should be tightened initially and then retightened during hydrostatic test of the boiler, applying the torque initially used.

Welded-type handhole fittings are designed to enter the header through a master opening. The master cap is of similar design but shaped to enter the header through the hole that it closes. In each case the shoulder of the cap, which seats on a machined surface of the opening, provides the mechanical strength of the closure. The ⅜-inch-throat seal weld of the cap on the outside of the header maintains fluid tightness of the joint. Headers with welded stubs for tube connections usually have one master handhole at each end for inspection.

Manhole openings in drums are either circular or elliptical, depending on design conditions. Woven gaskets are used on manhole covers for units of design pressures up to 500 psi, metallic gaskets for higher pressures. Woven gaskets are coated with a mixture of graphite and kerosine, metal gaskets are installed dry. Manhole covers are usually attached to the drum with a hinge bar. Although the covers are interchangeable, the outside yokes are fitted to the contour of the drum. The cover, yokes, and drumhead are match-marked to assure that all parts will be replaced as originally fitted. Manhole studs should be tightened when installed and again under hydrostatic test pressure.

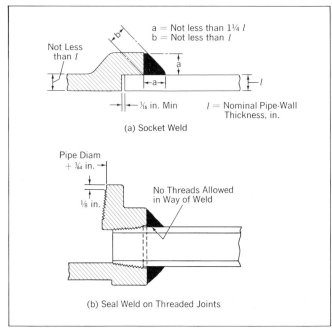

Fig. 18 Sketch (a), socket weld for pipe 3 in. and under in size. Sketch (b), seal weld for threaded connection.

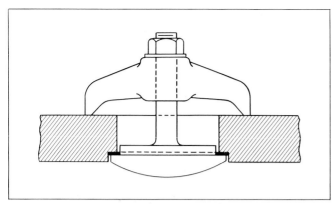

Fig. 19 Gasketed handhole fitting used to close header openings under conditions of moderate pressure and temperature.

Internal cleanliness of pressure parts

Many problems can develop during operations because of dirt or other foreign matter in the circulating system of a boiler. During the fabrication of drums, tubes, headers, pipes, or other pressure parts, precautionary measures are taken to assure that they will be clean internally. For boilers of welded-stub construction, the ends of all tubes and pipe as well as the stubs in drums and headers are closed with metal caps and sealed with plastic tape. This makes it unnecessary to clean these components in the field. Inevitably there will be a few closure caps displaced during unloading and handling. In such instances the erection crew must examine the components involved, perform any necessary cleaning, and replace the closures as soon as possible. During assembly, care must be taken that no foreign material enters the pressure-part system.

The pressure parts of boilers are searched before handhole and manhole closure fittings are installed. Reasonably straight tubes between headers or drums may be probed by passing a ball of correct size through them. Bent tubes which would not clear themselves of loose foreign material by gravity may be probed by blowing a tight-fitting sponge through them. Headers are checked with a light and mirror immediately before the extreme-end handhole fittings are installed.

The use of oil on water surfaces of boilers must be avoided. A water-soluble lubricant is used on tube expanders and tools for machining tube ends.

Cleanliness requirements for nuclear steam supply systems are particularly stringent. It is very important to avoid even small accumulations of solid materials which might block coolant flow, interfere with control rod movement, or damage coolant pumps. Most foreign materials in the reactor coolant become radioactive and can lead to troublesome deposits which hamper maintenance operations. Allowable limits for chlorine, fluorine and lead are low because of the potentially detrimental effect of small amounts of these substances on stainless steel and nickel alloys.

Nuclear components are thoroughly cleaned by wiping with pure solvents or halogen-free detergents prior to placing in service. Where detergents are used, demineralized water is used for solution and rinsing. All parts that are not accessible after final assembly must be cleaned during assembly.

Hydrostatic testing

When all pressure-part connections have been completed, the steam generating unit is tested at the pressure specified by the applicable code.

Before the test is applied, a final inspection is made of all welding. External connections are completed, including all fittings within code requirements. Connections for flanged safety valves are usually blanked. Welded safety valves are closed with an internal plug furnished by the valve manufacturer.

Water for hydrostatic testing must be clean and at a temperature which will result in a minimum pressure part metal temperature of not less than 70F. Nondrainable superheaters and reheaters are filled with demineralized water or condensate, if available. As a boiler is being filled, it is vented at every available connection, to allow water to fill every circuit.

After a boiler is filled, hydrostatic pressure is applied, usually by a pump made for testing purposes. If a boiler-feed or other high-capacity pump is used, precautions must be taken to keep the pressure under control at all times. While water is being pumped into the boiler, continuous inspection is made to observe any leakage conditions that might need repair or become dangerous. During the hydrostatic testing of any vessel, safety precautions must be observed and nonessential personnel kept from the test area.

Test pressure must be held long enough to allow minute leaks to be observed. Following this holding period, pressure is retained for an inspection period. On Universal-Pressure boilers, high-capacity pumps are used to cycle boiler pressure several times. The cycling uncovers leaks that might otherwise not show up until the first few operating cycles of the boiler. During final inspection, every area of the pressure system is viewed for leakage and repaired if necessary, to make the unit completely watertight.

Following inspection of the unit it is drained, and all nondrainable parts are protected from freezing if that possibility exists. The refractory, insulation, and casing work are completed in areas left open for test inspection.

The nuclear portion of the ASME Code outlines specific requirements for hydrotesting individual components, and the assembled system. In pressurized-water nuclear steam supply systems, the secondary (steam) side of the system is of a lower design pressure than the

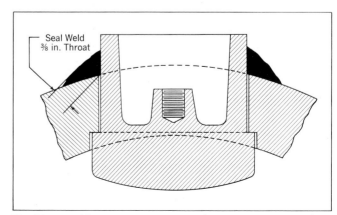

Fig. 20 Welded handhole fitting used to close header openings in higher-pressure boilers.

primary (reactor coolant) side, and the test pressures will be different for each of the two sides.

In the hydrostatic testing of a nuclear system, the tightness of the reactor head closure is an important item. The removable closure head is held in place by high-tensile alloy steel studs. In making the closure tight, the nut on each stud is tightened against the flange while the stud is held in tension by a stud tensioner (*see Reactor Vessel, Chapter 23*).

Assembly of nonpressure parts and auxiliaries

While pressure parts are being assembled and tested, work is in progress on nonpressure parts and auxiliary equipment. These include air heaters, fuel equipment, fans, duct work, refractory, insulation, and casing. These components require a large part of the manpower used on the unit. They must be scheduled to allow for access of large pieces and to take care of items that must be assembled in a prescribed sequence. Thus, air heaters are finished in time to allow for erection of flues and ducts. Pulverizers are located early enough for piping, drives, and other auxiliaries to be completed.

Refractory materials

The furnace and other wall areas of modern high-duty fossil-fuel boilers are made almost entirely of water-cooled tubes. The increased use of membrane walls has reduced the use of refractory on these areas. Castable and plastic refractories are used to seal flat-studded areas, wall penetrations, door and wall box seals.

Casing

Almost without exception, boiler casings today are of welded construction. It is essential that the strength of the weld equal the strength of the plate, that the welds be free of cracks and pinholes, and that they present a good appearance. With pressure casing, all seams are checked for air leakage under pressure. Nonpressure and external casings are given a thorough visual inspection.

Insulation

Insulation standards usually specify either insulation blocks or insulation blankets. Some plastic insulation is used for filling and pointing up voids. The thickness of the insulation for all surfaces is selected to give a specific surface temperature, e.g., 130F with 80F ambient air temperature and 50 ft/min surface velocity. The prime requisites for the installation of boiler insulation are that the application be tight, free of voids, well-anchored, and reinforced where necessary. The finished job must present a neat, workmanlike appearance. Various insulating materials having a wide range of temperature use-limits are available on the market today.

Duct work with heavy stiffeners at frequent intervals presents a difficult insulating job. The required thickness of insulation is applied for the temperature involved. With the stiffeners outside the flue and duct plate, the insulation thickness is often increased to assure adequate covering of the stiffeners. If the stiffeners are beyond the economic thickness of insulation, lagging is applied over the stiffeners and the minimum insulation thickness for the temperature requirement is used outside of this lagging. When insulation is applied at an appreciable distance from a hot surface with a long vertical run, there is a tendency for circulation of air to occur in the void. This increases heat transfer into the insulation, which is undesirable. Where vertical runs exceed 10 ft, horizontal barriers are installed between duct work and insulation.

As an optional design, where operating temperature of the equipment is 500F or less, a preinsulated panel made up of insulation and sheet metal lagging may be utilized. These panels are installed over the outside face of the existing stiffeners.

Sheet metal lagging

The increasing prevalence of outdoor boilers has given greater importance to the durability of insulation coverings. A light-gage metal lagging (galvanized steel or aluminum) is substituted for the plastic finish on walls, flues, ducts, air heaters, vestibules, windboxes, downcomers, steam lines, and other exposed components. The metal covering does not serve to seal against air infiltration but serves as a barrier to protect the insulation against water and physical damage. Metal lagging forms a hard, smooth surface that is easily painted and cleaned. It is reasonable in cost and is finding extensive acceptance with indoor as well as outdoor installations.

Mechanical equipment

The field installation of fans, stokers, pulverizers, feeders, and their driving motors follows standard methods for setting and alignment of machinery. In most cases, equipment manufacturers furnish special instructions that apply to the alignment of bearings, couplings, and other parts on each specific piece of apparatus.

Principal points of concern in erecting mechanical equipment are: 1) accurate location to center lines and elevation, 2) cleanliness and alignment of bearings, 3) alignment of couplings, and 4) homogeneous grouting between base plates and concrete foundations.

Preoperation inspection

After erection work is completed and the unit is ready for operation, a final overall inspection is made. Preferably this is a joint responsibility of representatives of the erection, service, and operating organizations.

Externally all components of the unit are checked for expansion clearances. Obscure corners are examined for any construction blocking or bracing that might have been left in place. Points of particular concern for expansion clearances are platforms and walkways constructed adjacent to external members that move with the unit.

Of special importance in fossil-fuel units is the removal of combustible materials that might present an explosion hazard during initial firing. Internal cavities are checked to see that all debris has been removed. Tubes are given a final inspection for alignment, particularly those tubes which might interfere with sootblower operations. Movable connections between tubes are examined for expansion clearances and to see that all attachments are properly anchored.

On most units construction schedules do not permit completion of all insulation before the unit goes into operation. It is important that work be completed on areas that will be inaccessible with the unit in operation.

Operation and maintenance

With proper design, manufacture and field erection, modern steam generating units are capable of operating for long periods of service. However, successful operation requires adherence to basic operating principles, and it requires that the unit be maintained in proper operating condition by performance of necessary in-service and outage maintenance.

The first fundamental is knowledge of operating conditions, so that the unit can be operated within design limitations. Chapter 33 describes the instruments and methods used for measuring the pressure, temperature and flow of steam, feedwater, air and flue gas, and the quality and purity of steam.

The greater part of this chapter is devoted to the measurement of temperature, which can be complex and difficult because of errors introduced by radiation and conduction. The basic principles used for the measurement of temperature are examined, and different types of thermometers and pyrometers are described. The thermocouple and its application are treated in considerable detail, including the measurement of fluid and tube temperatures, and the use of furnace tube temperatures to determine heat flux and to detect the presence of scale. The use of high-velocity thermocouples for the measurement of high temperatures of combustion gases in fossil-fuel units is also included.

Four methods for the measurement of steam quality and purity are examined. The use of orifices, flow nozzles, venturi tubes and flow tubes for the measurement of water, steam, gas and air flow is also described and illustrated.

Some important operating considerations are presented in Chapter 34. The greater part of the chapter deals with fossil-fuel units, including operator requirements, preparations for start-up, start-up of natural circulation and Universal-Pressure boilers, personnel safety, performance tests, handling of some abnormal operating conditions, and procedures for shutdown. The material under *Water Treatment for Fossil-Fuel Units* includes treatment of raw water, condensate, feedwater, and boiler water in natural circulation units and controls for water conditioning. The special requirements of water treatment for Universal-Pressure boilers are considered separately.

The latter portion of the chapter deals with the operation of nuclear steam supply systems, including operator requirements, pre-critical testing, fuel loading and zero-power testing, plant start-up, power testing and refueling. The material on water conditioning in a PWR comprises both the reactor-coolant and steam systems.

Chapter 34 concludes with a summary of the practical significance of pH values.

The operation of steam plants is greatly facilitated by modern control systems depicted in Chapter 35. This chapter begins with a discussion of basic boiler control theory with illustrative diagrams. This is followed by description of current feedwater control systems, and combustion control systems for oil, gas and coal with diverse types of firing. Several types of burner controls from manual to fully automatic are portrayed. The characteristics of control systems for once-through boilers are examined and the Integrated Boiler-Turbine-Generator Control System is described in some detail.

Instrumentation and controls for nuclear steam plants are also discussed in Chapter 35. Nuclear, in-core, and non-nuclear instrumentation is considered. The Integrated Control System for nuclear steam plants is described and illustrated. This system is the nuclear counterpart of the Integrated Boiler-Turbine-Generator Control System for fossil fuels.

The chapter concludes with a discussion of recent developments in instrumentation, power plant automation, and installation and service requirements.

Chapter 36 is devoted principally to the maintenance of fossil-fuel equipment.

In-service maintenance is directed primarily toward safe operation—avoidance of explosive fuel mixtures, and protection of pressure parts from overheating. It is also important to monitor and maintain efficiency, especially by keeping heating surfaces clean.

Outage maintenance of fossil-fuel units consists of inspection and cleaning of heating surfaces and the entire boiler setting and auxiliary equipment, and accomplishment of necessary repairs. Procedures for chemical cleaning of internal heating surfaces are described in detail in Chapter 36. Some of the methods used in making repairs and the requirements to be met are delineated. Also included are procedures for care of idle equipment.

Maintenance requirements for nuclear plants are discussed in the latter part of Chapter 36, with emphasis on the requirements that are unique to nuclear plants, including radiological safety.

Hammel-Dahl flow tube in a 36-in. diameter pipe, for measurement of reactor coolant flow in
a large nuclear steam supply system, being calibrated at St. Anthony Falls Hydraulic Laboratory of
the University of Minnesota. Water flow up to 83,000 gpm was used for this calibration.

Chapter 33

Pressure, temperature, quality and flow measurement

Instruments and methods for measuring pressure, temperature, flow and the quality and purity of steam are essential in the operation of a steam generating unit. Serving to assure safe, economical and reliable operation of the equipment, they range from the simplest manual devices to the measuring devices used to actuate the complete automatic control of boilers and all associated equipment (*see Chapter 35*).

Test instrumentation, often of a portable nature, is employed in the performance testing of equipment to determine flow, pressures and temperatures required to satisfy the user and the equipment supplier that the conditions of design and operation have been met. Requirements for these instruments are summarized in the *ASME Performance Test Codes*. These instruments require skilled technical operators, careful handling, and frequent calibration. They are generally not suitable for long-term continuous commercial operation.

Commercial instruments are those permanently installed and are expected to give satisfactory accuracy for extended periods. The emphasis is on dependability and repeatability. This often demands some compromise in absolute accuracy. However, the accuracy of commercial instruments is being improved, and they are being used increasingly for test purposes.

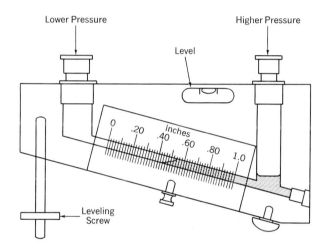

Fig. 2 Inclined differential manometer (*Dwyer Instruments, Inc.*).

Pressure measurement

The pressure gage is probably the earliest instrument used in boiler operation. Today more than one hundred years after the first "water-tube-safety boiler," the use of a pressure gage for determining steam drum pressure is still a requirement, even though modern controls and interlocks make overpressuring of a boiler virtually impossible. The Bourdon tube gage (Fig. 1) illustrates a type of gage which has been used for many years for pressure indication. Although improvements have been made in construction and accuracy, the basic principle has not changed.

Pressure-measuring instruments take various forms, depending on the magnitude of the pressure, the accuracy desired and other conditions.

Manometers, which may contain a wide variety of fluids, depending on the pressure, are capable of high accuracy with careful use. The fluids used vary from those lighter than water for low pressures to mercury for relatively high pressures. Fig. 2 illustrates an inclined manometer for reading small differentials at low pressure. Differential diaphragm gages using a magnetic

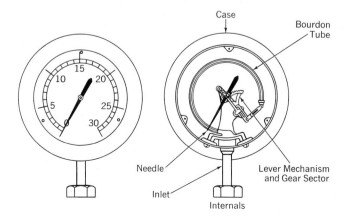

Fig. 1 Bourdon gage.

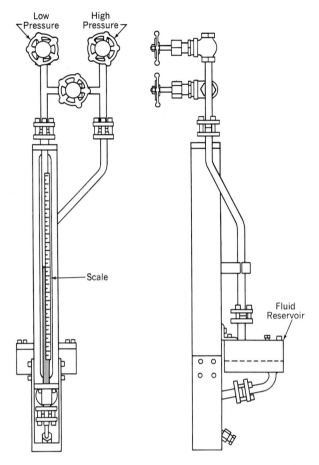

Fig. 3 High-pressure mercury manometer (*Meriam Instrument Company*).

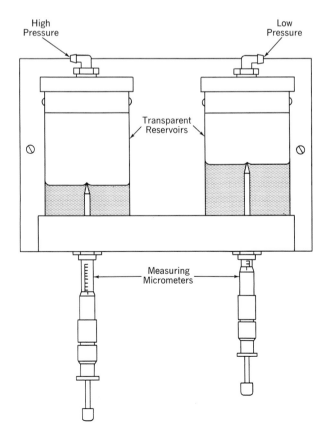

Fig. 4 Hook gage (*Dwyer Instruments, Inc.*).

linkage are now coming into use for low-pressure measurement. Fig. 3 shows a high-pressure mercury manometer. Manometers are considered an accurate means of pressure or pressure-differential measurement and are acceptable for *ASME Performance Test Code* purposes. For greater precision in measuring small pressure differentials, such as the accurate reading of flow orifice differentials, hook gages or micro-manometers may be used. A hook gage is illustrated in Fig. 4.

Bourdon tube gages are available for the measurement of a wide range of static pressures in varying degrees of precision and accuracy. The precision and accuracy necessary are determined by the requirements of the application. Pressure gages used as operating guides need not be of high precision and normally have scale subdivisions about 1% of full-scale range. For certain test procedures, such as hydrostatic testing of pressure parts and boiler efficiency tests, a higher degree of precision is required. Gages with scale subdivisions of 0.1% of full-scale range are available and should be used for these purposes. For efficiency testing, where temperatures and pressures should be known with high precision for accurate determination of enthalpy of steam and water, dead-weight gages are preferable to Bourdon gages for pressure measurement.

Diaphragm-type gages are used for the measurement of differential pressures. Fig. 5 illustrates a typical slack-diaphragm pressure gage for reading small differentials

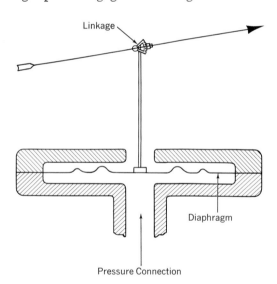

Fig. 5 Slack-diaphragm pressure gage.

in inches of water where total pressure does not exceed about one psig. For high static pressures, opposed bellows gages (Fig. 6) read a wide range of differential pressures. They are suitable for reading fluid pressure drops through boiler circuits and can be used to measure differentials from 2 to 1000 psi at pressures up to 6000 psi.

More sophisticated devices for the measurement of pressures and differential pressures are now on the market. These are generally described as transducers and are based on a variety of principles. Some examples are transducers using a strain gage mounted on a diaphragm, or those using a crystal which undergoes a change in electrical resistance as the element is deformed. Since such

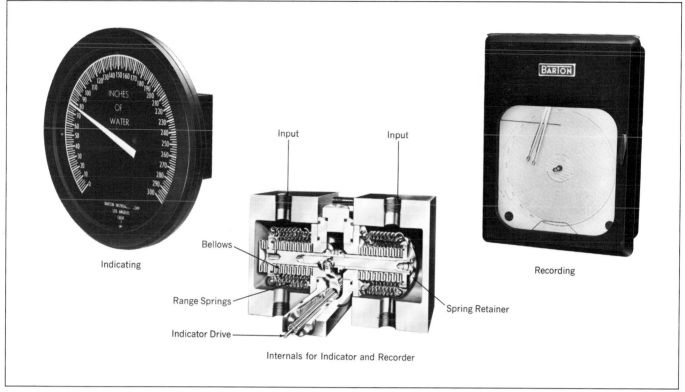

Fig. 6 Opposed bellows gage (*ITT BARTON, a unit of International Telephone and Telegraph Corporation*).

elements necessitate elaborate and frequent calibration they are not normally used as basic instruments for operating guides or test equipment. However, with their rapidly increasing reliability and ease of application, pressure transducers are finding wider application.

Pressure readings

In recording and reporting pressure readings, suitable correction to gage readings must be made for water leg, where it exists, and for converting to absolute pressure by the addition of atmospheric pressure, if required. Water leg is merely the added pressure imposed on the gage not contributed by the actual pressure, but by an effective leg of condensate or water standing above the gage. Fig. 7 illustrates the application of water-leg correction to a pressure-gage reading. For practical usage it is sufficient to reset the gage to zero with pressure off the system and the water leg completely filled.

Pressure drops across various types of devices such as orifices, nozzles, or pitot tubes provide a means of measuring flow and are described in a later section of this chapter.

Instrument connections for pressure measurement

The guiding principles governing the location of connections to the pressure source for measuring devices are in general the same regardless of the magnitude of the pressure, the type of measuring device, or the fluid being measured.

Pressure connections, or taps, in piping, flues or ducts, should be located in a position which avoids errors due to impact or eddies, thus assuring that a true static pressure is being measured. The connecting lines should be as short and direct as possible and free of leaks. For dif-

ferential-pressure readings it is preferable to use a differential-pressure-measuring device rather than to take the difference between the readings on two instruments.

Temperature measurement

Early in life everyone learns to distinguish between hot and cold. This sensory experience, supplemented by familiarity with such phenomena as the freezing and boiling of water, the cooking of food, and the flow of hot metals, gives rise to a general concept of temperature but does not provide a quantitative measure of degree of

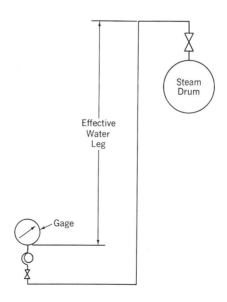

Fig. 7 Application of water-leg correction to pressure-gage reading.

hotness—in other words, a scale of temperature. One of the great contributions of thermodynamics was the establishment of a usable temperature scale (thermodynamic scale), completely independent of any actual substance, which forms the basis of the scales of temperature used in the quantitative measurement of degree of hotness.

Before the theory of temperature had been fully developed, various arbitrary scales had been devised. The Fahrenheit and Celsius (formerly centigrade) scales are the most common and firmly established.

The Fahrenheit scale is fixed at the freezing point (32F) and the boiling point (212F) of pure water, at atmospheric pressure, with 180 equal degrees between the two points. The centigrade scale was originally based on the same freezing (zero C) and boiling (100C) points of water at standard atmospheric pressure and utilizing the convenient 100 degree interval of the decimal system.

However, in 1960, the General Conference of Weights and Measures changed the defining fixed point from the ice point to the triple point (0.01C) of water. The triple point is the condition under which the three phases of matter (ice, water and steam) coexist in equilibrium. This point is more easily and accurately reproduced than the ice point. At standard atmospheric pressure the interval between the triple point for water and steam on the "centigrade" scale became 99.99 degrees instead of 100 degrees.

The word "centigrade" thus became a misnomer, and the name "Celsius" was accordingly substituted. The symbol, C, is today consequently standardized in all scientific and international work as degrees Celsius and commemorates the work of Anders Celsius in 1742.

The conversion from Fahrenheit to Celsius scales is effected by the formulas:

(1) $$F = (9/5)C + 32$$
(2) $$C = (5/9)(F - 32)$$

In the calibration of thermometers, the fusion or vaporization of various pure substances have been carefully determined and are known as "fixed points," namely:

Oxygen (liquid and gas in equilibrium @ 1 atm) = −182.97C

Sulfur (liquid and vapor in equilibrium @ 1 atm) = 444.00C

Silver (solid and liquid in equilibrium @ 1 atm) = 960.5C

Gold (solid and liquid in equilibrium @ 1 atm) = 1063C

Standard samples of the freezing points of metals are available from the National Bureau of Standards:

Tin	449.4F (231.9C)
Lead	621.2F (327.3C)
Zinc	787.1F (419.5C)
Aluminum	1220.2F (660.1C)
Copper	1981.4F (1083C)

Some less precise points are the melting points of:

Nickel	2646F (1452C)
Platinum	3223F (1773C)
Alumina	3722F (2050C)
Tungsten	6134F (3390C)

Two additional scales, useful in scientific work, use the absolute zero of temperature, i.e., −273.16C, or −459.69F. The absolute scale using Celsius degrees as the temperature interval is called the Kelvin scale (K); the absolute scale using Fahrenheit degrees is called the Rankine scale (R). The exact conversions are:

(3) $$K = C + 273.16$$
(4) $$R = F + 459.69$$

For most engineering work the following approximate conversions are sufficiently accurate:

(5) $$K = C + 273 = 0.555R$$
(6) $$R = F + 460 = 1.8K$$

Importance of temperature determination

Heat exchange, heat balance, and a multitude of other problems involving temperature are important in all phases of power generation. Means of indicating, recording and controlling temperatures are necessary in the design, fabrication, operation, and testing of power generating and associated apparatus; therefore, accurate measurement of temperatures is of prime interest to power engineers. Great strides have been made in developing suitable instruments and they are constantly being improved and simplified.

Methods of measuring temperature

Heat-affected properties of substances, such as thermal expansion, radiation and electrical effects are used by commercial temperature-measuring instruments. These instruments vary in their precision depending on the property utilized and substance used as well as the design of the instrument. The care taken in selecting the correct instrument for the particular application and its proper installation will determine to a large extent the accuracy of the results. Before readings are taken, it is the engineer's responsibility to make certain that the application is correct and that the results will not be affected by extraneous factors.

Changes of state

Fusion. For a pure chemical element or compound, such as mercury or water, fusion, or change of state from solid to liquid, occurs at a fixed temperature. The melting points of such materials are therefore suitable fixed points for temperature scales.

The fusion of pyrometric cones is widely used in the ceramic industry as a method of measuring high temperatures in refractory heating furnaces. These cones, small pyramids about 2-in. high, are made of selected mixtures of oxides and glass which soften and melt at established temperatures. The pyrometric cone is suitable for the temperature range from 1100 to 3600F. Its use in the power industry is generally limited to the laboratory.

Fusion pyrometers are also made in the form of crayon, paint, and pellets, which indicate a range of established temperatures up to 2000F. The crayon or paint is applied to a cold surface which produces a dull finish mark. This melts and changes to a glossy finish when the surface reaches the specified temperature. These marks,

therefore, indicate whether or not the surface temperature has reached or exceeded a selected value. The pellets begin to melt at specified temperatures when in contact with a hot surface.

Vaporization. The vapor pressure of a liquid depends on its temperature. When the liquid is heated to the boiling temperature, the vapor pressure is equal to the total pressure above the liquid surface. Therefore, the boiling points of various pure chemical elements or compounds at standard atmospheric pressure (29.92 in. Hg) can be used as thermometric fixed points.

The change of vapor pressure with temperature is utilized in the vapor-pressure thermometer, illustrated schematically in Fig. 8, which consists of a bulb partially filled with liquid and a capillary tube leading from the bulb to a pressure gage calibrated to read temperature directly. If the space between the liquid and the pressure gage is filled only with vapor from the liquid, the pressure will vary directly with the temperature of the liquid in the bulb. The capillary tube may be of considerable length, and its temperature does not affect the reading, but the accuracy of the instrument is affected by variations in atmospheric pressure and by elevation of the bulb above or below the gage. The temperature scale is nonuniform. The accuracy is not affected by changes in ambient temperature as long as the ambient temperature does not oscillate around that of the measuring bulb. The working range of a given instrument is limited to several hundred degrees and usually lies between minus 20 and plus 700F.

Expansion properties

Most substances expand when heated, and in many cases the amount of expansion is almost directly proportional to the change in temperature. This effect is utilized in various types of thermometers using gases, solids or liquids.

Gases. The expansion of gases follows the relationship:

$$(7) \qquad pv_M = RT$$

where:

p = absolute pressure, lb/sq ft
v_M = volume, cu ft/mole of gas
R = universal gas constant, 1545 ft lb/mole, T
T = absolute temperature, degrees Rankine = F + 460

At high pressures or near the condensation point, gases deviate considerably from this relationship. Under other conditions, however, the deviation is small.

Two types of gas thermometers are based on this relationship. In one a constant gas volume is maintained, and changes in pressure are used to measure changes in temperature. In the other a constant pressure is maintained, and changes in volume are used to measure changes in temperature. Very accurate instruments of this type have been developed for laboratory work. The constant-volume-type thermometer is widely used commercially.

Nitrogen is commonly used for the gas-filled thermometer in industrial applications. It is suitable for a temperature range of minus 200 to plus 1000F. The construction is similar to the vapor-pressure thermometer shown in Fig. 8, with nitrogen gas replacing the liquid and vapor. Expansion of the heated nitrogen in the bulb increases the pressure in the system and actuates the temperature indicator or recorder. The temperature scale is uniform, and the capillary tube may be of any length. Changes in temperature of the capillary tubing will introduce small errors.

Liquids. The expansion of liquids is used in a thermometer similar in design to the vapor-pressure instrument, shown in Fig. 8, except that the bulb and capillary tube are completely filled with liquid. Mercury is suitable for a temperature range of minus 40F to plus 1000F. The readings of instruments of this type are subject to error if capillary tubing is subjected to temperature changes.

The liquid-in-glass thermometer is a simple, direct reading, and conveniently portable instrument, widely used in many activities requiring the determination of temperature. Low-precision thermometers are inexpensive, and instruments of moderate precision are available for laboratory use.

This type of thermometer is usually made with a reservoir of liquid in a glass bulb connected directly to a glass capillary tube with graduated markings or with a scale attached. Mercury, the most commonly used liquid, is satisfactory from minus 40F, just above its freezing point, up to about 600F if the capillary space above the mercury is evacuated, or up to 900F or higher if this space is filled with nitrogen or carbon dioxide under pressure.

The use of unprotected glass thermometers is restricted to laboratory or field research applications. For more rugged service there are various designs of "industrial" thermometers, with the bulb and stem protected by a metal casing and usually arranged for use in a thermometer well. With this type of installation, response to rapid changes of temperature is not as fast as with the unprotected laboratory-type instrument.

Solids. The expansion of solids when heated is applied to temperature measurement in thermometers using a bimetallic strip. Flat ribbons of two different metals with unlike coefficients of thermal expansion are joined face-to-face by riveting or welding to form a bimetallic strip.

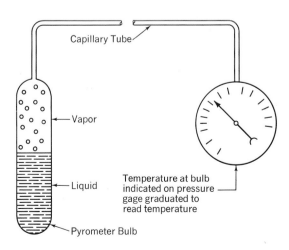

Fig. 8 Schematic assembly of vapor-pressure thermometer.

When the strip is heated, the expansion is greater for one side of the double layer than for the other, and the strip bends, if originally flat, or changes its curvature if initially in the spiral form frequently used. Bimetallic strips are seldom used in power plant thermometers but are widely used in inexpensive household thermometers, many designs of thermostats, and a variety of temperature control and regulating equipment. They are particularly useful for automatic temperature compensation in the mechanisms of other instruments.

Radiation properties

All solid bodies emit radiation. The amount is very small at low temperatures and large at high temperatures. The quantity of radiation may be calculated by the Stefan-Boltzmann formula (Equation 7, Chapter 4):

$$(8) \qquad q/S = \sigma\epsilon T^4$$

where:

q = radiant energy per unit time, Btu/hr

S = surface area, sq ft

σ = Stefan-Boltzmann constant, 1.71×10^{-9} Btu/sq ft, hr, T^4

ϵ = emissivity of the surface, a dimensionless number between 0 and 1 (usually between 0.80 and 0.95 for boiler materials)

T = absolute temperature, R = F + 460

At low temperatures the radiation is chiefly in the infrared range, invisible to the human eye. As the temperature rises, an increasing proportion of the radiation is in shorter wavelengths, becoming visible as a dull red glow at about 1000F and passing through yellow toward white at higher temperatures. The temperature of hot metals (above 1000F) can be estimated by their color. For iron or steel, the color scale is roughly as follows:

Dark red	1000F
Medium cherry red	1250F
Orange	1650F
Yellow	1850F
White	2200F

Two types of temperature-measuring instruments, the optical pyrometer and the radiation pyrometer, are based on the radiating properties of materials.

Optical pyrometers. By sighting an optical pyrometer on a hot object, brightness of the latter can be compared visually with the brightness of a calibrated source of radiation within the instrument, usually an electrically heated tungsten filament. A red filter may be used to restrict the comparison to a particular wavelength. This instrument is designed for measuring the temperature of surfaces with an emissivity of 1.0, which is equivalent to a "blackbody." By definition, a blackbody absorbs all radiation incident upon it, reflecting and transmitting none. When accurately calibrated, the pyrometer will give excellent results above 1500F, provided its use is restricted to the application for which it is designed. Measurement of the temperature of the interior of a uniformly heated enclosure, such as a muffle furnace, is such an application. When used to measure the temperature of a hot object in the open, the optical pyrometer will always read low, the error being small (20F) for high-emissivity bodies, such

as steel ingots, and considerable (200 to 300F) for unoxidized liquid steel or iron surfaces.

The optical pyrometer has a wide field of application for temperature measurements in heating furnaces and around steel mills and iron foundries. It is of no value for the commercial measurement of gas temperature, since clean gases do not radiate in the visible range.

Radiation pyrometers. In one type of radiation pyrometer, all radiation from the hot body, regardless of wavelength, is absorbed by the instrument. The heat absorption is measured by the temperature rise of a delicate thermocouple within the instrument, calibrated to indicate the temperature of the hot surface at which the pyrometer is sighted, on the assumption that the surface emissivity equals 1.0. The hot surface must fill the entire field of view of the instrument.

The radiation pyrometer has been developed into a laboratory research instrument of extreme sensitivity and high precision over a wide range of temperature. The usual industrial-type instrument gives good results above 1000F when used to measure temperatures of high-emissivity bodies, such as the interiors of uniformly heated enclosures. Since operation is independent of human judgment, radiation pyrometers may be used as remotely operated indicators or recorders, or in automatic control systems. Errors in measuring the temperatures of hot bodies with emissivities of less than 1.0, especially if they are in the open, are extremely large.

Radiation pyrometers sensitive to selective wavelengths have been developed and give good results measuring temperatures of bodies or flames utilizing, for example, the infrared band. Infrared radiation is produced by all matter at temperatures above absolute zero, and a detector sensitive to infrared, such as lead sulfide, may be used to sense the radiation. Using a system of lenses, a lead sulfide cell, an amplifier, and an indicator, temperature measurements may be made of radiating bodies.

A further variation on pyrometers is the so-called "two-color" pyrometer, which measures the intensities of two selected wave bands of the visible spectrum emitted by a heated object, computes the ratio of these emitted energies and converts it into a temperature indication. As with the optical pyrometer, indications depend on sighting visible rays, and hence its minimum range is 1000F.

Radiation pyrometers are not capable of determining gas temperatures.

Electrical properties

Two classes of widely used temperature-measuring instruments, the thermocouple and the electrical-resistance thermometer, are based on the relation of temperature to the electrical properties of metals.

Because of its versatility, convenience and ruggedness, the thermocouple is of particular importance in power plant temperature measurements. A separate section is devoted to the thermocouple and its applications.

Resistance thermometer. The electrical-resistance thermometer, used over a range of temperature from minus 400F to 1800F, depends on the increase in electrical resistance of metals with increase in temperature, which is almost in direct proportion. Therefore, if the electrical resistance of a wire of known and calibrated material is

measured (by a Wheatstone bridge or other device), the temperature of the wire can be determined.

In the simplest form of this instrument, shown by sketch (a), Fig. 9, the reading would be the sum of the resistances of the calibrated wire and the leads connecting this wire to the Wheatstone bridge. This value would thus be subject to error from temperature changes in the leads. By using a slightly more complicated circuit, shown by sketch (b), Fig. 9, the resistance of the leads can be eliminated from the instrument reading. In order to localize the point of temperature measurement, the resistance wire may be made in the form of a small coil. From room temperature to 250F, commercial instruments usually have resistance coils of nickel or copper. Platinum is used for higher temperatures and in many high-precision laboratory instruments over a wide range of temperatures.

The electrical-resistance thermometer does not require human judgment and can therefore be used for the remote operation of indicating, recording, or automatic-control instruments. If proper precautions are taken in its use, it is stable and accurate. However, it is less rugged and less versatile than a thermocouple.

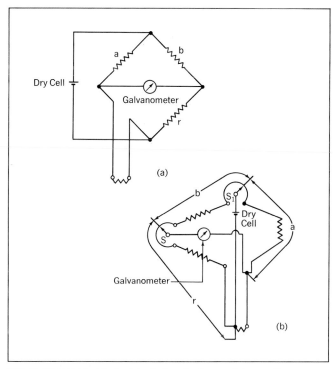

Fig. 9 Diagrams of electrical circuits for resistance thermometers (*Leeds & Northrup Company*).

Other properties

There are other properties of materials which vary with temperature and which could be used as the bases for temperature-measuring instruments. For example, the velocity of sound in a gas varies directly as the square root of the absolute temperature. While this phenomenon has been used in research, it has not been commercially applied because of difficulties in instrumentation. By using the flow of gas through two orifices in series, a method has been developed for measuring gas temperatures up to 2000F commercially and up to 4500F in the laboratory.

Temperatures in the range from absolute zero to 5000F have been determined with considerable accuracy by the use of an electric laboratory instrument that measures the motion of electrons. High-temperature research has been stimulated by gas-turbine and jet-propulsion problems, and the further development of new and improved temperature-measuring instruments is to be expected.

The thermocouple

A thermocouple consists of two electrical conductors of dissimilar materials joined at their extremities to form a circuit. If one of the junctions is maintained at a temperature higher than that of the other, an electromotive force (emf) is set up, producing a flow of current through the circuit, Fig. 10.

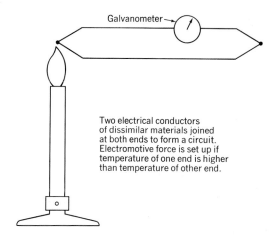

Galvanometer

Two electrical conductors of dissimilar materials joined at both ends to form a circuit. Electromotive force is set up if temperature of one end is higher than temperature of other end.

Fig. 10 Principle of the thermocouple illustrated.

The magnitude of the net emf depends on the difference between the temperatures of the two junctions and the materials used for the conductors. No unbalance or net emf will be set up if the two junctions of dissimilar materials are at the same temperature, or if the conductors are of the same material even though the two junctions are at different temperatures. If one junction of a thermocouple, which has been calibrated, is maintained at a known temperature, the temperature of the other junction can be determined by measuring the net emf produced, since this is proportional (almost directly) to the difference in temperature of the two junctions. The relationship between the electrical emf and the corresponding temperature difference between the two junctions has been established by laboratory tests throughout the temperature ranges for thermocouple materials in common use. These values are plotted in Fig. 11.

The principal advantages of the thermocouple in measuring temperatures are: versatility of application, rapidity of response through wide ranges of temperature, high degree of accuracy, durability, accurate reproducibility at relatively low cost, convenience of centralized reading or recording from one or many remote points, and simplicity of application to equipment for control and regulation of temperature.

In the thermocouple circuit illustrated by Fig. 12 the thermocouple wires of dissimilar materials extend from the hot junction to the cold or "reference" junction. In

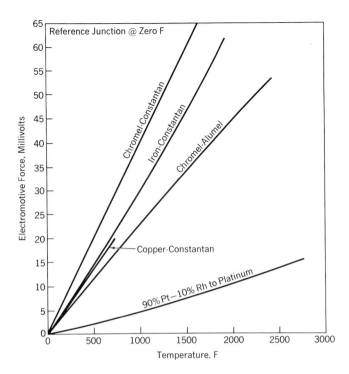

Fig. 11 Relation of temperature to electromotive force produced by several commonly used thermocouples.

the potentiometer circuit, copper leads may be run from the reference-junction terminals to the measuring instrument without affecting the net emf of the thermocouple. The pair of similar copper leads acts merely as electrical connectors to transfer the emf from the reference junction to the copper terminals of the potentiometer. If the instrument is at a uniform temperature throughout, no emf is set up between the copper conductors and slide-wire materials within the potentiometer itself. However, if temperature differences do exist within the instrument, there will be disturbing emfs in the circuit, and the readings will be affected.

Multiple circuits

If two or more thermocouples are connected in series, the total net emf at the outside terminals is equal to the sum of the emf developed by the individual couples. Where all of the individual hot junctions and all of the individual cold junctions are maintained at the same respective temperatures, as in the device known as the "thermopile," this multiplied value of emf makes it possible to detect and measure extremely small variations in temperature.

Two or more thermocouples may be connected in parallel for the purpose of obtaining a single reading of average temperature. In this case, the resistance of each thermocouple must be the same. The emf across the terminals of such a circuit is the average of all the individual emfs and may be read on a potentiometer normally used for single thermocouples.

To prevent short circuit or current flow between points of differing potential when two or more thermocouples are connected in series or parallel, it is important that both the hot-junction and cold-junction terminals of the individual couples be electrically insulated from one another. Also, for multiple-type circuits the simple conversion of average emf to temperature equivalent is strictly

true only if the emf-per-degree for the thermocouple materials is constant through the range of temperature of all thermocouple positions.

Practical application of thermocouples

For successful use of thermocouples in practical application, certain general principles and their corollaries, as outlined below, must be kept in mind.

There may be a difference between the temperature of the hot junction and that of the object or substance under investigation. This may be caused by inadequate thermal contact between thermocouple and object, by localized conduction of heat to or from the hot junction resulting from exposure of the thermocouple wires to media of higher or lower temperature, or by radiation effects of surrounding objects. The application of the thermocouple itself may in some cases distort the normal conditions of heat flow or temperature pattern within the object being studied. These factors should be minimized as far as possible by means that become apparent on consideration of the problem. Beyond that, the readings may sometimes be corrected by evaluating the possible errors by calculation or by reasonable estimate and comparison with correlated data.

If the composition of the thermocouple conductors is not homogeneous or a third material is present in the circuit, a temperature difference in the region of these conditions will cause intermediate or parasitic couples to be set up within the circuit, which may raise or lower the net emf in the circuit. Therefore, the use of brazing or soldering materials as a bond between two thermocouple wires at the hot junction would affect the readings unless all these materials were at the same temperature. The same is true if thermocouple wires, in close proximity to one another, are separately attached to an object for the purpose of determining its temperature. The object then becomes the hot junction, and any tem-

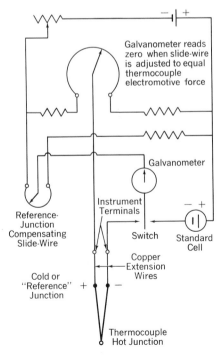

Fig. 12 Thermocouple circuit with manually adjusted reference-junction compensation.

perature gradient in it between the thermocouple wires affects the accuracy of the measurement. If the third material at each point of contact with the conductors is at the same temperature as the conductors, the net thermal emf at the cold-junction terminals will not be altered. By similar reasoning, it is wrong to assume that the structural parts of a boiler and its supports may be utilized without error as a common iron conductor, as is sometimes done for connecting a group of iron-constantan couples to a multipoint recorder or selector switch.

The emf developed by a thermocouple is independent of wire size or of change in size of conductors between the measuring junction and recorder terminals. Use of smaller wires at the hot junction will give a more rapid response to change of temperature because of the lesser mass of the hot junction. Their use also minimizes the disturbing effects of heat conduction in the wires adjacent to the hot junction. Offsetting these advantages, however, are the greater vulnerability of the smaller wires to physical damage and the shorter service life if subjected to oxidation at high temperature or to corrosive atmospheres. Also, in using smaller wires, if long leads are employed it is more difficult to balance the potentiometer because of the reduced sensitivity of the thermocouple-potentiometer assembly, since the current flow for a given emf is less because of the increased electrical resistance.

Selection of materials. Combinations of metals and alloys most frequently used for thermocouples are listed in Table 1 with their general characteristics and useful temperature range. Selection depends largely on ability to withstand oxidation attack at the maximum service temperature expected. Durability depends on size of wire, use or omission of protection tubes and nature of the surrounding atmosphere.

All thermocouple materials tend to deteriorate when exposed at the upper portion of their temperature range to air or flue gases and when in contact with other materials. Platinum in particular is affected by metallic oxides and by carbon and hydrocarbon gases when used at temperatures above 1000F and, in the course of time, is subject to calibration drift. Table 1 indicates that the upper limit of the useful range in temperature for all thermocouple materials listed is much below the maximum temperature at which rapid deterioration sets in.

For high-temperature duty in a permanent installation or where destructive contact is likely, service life may be extended, at some sacrifice in rapidity of response, by using closed-end protection tubes of alloy or ceramic material. The arrangement should permit removal of the thermocouple element from the protection tube for calibration and renewal when necessary. For use during short periods of time, as in some test work, protection tubes may be omitted if calibration is frequent, thus permitting correction of the data. For normal duty within the useful range of the thermocouple selected, the correction for change of calibration is usually negligible.

Sheathed-type thermocouples. In recent years, sheathed-type, magnesium-oxide insulated thermocouples have been in common use. The thermocouple wires are sheathed with inert magnesium-oxide insulation that protects them from the deteriorating effects of the environment. Sheaths can be made of stainless steel, insuring relatively long life, and resistance to oxidizing, reducing, or otherwise corrosive atmospheres. Sheathed thermocouples are available as grounded or nongrounded types illustrated in Fig. 13. The grounded-type thermocouple has more rapid response to temperature change but cannot be used for connection in series or parallel, because it is grounded to the sheath. For this purpose the nongrounded type should be used. The grounded type ap-

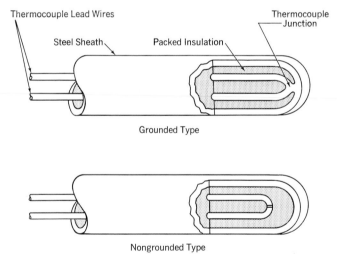

Fig. 13 Sheathed-type thermocouples.

Table 1
Types of thermocouples in general use

Type of Thermocouple*	Useful Temp Range, F	Maximum Temp, F	Millivolts at 500F†	Magnetic Wire
(+) Copper to Constantan (−)	− 300 to 650	1100	13.24	————
(+) Iron to Constantan (−)	0 to 1400	1800	15.01	Iron (+)
(+) Chromel to Constantan (−)	− 300 to 1600	1800	17.94	————
(+) Chromel to Alumel (−)	0 to 2300	2500	11.24	Alumel (−)
(+) 90% Pt − 10% Rh to Platinum (−)	900 to 2600	3190‡	2.048	————

* Nominal composition: constantan, 55% Cu, 45% Ni; chromel, 90% Ni, 10% Cr; alumel, 95% Ni, 5% Al, Si, and Mn.
† Reference junction, zero F.
‡ Melting point.

pears susceptible to separation or parting of the thermo-couple wire where long leads at high temperatures are used, whereas the nongrounded type appears satisfactory for this service.

Sheathed thermocouples may be equipped with pads for direct welding to tubes, as illustrated in Fig. 14. Pad-type thermocouples should not be used when the pad is exposed to temperatures that are markedly different from the temperature of the body being measured, since this added metal surface will either radiate or absorb heat depending on whether the ambient temperature is lower or higher. Typical applications of pad-type thermo-couples are for measuring temperatures of a drum, su-perheater-header or tube surface where these parts are not exposed to gas temperature (Fig. 15).

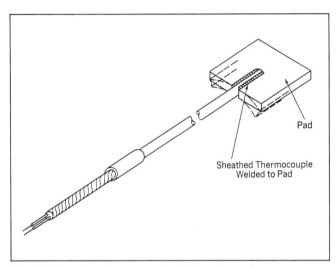

Fig. 14 Sheathed thermocouple with pad.

Thermocouple and lead wire. There are two classes of wire for thermocouples, the closely standardized and matched "thermocouple wire," and the less accurate "compensating lead wire." For thermocouples of noble metal, extension leads of copper and copper-nickel al-loy, which have an emf characteristic close to that of the noble-metal pair, are used to save cost. For thermo-couples of base metal, the extension leads in general use, while of the same nominal composition as the ther-mocouple wires, are less expensive since the control in manufacture and in subsequent calibration need not be as rigorous.

For accuracy, the matched "thermocouple wire" should be used at the hot junction and continued through the zone of greatest temperature gradient to a point sub-stantially at room temperature, where "compensating lead wire" may be spliced on for extension to the ref-erence junction. The reference junction is usually located at the recorder or central point of observation, but where a number of thermocouples are used it is sometimes eco-nomical to establish a "zone box" (*see Fig. 16*) from which copper conductors are extended to the measuring instrument.

Splicing of extension lead wires may be done by twisting the ends of the wires together, by the use of screw-clamp connectors, or by fusion welding, solder-ing, or brazing.

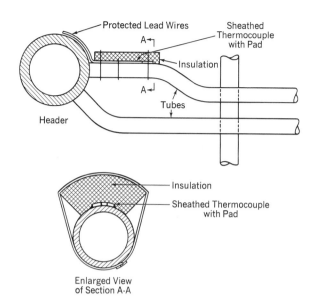

Fig. 15 Application of pad-type thermocouple.

Care should be taken to maintain correct polarity by joining together wires of the same composition. Polarity is usually identified by color code or tracers in the wire covering.

Hot junction. Wire and pipe-type elements for hot junctions may be purchased commercially or may be made from stock thermocouple wire, as shown by Fig. 17. These types are useful for direct immersion in a gas stream, for insertion into thermometer wells, or for thermal contact with solid surfaces.

Where the temperature of a metallic surface is to be measured, one of the most useful and versatile types of hot junction is formed by peening the wires separately into holes drilled into the surface of the metal. Steps in the procedure for making this type of junction are il-lustrated in Fig. 18.

The peened junction has the advantage of being com-pletely mechanical in application, with tight and re-

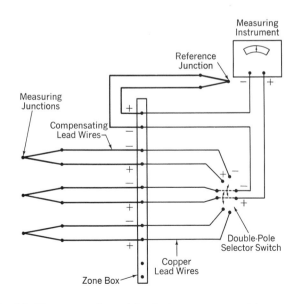

Fig. 16 Thermocouple and lead-wire arrangement to measur-ing instrument through selector switch.

markably strong attachment and minimum interference with the normal temperature of the object. The temperature indicated is essentially that of the metallic surface, which is the first point of contact with the conductors. The depth of the drilled hole has no effect other than for mechanical strength. The points of junction contact are subject to the effects of thermal conduction in the wires. Where this type of error is significant, precautions should be taken to prevent temperature gradients in the wires. Drilled holes for reception of the wire ends should allow for a snug fit before peening.

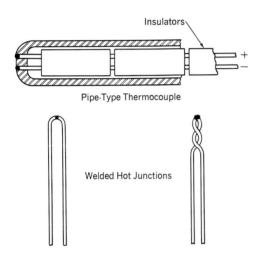

Fig. 17 Thermocouple elements and hot junctions.

Millivolt potentiometer

The temperature-emf relationships of standardized thermocouple wires, as established and published by the manufacturer, should be used to convert the potentiometer readings to the equivalent temperature values. These tabulated values represent the net emf impressed on the potentiometer terminals when the reference junction is at zero F and the measuring junction is at the temperature shown. The millivolt potentiometer may be employed with any type thermocouple and is frequently used in practice when several different types of couples are installed in the test setup.

It is usually impractical to maintain the reference junction at zero F while taking readings. Correction for any reference-junction temperature can be made by adding to each observed reading of emf the value of emf corresponding to the temperature of the reference junction and then entering the table with this sum to find the actual temperature of the measuring junction. Most millivolt potentiometers are equipped with a compensator, which should be adjusted to correct for the actual reference-junction temperature by setting the compensator at the value of emf from the table corresponding to the temperature of the reference junction. Direct millivolt readings will then correspond to the actual thermocouple temperature.

Direct-reading potentiometer

When calibrated for use with specific types of thermocouples, a potentiometer may be graduated to read the temperature of the hot junction directly instead of in millivolts. In this case, the reference-junction temperature is usually compensated automatically by resistor coils, built into the instrument circuit, which respond to deviations from a standard room temperature. It is necessary that compensating lead wires, or their equivalent, be extended to the instrument terminals, so that the reference junction is located at, or is at the same temperature as, the instrument. Characteristics of the compensating coils are specifically adapted to the type of thermocouple material for which the potentiometer is calibrated.

Temperature recorders

In temperature recorders, a power-operated mechanism automatically adjusts the slide-wire of a potentiometer circuit to balance the impulse received from the thermocouple. The action of the slide-wire is coordinated with the movement of a recording pen or print wheel that is drawn over, or impressed on, a temperature graduated chart that moves at a given speed.

In the modern recorder, change of thermocouple emf sets up an electrical imbalance which, upon being amplified, is used to drive a reversing motor that adjusts the slide-wire in the proper direction to restore the circuit to balance. Response to electrical imbalance is immediate, and extremely fast action of the driving mechanism is possible, so that an essentially continuous record may be traced for one thermocouple or a rapid scanning of many thermocouples may be recorded.

Checking recorder calibration. Compared with the manually operated potentiometer, all recorders are inherently less accurate because of wear and lost motion in driving gears, shrinkage or printing inaccuracies of paper and chart scales. Use of extremely long or unduly small-gage lead wires aggravates the lag. The resistance of long leads is of much less consequence where the energy of

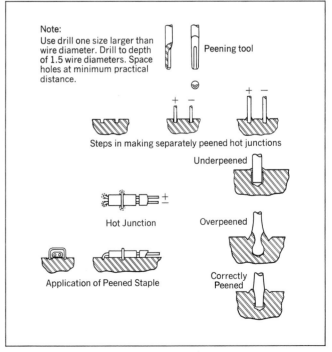

Fig. 18 Procedure for installing a peened-junction thermocouple to measure surface temperature of metal.

imbalance is amplified, as in the electronic type of recorder. However, the accuracy of recorders is sufficient for most commercial purposes and may be enhanced by the use of double or multiple-range circuits, which in effect increase the chart scale dimensions.

Temperature of fluids inside pipes

The temperature of a fluid (liquid, gas or vapor) flowing under pressure through a pipe is usually measured by a glass thermometer, an electrical-resistance thermometer or a thermocouple, each being inserted into a thermometer well projecting into the fluid, or by a thermocouple attached to the outside of the pipe wall. While the latter will give good results if all the necessary precautions are observed, the thermometer well is generally preferred, since the accuracy is greater.

A metal tube closed at one end, screwed or welded into a pipe wall, and projecting into the fluid serves as a thermometer or thermocouple well (Fig. 19). It must have the mechanical strength and rigidity to withstand hydrostatic pressure, bending caused by its resistance to fluid flow, and vibration. To minimize conduction of heat to the surroundings and to give rapid response to temperature changes, the dimensions of the well should be as small as compatible with the strength requirements. The part outside the pipe should be as small as possible. The material of the well must resist the erosive or corrosive action of the fluid. Since the temperature may be locally depressed by acceleration through a constriction in a pipe carrying a compressible fluid, the well should be carefully positioned. Projecting parts of the thermometer well and the pipe wall for some distance from the well should be thoroughly insulated against heat loss. The space between the outer end of the well and the thermal element should be tightly packed with insulating material to prevent circulation of air into the well. Omission of this packing could introduce a substantial error.

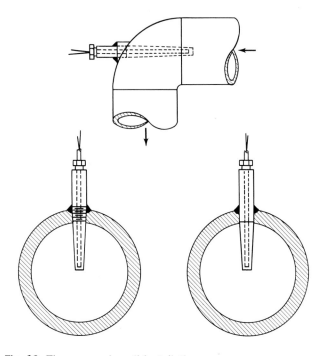

Fig. 19 Thermocouple-well installation.

The details of thermometer well designs vary. If the fluid is a liquid or a saturated vapor, good heat transfer is assured, and a plain well is satisfactory. If the fluid is a gas or superheated vapor, a finned well is sometimes used. The method of attachment to the pipe wall, either by screwing into the wall or boss or by welding or brazing, is optional with the designer provided safety-code requirements are met.

The thermometer well will tend to give an average temperature even if there is temperature stratification in the fluid, since thermal conduction along the well will serve to equalize the temperature.

Thermocouples may be attached to the outside of pipes by brazing, welding, or peening. Peening the thermocouple wires into holes drilled in the surface of the pipe is preferred as the easiest and most reliable method of installation. The thermocouple readings will give the temperature of the pipe wall at the exact point of contact with the wires, and any factor which causes the pipe-wall temperature at that point to differ from the temperature of the fluid inside the pipe will introduce an error.

Heat flow from the fluid to the surroundings will cause a temperature drop through the fluid film inside the pipe and through the pipe wall. Conversely, a temperature rise will occur if heat flows from the surroundings through the pipe wall to the fluid. If the pipe is not insulated, these temperature differences will usually be great enough to give appreciable variation from the fluid temperature. However, if the pipe is properly insulated, such changes in temperature will be negligible, and the readings will more accurately indicate the temperature of the fluid if that temperature has been constant for a sufficient time to allow the pipe wall to reach thermal equilibrium. Insulation restricted to the immediate vicinity of the thermocouple, with the remainder of the pipe bare, is not sufficient, since thermal conduction along the pipe wall will affect the readings.

Conduction of heat along the thermocouple wires is a frequent source of error. This can be prevented if the thermocouple wires are wrapped once or twice tightly around the pipe and held in place before the pipe insulation is applied. In this way the wires are brought to pipe-wall temperature in the region of the thermocouple junction, and thermal equilibrium is established. Extending the wires back and forth against the pipe wall will accomplish the same result. Both methods are illustrated in Fig. 20. In either case, fine wire will permit less heat conduction than heavy wire.

An additional source of error is the influence of "through steel"—uninsulated connections or valves which extend through the insulation and cause local cooling of the pipe wall. Locations remote from "through steel" should therefore be selected for thermocouples to determine the temperature of fluids inside pipes.

Tube temperature measurement

In steam boiler practice, it is frequently desirable to know accurately the metal temperature of tubes in different classes of service, such as furnace-wall or boiler-generating tubes that are cooled by water and steam at saturation temperature, economizer tubes cooled by water below the temperature of saturation, or superheater

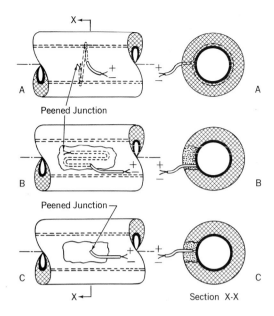

A—Good practice—Thermocouple wire wrapped around pipe underneath pipe insulation.

B—Good practice—Thermocouple wire laid along pipe wall before reinsulation.

C—Bad practice—Thermocouple wire led directly to outside.

Note: Any opening made in pipe insulation for access to pipe wall for installation of thermocouple must be carefully reinsulated with dry insulation firmly held in place.

Fig. 20 Thermocouple wires extending from hot junction disposed on pipe wall before leading outside.

and reheater tubes cooled by steam above saturation temperature. Such measurements may be for the purpose of determining the safety of pressure parts, for determining uniformity or unbalance conditions among tubes in parallel-flow circuits, for measurement of temperature increase of the fluid between inlet and outlet conditions, or for similar functional problems. In determining the temperature of the tube metal itself, measurement by thermocouple is a very practical and reliable method and is now used almost exclusively.

The peened type of hot junction, as illustrated by Fig. 18, is satisfactory in many cases and is probably the simplest form of thermocouple application. This couple measures essentially the temperature of the tube-metal surface, subject to errors caused by thermal conduction in the thermocouple wires to or from the junction contact. Conduction errors may be minimized as previously described and by shielding the wires from heat input or loss by wrapping with asbestos or other insulating material.

As noted previously, sheathed-type thermocouples with pads are in common use as a means of permanently monitoring tube temperatures where not exposed to external heat (Fig. 15).

Furnace wall tubes

In the measurement of water-cooled furnace-wall tube temperature it is necessary to provide special protection for the thermocouple and its lead wires because of the destructive high-temperature furnace atmosphere and, in some cases, the accumulation and shedding of ash and slag deposits. If a simple peened couple is used, the re-

sults may be of doubtful accuracy because of errors from conduction, and in most cases the service life would be short because of physical damage or deterioration of the wires from overheating. Cover plates welded to the tubes have been used to protect the wires, but these plates interfere with the normal heat flow and may be the cause of local ash deposits that create abnormal conditions at the point of temperature measurement.

The use of chord-drilled holes through which the thermocouple wires are laced (Fig. 21) was developed by B&W and has been found to be a very satisfactory method of application for furnace wall tubes. The tube surface is free from projections, the wires are protected, and the effect of thermal conduction at the hot junction is minimized because the wires pass through an essentially isothermal zone before emerging into cooler surroundings at the rear of the tube. To minimize the effect on the heat-flow pattern within the tube metal, the chord-drilled holes should be as small as possible. The effect of these holes on the strength of the tube is small. It is least in the critical direction of hoop stress and is readily tolerated in the direction of longitudinal stress. Use of chord-drilled holes in the thicker wall tubes for high steam pressure is therefore justified and practicable.

Gradient thermocouples

The measurement of the temperature gradient through the wall of a tube is a means of determining the heat flow rate through the tube wall, and of detecting buildup of certain types of internal deposit in the tube.

To obtain the best results, a large temperature gradient through the wall is desirable. However, ideal conditions must be compromised to permit an arrangement that provides tolerable metal temperatures, and at the same time is practical to fabricate. Fig. 21 shows a section

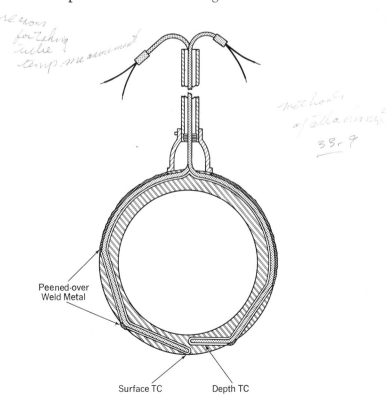

Peened-over Weld Metal

Surface TC   Depth TC

Fig. 21 Chordal thermocouples.

through a tube to illustrate the drilling and installation of typical surface and depth thermocouples and Fig. 22 the completed installation.

Calibration. The thermocouples used are bought to a specified accuracy. For greater accuracy they can be calibrated in the laboratory against a standard platinum-to-platinum-rhodium thermocouple, although, as purchased, the accuracy is consistent with that expected in this type of application.

No way has been found to date of accurately or economically calibrating the thermocouple tube assembly in the laboratory. The most satisfactory method is, following installation, to obtain a series of temperature readings on all thermocouples at two or three different ratings on the boiler, from a low rate to maximum rate, while the tube is still known to be clean internally, and reading all temperatures as nearly simultaneously as possible. Several series of readings should be taken on the thermocouples at each rating and an average calculated for each thermocouple used, in order to correct for minor differences in temperatures resulting from variations in heat input. This will also compensate for the time lag between surface and depth thermocouples. By using the surface and depth dimensions, the "equivalent lengths"

Fig. 22 Chordal thermocouple installed in a tube.

can be determined and the temperature gradients plotted. In an actual tube wall the heat flows through a path of decreasing sectional area and the temperature gradient through the metal is not linear with respect to thickness. The gradient, however, may be drawn as a straight line if temperatures are plotted against "equivalent length" of flow path (ℓ_e) which represents an equivalent flat plate having a uniform flow path with an equivalent but greater thickness. This is illustrated in Fig. 23.

The equivalent plate thickness is calculated in the following manner:

$$(9) \qquad \ell_e = R \log_e(R/r)$$

where:

R = outside radius of tube, in.
r = inside radius of tube, in.
ℓ_e = equivalent flat plate thickness, in.

In many cases thermocouple error may represent a significant portion of the gradient to be measured. Ideally, lines drawn through the surface and depth temperatures (Fig. 24) should intersect the inner surface equivalent-thickness line slightly above fluid temperature as measured by a thermocouple peened on the inside face of the tube. The amount above fluid temperature represents the temperature drop across the fluid film, and this drop will increase with increased heat input. Practically, it is impossible to obtain consistently precise enough drilling to assure that the pattern shown in Fig. 24 will always be obtained. If, at low inputs, the line drawn through surface and depth temperatures intersects the inner-surface equivalent thickness line at fluid temperature or slightly above, it may be considered as satisfactory. If it falls below or well above this point, a correction or calibration may be made by ignoring the measured equivalent depth dimension, plotting a line through the outer surface temperature and the temperature at the inner surface, then adjusting the equivalent depth to a value represented by the intersection of the adjusted gradient and depth couple temperature (Fig. 25).

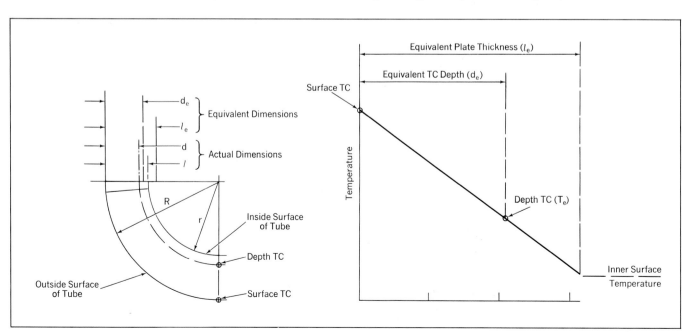

Fig. 23 Thermocouple installation.

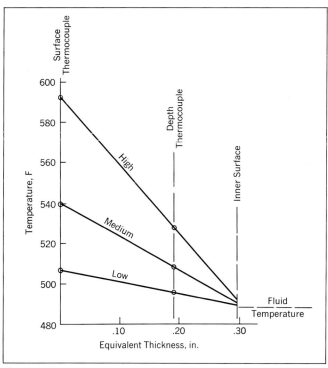

Fig. 24 Sample plot of temperature gradients for low, medium and high heat rates.

Heat flux measurement. Once a series of plots, as suggested under *Calibration*, shows consistent results, heat inputs may be calculated using formula (2), Chapter 4:

$$(10) \qquad q/S = \frac{k(t_1 - t_2)}{\ell_e}$$

where:

q/S = heat flow, Btu/sq ft, hr
k = thermal conductivity, Btu/sq ft, hr, F/in. (Fig. 1, Chapter 4)
t_1 = outside surface thermocouple temperature, F
t_2 = depth thermocouple temperature, F
ℓ_e = equivalent plate thickness (surface to depth) in. (Fig. 23)

Scale detection. If the temperature gradients are to be used as a scale detector, then thermocouples should be read periodically, plotted, and checked for a possible change in the temperature above saturation.

To assure a close comparison, the thermocouple temperatures should always be read the same way, with the same equipment, and under operating conditions as close to those existing during the original set of readings as possible (*see Calibration*). An accumulation of internal deposit in the thermocouple zone will be marked by an increased temperature difference from inner surface to saturation when compared to initial or previous plots of similar readings as shown in Fig. 26.

When the average of surface and depth temperatures rises to the point where the corresponding stress approaches the allowable limit for the tube metal in question, the boiler should be removed from service for internal cleaning. Sufficient allowance should be made for the possibility that other tubes in the unit, of which temperatures are not being measured, may be operating at a higher temperature than the indicator tube.

Limitations of gradient thermocouples. It should be recognized that the use of the gradient-thermocouple method of measuring heat flow through the tube walls is a guide rather than an absolute measure. Relatively small demensions and small differential temperatures exist between surface- and depth-thermocouple locations and any small error in determining temperatures or in thickness of metal between thermocouples usually represents a large percentage of this small difference.

The effectiveness of the gradient-temperature plot as a scale detector is dependent on the nature of the scale. Certain types of scale deposit rather uniformly, such as carbonate or silica deposits, while iron oxide deposits tend to accumulate in patches. Since there is no way to assure locating thermocouples in an area where nonuniform or patch-type deposits may accumulate, the

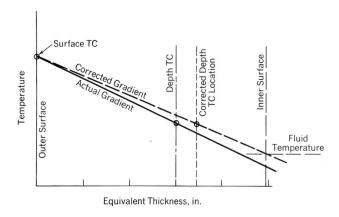

Fig. 25 Adjustment of temperature gradient.

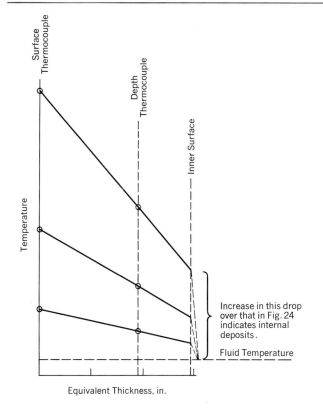

Fig. 26 Sample thermocouple plot after deposit formation in tubes.

gradient-thermocouple method of scale detection is not reliable for such accumulations.

For a quick indication of a change in conditions, indicating the presence of internal tube deposits, the difference between surface and depth temperature readings can be plotted against the difference between surface and fluid temperature readings. With a clean tube, points should fall along a straight line over a range of inputs. As deposits form, the difference between surface and fluid temperature will increase for an unchanging surface and depth temperature difference. Fig. 27 shows a typical plot of such conditions. When surface temperatures begin to approach dangerous limits, the boiler should be shut down for internal cleaning.

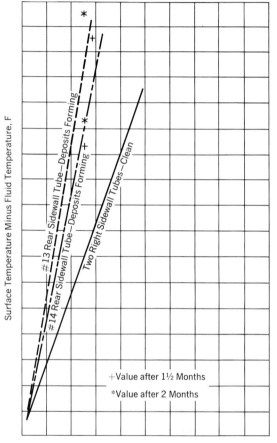

Fig. 27 Plot of chordal thermocouple temperatures showing effect of internal deposits.

Superheater and reheater applications

Where it is desired to measure metal temperatures of superheater or reheater tubes in the gas stream, chordal surface thermocouples can be installed using the principles previously described. However, special provision must be made to protect the length of wires between the point of measurement and the exit from the boiler setting. This can be done by containing the sheathed thermocouple in stainless steel tubing, welded to the superheater or reheater tube, to maintain the sheath and protection tubing at a temperature approximately that of the superheater or reheater tube.

Gas temperature measurement

Gas temperature is one of the most important items of the data required in testing or recording the performance of steam generating units. It is also of equal importance in safe and efficient operation. In the measurement of gas temperature, therefore, care must be taken 1) to make certain that the instrument used indicates the temperature correctly and 2) to interpret the temperature readings to give a true-average temperature of the gas stream, which is usually not uniform.

In all cases of gas temperature measurement, the temperature-sensitive element approaches a temperature in equilibrium with the conditions of its environment. While it receives heat primarily by convection transfer from the hot gases in which it is immersed, it is also subject to heat exchange by radiation to and from the surrounding surfaces and by conduction through the instrument itself. If the temperature of the surrounding surfaces does not differ from that of the gas (gas flowing through an insulated duct), the temperature indicated by the instrument should accurately represent the temperature of the gas. If the temperature of the surrounding surfaces is higher or lower than that of the gas, the temperature indicated by the instrument will be correspondingly higher or lower than the temperature of the gas.

The amount of variation from the true temperature of the gas depends on the temperature and velocity of the gas, the temperature of the surroundings, the size of the temperature-measuring element, and the physical construction of the element and its supports. To correct for the errors in temperature caused by the surroundings in any particular installation, it is best to calibrate the instrument against a known and reliable determination of the gas temperature.

When gas temperatures below 1000F are to be measured, a bare thermocouple, resistance thermometer, mercury-in-glass thermometer, or one of the various bulb-type thermometers may be used.

When a 22-gage bare thermocouple is used to measure the gas temperature in boiler, economizer, and air-heater cavities with surrounding walls colder than the gas, the magnitude of the error in the observed readings may be found from Fig. 28.

High-velocity thermocouple

Progressive design and operation of modern steam generating units depends, to an increasing extent, on the critical evaluation of gas temperature conditions in the furnace and superheater sections of the equipment. Successful performance must take into account the limitations imposed by metal temperatures of superheater tubes, and by the fusing characteristics of ash and slag from the fuel in current or expected use. While the overall complexity of combustion and heat-transfer relationships prevents exact calculation, much valuable information can be obtained by taking direct and accurate measurement of the gas temperatures occurring in operating units, and making comparative studies of related factors.

The optical pyrometer and radiation pyrometer are not designed to measure gas temperature, and should not be used, as results may be extremely misleading. Excessive error is also encountered when gas temperatures in

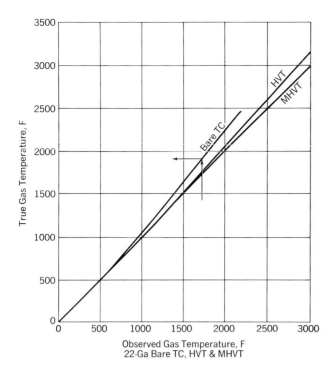

Fig. 28 General magnitude of error in observed readings when measuring gas temperature in boiler cavities with thermocouples.

the furnace and superheater areas are measured with a bare thermocouple.

The high-velocity and multiple-shield high-velocity thermocouples (HVT and MHVT), developed to correct for radiation effects, are the best instruments available for the measurement of high gas temperature in colder surroundings or low gas temperature in hotter surroundings. Cross sections through single and multiple-shield high-velocity thermocouples, developed for use in boiler testing, are shown in Fig. 29.

The surfaces (water-cooled walls, superheater or boiler tube banks) surrounding the usual location of a gas traverse are cooler than the gases. Consequently, the readings from a bare unshielded thermocouple will indicate lower temperatures than those obtained with an HVT. For the same reason, an HVT will generally indicate lower values than an MHVT. A comparison between the readings for bare, HVT, and MHVT thermocouple temperatures in typical boiler furnaces and cavities is given in Fig. 28.

Measurements with the MHVT closely approach true gas temperature. In the MHVT, the thermocouple junction is surrounded by multiple shields, all of which receive heat by convection induced by the high rate of gas flow. In this manner, the transfer of heat by radiation is so reduced that there is virtually no exchange of heat between the junction and the innermost shield. Because of the small flow areas which rapidly become clogged by ash, practical use of the MHVT is limited to clean gas conditions. Where traverses are taken in dust- or slag-laden gases, it is usually necessary to use the HVT and correct the readings by comparison with the results from an MHVT obtained under clean-gas conditions.

For temperatures exceeding 2200F, noble-metal thermocouples are required, and it is important to protect

the couple from contamination by the gases or entrained ash. The tube covering, shown in Fig. 29, provides some protection for the wires especially when fouling occurs from molten slag at temperatures above 2400F. When platinum couples are used in gases ranging from 2600 to 3000F or higher, appreciable calibration drift may occur even while taking measurements requiring only several minutes of exposure time. The thermocouple elements should be checked before and after use with corrections applied to the observed readings. When the magnitude of error reaches 40 to 60F, the contaminated end of the couple should be removed and a new junction made using the sound portion of the wire. Calibration of the service couple may be checked by comparing its readings with those of a standard couple of the same material when both couples, bound together, are inserted in a specially designed tubular resistance-wound electric furnace. Care should be taken that cold-junction temperature during calibration is approximately what it will be during the test period.

Since the transfer of heat by radiation is proportional to surface area, emmissivity, and the difference of the fourth powers of the absolute temperatures of source and receiver, it follows (the gases being considered as nominally transparent to the passage of radiant energy) that the effects of radiation increase as the temperature difference between the thermocouple hot junction and the surrounding surfaces increases. Also, since transfer of heat to the thermocouple by convection is proportional to a power of gas mass velocity and to the first power of the temperature difference between gas and thermocouple, it follows that the temperature of the junction may be brought more nearly to the true temperature of the

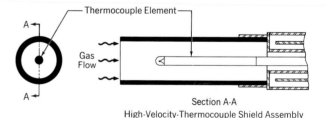

Section A-A
High-Velocity-Thermocouple Shield Assembly

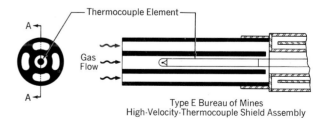

Type E Bureau of Mines
High-Velocity-Thermocouple Shield Assembly

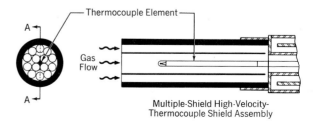

Multiple-Shield High-Velocity-
Thermocouple Shield Assembly

Fig. 29 Shield assemblies for high-velocity thermocouple (HVT) and multiple-shield high-velocity thermocouple (MHVT).

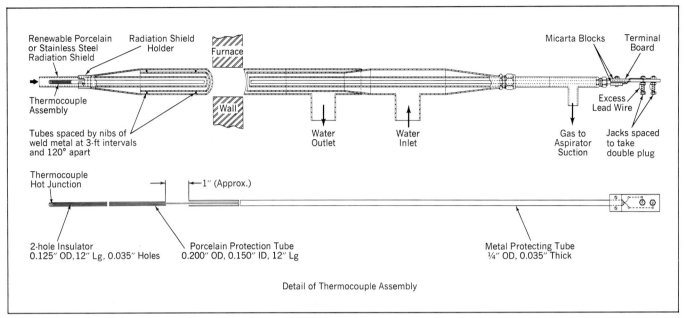

Fig. 30 Rugged water-cooled high-velocity thermocouple (HVT) for determination of high gas temperatures.

gas by increasing the rate of mass velocity and convection heat transfer while shielding the junction from the influence of radiation.

A special high-velocity thermocouple probe for measuring high gas temperatures in boilers is illustrated in Fig. 30. This portable assembly is used primarily for making test traverses in high-duty zones by insertion through inspection doors or other test openings in the setting.

The thermocouple is supported by a water-cooled holder consisting of concentric tubes of suitable length to span the traverse distance. The measuring junction is surrounded by a tubular porcelain radiation shield through which gas flow is induced at high velocity by an aspirator attached to the external connections. The gas aspiration rate over the thermocouple can be checked by an orifice incorporated with the aspirator and connected to the probe by a length of hose. The gas mass velocity over the thermocouple junction should be not less than 15,000 lb/sq ft, hr (*see Fig. 31*). Heat transfer to junc-

tion and shield by convection is simultaneous, so that both approach the temperature of the gas stream. Radiation transfer at the junction is diminished by the shield. However, since the shield is exposed externally to the radiation effect of the surroundings, it may gain or lose heat, and its temperature may be somewhat different from that of the junction.

With the increasing size of steam generators, handling of HVT probes of suitable length has become more difficult, but to date no acceptable substitute method for the measurement of high temperature gases has been developed. To minimize the effort involved in HVT gas temperature measurement, the probe itself has been lightened by using lighter gage stainless steel tubing and fittings, sheathed-type thermocouples and a track-type support. Temperatures are recorded on a strip chart allowing a reduction of manpower and providing a permanent record.

Evaluation of gas temperature

If the entire gas stream is at a uniform temperature, a single temperature reading at any point in the stream will be representative. However, such a condition is unusual, and it is generally necessary to make a traverse, taking readings at a number of points distributed across the gas stream. In order to evaluate the temperature reading properly, it is necessary to know, or to estimate, the direction and velocity of the gas flow at the various points in the gas stream where the temperatures are measured. Sometimes the gas velocity will be constant at all points, but there will be temperature stratification in the gas stream. More frequently, both gas temperature and gas velocity will be stratified. Occasionally there is recirculation, with some of the gas flowing through the traverse plane in one direction and some in the opposite direction.

The degree of accuracy required in the determination of the gas temperature depends on the use to which the data are applied. For instance, if a heat balance is to be determined for a section of the unit, such as the furnace,

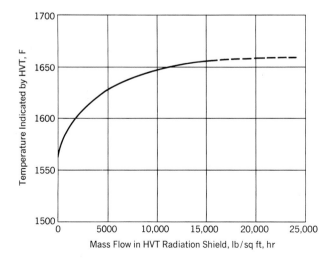

Fig. 31 Gas mass velocity over high-velocity-thermocouple junction greatly affects indicated temperature.

the average temperature required must be the one which, in combination with the total gas weight, will give a true measure of the quantity of heat leaving the section. In this case a higher degree of accuracy is necessary, and the correct procedure (though often in practice it can be only approximated) for the determination of an average temperature is as follows:

Select an arbitrary imaginary surface (a surface in one plane is often, but not always, the most convenient) in which the temperature and gas velocity traverses are to be made. Divide this surface into a number of small areas, which may be unequal, for comprehensive coverage. Measure the gas temperature, gas-flow direction, and gas velocity at a number of points. From the measurements taken, establish the gas temperature, gas-flow direction, and gas-flow velocity representative of each small area. Next, calculate the vector component of gas velocity normal to the surface of each small area. If there is recirculation, some of these vector components will be negative. For each small area, set down separately the product of temperature, area, and component of velocity, and the product of area and component of velocity. To obtain the true average temperature, divide the sum of the first set of products by the sum of the second set of products. Should the gas temperature vary over such a wide range that the assumption of a constant average value of specific heat for all parts of the gas stream is not warranted, gas enthalpy must be substituted for gas temperature. This procedure is based on a general mathematical theorem (Gauss's theorem) which finds wide application in various branches of physics.

This method for obtaining a weighted average temperature becomes time-consuming on a large steam generator and the need for such accuracy must be justified. Usually an arithmetic average of temperature points will suffice, if a sufficient number of points is obtained. For example, where unit-exit-gas temperatures are obtained for determination of dry gas loss, on a heat-loss efficiency test, the frequency of points called for by the *ASME Performance Test Code* permits a degree of accuracy corresponding to errors in efficiency not greater than a few hundredths of a percentage point.

When bulb-type or resistance pyrometers are installed permanently to measure gas temperature in a flue or duct, it is common practice to extend the bulb or resistance element from one side of the gas pass to the other in order to obtain a representative average temperature.

To assure against overheating of superheater or reheater tubes during a pressure-raising operation before steam is flowing through the tubes, it is satisfactory to use bare thermocouples temporarily installed in the gas stream immediately before the tubes involved and in sufficient number or proper location to assure indicating the highest gas temperature. The normal procedure is to remove these thermocouples after steam flow through the tubes is adequate to cool them. Gas temperature may then be increased. Future pressure-raising procedures can be based on this established rate or, if close control over the procedure is desired, gas temperatures can be monitored and recorded for each procedure. On units designed for remote operation, it is possible to retract and insert these thermocouples remotely, using a retractable sootblower carriage, as illustrated in Fig. 32.

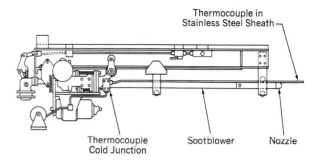

Fig. 32 Retractable thermocouple for measuring furnace-exit-gas temperatures as used for regulating firing rates during boiler pressure-raising.

When gas temperature and flue-gas analysis are required at the boiler or air-heater exit, a series of probes such as shown in Fig. 33 may be used. A number of these probes installed in a flue with the thermocouples connected to either a data logger or strip-chart recorder permits obtaining both a pattern and an arithmetic average of gas temperature. The flue-gas sampling tubes may be attached to a bubbler unit, also shown in Fig. 33, which will provide an average gas sample for analysis by either an Orsat apparatus or automatic analyzer.

Insulation and casing temperature

Inner surfaces

The thermocouple is particularly well suited for the measurement of temperatures at interfaces between successive layers of insulation, or at other points inside insulation. The temperature-sensitive hot junction may be buried out of sight, and the temperature may be read remotely. Furthermore, the hot junction and lead wires of the thermocouple are of small dimensions, which is important since it is imperative that the temperature-sensitive elements should be accurately located because of the steep temperature gradient through insulation.

Because of its low thermal conductivity, the rate of heat transfer through insulating material is low. This accentuates the effect of any heat conduction along the thermocouple lead wires, which is therefore a potential source of large error. To minimize or to eliminate this conduction error, leads must extend for some distance in a constant temperature zone, and small diameter wire should be used. If, for instance, in a composite wall the temperature of the interface between high-temperature block and 85% magnesia block is to be determined, the hot junction should be located between the layers of block, and the lead wires should be extended at least one foot between the layers before being brought to the outside (*see Fig. 34*). The block surfaces should be grooved sufficiently to accommodate the wire without being separated by it.

Outer surfaces

To avoid errors of considerable magnitude in the measurement of the temperature of the outer surface of insulation, thoughtful attention and careful workmanship are essential. Portable contact thermocouple instruments, designed to be pressed against a surface to measure its temperature, are unsatisfactory for this application and

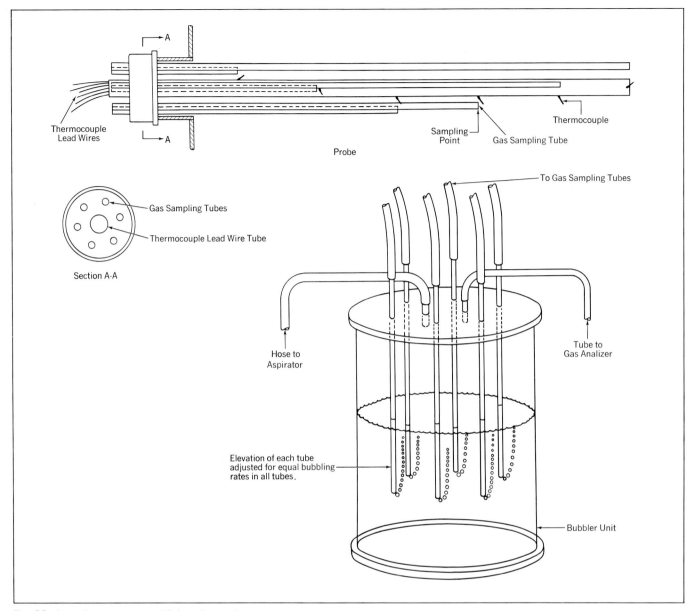

Fig. 33 Combination-type multiple-point probe.

will not read correctly when applied to hot uncased insulation. Such instruments cool the surface at the point of contact, and the low rate of heat transfer through the insulating material prevents the restoration of normal surface temperature by heat flow from surrounding areas.

For satisfactory results, the means of attachment of the thermocouple at the surface of the insulation must not appreciably alter the normal rate of heat transmission through the insulation and from the surface of the insulation to the surroundings. If serious errors from conduction are to be avoided, it is essential that the lead wires be maintained at the temperature of the surface. Fine wires can be attached more easily than heavy wires. If the insulation is plastic at the time of application, it may be possible to press the thermocouple junction and several feet of lead wires into the very surface of the insulation, with assurance that the thermocouple will adhere when the insulation hardens. If the insulation is already hard and dry, it may be possible to cement the junction and lead wires to the surface, using a minimum amount

of cement (*see Fig. 34*). Fastening the wires to the surface with staples introduces conduction errors; covering the wires with scotch tape or friction tape changes the heat transfer characteristics of the surface and imposes an undesirable insulation layer between the wires and the ambient air. Each specific installation is a challenge to the ingenuity and heat transfer knowledge of the test engineer.

Steel casings

The temperatures of steel casings of boilers may be measured with greater ease and accuracy. Portable contact thermocouple instruments give good results, since lateral heat flow from adjoining metal areas quickly compensates for the small quantity of heat drawn by the instrument from the point of contact. Thermocouple wire may be peened into or fused onto the metal surface to form the hot junction, and leads may be cemented to the surface for several feet. It is desirable to have the best possible thermal contact between the lead wires and the

surface and the least possible covering of the wire or disturbance of heat transfer from the surface to the surrounding air.

Approximate surface temperatures may be conveniently measured with fusion paints or crayons (*see Fusion*).

In power plants, thermometers are sometimes fastened to metal surfaces by wads of putty. This method of measuring temperatures gives a reliable approximate surface temperature indication if the metal is massive and not far from room temperature. It is not recommended for boiler-casing-temperature measurement and is completely unsatisfactory for the measurement of insulation-surface temperature.

"Through steel," such as metal ribs imbedded in insulation, studs or door frames extending through insulation causes considerable local upsets in surface temperatures, and its influence may spread laterally for some distance along a metal casing. These effects must be given careful consideration in the planning and interpretation of surface temperature measurement.

Measurement of steam quality and purity

Of the approved methods of field testing for steam purity or quality, the most widely used are:

1. Sodium tracer (flame photometry)
2. Electrical conductivity (for dissolved solids)
3. Throttling calorimeter (for direct determination of steam quality)
4. Gravimetric method (for total solids)

Each of these methods is described in *ASME Performance Test Code* 19.11, Water and Steam in the Power Cycle. The throttling calorimeter determines steam quality directly, whereas the other three methods determine the solids content of steam.

Most of the solids content of steam comes from the boiler water, largely in the carry-over of water droplets (*see also Steam Separation and Purity, Chapter 1*). It is customary to relate steam quality and solids content of steam by the formula:

$$(11) \qquad x = 100 - \left[\frac{\text{Solids in Steam} \times 100}{\text{Solids in Boiler Water}} \right]$$

where $x = \%$ steam quality, and solids are expressed as equivalent ppm (by weight) of steam or water.

By the use of formula (11), steam quality can be determined if the solids content in steam is known, and vice versa. This relationship is subject to error resulting from carry-over of solids in solution in the steam or in vaporized form. This effect occurs principally with silica at pressures above 2000 psi (*see Fig. 12, Chapter 1*).

Each of the four methods listed will be discussed separately with its advantages and disadvantages. Briefly:

1. For the best possible accuracy, the sodium tracer method, with continuous recording of total dissolved solids in steam, should be used.
2. Conductivity methods are useful within limitations.
3. The calorimeter method of testing for steam purity is not suitable for measuring extremely small quantities of carry-over, particularly at pressures in excess of 600 psi.
4. Gravimetric analyses require a large sample and do not detect carry-over peaks.

Obtaining the steam sample

If the results of steam quality or purity determinations are to be accurate, it is necessary that the instruments be supplied with a representative steam sample. The method of obtaining a steam sample and the boiler operating procedure during testing are fundamentally the same for each method of testing.

The sampling nozzle should be of the design recommended by the *ASME Performance Test Code*. It should be located after a run of straight pipe (or tube) of a length equal to at least ten diameters. Locations in the order of preference are:

1. Vertical pipe, downward flow.
2. Vertical pipe, upward flow.
3. Horizontal pipe, vertical insertion.
4. Horizontal pipe, horizontal insertion.

The nozzle should be installed in the saturated steam pipe (or tube) in the plane of a preceding bend, and in such a position that the sampling ports will directly face the steam flow.

On boilers with multiple superheater-supply tubes, sampling nozzles should be located in tubes spaced across the width of the drum. Such sampling points should be at no greater than 5-ft intervals.

When a calorimeter is used, the connection from the sampling nozzle to the calorimeter must be short and well insulated, so that radiation losses will be at a mini-

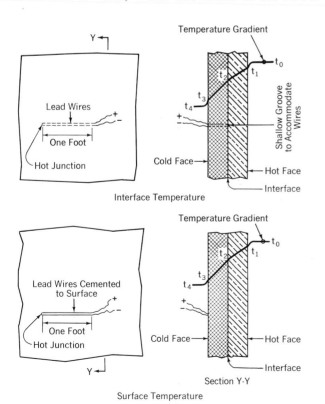

Fig. 34 Thermocouples for measuring surface or interface temperature of insulation.

mum. Connections must be steamtight so that the insulation will remain dry.

When steam purity is tested by conductivity or sodium tracer methods, the connection from the sampling nozzles to the condenser should be of steel pipe, and preferably stainless steel, with an inside diameter not exceeding $\frac{1}{4}$ in. and should be of minimum length, to reduce the storage capacity of the line. Multiple connections can be run to a common line and then to the condenser, but should be valved so that each connection can be sampled individually, to isolate possible selective carry-over. In any case, cooling coils, or condensers, should be located as close to sampling nozzles as possible, to minimize settling of solids in the sample line which could cause erratic sample measurement.

Sodium tracer method

The sodium tracer technique permits measuring dissolved-solids impurities (carry-over) in steam condensate to values as low as 0.001 ppm.

Sodium is a constituent present in all boiler waters where chemical treatment is in the form of solids. The ratio of the total dissolved solids in the steam condensate to the total dissolved solids in the boiler water is proportional to the ratio of the sodium in the steam condensate to the sodium in the boiler water. By determining the sodium content of the steam condensate and boiler water and the total dissolved solids in the boiler water, the solids content of the steam and the percent moisture carry-over may be calculated. The usual method of de-termining the sodium content of steam condensate and water is by the use of a flame photometer.

Fig. 35 illustrates a flame photometer modified to accept and monitor a continuously flowing sample of condensed steam. This modification permits prompt indicating and recording of the effect on carry-over of any change in boiler operating conditions, facilitating prompt analysis of problems.

The flame photometer is illustrated in schematic form in Fig. 36. The condensed steam sample is aspirated through a small tube in the burner into the oxygen-hydrogen flame. The temperature of the flame (3000-3500F) vaporizes the water and excites the sodium atoms which emit a characteristic yellow light having a definite wavelength. The intensity of the yellow light emitted is a measure of the amount of sodium in the sample. The intensity of the light is measured with a spectrophotometer equipped with a photomultiplier attachment.

The light from the flame is focused by the condensing mirror and directed in a beam to the diagonal entrance mirror. The entrance mirror deflects the light through the entrance slit and into the monochromator to the plane mirror. Light striking the plane mirror is reflected to the fiery prism where it is dispersed into its component wavelengths. The desired wavelength of light is obtained by rotating a wavelength selector (Fig. 35) which adjusts the position of the prism. The selected wavelength of light is directed back to the plane mirror where it is reflected through the adjustable exit slit and lens. The light impinges on the photomultiplier tube

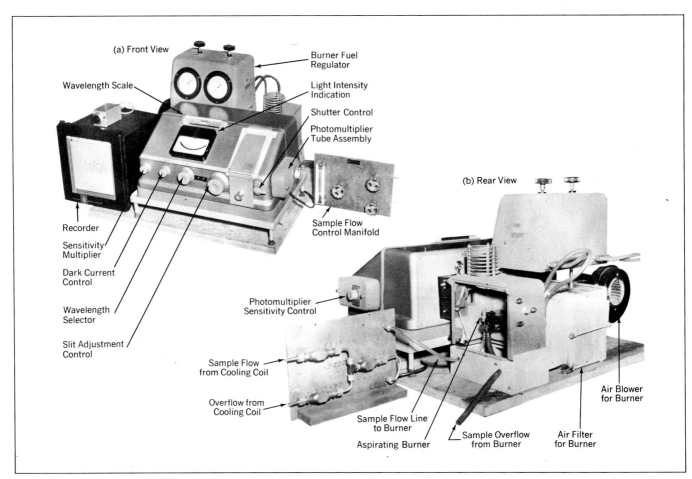

Fig. 35 Flame photometer (*by Beckman Instruments, Inc. with modifications by B&W*).

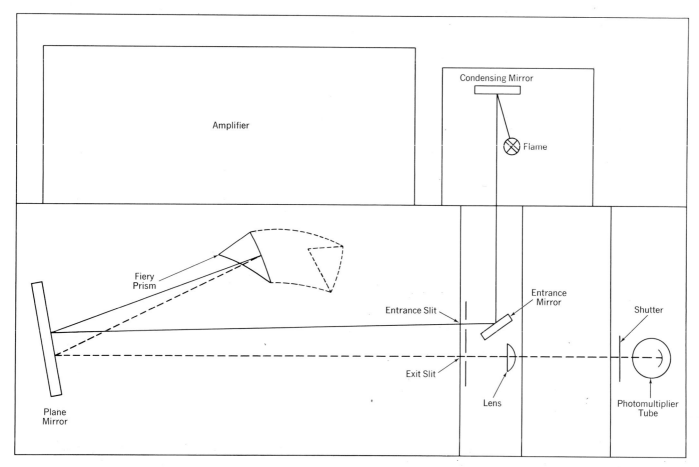

Fig. 36 Schematic arrangement of flame photometer.

causing a current gain which registers on the meter. The amount of sodium in the sample is then obtained from standard curves previously determined from solutions of known sodium concentrations.

Conductivity method

Electrical conductivity can be used to determine steam purity in units operating with significant solids concentration in the boiler water and total solids content in the steam in excess of 0.5 ppm.

This method of determining solids carry-over in steam by electrical conductivity is based on the fact that dissolved solids, whether acids, bases or salts, are quite completely ionized in dilute solution, and therefore conduct electricity in proportion to the total solids dissolved. On the basis of solids normally present in boiler water, the solids content of the steam in parts per million (ppm) equals the electrical conductivity of the sample in micromhos per centimeter times 0.55.

The condensed sample should ideally be completely free from dissolved gases, especially ammonia (NH_3) and carbon dioxide (CO_2), which contribute nothing to the solids content of the steam, but have a marked effect on conductivity. The major effort in carry-over testing by conductivity is directed toward elimination of ammonia and carbon dioxide from the condensed steam sample, and analyzing and correcting for the traces which remain. These objectives can be accomplished by any of several analyzing systems, which are described in *ASME Performance Test Code* 19.11.

Throttling calorimeter

When steam expands adiabatically without doing external work, as through an orifice, the enthalpies of the high pressure and low pressure steam are equal (provided there is no net change in steam velocity). Such an expansion is termed "throttling." As can be seen from a Mollier chart, wet steam with an enthalpy exceeding 1150.4 Btu/lb becomes superheated when throttled to atmospheric pressure. The measured temperature of the expanded steam fixes its enthalpy, which may be used with the measured pressure of the wet steam to determine the percent moisture in the wet steam sample.

The foregoing principle is used in various forms of throttling calorimeters, each of which incorporates a small orifice for expansion of the steam sample into an exhaust chamber where the temperature of the expanded steam is measured at atmospheric pressure. Velocity changes in properly designed calorimeters are negligible. The variations in the different designs of calorimeters are chiefly in the means of shielding the calorimeter from external temperature influences. At pressures below 600 psi the calorimeter shown in Fig. 37 is used. This is a small, low-cost, simple and accurate instrument which gives good results for steam having appreciable quantities of moisture, up to 4.3% at 100 psi, 5.6% at 200 psi, and 7.0% at 400 psi.

Fig. 37 shows the calorimeter installed ready for use. The connection should be short; it and the calorimeter itself should be well insulated. It is essential that the calorimeter discharge be completely unobstructed so that

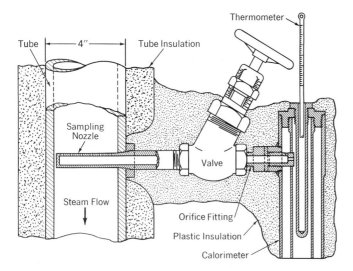

Fig. 37 Throttling calorimeter showing sampling tube installed in steam header or pipe.

no back pressure can be built up in the exhaust chamber. The calorimeter orifices must be clear, of full opening, and of the correct diameter—⅛ in. for pressures from atmospheric to 450 psi and 1⁄16 in. from 451 to 600 psi. The thermometer should be immersed in oil of suitably high flashpoint or mercury. The calorimeter is operated by opening wide the shut-off valve and letting the steam discharge through the calorimeter to the atmosphere. It is extremely important that the calorimeter be thoroughly warmed up and in temperature equilibrium before normal temperature or test readings are taken.

In obtaining calorimeter readings, the temperature of the expanded and superheated steam is measured by a thermometer inserted in the thermometer well. Due to errors arising principally from radiation from the calorimeter installation, thermometer corrections, and orifice irregularities, the observed temperature will tend to be lower than the theoretical temperature. To determine the difference so that a suitable correction may be applied, the "normal temperature" of the calorimeter as installed should be determined. This can be done by taking calorimeter readings when it is known that the boiler is delivering dry saturated steam, as when the boiler output is steady at about 20% of rated capacity with low boiler water concentration and steady water level. The "normal correction" is obtained by subtracting the "normal temperature" from the theoretical temperature as read from the zero moisture curve of Fig. 38. The normal correction should not exceed 5F. If it does, the calorimeter orifice is clogged, the insulation is faulty, or some other test feature is incorrect. When the calorimeter is used to determine the quality of a wet steam sample, the percent moisture can be found from the curves of Fig. 38 using measured drum pressure and corrected calorimeter temperature.

The calorimeter is a simple, easily used instrument and when properly installed, insulated, and operated, can give accurate results for steam moisture contents as low as 0.5 or 0.25% for low pressure boilers. For pressures above 600 psi and for greater accuracy of steam purity measurement, in the low ppm range, other methods of measurement should be used.

Gravimetric analysis

Gravimetric, or "evaporation to dryness," analysis is an acceptable code procedure for determining solids, particularly total solids, in a condensed steam sample. It consists of evaporating a known quantity of condensed steam to complete dryness, and weighing the residual. This can be done on a batch basis, or by use of a continuous sample system.

While a gravimetric analysis provides an accurate measure of total solids in water, its main disadvantage is that it requires a relatively large quantity of water obtained over an extended period of time and therefore does not localize carry-over peaks, when they occur. Time lag in other methods of steam purity measurement is usually small enough to permit attributing peaks of carry-over to periods of high water or high boiler-water solids, or other operating upsets.

Flow measurement

The measurement of fluid flow is necessary to permit intelligent, safe and efficient operation of steam generating equipment. This includes measurement of water, steam, air and gas flow. While there are many means of measuring flow, the basic acceptable methods, for the type of accuracy required by the *ASME Performance Test Code*, are by use of orifice, flow nozzle (flow tube), or venturi tubes as primary elements. The pressure drop or differential pressure created by these restrictions can be converted by calculation into a flow rate. Other methods of flow measurement will be discussed later.

The flow of any fluid through an orifice, nozzle or venturi tube may be determined by the equation:

$$(12) \qquad w = C_q \, YA \sqrt{\frac{2g\rho_1(p_1 - p_2)}{1 - \beta^4}}$$

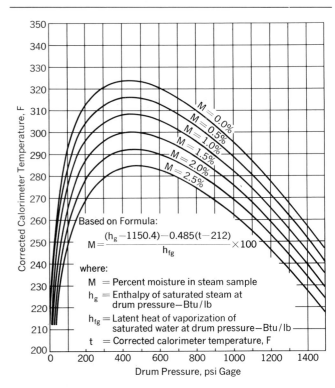

Based on Formula:

$$M = \frac{(h_g - 1150.4) - 0.485(t - 212)}{h_{fg}} \times 100$$

where:

M = Percent moisture in steam sample
h_g = Enthalpy of saturated steam at drum pressure—Btu/lb
h_{fg} = Latent heat of vaporization of saturated water at drum pressure—Btu/lb
t = Corrected calorimeter temperature, F

Fig. 38 Percent moisture in steam vs. calorimeter temperature.

where:

C_q = coefficient of discharge, a dimensionless number dependent on the device used, its dimensions and installation

Y = compressibility factor, a dimensionless number which equals 1.0 for most liquids and for gases where the pressure drop across the device is less than 20% of the initial pressure

A = cross-section area of throat, sq ft

g = gravitational acceleration, 32.17 ft/sec^2

ρ_1 = density at upstream temperature and pressure, lb/cu ft

w = flow rate, lb/sec

p_1 = upstream static pressure, lb/sq ft

p_2 = downstream static pressure, lb/sq ft

β = ratio of throat diameter to pipe diameter, dimensionless

Details of primary element sizing, fabrication and flow calculations can be obtained from the ASME publication *Fluid Meters, Their Theory and Application.*

Table 2 is extracted from the *ASME Performance Test Code* 19.5; 4, Flow Measurement, to show the relative merits and demerits of the three above named types of primary elements. The throat-tap nozzle has the highest accuracy of the primary flow-measuring devices.

The primary elements listed should be fabricated of erosion- and corrosion-resistant materials, and machined to definite tolerances in order to deliver the accuracies required. The orifice and flow nozzles are shown in Fig. 39; the venturi tube in Fig. 40.

Even though these elements can be sized with considerable accuracy by calculation, they should be calibrated by reputable laboratories prior to any precision testing. Calibration is usually by weighed water tests using precision weight scales. For normal commercial use, calculated flow rates or rates based on prototype testing or calibration are usually adequate.

Regardless of the primary element selected, certain important factors of its installation should be considered to assure accurate measurement:

1. Location in the piping in relation to bends or changes in cross section.
2. Possible need for approach straightening vanes.
3. Location and type of pressure taps.
4. Dimensions and condition of surface of piping before and after element.
5. Position of element relative to direction of fluid flow.
6. Type and arrangement of piping from primary element to differential pressure measuring instrument.

Details of these requirements for precision use or testing are also covered in ASME's *Fluid Meters, Their Theory and Application.* Since these devices produce a differential pressure across the element, a single differential gage as discussed under *Pressure Measurement* should be used for the measurement of flow.

For the flow measurement of combustion air or flue gas, where a high degree of precision is normally not

Table 2
Advantages and disadvantages of various types of primary elements

Advantages	Disadvantages
Orifice	
(1) Lowest cost	(1) High nonrecoverable head loss
(2) Easily installed and/or replaced	(2) Suspended matter may build up at the inlet side of horizontally installed pipe unless eccentric or segmental types of orifices are used with the hole flush with the bottom of the pipe
(3) Well established coefficient of discharge	
(4) Will not wiredraw or wear in service during test period	(3) Low capacity
(5) Sharp edge will not foul up with scale or other suspended matter	(4) Requires pipe line flanges, unless of special construction
Flow Nozzle	
(1) Can be used where no pipe line flanges exist	(1) Higher cost than orifice
(2) Cost less than venturi tubes and capable of handling same capacities	(2) Same head loss as orifice for same capacity
	(3) Inlet pressure connections and throat taps when used must be made very carefully
Venturi Tube	
(1) Lowest head loss	(1) Highest cost
(2) Has integral pressure connections	(2) Greatest weight and largest size for a given size line
(3) Requires shortest length of straight pipe on inlet side	
(4) Will not obstruct flow of suspended matter	
(5) Can be used where no pipe line flanges exist	
(6) Coefficient of discharge well established	

Source, *ASME Performance Test Code* 19.5;4-1959

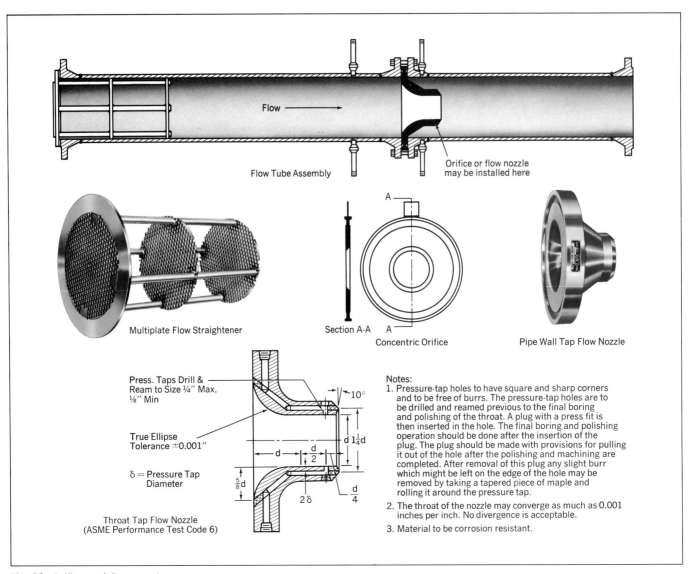

Notes:
1. Pressure-tap holes to have square and sharp corners and to be free of burrs. The pressure-tap holes are to be drilled and reamed previous to the final boring and polishing of the throat. A plug with a press fit is then inserted in the hole. The final boring and polishing operation should be done after the insertion of the plug. The plug should be made with provisions for pulling it out of the hole after the polishing and machining are completed. After removal of this plug any slight burr which might be left on the edge of the hole may be removed by taking a tapered piece of maple and rolling it around the pressure tap.

2. The throat of the nozzle may converge as much as 0.001 inches per inch. No divergence is acceptable.

3. Material to be corrosion resistant.

Fig. 39 Orifice and flow nozzles.

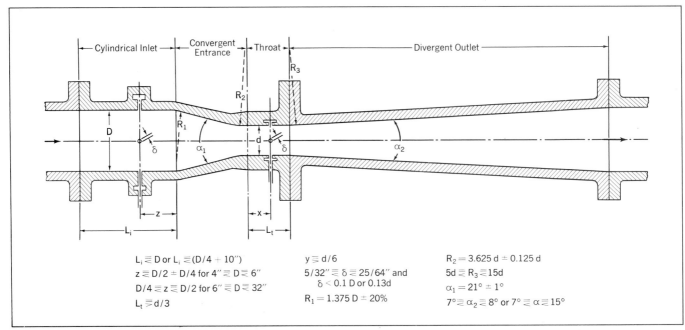

$L_i \gtrless D$ or $L_i \gtrless (D/4 + 10'')$

$z \gtrless D/2 \pm D/4$ for $4'' \gtrless D \gtrless 6''$

$D/4 \gtrless z \gtrless D/2$ for $6'' \gtrless D \gtrless 32''$

$L_t \gtrless d/3$

$y \gtrless d/6$

$5/32'' \gtrless \delta \gtrless 25/64''$ and
  $\delta < 0.1\,D$ or $0.13d$

$R_1 = 1.375\,D \pm 20\%$

$R_2 = 3.625\,d \pm 0.125\,d$

$5d \gtrless R_3 \gtrless 15d$

$\alpha_1 = 21° \pm 1°$

$7° \gtrless \alpha_2 \gtrless 8°$ or $7° \gtrless \alpha \gtrless 15°$

Fig. 40 Dimensional proportions of classical (Herschel) venturi tubes with a rough-cast, convergent inlet cone. (Source, ASME, *Fluid Meters, Their Theory and Application,* Sixth Edition, 1971).

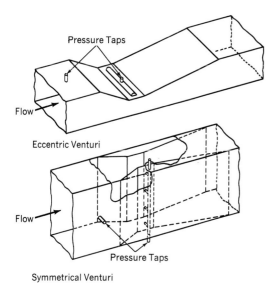

Fig. 41 Venturi sections for air ducts.

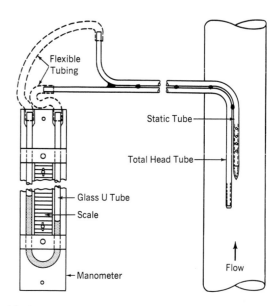

Fig. 43 Arrangement of pitot tube.

required, orifices, flow nozzles or venturi are also used, but the rigid requirements of construction and location for code testing are usually not possible because of space limitations, and hence normally not followed. Sometimes, as a substitute, a component of the steam generator, which because of its position in the path of flow creates a suitable pressure drop, is used to obtain a measure of the flow. For example, the draft loss across the gas side of an air heater may be used as an index of the flue gas flow. Because pressure drop will vary with a change in cleanliness, these are not highly reliable methods. The use of orifices, flow nozzles, venturi air foils or impact-suction tubes in areas free of entrained

dust, and at relatively stable temperatures prove more satisfactory. Fig. 41 illustrates two types of venturi sections used in air ducts for measurement of combustion air flow. Fig. 42 illustrates an impact-suction pitot-tube arrangement for metering primary air flow in a pulverizer system.

For a dependable determination of air flow, the primary element used should be calibrated, preferably at normal operating pressure and temperature. Test connections, or sampling points, for this purpose are located at a zone in the duct or pipe where good flow characteristics are obtainable, and the calibrating flow measurements are made using a hand-held pitot tube or equiva-

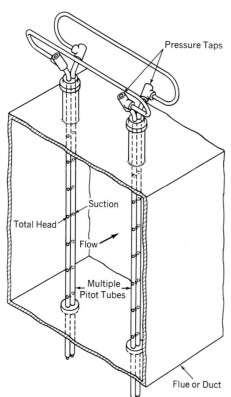

Fig. 42 Averaging pitot tubes.

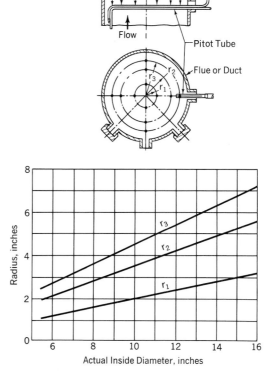

Fig. 44 Pitot tube traverse.

lent. The pitot tube, when inserted facing the air or gas flow stream measures velocity pressure, that is, the difference between total and static pressure. The velocity pressure measurement can be converted into a velocity reading by:

$$(13) \qquad V = 1097 \sqrt{\frac{h_v}{\rho}}$$

where:

V = velocity, ft/min
h_v = velocity head as indicated by pitot tube differential, in. of water
ρ = density at the temperature of the sampling location, lb/cu ft

A typical pitot tube and measuring manometer is illustrated in Fig. 43. The pitot tube has a factor or coefficient, of 1.0, to be applied to velocity head readings, eliminating the need for corrections to the head readings. Fig. 44 shows a method of traversing a round duct using a pitot tube.

An additional, portable, flow-measuring device that can be used for calibration purposes is the Fecheimer probe. It also has a coefficient of 1.0. It incorporates a null balance feature that permits determining when the probe faces the direction of gas flow. This probe is illustrated in Fig. 45. In the schematic, the outer holes in the probe are each at exactly 39-$\frac{1}{4}$° from the centerline hole, placing them at a point of zero impact pressure, and hence will give a reading of true static pressure. When the probe faces the flow of gas, a manometer connected across the two outer holes will give a zero, or null, balance. Since the centerline hole receives a full impact or total pressure, when facing into the gas stream, a manometer connected across one outer hole and the center-

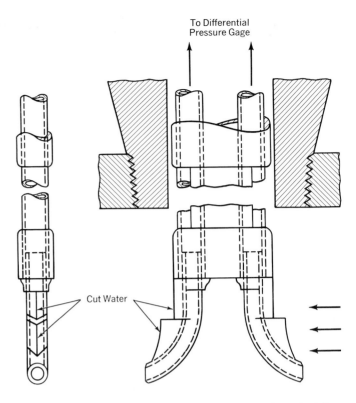

Fig. 46 Pitot tube, combined type with reversed static tube. (Source, ASME, *Fluid Meters, Their Theory and Application,* Sixth Edition, 1971).

line hole will give true velocity pressure, that is, impact pressure less static pressure. The impact-suction or reversed-type pitot tube, illustrated in Fig. 46, produces a differential pressure greater than one velocity head, which gives a magnified reading. Also, this type of pitot tube will measure flow in either direction. In order to use the reversed-type pitot tube for the measurement of flow, calibration is required for the Reynolds number range as well as for the geometry of the flow channel and its position in the stream.

Permanently installed pitot tubes are used in cases where relatively high pressure losses due to the primary measuring element are undesirable.

Flow tubes are also used in such cases, e.g., in the reactor coolant loops of nuclear steam supply systems (*see frontispiece to this chapter*). These flow tubes differ from most other primary elements in that the flow channel cross section varies in a geometrically similar manner in the inlet and exit directions from the contoured throat section.

The throat section is equipped with two sets of pressure taps, one set pointing upstream and one downstream similar to impact-suction pitot tubes. Thus the flow tube will sense flow in either direction.

Each set of taps is interconnected and the two sets in turn are connected to a differential pressure gage. The pressure taps are located at cross sections of equal area so that the differential developed is a result of impact and suction pressure differences only and is thus a function of the velocity head alone.

Many types and makes of commercial flow-measuring devices are described in the literature.

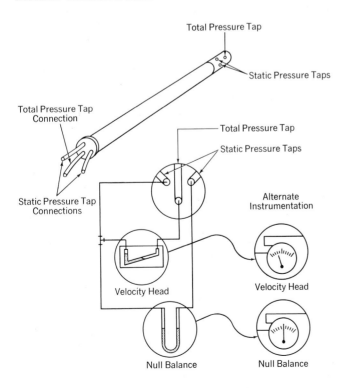

Fig. 45 Fecheimer probe.

Chapter 34   Operation of steam generating equipment

Operation of fossil-fuel boilers

Many boilers are operating day after day at or near test-condition efficiencies and with a minimum number of unscheduled outages. These boilers and their auxiliary equipment have received the proper attention not only while they were being designed, manufactured and erected, but also, of equal importance, while they are in service. The operators of these boilers have the knowledge and interest to operate within the limitations of the equipment, to institute and practice safe procedures, and to apply preventive maintenance on schedule.

Operator requirements

Good operation begins before equipment installation is complete. It includes training of the operators as well as preparation of the equipment.

Every operator must be trained to understand and fulfill the responsibility he assumes for the successful performance of the equipment and for the safety of all personnel involved. To be prepared for all situations that may arise, he must have a complete knowledge of all components—their designs, purposes, limitations, and relationships to other components. This includes thoroughly inspecting the equipment and studying the drawings and instructions.

Operators must stay abreast of the rapid progress in the steam generation field, especially in the area of controls and operating procedures. The ideal time to become familiar with new equipment is during the pre-operational phase when the equipment is being installed.

Preliminary operation should not be entrusted to inexperienced personnel who are not familiar with the equipment and the correct operating procedures. Considerable damage can result from improper preparation of equipment or its misuse during preliminary checkout. All preliminary operations for testing fans, pumps, fuel burning equipment, or for cleaning, drying, boiling out, and blowing steam lines should be by regular operators who have the knowledge and experience to protect the equipment.

Operator training takes on special significance during the initial operating period required to prepare the unit for commercial operation. Knowledgeable and experienced operators are valuable during this period when the controls and interlocks are being adjusted, fuel burning equipment is being regulated, operating procedures are being perfected, and preliminary tests are being conducted to determine the performance and capabilities of the unit. Experienced men with a knowledge of the equipment can eliminate the confusion that may otherwise exist during this period. The additional experience gained during the initial period can also pay dividends in the future performance of the unit.

Preparations for start-up

A systematic approach is required in the preparation for service of a new boiler or any boiler that has undergone major repairs or alterations. The procedure varies with boiler design; however, certain steps are required for all boilers. Some procedural steps may be continuous throughout the start-up period; some steps may be combined; others may be intermittent. The steps may be classified as inspection, cleaning, hydrostatic testing, precalibration of instruments and controls, auxiliary equipment preparation, refractory conditioning, chemical cleaning, steam line cleaning (blowing), safety valve testing and setting, and initial operations for adjustments and testing.

Inspection. An inspection of the boiler and auxiliary equipment serves two purposes: 1) it familiarizes the operator with the equipment, and 2) it verifies the condition of the equipment. The inspection should begin sometime during the construction phase and continue until all items are completed. In cases where inspection is delayed until construction or repairs are completed, it is necessary to rely on the erection or repair supervisor for verification of the completeness and fitness of some components for operation.

One item frequently overlooked during the inspection is the provision or lack of provision for expansion. The boiler expands as the temperature and pressure are increased and so also do steam lines, flues and ducts, sootblower piping, and drain piping. Before pressure is raised in the boiler, provision must, therefore, be made

for expansion. Temporary braces, hangers, or ties used during construction must be removed.

Cleaning. Debris and foreign material which accumulate during shipment, storage, erection, or repairs should be removed. Debris on the waterside can restrict circulation or plug drain lines. Debris on the gas side can alter gas or air flows. Combustible material on the gas side can ignite and burn at uncontrollable rates and cause considerable damage. Glowing embers can be the source of ignition at times when ignition is not desired.

Fuel lines, especially oil and gas lines, should be cleaned to prevent subsequent damage to valves and the plugging of burner parts. Steam cleaning is recommended for all oil and gas lines. Atomizing-steam and atomizing-air lines should be cleaned.

Hydrostatic test. After the pressure parts are assembled but before the refractory and casing are installed, a hydrostatic test at $1\frac{1}{2}$ times the boiler design pressure is applied to all new boilers and maintained for a sufficient time for the detection of any leaks. Gags are used to prevent safety valve opening during this test. Gags must be applied even if the valves are equipped with the special internal plugs often supplied with high-pressure welded valves. Blanks are often installed in flanged valves.

Any blanks, gags, and plugs used during the hydrostatic test are removed when the test is completed. Hydrostatic plugs alone do not prevent the safety valve from opening; they affect closure at a point other than the regular seating surface; therefore, gags are required to prevent the valves from opening during the hydrostatic test. Gags used with or without the hydrostatic plugs should not be applied until 80 to 90% of the set-point pressure is obtained. Conversely, the gags are removed when the boiler pressure has been reduced to 80 to 90% of the set-point pressure. This procedure protects the seating surfaces of the valve and prevents excessive pressure on the valve stem.

The hydrostatic test is normally the first time the new boiler is filled with water; therefore, this is the time to begin the practice of using high-quality water for the prevention of internal fouling and corrosion. Demineralized water or condensate treated with 10 ppm of ammonia for control of pH and 500 ppm of hydrazine for control of oxygen should be used for all nondrainable superheaters and reheaters. A clear, filtered water, on the other hand, is suitable for components that will be drained immediately after the hydrostatic test.

Temperature plays an important part in hydrostatic testing. First, the metal temperatures and, therefore, water temperature should be above the dew-point temperature of the surrounding air to prevent the formation of condensate on the parts being tested. Condensation obscures and practically prevents the detection of small leaks. Second, the water temperature should be kept low enough so that the pressure parts can be touched and close inspections made. It should not be so high that water escaping from small leaks evaporates immediately or flashes to steam.

Finally, no air should be trapped in the unit during the hydrostatic test. As the unit is being filled, each available vent should be open until water appears.

Instrumentation and controls. Every natural-circulation boiler has at least two indicating instruments—a pressure gage and a gage glass. If a superheater is involved, some type of steam-temperature indicator is also used. Once-through type boilers have pressure gages, flow meters, and temperature indicators. These indicators are important in that the pressure, temperature, levels, and flows indicated by them must be controlled within design limits. The indicators must, therefore, be correct. Operation should not be attempted until these instruments are calibrated. The calibrations should include corrections for actual operating conditions. Water-leg correction for the pressure gage is one example.

Most modern day boilers are controlled automatically. Before these boilers can be started up, the automatic controls must be adjusted or provisions made for manual controls until the automatic controls can be adjusted during operation.

Auxiliary equipment. The auxiliary equipment must also be prepared for operation. This equipment includes fans to supply air for combustion, feedwater pumps to supply water, fuel equipment to prepare and burn the fuel, air heaters to heat the air for combustion, and a drain system to drain the boiler when required.

Refractory. Many boilers contain refractories in one form or another, including firebrick, special tile, plastic chrome ore or castables. Some refractory materials must be kept wet until the necessary chemical reaction is completed for maximum strength, some require air drying, others require heat. Correct curing or drying will result in longer service life from the refractory.

Chemical cleaning. Waterside cleanliness is important for all boilers. It becomes increasingly important with higher heat transfer rates, higher availability requirements, and higher steam pressures with their associated higher saturation temperatures. Waterside impurities can lead to boiler tube failures. They can also lead to carry-over of solids in the steam, resulting in superheater tube failure or turbine-blade deposits. Oil, grease, and paint will bake on boiler tubes and form heat-transfer barriers, causing the tubes to overheat and fail. In natural-circulation boilers, oil can cause foaming, resulting in carry-over and a false indication of water level. Silica can also form heat-transfer barriers and, at the higher saturation temperatures, will volatilize and carry over with the steam to form deposits on the turbine blades.

The flushing of all loose debris from the feedwater system and boiler and the use of high-quality water for the hydrostatic test must be supplemented by proper waterside cleaning before start-up. To remove accumulations of oil, grease, and paint, the natural-circulation boiler is given a caustic and phosphate boil-out after the feedwater system has been given a phosphate flush. The once-through boiler and its associated pre-boiler equipment are given a similar flushing. This boiling out and/or flushing should be accomplished before operation.

After boiling out and flushing are completed, products of corrosion still remain in the feedwater system and boiler in the form of iron oxide and mill scale. It is recommended that acid cleaning for the removal of this mill scale and iron oxide be delayed until operations at

fairly high capacities have carried all loose scale and oxides from the feedwater system to the boiler. This results in a cleaner boiler for subsequent operations. Chemical cleaning of internal heating surfaces is described in Chapter 36.

Steam-line blowing. Fine-mesh strainers are customarily installed in turbine-inlet-steam lines to protect turbine blades or valves against damage from scale or other solid material that may be carried in the steam. In addition, many operators use high-velocity steam to clean the superheater and steam lines of any loose scale or foreign material. The actual procedure used depends on the design of the unit. Temporary piping to the atmosphere is required with all procedures. This piping must be anchored to resist the high nozzle reaction created during the blowing period.

Several methods are used for blowing steam lines, including particularly high-pressure air and steam blowing. The recommended method and the one most used is steam blowing because temperature shock is the most effective means of removing loose scale. Experience has shown that a combination of high velocity and temperature shock is effective. Sufficient shock is obtained with a series of blows where the steam temperature changes during each blow.

Steam line blowing is usually done in two steps:

1. The superheater, main steam piping, and cold reheat piping are included in the first step. A temporary crossover is required between the main steam piping and the cold reheat piping. The turbine stop valve is constructed so that the flanged top of the valve can be removed and a temporary-piping connection can be bolted in place. Successive steam blows are made through the piping to atmosphere until it is determined that the targets located at the discharge nozzle of the temporary piping are clean.

2. The second step includes the superheater, main steam piping, reheater, and the cold and hot reheat piping, through temporary piping to the atmosphere. Successive blows are made until it is determined that the targets at the discharge nozzle of the temporary piping are clean.

This two-step procedure prevents blowing of a dirty line through the reheater.

There are two basic methods of supplying steam for steam-line blowing with a Universal-Pressure boiler. The first method is to use steam returning from the flash tank to the superheater. The second method is to use high pressure steam directly from the boiler. The latter method supplies large quantities of steam at higher pressures. Temporary valving is required to control the blowing rate and duration of the blowing period.

Boiler pressure and temperature can be maintained during the blowing period by continuous firing. If firing is discontinued during the blowing period, it must be remembered that any change in boiler pressure changes the saturation temperature throughout the drum-type boiler. To avoid excessive thermal shock, changes in boiler pressure should be limited to those corresponding to 75F in saturation temperature during the relatively short blowing periods. This is not a problem on the once-through type boiler because the boiler is normally below saturation temperature at the beginning of the blow.

Safety valves. The set point of each safety valve is normally checked, and adjusted if necessary, immediately after reaching full operating pressure for the first time with steam. Safety-valve seats are susceptible to damage from wet steam or grit. This is an essential reason for cleaning the boiler and blowing out the superheater and steam line before testing safety valves.

Safety valves on drum-type boilers are normally tested both for set-point pressure and for the closing pressures. This requires that the boiler pressure be raised until the valve opens and relieves sufficient pressure for the valves to close.

Normally on once-through boilers, safety valves are set 17% above the design pressure of the superheater outlet header (master stamping pressure). Therefore, it is not practical to test safety valves by raising the boiler pressure to the set point.

In order to remain tight, higher-pressure safety valves cannot tolerate any damage to the seats. They are normally not tested for closing pressure. Two methods are common for checking high-pressure safety valves without permitting them to open fully. One method uses special gags to restrict valve lift and to close the valve as soon as it starts to simmer. Cold water may be used but the set-point pressure must be corrected for temperature. A second method uses special calibrated hydraulic jacks or air-operated motors to open the valves while the boiler is operating at normal temperature and pressure. This procedure does not require any correction for temperature. The popping pressure is determined by adding the effective jack pressure to the boiler pressure.

Regulating the steam pressure to test reheat safety valves is difficult because of the reheat turbine and valving arrangement. In many cases, reheat safety valves are tested utilizing the temporary piping installed for blowing out the reheat steam lines.

The testing of safety valves always requires caution. Safety-valve exhaust piping and vent piping should not exert any excessive forces on the safety valve. The lowest-set safety valves should be tested first and then gagged to prevent their opening while testing the higher pressure valves. Gags should always be used as a safety measure while making adjustments to the valves.

Start-up

Operating procedures vary with boiler design. However, certain objectives should be included in the operating procedures of every boiler: 1) protection of pressure parts against corrosion, overheating, and thermal stresses; 2) prevention of furnace explosions; and 3) production of steam at the desired temperature, pressure and purity.

Filling. In filling the boiler for starting up, certain precautions should be taken to protect the pressure parts. First, a high-quality water should be used to minimize waterside corrosion and deposits. Second, the temperature of the water should be regulated to match the temperature of the boiler metal to prevent thermal stresses. High temperature differentials always cause thermal

stresses in the pressure parts and, if severe, will limit the life of the pressure parts. High temperature differentials can also distort the pressure parts enough to break studs, lugs, and other attachments. Differentials up to 100F are generally considered safe and can usually be maintained in practice.

A third precaution taken during the filling operation is the use of vents to displace all air with water. This reduces oxygen corrosion and assures that all boiler tubes are filled with water.

A fourth precaution on drum-type boilers is to establish the correct water level before firing begins. The water level rises with temperature; therefore, only one inch of water is required in the gage glass except with certain special designs that may require a starting level higher in the gage glass to fill all circulating tubes exposed to the hot flue gases.

Circulation. Overheating of boiler tubes is prevented by the flow of fluid through the tubes. Flow is produced in the natural-circulation type boiler by the force of gravity acting on fluids of different densities. Flow starts when the temperature of the water in the generating tubes is greater than that in the downcomers and increases as firing rate is increased. Some drum-type boilers are designed for forced circulation and depend on a circulating pump to produce this flow.

The once-through type boiler depends on the boiler feedwater pump to produce the necessary flow. Whenever the once-through boiler is being fired, a minimum design flow must be maintained through the furnace circuits. With the use of the bypass system, the fluid can bypass the superheater and turbine to maintain this minimum design flow until saturated steam is available for admission to the superheater and until the turbine is using sufficient steam to maintain the design minimum furnace flow (see *Start-Up of Universal-Pressure Boilers*).

Purging. Considerable attention has been given to the prevention of furnace explosions, especially on units burning fuel in suspension. Most furnace explosions occur during the starting-up and low-load periods. Whenever the possibility exists for the accumulation of combustible gases or combustible dust in any part of the unit (and that possibility exists if a fuel line is connected to the unit) no attempt should be made to light the burners until the unit has been thoroughly purged. The accepted practice on multiple-burner units is to purge with 25% of full-load rated-air flow until five volume changes are made. The smaller single-burner units are normally purged with 70% of full-load air flow until eight volume changes are made. A volume change includes the windbox, furnace, boiler passes, flues and ducts, and any other place likely to contain gas (see *Safety Precautions, Chapters 7 and 9*).

Protection of economizer. Very little water, if any, is added to the drum-type boiler during the pressure-raising period; consequently there is no feedwater flow through the economizer. Economizers are located in relatively low temperature zones; nevertheless, some economizers generate steam during the pressure-raising period. This steam remains trapped in the economizer until feedwater is fed through the economizer. It not only

makes the control of steam-drum water level difficult but causes water hammer. This difficulty is overcome by supplying feedwater continuously, by venting the economizer of steam, or by recirculating boiler water through the economizer. If a recirculating line is used, the valve in this line must remain open until feedwater is being fed continuously through the economizer to the boiler.

Protection of superheater. During normal operation, every superheater tube must have steam flow sufficient to prevent overheating. During start-up, before there is steam flow through every tube, the flue gas temperature entering the superheater section must be controlled to limit superheater-metal temperatures to safe values, 900F for carbon-steel tubes and 950 to 1000F for various alloy tubes. While firing rate is used primarily to control flue-gas temperatures, other means are useful: excess air, flue-gas recirculation, and burner selection.

Gas temperature entering the superheater during start-up is measured with retractable thermoprobes which are removed as soon as steam flow is established in every superheater tube. These probes are required for the first few start-ups to establish safe firing rates. When fast start-ups are required with firing rates exceeding those previously established as safe, thermocouples are required for every start-up. They are always used on the once-through type boiler.

The two prerequisites for steam flow through every superheater tube are 1) removal of all water from each tube and 2) a total steam flow equal to or greater than 10% of rated steam flow. Water is removed from drainable superheaters by simply opening the header drains and vents. Nondrainable superheaters are not so simple, because the water must be boiled away. There will be no steam flow through a tube partially filled with water, and those portions of the tube not in contact with water will be subjected to excessive temperatures unless the flue-gas temperature is limited.

Thermocouples attached to the outlet legs of nondrainable superheater tubes, where they pass into the unheated vestibule, will read saturation temperature at the existing pressure until that tube is cleared and there is a flow of steam through the tube. The temperature of these outlet legs rises sharply to significant increases above saturation immediately after flow is established. Superheater tubes adjacent to sidewalls and division walls are normally the last to boil clear. These should, therefore, have thermocouples.

Thermocouples attached to the outlet legs are used to indicate not only steam flow during start-up but also excessive temperatures during normal operations. The firing rate and steam flow must, of course, be properly related, but on wide units temperature unbalance can occur as a result of uneven firing from side to side. Units with interstage attemperation can, as a result of over-attemperation, maintain the correct steam temperature and still exceed safe superheater-metal temperatures because the proper relationship is not maintained between firing rate and steam flows. Thermocouples, therefore, should be evenly spaced across the width of the superheater at four- to six-ft intervals.

Nondrainable superheater tubes will always collect some condensate when firing is stopped. More condensate will collect during the longer outages and more time

will be required to boil the superheater clear. The first start-up normally requires the longest time to clear the superheater because it is full of water from the hydrostatic test.

Protection of reheaters. Since reheaters are, in effect, superheaters interposed between the outlet of the high pressure turbine and the inlet of the low pressure turbine, they require the same protection as the superheaters, and the same precautions are used. In present-day installations, where a boiler and a turbine are operated as a single unit, the reheater goes into normal operation in tandem with the superheater, and reheater steam flow, like superheater steam flow, must be properly related to the firing rate.

Protection of drums and headers. In the majority of installations, the time required to place a boiler in service is limited to the time necessary for the protection of the superheater and the reheater against overheating. In some cases, however, the time for both starting up and shutting down may be determined by the time required to limit the thermal stresses in the drums and headers.

Various rules based on thermal stress analysis, and supported by operating experience, have been formulated and accepted as general operating practice. The rules fall into three categories: one for drums and headers with rolled tube joints, a second set for headers with welded tube joints, and a third set for steam drums with welded tube joints.

On drums and headers with rolled tube joints, the relatively thin tubes contract and expand at a much faster rate than the thicker tubesheets; therefore, tube-seat leaks are likely to occur if heating and cooling rates are not controlled. Heating and cooling rates have, therefore, been established at 100F change in saturation temperature per hr. This rate also limits the temperature differential between the top and bottom of the steam drum to 100F which minimizes the drum distortion and the resulting strains on tube seats.

Headers with welded tube connections present no problem with tube-seat leaks or with header distortion because the tubes are welded to the headers and the headers are normally filled with fluid at a constant temperature. The concern here is mainly with temperature differentials through the header wall and the resulting incipient cracking if excessive thermal stresses occur. All headers used today are safe if the heating and cooling rates are limited to 400F per hr.

Steam drums with welded tube connections are not subject to tube-seat leaks but, since they are filled with water in the bottom and steam in the top, the heating and cooling rates vary between the top and the bottom. This results in temperature differences between the top and the bottom. Stress analyses show that the principal criterion for reliable rates of heating and cooling should be based on the relationship between the temperature differential through the drum wall and the temperature differential between the top and bottom of the drum, both measured in the same circumferential plane. Stress analysis also shows that the allowable temperature differentials are based on tensile strength, drum diameter, wall thickness, and pressure; therefore, each steam drum has its own allowable temperature-differential curves, one set

for cooling and one set for heating. Curves for a typical drum are shown in Fig. 1. Actual temperature differentials must be below the allowable differentials shown.

To determine the temperature differences during the periods of starting up and shutting down, it is necessary to obtain continuously and accurately the outside- and inside-surface temperatures of the drum shell. Temperatures of the outside of the drum shell are best determined by thermocouples. At least six outside thermocouples are required: two on each end, one top and one bottom (all outside the baffle and scrubber area), and two in the center, one top and one bottom.

Temperatures of the inside surface may be determined by thermocouples attached to the saturated steam tubes and boiler riser tubes (Fig. 15, Chapter 33), or by saturation temperatures obtained from steam tables. The inside surface temperature may be assumed to be the same as the water or steam inside the drum.

There are two periods when the steam in the top of the drum is hotter than the water occupying the lower half. One period is soon after firing begins on boilers with large nondrainable superheaters. Steam forms first in the superheater and flows back to the steam drum where it heats the top of the drum. A second period is during cooling when cold air is pumped through the boiler by the forced draft fans. The boiler water cools, but the steam in the top of the steam drum remains at essentially the same temperature.

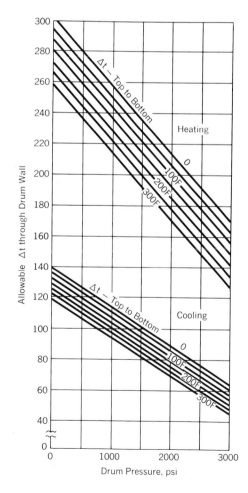

Fig. 1 Allowable temperature differential limits for a typical steam drum.

The temperatures of the top and bottom can be brought close together by flooding the steam drum with water. Firing must be stopped and water must not be allowed to spill over into the superheater. A high-level gage glass is useful for this operation. However, thermocouples attached to the superheater supply tubes can be used to indicate when the drum is flooded since there is a sharp change in temperature when water enters these supply tubes. Allowable temperature differentials for cooling are stringent, considerably more so than for heating. Fast cooling should, therefore, be supervised with the use of allowable temperature-differential curves, thermocouples, and a high-level gage glass.

Cooling is particularly important when the boiler is to be drained for short outages for inspections or repairs. The steam drum must be cooled to permit filling with the available water without exceeding the allowable temperature differentials. A wider latitude is permitted if the water used for filling is hotter than the steam drum because this becomes a heating cycle (see Fig. 1).

Before removing the unit from service, a more uniform cooling can be achieved by reducing pressure to approximately two-thirds of normal operating pressure. This reduces the temperature of both the water and steam in the steam drum.

Start-up of Universal-Pressure boilers

The Universal-Pressure boiler is designed to maintain a minimum flow inside the furnace circuits to prevent overheating of furnace tubes during all operating conditions. This flow must be established before start-up of the boiler. A bypass system, integral with the boiler, turbine, condensate and feedwater system (Fig. 2), is provided so that the minimum design flow can be maintained through pressure parts which are exposed to high-temperature combustion gases during the start-up operations and at other times when the required minimum flow exceeds the turbine steam demand.

The bypass system performs the following additional functions:

1. Reduces pressure and temperature of the steam leaving the boiler during start-up to conditions suitable for turbine, condenser and auxiliary equipment.

2. Provides means for recovering heat flowing to the bypass system, during start-up and low-load operation, utilizing the feedwater heaters.

3. Provides means for conditioning the water during start-up without delaying boiler and turbine warming operations.

4. Protects the high-temperature (secondary) superheater against shock from water during start-up.

5. Provides means for relieving excessive pressure in the system after a load trip.

Bypass arrangements provided in different plants differ considerably in detail, as they are designed to accommodate the needs of the turbine as well as the Universal-Pressure boiler. Fig. 2 illustrates in simplified form an arrangement which is used in a number of installations.

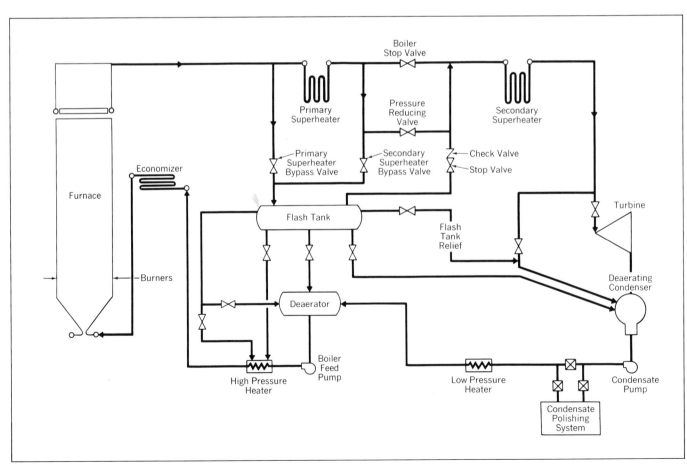

Fig. 2 Bypass system for Universal-Pressure boiler.

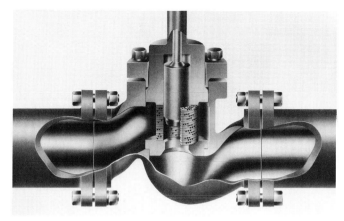

Fig. 3 The Self "Drag" Velocity Control Element.

Fig. 4 Stack of etched discs.

Self "Drag" Control Elements. The primary and secondary superheater bypass valves (Fig. 2) have the important function of reducing the boiler pressure to the rather low values suitable for the turbine during start-up. The pressure drop through these valves during start-up may be as much as 3500 psi, and a highly special valve is required to accommodate this large pressure drop without noise and vibration.

The Self "Drag" Velocity Control Element (Fig. 3), manufactured by Control Components, Inc., is used for this service. The heart of this new device is a stack of etched discs (Fig. 4). A large pressure reduction is accomplished much more readily in this stack than at the single opening between plug and seat in a conventional throttling valve. The Self "Drag" elements divide the incoming flow stream into many smaller flow streams which are then directed through individual passages containing a series of right angle turns. Each turn reduces the pressure by one velocity head. This concept and technique allow complete control of velocity and pressure, resulting in a quiet system free of cavitation, vibration and wear.

In addition to their use in the superheater bypass lines, these valves have other applications in the Universal-Pressure system. Valves of this type can also be used as power-operated relief valves where quiet operation is desired.

Bypass system operation. During the course of a plant start-up, the Universal-Pressure-boiler bypass system is operated in four different modes, as follows:

1. *Cold cleanup mode.* Before firing, water is circulated at the full start-up or minimum-design flow rate (usually about 25% of maximum) through the boiler, primary superheater, flash tank, condenser and "condensate-polishing" system to reduce impurities. The condensate-polishing system is an arrangement of demineralizers designed to purify the condensate to meet the feedwater purity requirements of a once-through boiler. This equipment is used to reduce impurities in the boiler water to a level corresponding to a cation conductivity of one micromho at the economizer inlet before firing is started. During cold cleanup operation, the turbine is sealed, the condenser is under vacuum and every effort is made to keep oxygen out of the system (*see also Water Treatment for Universal-Pressure Boilers*). A nitrogen blanket may be provided for the deaerator, a vacuum line may be connected to the condenser, or the vents closed on the deaerator. Auxiliary steam should be used, if available, to obtain deaeration.

2. *Hot cleanup mode.* The furnace is fired and the temperature of the water circulated is slowly increased. During this period, the boiler and economizer slough off some deposits (primarily iron oxide) as they heat up. If the system is dirty, as happens with a new system or after acid cleaning, cleanup must be completed before exceeding a water temperature of 550F in the boiler. Considerable fuel is saved by directing the drains first to the heat recovery equipment and then to the condensate-polishing system for cleanup until iron content leaving the condensate polisher falls below 10 ppb. Since early turbine sealing and feedwater deaeration are necessary to protect the unit from oxygen corrosion, hot flash-tank drains are routed to the deaerator at a low pressure until flash-tank steam is available. After the deaerator is supplied, excess flash-tank steam can be used to warm, roll, and load the turbine. Before deaeration is obtained, every effort should be made to keep oxygen out of the system.

3. *Start-up mode.* This mode is used after hot cleanup is accomplished, or when it is not required. Flash-tank steam is used first to warm, roll and load the turbine. Any excess steam is used for deaeration and feedwater heaters. Flash-tank drains are also used for deaeration and heating. Excess drains and steam go to the condenser.

   As the system is warmed up and sufficient heat becomes available, flash-tank pressure is increased to its maximum operating value. At synchronous speed or initial electrical load, the turbine control valves are slowly throttled while the turbine stop valve is slowly opened.

4. *Pressurization.* When the turbine control valves are at their normal minimum-load-flow full-pressure position, flash-tank steam can be replaced with boiler steam by opening the pressure-reducing valve in the bypass around the boiler stop valve. This increases the superheater pressure and the flow to the turbine.

During the initial pressurization period, flash-tank steam to the secondary superheater is replaced with high pressure steam through the pressure-reducing valve.

During this period, the control of steam temperature is very important. It is accomplished by increasing firing at a rate relative to the increase in gross generator megawatt output. The pressure-reducing valve is opened at a controlled rate to prevent steam temperature excursions.

When flow to the turbine is equal to minimum boiler-design flow, the valves to the flash tank are closed and the bypass is out of service. Steam flow to the turbine is then equal to water flow through the boiler.

Personnel safety

Operating instructions usually deal primarily with the protection of equipment. Rules and devices for personnel protection are also essential. The do's and don'ts listed here are based on actual operating experience, and point out some personnel safety problems.

1. When viewing flames or furnace conditions, always wear tinted goggles or a tinted shield to protect the eyes from harmful light rays and flying ash or slag particles.

2. Do not stand directly in front of open ports or doors, especially when they are being opened. Furnace pulsations caused by firing conditions, sootblower operation, or tube failure can blow hot furnace gases out of open doors, even on suction-fired units. Aspirating air is used on inspection doors and ports of pressure-fired units to prevent the escape of hot furnace gases. The aspirating jets can become blocked, or the aspirating air supply can fail. In some cases, the entire observation port or door can be covered with slag, causing the aspirating air to blast slag and ash out into the boiler room.

3. Do not use open-ended pipes for rodding observation ports or slag on furnace walls. Hot gases can be discharged through the open-ended pipe directly onto its handler. The pipe can also become excessively hot.

4. Never enter a vessel, especially a boiler drum, until all steam and water valves, including drain and blowdown valves have been closed, and locked or tagged. It is possible for steam and hot water to back up through drain and blowdown piping, especially when more than one boiler or vessel is connected to the same drain or blowdown tank.

5. Do not enter a confined space until it has been cooled, purged of combustible and dangerous gases, and properly ventilated with precautions taken to keep the entrance open. Station a man at the entrance, notify a responsible person, or run an extension cord through the entrance.

6. Use low-voltage extension cords, or cords with properly-connected grounds. Bulbs on extension cords, and flashlights should be explosion proof.

7. Never open or enter rotating equipment until it has come to a complete stop and its circuit breaker is locked open. Some types of rotating equipment can be set into motion with very little force. This type should be locked with a brake or other suitable device to prevent rotation.

8. Be prepared for falling slag and dust when entering the boiler setting or ash pit.

9. Always secure the drive mechanism of dampers, gates, and doors before passing through them.

10. Never step into fly ash. It can be cold on the surface yet remain hot and smoldering underneath for weeks.

11. Be prepared for hot water in drums and headers when removing manhole plates and handhole covers.

12. Never use toxic fluids such as carbon tetrachloride in confined spaces.

13. Be prepared for slag leaks. Iron oxides in coal can be reduced to molten iron or iron sulfides in a reducing atmosphere in the furnace resulting from combustion with insufficient air. This molten iron can wash away refractory, seals, and tubes and leak out onto equipment or personnel.

14. When handling any type of rod or probe in the furnace—especially in pulverized-coal-fired furnaces—be prepared for falling slag striking the rod or probe. The fulcrum action can inflict severe injuries.

Performance tests

As stated before, many steam generating units are operating day after day with efficiencies at or near test-condition values. Any unit can operate at these efficiencies with the proper instrumentation, a reasonable equipment- and instrument-maintenance program, and proper operating procedures.

Early in the life of the unit when the gas side is clean, the casing is tight, the insulation is new, the fuel burning equipment has been adjusted for optimum performance, and the fuel-air ratio has been set correctly, performance tests should be conducted to determine the major controllable heat losses. These losses are the dry gas to the stack and, on coal-fired units, combustible in the refuse (*see also Maintaining Efficiency, Chapter 36*).

During these tests accurate data should be taken to serve as reference points for future operation. Sampling points which give representative indications of gas temperatures, excess air, and combustibles in the refuse should be established and data from these points recorded. Items related to the major controllable losses should also be recorded at this time: draft losses, air flows, burner settings, steam flow, steam and feedwater temperatures, fuel flow and air temperatures.

Procedures for performance tests are provided in *ASME Performance Test Codes*—PTC 4.1, Steam Generating Units; PTC 4.2, Coal Pulverizers; and PTC 4.3, Air Heaters.

Abnormal operation

Low water. Upon loss of water level to a point where the water level is not shown, it is recommended that firing be stopped and the unit allowed to cool unless sufficient thermocouples are used to measure the temperature differential through the drum shell. Some boil-

ers have the feedwater discharge located above baffles and the fall of feedwater through the steam space heats the water sufficiently to prevent temperature shock. Even so, the use of thermocouples is recommended. Other boilers have the feedwater discharge located so that the feedwater comes into direct contact with the drum shell. In this case thermocouples are definitely needed. If the water-level recorder indicator shows that the bottom of the drum is covered with water, then water may be added. But at any time if the allowable temperature differentials are exceeded, feedwater flow should be stopped until safe temperatures are obtained by allowing the unit to soak.

Tube failures. Operating a boiler with a known tube leak is not recommended. Steam or water escaping from a small leak can cut other tubes by impingement and set up a chain reaction of tube failures. By the loss of water or steam, a tube failure can alter boiler circulation or flow and result in other circuits being overheated. This is one reason why furnace risers on the once-through type boilers should be continuously monitored. A tube failure can also cause loss of ignition and, if reignition occurs, a furnace explosion.

Any unusual increase in furnace-riser temperature on the once-through type boiler is an indication of furnace-tube leakage. Small leaks can sometimes be detected by the loss of water from the system, the loss of chemicals from a drum-type boiler, or by the noise made by the leak. If a leak is suspected, the boiler should be shut down as soon as normal operating procedures permit. After the leak(s) is located by hydrostatic testing, it should be repaired by replacing the tube or a section of it with new tubing (*see Repairs to Fossil-Fuel Equipment, Chapter 36*).

Several items must be considered when a tube failure occurs. In some cases where the steam-drum water level cannot be maintained, shut off all fuel flow and shut off completely any output of steam from the boiler. When the fuel has been turned off, purge the furnace of any combustible gases and stop the feedwater flow to the boiler. Reduce the air flow to a minimum as soon as the furnace purge is completed. This procedure reduces the boiler pressure drop and its corresponding drop in water temperature within the boiler. It also protects the steam drum against temperature shock caused by the introduction of relatively cold feedwater.

The firing rate or the flow of hot gases cannot be stopped immediately on some waste-heat boilers and some types of stoker-fired boilers. Several factors are involved in the decision to continue the flow of feedwater, even though the steam-drum water level cannot be maintained. In general, the feedwater flow should be continued as long as the temperature of the waste-heat gases entering the unit is hot enough to damage the unit. On the other hand, if the possibility exists of a smelt-water reaction or a slag-water reaction, the feedwater flow should be discontinued. The thermal shock resulting from feeding relatively cold feedwater to an empty steam drum should also be considered. Thermal shock is minimized if the feedwater is hot, the unit has an economizer, and the feedwater mixes with the existing boiler water or is sprayed into the steam space of the steam drum.

After the unit has been cooled, make a complete inspection for evidence of overheating and for incipient cracks, especially to headers and drums. All repairs should be approved by the insurance carrier.

An investigation of the tube failure is very important so that the condition(s) causing the tube failure can be eliminated and future failures prevented. This investigation should include a careful visual inspection of the failed tube. In some cases a laboratory analysis or consideration of background information leading up to the tube failure is required. This information should include the location of the failure, the length of time the unit has been in operation, load conditions, start-up and shut-down conditions, and feedwater treatment.

Shutdown

Boiler units should be taken out of service at regular intervals for internal inspection, cleaning, and repair.

In shutting down the fuel-burning, fuel-preparation, and draft equipment, while taking a boiler out of service, the instructions for the type of firing system used should be followed. To avoid possible damage from overheating or an explosion during or subsequent to shutting down, careful attention should be given, before and after shut-down, to the condition of the fuel equipment, particularly with reference to temperature and cleanliness.

After the firing equipment and fans are out of service, the dampers, including the superheater and superheater bypass dampers when fitted, should be closed to permit the unit to cool slowly and uniformly. When feed to the boiler is no longer required and the non-return steam valve has closed, the main steam stop valve should be closed. For economizers with recirculating connections, which are used on some boilers, the economizer recirculating valve should be opened only when there is a fire in the unit and there is no feedwater flow. During shutdown, when the boiler has reached the point where the fire has been extinguished and there is no feedwater flow, the economizer recirculating valve should be closed. The pressure should be allowed to drop naturally, without open vents or other intentional means of taking steam from the unit to hasten the lowering of the steam pressure. The superheater drains, however, should be opened sufficiently to keep all condensate out of headers. To avoid brickwork difficulties and unnecessary stresses in the pressure parts, cooling of the furnace should not be hastened by allowing large quantities of cool air to pass through the setting. After the furnace brickwork has lost its color, the use of a moderate amount of induced or natural draft is permissible.

To prevent a vacuum from condensation of steam within the boiler, the steam drum vent valve should be opened when the steam pressure has dropped to about 25 psi. A vacuum within the unit may cause future leakage of gasketed joints.

Since shutting down large high pressure boilers by the foregoing procedure takes such a long time, it is desirable, in many instances, to adopt other methods, such as thermocouples distributed over the pressure parts of the unit, to establish the maximum allowable rate of cooling. Specific procedures for alternative methods to accelerate shutdown are outlined under *Protection of Drums and Headers.*

The boiler should not be emptied until the furnace has cooled to a temperature at which a man can enter and remain in the furnace. If the heating surfaces are to be cleaned externally, the operation should be carried out as completely as possible before the fire has died out and should be finished by means of air lances and scrapers after the unit has cooled off.

Boilers equipped with reheaters are shut down in much the same manner as outlined above. The principal additional precaution made necessary by the reheater is that the reheater drains should not be opened until after the intercepting valve on the low pressure turbine has been closed, so that air will not be drawn into the condensate system.

With the use of the reheat cycle in its high-temperature form, it may be desirable, in shutting down, to control the rates of temperature drop in the different parts of the turbine and boiler equipment. Exact procedures cannot properly be given as applicable to the many different plants. However, it is appropriate to suggest that shutting down the high pressure turbine, low pressure turbine, superheater, and reheaters be coordinated with the dropping of pressure in the boiler proper, so that the rates of change in temperatures of the heavy boiler sections, even though their absolute values are lower, may be coordinated with the rates of change of the higher temperatures in the steam system.

Water treatment for fossil-fuel units

The advantages of modern boilers can be realized to the fullest only if proper attention is given to water treatment. No boiler can operate efficiently or dependably if its heat-transfer surfaces are allowed to foul with scale or if corrosion is permitted to occur.

Water treatment must include conditioning of the:

1. Raw-water supply.
2. Condensate returns from process steam or turbines.
3. Boiler water.

Proper conditioning will result in:

1. Freedom from deposits on internal surfaces.
2. Absence of corrosion of internal surfaces.
3. Prevention of carry-over of boiler water solids into the steam, caused by foaming and/or high total dissolved solids.

Some definitions of the water terminology in various parts of the boiler cycle are desirable. Steam that is condensed and returned to the boiler system is termed condensate. Steam lost due to process requirements, blowdown or leakage out of the system, has to be replaced; the replacement water added to the system is termed makeup water. The condensate together with the makeup water comprise the feedwater to the boiler. In some plants only a small percentage of condensate is returned; in others, almost all the steam generated is recovered as condensate. Feedwater enters the boiler and is evaporated into steam, leaving behind solids to concentrate in the boiler water. If the concentration of solids in the boiler water exceeds certain limits, the quality of steam can be impaired by carry-over. Also, boiler-water solids may settle out on the boiler surfaces as sludge. The concentration of solids in the boiler water can be controlled by removing a portion of the water either intermittently or continuously. This bleeding of a portion of the boiler water from the drum is termed blowdown.

In Universal-Pressure boilers, there are no drums to concentrate the boiler-water salts and impurities, and blowdown is not utilized. Purification takes place by continuously passing all or part of the condensate through demineralizers in a process called condensate polishing.

The treatment of raw water, condensate, feedwater and boiler water, and the subjects of carry-over and steam purity are considered in detail in the sections which follow.

Raw-water treatment

Water never exists in the pure form. All natural waters contain varying amounts of dissolved and suspended matter. The type and amount of matter in water varies with the source, such as lake, river, well or rain, and also with the section of the country.

As rain, water brings into solution the atmospheric gases of oxygen, nitrogen and carbon dioxide. As it percolates through the soil, it dissolves and picks up many minerals harmful to boiler operation. Surface waters frequently contain organic matter that must be removed before the water is satisfactory for use in a boiler.

Suspended solids are those that do not dissolve in water and can be removed or separated by filtration. Examples of suspended solids are mud, silt, clay and some metallic oxides.

Dissolved solids are those which are in solution and cannot be removed by filtration. The major dissolved materials in water are silica, iron, calcium, magnesium and sodium. Metallic constituents occur in various combinations with bicarbonate, carbonate, sulfate and chloride radicals. In solution these materials divide into their component parts called ions, which carry an electrical charge. The metal ions carry a positive charge and are referred to as cations. The bicarbonate, carbonate, sulfate and chloride ions are negatively charged and are referred to as anions.

Scaling occurs when calcium or magnesium compounds in the water ("water hardness") precipitate and adhere to boiler internal surfaces. These hardness compounds become less soluble as temperature increases, causing them to separate from solution. Scaling causes damage to heat-transfer surfaces by decreasing the heat-exchange capability. The result is overheating of tubes, followed by failure and equipment damage.

Porous deposits will allow concentration of boiler-water solids. This concentration of boiler-water solids, particularly if strong alkalies are present, will result in severe corrosion of the tube surfaces.

Since water impurities cause boiler problems, careful consideration must be given to the quality of water in the boiler. External treatment of water is required when the amount of one or more of the feedwater impurities is too high to be tolerated by the boiler system.

The selection of equipment for raw-water preparation should only be made after a careful analysis of the raw-water composition, quantity of makeup required, boiler type and operating pressure. Generally, the first step in the water processing involves coagulation and filtration

of the suspended material. Natural settling in quiescent water will remove relatively coarse suspended solids. The required settling time depends on specific gravity, shape and size of particles and currents within the settling basin. This process can be speeded up by coagulation. Coagulation is the process by which finely divided materials are combined by the use of chemicals to produce large particles capable of rapid settling. Typical coagulant chemicals are alum and iron sulfate. The preliminary treatment involves chlorination of the water for the destruction of the organic matter. Several manufacturers offer equipment to operate on a completely automated basis, as illustrated in Fig. 5.

Following coagulation, settling and chlorination, the water should be passed through filters. Filtration removes the finely divided suspended particles not removed in the coagulation and settling tanks. Special equipment such as activated-charcoal filters may be necessary to remove the final traces of organic and excess chlorine. After the removal of the suspended material in the raw water, the hardness or scale-forming materials are still present in solution. Further treatment is required to remove these materials. This treatment consists of precipitating the hardness constituents and/or exchanging the hardness for non-hardness constituents in a process called ion exchange. Brief descriptions of each of these processes follow. It is recommended that assistance be obtained from a water consultant in order to select the best process and equipment for a specific installation.

Sodium-cycle softening. This process, called sodium zeolite softening, utilizes resin materials that have the property of exchanging the hardness constituents, calcium and magnesium, for sodium. The process continues until the sodium ions become depleted or, conversely, the resin capacity to absorb the calcium and magnesium no longer exists. When this occurs, the resin is said to be exhausted, and is regenerated by passing a solution of salt through it.

Water, after passing through the zeolite process, contains as much bicarbonate, sulfate and chloride as the raw water, only the calcium and magnesium having been exchanged for the sodium ions. There is no reduction in the overall amount of dissolved solids and neither is there a reduction of alkalinity content. When it is necessary to reduce the amount of total dissolved solids, zeolite must be coupled with other methods such as hot lime zeolite softening. The reduction of alkalinity is discussed under *Hot Lime Zeolite — Split Stream Softening.*

Hot lime zeolite softening. In this process hydrated lime is employed to react with the bicarbonate alkalinity of the raw water. The precipitate is calcium carbonate and is filtered from the solution. To reduce silica, the natural magnesium of the raw supply can be precipitated as magnesium hydroxide, which acts as a natural absorbent for silica. These reactions are carried out in a vat or tank that is located just ahead of the zeolite softener tank. The effluent from this tank is filtered and then introduced into the zeolite softener. There is always some residual hardness leakage from the hot-process softener to be removed in the final zeolite process. The hot lime process operates at about 220F. At this temperature the potential for the exchange of sodium for hardness ions is greater than at ambient temperature, and the result is a lower hardness effluent than is achieved at ambient temperatures. This system is shown schematically in Fig. 6.

Hot lime zeolite — split stream softening. Many raw waters softened by the first two processes would contain more sodium bicarbonate than is acceptable for boiler feedwater purposes. Sodium bicarbonate will decompose in the boiler water to give caustic soda. Caustic soda in high concentrations is corrosive and promotes foaming. The American Boiler Manufacturers Association has adopted the standard that the alkalinity content should not exceed 20% of the total solids of the boiler water. Split stream softening provides a means for reducing the alkalinity content.

This requires a second zeolite tank that has a zeolite resin in the hydrogen form in addition to the usual tank with the resin in the sodium form. The two tanks are operated in parallel. In one tank, calcium and magnesium ions are replaced by hydrogen ions. The effluent from

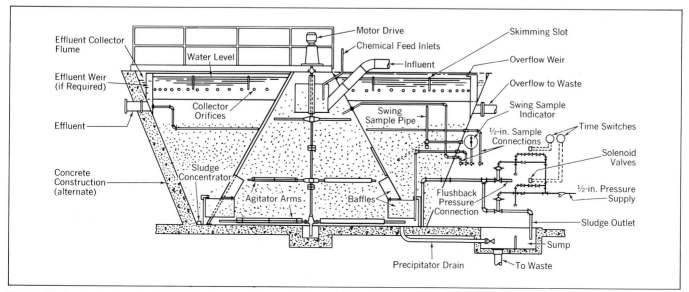

Fig. 5 Sludge contact softener. (*Source, Betz Handbook of Industrial Water Conditioning.*)

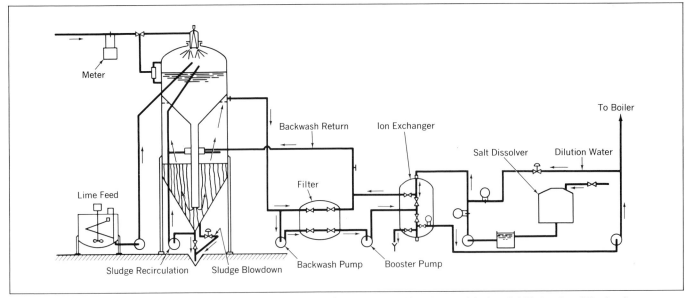

Fig. 6 Flow sheet of typical hot lime zeolite softening process. (*Source, Betz Handbook of Industrial Water Conditioning.*)

this tank with the resin in hydrogen form is on the acid side and has a lower total-solids content. The total flow can be proportioned between the two tanks to produce an effluent with any desired alkalinity as well as excellent hardness removal. When the hydrogen resin is exhausted, it is regenerated with acid.

Demineralization and evaporation. At drum pressures over 1000 psi, demineralization or evaporation of the makeup water is generally desirable. A water that closely approaches theoretical chemical purity can be obtained by either of these processes.

Evaporation as a source of purified water does not involve ion exchange. It is actually a distillation process, consisting of evaporation, leaving most of the solids behind, and recondensation of the purified water. While evaporated water is quite satisfactory, economics generally favors demineralization.

Demineralization, like the zeolite process, involves ion exchange. The metal ions are replaced with hydrogen ions by means of the process and equipment described for the hydrogen-zeolite system (*see Hot Lime Zeolite— Split Stream Softening*). In addition, the salt anions (bicarbonate, carbonate, sulfate and chloride) are replaced by hydroxide ions by means of a specially prepared resin saturated with hydroxide ions.

The two types of resins can be located in separate tanks. In this system, the two tanks are operated in series in a cation-anion sequence. The anion resin is regenerated after exhaustion with a solution of sodium hydroxide. The cation resin is regenerated with an acid, either hydrochloric or sulfuric. Some leakage of cations always occurs in a cation exchanger, resulting in leakage of alkalinity from the anion exchanger.

In another arrangement, known as the mixed-bed demineralizer, the two types of resins are mixed together in a single tank. In the mixed-bed demineralizer, cation and anion exchanges take place virtually simultaneously, resulting in a single irreversible reaction that goes to completion. Regeneration is possible in a mixed bed because the two resins can be hydraulically separated

into distinct beds. The cation resin is approximately twice as dense as the anion resin. Resins can be regenerated in place or sluiced to external tanks for this purpose.

The raw water for drum-type boilers operating above 2000 psi drum pressure and for once-through units should be prepared by passing water through a mixed-bed demineralizer as a final step before adding to the cycle.

The effluent from demineralization is approximately neutral. With nearly all salts removed, the problem of chemical control of the boiler water is minimized.

Treatment of condensate

In most cases, condensate does not require treatment prior to reuse. Makeup water is added directly to the condensate to form boiler feedwater. In some cases, however, especially where steam is used in industrial processes, the steam condensate is contaminated by corrosion products or by the in-leakage of cooling water or substances used in the process. Hence steps must be taken to reduce corrosion or to remove the undesirable substances before the condensate is recycled to the boiler as feedwater.

The presence of acidic gases in steam makes the condensate acidic with consequent corrosion of metal surfaces. In such cases, the corrosion rate can be reduced by feeding to the boiler water chemicals that produce alkaline gases in the steam. The addition of neutralizing and filming amines to boiler water or to condensate to minimize corrosion by condensate and feedwater is discussed under *Control of* pH.

Many types of contaminants can be introduced to condensate by various industrial processes. They include liquids, such as oil and hydrocarbons, as well as all sorts of dissolved and suspended materials. Each installation must be studied for potential sources of contamination. The recommendations of a water consultant should be obtained to assist in determining corrective treatment.

Fig. 7 shows a condensate purification system used in a paper-mill boiler cycle. The resin beds not only remove dissolved impurities by ion exchange but also serve as filters to remove suspended solids. It is necessary to

backwash and regenerate these resin beds periodically. Several types of condensate purification systems are available from various vendors. Some of these are capable of operation at temperatures as high as 300F.

One such example of a condensate purification system is the use of ion exchange equipment as shown in Fig. 7 for a typical paper-mill boiler cycle. The resin beds not only remove dissolved impurities by ion exchange, but also serve as filters to remove suspended solids, such as products of corrosion. It is necessary to backwash and regenerate such resin beds periodically. These resin beds can be purchased for in-place regeneration or for regeneration in external tanks. External regeneration facilitates more efficient removal of suspended metal oxides from resin beds.

Where significant quantities of magnetic oxide or other magnetic species are present in the condensate-feedwater system, the application of an electro-magnetic filter "EMF" to effectively remove these suspended solids has been proved to be quite successful in both operation and performance. The EMF, Fig. 8, consists of a pressure vessel, coil, spheres, and a power control unit. The pressure vessel is constructed of a non-magnetic material and contains a featherbed of magnetizable spheres approximately ¼-in. diam. The pressure vessel is surrounded by a magnetic coil which is supplied with direct current from the power control unit. Flow is upward through the filter both during operation and when flushing the filter, thereby minimizing and simplifying the piping and valving system. Some other advantages that the electro-magnetic filter offers are low pressure drop through the filter, minimum quantity of flush water, entire backwash process only takes several minutes and no chemicals are required in its use.

Laboratory analysis of flush water indicates that some non-magnetic iron oxide may also be retained by the EMF. The non-magnetic iron removal is believed to be due to the presence of magnetic/non-magnetic composite particles, which are magnetically attracted by the filter.

Condensate-polishing systems. Demineralizer systems, installed for the purpose of purifying condensate, are known as condensate-polishing systems. A condensate-polishing system is a requisite to maintain the purity required for satisfactory operation of once-through boilers (*see Water Treatment for Universal-Pressure Boilers*). High-pressure drum-type boilers (over 2000 psi) can and do operate satisfactorily without condensate pol-

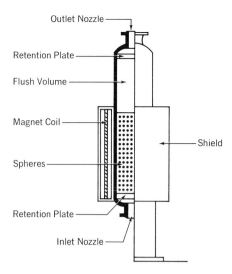

Fig. 8 Sectional view of electro-magnetic filter.

ishing. However, many utilities recognize the benefits of condensate polishing in high-pressure plants, including:

1. Improved turbine capability and efficiency.
2. Shorter unit start-up time.
3. Protection from the effects of condenser leakage.
4. Longer intervals between acid cleanings.

Two types of condensate-polishing systems are available, both capable of removing suspended material, such as corrosion products, as well as ionized solids.

Deep-bed demineralizers operate at flow rates of 40 to 60 gpm per sq ft of bed cross section. This type requires external regeneration facilities. The deep-bed system has a higher initial cost with possible lower operating costs, especially during initial unit start-up. Its greater capacity for removing ionized solids permits continued operation with small amounts of condenser leakage. The deep-bed system is usually operated with the cation resin in the hydrogen form, but the ammonium form can also be used. The cost of regenerating the resin in the ammonium form is greater than for the hydrogen form, but the time period between regenerations is much longer.

The cartridge-tubular type, such as the Powdex system, uses smaller amounts of disposable resins, eliminating the need for regeneration. The Powdex system uses cation resin in the ammonium form. Because of the many considerations involved, an evaluation of alternate types should be made before a system is selected for any given installation.

Use of the EMF with ion exchange equipment in a condensate purification system provides the ultimate in condensate polishing. Location of the EMF upstream of the resin beds offers the advantages of longer operating periods for the beds, thereby reducing the frequency of bed regeneration, and, subsequently, lesser costs for regeneration chemicals.

Treatment of feedwater

The following discussion outlines what is required to produce and maintain the quality of feedwater recommended in Table 1.

The pre-boiler equipment, consisting of feedwater heaters, feed pumps and feed lines, is constructed of a

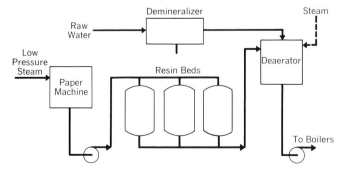

Fig. 7 Condensate purification system. (*Courtesy Cochrane Division of Crane Company.*)

Table 1
Recommended limits of solids in boiler feedwater

Drum Pressure	Below 600 psi	600 to 1000 psi	1000 to 2000 psi	Over 2000 psi
Total solids, ppm			0.15	0.05
Total hardness as ppm CaCO₃	0	0	0	0
Iron, ppm	0.1	0.05	0.01	0.01
Copper, ppm	0.05	0.03	0.005	0.002
Oxygen, ppm	0.007	0.007	0.007	0.007
pH	8.0-9.5	8.0-9.5	8.5-9.5	8.5-9.5
Organic	0	0	0	0

variety of materials, including copper, copper alloys, carbon steel, and phosphor bronzes. To reduce corrosion, the makeup and condensate must be at the proper pH level and free of gases such as carbon dioxide and oxygen. The optimum pH level is that which introduces the least amount of iron and copper corrosion products into the boiler cycle. This optimum pH level should be established for each installation. It generally ranges between 8.0 and 9.5.

Control of pH. The control of corrosion in the condensate system is generally accomplished by adding one of the following chemicals:

1. Neutralizing amines—ammonia, morpholine, cyclohexylamine and hydrazine.
2. Filming amines—octadecylamine acetate.

Neutralizing amines are volatile alkalizers that distill with the steam and neutralize acids that form in the condensate. Hydrazine, which is also an excellent oxygen scavenger, is included with the volatile alkalizers. It decomposes in the boiler, forming ammonia, hydrogen and nitrogen. The ammonia provides pH control in the condensate. The use of hydrazine as an oxygen scavenger is discussed under *Chemical Scavenging of Oxygen by Hydrazine.*

Selection of the proper alkalizer should be considered for each plant to minimize the pickup of iron and copper in the condensate and feedwater. Optimum conditions should be established by tests during the early operation of the unit. Factors to be considered in selecting the alkalizer are steam temperature, makeup requirements, and carbon-dioxide concentration in the condensate.

Condensate corrosion rates are increased by the partial pressure of carbon dioxide in the steam. Carbon dioxide originates in the breakdown of carbonates in the boiler water. If steam has a high carbon-dioxide content, filming amines should be considered as a corrective. Filming amines reduce corrosion rates by forming a protective coating on the surfaces contacted by the steam and condensate. Since this is a surface phenomenon, the amount of metal surface to be protected is more important economically than the concentration of gas in the steam. Control of filming amine feed rate is critical. The protective film will not form if the feed is insufficient while excessive feed of this waxlike substance can plug the flow passages of the equipment.

In units with a high percentage of makeup feed, it may not be necessary to add chemicals specifically for pH

control. When the makeup is treated by the lime-soda process or a lime-soda-zeolite system, the effluent is normally within the recommended pH range or slightly higher. If pH exceeds the recommended limits, the high alkalinity may lead to foaming and carry-over. For corrective action, see *Hot Lime Zeolite—Split Stream Softening.*

Control of oxygen. The presence of gases, particularly oxygen, leads to corrosion of the boiler and cycle equipment. This type of attack will occur in an operating boiler as well as an improperly stored idle boiler. The consequent effect of dissolved oxygen in feedwater is pitting of the internal surfaces. This is most prevalent in the economizer, the steam drum and the supply tubes. The pitting may be general or selective. In either case, if allowed to proceed unchecked, it will adversely affect the reliability of the unit and shorten its service life.

The most logical approach to the prevention of corrosion by gases is to expel them from the system at the first opportunity. The usual method is by means of a deaerating heater. This equipment must be kept in prime operating order over the complete load range. If the deaerator operates under vacuum at low loads, the entrance of air must be prevented. Oxygen concentrations at the deaerator outlet should be consistently less than 0.007 ppm. As a further assurance against the destructive effect of dissolved oxygen, a residual quantity of an oxygen-scavenging compound should be maintained in the system.

Chemical scavenging of oxygen by sodium sulfite. Most operators use sodium sulfite for the chemical scavenging of oxygen. Fig. 9 shows the recommended sulfite concentration as a function of boiler pressure. The amount of sulfite that can be safely carried decreases as pressure increases. At the high temperatures associated with the higher pressures, sulfite decomposes into acidic gases that can cause increased corrosion. Consequently, sulfite should not be used at pressures greater than 1800 psi. On boilers having spray attemperation, the sodium sulfite should be added after the attemperator take-off point. About 8 ppm is required to remove 1 ppm of oxygen.

Chemical scavenging of oxygen by hydrazine. Hydrazine is an alternate scavenger, offering two principal advantages:

1. The decomposition and dissolved-oxygen reaction products of hydrazine are volatile. Consequently, they do not increase the dissolved-solids content of the boiler water, nor do they cause corrosion where steam is condensed.

2. Experience has shown that condensate pH will usually stabilize in the range of 8.5-9.5 if a 0.06-ppm hydrazine residual is maintained at the boiler inlet. This eliminates the need for pH treatment of the condensate-feedwater.

It is apparent that a residual of 0.06 ppm of hydrazine will provide only a limited protection against oxygen entering the boiler. Thus it is not practicable to utilize this scavenger as a substitute for an airtight system.

Changes in feedwater treatment. Any changes in feedwater treatment or boiler water conditions can have

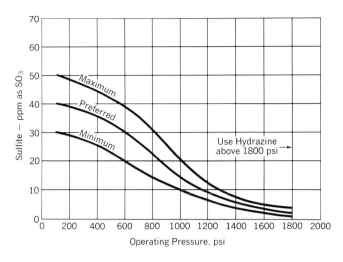

Fig. 9 Recommended sulfite residual in boiler water.

troublesome results. Changes should therefore be made gradually and with close observation. For instance, if sulfite treatment is to be replaced by hydrazine, initial dosage should be small and changes in the iron and copper concentration in the feedwater should be carefully monitored. If iron and copper concentrations in the feedwater and boiler water increase significantly, load should be reduced and blowdown increased. It may require days or weeks for conditions to stabilize, so results must be observed and evaluated over a significant period.

Treatment of boiler water for natural-circulation units

Direct treatment of boiler water, usually referred to as internal treatment, is used 1) to prevent scale formations caused by hardness constituents, and 2) to provide pH control to prevent corrosion. Treatment that is incorrect or inadequate in either respect can lead to tube failures and result in costly unscheduled outages. The permissible limits on contaminants entering the boiler and also on treatment chemicals that can be added to the boiler decrease with rising boiler pressures. Fig. 10 illustrates internal deposits resulting from poor water treatment.

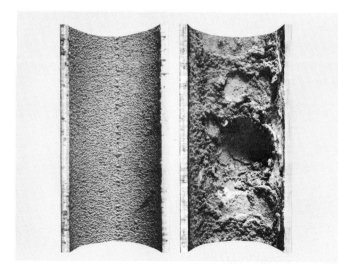

Fig. 10 An example of internal deposits resulting from poor boiler water treatment. These deposits, besides hindering heat transfer, allowed boiler water salts to concentrate, causing corrosion.

Fig. 11 shows the relationship between dissolved solids in boiler water and solids in steam at various drum operating pressures. This correlation agrees reasonably well with both laboratory and field data. If a boiler-water total-solids concentration of 15 ppm is assumed, Fig. 11 indicates that 15 ppb solids would be expected in the steam at 2400 psi drum pressure, while at 2800 psi drum pressure about 75 ppb would be expected in the steam. Fig. 12 indicates the great reduction in silica concentration in boiler water that must occur as pressures increase if silica in the steam is to be limited to 20 ppb. Experience has demonstrated that a concentration of 20 ppb will pass through the superheater and turbine without deposition. This curve is valid for a boiler water pH of 9.5. At the higher pressures, boiler water additives must be reduced to low levels in order to avoid deposits on turbine parts.

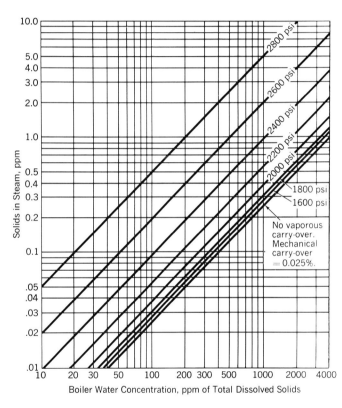

Fig. 11 Solids in steam vs dissolved solids in boiler water.

There are four methods of internal treatment in common use on natural-circulation drum-type boilers:

1. Phosphate-hydroxide (conventional-treatment).
2. Coordinated phosphate.
3. Chelant.
4. Volatile.

The method of treatment is generally dictated by the pressure range of the unit.

Methods 1 and 2 are intended to control the boiler water pH and to precipitate the calcium and magnesium compounds as a flocculent sludge, so that they can be removed in the boiler blowdown rather than being deposited on heat-transfer surfaces. Method 1 maintains an excess of hydroxide alkalinity. The effects of alkalinity

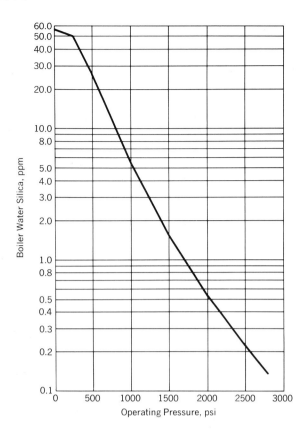

Fig. 12 Recommended maximum silica concentrations in boiler water at pH 9.5 (drum-type boilers).

are discussed under *Steam Purity.* Method 3 involves the addition of a complex metal-chelant compound such as ethylenediamine-tetraacetic acid (Na_4EDTA) or nitrilotriacetic acid (NTA). In Method 4, as the name implies, no solid chemicals are added to the boiler or pre-boiler cycle. The pH of the boiler water and condensate cycle is controlled by adding a volatile amine.

In Methods 1 through 3, either sulfite (up to 1800 psi) or hydrazine can be used as the oxygen scavenger. Above 1800 psi, or with the volatile treatment (Method 4), hydrazine is used.

Phosphate-hydroxide (conventional-treatment) method.
This is the most prevalent method of treatment for industrial boilers operating below 1000 psi. It involves the addition of phosphate and caustic to the boiler water. Caustic is added in sufficient quantity to maintain a pH of 10.5 to 11.2. A boiler treated with caustic and phosphate is less sensitive to upsets than with other methods of feedwater control.

The primary purpose of phosphate addition is to precipitate the hardness constituents. The calcium reacts with phosphate under the proper pH conditions to precipitate calcium phosphate as calcium hydroxyapatite, $Ca_{10}(PO_4)_6(OH)_2$. This is a flocculent precipitate that tends to be less adherent to boiler surfaces than simple tricalcium phosphate, which is precipitated below 10.2 pH. Caustic reacts with magnesium to form magnesium hydroxide or brucite, $Mg(OH)_2$. This precipitate is formed in preference to magnesium phosphate at a pH above 10.5 as it is less adherent.

The recommended phosphate concentration for a given

boiler operating pressure is shown in Fig. 13. At the higher pressures, comparatively low phosphate residuals must be maintained in order to avoid appreciable phosphate "hideout." Hideout is the term used to identify the phenomenon of the temporary disappearance of phosphate in the boiler water upon increase in load and its reappearance upon load reduction. The recommended alkalinity as a function of pressure is given in Fig. 14.

Phosphate hideout does not appear to be as important below 1500 psi, and even at this pressure, phosphate concentrations of 12 to 25 ppm as PO_4 can be carried without appreciable hideout. Either sulfite or hydrazine may be used to scavenge oxygen.

Coordinated phosphate method. In this method of treatment, no free caustic is maintained in the boiler water. Fig. 15 shows the phosphate concentration versus the resulting pH when trisodium phosphate is dissolved in water. Recent laboratory tests show that the crystals which precipitate from a concentrated solution of trisodium phosphate at elevated temperatures contain disodium phosphate and that the supernatant liquid is rich

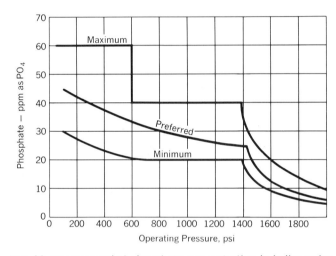

Fig. 13 Recommended phosphate concentration in boiler water at various boiler operating pressures (phosphate-hydroxide treatment).

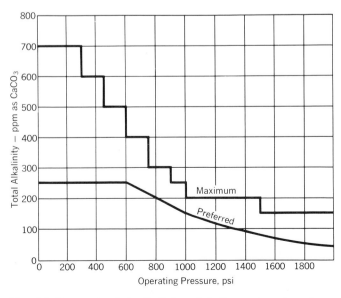

Fig. 14 Recommended alkalinity of boiler water at various boiler operating pressures (phosphate-hydroxide treatment).

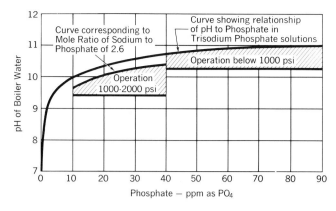

Fig. 15 Recommended phosphate content of boiler water for drum boilers, using coordinated phosphate treatment.

in sodium hydroxide. The sodium hydroxide can destroy the magnetite protective film on boiler surfaces. To assure that no free caustic is present, a boiler-water phosphate concentration that corresponds to a sodium-to-phosphate mole-ratio of 2.6 is recommended above 1000 psi, as shown in Fig. 15. The precaution against free hydroxide alkalinity is less critical in boilers operating below 1000 psi. The shaded areas on Fig. 15 indicate the recommended operating range of PO_4 and the resulting pH for boiler pressures to 2000 psi. For drum pressures from 2000 to 2835 psi the boiler water should contain from 3 to 10 ppm Na_3PO_4 with corresponding pH of 9.0 to 9.7.

When using the regular commercial grades of chemicals, caution should be used in calculating the weights needed to provide the proper mole ratios. Commercial phosphates commonly are in the form of $Na_3PO_4 \cdot 12H_2O$ and $Na_2HPO_4 \cdot 7H_2O$. A mixture of 65% $Na_3PO_4 \cdot 12H_2O$ and 35% $Na_2HPO_4 \cdot 7H_2O$ corresponds to a mole ratio of Na to PO_4 of 2.6. If the pH is too low, it may be corrected by increasing the ratio of trisodium to disodium phosphate. If the pH is too high, the ratio should be decreased.

Use of chelants. This method of water treatment has become popular in recent years with industrial boiler operators. These organic agents react with the residual divalent metal ions, calcium, magnesium and iron, in the feedwater to form soluble complexes. The resultant soluble complexes are removed through continuous blowdown. This method of treatment has been used in boilers operating as high as 1500 psi, although present B&W recommendations limit its use to units below 1000 psi.

Certain precautions are necessary in using this treatment. The chelating agents do not chelate ferric iron or copper. The presence of chelating agents and oxygen together, in the boiler or pre-boiler cycle, must be avoided. During operation, deaeration must be good at all times, and measures must be taken to protect the boiler from oxygen at all times during off-line periods (*see Care of Idle Equipment, Chapter 36*).

Experience indicates that it is difficult to control chelant feed based on chelant residual in the boiler water. Excess chelant will attack clean boiler surfaces. B&W therefore recommends that chelant feed be based on known quantities of hardness and iron present in the feedwater, with the objective of maintaining a residual approximating 1 ppm of chelant in the boiler water. To protect the boiler from upsets resulting from heat-exchanger leakage or makeup plant overrun, a phosphate residual of 15 to 30 ppm should be maintained in the boiler water. The boiler internal surfaces should be inspected whenever opportunity permits. If sludge deposits accumulate, the chelant feed should be increased by 1 to 2 ppm. If the boiler is found to be exceptionally clean and shiny surfaces are in evidence, the chelant feed should be decreased. A light gray dust on the internal boiler surfaces appears to characterize the ideal condition.

For handling chelants, chemical feed piping must be made of stainless steel or some other corrosion-resistant material.

Volatile treatment. This method of treatment may be used for units operating above 2000 psi drum pressure. In this method, no solid chemicals are added to either the boiler or pre-boiler cycle. By eliminating solid treatment, the volatile carry-over of solids is eliminated and consequently turbine deposits are avoided. Cycle pH is controlled at 9.0 to 9.5 with a volatile amine such as ammonia. Hydrazine is added as an oxygen scavenger in quantity sufficient to provide a concentration of 20 to 30 ppb at the economizer inlet.

With volatile treatment, the feedwater must not contain hardness or condenser-leak constituents. Since no phosphate is present to remove hardness, any contamination assumes major importance. Prompt detection and remedial action is required. Failure to take such action endangers the future availability of the unit. A condensate-polishing system in the cycle is the best insurance against condenser leakage and hardness constituents.

Steam purity. The trend toward higher pressures and temperatures in steam power plant practice imposes a severe demand on steam-purification equipment for elimination of troublesome solids in the steam (*see Steam Separation and Purity, Chapter 1*). Carry-over may result from ineffective mechanical separation and from the vaporization of boiler-water salts. Total carry-over is the sum of the mechanical and vaporous carry-over of all impurities.

Mechanical carry-over is the entrainment of small droplets of boiler water in the separated steam. Since entrained boiler-water droplets contain solids in the same concentration and proportions as the boiler water, the amount of impurities in steam contributed by mechanical carry-over is the sum of all impurities in the boiler water multiplied by the moisture content of the steam. Foaming of the boiler water results in gross mechanical carry-over. The common causes of foaming are excessive boiler-water solids, excessive alkalinity or the presence of certain forms of organic matter, such as oil.

Maintaining dissolved solids at the level required to prevent foaming requires continuous or periodic blowdown of the boiler. Table 2 gives the recommended total solids concentration for the prevention of excessive carry-over at various operating pressures. Most operators find it convenient and advisable to run well below these limits. Exceeding them may endanger the superheater, the turbine, or the process application.

High boiler-water alkalinity tends to increase carry-

Table 2
Limits for total solids content in boiler water (drum boilers)

Drum Pressure, psi	Total Solids, ppm	Drum Pressure, psi	Total Solids, ppm
0-300	3500	901-1000	1250
301-450	3000	1001-1500	1000
451-600	2500	1501-2000	750
601-750	2000	Over 2000	15
751-900	1500		

over, particularly in the presence of an appreciable quantity of suspended matter. This effect may be corrected by various methods, dependent on the cause of the high alkalinity. For example, if trisodium phosphate is being added to the boiler water, a less alkaline phosphate, such as disodium or monosodium phosphate will help in reducing alkalinity.

The presence of oil in boiler water is intolerable, as it causes foaming and carry-over. Steps should be taken to prevent its entry into the boiler through the feedwater system or leakage through pressure seals and joints. Organic antifoaming agents are a recent development with some successful application. However, their use should not be considered a cure-all.

Spray water for use in a spray attemperator should be of the highest quality. Solids entrained in the spray water enter the steam and can cause troublesome deposits on superheater tubes and turbine blades.

Carry-over of volatile silica is generally a problem only at pressures of 1000 psi or above, although it can be encountered at pressures as low as 600 psi. For the protection of the turbine, it is important that silica carry-over be prevented in this pressure range by adherence to the silica limits of Fig. 12.

The prevention of vaporous carry-over is much more difficult than the correction of mechanical carry-over. The only effective method is to reduce the solids concentration in the boiler water.

Controls for water conditioning

The safe and efficient operation of boilers at pressures over 1000 psi requires continuous monitoring of the water conditioning system. Early detection of any contamination entering the system is essential, so that immediate corrective action can be taken before the boiler and its related equipment are damaged.

Electrical conductance, the reciprocal of resistance, affords a rapid means of checking for contamination in a water sample. Electrical conductance of a water sample is the measure of its ability to conduct an electric current. It can be related to the ionizable dissolved solids in the water. A single instrument will measure and record important conductivities of the water from as many as twenty different locations in the system. The electrical conductivity signal can be used to actuate alarm systems or to operate equipment in the water system. The micromho (1×10^{-6} mho) is normally the unit of measurement. For most salts in low concentrations, 2 micromhos is equal to 1 ppm concentration when corrected to 77F.

Ammonia or amines used for pH control affect the conductivity. To obtain an accurate indication of solids, a cation ion exchanger removes the volatile alkalizers and converts the salts to their corresponding acids. Seven micromhos are equivalent to 1 ppm concentration for most salts.

For boilers with operating pressures over 1000 psi, cation conductivity of the condensate should normally run between 0.2 and 0.5 micromhos. A reading above this limit indicates the presence of condenser leakage or contamination from some other source. The source of the contamination should be investigated and remedied at the first opportunity. However, when a cation conductivity limit of 1.0 is reached, the internal water treatment and blowdown must be changed appropriately.

Dissolved oxygen should be monitored at the condensate pump discharge and the deaerator outlet. Sulfite or hydrazine can be used for oxygen scavenging. Over 1800 psi drum pressure, sulfite should not be used; only hydrazine is recommended. Sulfite or hydrazine can be added to the condensate on a manual or automated basis.

Feedwater pH is monitored at the condensate pump discharge and the economizer inlet. Chemical-injection pumps are usually adjusted manually to maintain the proper pH for the conventional and coordinated phosphate water-treatment systems. Where volatile water treatment is used, pH can be controlled automatically by using conductivity to transmit signals to the ammonia injection pumps. It is generally preferable to use conductivity rather than pH to transmit signals to the ammonia pumps. Conductivity equipment has been found to be more reliable for this purpose and the linear, rather than logarithmic relationship to concentration, enables better control. Ammonia should be added at the hotwell effluent, or, if condensate polishing is used, at the effluent of the demineralizing system.

Hydrogen should be monitored at the economizer inlet and the superheater outlet. A hydrogen analyzer-recorder can actuate an alarm when the hydrogen concentration of the feedwater or steam deviates from the safe value, which is specified for the plant. Deviation from the normal hydrogen concentration can indicate that corrosion is taking place within the water-steam system.

Automated equipment is commercially available for the continuous on-stream analysis of the critical constituents of the boiler water, such as hardness, phosphate, iron, copper and silica. Most laboratory analytical procedures that depend on the development of a color, and then measuring the intensity of that color to indicate the concentration of the constituent in the water sample, can be put on an automatic basis.

Water treatment for Universal-Pressure boilers

Satisfactory operation of the once-through boiler and associated turbine requires that the total solids in the feedwater be less than 0.05 ppm. Table 3 lists recommended maximum limits for feedwater contaminants and typical values obtained during operation.

Recommended limits should be low because all solids in the feedwater will either deposit in the boiler or be carried over with the steam to the turbine. Consequently, water-treatment chemicals must be volatile. All cycles should have condensate-polishing systems to meet the limits shown in Table 3. A schematic diagram is shown

Table 3
Recommended limits of solids in feedwater
for Universal-Pressure boilers

	Maximum Limit	Typical Concentrations
Total solids	0.050 ppm	0.020 ppm
Silica as SiO_2	0.020 ppm	0.002 ppm
Iron as Fe	0.010 ppm	0.003 ppm
Copper as Cu	0.002 ppm	0.001 ppm
Oxygen as O_2	0.007 ppm	0.002 ppm
Hardness	0.0 ppm	0.0 ppm
Carbon dioxide	0.0 ppm	not measured
Organic	0.0 ppm	0.002 ppm
pH	9.2-9.5	9.45

in Fig. 16. Laboratory tests as well as field studies show that high-flow-rate condensate-polishing systems (25 to 50 gal per min per sq ft of cross-sectional bed area) perform as filters of suspended material and ionized particles. Ammonia is added to control the pH in the system. Fig. 17 indicates the amount of ammonia required, in terms of ppm or solution conductivity, to give a certain pH in the system. Hydrazine is added to the cycle for oxygen scavenging.

Most of the iron entering the boiler originates in the condensate-feedwater cycle downstream of the polishing demineralizers or in the shell side of feedwater heaters where drips bypass the polishing demineralizers. Studies on a number of installations with carbon-steel feedwater heaters have shown that iron pickup can be minimized by operating with feedwater pH in the range of 9.3 to 9.5. The best pH for minimizing iron pickup should be determined for each cycle during the first several months of operation.

Ammonia is injected downstream of the condensate polishers and controlled from a sample taken far enough downstream of the injection point to assure good mixing. Hydrazine is generally fed at the exit of the condensate-polishing system and/or at the boiler feed-pump suction. Automatic controls are available to regulate the positive displacement pumps that meter ammonia and hydrazine introduction. The signal to the pump-controller for ammonia usually comes from a specific conductivity-recording instrument that is compensated for temperature changes of the cycle water. Hydrazine feed is frequently automatic, utilizing an analyzer and controller. Hydrazine residuals of 10-20 ppb are normally maintained at the boiler inlet.

Prior to plant start-up, either initially or after long outages, water must be circulated through the condensate-polishing system to reduce the dissolved material and suspended particles (*see Start-Up of Universal-Pressure Boilers*). The cation conductivity of the cycle water must be reduced to less than 1.0 micromho before a fire is lighted in the unit. Temperatures are not allowed to exceed 550F at the convection pass outlet until the iron levels are less than 100 ppb at the economizer inlet. Cation-conductivity and suspended-iron requirements are generally met after 4 to 5 hours of circulation with cycles having the bypass arrangement shown in Fig. 2.

Many units have instrumentation that will trip the unit in case of excessive feedwater contamination. Trip-limit recommendations are based on the measurement of cation conductivity at the boiler inlet. An actual unit trip is usually preceded by alarms at the hotwell discharge to warn the operator of feedwater contamination and possible load reduction. In setting feedwater trip limits, protection of both the boiler and the turbine must be considered. A common arrangement consists of two cation conductivity alarm devices, both required to read high

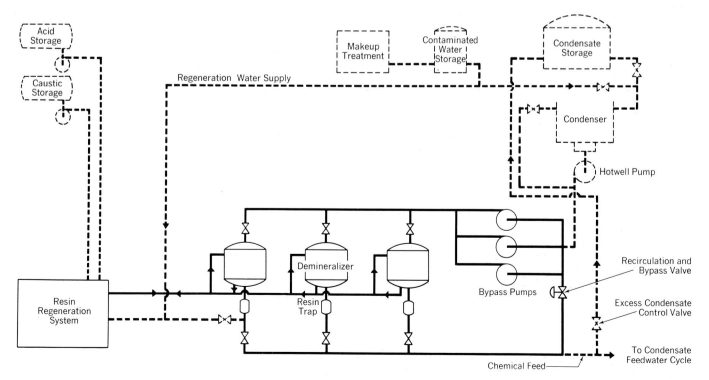

Fig. 16 Schematic diagram of condensate-polishing system with high quality makeup treatment (4-bed ion exchange or equivalent).

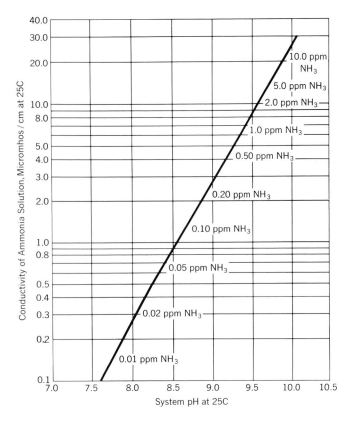

Fig. 17 Theoretical relationship between conductivity and pH for ammonia solutions.

to initiate the trip sequence. A conductivity of 2 micromhos for five minutes or 5 micromhos for two minutes, results in a unit trip. Properly installed and maintained, these trip devices are highly reliable.

Operation of steam generating equipment — nuclear

Since the inception of NRC licensing procedures for nuclear power plants, the testing of designs and equipment has had a degree of formality and emphasis uncommon to non-nuclear power plants. The procedures include a formal field test program conducted on each nuclear power plant. The objective of this program is to provide the means for the user, the equipment supplier, and the Nuclear Regulatory Commission to be assured that the design objectives of the plant are met, and that it may be operated safely. The program includes testing of those structures, systems and components that prevent or mitigate the consequences of postulated accidents that could cause undue risk to the health and safety of the community.

The program discussed in this section is applicable to Pressurized-Water-Reactor systems and is modeled on programs conducted by B&W for utility customers. The three consecutive phases are discussed in the subsections entitled Pre-critical Testing, Fuel Loading and Zero-Power Testing, and Power Ascension Tests. The Office of Inspection and Enforcement of the NRC reviews test procedures, witnesses tests and performs data evaluation for testing of many of the safety-related systems or components. This is done to aid the NRC in determining whether the plant has been constructed in accordance with the selected design criteria.

Operator requirements

In contrast to the state-by-state licensing requirements for fossil plant operators, nuclear plant operators are licensed for a specific plant by the Nuclear Regulatory Commission. Licensing requirements are defined by the Atomic Energy Act of 1954.

There are two classes of licenses—senior reactor operator and reactor operator. The reactor operator manipulates the plant controls under the direction and supervision of a senior reactor operator.

Training and qualification standards have been well defined and each operator is required to pass an extensive written and oral examination, administered by the NRC, for the particular class of license he receives. A license is issued for a two-year period after which it can be renewed by application to the NRC.

Pre-critical testing

Pre-critical testing involves the testing of components, equipment, instrumentation, controls and, finally, complete systems, to demonstrate that all systems and components required to support reactor operation function properly. One of the main objectives of pre-critical testing is to demonstrate by tests that all structures, systems and components, which can affect safety, perform their functions as designed. This is prerequisite to the issuance of an operating license by NRC. Until this license has been obtained, nuclear fuel may not be loaded into the reactor.

The testing schedule is integrated with the plant erection schedule to assure that erection and testing events are consistent and that the overall schedule progresses as rapidly as possible. Testing begins as soon as erection has progressed to the point where meaningful tests may be conducted, and continues for several months until all systems and components necessary for reactor operation have been demonstrated to perform as designed. In general, pre-critical testing follows the sequence of events listed below:

1. *Inspection.* Examine all equipment for cleanliness, and proper installation.
2. *Electrical tests.* Verify proper hookup of all electrical equipment and complete "no load" performance tests.
3. *Instrumentation tests.* Verify proper instrument installation. Calibrate instrumentation and control systems.
4. *Hydrostatic tests.* Hydrostatically test all fluids components and systems in accordance with the industry codes to which they were designed.
5. *Functional tests.* Demonstrate by operation of the components or systems that they will perform the functions for which they are designed.
6. *Operational tests.* Under conditions as close to normal operating conditions as possible, demonstrate that each component or system will perform the function for which it is designed.

Items 1-4 above are normally completed on a system basis as plant erection permits. Functional tests represent the first time that all components of a system are operated together to perform the functions for which the

system is designed. These tests demonstrate that the system will perform its design functions under conditions that are less demanding than normal operating conditions. This allows some degree of operating experience with each system and provides a period for equipment run-in prior to operating the system under full design conditions. Since this is the first time complete systems have operated, instruments, controls and equipment are thoroughly checked and adjustments are made as necessary to give the desired system performance.

Following the completion of functional testing on all components and systems required for reactor operation, the reactor coolant system is heated to hot standby conditions of temperature and pressure using the reactor coolant pumps as a heat source. Heating up of the reactor coolant system begins several weeks of testing during which systems-operational testing is performed. Systems and components are tested for performance, and final adjustments are made as necessary. This period of simulated reactor operation also provides the opportunity to verify the normal plant operating procedures and, since the reactor does not contain nuclear fuel, allows the demonstration and verification of control procedures for several unusual operating conditions.

Since plant conditions are very close to those which will be experienced during normal power operation, a significant portion of this period is allocated to operator training. In performing operational tests, the operator gains valuable experience in operating the systems, under both normal and emergency conditions. This experience constitutes the final stage of operator training before the operators are given the NRC Operators License Examination.

The period of simulated operation, with the reactor-coolant system under hot standby conditions, is terminated when all systems or components have been thoroughly tested in each of their operating modes. When this phase is complete, nuclear fuel may be loaded into the reactor.

Fig. 19 View inside of reactor vessel of large nuclear unit prior to initial testing, showing dummy fuel elements fitted into the lower grid plate.

Fuel loading and zero-power testing

The nuclear fuel is loaded into the reactor vessel only after many pre-loading tests and practice fuel-handling operations are successfully completed. Neutron detectors and neutron sources are placed in the vessel. These sources and instruments are used to monitor the core-assembly process.

Loading takes place with the reactor vessel and fuel-handling pool filled with ambient-temperature demineralized water containing about 2000 ppm of boron in the form of boric acid. This borated water assures a nuclear multiplication factor of 0.95 or less with a fully loaded core.

With the system prepared, loading begins. Multiplication measurements, slow fuel insertion, and frequent pauses to relocate sources and monitors and to check results, continue until all fuel assemblies are installed.

After fuel loading, the system is secured and all preparations for initial low-power operation completed. Initial operation is normally conducted at normal operat-

Fig. 18 Reactor vessel closure head prior to start-up.

Fig. 20 Inspection of control-rod-drive rotor assembly prior to start-up.

ing reactor coolant system temperature and pressure. The steam bypass system is used to remove the excess reactor coolant heat to maintain constant-temperature conditions.

After initial criticality is attained, a series of zero-power physics tests are performed. These tests are performed for the following reasons:

1. To prove compliance with safety standards set during U.S. NRC licensing procedures.
2. To measure those parameters necessary for proper operation.
3. To determine the feasibility of eventual uprating of the reactor power.
4. To obtain information for use in design improvements.

The parameters measured are control-rod reactivity worths, reactor reactivity coefficients, soluble-poison reactivity worths, and core excess reactivity. Nuclear instrumentation range overlap checks, shutdown margin verifications and pseudo-rod ejection tests are also performed. Special-purpose equipment is used to obtain data and evaluate results. This equipment, called a reactimeter and data acquisition system, is built around a portable digital computer.

Power ascension tests

After completion of the low power tests, power is raised in steps during the power escalation sequence. Important plant parameters are extrapolated to the next higher plateau prior to raising power. The objectives of this testing phase are to:

1. Determine the plant operating characteristics.
2. Verify that the plant is capable of operating safely within design specifications.
3. Verify that operating procedures provide for safe and proper operation.
4. Bring the unit to rated capacity.

Tests performed during this phase include:

a) Radiochemistry
b) Reactor-coolant system chemistry
c) Steam generator chemistry
d) Plant shutdown from outside control room
e) Reactor coolant system hot leakage
f) Vibration and loose parts baseline
g) Effluent monitoring
h) NSS heat balance
i) Integrated-Control system steady-state
j) Integrated-Control system transient
k) Loss of offsite power
l) In-core monitoring system
m) Nuclear instrumentation calibration
n) Biological shield survey
o) Plant computer
p) Core power distribution
q) Ejected rod
r) Dropped rod
s) Reactivity coefficients at power
t) Power imbalance detector correlation
u) Reactor trip
v) Turbine trip
w) Natural circulation (first-of-a-kind)

Acceptance testing. The final phase of power testing is the acceptance test. The plant is operated up to 100% rated power at both design transient rates and steady-state conditions. Data are used for plant evaluation as before; in addition the warranty requirements must be satisfied prior to commercial operation.

Refueling

When making distinctions between nuclear- and fossil-fueled power generating plants, there is one aspect of nuclear power-generation experience which has no analogy to fossil-fueled steam production. This is the shutdown and disassembly of the primary heat-generating mechanism in order to remove spent fuel and add new fuel. Whereas fueling and ash removal in a combustion process is continuous while the unit is producing steam, the refueling and spent-fuel removal process in a commercial nuclear reactor requires that the plant be shut down and the reactor vessel opened for a significant period of time (*see Utilization of Uranium, Chapter 19*). The frequency of refueling varies. Normally it is within 1 to 1½ years for commercial power reactors.

The refueling outage is planned long in advance of the expected date. Based on the operating history of the reactor, positions for new and partially-spent fuel assemblies are assigned and a fuel-removal, shuffle, and insertion sequence is prepared. In order to minimize carrying charges, a new batch of fuel assemblies is fabricated as close as practicable to the time of loading into the reactor. This batch may represent replacements for only one-third of the fuel assemblies in the core. The new fuel assemblies are shipped to the reactor site, inspected, and then transferred to a protected storage area.

At the designated point in the power history of the al-

most exhausted core, the reactor is shut down, cooled down, and depressurized. During cooling and depressurization, the refueling equipment, including the reactor-vessel head, stud tensioner, internals-handling apparatus, the fuel and control-rod handling machinery, and miscellaneous specially designed tools are inspected and any necessary preliminary work is done.

When the reactor-coolant-system pressure has been reduced below the required point, the system is vented and the coolant level is lowered to a point just below the flange separating the vessel and head. The control-rod-drive service lines to all drives, except those which require power for uncoupling, and other attachments to the head are disconnected and the thermal insulation removed from the head flange area. The control-rod drives are uncoupled from the rods and the remaining control-rod-drive service lines are disconnected. In parallel with the uncoupling of the drives, the large studs and nuts holding the vessel and head together are detensioned and removed from the vessel flange and stored on the head flange. The head is then lifted from the vessel and placed on a specially built storage stand. A lifting attachment is connected between the building crane and the upper portion of the reactor-internals assembly and left in place. At this time the area above the open vessel is flooded with water to provide a radiation shield. After the upper internals-assembly has been removed and stored, the core is exposed and the fuel-handling sequence begins. The spent fuel assemblies of the core are removed first and transferred to the underwater storage pool where, after a period of cooling-off and radioactive decay, they are loaded into shielded casks and shipped to a fuel-reprocessing plant. The partially-spent fuel assemblies are then transferred to new locations, and the new fuel assemblies are loaded into the core. In a similar manner, spent control rods are removed, partially-spent control rods are in some cases relocated, and new ones are added to provide the original configuration. A complete visual check by television or periscope is made of the core to verify the correct locations of all fuel assemblies and control rods. While the vessel is open, its interior is inspected using remote techniques. Metallurgical surveillance specimens may be removed for later testing to ascertain the effects of radiation on the vessel material.

The reactor is reassembled by the reverse of the disassembly procedure. During heatup and pressurization of the reactor-coolant system, all seals in the reactor-coolant system which were breached during refueling are inspected for leakage.

After the system is heated up and pressurized, the new core is brought to criticality and physics tests, including induced reactivity and temperature transients with various control-rod patterns, are performed to verify the predicted characteristics of the new core.

Total downtime requirements (shutdown time) for refueling current pressurized-water reactors is in the range of three to six weeks for a routine operation, although the actual fuel-handling time may be as little as eight days. Considerable effort is being devoted to reducing this time, particularly on future units, by improved planning and better handling equipment.

Plant operation summary

The actual operation of a nuclear power station is no more difficult than the operation of a modern supercritical boiler of equivalent capacity, but knowledge of the new technology is most important. The emphasis on safety has led to the requirement for documentation of procedures, and also to stringent requirements for operator qualification.

Following proven power-station design philosophy, all control stations, switches, controllers, and indicators necessary to start up, operate, and shut down the nuclear units are located in one control room. Fig. 21, a photograph taken during construction, shows a console for the control of two large nuclear units from a single control room. Operation of functions necessary to maintain safe conditions after a loss-of-coolant accident is initiated from the centrally-located control room. Controls for certain auxiliary systems may be located at remote stations when the system controlled does not involve power-generation control or emergency functions.

The necessary information for routine monitoring of the nuclear units and the station are displayed on the control-room console or on visible panel boards in the immediate vicinity of the operator. Information display and control equipment frequently employed on a routine basis, or protective equipment quickly needed in case of an emergency, is mounted on the operating console. Recorders and radiation monitoring equipment are mounted on panels in the control room. Indicators and controllers needed primarily during start-up or shutdown, are mounted on adjacent side panels.

A station computer is available in the control room for

Fig. 21 Portion of control console for two large nuclear units (photographed during construction).

alarm monitoring, performance monitoring, and data logging. On-demand printout is available to the operator at his discretion in addition to the computer periodic logging of the station variables.

Visible and audible alarm units are placed in the control room to warn of any approaching unsafe condition.

Water conditioning in a PWR

In a pressurized-water reactor (PWR) system, water quality must be considered from two different viewpoints—the primary or reactor-coolant system, and the secondary or steam-generator feedwater system.

Reactor coolant

In the reactor-coolant system, the water is conditioned to prevent corrosion by oxygen generated through dissociation of the water coolant by radiation in the reactor. To minimize oxygen, an excess of hydrogen is maintained. Another important consideration is the fact that the metal enclosure of the primary system consists principally of stainless steel; this requires that halogen impurities (chlorides and fluorides) be essentially eliminated. Lithium-7, which is not activated by neutrons, is used to control pH. An additional special feature is the use of rather large quantities of boric acid in solution as a reactor-control device (see Physics, Chapter 21). Table 4 lists water quality specifications for the water coolant in a commercial pressurized water reactor.

Table 4
PWR coolant-water quality

Total solids (including dissolved and undissolved, but excluding lithium-7 hydroxide and boric acid), ppm maximum	1.0
Boric acid, ppm	<13,000
Lithium-7, ppm	0.2-2.0
pH at 77F	4.8-8.5
Dissolved oxygen as O_2, ppm	0.1 (Controlled by excess hydrogen)
Chlorides as Cl^-, ppm maximum	0.1
Fluorides as F^-, ppm maximum	0.1
Hydrogen as H_2, standard cc/ kg H_2O	15-40
Total gas, standard cc/kg H_2O, maximum	100

With reference to the first item of Table 4, there are no analytical procedures by which undesirable solids of varying constituents in the range of 1.0 ppm can be readily measured when a large quantity of another solid, such as boric acid, is also present. This specification is therefore primarily a guide for the control of undesirable solids at their sources. The main potential sources for these solids in the coolant are corrosion products, impurities in the boric acid itself, and impurities in the makeup water.

Steam-generator feedwater

Water-quality requirements for the steam-generator feedwater are generally similar to those of a large fossil-fuel boiler. One significant difference is the consequence of using Inconel Alloy 600 in the steam-generator tubes. This material has demonstrated its compatibility with the water environment on both primary and secondary sides of a pressurized-water-reactor steam generator. However, some problems with Inconel Alloy 600 in oxygenated water containing lead have been reported. Hence zero lead is customarily specified. This means that the level must be kept below the lowest values detectable by acceptable referee methods (see also Chapter 29).

Table 5 lists minimum purity specifications for steam generator feedwater.

Table 5
PWR steam generator feedwater quality

Max total solids (dissolved and suspended), ppb	50
Max dissolved oxygen, ppb	7
Max total silica (as SiO_2), ppb	20
Max total iron (as Fe), ppb	10
Max total copper (as Cu), ppb	2
pH at 77F (adjusted with ammonia)	9.3-9.5
Total hardness	*
Organics	†
Lead	0
Max cation conductivity, μmho/cm	0.5

* No specification is listed owing to control analysis limitations; however, care should be taken to eliminate hardness constituents to prevent possible steam-generator deposition problems.
† Any organic contamination should be avoided in condensate-polishing systems to prevent possible resin fouling.

The practical significance of pH values

The term "pH" is used to express the degree of acidity or alkalinity of a solution. Acidity is commonly associated with a sour taste, while alkaline or basic materials impart a somewhat bitter taste.

When substances such as acids, bases, or salts are dissolved in water, ions are formed in the solution. These ions consist of electrically charged atoms or groups of atoms that result from the partial or complete dissociation of the solute molecules. The formation of the ions is termed "ionization," and the extent to which it occurs can be expressed by an "ionization constant," which has a fixed value for a given solution at a specified concentration and temperature.

Though many different ions may be formed in solution, those that establish whether the solution is acid or alkaline are the hydrogen (H^+) and the hydroxyl (OH^-) ions, respectively. When the hydrogen ions exceed the hydroxyl ions in number, the solution is acid. When they are equal, it is neutral. Alkalinity or basicity denotes that the hydroxyl ions exceed the hydrogen ions.

Acids and alkalies vary in the degree to which they form ions in solution. Those which almost completely ionize are called strong acids or bases. Hydrochloric acid

and sodium hydroxide are examples of this type. Other acids and bases ionize to only a small degree and are, therefore, called weak acids or bases. Acetic acid and ammonium hydroxide are typical examples.

Even pure water dissociates to a minute degree into hydrogen and hydroxyl ions. It has been found that pure water at 25C always contains 1.0×10^{-7} gram equivalents per liter of hydrogen ions and, since pure water is neutral, an equal concentration of hydroxyl ions. The product of these concentrations is a constant equal to 1.0×10^{-14} at 25C. Thus, if the hydrogen ion concentration of a solution were 1.0×10^{-5} gram equivalents per liter, the hydroxyl ion concentration would be equal to 1.0×10^{-9} gram equivalents per liter. Since, for this case, the hydrogen ion concentration is greater than the hydroxyl ion concentration, the solution is acidic.

In order to express hydrogen ion concentrations more conveniently than by the use of decimals or by negative exponents, the term "pH" was adopted. Expressed mathematically, pH is equal to the negative logarithm to the base 10 of the hydrogen ion concentration. This is expressed as:

Hydrogen ion concentration $= 1 \times 10^{-x}$ where "x" equals the pH. A neutral solution, since it contains 1×10^{-7} gram equivalents of hydrogen ion per liter, has a pH value of 7. Since acid solutions contain more than 1×10^{-7} gram equivalents of hydrogen ion per liter, the pH values of these solutions are less than 7. Conversely, alkaline solutions have pH values greater than 7.

The commonly accepted range within which pH values are expressed covers the scale of 0 to 14. The extremes of this scale correspond to 10^{0} and 10^{-14} gram equivalents of hydrogen ion per liter. Acidities or alkalinities greater than those represented by pH values of 0 and 14, respectively, are more conveniently expressed as percent concentrations.

Examples of acid solutions encountered in everyday life are lemon juice with a pH value of approximately 2.0 and carbonated soft drinks with a pH of about 6.5. On the other hand, a solution of 1 teaspoon of baking soda in a cup of water would be alkaline and have a pH value of nearly 10.

Since the pH value of a solution varies with temperature, it is the usual practice to measure and report all pH values at 25C. Notwithstanding the scarcity of accurate values at elevated temperatures, such data as are available indicate that pH decreases with increase in temperature, the neutral point decreasing in like manner.

The pH value may be estimated conveniently by the use of specially prepared papers containing dyes which vary in color according to the pH. For feedwater and boiler-water pH determinations, where a higher degree of accuracy is required, it is usual practice to employ an instrument which measures the potential difference established between two suitable electrodes and indicates this reading on a scale graduated in pH units.

The following table is helpful in understanding the relation between hydrogen ion concentration and pH.

Hydrogen ion concentration, gram equivalents per liter			pH
1.0		10^{0}	0
0.1		10^{-1}	1
0.01		10^{-2}	2
0.001	Acid	10^{-3}	3
0.0001		10^{-4}	4
0.00001		10^{-5}	5
0.000001		10^{-6}	6
0.0000001	Neutral	10^{-7}	7
0.00000001		10^{-8}	8
0.000000001		10^{-9}	9
0.0000000001		10^{-10}	10
0.00000000001	Alkaline	10^{-11}	11
0.000000000001		10^{-12}	12
0.0000000000001		10^{-13}	13
0.00000000000001		10^{-14}	14

Control console for a large fossil-fuel unit in an Eastern central station.

Chapter 35

Controls for steam power plants

Instruments and controls are an essential part of all steam generating installations. They serve to assure safe, economic, and reliable operation of the equipment. They range from the simplest manual devices to the complete automatic control of the boiler, or nuclear steam supply system, and all associated apparatus. The subject of instrumentation and control is consequently so diverse and extensive that any brief treatment, as in this chapter, must be limited to basic concepts.

Boiler control systems, particularly as they are applied to boiler-turbine-generator units, are made up of several types of control systems to perform several specific control functions (see Basic Boiler Control Theory). In the past the accepted practice has often been to identify these as separate and independent systems, frequently applied to the same boiler by different control system suppliers. Today a boiler- or unit-control system is most often applied as a complete system with demand requirements applied simultaneously to steam-generating and -using equipment to minimize the effect of interactions between control subsystems.

Various types of boiler control systems for fossil-fuel boilers include:

1. Boiler instrumentation systems (see also Chapter 33).
2. Combustion control systems.
3. Steam temperature control for superheater and reheater outlet (Chapter 12).
4. Drum level control.
5. Burner-sequence-control systems.
6. Once-through boiler controls.
7. Integrated control systems to integrate all the foregoing with the turbine and electric-generator control.
8. Data processing and display.
9. Plant automation.

To illustrate how control subsystems can be integrated into a complete control system, an integrated control system for a fossil fuel, once-through boiler is described.

The basic principles of nuclear reactor control are described in Chapter 21 and some of the equipment used is described in Chapter 23. An integrated control system for a nuclear steam plant is described in this chapter.

Basic boiler control theory

Boiler control is the regulating of the boiler outlet conditions of steam flow, pressure, and temperature to their desired values. In control terminology, the boiler outlet steam conditions are called the output or controlled variables, and the desired values of the outlet conditions are the set points or input-demand signals. The quantities of fuel, air, and water are adjusted to obtain the desired outlet steam conditions and are called the manipulated or controlled variables.

The boiler is referred to as the system, plant, or process, and disruptive influences on the boiler, both internal and external, such as variations in heat content of fuel or cycle efficiency are the disturbance inputs. The controller or control system has the function of "looking at" the desired (set points) and actual values (output variables) of the outlet steam conditions and adjusting the amounts of fuel, air, and water (manipulated variables) to make the outlet conditions match their desired values. The controller can be manual with an operator making the adjustments or it can be automatic with a pneumatic or electronic analog computer or a digital computer making the adjustments. A block diagram of the controlled boiler system is shown in Fig 1.

While it is theoretically possible to operate a boiler satisfactorily with manual control, the operator must maintain a tedious constant watch for the occurrence of a disturbance. Time is required for the boiler to respond to a correction, and this can lead to overcorrection with further "upset" to the boiler. An automatic controller, on the other hand, does not experience tedium and, once properly adjusted, will always make the proper adjustment to minimize the upsets to the boiler and, therefore, will control the system more accurately and reliably.

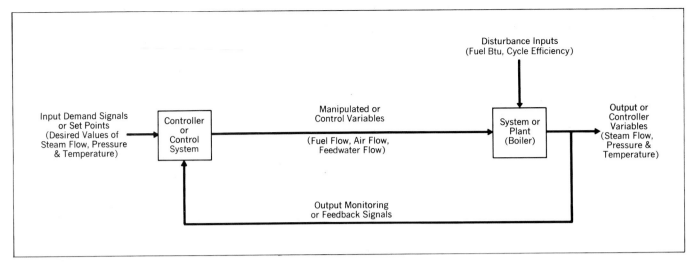

Fig. 1 Block diagram of a controlled boiler system.

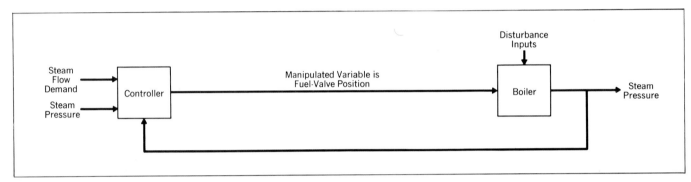

Fig. 2 Simplified block diagram of a boiler control function.

The various types of automatic control can be illustrated by use of the block diagram in Fig. 2, which represents the control of one output variable, namely, steam pressure, in a hypothetical boiler. The set points for steam pressure and steam flow will be used as reference values, and the manipulated variable is the fuel-valve position. Disturbance inputs come from the boiler, which is the system to be controlled.

Open-loop control

The simplest control mode is the open-loop, feedforward, or non-feedback control, where the manipulated variables of fuel, air, and water are adjusted only from the input-demand signals without monitoring the outlet conditions or output variables. As an example, Fig. 3 illustrates an open-loop control system to accomplish the control function illustrated by Fig. 2. Fig 3a is a block diagram, representing the action to be taken, which is "feedforward" only. Fig. 3b is a calibration curve, expressing fuel-valve position as $f(D)$, a function of steam demand. This calibration curve, established by manually determining the fuel-valve position required to maintain the desired steam flow with a constant steam pressure, is entered into the controller. The response of this open-loop control is very fast and depends only on the accuracy of the calibration curve.

One of the difficulties with open-loop control is that the calibration curve is accurate only as long as the boiler conditions remain as they were when the calibration was established.

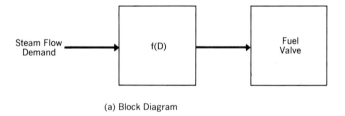

(a) Block Diagram

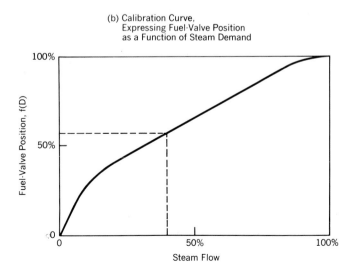

(b) Calibration Curve,
Expressing Fuel-Valve Position
as a Function of Steam Demand

Fig. 3 Open-loop mode to control steam pressure by varying fuel input.

Another problem with open-loop control is that the output changes as the load changes on the output signal (the fuel valve in Fig. 3). For example, a change in friction on the valve stem will cause a variation in valve position in response to a given input-demand signal, thus introducing an error into the performance of the open-loop control. Such disadvantages normally outweigh the open-loop advantages of stability and simplicity.

Closed-loop control

If the system requirements cannot be met by an open-loop control, then a closed-loop or feedback control must be used. In closed-loop control mode, the actual output of the system is measured and compared to the input-demand signal with the difference between the two signals (the error signal) used to reduce the difference between the demand and output signals to zero.

The open-loop system of Fig. 3 could be closed by having an operator observe the measured steam pressure and then manually adjust the fuel valve position to obtain the fuel flow necessary to maintain the desired steam pressure at the required steam flow. To avoid the disadvantages of manual control, an automatic controller can be provided in a closed-loop or feedback system.

Proportional control. The simplest type of closed-loop system is proportional control where the manipulated variable or controller output is proportional to the deviation of the controlled variable from its desired or set-point value. The deviation of the controlled variable from its set point is called the error signal. Depending on the arrangement of the controller, the output signal of a proportional-control system will always be either directly or inversely proportional to the controlled variable.

Fig. 4 illustrates the application of proportional control to the control function of Fig. 2 (*See Table 1 for explanation of △ and K in Fig. 4 as well as other symbols in*

subsequent figures in this chapter.) In the system of Fig. 4, for every deviation of steam pressure from its set point, the fuel valve will be moved to a specific position, as shown in Fig. 5, for three values of "relative proportional gain." In Fig. 5 the relative proportional gain is arbitrarily said to have a value of 1.0 if the control is set so that a pressure error of 10 psi initiates a 50% change in position of the fuel valve. If the control is set to be twice or four times as sensitive, the relative proportional gain is said to be two or four respectively. In the latter case, a change of 2.5 psi in steam pressure initiates a 50% change in fuel valve opening.

The response of steam pressure to step increases in load on the boiler is shown in Fig. 6 for two values of proportional gain on the controller. The application of a

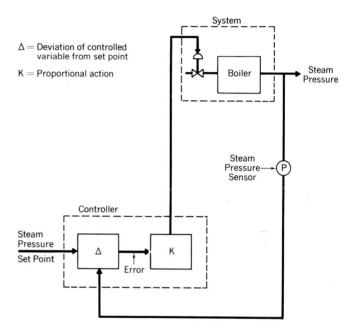

Fig. 4 Proportional-control system.

Table 1
Control Symbols

○ —Transmitter
K —Proportional action (gain)
∫ —Integral action
Σ —Summing action
△ —Difference or subtracting action
< —Low select auctioneer
> —High select auctioneer
≮ —Low limiting
≯ —High limiting
d/dt —Derivative (rate)
Σ/n —Averaging
⬦ —Hand-automatic selector station
    (analog control)
⬦ —Hand-automatic selector station
    (analog control) with bias
H/A —Hand-automatic selector station
    (digital control)
T —Transfer
± —Bias action
f(x) —Power device (valves, drives, etc.)

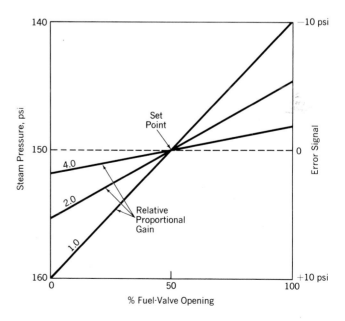

Fig. 5 Fuel-valve opening for various pressure deviations in a proportional-control system.

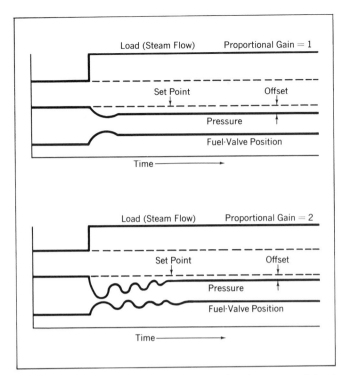

Fig. 6 Response of steam pressure to step increases of load in a proportional-control system.

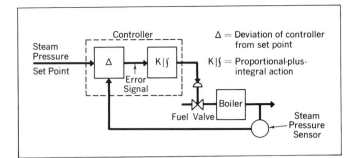

Fig. 7 Proportional-plus-integral control.

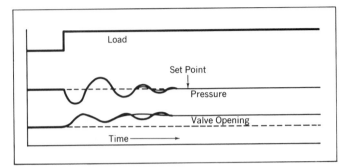

Fig. 8 Response of steam pressure to step increase of load in a proportional-plus-integral-control system.

step increase in load or steam flow immediately decreases the steam pressure which, through the proportional controller, causes the fuel valve to open by a proportional amount. The additional heat input due to the increased fuel flow causes the steam pressure to return toward its set point, which in turn reduces the fuel valve opening.

There may be a certain amount of cycling or hunting, depending on the proportional gain of the controller, before the steam pressure stabilizes. It can be noted in Fig. 6 that the steam pressure does not stabilize at its set point, but is offset to a value below the set point. A characteristic of "proportional-only" control is that an error or offset is necessary to provide a steady-state fuel valve opening which will support the desired load, except for a single load condition.

An increase in the relative proportional gain or sensitivity will reduce the final offset in the steam pressure as shown in Fig. 6. An increase in proportional gain may increase the time required for the system to reach a steady-state condition. This offset is always present with proportional control and, if the gain is increased even more to reduce the offset, undamped oscillations will result.

Integral or reset control. This offset may be eliminated by the addition of the integral or reset mode of control to the proportional-control system, as illustrated in Fig. 7. The response of the hypothetical boiler to a step increase in load when using a proportional-plus-integral control system is shown in Fig. 8. The steam pressure is returned to its set point without the offset which is present with the proportional-only control. However, the system may be less stable as it takes a longer period of time for the steam pressure to stabilize with the offset completely eliminated.

Integral control, as its name implies, is based on the integration of the deviation between the controlled variable and its set point over the time the deviation occurs. Integral control is also referred to as reset control since the band of proportional action is shifted or reset so that the manipulated variable operates about a new base point.

Derivative control. The stability and response of the system can be improved still further by adding a third mode of control action to the controller called derivative or rate control. Derivative control is a function of the rate of change of the controlled variable from its set point, as shown in Fig. 9. The addition of the derivative control mode to the controller-boiler is shown in Fig. 10. As soon as the step change is made, the pressure starts to drop and the proportional mode begins to open the fuel valve. The derivative mode will also open the fuel valve further as a function of the rate at which the pressure is changing, providing anticipation of where the fuel valve should be positioned. When the rate of change of the steam pressure decreases, the derivative control has less effect and the proportional and integral modes do the final positioning of the fuel valve.

Feedforward-feedback control

In a closed-loop control system, the controlled variable always has to deviate from its set point before any corrective action is initiated by the controller. In this respect the open-loop system has a faster response since it takes corrective action before the controlled variable starts to change. When the open-loop or feedforward system is combined with the closed-loop or feedback system, the result is a system with fast response that is able to compensate for changes in the calibration curve. Fig. 11 represents a feedforward-feedback control system to accomplish the control function of Fig. 2.

As the step change in load occurs, the feedforward signal immediately positions the fuel valve to meet the requirements of the calibration curve. If this curve is exact, no error develops and the feedback loop has no work to do. If the calibration curve is in error, the feedback loop readjusts the fuel valve position to eliminate any pressure error which may develop due to shifts in the calibration. However, the response will be faster and the magnitude of the system upset will be smaller since the feedforward signal positions the valve near its final steady-state position, leaving a smaller range of action to be accomplished by the feedback loop.

Requirements of the controller

The requirements to be met with a controller are that the overall controlled boiler system be stable and responsive. This means that the values of the controlled variables or outlet steam conditions are maintained close to their desired values under equilibrium or steady-state conditions with no cycling or self-sustained oscillations, and that the system recovers quickly without excessive hunting, overshoot or oscillations from system disturbances and changes in the reference values or set points.

The discussion illustrated by Figs. 2 to 11 considers only one of the sub-loop controls on the boiler. However, each of the other boiler-output variables will be controlled by one of these same modes in its control sub-loop, depending on the accuracy and speed of response required in order that the overall controlled system be stable and have fast response.

Feedwater control systems

The purpose of the feedwater control is to regulate the flow of water to a drum-type boiler so as to maintain the level in the boiler drum between the desired limits. The control system will vary with the type and capacity of the boiler as well as the characteristics of the load.

Most shop-assembled boilers in the lower capacity range and the lower operating-pressure range are equipped with self-contained feedwater control systems of the thermo-hydraulic or thermostatic types. The thermo-hydraulic type is generally applied to boilers having an operating pressure in the range between 60 and 600 psi and capacities not exceeding 75,000 to 100,000 lb/hr under steady load conditions.

The self-operated feedwater regulator, illustrated in Fig. 12, is actuated by a closed hydraulic system consisting of the annular space between the two concentric tubes of a "generator," the connecting copper tubing, the metal bellows of the regulating valve, and the water necessary to fill the system. The inner tube of the generator is connected to the steam drum of the boiler, the lower end to the water space and the upper end to the steam space, as shown in Fig. 12.

The water level in the inner tube of the generator follows the actual level in the drum. When the water level in the drum decreases, the heat from the steam in that portion of the tube vacated by the drop in level causes water in the outer tube to flash into steam, displacing water from the outer tube through the connecting tubing into the bellows. This causes the bellows to expand, increasing the regulating-valve opening to admit more water to the drum.

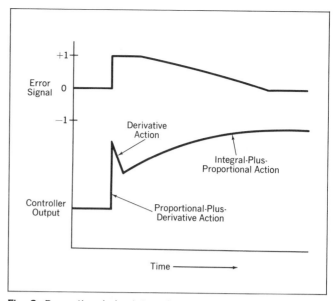

Fig. 9 Proportional-plus-integral-plus-derivative action.

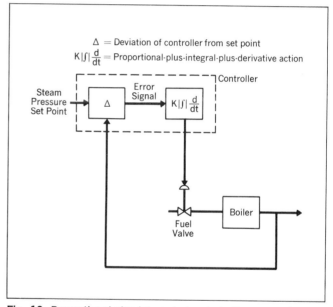

Fig. 10 Proportional-plus-integral-plus-derivative control.

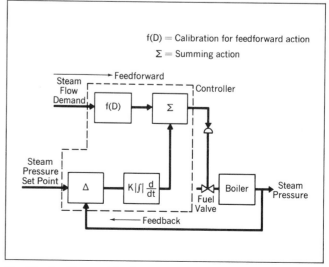

Fig. 11 Feedforward-feedback control.

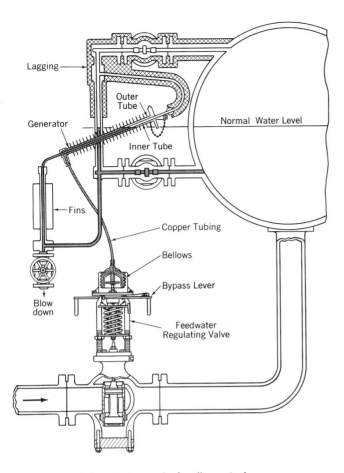

Fig. 12 Self-operated thermo-hydraulic control.

In the thermo-hydraulic regulator, water input is controlled in proportion to drum level, not to load. As a result, the level maintained at higher loads will be somewhat lower than the level maintained at relatively lower loads. The amount of this regulated level variation will depend on the extent of the load variation, the sizing of the regulating valve, and the slope of the "generator" (Fig. 12). The unregulated level variation will depend on the extent of "swell and shrink" effects, drum pressure changes, and supply water variations.

For higher capacity boilers and those operating at higher pressures, a pneumatic or electrically operated feedwater control system is applied. Controls of these types utilize varying degrees of control action to suit the particular application. They are classified as single-, two-, or three-element feedwater control systems. The details of these systems are illustrated in Figs. 13, 14 and 15, using the symbols given in Table 2.

Single-element feedwater control

In single-element feedwater control (Fig. 13), the water in the drum is at the desired level when the signal from the level transmitter equals its set point.

If an undesirable water level exists, the controller applies proportional-plus-integral action to the difference between the drum-level and set-point signals to change the position of the regulating valve. A hand-automatic station gives the operator complete control over the valve. A valve positioner can be included in the control-

valve assembly to match the valve characteristics to the individual requirements of the system.

Single-element control will maintain a constant drum level for slow changes in load, steam pressure, or feedwater pressure. However, since the control signal satisfies the requirements of drum level only, excessive "swell or shrink" effects will result in wider drum-level variations and a longer time for restoring drum level to set point following a load change with single-element control than with two- or three-element control.

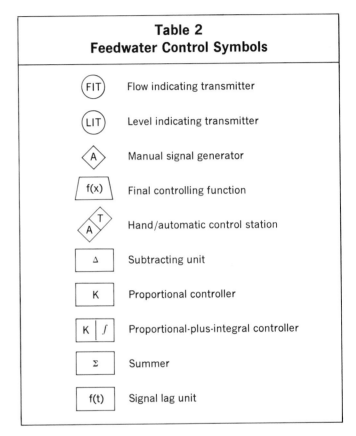

Table 2
Feedwater Control Symbols

(FIT)	Flow indicating transmitter
(LIT)	Level indicating transmitter
A	Manual signal generator
f(x)	Final controlling function
A / T	Hand/automatic control station
Δ	Subtracting unit
K	Proportional controller
K ∫	Proportional-plus-integral controller
Σ	Summer
f(t)	Signal lag unit

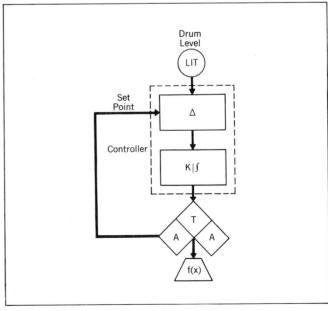

Fig. 13 Single-element feedwater control.

Two-element feedwater control

Two-element control (Fig. 14) comprises a feedforward control loop which uses steam-flow measurement to control feedwater input, with level measurement assuring correct drum level.

The drum-level element of the controller applies proportional action to the difference between the drum-level signal and its set point. The sum of the drum-level error signal and the flow signal determines the valve position. Thus, the steam-flow measurement maintains feedwater flow proportional to steam flow; the drum-level measurement corrects for any imbalance in water input vs steam output caused by deviations in the valve-position/water-flow relationship, and provides the necessary transient adjustments to cope with the "swell and shrink" characteristics of the boiler.

Three-element feedwater control

Three-element control (Fig. 15) is a cascaded-feedforward control loop which maintains water-flow input equal to feedwater demand. Drum-level measurement keeps the level in the drum from drifting due to flow meter errors, blowdown, or other causes.

The drum-level element of the controller applies proportional action to the error between the drum-level signal and its set point. The sum of the drum-level error signal and the steam-flow signal is the feedwater-demand signal. This is the output of the "summer." The feedwater demand signal is compared with the water-flow input and the difference is the combined output of the controller. Proportional-plus-integral action is incorporated to provide a feedwater correction signal for valve regulation or pump speed control.

In single boiler-turbine units, the turbine first-stage shell pressure can be used as a substitute variable for steam flow.

Three-element feedwater control systems can be adjusted to restore a predetermined drum level at all loads; or in boilers with severely fluctuating loads, the system can be adjusted to permit water level in the drum to vary with the boiler loading to compensate for "swell and shrink" effects. If the drum level is allowed to vary in this manner, a nearly constant inventory of water, as opposed to a constant level, is maintained.

Bailey three-element feedwater control systems of this type can be precalibrated so that only a few simple adjustments are needed to match the system to the individual requirements of the boiler. Control characteristics can be easily changed by direct adjustment.

Combustion control systems

The function of a combustion control system is to control the fuel and air input or firing rate to the furnace in response to a load index representing a demand for the level of fuel input. The demand for firing rate is, therefore, a demand for energy input into the system to match a withdrawal of energy at some point in the cycle through increased steam flow and, in turn, increased power generation in an electric generating plant. For boiler operation and control systems, variations in the boiler outlet pressure are often used as an index of an unbalance between fuel-energy input and energy withdrawal in the output steam.

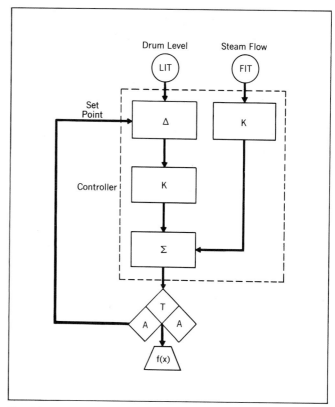

Fig. 14 Two-element feedwater control.

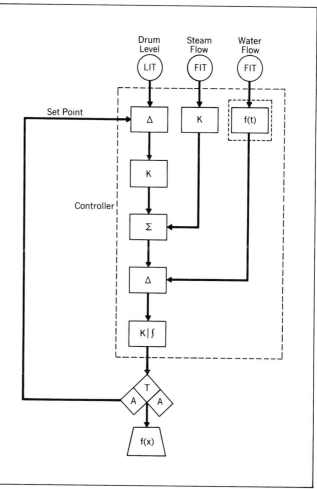

Fig. 15 Three-element feedwater control.

A great variety of combustion control systems have been developed over the years to fit the needs of particular applications. Load demands, operating philosophy, plant layout, and types of firing must be considered before the ultimate selection of a system is made. The following examples show a few of the systems that have been developed for various types of fuel firing. The control symbols shown on these figures have been tabulated in Table 1 for easy reference.

Stoker-fired boilers

Stoker-fired boilers are regulated by positioning fuel and combustion air from changes in steam pressure. A change in steam demand initiates a signal from the steam-pressure controller, through the boiler master controller, to increase or decrease both fuel and air simultaneously and in parallel to satisfy the demand. As long as an error in pressure exists (a departure of actual pressure from the set-point value), the steam-pressure controller will continue to integrate the fuel and air until the pressure has returned to its set point (see Fig. 16).

A combustion guide, in this case steam-flow air-flow, compares pressure error to a calibrated air-flow demand to modify the rate of fuel being burned (proportional to steam flow) and initiate any required readjustments to the forced draft damper so that the desired fuel-air ratio is continuously maintained.

Furnace draft is regulated separately through the use of a furnace-draft controller and a power operator that positions the uptake damper.

Gas- and oil-fired boilers

Fig. 17 illustrates a system applicable to the burning of gas and oil, separately or together. The fuel and air flows are controlled from steam pressure through the boiler master with the fuel readjusted from fuel-flow air-flow. The oil or gas header pressure may be used as an index of fuel flow and the windbox-to-furnace differential as an index of air flow on a per-burner basis. Such indices are commonly used for single-burner boilers.

Pulverized-coal-fired boilers

Fig. 18 illustrates a more sophisticated combustion control that would be used on larger boilers having several pulverizers, each supplying a group of burners compartmented off from the others with both primary and secondary air being admitted and controlled on a per pulverizer basis.

The boiler firing-rate demand is compared to the total measured fuel flow (summation of all feeders in service delivering coal) to develop the demand to the pulverizer master. The pulverizer master demand signal is then applied in parallel to all operating pulverizers. All pulverizers have duplicate controls.

The individually biased pulverizer demand signal is then applied in parallel as demands for coal-feeder speed, primary-air flow, and total pulverizer group air flow (primary plus secondary air flows). When an error develops between demanded and measured primary-air flow or total air flow, proportional plus integral action will be applied through the controllers to adjust the primary or secondary air dampers to reduce the error to zero. A low primary-air flow or total air flow cutback is applied in the individual pulverizer control. If either measured primary-air flow or total air flow is low relative to coal rate (feeder speed) demand, this condition is recognized in the "low-select" auctioneer in the coal-feeder demand to reduce the demand to that equivalent

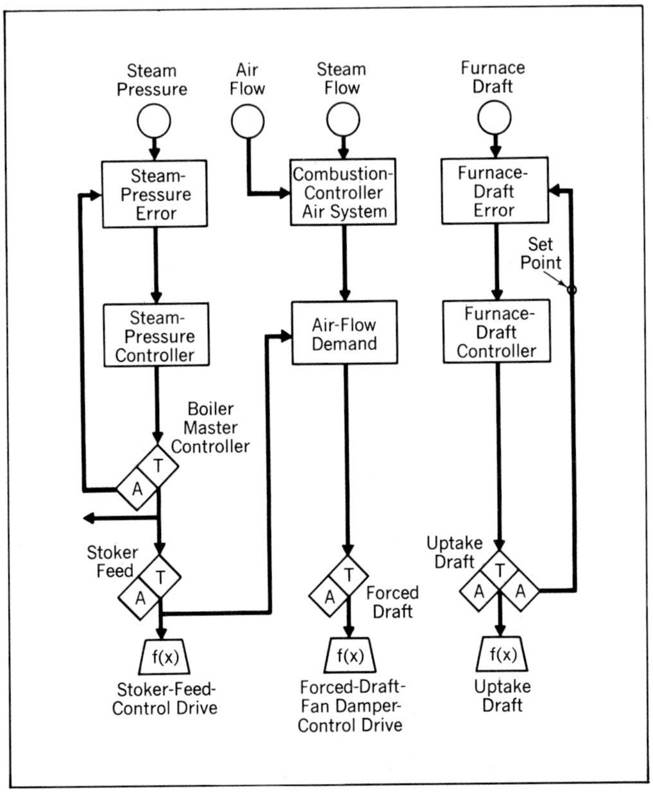

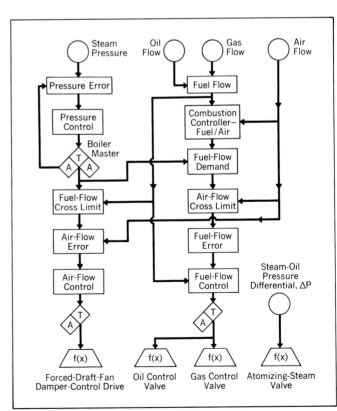

Fig. 16 Diagram of combustion control for a spreader-stoker-fired boiler.

Fig. 17 Diagram of combustion control for a gas- and oil-fired boiler.

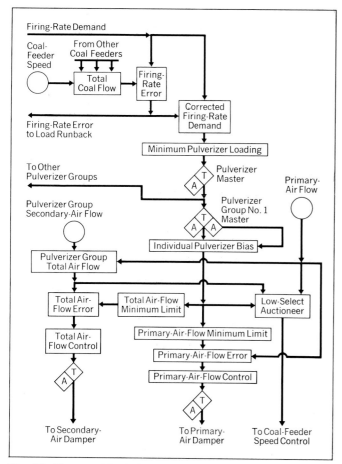

Fig. 18 Diagram of combustion control for a pulverized-coal-fired boiler.

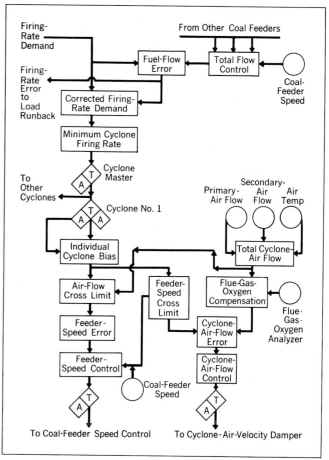

Fig. 19 Diagram of combustion control for a cyclone-fired boiler.

to the measured air flows. A minimum pulverizer loading limit, a minimum primary-air flow limit and a minimum total air flow limit are applied to the respective demands to keep the pulverizers above their minimum safe operating load, to maintain sufficient burner nozzle velocities at all times, and to maintain primary air-fuel and total air-fuel ratios above prescribed levels at all times.

Cyclone-Furnace-fired boilers

The cyclone controls shown in Fig. 19 are similar to those described for pulverized-coal-fired units. Although the cyclone functions as an individual furnace, the principles of combustion control are the same.

On multi-cyclone installations the feeder drives are calibrated so that all feeders run at the same speed for the same master signal. The total air flow is controlled by the velocity damper in each cyclone to maintain the proper fuel-air relationship. This air flow is automatically temperature-compensated to provide the correct amount of air under all boiler loads. The total air flow to the cyclone is controlled by the windbox-to-furnace differential pressure, which is varied as a function of load to increase or decrease the forced-draft-fan output. Automatic compensation for the number of cyclones in service has been incorporated along with the additional feature of an oxygen analyzer. This gas analyzer is a component for most control systems and serves as an important aid to the operator in monitoring excess air

for optimum firing conditions. Another useful combustion guide is the relationship between power generation and air flow.

Combustion guides

It is necessary to provide the operating personnel with a device to allow manual or automatic proportioning of the amount of air to the amount of fuel.

The level of excess air is one index that is commonly used to determine the performance of the unit and to guide its everyday operation. Excess air is the amount of air supplied over and above that required for theoretically perfect combustion. It is always necessary to supply some excess air to assure complete combustion of all the fuel. Any excess air not actually required constitutes a substantial loss in the form of decreased boiler efficiency, and thus a higher fuel bill.

On the other hand, operating with a deficiency of air flow for the fuel being burned can also result in decreased boiler efficiency as well as the formation of combustible products that can present a hazardous condition in convection passes and air heaters, as well as in the furnace.

Three basic types of combustion guides are applied in steam generating units. They are steam-flow air-flow, fuel-flow air-flow, and gas analysis. Each has distinct advantages. The individual boiler and the fuel properties must be studied to determine the best guide for a particular unit. A combination is often incorporated in

the instrumentation system. A fourth type now being initiated is megawatt-generation air-flow. All guides are based on the fact that theoretical air flow and Btu release in the fuel have a close and predictable relationship. This relationship is discussed in Chapter 6 and in *Output of the Unit*, Chapter 14.

Steam-flow air-flow. The steam-flow air-flow concept (Fig. 20) can be applied to obtain an instantaneous indication of the efficiency of fuel consumption. Because boiler efficiency at a specific load remains essentially constant for a given excess air, fuel consumption can be determined from steam flow, which is established by the use of standard flow-measuring devices. Steam flow is used as an index of heat absorption.

The air-flow indication or index can be established by primary elements located on either the air side or the flue-gas side of the unit.

Air-flow measurement. From a control standpoint, the preferred location for air-flow measurement is in the clean air duct between the air heater and the burners. Available air-measuring devices are discussed under *Flow Measurement* in Chapter 33.

The alternate location for air-flow measurement is on the flue gas side with connections located so that the differences in pressure resulting from the flow of combustion products through a section of the main boiler or air heater can be measured. The products of combustion at a given flue gas temperature are proportional to the amount of air supplied, and thus the flue-gas flow can serve as an index of air flow.

The measurement of combustion air supplied to a boiler is made difficult by several factors:

1. The air-measuring device is a restrictive type, similar to the primary elements used in other flow measurements. The resulting unrestored head loss means added fan power.

2. On large and complicated units it is usually impossible to find one duct through which all of the combustion air passes. Metering equipment capable of accurately totaling several flows must then be employed.

3. Air density must be considered in both the calibration and operation of any air-flow meter. Either manual or automatic temperature compensation must be applied to the air-flow indication for it to reflect the mass rate of air flow.

The steam-flow air-flow meter is calibrated after the unit is placed in operation. The calibration is based on results obtained from a number of combustion tests. Proper calibration makes possible a visual presentation of the relative correctness of the fuel-air proportioning. The operator is able to achieve optimum firing conditions by maintaining the correct relative positions of the two measurement pens.

Fuel-flow air-flow. Where it is practicable to measure the rates of admission of fuel and air prior to combustion, a fuel-flow air-flow ratio guide can be established. This may be direct control or backup for adjustment or setting up limits of fuel or air flow.

Fuel-flow measurement. The measurement of gaseous fuels requires consideration of the physical properties of

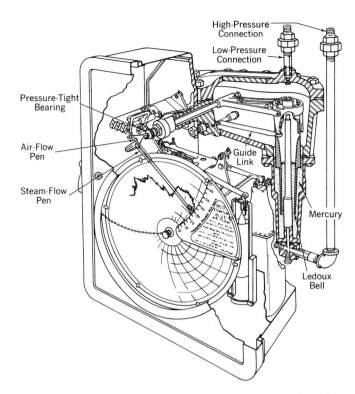

Fig. 20 A steam-flow air-flow combustion guide for maintaining desired excess air. Fuel-flow air-flow device is similar but may have different flow-measuring mechanism.

the gas, particularly temperature, pressure, and specific gravity. Where widely changing properties are encountered, automatic compensation should be provided. A primary element installed in the main header will produce a differential to actuate a recording meter. On less complex installations, particularly those with single burners, the pressure at the burner can be used as an indication of flow.

With liquid fuels, various types of flow meters can be installed directly in the supply header to indicate and record fuel flow. As with gaseous fuels, oil-header pressure can be used as an indication of flow.

The measurement of solid-fuel flow can be accomplished through the use of weight scales or feeder speeds. The use of feeder speed, however, is more applicable to the control and indication of fuel flow. The feeder can be calibrated in pounds of fuel flow per feeder revolution to produce a continuous flow rate. On large units several feeder speeds can be totalized to give the total fuel flow to the unit.

The new concept of "megawatt-generation" air-flow is now being applied in new boiler instrumentation and control systems for steam-electric generating plants. "Megawatts generated" is a direct index of Btu input to the unit and is essentially unaffected by variations in feedwater temperature or fuel properties.

Gas analysis. Gas analyzers are used to ascertain correct fuel-air relationships. Representative flue gas samples are continuously analyzed either chemically or electronically to produce chart records of the oxygen and combustibles present in the products of combustion. Since there is direct correlation between the percentage of oxygen in the flue gases and the quantity of excess air

supplied to the combustion zone, the operator is furnished with a continuous and direct reading of combustion efficiency. The indicated or recorded oxygen signal can be used for control purposes in adjusting the total air flow.

Comparison of combustion guides. Each combustion guide has its particular merits; none is infallible. The informed combustion engineer utilizes the advantages of one to overcome the disadvantages of another.

The fuel-flow-air-flow-ratio guide proportions fuel and air continuously during severe load swings. It is, therefore, popular on gas- and oil-fired units. It has the disadvantage of being in error for wide variations in heating value of the fuel. When the fuel heating value changes, the calibration of the correct fuel-air relationship also changes. Hence, to maintain a given excess air, the proportions of air and fuel must also be changed. Often the fuel-flow-air-flow-ratio guide is used for coal-fired units having a variable-Btu fuel but with a feedback calibration of air flow based on oxygen measurement or a Btu-input index such as steam flow or megawatt generation.

On major load changes, the steam-flow air-flow device is temporarily in error, i.e., the fuel consumption is normally higher or lower than indicated by the steam-flow load index, because of the overfiring and underfiring necessary for steam pressure control. This guide is also affected by changing feedwater or steam temperatures, since a variation of either temperature demands more or less transfer of heat to each pound of steam produced at the specified pressure and temperature. These errors are inherently minimized where megawatt generation is used as the index of Btu absorption. It is necessary, when substantial changes may occur in steam or feedwater temperature, to provide manual or automatic compensation to the steam-flow air-flow calibration.

A gas analyzer gives true excess-air determinations. Some delay is introduced, since combustion must be completed before a correct sample can be obtained. If the sample is withdrawn close to the combustion zone, this delay is not usually objectionable. Considerable study may be required to locate sample points that will give correct average excess-air values. The dirty, hot, and corrosive conditions of the flue gases at these points make periodic maintenance necessary for continuous dependable sampling. The gas analyzer is an accurate index for feedback control.

It should be pointed out that at least one of these combustion guides is needed for proper control of the combustion process. The flow-index guides serve as a direct signal to the firing equipment and act to maintain correct relationship of the combustion conditions.

Burner controls

Types

Burner control systems of various types are now applied to almost all boilers to prevent continued operation of a boiler where a hazardous furnace condition could exist and to assist the operator in starting and stopping of burners and fuel equipment.

The most important burner-control function is to prevent furnace or pulverizer explosions which could threaten the safety of operating personnel and damage

the boiler. The control system must also prevent damage to burners and fuel equipment from maloperation while avoiding false trips of fuel equipment when a truly unsafe condition does not exist.

Other important factors in the design of the burner control system are the method and location to be used in the start-up, shutdown, operation, and control of the fuel equipment. These factors must be understood before purchase, design, or application of a burner control system.

The different categories of burner control are summarized in the following discussion.

Manual control. With complete manual control (Fig. 21) it is necessary to operate the burner equipment at the burner platform. Positioning of the burner components is performed manually. Checks on the existing conditions are dependent on observation and evaluation by the local operator. Good communication between the local operator and the control room is required to coordinate the start-up and shutdown of burner equipment. Manual supervision and control are of interest principally on older boilers, since some form of automatic burner control is provided with almost all boilers now being purchased.

Manual control with lighter-flame-proving system. The recommended initial step is to apply a semiautomatic lighter control including a flame-proving and interlock system (Fig. 22). From local-panel-board initiation, assuming first that various pre-firing and purge interlocks

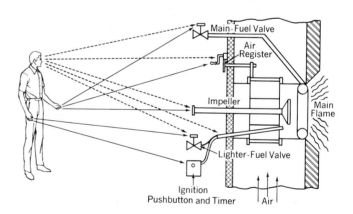

Fig. 21 Fuel-burner manual control.

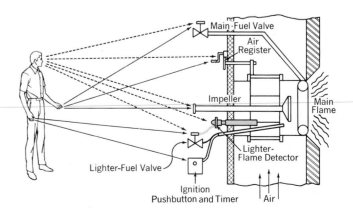

Fig. 22 Manual control with lighter-flame-proving system.

are satisfied, the lighter will be started and proved continuously, and thus provide a permissive signal for introduction of main fuel to that burner.

Flame detectors or other means to prove lighters in service are recommended by the Boiler-Furnace Explosions Committee of the NFPA (National Fire Protection Association). This is the recognized industry committee for establishing standards for boiler furnace safety.

For this type of limited system the fuel equipment should still be operated only from the burner platform as with complete manual control.

Manual control with lighter- and main-flame proving. Many industrial boilers with gas and/or oil firing by multiple burners are protected by a burner interlock and trip system using individual-burner supervisory cocks and trip valves from main-flame detection (Fig. 23). The lighter is initiated from a local panel with manual operation of the air registers and supervisory cocks. After a short ignition-time delay, the individual burner valve will trip on loss of main flame. Normally no other monitoring is provided at each burner except by the operator's intelligence. This is a local manual system and should not be operated from a remote location. Such systems have limited burner interlocks and trips, or none, except from lighter- and main-flame detectors. Cross interlocks between burners are also nonexistent or limited. This relatively inexpensive burner control system has proved satisfactory where only a few burners are

operated from the burner platform. NFPA now requires a system of this scope as a minimum for oil- and gas-fired boilers.

Remote manual sequence control. Illustrated in Fig. 24, this system represents a major step, permitting remote manual operation, and using instrumentation systems and position switches in the control room for intelligence. This system is not recommended for remote operation where safety is dependent only on flame detection. Various burner permissives, interlocks, and trips should also be provided to account for the position of fuel valves and air registers in addition to main-flame detection. With this system the operator participates in the operation of the fuel equipment. He controls each sequence of the burner-operating procedure from the control room, and no steps are taken except by his initiation.

Automatic sequence control. The next logical step (Fig. 25) is to automate the sequence control to permit start-up of burner equipment from a single push button or switch control. Automation then replaces the operator in control of the operating sequences. Since the operator initiates the demand for each fuel-utilization unit, it is expected that he participates, or that he at least monitors with his intelligence the operating sequence, as indicated by signal lights and instrumentation signals, as the start-up process proceeds to completion with the fuel-utilization unit in service on automatic control. This

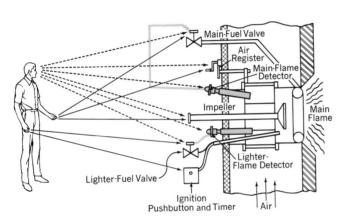

Fig. 23 Manual control with lighter- and main-flame-proving systems.

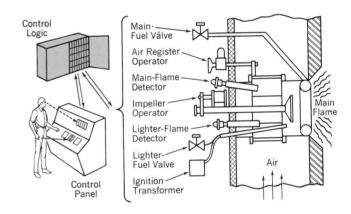

Fig. 25 Automatic sequence control.

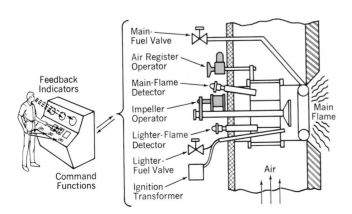

Fig. 24 Remote manual sequence control.

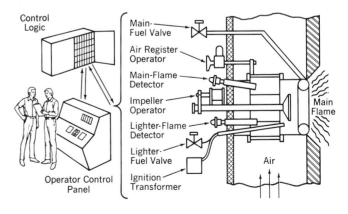

Fig. 26 Fuel management.

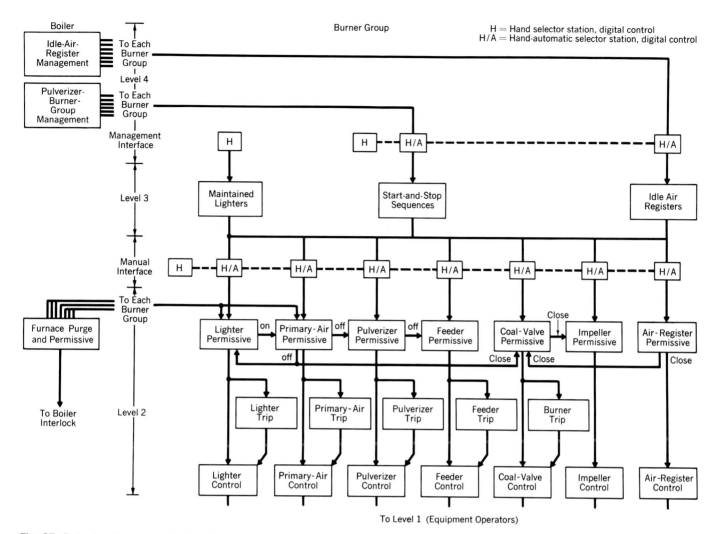

Fig. 27 Pulverizer-burner control system.

category has been widely applied to gas burners but also to oil- and coal-burning systems as well.

Fuel mangement. Finally a degree of fuel system automation can be achieved that will permit fuel equipment to be placed in service without supervision by the operator (Fig. 26). A fuel-management system can be applied that will recognize the level of fuel demand to the boiler, will know the operating range of the fuel equipment in service, will reach a decision concerning the need for starting up or shutting down the next increment of fuel equipment, and will select the next increment based on the firing pattern of burners in service. Such demands for the start-up or shutdown of fuel preparation and burning equipment can be initiated by the management system without the immediate knowledge of the operator and, in fact, his attention may be diverted from the firing and fuel preparation equipment at this time.

The degree of operating flexibility allowed with a burner control system is closely related to the degree of operator participation. A higher level of automation reduces the flexibility of the operator in handling situations where a piece of equipment fails to perform as expected. One method used to provide more operating flexibility is to allow operator participation at two or more levels. Increased flexibility is also obtained by careful grouping of equipment so that a fault anywhere in the system will affect a limited amount of equipment. An example of this is the grouping of burners on a pulverizer so that the failure of a piece of hardware on a burner will only affect the failed burner, and not the pulverizer and its remaining burners.

Fig. 27 illustrates provision for manual intervention in a fuel-management-type system. In this figure, functions are detailed at four levels of a pulverizer-burner control system. Manual intervention is provided at level 2 to permit remote manual operation with interlock protection features.

The cost of the burner control system is also important, but varies significantly with the functional requirements and degree of operating flexibility, as well as the type of logic* equipment (solid state or relay) and packaging desired for the system, so that a true evaluation of cost cannot be reached without a complete understanding between the customer and vendor of the factors involved.

A very common error in applying burner controls is attempting to use a local manual-control system as a limited-scope remote-manual-control system.

---

* The term "logic" is used to indicate devices which receive information, compare it against predetermined instructions, and take the action required.

Flame detection

One of the most important items required for a burner control system is the means of assuring the presence or absence of flame on each individual burner regardless of the type of fuel being burned.

Ultraviolet (UV) flame detectors have been successfully applied to all types of fuels. The UV detector is especially well suited to natural-gas-fired burners due to abundance of ultraviolet radiation produced by the combustion of the hydrogen in natural gas. The Flicker detector uses the high-frequency dynamic flickering of the primary combustion process in combination with the intensity of the visible radiation of the flame. Initial application of this dual-signal detector indicates that the Flicker detector provides greater discrimination and reliability than the UV detector on oil and coal firing. The two detectors can be used in combination on a burner where it is necessary to monitor both gas and oil or coal firing on the same burner, such as on a coal burner with a gas lighter.

Present philosophy in applying flame detectors to any type of fuel requires either the use of self-checking detectors or the use of redundant detectors on each burner in order to provide the reliability necessary for operation with a burner control system.

The proper location of the flame detectors on a burner is dependent on many factors, including burner-control-system design and, therefore, should be determined by the burner-control manufacturer as an integral part of burner-control-system design.

Flame monitoring devices in current use are designed for on-off type of operation based on the presence or absence of flame. Although the basic detector units provide a variable analog output signal which can be read on a meter, there is no direct claim to an established relationship between this relative output signal and the flame quality. Therefore, the analog signals should never be relied upon as flame quality indicators. They should be used only to provide helpful information for initial setup adjustments and continuous "on-line" observance.

Several power plants today are using closed-circuit television to provide a means of continuous furnace observation by the operator from the control room. Closed-circuit TV has been successfully applied to all fuels and more applications are expected in the future.

Control system design for Universal-Pressure boilers

The introduction and increased use of the once-through boiler design in the United States stems from the continuing efforts of the utility industry and its suppliers to reduce the cost of generating electric power. The once-through boiler makes possible the increase in cycle efficiency obtainable from operation at full steam temperature over a wider load range and operation at supercritical pressures. The Universal-Pressure boiler, manufactured by B&W, is one type of a once-through boiler (*see Chapter 22*). This boiler type, as its name implies, can be designed to operate at either subcritical or supercritical pressures.

Operation of the once-through boiler

The once-through concept can best be described by thinking of the boiler as a single tube. Feedwater is pumped into one end, heat is applied along the length of the tube, and steam flows out of the other end. The output from the tube is a function of the feedwater flow and the amount of heat supplied. The outlet fluid enthalpy, or heat content, depends only on the ratio of the heat input to the feedwater flow. The presence of a valve at the outlet of this one-tube boiler provides a means of varying the pressure level. When the pressure level is maintained constant, the outlet steam temperature also is dependent only on the ratio of the heat input to the feedwater flow.

At steady-state conditions the feedwater flow-in equals the steam flow-out. The pressure level will be influenced not only by the valve restriction at the outlet, but also by the density of the fluid throughout the system. Therefore, it is important to note that a change in heat input will influence both pressure and temperature. It is possible to vary the flow and pressure at the outlet by changing the amount of valve restriction, or at the inlet by changing both the feedwater flow and the heat input. It is important to note that a change in feedwater flow without a corresponding change in the heat input will result in a change in the outlet steam temperature. During transient conditions other factors, such as the fluid and energy storage requirements which change with load, must be considered since they influence the feedwater flow and heat inputs.

Characteristics of control systems

Experience with once-through boiler operation has indicated the importance of a control system which fully exploits the capability of the once-through concept. The three most important control systems, which have been used with the Universal-Pressure boiler, are the Turbine-Following, the Boiler-Following, and the Integrated Boiler-Turbine-Generator Control systems. The latter combines the advantages of the first two.

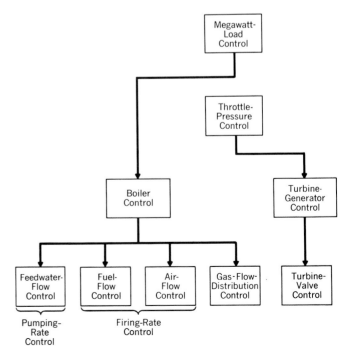

Fig. 28 Turbine-following control system.

Turbine-following control. A conventional turbine-following control system is shown diagrammatically in Fig. 28. With a turbine-following system the turbine-generator is assigned the responsibility of throttle-pressure control while megawatt load control is the responsibility of the boiler. When an increase in load is demanded, the boiler control increases the pumping and firing rates which in turn starts raising the throttle pressure. In order to maintain a constant throttle pressure, the turbine control valves open and accept the additional boiler output, thus increasing the load. When a decrease in load is demanded, the same procedure occurs in the reverse direction. Load response with this type of system is rather slow since the turbine generator must wait for the boiler to change its output before repositioning the turbine control valves to change load.

Boiler-following control. A conventional boiler-following control system is illustrated in Fig. 29. With a boiler-following system the boiler is assigned the responsibility of throttle-pressure control while megawatt-load control is the responsibility of the turbine-generator. The demand for a load change goes directly to the turbine control valves to reposition them to achieve the desired load. Following a load change, the boiler control modifies the pumping and firing rates to reach the new load level and restore throttle pressure to its normal operating value. Load response with this type of system is very rapid, since the stored energy in the boiler is used to provide the initial change in load. The fast load response is obtained at the expense of less stable throttle-pressure control.

Integrated control. While both these systems can provide satisfactory control of the unit, each has certain inherent disadvantages and neither exploits fully the capabilities of both the boiler and turbine-generator. The turbine-following and boiler-following systems have

been combined into an integrated-control system which provides the advantages of both systems while minimizing the disadvantages.

The Integrated Boiler-Turbine-Generator Control system is shown diagrammatically in Fig. 30. Megawatt-load control and throttle-pressure control are the responsibility of both the boiler and the turbine-generator. One type of an integrated system assigns the responsibility of throttle-pressure control to the turbine-generator, thus taking advantage of the stability of a turbine-following system. In addition the system utilizes the stored energy in the boiler, thus taking advantage of the fast load response of a boiler-following system.

Since the boiler is not capable of producing rapid changes in steam generation at constant pressure, the turbine is used to provide the initial load response. When a change in load is demanded, the throttle-pressure set point is modified using megawatt error (difference between the actual load and the load demand), and the turbine control valves respond to the change in set point to give the new load level rather quickly. As the boiler modifies the pumping and firing rate to reach the new load and restore throttle pressure, the throttle-pressure set point returns to its normal value. The result is a fast and efficient production of electric power through proper coordination of the boiler and turbine-generator. The speed of response is much faster than a turbine-following system, as shown in Fig. 31. However, it is not as fast as a boiler-following system because the effect of megawatt error is limited to maintain a balance between boiler response and boiler stability. Wider limits would provide more rapid response while narrower limits would provide more stability.

Development of the Integrated-Control system received added impetus from the introduction by the electric power generating companies of the wide-area economic-load-dispatch system. This new system, through a means involving incremental cost control, re-

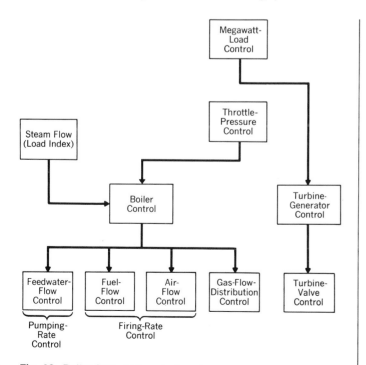

Fig. 29 Boiler-following control system.

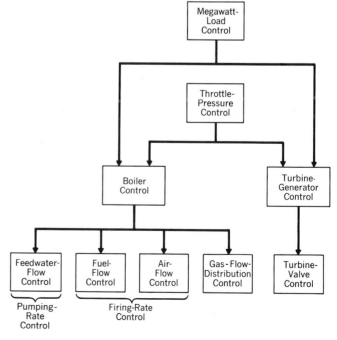

Fig. 30 Integrated Boiler-Turbine-Generator Control system.

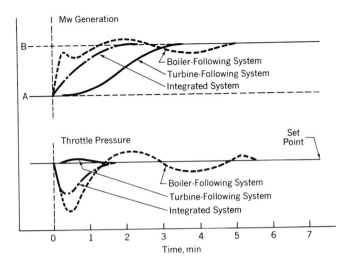

Fig. 31 Comparison of response characteristics of various arrangements of boiler-turbine-generator control systems for a large change in load demand.

quires precise load control. Each unit under control is required to produce a specific level of megawatt generation and the area-load-control system continues to readjust the turbine control valves until this level is reached. Now, even relatively minor interactions between steam flow and throttle pressure can create a continuous interaction between the boiler, the turbine-generator, and the area-load control. The conventional boiler-following system, which is subject to such interactions between steam flow and throttle pressure, does not lend itself to use with this type of an area-load control. This is not due to any incapability of the boiler-following system as such but is the result of combining two highly responsive systems.

Since wide-area economic-load-dispatch systems are being utilized increasingly, greater emphasis is placed on controlling the boiler and turbine-generator together in an integrated system to achieve automatic control of megawatt generation over a wide operating-load range. While the Integrated-Control system was developed primarily for use with the once-through boiler, it can also be applied to drum boilers especially where wide-area

economic-load-dispatch systems are in service. A description of the Integrated Boiler-Turbine-Generator Control system is presented in the following section.

Integrated Boiler-Turbine-Generator Control system

The Integrated-Control system in its basic form consists of a number of ratio controls which compare related pairs of controlled inputs, such as:

> Boiler energy input to generator energy output.
> Superheater-spray-water flow to feedwater flow.
> Fuel flow to feedwater flow.
> Fuel flow to air flow.
> Recirculated-gas flow to air flow. This in effect is a ratio of reheater absorption to absorption in primary water and steam.
> Fuel flow to primary-air flow for pulverized-coal-fired units.

Fig. 32 is a simplified diagram showing all system inputs controlled in a parallel relationship from the Mw-load demand by means of ratio controls.

The Integrated-Control system coordinates the boiler and turbine-generator for fast and efficient production of electrical power in response to load demands initiated by the automatic load-dispatch system. A functional description of the Integrated-Control system, shown in Fig. 33, is presented in the sections following.

Megawatt-load control. Most electric utility companies have an area-load-control system which introduces a demand on the boiler-turbine-generator unit. The megawatt-load control conditions these demands to make them compatible with the state of the unit and its ability to change load. Also considered are such factors as maximum and minimum load limits and maximum permissible rate of load change. The Mw-load demand is modified for any frequency error, recognizing that, whenever a frequency error occurs, the turbine-speed governor will change the turbine-control-valve position, thus changing load. This avoids any interaction between the turbine-speed-governor control and the analog control systems.

A control feature is included which will "runback" (i.e., reduce) the Mw-load demand whenever unit capability is limited for any reason such as the loss of a

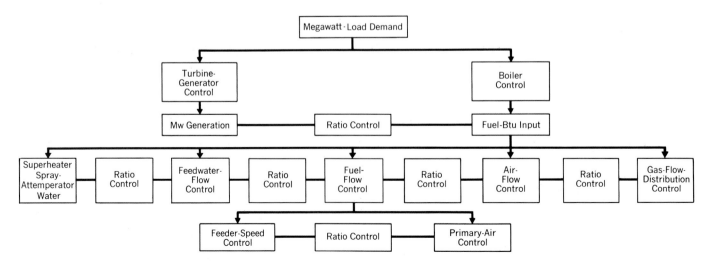

Fig. 32 Simplified diagram of ratio controls.

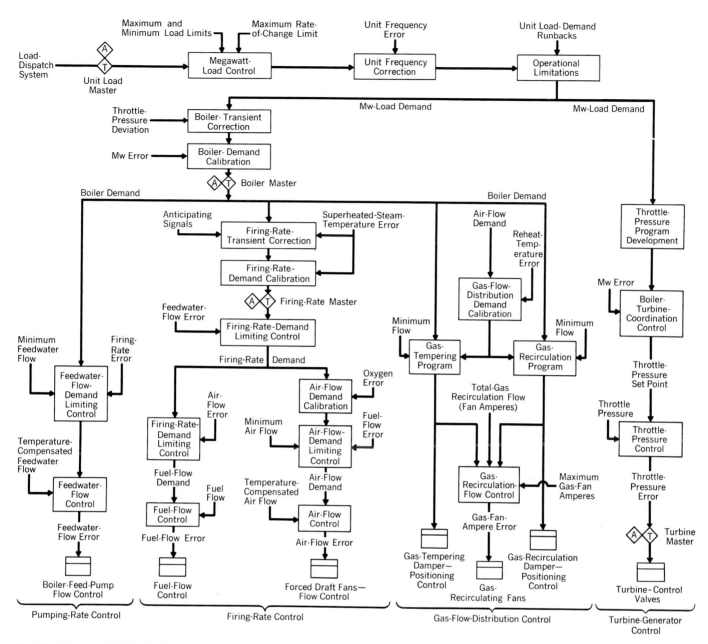

Fig. 33 Integrated Boiler-Turbine-Generator Control system.

boiler feed pump. The unit-load master permits the unit to be separated from the load-dispatch system and placed on manual control with the operator establishing the unit's output. The final Mw-load demand signal is applied in parallel to the boiler and turbine-generator.

Throttle-pressure control. Throttle-pressure control is the responsibility of both the boiler and the turbine-generator. During steady-state operation, the turbine-control valves maintain a constant pressure at the throttle. During load transients the throttle pressure is controlled within ± approximately 100 psi of its normal set point. The amount of pressure variation from the normal set point depends on the size of the Mw-load error, i.e., the size of the load change on the unit. This is discussed further under *Turbine-Generator Control.*

Whenever throttle pressure deviates from its normal set point, a signal proportional to the size of the error modifies the basic boiler demand to return pressure to

its normal operating value. This corrective action provides a means of over- or under-pumping and firing during load changes to accommodate the changes required in the boiler-fluid and energy-storage levels.

Turbine-generator control. The Mw-load demand is used to develop a steady-state throttle pressure program. The normal program for a unit operating at supercritical pressure requires maintaining a throttle-pressure set point of 1000 psi up to approximately 8% of load. This is "ramped" up to 3500 psi as the load is increased to 25%. Above this load, throttle pressure is maintained at 3500 psi.

The normal steady-state throttle-pressure set point is compared with the actual measurement of throttle pressure. Any error causes the throttle-pressure control to adjust the position of the turbine-control valves to maintain the desired throttle pressure. When a change in load is demanded, the boiler-turbine-coordination control uses

Mw error to modify the steady-state throttle-pressure set point and program the opening and closing of the turbine-control valves in a controlled manner in order to provide a fast response to the Mw-load demand while maintaining stable throttle-pressure control. As the Mw generation changes to satisfy the Mw-load demand, the throttle-pressure set point returns to its normal value. The turbine master permits the operator to change the turbine-control valves manually to establish the desired unit load, in which case the boiler is controlled in a "boiler-following" mode.

Boiler control. The Mw-load demand is used by the boiler control to establish demands for feedwater, fuel and air flows, and gas-flow distribution. The Mw-load demand is modified for any deviation in throttle pressure as discussed under *Throttle-Pressure Control* in order to change the fluid- and energy-storage levels of the boiler. This correction assists in maintaining boiler output consistent with turbine steam requirements.

The boiler and turbine must be maintained in the proper relationship at all times in order to produce the load demanded by the system. Any permanent change in the normal relationship between the boiler and turbine, such as a change in the turbine efficiency, will show up under steady-state conditions as a Mw error. Consequently, Mw error is used to calibrate the boiler demand to keep the boiler and turbine in the correct relationship. The boiler master permits the operator to establish the boiler demand manually. The boiler demand is applied in parallel to feedwater-flow, firing-rate, and gas-flow-distribution controls.

Feedwater-flow control. The boiler demand is used to establish a demand for feedwater flow. A minimum feedwater-flow demand (usually 25% or 33% of full load) assures that an adequate feedwater flow is maintained at all loads to protect the furnace tubes from overheating. Whenever the firing rate is unable to satisfy its demand, a firing-rate error will modify the demand for feedwater flow. This assists in maintaining the feedwater flow and the firing rate in the proper relationship, thus minimizing steam-temperature upsets.

The feedwater-flow demand is calibrated using feedwater-temperature error since any deviation from the expected feedwater temperature requires more or less feedwater flow to compensate for the change in extraction flow to the feedwater heaters.

Firing-rate control. Boiler demand is used to establish the base-firing-rate demand. Various control signals are used to correct the firing-rate demand during transient conditions in anticipation of and in response to steam-temperature or gas-temperature changes. This minimizes the steam-temperature upset associated with a load change. Gas temperature is used at low loads to improve the response of the steam-temperature control.

The proper calibration of firing rate to feedwater flow is required in order to maintain the desired superheat temperature. Continuous calibration of the firing-rate demand is provided to correct for steam temperature errors which result from changes in boiler cleanliness, and changes in the fuel Btu content.

Spray attemperation is used above half load to achieve a rapid, temporary correction of steam temperature while the firing-rate demand is being modified to produce a slower, permanent change. Whenever the feedwater flow is unable to satisfy its demand, a feedwater-flow error will modify the demand for firing rate. This assists in maintaining feedwater flow and firing rate in the proper relationship, thus minimizing steam-temperature upsets.

The final firing-rate demand is used to establish a demand for air and fuel flows. This arrangement produces fast firing-rate response to load changes by moving the fuel and air simultaneously. The firing-rate master permits manual operation of the fuel- and air-flow controls.

The fuel-flow demand is compared with the measured fuel flow. Any error will cause the fuel-flow control to modulate the control valve to satisfy the fuel-flow demand. Whenever the air-flow demand cannot be satisfied, an air-flow error will modify the demand for fuel flow. This assists in maintaining fuel and air flow in the proper relationship to assure safe and efficient boiler operation.

An air-flow demand calibration is included in the control system to account for any disturbance caused by fuel and/or air-flow metering errors or by changes in the Btu content of the fuel. This assists in maintaining the correct amount of excess air required for the combustion process. Air-flow demand is compared with the measurement of air flow which has been temperature-compensated for accuracy. Any error will cause the air-flow control to reposition the forced-draft-fan controls to satisfy the air-flow requirements.

A minimum air-flow demand (usually 25% of full-load-air flow) assures safe boiler operation at low loads. Whenever the fuel-flow demand cannot be satisfied, a fuel-flow error will modify the demand for air flow. This assists in maintaining the proper relationship between the fuel and air flows.

Gas-flow-distribution control. Combustion gases leaving the economizer are recirculated and introduced through the bottom of the furnace as gas recirculation for the dual purpose of controlling reheat-steam temperature at high loads and for furnace protection throughout the load range, particularly at low loads. Gas recirculation alters the heat-absorption pattern throughout the unit. On coal-fired units combustion gases leaving the economizer are introduced near the furnace outlet as gas tempering to control the furnace-exit-gas temperature.

The air-flow demand is used to develop the high load program for gas flow distribution. This program is continuously calibrated to control the reheater absorption in order to maintain the desired reheat-steam temperature. The boiler demand is used to develop the low-load program for gas recirculation and gas tempering. Whenever the reheat steam temperature is higher than desired, the amount of gas-recirculation flow is reduced. When gas-recirculation has been reduced to its minimum value and reheat temperature is still high, reheat spray-attemperation is used to control reheat temperature.

The sum of the gas-recirculation and the gas-tempering demands is the total flow required from the gas recirculation fans. The gas-fan amperes, which represent an accurate measurement of flow, are used to control the gas-recirculation flow. The total gas-recirculation-flow demand is a demand for gas-fan amperes and is com-

pared with the actual measurement of gas-fan amperes. Any error will cause the gas-recirculation-flow control to reposition the fan-inlet damper to satisfy the demand for gas-fan amperes. Fan overload protection is provided through a maximum gas-fan-amperes limit. On some units excess air may be used instead of gas recirculation to control reheat-steam temperature and provide furnace protection.

Start-up and low-load control. During start-up and operation at loads below the minimum feedwater flow, some or all of the flow is diverted through a bypass system to the flash tank. This enables the boiler to provide the desired steam flow to the turbine while maintaining a minimum feedwater flow for protection of the furnace tubes from overheating. Operation of various valves in the bypass system provides load and pressure control.

The flash-tank control automatically maintains control of both flash-tank pressure and flash-tank level while the unit is operating on the bypass system. The controls selectively distribute the flash-tank drains and steam flow to the condenser, deaerator and the high pressure heaters, initially to clean up the water and then to recover heat from both the steam and drain flows. See also *Start-Up of Universal-Pressure Boilers*, Chapter 34.

Instrumentation and controls for nuclear steam plants

The instrumentation and control for the nuclear plant should be organized for maximum "on-line" operation and load-following capability with a minimum of functions to be performed by the operating staff. B&W accomplishes this by using techniques developed especially for the utility industry. The organization of functions is shown in Fig. 34. The white boxes represent equipment components in the reactor coolant and steam systems. The heavy black lines represent reactor coolant, steam, condensate or feedwater lines.

The broken lines represent the instrumentation inputs from the plant, including reactor measurements by the nuclear and in-core instrumentation, and reactor coolant loop, steam, feedwater, turbine, and generator measurements by the non-nuclear instrumentation.

The shaded boxes contain the various subsystems of the Integrated-Control system, including the integrated master, which sends signals in parallel to the turbine-valve control, the feedwater control, and the reactor control. The heavy gray lines denote the outputs of the integrated master and the control subsystems, which

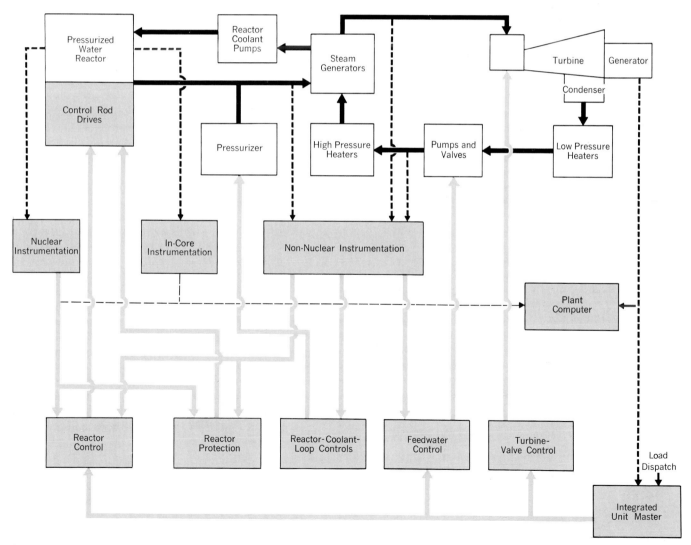

Fig. 34 Instrumentation, control and protection functions for a nuclear (PWR) steam-electric-generating unit.

drive the turbine governor and feedwater valves, feed pump, turbine-speed controls, and the control rod drives. The thin dashed lines represent inputs to the information and computing system, which acquires and processes data from all the instrumentation systems.

Instrumentation systems

Nuclear instrumentation. The nuclear instrumentation system (Fig. 35) monitors the reactor neutron power from below source level when the reactor is shutdown to over 125% of full power, and provides signals to the operator, the reactor protection system, and the reactor controls. Technical specifications require the system to be in operation whenever fuel is loaded in the reactor. All system neutron detectors are located in vertical wells immediately outside the reactor vessel but inside the primary shielding. The normal signal span from source level to overpower trip is approximately 10 decades (a range of 10^{10}). The nuclear instrumentation provides 13 decades (a range of 10^{13}) of neutron flux information to include margins at both ends of the operating scale and allow for variations in source strength and leakage flux at full power.

As shown in Fig. 35, the nuclear instrumentation has eight channels of neutron information divided into three ranges of sensitivity—the source range, the intermediate range, and the power range. Only one channel in each range is shown in detail in Fig. 35.

The two source-range channels are identical and use proportional counters in lead-shielded thimbles on opposite sides of the core at the axial centerline to provide seven decades of log-count-rate information from below-source level up to a two-decade overlap with the intermediate range. The source-range channels also provide

rate-of-power-change information for control rod withdraw-hold interlocks. The source-range preamplifiers are located close to the detectors in the reactor building. The neutron flux level is read on the level indicator and the rate of change on the rate indicator.

The two identical intermediate-range channels use compensated-ion chambers in lead-shielded thimbles on opposite sides of the core at the axial centerline to provide eight decades of logarithmic power (expressed as log n where n is neutron density) information from about seven decades below full power up to several hundred percent power, and rate-of-power-change information for control rod withdraw-hold interlocks.

The four full-power-range channels use full-core-length uncompensated ion chambers in unshielded thimbles opposite the quadrants of the core to provide highly accurate linear measurements of reactor power from zero to 125% of rated power to the reactor protection system and reactor controls. Each full-length power-range neutron detector consists of two half-length sections opposite the upper and lower halves of the core to determine the distribution of power along the axis of the reactor. The system derives signals from both the sum of the two detector halves and the difference between the two detector halves. The sum of power signals from upper and lower sections can be calibrated against a reactor heat balance calculated by the plant computer. The difference signal can be used by the operator to equalize power generation in the upper and lower halves of the reactor core. The output of the four power range channels is combined in the "averaging logic" for input to the Integrated-Control system and all four are used in the protection system (*see footnote under Fuel Management for definition of "logic"*).

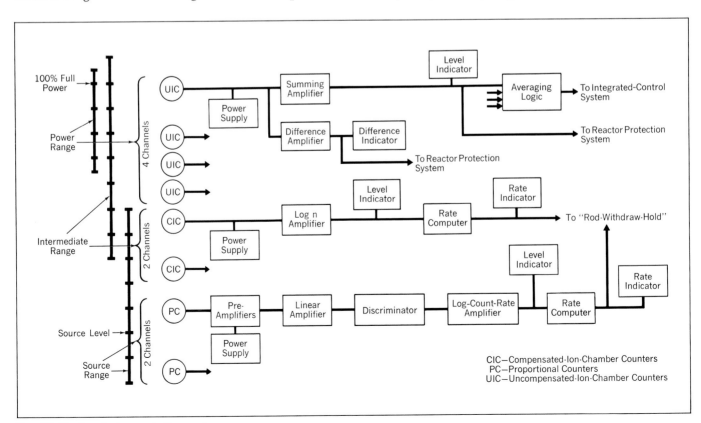

Fig. 35 Nuclear instrumentation system.

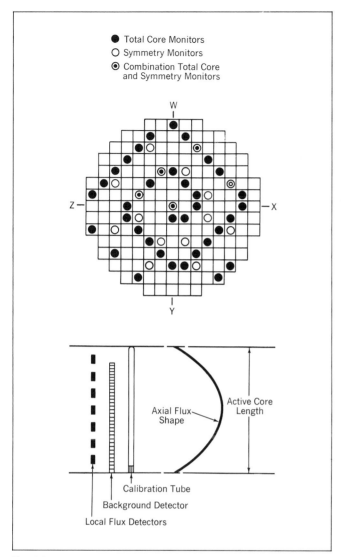

Fig. 36 In-core detector locations.

In-core instrumentation. The in-core instrumentation system monitors the power distribution within the reactor core using self-powered neutron detectors and temperature detectors distributed throughout the core. The system performs neither protective action nor control functions. Fig. 36 shows a typical arrangement of the in-core instrumentation. In-core detector assemblies are located in instrumentation tubes in approximately 30% of the fuel assemblies. Each detector assembly has seven local neutron-flux detectors spaced evenly along the axis of the reactor, one background detector extending the full height of the reactor core. The plant computer is used to provide the operator with indicated outputs from the in-core detectors and calculated power distribution and core performance data, by combining measurements from the total core monitors and symmetry monitors.

Non-nuclear instrumentation. The non-nuclear instrumentation system monitors variables such as temperature, pressure, level, and flow in both the reactor coolant system and the steam and feedwater systems and provides signals for reactor protection, reactor control, reactor-coolant-loop control, and feedwater control.

Plant computer. The plant computer monitors signals from all the instrumentation systems and plays an active part in helping the operator improve the operation of the plant. Typically the computer collects inputs from over 2000 points throughout the plant and provides both collected and calculated data on equipment and fuel performance to optimize the operation of both the nuclear steam system and the rest of the plant. The functions of the computer can also be extended to monitor or control the start-up and loading of the turbine-generator.

Integrated-Control system for nuclear steam plants

The Integrated-Control system summarized in Fig. 37 is the nuclear counterpart of the Integrated Boiler-Turbine-Generator Control system for fossil fuels. This system combines the stability of a turbine-following system with the fast response of a boiler-following system to provide optimum response from the reactor-boiler-turbine unit.

The turbine and two steam generators are capable of automatic control from zero power to full power with optional manual control. The reactor controls are designed for manual operation below 15% full power and automatic or manual operation above 15% full power.

Increasing power transients between 20 and 90% power are limited to ramp changes of 10%/min and step increases of 10%. Power increases above 90% are limited to 5%/min. Decreasing power transients between 100 and 20% power are limited to ramp changes of 10%/min and step decreases of 10% without turbine-bypass or safety-valve action. The turbine-bypass system permits

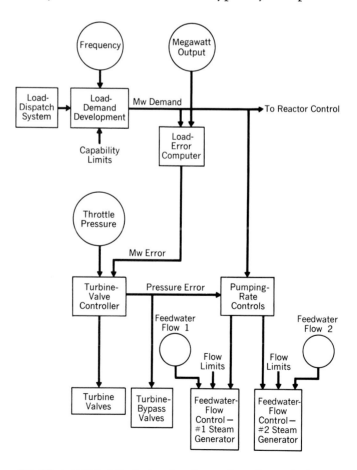

Fig. 37 Integrated-Control system for nuclear steam plants.

a load drop of 40% or a turbine trip from 40% load without safety valve operation or reactor trip. The turbine-bypass system and safety valves permit a 100% load drop without turbine trip or reactor trip to satisfy "blackout" requirements.

Optimum overall plant performance is maintained by limiting steam pressure variations; by limiting the imbalance that can exist between the steam generator, turbine, and reactor; and by limiting the total plant-load demand upon loss of capability of the steam-generator-feed system, the reactor, or the turbine-generator. The load demand is restrained by a maximum load limiter, a minimum load limiter, a rate limiter, and a runback limiter. In normal operation the limits would be set as follows:

Maximum load limit, %	100
Minimum load limit, %	15
Rate limit, %/min	10

The runback limiter acts to limit the load demand if one or more reactor coolant pumps are inoperative, or total feedwater flow lags total feedwater demand by more than 5%.

The output of the limiters is a megawatt-demand signal which is applied to the turbine controls, steam generator controls, and reactor controls in parallel.

The control system receives inputs of megawatt demand, system frequency, and steam pressure, and supplies output signals to the turbine-bypass valve, turbine valve controller and steam-generator feedwater pumps and valves with changing operating conditions. The Mw demand, limited as required by system capability, is applied to the feedwater, reactor and turbine controls, all in a parallel relationship.

Turbine controls. The megawatt demand is compared with the generator megawatt output, and the resulting megawatt-error signal is used to change the steam pressure set point (Fig. 37). The pressure error positions the turbine valve controller so that the turbine valves then change position to control steam pressure. The result is rapid response to megawatt-demand changes although the turbine is being controlled in the turbine-following mode. As the megawatt error reduces to zero, the steam-pressure set point is returned to the steady-state value. By limiting the effect of megawatt error on the steam-pressure set point, the system can be adjusted to permit controlled variations in steam pressure to achieve any desired rate of turbine response to megawatt demand. Although the valve controller is being driven to control steam pressure much like a turbine-following system, the turbine remains on governor control so that large frequency upsets will draw rapid response from the turbine-generator to restore system frequency.

Steam generator controls. Control of the two steam generators (Fig. 37) is based on matching the feedwater flow to megawatt demand with adjustment between the two steam generators provided by the error between steam-pressure set point and steam pressure. The pressure error increases the feedwater-flow demand if the pressure is low and decreases the feedwater-flow demand if the pressure is high.

The basic control actions for parallel steam generator operation are:

1. Megawatt demand converted to feedwater demand.
2. Steam pressure compared to set pressure and the pressure error converted to feedwater demand.
3. Total feedwater demand computed from the sum of items 1 and 2.
4. Total feedwater-flow demand split into feedwater-flow demand for each steam generator.
5. Feedwater demand compared to feedwater flow in each steam generator. The resulting error signals position the feedwater control valves and feed-pump turbine-speed controls to match feedwater flow to feedwater demand in each steam generator.

For operation below 15% load, the steam generator controls act to maintain minimum steam-generator water level. The conversion to level control is automatic. At loads below 15%, the turbine-bypass valves operate to limit steam pressure rise.

The steam generator controls also provide ratio, limit, and runback actions. In a unit with two steam generators, these include:

1. *Steam-generator load-ratio control.* Under normal conditions the steam generators will each produce one-half of the total load. Steam-generator load-ratio control is provided to proportion the load as permissible for the number of reactor coolant pumps operating in each loop.
2. *Rate limits.* Rate limiters restrict loading or unloading rates to those which are compatible with the turbine and/or the steam generator.
3. *Water level limits.* A maximum-water-level limit prevents gross overpumping of feedwater and assures superheated steam under all operating conditions. A minimum-water-level limit is provided for low load control.
4. *Reactor-coolant-pump limiters.* These limiters restrict feedwater demand to match reactor-coolant-pumping capability. For example, if one reactor coolant pump is not operating, the maximum feedwater demand to the steam generator in the loop with the inoperative pump is limited to approximately half of normal.
5. *Reactor-outlet and feedwater low-temperature limiters.* These limiters reduce feedwater demand when the reactor outlet temperature is low or the feedwater temperature is low.
6. *Feedwater pump capability.* A feedwater pump capability runback signal limits the megawatt-demand signal whenever total feedwater flow lags total feedwater demand by 5%.

Reactor-coolant-loop controls. The reactor-coolant-loop controls act independently of the integrated control to maintain reactor coolant pressure and pressurizer level constant (Fig. 38). The pressure controller energizes pressurizer heater banks in sequence as the pressure falls and opens the pressurizer spray valve when the pressure rises. The level controller positions the pressurizer-level control valve in the makeup line to maintain constant

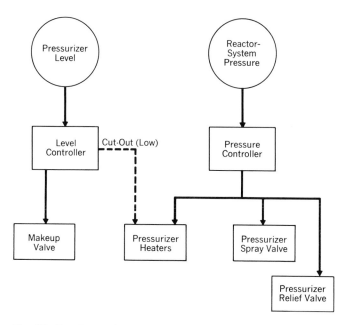

Fig. 38 Reactor-coolant-loop controls.

pressurizer level. A low-pressurizer-level cutout interrupts the pressurizer heater power to prevent heater and pressurizer damage.

Reactor control. The physics requirements for reactor control are discussed in Chapter 21, as is the accomplishment of reactor control by means of control rods and soluble poison. Control rods and their drive mechanisms are discussed in Chapter 23. The organization and functions of a reactor control system are summarized in Fig. 39.

The reactor control positions control rods to regulate the power output of the reactor and maintain constant reactor average temperature. The Mw demand is summed in the power controller with reactor-average-temperature error to form a reactor-neutron-power demand. The output of the power controller is a control rod drive "withdraw" or "insert" command resulting from a difference between the reactor-neutron-power demand and the actual neutron power as measured by the power-range neutron detectors. One of three control-rod-drive groups selected in sequence by the control rod program will respond to this command through the normal control functions as long as there is no input from the protection functions to the protection logic which compares the input information with predetermined instructions and takes the necessary action.

When protection-function action is required, the protection logic interrupts the control commands and routes the action to the appropriate channel for the level of action required. A rod "withdraw hold" inhibits all control rods from responding to withdraw commands. A trip signal bypasses the control rod program and drops all control rods into the core. The soluble-poison control is initiated manually and terminated automatically. The control rod program acts as a permissive to restrict the start of dilution to a "safe" rod position pattern.

The reactor controls are designed to maintain a constant average reactor coolant temperature over the load range from 15 to 100% of full power. The steam system

operates on constant pressure at all loads. The average reactor coolant temperature decreases over the range from 15% load to zero load.

Input signals to the reactor controls (Fig. 39) include reactor-coolant average temperature, megawatt demand, and reactor power as indicated by out-of-core neutron detectors in the power range of the nuclear instrumentation. The output of the controller is an error signal that causes the control rod drive mechanism to be positioned until the error signal is within a dead band.

Reactor power level demand, N_d, is computed as a function of time, t, the megawatt demand, Mw_d, and of the reactor coolant system average temperature deviation $\overline{\Delta T}$, from the set point, according to the following equation:

$$N_d = K_1 Mw_d + K_2 (\overline{\Delta T} + \int \overline{\Delta T}\, dt)$$

Megawatt demand is introduced as a part of the demand signal through a proportional unit having an adjustable gain factor, K_1. The temperature deviation is introduced as part of the demand signal after proportional-plus-integral action is applied. For the temperature deviation, K_2 is the adjustable gain and the adjustable integration factor.

The reactor power level demand, N_d, is then compared with the actual reactor power level signal, N_i, which is derived from the nuclear instrumentation. The resultant error signal, $N_d - N_i$, is the reactor-power-level error signal, E_p.

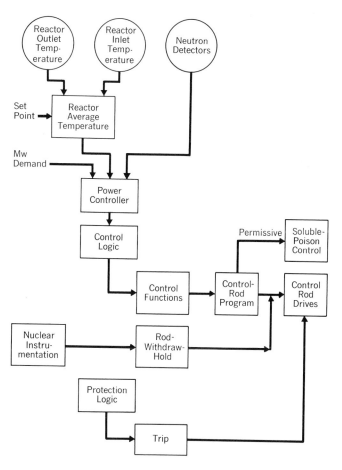

Fig. 39 Reactor control system.

When the reactor-power-level error signal, E_p, exceeds the dead-band settings, the control rod drive assembly receives a command that withdraws or inserts rods, depending on the polarity of the power error signal.

The following additional features are provided with the reactor power controller:

1. An adjustable low limit on megawatt-demand signal, Mw_d, to cut out automatic reactor control action.
2. A high limit on reactor-power-level demand, N_d.
3. An adjustable low limit on reactor-power-level demand, N_d.

Part of the control rods are assigned to automatic control of reactor power level. These control rods are arranged in three symmetrical groups which operate in sequence. An automatic-sequence logic unit is used for reactor control with the three regulating rod groups. This unit allows operation of no more than one control-rod group simultaneously, except over the last 25% travel of one group and the first 25% travel of the next group, when overlapping motion of two groups is permitted.

The position of one automatic group is used as an index to soluble poison dilution. Soluble poison adjustment is initiated manually and terminated automatically. The position of this group acts as a "permissive" to restrict the start of dilution to a "safe" rod position pattern, or to terminate dilution automatically.

As fuel burnup progresses, dilution of the soluble poison is controlled as follows:

When a partially-withdrawn active control-rod group reaches the fully withdrawn point, interlock circuitry permits setting up a flow path from a demineralized water tank in lieu of the normal flow path of borated makeup to the reactor coolant system. Demineralized water is fed to the reactor coolant system, and borated reactor coolant is removed.

The reactor control system inserts the active regulating group to compensate for the reduction in poison concentration. When the control group has been inserted to the 75% withdrawn position, the dilution flow is automatically blocked. The dilution cycle is also terminated automatically by a preset volume control, which is independent of rod position. Normally a dilution cycle is required every several days.

During reactor start-up, control rods are withdrawn in a predetermined sequence in symmetrical groups of four or more rods. The group size is preset, and individual control-rod assignments to a group are made at a control-rod grouping panel. However, the operator can select any individual control rod and any control-rod group for motion as required.

Protection systems

Reactor protection system. The reactor protection system acts to trip the reactor when unsafe conditions exist. A trip signal fully inserts all control rods into the reactor. The reactor protection system consists of four identical channels of redundant measurements which trip the reactor whenever any two of the four channels reach a trip value. Above 10% of full power, five signals will trip the reactor—reactor power, axial power imbalance, power-flow ratio, reactor pressure, and reactor temperature. For each reactor coolant pump combination, there is a maximum allowable reactor neutron power. Exceeding the allowable power will trip the reactor. At any given power level there is a maximum allowable axial power imbalance. Exceeding the allowable imbalance will trip the reactor. High reactor-coolant pressure trips the reactor to prevent damage to the reactor coolant system. Low reactor-coolant pressure and high reactor-coolant temperature trip the reactor to prevent a departure from nucleate boiling. See also *Reactor Protection System*, Chapters 21 and 23.

Engineered safeguards actuation system. To limit the consequences of a possible accident, engineered safeguards systems are provided to perform the functions described in Chapter 21. More detailed discussion is given in *Engineered Safeguards Systems*, Chapter 23. These systems are actuated by the engineered safeguards actuation system. This system consists of three channels of identical redundant reactor-coolant pressure and reactor-building pressure measurements, which act to energize the engineered safeguards systems whenever any two of three channels reach a trip value.

Recent developments in instrumentation

Most instrumentation in a power plant today depends on a mechanical linkage to convert a measured variable such as pressure or flow into an analog signal. Utilizing the solid-state technology used to produce transistors and integrated circuits, solid-state transducers have been developed, which directly convert the measured variable into an electric analog signal. These solid-state transducers offer faster response, better repeatability, simpler instruments, and greater reliability than the mechanically coupled transducers. Solid-state technology has also produced thin-film thermocouples which, because of their smaller size and mass, offer faster response in measurement while introducing less disturbance to the item being measured.

The increasing use of digital computers in the power plant is requiring that analog signals representing temperatures, pressures, and other measurements be converted to digital signals compatible with the digital computer. Since the conversion of analog to digital signals requires additional hardware, work is under way to develop transducers that produce their output signal directly, representing the measured value in a digital form acceptable to the digital computer without further conversion.

Simplifying information display

Large boiler-turbine units have as many as 2200 indicators, recorder lights, annunciator points, and position indicators. With such a large amount of information being presented, operators may find it difficult to analyze the best action to follow in an emergency situation.

One effort to simplify the information display is the use of alarm printers, which log all points going into alarm and returning to normal, any measured values exceeding predetermined limits, and the starting and stopping of major equipment groups. This provides the operator with a single source of information for all off-normal conditions, as well as a time log of the sequence in which the events occur.

Current systems print out a verbal description of the condition which is causing the alarm. Since this operation is slow compared to the time available in emergency, cathode-ray-tube displays, similar to a TV screen, are being used in some systems.

Another approach is to have the computer store and display analog values on demand. By storing in the computer the calibration curves for the individual transducers, the display can be made in engineering units. Some high-speed electronic displays allow the readings to be updated on each data collection cycle after the point is selected.

Performance computations

The continuing growth in size and complexity of units has added importance to the frequent analysis of performance. Many operating companies are analyzing their performance-evaluation programs and developing monitoring techniques that make possible the detection of malfunctions before substantial losses have occurred.

A number of performance-evaluation procedures are practiced today. In some power companies, the performance of each unit is checked periodically by extensive heat-rate tests. Techniques and procedures for performing such evaluations are covered under *ASME Performance Test Codes*.

The digital computer is also being used to conduct on-line performance calculations periodically (hourly and daily in most systems). This information can be compared with expected performance data stored in the computer with any deviation recorded for future correction.

Future application of the performance computer will include its use as an on-line control where the performance calculations will be used to obtain optimum plant performance by automatically modifying set points and programs in the normal on-line control system.

The performance computer can also be used to totalize hours of operation accumulated on pieces of equipment and provide notification when maintenance is due on different items of hardware, as well as to provide a record of the operation of a piece of equipment.

To date a few computer programs have been developed to scan several criteria, evaluate the data and report to the operator an impending maloperating condition. As improved instrumentation systems and more knowledgeable techniques are developed, it is expected that greater use will be made of such programs.

Power plant automation

Many power plants today are essentially automatic in operation between one-third and full load using the conventional systems discussed earlier in the chapter. To achieve complete automation of a plant, it is first necessary to add control sub-loops for the auxiliaries which were previously considered to be the exclusive responsibility of the operator. All of these sub-loops must then be integrated through a unit management control to provide complete plant automation. Fig. 40 shows diagrammatically the arrangement of such a control system.

The basic concept for full automation is to provide the maximum amount of control and monitoring at the lowest possible level. The organization of the different levels as shown in Fig. 41 for a fossil-fuel plant is summarized below:

Level 1 — The equipment hardware being controlled.
Level 2 — The internal control of the individual equipment items or group of functionally identical items of equipment always operated in parallel.
Level 3 — Coordination of the sequence of actions and interlocking with respect to more than one equipment group.
Level 4 — The modulation and sequencing of major cycle components involving the entire unit.
Level 5 — Generation of the major load-demand signals to coordinate the operation of the overall plant.

Advantages obtained with the hierarchical-control concept are self-regulation of equipment groups, allowing the equipment group to protect itself through the low-level interlocking, thus providing greater reliability and

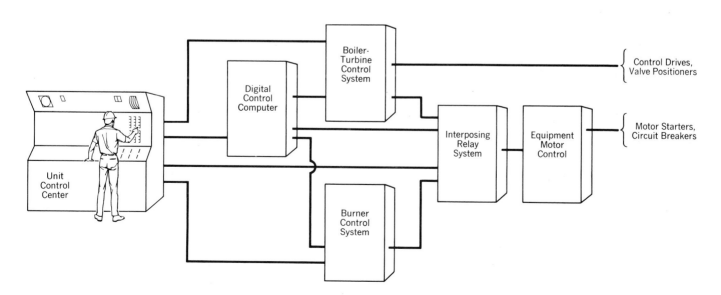

Fig. 40 Composite of automation components.

control decentralization and permitting continued plant operation with some portions of the control system out of service.

Some of the advantages of overall unit automation are:

1. Improved protection of personnel and equipment through more complete instrumentation, simplified information display, and more extensive and thorough supervisory control.
2. Reduced outages, reduced maintenance, and longer equipment life through more uniform and complete control procedures of start-ups, on-line operation, and shutdowns.
3. Better plant efficiency through continuous and automatic adjustments to the controls with the objective of optimizing plant operation.
4. More efficient use of manpower during start-up and on-line operation.

The trend of boiler automation is clear, and its future scope can be predicted with considerable confidence. The achievement of some goals will be difficult. There are operating problems to be solved, traditions to be overcome, and new philosophies and approaches to be accepted. Reliable and adequate equipment is already available and its application, through the cooperation of manufacturers and users, will make the automatic power

plant a complete reality. More work needs to be done to improve the peripheral equipment such as instrumentation systems, position indicators, equipment operators, and other sensors to couple the control system in a reliable manner to the equipment it is controlling.

Installation and service requirements

It is important to make certain that instrumentation and control equipment is properly installed and serviced. Supervision of installation and the required calibration adjustments should be performed by qualified and experienced personnel. Adequate time for tune-up of controls should be provided during initial boiler operation.

Experienced field engineers, employed by control manufacturers, are available to assist customers. The field adjustment of a sophisticated control system is a job for an expert. Once done, maintenance can be performed by trained plant personnel. The plant personnel who will be responsible for this maintenance should be available to observe and assist the control manufacturer's representatives in the installation and calibration of the control system. Most control manufacturers offer training programs to familiarize customer personnel with the control equipment. A planned program of preventive maintenance should be developed for the control system.

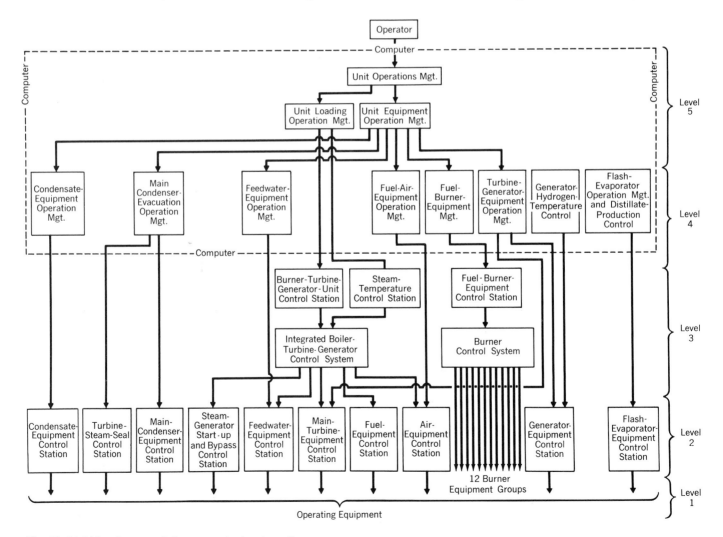

Fig. 41 Multi-level approach to power-plant automation.

Chapter 36

Maintenance

The capability of steam generating equipment to operate safely and to remain in operation in accordance with plans and schedules is of prime importance. The maintenance of equipment in condition to assure this capability has come to be known as "preventive maintenance." Preventive maintenance includes a policy of operating equipment properly and within its range of capability. It includes maintaining equipment clean and in prime operating condition. This is verified by instrumentation and in-service observations. Preventive maintenance also includes regularly scheduled outages to make those inspections which cannot be made during operation, and to perform necessary repairs.

In-service maintenance — fossil-fuel equipment

Safety

First emphasis is on safe operation, the avoidance of conditions that could result in explosive mixtures of fuel in the furnace or other parts of the setting, and the protection of pressure parts to prevent excessive thermal stresses or overheating, resulting in failure.

Furnace and setting. The prevention of furnace explosions deserves top priority because of potential personnel injury, the high cost of repairs, and the effect of outage time on electric utility systems and industrial processes. Four items are of major importance in the prevention of furnace explosions:

1. Optimum operating procedures and operator training.
2. Optimum burner observation with prompt detection of flame failure.
3. Detection of unburned combustibles in the flue gas.
4. Positive, immediate indication of fuel-air relation at the burners.

Procedures for safe operation are the same whether they are followed manually or automatically, and can be carried out by the "human" operator or programmed for computer control. It is important that these procedures be recognized and followed and that operators understand basic principles, even though fully automatic control may be used.

The majority of furnace explosions result from failure to detect a loss of ignition, even though other indications, such as dropping boiler pressure, steam temperature and exit-gas temperature, show that fuel is either not being burned or is being burned incompletely. This emphasizes the fact that nothing takes the place of seeing the fire. On-the-spot burner observation with today's large, centrally controlled stations is no longer practicable. Hence reliable, remote indication of positive ignition on all burners must be relayed to the operator at the central control point. A "combustibles alarm" to indicate the presence of unburned combustibles in the flue gas is considered as a good backup for flame observation.

The differential air pressure, between burner windbox and furnace, is an essential aid in purging the furnace and setting, lighting off, and normal operation. It is an excellent guide in the establishment of correct fuel-air relationship to prevent loss of ignition or the accumulation of unburned combustibles in the furnace or setting.

The sections entitled *Safety Precautions* in Chapters 7 and 9 provide more specific information concerning the safe handling and burning of oil and gas, and pulverized coal respectively. Means to avoid the accumulation of oil or soot on air-heater and economizer surfaces in oil-fired units, to avoid fires in these areas, are discussed under *Starting Cold Boilers and Operating at Low Loads,* Chapter 7.

Pressure parts. A very important item of safety equipment is the boiler safety valve. The capacity, relief pressure and procedures for installation and testing of safety valves have been codified and are written into the law in nearly all jurisdictions (*see also Design of Pressure Parts, Chapter 12*). Modern safety valves are highly dependable when properly installed, and their installation is checked by state and insurance inspectors.

Next on the list of safety equipment is a reliable means to determine that the boiler is filled with water. For a drum-type boiler, this consists of adequate water

level detection. For a once-through boiler, this is accomplished by reliable measurements of water flow and firing rate so that the operator can be assured at all times that feedwater flow is matched to the firing rate. (*See Control System Design for Universal-Pressure Boilers, Chapter 35.*)

Monitoring of feedwater and boiler water conditions, as well as steam purity, are essentials of any boiler operation today, whether it is a drum-type or a once-through boiler (*see Water Treatment for Fossil-Fuel Units, Chapter 34*). The chordal type thermocouple, installed in tubes in strategic locations in the furnace, serves as an excellent guide to internal cleanliness of the boiler and can be used as an indicator of the need for chemical cleaning, which is discussed later in this chapter. The use of chordal thermocouples is treated in Chapter 33 under the captions *Furnace Wall Tubes* and *Gradient Thermocouples.*

Monitoring temperatures. Reliable measurement of various temperatures is a necessity for safe operation and reasonable maintenance of the boiler unit. In general these temperatures fall into three categories—metal temperatures, gas temperatures, and temperatures of steam and water.

1. The measurement of superheater and reheater tube temperatures is essential to prevent exceeding safe metal temperatures. Tube temperatures in various circuits of once-through boilers must also be monitored as an operating guide. With current designs of drum-type boilers there is no great concern over stresses in thick-walled drums since data indicate that a firing rate regulated to protect superheaters and reheaters also takes care of safe pressure-rise rates on the drum. During rapid cooling of a drum-type unit, however, it is still advisable to check drum differential temperatures. Air heater tube temperatures must be monitored to make sure that they remain above the dew point to insure against sulfur corrosion.

2. Gas temperatures in several areas should be monitored during pressure-raising periods. Temperatures entering the superheater are checked for protection of the superheater metal.

   For gas-fired units equipped with regenerative air heaters it is possible, during pressure and temperature-raising periods of operation, for the relatively cold, rotating, air-heater elements to condense moisture generated in the flue gas by the hydrogen in the fuel. As the air heater rotates into the air stream the condensed moisture can be swept into the air and carried to the burners, depressing flame temperature below ignition point, with consequent flame failure. For regenerative-type air heaters, gas temperature entering the heater should be measured to indicate when the air heater may be safely rotated and not cause loss of ignition. For protection against explosion on gas-fired units, it has been found that gas temperature entering the air heater should be at least 400F before rotating the air heater. The recent practice of operating with an air-rich furnace atmosphere during start-up may make this precaution unnecessary.

   Gas temperatures leaving the regenerative air heater are also monitored to prevent air heater corrosion.

3. Monitoring of steam and water temperatures has been conventional procedure for years. Quick start-ups and the matching of steam temperatures to allowable turbine temperatures expand the requirements for good monitoring.

Monitoring pressures. The measurement of certain pressures and pressure differentials is mandatory for safe operation.

1. Water and steam pressure should be measured on a drum-type boiler as an operating guide, once the safe pressure rise or pressure reduction rate has been established. On a once-through boiler, water pressure should be measured to make sure that a safe pressure exists prior to firing. Differential pressure on a once-through unit is required to establish adequate, safe, minimum flow. When measured across various portions of the unit, differential pressure serves as an index of internal cleanliness.

2. The measurement of furnace pressure on both pressurized and suction-type units is required to assure that design pressures of the casing or containment are not exceeded. Some form of differential gas or air pressure measurement, in conjunction with time lapse, is required as an indication that the setting has been adequately purged prior to firing. This is a necessary operating guide to assure proper fuel-air relation at the burners.

Maintaining efficiency

The best way to analyze the problem of maintaining efficiency is to examine the major losses in efficiency, what affects them, and what can be done to control them. A typical heat balance for a pulverized-coal-fired utility boiler would be:

Dry gas loss	5.16%
Loss due to hydrogen and moisture in the fuel	4.36%
Loss due to unburned combustible	0.50%
Loss due to radiation	0.30%
Loss due to moisture in air	0.13%
Manufacturers margin and unaccounted loss	1.5 %
Overall efficiency	88.05%

Minor losses are usually lumped into one percentage figure and labeled "unaccounted for." These minor losses are quite extensive in number, but they are small with regard to heat loss. Of these minor "unaccounted for" losses, the largest is the loss due to sensible heat in the ash or slag.

The boiler operator has a significant amount of control over the losses listed as dry gas loss and loss due to unburned combustible, by adjusting boiler operation.

Variables in efficiency losses. There are two variables in dry gas loss—stack temperature of the gas, and the weight of the gas leaving the unit. Stack temperature varies with the degree of deposit on the heat-absorbing surfaces throughout the unit, and it varies with the amount of excess combustion air. The effect of excess air is two-fold: 1) it increases the gas weight and 2) it raises the exit-gas temperature. Both effects increase dry

gas loss and thereby reduce efficiency. A rough rule-of-thumb gives an approximate one-percent reduction in efficiency for about a 40F increase in stack gas temperature on coal-fired installations.

In coal-fired units, unburned combustible loss includes the unburned constituents in the ash-pit refuse and in the flue dust. These constituents may include a variety of compounds. However, in calculating the unburned loss, all constituents are customarily treated as pure carbon.

The unburned combustible loss will vary with the volatile matter and the ash content of the coal, but these conditions are normally beyond the operator's control. Excess combustion air once again is the controllable variable affecting this loss. The normal result of increasing air is to reduce combustible in the refuse, thus increasing efficiency. There is no ready rule for approximating this loss, since coal volatility and ash content vary too widely. The curves of Fig. 1 illustrate the change in efficiency loss due to combustible in flue dust with changes in combustible content of the flue dust, percent ash in the coal, and percent of ash up the stack. This figure indicates that the higher the combustible ash content of the coal and the greater the percentage of flue dust to the stack, the greater the loss in efficiency.

Fig. 2 shows the effect on dry gas loss, unburned combustible loss, and gross unit efficiency of increasing excess air from the normal operating range to an abnormally high value. The numbers on the curves indicate the three following units from which the data were obtained:

1. A stoker-fired industrial boiler, 35,000 lb/hr capacity.
2. A pulverized-coal-fired utility boiler of 600,000 lb/hr capacity.
3. A pulverized-coal-fired utility boiler, 1,170,000 lb/hr capacity.

Fig. 2 shows a net loss of efficiency with increasing excess air in all cases. In each case a small reduction in unburned combustible loss is more than offset by the increased dry gas loss.

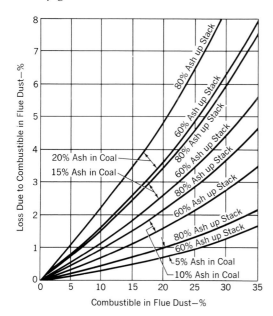

Fig. 1 Variation of flue dust combustible losses for coals of different ash content and percent of ash up the stack.

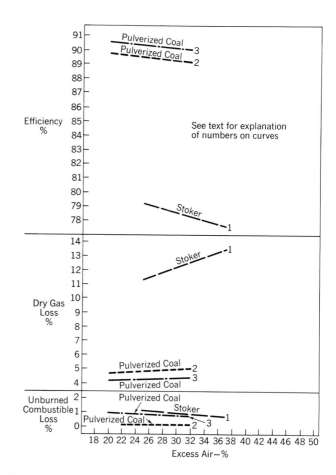

Fig. 2 Efficiency and heat losses vs excess air.

Monitoring efficiency. Continuous monitoring of flue-gas temperatures and flue-gas oxygen content by regularly calibrated recorder or indicator and by periodic checks on combustibles in the refuse will indicate if original efficiencies are being maintained. If conditions vary from the established performance base, corrective adjustments or maintenance steps should be taken.

High exit-gas temperatures and high draft losses with normal excess air indicate dirty heat-absorbing surfaces and the need for sootblowing.

High excess air normally increases exit-gas temperatures and draft losses and indicates the need for an adjustment to the fuel-air ratio. The high excess air may, however, be caused by excessive casing leaks, cooling air, sealing air, or air heater leaks.

High combustible in the refuse indicates a need for adjustments or maintenance of fuel-preparation and burning equipment.

Outage maintenance — fossil-fuel equipment

Outages for preventive maintenance are scheduled as required to prevent equipment failures. In the electric power industry, schedules must take account of system load variations. It is generally preferable not to shut down large electric generating units during the peak load seasons of midsummer or midwinter. The ability of a steam generating unit to remain in operation until the scheduled outage time must be continually monitored by instruments and visual observations.

Internal cleanliness and inspection

One of the best preventive steps that can be taken to assure safe, dependable operation is the maintenance of boiler water conditions that will insure against any internal tube deposits that could cause overheating and failure of tubes. The chordal-type thermocouple (*see Gradient Thermocouples, Chapter 33*) can be used to measure the extent of internal deposits and to indicate the need for chemical cleaning. The measurement of waterside pressure drop across a once-through boiler is also a means of establishing when internal chemical cleaning is required. With some types of water-treatment programs the ability, or inability, to maintain normal boiler water conditions can indicate the existence of a tube leak.

Where in-service measurements are not taken, or when they do not indicate a need for cleaning, checking during regularly scheduled out-of-service periods is recommended for assuring continued operating availability. Low pressure, drum-type boilers still lend themselves to careful, visual inspection to establish the need for internal cleaning. Inspection and determining the amount and type of deposit by turbining and weighing the deposit will establish what has to be removed and what will remove it. Today's modern, high pressure generating units, with complex circuitry and all-welded construction makes visual examination very difficult and non-conclusive. It is preferable and much easier to remove one or more representative tube sections from the high heat input zone of the unit for examination and measurement of the internal deposit. Comparison of the internal area and weight of deposit per unit of area, expressed as grams per square foot, is compared with empirically confirmed weight limits and the physical and chemical nature of the deposit is investigated and the need for internal cleaning established.

Inspection of steam-drum internals should be a part of any out-of-service inspection, particularly if operating checks of steam leaving the drum have given evidence of excessive solids in the steam. All baffling and steam-separating equipment should be in its proper place, and any joints designed to seal against leakage should be tight. It is usually possible to observe evidence of carry-over-producing leaks if the drum is inspected shortly after the boiler is drained, and before any internal cleaning is begun. In removing baffles, plates or steam separators for inspection, it is wise to match-mark parts to assure a proper fit upon reassembly.

Internal cleaning. Chemical or acid cleaning is the quickest and most satisfactory method for the removal of waterside deposits. The guidelines and precautions that must be followed for the safe and effective use of chemicals are discussed under *Chemical Cleaning of Internal Heating Surfaces—Fossil-Fuel Equipment.*

External cleanliness and inspection

Boiler and air heater gas temperatures, and gas-side pressure drops, measured during the operating period of the unit, will show whether external fouling, not removable by normal sootblower operation, is progressing, and will give some clue as to where the accumulation is occurring. During outage periods, the entire unit should be thoroughly inspected with the following objectives:

1. To detect any possible signs of overheating of tubes, particularly if thermocouples have indicated this possibility. Furnace wall tubes should be examined for swelling, blistering, or warping. If signs exist, it may be necessary to gage tubes either by mechanical or ultrasonic methods to establish the amount of swelling or wall thinning. Superheaters, reheaters, and economizers should be inspected with the same objective.

2. To discover any possible signs of erosion or corrosion. A thorough inspection of heat-absorbing surfaces should always be a part of annual outages, and this inspection should be given added importance if any unusual operating conditions have preceded the outage. For example, it is possible by operating with high-ash coals and high excess air to increase gas velocities and dust loadings sufficiently to cause tube erosion. Operating with insufficient combustion air, i.e., with a reducing atmosphere in the furnace, can cause wastage of furnace tubes when the appropriate conditions of temperature and ash deposit exist. High temperature corrosion of superheater tubes or support brackets can occur at elevated temperatures and with oil having significant amounts of vanadium.

   In general, erosion appears as a smooth, sometimes shiny, loss of metal. It can be caused by impingement of sootblower jets, possibly dictating the need for reducing blowing pressure or for realignment of the blower. Corrosion associated with ash deposit may be hidden, and sandblasting or washing of surfaces may be required for detection and measurement.

3. To detect any misalignment of tubes from warpage or from disengagement of support hangers, brackets or spacers. Maintenance of proper tube alignment is of extreme importance to prevent erosion or rubbing from sootblowers, and erosion from flue dust as a result of unequal gas flow lanes.

4. To locate any deposits of ash or slag, not removed by sootblowing, that interfere with heat transfer or free gas flow through the unit. Any heavy deposits that block a major portion of gas lanes can indirectly contribute to erosion problems by creating channels of high velocity in remaining open areas. The presence of deposits indicates a need to check the operation and blowing pressure of sootblowers in that area.

5. To determine the condition of fuel-preparation and burning equipment, particularly if routine sampling of ash has indicated the presence of increasing amounts of unburned combustible material. Any air-flow regulating or adjusting equipment such as dampers, or burner-register doors, should be free of warpage or overheating, and operate freely over its control range. Fuel distribution equipment, such as burner impellers or burner-line distributors should be examined for signs of erosion or, if coking of burners has occurred during operation, for signs of burning or overheating. Coal conditioners, pulverizers and feeders should be inspected to determine whether wear parts need replacing, particularly if coal output has been decreasing, or if routine fineness checks of ground or pulverized coal have shown low product fineness.

6. To determine the condition of any refractory exposed to flue gases, such as burner throats or walls, and areas

in convection passes, particularly if operating conditions have been unusually severe, as when operating intermittently or with a known reducing atmosphere.

External cleaning

When ash deposits contain an appreciable amount of sulfur, they should be removed prior to any extended outage, since these deposits can absorb ambient moisture to form sulfuric acid that will corrode pressure parts. Many ash deposits that result from burning severely fouling solid and liquid fuels are removable by water washing. Units can be, and are, designed for water washing with ample drainage of the wash water and sluiced ash. An out-of-service period is required for all pressure parts. Air heaters can be sectionalized so that areas may be isolated and washed without shutdown of the unit. The washing facilities should be supplied with a means for providing various degrees of alkalinity with hot water for water washing the air heater. This is to avoid acid corrosion with varying quantities of sulfur as the drain from the air heater should be maintained at a neutral condition. Hot alkaline water in the presence of sulfur deposits results in precipitation of iron salts. This is especially necessary with sulfur-bearing fuels. The normal sootblower system is successfully used in many plants by connecting the supply of wash water to the sootblower steam-header system. Drain facilities should be open and ready for discharge of the wash water to catch-basins. Wall areas or tubes in wide-spaced arrangement lend themselves to cleaning by protracted soaking with the wash water. Areas where surfaces are closely spaced, as in regenerative air heaters, can be cleaned by high-pressure water jets. Inspection will indicate what areas require particular attention. The wash water effluent should be checked periodically during washing to maintain an alkaline pH. Out-of-service washing should be scheduled so that surfaces can be dried immediately after cleaning. A good approach is to water wash just before returning a unit to service. A unit that must remain out of service after washing should be dried out at a low firing rate to prevent corrosion.

During a maintenance outage, corrective steps should be taken to prevent recurrence of problems revealed by inspection or by information obtained from monitoring instruments. Some examples are:

1. Overheating of superheater tubes may have occurred from too rapid start-up, or from carry-over of solids in steam. The start-up procedure should be rechecked. Superheater metal temperatures and entering gas temperatures should be closely monitored. Calibration of steam-purity measurement equipment should be checked. A complete carry-over test run under widely varying conditions to determine the exact cause of the problem is often beneficial.

2. Additional gas baffling may be required to prevent external erosion caused by channeling of gases between convection surfaces and walls.

3. Readjustment of sootblowing pressures may be required to increase cleaning effectiveness, or to eliminate sootblower erosion in localized areas.

4. On suction-fired units, resealing of the boiler setting may be required to reduce air infiltration evidenced by an increase in unburned combustible in the ash. Sources of leaks are best identified by use of a non-toxic chemical smoke under slightly positive pressure.

5. A recalibration of all instruments is advisable to assure their functional reliability.

Chemical cleaning of internal heating surfaces—fossil-fuel equipment

Chemical cleaning of internal heating surfaces was first proposed where it was difficult or impossible to clean by other methods. The process is now widely used with complete confidence as the quickest, cheapest, and most efficient method of cleaning these surfaces in boilers of all sizes. It is, however, extremely important to use a procedure of known reliability under careful control.

The procedures outlined are suggested with the understanding that the user must depend on competent chemical supervision of his own choice, supplemented by consultants on boiler-water and scale problems. There are specialist companies equipped to provide a complete chemical-cleaning service.

Advantages of chemical cleaning

In comparison with the removal of scale and deposits from internal heating surfaces by mechanical means, the more important advantages of chemical cleaning may be listed as follows:

1. Outage time is reduced. Usually a boiler can be cleaned in less than 36 hours. More than 48 hours are seldom required.

2. Extensive dismantling of the unit is not required. The solvents can be introduced and discharged through existing connections. The only dismantling necessary is the removal of drum-manhole covers and a few header-handhole closures for inspection.

3. Inaccessible areas, such as small tubes, short-radius tube bends, and irregular surfaces, are readily cleaned, since the cleaning medium has access to all locations reached by steam or water. The result is a better cleaning job. More thorough removal of scale reduces the subsequent rate of deposit formation.

4. New equipment can be designed with complete flexibility and simplicity for best economy, efficiency, and overall cost, since no compromise is required to provide accessibility for cleaning.

5. The total cost is less.

General procedures and methods

In general, four steps are required in a complete chemical-cleaning process for a boiler:

1. The internal heating surfaces are washed with an acid solvent containing a proper inhibitor to dissolve the deposits completely or partially and to disintegrate them.

2. Clean water is used to flush out loose deposits, solvent adhering to the surface, and soluble iron salts. Any corrosive or explosive gases that may have formed in the unit are displaced.

3. The unit is treated to neutralize and "passivate" the heating surfaces. The passivation treatment produces a passive surface or forms a very thin protective film

on ferrous surfaces so that formation of "after-rust" on freshly cleaned surfaces is prevented.

4. The unit is flushed with clean water as a final rinse to remove any remaining loose deposits.

The two generally accepted methods in chemical cleaning are: 1) continuous circulation of the solvent through the parts to be cleaned (Fig. 3), and 2) filling the unit with the solvent and allowing it to soak for a prescribed length of time (Fig. 4).

Circulation. In the circulation method (Fig. 3), after filling the unit the hot solvent is recirculated until cleaning is completed. Samples of the return solvent are tested periodically during the cleaning. Cleaning is considered complete when the acid strength and the iron content of the returned solvent reach equilibrium (Fig. 5), indicating that no further reaction with the deposits is taking place. In the circulation method a solvent of lower strength may be used, as compared with the soaking method, and the solvent is drained from the unit as soon as the reaction is complete. Hence the possibility of damage to the surface cleaned is less in using the circulation method.

The circulation method is particularly suitable for cleaning once-through boilers, superheaters, and economizers with positive liquid flow paths to assure circulation of the solvent through all parts of the unit. A complete cleaning job cannot be anticipated by this method unless the solvent reaches and passes through every circuit of the unit.

Cleaning by the circulation method is aided mechanically by the constant change of solvent which flows over

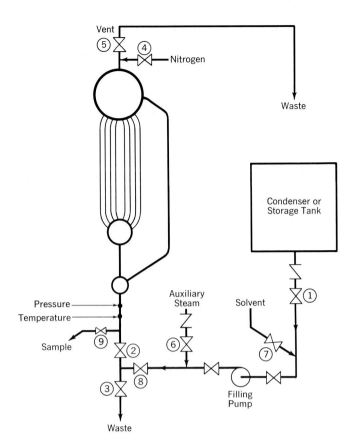

Fig. 4 Chemical cleaning by the soaking method—simplified arrangement of connections.

the deposits on the surface. This feature is of particular advantage when foaming may occur, as with deposits of a calcareous nature. The continuously circulating solvent also carries disintegrated undissolved materials through the unit. This is especially helpful in preventing clogging of small tubes.

Soaking. In cleaning by the soaking method (Fig. 4), after filling with the hot solvent, the unit is allowed to soak for a period of 4 to 8 hours depending on deposit conditions. To assure complete removal of deposits, the acid strength of the solvent must be somewhat greater than that required by the actual conditions, since, unlike the circulation method, control testing during the course of the cleaning is not conclusive, because samples of solvent drawn from convenient locations may not truly represent conditions in all parts of the unit.

The soaking method is preferable for cleaning units where definite liquid distribution to all circuits by the circulation method is not possible without the use of many chemical inlet connections or where circulation through all circuits at an appreciable rate cannot be assured except by using a circulating pump of impractical size. These conditions may exist in large natural-circulation units that have complex furnace-wall cooling systems.

Advantages of the soaking method compared with the circulation method are simplicity of piping connections, assurance that all parts are reached by a solvent of adequate acid strength, and less chemical supervision during the cleaning operation.

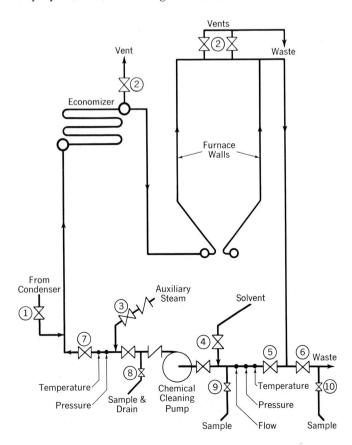

Fig. 3 Chemical cleaning by the circulation method—simplified arrangement of connections.

Solvents, deposits and inhibitors

Solvents. For the removal of boiler deposits, various solvents have been suggested or tried, including many acids and a number of alkaline compounds.

In general, the use of alkaline compounds requires considerable time and temperature and, while the attack on steel is nonexistent or negligible, the surface will not be as clean as with the acid solvents.

On the basis of cost, availability, suitable inhibitors and rapid removal of deposits, extensive experience indicates that hydrochloric acid is the most practical cleaning solvent when using the soaking method on natural circulation boilers. It is recognized that other methods and solvents can be used for chemical cleaning. Solvents, such as chelants, sulfuric acid, and other acid formulations have been used. These solvents are capable of producing good results on deposits of certain physical and chemical characteristics. However, no other solvent available today is able to handle such a wide range of deposits as hydrochloric acid. The chelant base solvents exhibit a degree of versatility in that they can be employed in both the fill and soak and continuous circulation type procedures for cleaning.

Experience in the last 10 years has indicated that an organic acid mixture (hydroxyacetic-formic) is the safest solvent when applying the circulation cleaning method to once-through boilers. Hydroxyacetic-formic acids, now most widely used in once-through boilers, offer a greater degree of safety over mineral acids in the event of some unforeseen incident during the cleaning and rinsing operation. The organic acids decompose into harmless gases in the event of incomplete flushing.

A small percentage of ammonium bifluoride has been found to enhance greatly the solubility of iron in both hydrochloric and hydroxyacetic-formic acids. The ammonium bifluoride should be added to the acid solvent to obtain optimum results from the cleaning operation. For deposits of certain characteristics, the solvent may require additional reagents, such as intensifiers to react with certain constituents or wetting reagents to promote solvent penetration of the deposit. The need for these auxiliary chemicals should be decided by the chemist in charge of the cleaning operation.

Pressure parts of alloy steels, particularly those high in chromium, should not be cleaned with acid solvents without competent chemical advice on the type of acid and inhibitor and the conditions of application in each specific case.

Prior to performing the chemical cleaning of the unit, it is strongly recommended that a representative tube section with the internal deposit intact be subjected to a chemical cleaning test in the laboratory to determine the proper solvent chemical and concentrations of that solvent to achieve a safe and satisfactory cleaning agent.

Deposits. Generally, scale deposits formed on the internal heating surfaces of a boiler unit come from the water. Most of the constituents belong to one or more of the following groups: oxides of iron, metallic copper, carbonates, phosphates, sulfates of calcium and magnesium, silica and silicates. The deposits may also contain various amounts of oil, which are sometimes appreciable in boilers on return to service.

For the most efficient and economical chemical cleaning, certain procedures should be performed prior to the actual cleaning operation, since they greatly influence the success or failure of the chemical cleaning. These procedures include analysis of the deposit for which solvent is specified, and cleaning tests to determine solvent strength, contact time, and temperature. The deposit analyses should include a deposit weight in grams per sq ft, spectrograph analysis to detect the individual cation elements and X-ray diffraction to identify the major crystalline constituents present in the deposit. The deposit is usually a mixture of several constituents, and the solvent composition that will best dissolve the major constituents is generally selected, since the dissolution of the soluble components will free any insoluble compounds present, which can then be removed by flushing.

If the analysis of the deposit indicates the presence of copper which usually derives from corrosion in the economizer or other equipment ahead of the boiler, two procedures are commonly used:

1. Addition of a copper complexing agent directly to the acid solvent.

2. Separate cleaning step using a copper solvent. This step is followed with the acid solvent.

The decision to use (1) or (2) should depend on the estimated quantity of copper present as based on the deposit examination.

In the case of silica or silicates, no general recommendation can be made. Some silicates react more readily with hydrochloric acid, some with sulfuric acid, and still others with a combination of strong alkalies and heat. Boiling for several hours with a 5 to 10% soda ash solution, before acid cleaning, has been found effective in changing the silica scale to a more acid-soluble form. In some instances, to remove silica scale, hydrofluoric acid has been included in the solvent. Except under expert chemical advice and supervision, this procedure is not recommended. Ammonium bifluoride is also known to remove silica-type scales.

When deposits are dissolved and disintegrated, oil is removed simultaneously, provided it is present only in small amounts. For higher percentages of oil contamination, it may be necessary to use a wetting agent in the solvent to promote penetration of the deposit. If the

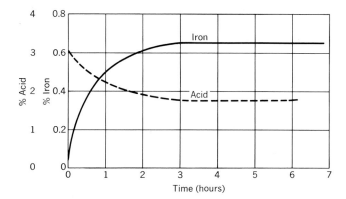

Fig. 5 Solvent conditions during cleaning.

deposit is predominantly oil or grease, boiling out with alkaline compounds must precede the acid cleaning.

Inhibitors. The following equations represent the reactions of acids (in this instance hydrochloric) with constituents of boiler deposits:

$$Fe_3O_4 + 8HCl = 2FeCl_3 + FeCl_2 + 4H_2O$$

$$CaCO_3 + 2HCl = CaCl_2 + H_2O + CO_2$$

At the same time, however, the acids will also react with and waste away the metal of the boiler, as represented by the equation:

$$Fe + 2HCl = FeCl_2 + H_2$$

unless means are provided to prevent or retard this reaction without affecting the attack on deposits.

For this purpose arsenic compounds, barium salts, starch, quinolin, pyridine, or other products were formerly added to the acid solvent as inhibitors, to prevent or materially reduce this reaction with the metal. Today, however, a number of excellent commercial inhibitors are available. They are sold under various trade names, and still others are made and used by companies furnishing complete acid-cleaning services including the prepared solvents. If the cleaning is done by the operator's own organization rather than by a company specializing in this work, the use of commercial inhibitors offered by reputable chemical concerns is recommended.

The effectiveness of acids in attacking boiler deposits as well as steel increases rapidly with rise in temperature. However, the inhibiting effect decreases as the temperature rises and, at a certain temperature, likely to vary for each inhibitor, the inhibitor may be decomposed into compounds devoid of inhibiting properties. Additionally, it should be noted that not all inhibitors are effective with all acids.

Important points in the use of inhibited acid solvent may be summarized as follows: Selection of the acid and auxiliary chemicals should depend on the type of deposit to be removed. The inhibitor must be suitable for the acid selected. The temperature of the solvent must be kept below that at which the effectiveness of the inhibitor is reduced or destroyed. The limiting temperature for use of the inhibitor should be obtained from the maker.

Determination of solvent conditions

Deposit samples. The preferred type of deposit sample is a small section of tube with adhering deposit. In any case a sample of the deposit, down to the bare metal, representing the worst condition in the unit, should be obtained. Selection of the solvent and auxiliary chemicals is usually specified from deposit analyses made as described previously under *Deposits.* After selection of the acid, it is necessary, to assure complete removal of the deposits, to determine the acid strength of the solvent, the solvent temperature, and the length of time required for the cleaning process.

Acid strength. Technically, the acid strength would be in proportion to the amount of deposit in the unit to be cleaned. However, the amount of deposit is usually known only approximately. On the basis of experience, it is recommended that the acid strength of the solvent

and ammonium bifluoride concentration, as fed to the unit, should be:

1. Natural circulation boilers (soaking method)
   (a) Preoperational: Inhibited 5% hydrochloric acid + 0.25% ammonium bifluoride.
   (b) Operational: Inhibited 5 to 7½% hydrochloric acid and ammonium bifluoride based on deposit analysis.
2. Once-through boilers (circulation method)
   (a) Preoperational: Inhibited 2% hydroxyacetic–1% formic acids + 0.25% ammonium bifluoride.
   (b) Operational: Inhibited 2% hydroxyacetic–1% formic acids + 0.25% ammonium bifluoride.

Commercial hydrochloric acid is sold in two grades in 13-gallon carboys. The principal specifications for each grade and the approximate dilution required for a 5% and 7.5% solution are noted below:

Degrees Baumé	18	20
Specific gravity	1.142	1.160
Acid strength, %	27.92	31.45
For a 5% solution, gal H$_2$O/gal acid	6.1	6.9
For a 7.5% solution, gal H$_2$O/gal acid	4.0	4.6

Commercial hydroxyacetic and formic acids are available in 70 and 90% concentrations, respectively.

Solvent temperature. To aid in the acid attack on the deposits, the temperature of the solvent should be as high as possible without seriously reducing the effectiveness of the inhibitor.

When using hydrochloric acid, commercial inhibitors lose their effectiveness above 170F and corrosion rate increases rapidly. It is therefore recommended that the temperature of the solvent as fed to the unit be in the range of 160 to 170F. In using the circulation method with hydroxyacetic-formic-acid mixture, experience indicates that a temperature of 200F is a necessity to assure an adequate chemical cleaning. With the present commercially available inhibitors, the temperature limitation should be 220F. The only exception to this rule is the use of certain chelant base solvents in cleaning the boiler components of natural circulation and pump assisted units. In this procedure the boiler metal temperatures are warmed to a specific temperature range. The chelant chemicals are introduced into the boiler and the boiler metal temperatures are further raised to predetermined limits.

In making up the solvent to the required strength, it will be necessary to supply steam from an auxiliary source to heat the acid as fed to the unit or, when using the circulation method, to heat the circulating water to 200F before injecting the acid solution to produce the desired concentration. Heat should be added by either direct-contact or closed-cycle heat exchangers. The temperature of the solvent should never be raised by firing the unit.

Cleaning time. When cleaning by the circulation method, completion of the process is determined by analyzing samples of the return solvent for iron concen-

tration and acid strength and noting when both reach equilibrium (Fig. 5). However, acid circulation for a minimum of four hours is recommended to make sure that the iron content of the acid becomes constant.

In using the soaking method, the length of time the solvent is to be retained in the unit should be decided upon beforehand. While the type and quantity of the deposit and laboratory determination of the reaction rate of the solvent on samples of the deposit should apply in setting the length of time, a practical guide in determining the solvent retention time for the first few cleanings, using the acid strength noted above, is given as follows:

1. For preoperational cleaning, four hours minimum.
2. For moderate thickness of relatively soft sludges or for conditions that would otherwise require turbining at not less than yearly intervals, the solvent retention time should be a minimum of four hours.
3. For thin coatings ("eggshell" thickness) of relatively hard scale formation, the solvent retention time should be six hours.
4. For deposits such as might result from a severe upset in the feedwater-conditioning system, the solvent retention time should be a maximum of eight hours.

The periods noted are for the actual retention of the solvent in the unit, including the time of filling and draining. In establishing permanent schedules, the periods recommended should be extended or shortened on the basis of the results achieved for specific conditions during the first few cleanings, as indicated by visual inspection or examination of sample sections of tubing cut out of the unit before and after cleaning, in areas typical of the worst deposit conditions.

Preparation for cleaning

Heat transfer equipment. All parts not to be cleaned should be isolated from the rest of the unit. To exclude acid, appropriate valves should be closed and checked during the cleaning to make sure that they are not leaking. Also, connections may be broken and blanked. Where arrangements permit, parts of the unit, such as the superheater, can be isolated by completely filling with demineralized water. Temporary piping should be installed to flush dead legs after cleaning. With once-through type units, besides filling the superheater with demineralized water, it should be pressurized with a pump or nitrogen. The pressure should be in excess of the chemical cleaning pump head.

Bronze or brass parts should be removed or replaced temporarily with steel. All valves should be steel or steel alloy. Gage and meter connections should be closed or removed from the unit.

All parts of the unit not otherwise protected by blanking off or by flooding with water should be covered by the inhibited solvent. Vents to a safe discharge should be provided wherever vapors might be pocketed, since acid vapors from the cleaning solution do not retain the inhibitor.

Cleaning equipment. The cleaning equipment should be connected as shown in Fig. 3 if the continuous-circulation method is used, or as shown in Fig. 4, if the soaking method is used. Continuous circulation requires an inlet connection to assure distribution and to promote circulation through all circuits. It also requires a return line to the chemical cleaning pump from the highest point of the unit. The soaking method does not require a return line, but means should be provided, such as a rubber hose, to carry the spill-over from the vent to a safe location, and the pump discharge should be connected to the lowermost inlet to the unit. Depending on the volume of the liquid to be handled, the pump discharge and the return or vent spill-over lines, as the case may be, are usually $1\frac{1}{2}$ to 3-in. pipe size.

The filling or circulating pump should not be fitted with any bronze or brass parts, or flexible expansion joints. A standby pump is recommended. A filling pump should have the capacity to deliver, in not over two hours at 100 psi, a volume of liquid equal to the content of the vessel to be cleaned. A circulating pump should have a capacity high enough to meet recommended cleaning velocities for a particular unit. With modern once-through boilers, a capacity of 3600 gpm at 300 psi is not uncommon. An acid pump, closed mixing tank and suitable thermometers, pressure gages, and flow meters are required. An adequate supply of clean water and steam for heating the solvent to the desired temperature should be provided, along with equipment for adding steam. Provision should be made for adding the inhibited acid to the suction side of the filling or circulating pump (Figs. 3 and 4).

Cleaning solutions. To determine the amount of solvent required, an estimate should be made of the content of the vessel to be cleaned, adding 10% to allow for wastage and other contingencies. Commercial acid suitable for the deposit to be removed should be procured in the quantity required, when mixed with water, to make a solvent of the amount and acid strength desired.

An inhibitor suitable for the acid to be used should be procured. In obtaining the manufacturer's recommendation for the amount of inhibitor to be used, care should be taken to make certain that this recommendation is based on full knowledge of the acid strength of the solvent and what it is to be used for, to avoid any possibility of a higher corrosion rate than can be tolerated when cleaning a boiler. The amount of inhibitor specified for each carboy or drum of acid should be completely dissolved or suspended in about 1 gallon of acid removed from the container, taking care not to let the solution heat. After pouring the mixture of inhibitor and acid back into the container, the contents should be thoroughly mixed.

Neutralizing-passivating solutions.

1. Natural circulation boilers

   Prior to the neutralizing process, a sufficient quantity of soda ash solution should be prepared to fill the unit completely. The proportion is 10 lb of commercial soda ash to 100 gal of water. This produces a solution strength of about 1%.

2. Once-through boilers

   Ammonia and hydrazine should be added to the circulating water in concentrations of 40 ppm and 500 ppm respectively.

If the operator retains an organization specializing in chemical cleaning of heat transfer equipment, the spe-

cialist organization ordinarily determines and supplies the type of cleaning solvent, neutralization-passivation solutions, and handling equipment best suited for the specific conditions. However, the boiler manufacturer should always be consulted so that consideration can be given to internal-boiler-circuitry problems that may be unknown to the cleaning contractor.

Circulation-method procedure

To expedite cleaning, the preparations should be carried out as far as possible before the unit is taken off the line. When the unit is removed from service, it is allowed to cool in the normal manner, and then drained. The superheater is back-filled with demineralized water and pressurized. Pressure in the superheater should be checked periodically during the cleaning procedure.

The unit, Fig. 3, is filled with demineralized water through connection 1, and all air is vented from the system through vents, 2. The chemical cleaning pump is started and circulation is established. Optimum circulation velocity is about 2 ft/sec; however, the velocity should not be less than ½ ft/sec (where flow cross section is a maximum) and should not exceed 4 ft/sec (where flow cross section is a minimum). To assure a full system at all times, the pressure at the cleaning pump suction should be 20-30 psi in excess of that due to hydrostatic head. Low pressure steam is added to the system through connection 3 until the circulating water reaches a temperature of 200F. Circulation should be checked during heating.

After the water temperature has reached 200F, the inhibited concentrated acid and ammonium bifluoride should be injected at a flow rate to produce the desired solvent concentration. To provide a solvent solution of the required uniform concentration, the solvent injection time should be equal to the time required for the water to make one complete circuit. The 200F temperature is maintained by the addition of steam at the required rate. No firing should take place while acid remains in the boiler. During the first hour, every vent along the acid path should be opened every 15 minutes and once every hour thereafter to relieve any hydrogen gas accumulations. Temporary hoses should be attached to the vents in order to direct the acid effluent to an appropriate drain location. Acid circulation should continue for four to six hours after acid first appears at location 9, Fig. 3. As the volume of the liquid increases because of solvent addition and heating, it may be necessary from time to time during the cleaning operation, to close return valve 5 and open the waste valve, 6. Iron concentration and acid strength analyses should be performed at least once every hour and preferably every half hour during the cleaning. It will be helpful to plot solvent conditions, as indicated in Fig. 5.

Laboratory testing has revealed that a solution of 2% hydroxyacetic-1% formic acids will dissolve up to 1.3% iron. At this concentration, the acid solution becomes saturated and will not dissolve any more iron. If, during the cleaning operations, the iron concentration should reach 1.3%, it would be necessary to displace the spent solvent and begin injection of fresh solvent to the desired concentration to complete cleaning. However, unless the surfaces are especially dirty, the inhibitor concentration

should be checked if the iron content reaches 1.3%.

If for any reason, the unit has to be drained during or subsequent to the chemical cleaning, it must be drained under a positive pressure of nitrogen to minimize oxidation of the heat transfer surfaces.

When it has been determined from chemical analyses that the solvent-deposit reaction is complete or the solvent has circulated for a minimum of 4 hours, the chemical cleaning pump is stopped. The solvent is then displaced from the unit by closing return valve 5 and opening waste valve 6. Demineralized water is admitted through 1. Displacement of the solvent should be accomplished with flow rates as high as possible and continue until the electrical conductivity of the effluent, 10, is within 50 micromhos/cm of the influent water. At the completion of the displacement, circulation should be reestablished with the chemical cleaning pump and ammonia and hydrazine added to the circulating water in concentrations of 40 ppm and 500 ppm respectively. The system should again be heated to 200F and maintained for two hours as a neutralization-passivation step. During this period, all drains, vents, instrument connections and piping "dead ends" should be flushed with the solution. It is also advisable to flush out the superheater. At the end of the neutralization-passivation step, the solution is displaced with demineralized water. A conductivity end point of 50 micromhos should be used.

As a final step in the cleaning operation, the system is again recirculated to allow injection of large excesses of ammonia and hydrazine (10 ppm of ammonia and at least 200 ppm of hydrazine). Circulation should continue for approximately 1 hr after chemical concentrations are detected at location 9. This completes the chemical cleaning. The unit is ready for start-up or a period of short wet storage.

If inspection of tubes and headers is warranted to determine the effectiveness of the cleaning, the last step in the cleaning procedure, that of injecting 10 ppm ammonia and 200 ppm hydrazine, can be omitted. After displacement of the neutralization-passivation solution, the unit is drained under nitrogen pressure and appropriate headers opened for inspection. Any heavy deposits found should be removed by thorough flushing.

Soaking-method procedure

The unit must be removed from service to prepare it for chemical cleaning. Preparations include installation of temporary connections shown in Fig. 4. Necessary thermocouples should be installed, if this has not already been done, at the following locations: 1) steam drum, 2) near the center of each furnace wall, 3) on one of the lower furnace wall headers. The unit is filled with treated water, preferably demineralized, and brought to temperature with the use of ignitors or light firing. When temperatures throughout the boiler have stabilized in the 170-180F range, as indicated by the installed thermocouples, firing is discontinued and the unit is drained. The hot water drained from the unit can be saved and used during the subsequent solvent-addition stage. During the draining period, the superheater should be back-filled with treated condensate. This is a precautionary measure to prevent introducing hydrochloric-acid vapors to the superheater.

The drum-level gage glass should be removed from service and a temporary plastic tube gage installed to indicate the height of the acid in the steam drum.

With boiler metal temperatures in the range of 170-180F (Fig. 4) and drum vents open, valve 1 is opened, the filling pump is started, and heating steam is admitted through valve 6, and adjusted to heat the water to the unit to 160-170F. Addition of inhibited concentrated solvent, through valve 7, is started. The heating steam will require slight adjustment to maintain 160-170F solvent temperature. The rate of solvent feed is adjusted to bring the solution to the desired acid strength at sampling point 9. During the filling operation, frequent checks should be made and conditions adjusted so that the solvent fed to the unit is held at the desired strength and temperature. Filling of the unit should continue until the solvent level is at normal operating level in the steam drum. When the unit is full of solvent, the filling pump, auxiliary steam, and solvent feed are stopped. Valves 2 and 8 are closed and drum vent 5 is left open. The unit should then be allowed to soak for a period of time suitable for the conditions (*see Cleaning Time*).

On large units equipped with an economizer and where it is desirable to clean the economizer as well as the boiler, filling should be through the cleaning connections (Fig. 4) and to the economizer through the economizer drain lines. Since it usually takes longer to fill the economizer than to fill the boiler, filling of the boiler should be stopped when a level of solvent is sighted in the steam drum. Filling of the economizer should continue until a noticeable increase in solvent level in the steam drum occurs. The boiler should then be filled up to the normal operating level in the steam drum.

After having held the solvent in the unit for the prescribed length of time, the unit should be completely drained under nitrogen pressure by closing vent 5 and opening valves 2, 3 and 4. Nitrogen pressure of approximately 5 psi is sufficient.

During the draining, samples of the discharge solvent should be collected (location 9) at predetermined intervals and a composite sample prepared. Analysis of this sample for iron content and acid strength provides a basis for estimating the quantity of deposits removed and the amount of acid spent during the cleaning.

When the solvent has been drained from the unit until nitrogen is emitted from drain valve 3, valves 3 and 4 are closed and valves 1, 5 and 8 are opened. The pump is started and the unit filled with treated water, preferably demineralized, with a pH less than 8. If the economizer has been cleaned, the unit may be filled through the economizer. This will assure removing all acid from the economizer. In any case, the unit should be filled until a level is sighted in the steam drum. Filling is stopped and water is flushed through the feedwater stop-check valve until a noticeable increase in drum level appears. This will insure against a leaking valve and acid backing into the feedwater system. In addition, the superheater should be back-flushed until a level increase is observed in the drum. Continuing to fill the unit, until water overflows through vent 5, will assure removing uninhibited acid vapors that condense on the top of the drum. The unit is then drained under nitrogen pressure and the fill-and-flushing step is repeated. After draining

the unit again under nitrogen pressure, the pH of the rinse water is checked. If pH is less than 5, the fill-and-flushing step must be repeated.

When the flushing operation is complete, as indicated by pH measurement, the surfaces should be neutralized and passivated. After removing the temporary gage and cutting in the drum-level gage glass, the unit is filled with a solution of soda ash (10 lb per 100 gal water), to slightly below normal operating level. The unit is then fired and boiled out for 4 to 6 hours. Recommended boiling-out pressures are:

1. Operating pressure, for all boilers operating at 200 psi and less.
2. 200 psi or one-half the operating pressure, whichever is higher, for boilers operating above 200 psi. It is not necessary to exceed 600 psi.

During the duration of the boil-out, the economizer should be blown down several times by opening and closing drain valves to assure circulation. After completion of boil-out, firing is discontinued and the pressure allowed to decay to 20-25 psi. The unit is then drained. Draining under nitrogen pressure is not necessary at the completion of boil-out.

It is recommended that:

1. All inclined tubes with a slope of less than 60°, where the bottom of the tube in the sloped section is exposed to heat, should be flushed individually.
2. If the unit is cyclone fired, the Cyclone-Furnace tubes should be flushed individually.
3. Two upper wall headers and two lower wall headers should be flushed so that some water reaches each tube. If drains indicate a substantial amount of loose material being removed, then all headers should be opened and flushed toward the drain points.

The above recommendations are made to prevent tube failures by flushing out undissolved heavy iron deposits that are sometimes loosened by acid cleaning. If such deposits were allowed to remain in the tubes, they could cause overheating and failure when the unit is fired.

Chemical cleaning of superheater, reheater and steam piping

In the past, chemical cleaning of superheaters and reheaters were not generally performed because it was considered both unnecessary and needlessly expensive for so doing. With the advent of further problems due to the use of higher steam temperatures, the need for and the development of safe and satisfactory cleaning procedures for the cleaning of superheaters, reheaters and steam piping was accomplished and has gained acceptance. In particular, this has been further brought about because of:

1. With the advent of more stringent restrictions for steam line blowing during the initial operating stages of a unit start-up, chemical cleaning of these surfaces appears attractive from the standpoint of reduced periods of steam line blowing and affording more positive cleaning results.
2. Solid particle erosion damage to turbine components from the exfoliation of oxide scale is costing the utility industry millions of dollars per year in unscheduled downtime, maintenance and replacement parts.

Recent experience with chemical cleaning of the affected areas indicates that at least temporary relief from this problem can be achieved.

Adequate inspection, chemical cleaning tests and careful preparation are essential to the success of such an operation. Both drainable and non-drainable surfaces have been successfully cleaned.

In performing a chemical cleaning of surfaces that have experienced severe exfoliation, it is important to remove a tube sample that is representative of the worst condition. Generally, oxidation progresses at about the same rate on the outside of the tubes as on the inside and will usually exfoliate in the same manner. Thus, if one removes a tube sample which has the worst external appearance, it will probably also exhibit the worst internal condition.

The tube sample should be tested in a chemical cleaning test facility capable of producing a flow rate similar to those to be used in the actual cleaning. This facilitates development of a solvent mixture capable of cleaning the affected surfaces.

To determine the circulating pump size and flows required to achieve the desired velocities, it will usually be necessary to contact the boiler manufacturer for detail drawings and flow areas of the various circuits. Specific piping arrangements will vary greatly from one plant to another, depending on unit design and the particular areas to be cleaned.

Figs. 6 and 7 show possible piping schematics for a drum boiler system and once-through boiler system respectively.

In the case of a drum boiler, if it is desired to clean the boiler along with the superheater and reheater, it will usually be necessary to orifice the downcomers in order to obtain the desired velocities through the furnace walls.

A steam blow to purge all air and totally flood the system must precede the cleaning in all systems containing pendant non-drainable surfaces. Most drainable systems benefit from such a steam blow since most contain an inverted loop which makes air displacement difficult to achieve when filling.

Presently, two solvent mixtures are available that have successfully cleaned superheater, reheater and steam piping. One is a combination of hydroxyacetic and formic acids containing ammonium bifluride and the other is EDTA base solvent. Solvent strengths, temperature and cleaning period are best determined by subjecting tube samples to chemical cleaning tests under conditions similar to the actual cleaning operation.

Since the chemical cleaning of superheater and reheater requires special attention, it is strongly recommended that the services of a competent chemical-cleaning specialist be employed to assist in the system engineering and cleaning operations.

Precautions

Cleaning must not be considered a substitute for proper water treatment. The rigid control maintained in well-operated plants to achieve the best possible water treatment should not be relaxed because of the relative ease of cleaning by the chemical method. Chemical cleaning ordinarily is not necessary more often than once a year.

Intervals between cleanings should be extended or reduced as conditions warrant. This is essential, since each time a unit is chemically cleaned, the metal surfaces are depassivated or stripped of their protective oxide coating and, in addition, a slight amount of parent metal is dissolved because none of the known inhibitors is completely effective.

In handling acids, the recognized precautions of using goggles, rubber gloves, and rubber aprons should be observed. Acid should be poured slowly into water; never pour water into acid.

Acid cleaning removes mill scale and products of oxidation. A thorough visual inspection should be made after cleaning to determine whether any parts need to be replaced.

In riveted joints the solvent may enter seams, and damage can occur without being detected. Therefore, chemical cleaning of riveted drums is usually avoided. This applies particularly to drums calked on the outside.

The possibility of hydrogen gas being generated during the acid cleaning of internal heating surfaces should never be overlooked. The quantity of hydrogen released is a measure of the ineffectiveness of the inhibitor. A portion of the hydrogen will be absorbed by the metal, while the remainder will form part of the atmosphere in the vessel. The portion absorbed by the metal will be liberated gradually, the time required decreasing as the temperature of the metal increases. While the metal wastage indicated by its generation may be inconsequential, the hydrogen is a source of two potentially dangerous conditions—embrittlement of the steel and an explosive atmosphere in the vessel.

On the completion of acid cleaning, because of the possibility of hydrogen embrittlement, the steel should not be cold-worked (tubes rolled, flanges tightened, seams calked, etc.) in any manner for at least four or five days until the pressure boiling-out has been completed or the boiler has been brought up to steam pressure in the normal manner.

In opening a unit for inspection following an acid cleaning, the possibility of an explosion from the presence

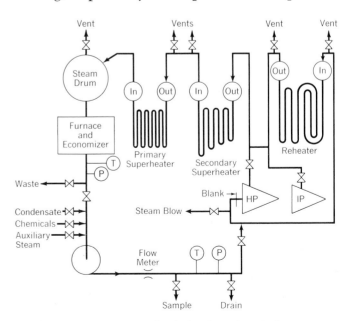

Fig. 6 Chemical cleaning circuit for drum-type boiler.

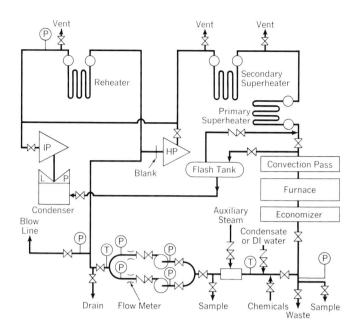

Fig. 7 Chemical cleaning circuit for once-through boiler.

of free hydrogen in the atmosphere within the unit must be recognized. There have been explosions of hydrogen in boiler atmospheres after acid cleaning, and fatal injuries have resulted. At atmospheric pressure and ordinary temperatures, the values indicated for the flammability of a mixture of hydrogen in air lie in the range from 6.2% as the lower limit to 71.4% as the upper limit. The ignition temperature of hydrogen in air, at atmospheric pressure, is between 1076 and 1094F.

It is imperative, therefore, because of the possibility of an explosion, to observe the following precautions: After an acid cleaning, no one should enter the unit or get in the way of any openings to the pressure parts unless the atmosphere within has been cleared of explosive gases. Until this has been done, open flames, flashlights, any other lighting equipment, or anything that might produce a spark of any kind must not be used within or near the openings of pressure parts.

The following steps may be taken to clear the atmosphere of explosive gases within the pressure parts: After acid cleaning, apart from other reasons the unit should be thoroughly flushed with warm water to a positive overflow from the topmost vent, to make certain that all the atmosphere within has been displaced. To warm the unit and thus accelerate the liberation of hydrogen absorbed in the metal, the temperature of the water should be held as nearly as possible at 212F by light firing or other means.

After the unit has been opened, air eductors, placed at locations such as open drum manholes, should be used to circulate air through the unit to remove hydrogen being liberated from the metal. This procedure should continue until analysis by a Burrell or other suitable instrument shows that the air inside is free of explosive gases.

Evaluation of results

Determination of the type and approximate amount of different kinds of scale and impurities removed from a unit at a cleaning will be possible if, at periodic intervals

during the operation, the spent cleaning solvent and the water solid matter ejected are properly sampled and analyzed and a record is kept of the total amount involved. This information will serve as a valuable guide for further boiler-water treatment and the determination of the required frequency of cleaning.

Repairs to fossil-fuel equipment

Repairs to steam generating equipment must meet exacting requirements. This is not surprising in view of the rigid requirements for design, fabrication and field erection of steam generating equipment. Three resources—experienced supervision, skilled manpower and adequate tooling—are necessary for the effective performance of repairs. In some situations, the assistance of the manufacturer is required, particularly when engineering design, metallurgy, welding technology, and special tool development are involved. The manufacturer's construction capabilities can often reduce the minimum downtime required to accomplish maintenance and repairs.

Performance monitoring and inspection establish the nature and amount of repair and adjustment to equipment that are required to return the unit to dependable operation. The equipment manufacturer can recommend, guide, or carry out the work, but final decision on what will be an acceptable, dependable repair rests with the operating company and insurance or state inspectors.

Repairs to pressure parts by welding

The ASME Code is not written specifically for repair work, but all materials and constructions used in repair work must meet code requirements. Repairs to pressure parts are made under the guidance of the *National Board Inspection Code* published by the National Board of Boiler and Pressure Vessel Inspectors, Columbus, Ohio. This code covers problems of inspections and repairs to boilers and auxiliary equipment that are not otherwise covered in the ASME Code. It suggests laws and regulations for inspection of pressure vessels, and rules for repairs by fusion welding. These rules are acceptable in practically all states.

No repairs by welding are to be made to a boiler without the approval of an authorized inspector. Where the strength of the structure depends on the strength of the weld, the repair must be made by a qualified operator. For repair work the welder need not be qualified by the manufacturer. The only requirement is that the inspector be satisfied with the welder's qualifications. Frequently a power station management will request that welders in its maintenance force be qualified by the manufacturer.

For certain repairs where the strength of the structure does not depend on the strength of the weld, as in building up corroded surfaces, the National Board rules permit the use of an "approved operator." The requirements for an approved operator, as outlined in the rules, are somewhat less rigid than those for a qualified operator.

Repairs defined by the *National Board Inspection Code* include:

1. Replacement of sections of tubes, provided the remaining part of the tube is not less than 75% of its original thickness.
2. Seal welding of tubes.

3. Building-up of certain corroded surfaces.
4. Repairs of cracked ligaments of drums or headers within certain definite limits.

Replacement of sections of tubes. The replacement of a section of failed tube can be done by a qualified operator. The length of the replaced section should be a minimum of 12 inches. Usual practice is to cut out the defective section with an oxyacetylene torch. Care must be taken to prevent slag from entering the tube. The ends are scarfed by grinding with special tools (Fig. 8). The use of backing rings (Fig. 17, Chapter 32) is generally recommended when sections are welded into existing tubes. However, where the backing ring is not used, as in high-heat-input zones of high pressure boilers, the space between tube ends should be a minimum and the first bead of the weld metal should be run with a $\frac{3}{32}$-in. diameter electrode. Use of the gas tungsten arc process is recommended for the root pass (Fig. 9). This is a gas-arc-welding process, which uses an inert gas to protect the weld zone from the atmosphere. It is described under *Gas-Shielded Tungsten-Arc Welding* in Chapter 31. If the tube to be replaced is of alloy material, the boiler manufacturer should be consulted for procedures and welding techniques.

Seal welding. Seal welds are used under some conditions for fluid tightness. Structural strength must be secured by some other means such as an expanded joint (*see Figs. 11, 12 and 13, Chapter 32*).

In new construction the ASME Code permits the elimination of the "flare" or "bell" on tubes to be seal welded, provided the throat of the seal weld is not less than $\frac{3}{16}$ in. nor more than $\frac{3}{8}$ in. This applies to a seal weld either inside or outside of the drum or header. For repair work the *National Board Inspection Code* permits seal welding.

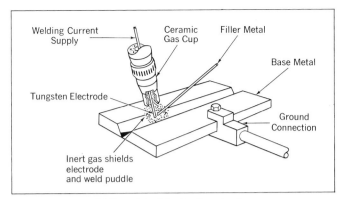

(a) Essentials of the Gas Tungsten Arc

(b) Applying Gas Tungsten Arc First-Pass Weld to Membrane Panel Repair

Fig. 9 Gas Tungsten Arc (GTA) welding.

Both codes require that tubes be reexpanded after seal welding. The reexpanding should be done lightly and the seal weld examined for cracks after the expanding operation is completed.

Building-up corroded surfaces and repairing cracked ligaments. Repairs included in these two categories vary considerably and can be extremely complex. It is recommended that each individual case be reviewed with the boiler manufacturer, operator, and authorized inspector to establish acceptable procedures.

Following all weld repairs, postweld heat treatment and inspection procedures should be implemented as required by the *National Board Inspection Code* and inspection authorities.

Removing tubes and fittings from drums and headers

Occasionally tubes must be removed and replaced because of damage or defects or because the boiler is to be dismantled and relocated. There are a variety of ways for removing tubes, depending on whether the tubes are to be salvaged, wholly or in part, or scrapped.

Expanded tubes. With light-gage tubes it is often possible to cold-crimp both ends of the tubes to loosen them in the seats and then drive or "jack" the tubes out.

When the tubes are too heavy for cold-crimping, the two-stage heating method may be used. The heat is applied to the inside of the tube end with a torch. Heat is first applied for a short period—not long enough for it to be transfered to the tubesheet. When the tube end

Fig. 8 Preparing tube ends for welding.

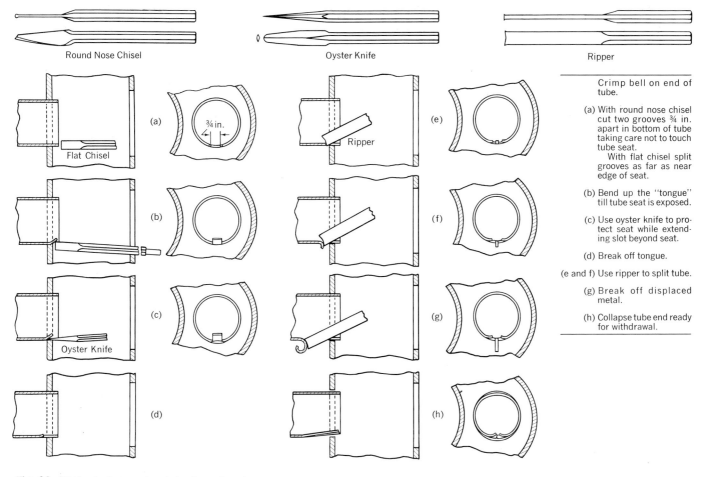

Crimp bell on end of tube.

(a) With round nose chisel cut two grooves ¾ in. apart in bottom of tube taking care not to touch tube seat.

    With flat chisel split grooves as far as near edge of seat.

(b) Bend up the "tongue" till tube seat is exposed.

(c) Use oyster knife to protect seat while extending slot beyond seat.

(d) Break off tongue.

(e and f) Use ripper to split tube.

(g) Break off displaced metal.

(h) Collapse tube end ready for withdrawal.

Fig. 10 Method of removing tube from header.

cools, the joint will have loosened enough so that the second heat will not be transferred readily to the tubesheet. The tube end can then be heated sufficiently for crimping and the tube can be pushed out of its seat.

If neither of these methods is applicable, the tubes are usually cut off close to the outside of the shell, and the stubs are removed later in a separate operation. To remove light tube stubs, it is advisable to cut grooves about ¾ in. apart with a round-nose chisel. When the tongue (the metal between the two grooves) is knocked free, the stub can be collapsed and removed (Fig. 10).

When a heavy gage tube must be replaced and the expanded end is a good joint, it is better not to disturb the expanded end provided there is outside access to the tube. It is simpler to cut off the tube at a convenient distance from the drum and join the stub end to the new tube with a ring weld. However, if there is no access for such a repair, the cutting can be done from inside the drum by careful use of a cutting torch. The tongues can be prepared without damage to the seat with the grooving tool shown in Fig. 11.

When it is impossible or inadvisable to use a torch, a cutting tool of the type illustrated in Fig. 12 is used.

Seal welded tubes. Seal welds are removed from tubes by using tools or cutters such as the one shown in Fig. 13. This particular tool will remove seal welds from 2½-in. OD tubes inside headers. It can also be used to cut off excess stock from 2½, 3 and 3¼-in. OD tubes.

Fig. 14 shows another type of cutter used for removing

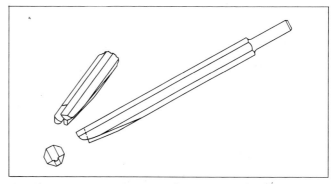

Fig. 11 Grooving tool for tube-stub removal.

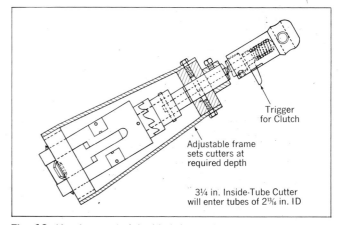

Trigger for Clutch

Adjustable frame sets cutters at required depth

3¼ in. Inside-Tube Cutter will enter tubes of 2¹³⁄₁₆ in. ID

Fig. 12 Hand operated inside-tube cutters.

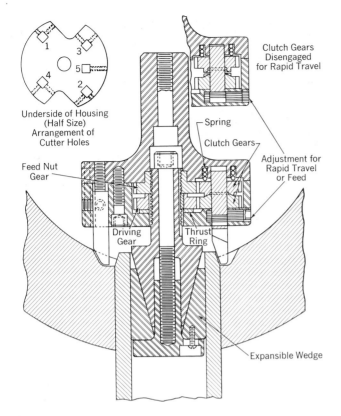

Underside of Housing
(Half Size)
Arrangement of
Cutter Holes

Feed Nut
Gear

Driving
Gear

Thrust
Ring

Clutch Gears
Disengaged
for Rapid Travel

Spring

Clutch Gears

Adjustment for
Rapid Travel
or Feed

Expansible Wedge

Fig. 13 Tool for removing weld from inside-seal-welded 2½-in. OD tubes; also for cutting off 2, 2½, 3 and 3¼-in. OD tubes.

the seal weld of small-diameter (marine superheater) tubes. The pilot and cutter assembly is placed in the tube, and driven through a universal joint and extension by an air motor located outside the header.

After removing the seal welds, the tubes and tube stubs may be removed as previously described.

Removal of seal-welded handhole fittings

In the course of repair and maintenance work it is often necessary to remove one or two handhole fittings that have been seal welded. The most practical way to do this, when no alloy material is involved, is to remove the seal weld with a cutting torch. Considerable care is required to prevent damage to the header in this process. Alternatively, the seal weld can be removed by grinding or chipping. While these methods are slower, they do not present the hazard involved in the burning process, and alloy materials can be handled without damage.

If a great number of fittings are to be removed from alloy headers, it may be advantageous to use special tools like the one shown in Fig. 15. This type of cutting tool is used outside the header to remove seal welds from 3¼, 4 and 4½-in. expanded-type cup caps and blind nipples, and welded-type handhole plugs.

Repairs to stud surfaces

During the construction, repair, and maintenance of boilers it is sometimes necessary to replace or provide additional welded studs on tubes and ductwork for attaching insulation, casings, doors, or refractories. In most applications the semi-automatic stud welder may be used (Fig. 16). The apparatus consists of a welding machine, a weld-timer and a welding gun. The surface to which

the stud will be welded should be free of dirt, but it is not necessary to remove paint or mill scale. The stud locations should be laid out accurately and the gun held in position to assure that the stud will be square with the plane of the wall or surface. It is important that the operator not permit the gun to slip while making the weld. The semi-automatic stud welder is not recommended for tubes less than 0.125-in. thick. Hand welded studs should be used for these.

Pulverizer maintenance

B&W manufactures two types of vertical shaft air swept pulverizers: 1) the EL (Fig. 17a) which operates on the ball-and-race principle, and 2) the MPS (Fig. 17b) which operates on the roll-and-race principle. (See also B&W Type MPS and Type EL Pulverizers, Chapter 9.)

In most power station applications, there is a spare pulverizer when firing the performance design coal. This permits scheduling of maintenance without impairing unit operation.

The operating and maintenance instructions for each type of pulverizer cover the specific items and procedures to be used. Contract documentation provides the operating coordination of the pulverizers to the system to be fired for the design coal.

Prior to placing a pulverizer system in service, initial inspections and recording of the items noted in the instructions should be made. This information sets the basis by which further maintenance work and spare part ordering can be planned. Good records will also show what a change in coal supply can mean in terms of man-

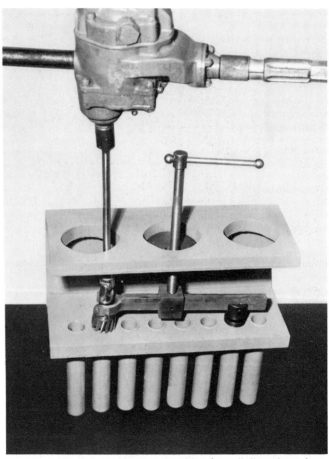

Fig. 14 Cutter for removing seal welds of small-diameter tubes.

power levels or budgetary costs for grinding the coal.

For many maintenance operations, specific tooling is provided as a means to do the work quickly and safely. Inspection and maintenance of this equipment is also essential to insure continued safe operation.

The normal replacement items such as wear parts are manufactured with tolerance on critical dimensions. The pulverizer has crucial settings such as mounting flatness, throat gap dimension or alignment, ring centering means, etc., and after periods of operation, rework of components may be necessary. In the case of the large roll wheel assemblies in the MPS pulverizer, the condition and tightness of the lip seals, the bearing tolerance, and the condition of the oil should be checked at convenient maintenance points during the wear cycle or over the life of the equipment. Preventive maintenance such as this helps insure high equipment availability.

Maintaining the operating variables such as air flow, spring tension and instrument calibration is essential to sustaining proper pulverizer operation. Low air flows will permit rejecting coal into the air plenum causing undue wear and possibly premature failure of components.

Rotating machinery

Balancing. The balancing of rotating machinery is given careful attention by the manufacturer and therefore field balancing is seldom necessary. However, it is sometimes impracticable to balance rotors dynamically for field-assembled fans in the manufacturer's shop. These rotors are made with very close tolerances for uniformity of section and are statically balanced with care,

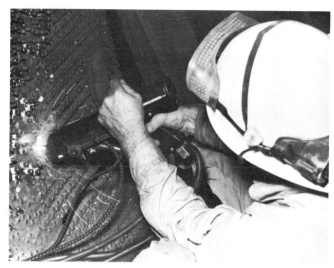

Fig. 16 Applying self-welding studs for refractory application.

and this is usually sufficient. However, when a fan under operating conditions sets up vibrations greater than the foundation can absorb, it is necessary to balance the rotor in the field.

Ball bearings. During the storage and field assembly of ball bearings, care must be taken to prevent the entrance of dirt which is the cause of 90% of the failures of bearings of this type. A ball bearing is not removed from its shipping container until immediately before installation when it should be laid on a clean sheet of paper and covered. It is not customary to wash off the factory lubricant. Bearings should be wiped with clean rags; cotton waste should not be used.

Ball bearings are usually assembled on shafts with the aid of a drift pipe (Fig. 18). They can either be pressed on with a hand or light power press (Fig. 18a) or driven on with a drift pipe and hammer (Fig. 18b).

If the hot-oil method is used in preparing a bearing for assembly, overheating must be avoided. About 225F is the highest permissible temperature. The shaft size should be checked to determine the tightness of fit. The bearing must be held against the shaft shoulder until it cools enough to grip the shaft tightly or, if there is a lock nut, it should be pulled down before the bearing cools. The bearing should be greased directly after assembly.

The same general precautions should be observed in removing a bearing (if it is to be used again) as when installing it. Correct methods of removal are illustrated in Fig. 19, sketches (a), (b) and (c). When a gear or some other part on the shaft abuts the inner ring, the bearing can be forced off ahead of the part, without injury, by tapping it lightly.

In arc welding on machinery having ball bearings, welders must be cautioned to attach the ground connection so that the current will not pass through the bearing. If this precaution is not observed, possible arcing between the bearing races and the balls may not only cause pitting but may also reduce the hardness of the courses with consequent quicker wear of the bearing.

After installation or repairs and before operation, it is necessary to make certain that all bearings of pulverizers, fans, feeders, pump motors and other rotating equipment are lubricated in accordance with approved practice.

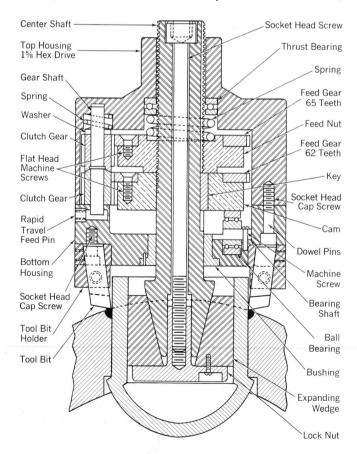

Center Shaft
Top Housing 1⅝ Hex Drive
Gear Shaft
Spring
Washer
Clutch Gear
Flat Head Machine Screws
Clutch Gear
Rapid Travel Feed Pin
Bottom Housing
Socket Head Cap Screw
Tool Bit Holder
Tool Bit

Socket Head Screw
Thrust Bearing
Spring
Feed Gear 65 Teeth
Feed Nut
Feed Gear 62 Teeth
Key
Socket Head Cap Screw
Cam
Dowel Pins
Machine Screw
Bearing Shaft
Ball Bearing
Bushing
Expanding Wedge
Lock Nut

Fig. 15 Tool for removal of seal welds from cup caps and blind nipples.

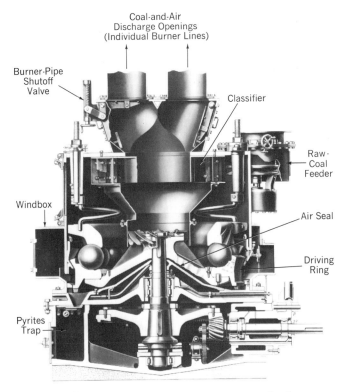

Fig. 17a B&W Type EL single-row ball-and-race pulverizer.

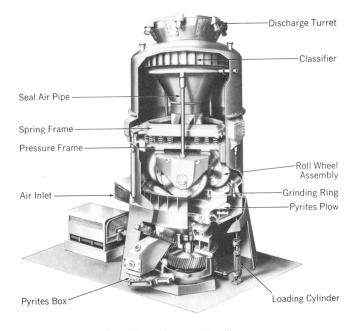

Fig. 17b Babcock & Wilcox Type MPS mill.

Care of idle equipment—fossil fuels

To minimize the possibility of corrosion, boilers to be removed from service must be carefully prepared for the idle period and closely watched during the outage. There are two methods available for storing the unit, wet storage and dry storage. Although the wet storage procedure is preferred, such factors as availability of good quality water, ambient weather conditions, integrity of boiler, length of storage period, etc., may dictate that the dry storage procedure is more practical.

Protection of internal surfaces — dry storage

When it is known that a boiler is to be idle for a considerable length of time and that a brief period will be allowed for preparation to return it to service, the dry storage method is recommended. In this method the unit is emptied, thoroughly cleaned internally and externally, dried, and then closed up tight to exclude both moisture and air. Trays of lime, silica gel, or other moisture absorbent may be placed in the drums to draw off the moisture in the air trapped by the closing up of the boiler.

The following general procedure is recommended when placing a unit into dry storage:

1. Fire the boiler according to the normal start-up procedure and establish 50 psig drum pressure. Secure the boiler and when the pressure decays to 20 psig, drain immediately under air. As soon as possible, open the drums to allow air to circulate for drying of all internal surfaces.

2. Install a tray containing a moisture absorbent (silica gel is preferred) into the drums. To insure against overflow of corrosive liquid after the moisture has been absorbed, the trays should not be more than three-quarters full of dry absorbent. The amount of moisture absorbent can vary but 1 lb per 1000 lb/hr steam flow capacity seems adequate.

3. Attach a source of nitrogen to the steam drum vent, close all other vents and drains and pressurize the boiler to 10 to 15 psig with nitrogen. The amount of nitrogen required will vary according to the volume of the unit.

4. With the boiler and superheater pressurized, alternately open all boiler drains (including superheater) to purge air from the unit until pressure decays to zero. It may be necessary to repeat this process several times to reduce the amount of oxygen left in the boiler to a minimum.

5. The unit should now be stored under 5 to 10 psig nitrogen pressure maintained at the steam drum.

6. We would recommend that periodic inspection of the unit be performed every 3 to 6 months to assure that no corrosive action is taking place and to replenish the absorbent as required. Since air will enter the unit during this inspection, it will be necessary to repeat steps 3 and 4 to expel this air.

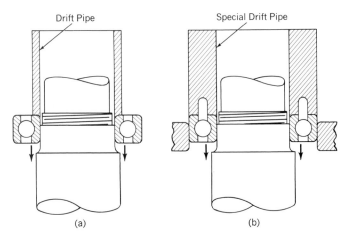

Fig. 18 Typical use of drift pipes in lightly pressing or driving ball bearings on shaft.

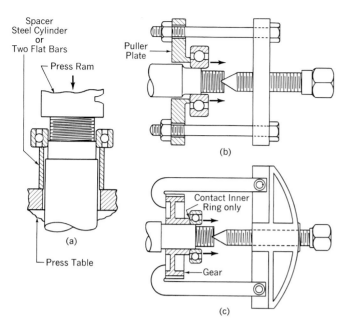

Fig. 19 Two general methods used for the safe removal of ball bearings. Sketch (a) shows use of arbor press and spacer. Sketches (b) and (c) show two types of conventional gear pullers adapted for this light service.

It is important to note that the unit should be properly tagged and the appropriate warning signs attached noting that the boiler is stored under nitrogen pressure and that complete exhaustion of the nitrogen must occur before anyone enters the drum. Otherwise, death by suffocation can result.

The above procedure is intended to include the economizer and superheater.

Protection of internal surfaces — wet storage

Where boilers go into standby service but must be available for immediate operation, they should be steamed in service, so that boiler water conditions may be stabilized and oxygen bubbles cleared from the boiler surfaces. The advantage of employing the wet storage procedure is that the unit is stored completely wet with the recommended levels of chemicals to eliminate a wet-dry interface where possible corrosion can occur. It is suggested that volatile chemicals be used to avoid increasing the level of dissolved solids in the boiler water which should be reduced to a minimum prior to the storage period.

In preparing a unit for wet storage, the following procedure is recommended:

1. Reduce the amount of total dissolved solids in the boiler water to a minimum consistent with good boiler operation.

2. The unit should be filled with deaerated, demineralized water treated with 500 ppm hydrazine (N_2H_4) for oxygen removal and sufficient ammonia (NH_3) to attain a pH of 10 (for demineralized water or condensate, this will require approximately 10 ppm ammonia).

3. We strongly recommend pre-mixing of the chemicals with the water to insure a uniform mixture entering the boiler. This can be accomplished by the blend-fill method, or if possible, by pre-mixing of the chemi-

cals in the condenser. Simply introducing the chemicals through the drum manhead after establishing water level will not insure adequate dispersion of chemicals to all internal surfaces, unless sufficient heat is delivered to the furnace (i.e., firing the boiler) to induce natural circulation throughout the boiler.

4. Fill the unit with the treated demineralized water until flooding occurs at the steam drum vent. The superheater can be filled via overflow from steam drum. An alternative is to fill the superheater through the header drains. Once the unit is completely filled, close all vents.

5. A source of low pressure nitrogen should be connected at the steam drum to maintain 5 to 10 psig to prevent air entering the unit.

6. If storage continues into the winter, ambient temperatures below freezing point of water create a real hazard to the boiler pressure parts and it will be necessary to provide a means of keeping the unit warm to avoid damage.

7. At some later date when the unit is to be returned to service, the boiler can be drained to normal start-up water level and placed into operation.

Even with the above procedure, the possibility of corrosion must not be underestimated. The boiler should be inspected periodically to inspect for possible corrosion damage. Analysis of the boiler water should be conducted periodically and, when necessary, sufficient chemicals added to establish the proper levels recommended. To insure uniform dispersion of the volatile chemicals, it will be necessary to repeat one of the methods outlined in step 3.

Protection of idle superheaters and reheaters

Superheaters during out-of-service periods, except when the wet storage method is used, should always be kept dry and closed from contact with air. Reheaters should be taken care of in the same manner as superheaters except that the wet storage method is never used. When it is almost impossible to pressurize the reheater with nitrogen, the following procedure may be employed. Before shutdown is complete, condenser vacuum should be maintained as long as possible to facilitate the removal of moisture in the reheater. With sufficient vacuum on the condenser, open the vents or drains on the primary inlet of the reheater to allow air to pass through to remove all moisture.

No unit should be wet stored when there is any probability of a temperature drop to the freezing point unless sufficient heat can be provided to the unit to eliminate the danger of water freezing and damage to pressure parts.

Protection of external surfaces

The external surfaces of all pressure parts and other metallic surfaces should be completely cleaned of all ash and soot deposits. Other ash, cinder, or fuel accumulations, such as on the grates, furnace floors, shelf baffles, and in the cinder hoppers, should be removed.

The settings should then be closed and kept closed, but periodic inspection should be made regularly to guard against sweating and corrosion of the external

surfaces of the pressure parts, particularly when the wet storage method is used. In this connection it may be necessary to use coke stoves, or similar heating devices at convenient points to keep all metal surfaces above the dew point, particularly during protracted spells of damp weather accompanied by rising temperature.

Equipment for nuclear fuels

Maintenance in a nuclear power plant, whether preventive or corrective, usually involves techniques and equipment necessitated by the requirements of radiological safety, quality control, and operational testing which govern the performance of nuclear plant repair work. The most frequent maintenance problems which affect the operation of a nuclear plant include primary coolant leaks, instrumentation and control-equipment failures, and steam-system equipment malfunction. Other maintenance problems, which are unique to nuclear plants, include auxiliary-system-fluid leaks that require a reactor to be shut down, inaccessibility of major components during reactor operation, reactor containment integrity and leak isolation, and the size and complexity of reactor coolant pumps.

Nuclear radiation

The greatest maintenance problem and one that affects nearly all nuclear repair operations is the potential hazard imposed by nuclear radiation. An area of high radiation restricts a worker to severe controls and requires supporting activities and equipment. A large part of the primary planning, design and administrative considerations governing plant maintenance are concerned with providing the ability to work safely, in spite of the presence of dangerous substances. Nuclear maintenance operations are planned as no-risk activities. A job does not start until the equipment and procedures necessary to ameliorate all existing and potential problems are made available. The extensive forethought and design sophistication demanded by today's large nuclear power plants have afforded the industry a safety record second to none.

The area in which the job is to be done must be completely surveyed so that the extent and location of the varying radiation fields and contaminated areas and the concentration of airborne activity are known. On the basis of this information the worker may be restricted as to where he may work, how long he can spend in a particular location, and what protection he must have, such as protective clothing, respiration equipment, or portable shielding. These preparations are time-consuming. Additional manpower may also be required so that, by rotation, a worker is prevented from receiving the permissible radiation exposure, which would prevent him from further radiation work for a specified period of time. Delegation of portions of a particular job allow key personnel to cover several jobs at once without overexposure to radiation.

Special tools and equipment. Special tools are required in many cases to facilitate unique requirements such as the disassembly of a radioactive component in a pool of water or behind a wall of shielding. Optical devices such as borescopes, periscopes, and closed-circuit television are also employed.

Temporary shielding is used occasionally in areas where a worker must perform a task close to a point of concentrated radiation. For example, to replace a temperature detector near a primary coolant piping elbow (a common "crud trap"), lead blankets and bricks are laid around the piping until the radiation level is reduced to the point where the worker can spend the time necessary to do the job.

Considerable design effort must be directed toward radiation problems associated with the use or location of a particular component. A current improvement in this direction involves the modularization of components. A modularized, or one-piece, pump-motor-stand combination allows quick removal and replacement of a spare unit. The effect on plant downtime as well as the potential personnel radiation exposure is reduced because the repairs to the unit are made while the replacement unit is already in service.

Preparation for maintenance

Preparations for some maintenance operations include provisions for preventing the spread of surface or airborne radioactivity to areas outside of the immediate work area. For such operations as "burning," grinding, and welding, the work area is isolated by constructing a "clean room" around the area by use of plastic sheet and other disposable materials. Personnel working inside the room wear protective clothing and respirators. An area outside the room entrance is cordoned off as a monitored entry and exit station. When the job is completed, the room is carefully dismantled and the work area is decontaminated. Contaminated trash from the job is packaged and marked for disposal, usually by a licensed radioactive-waste-disposal contractor. All tools and equipment used in the job are enclosed in plastic and removed to a radiological workshop for decontamination. It is common practice to leave some tools in the work area, where frequent reuse makes decontamination futile. The work area, especially if it is open to normal entry during plant operation, will be decontaminated and surveyed. Any radiation or contamination remaining after the survey is noted by posting a standard radiation warning at the entrance to the area.

Other maintenance-related factors that are unique to nuclear steam supply systems are the inability to drain the reactor coolant system while the nuclear fuel is in the reactor vessel and the requirement to continue removing decay heat long after the reactor is shut down. The radioactive decay of fission products and irradiated core structural material continues to generate considerable heat and radiation after the fission process is stopped. The heat generated is sufficient to melt the cladding around the fuel unless a cooling medium is available to absorb the heat and carry it away from the core (see Decay-Heat-Removal System, Chapter 21).

The two factors mentioned must be carefully considered in the layout of components and piping, particularly with respect to the relative elevations of components. For example, Oconee Nuclear Station, Unit 1 (Chapter 23) is arranged to permit draining of the steam generators, the reactor coolant pump volutes, and

the pressurizer for inspection and maintenance while maintaining the reactor vessel water level and recirculating the coolant in the vessel through a decay-heat-removal system.

Steam generators

The steam generators, which are actually tubular heat exchangers, are similar functionally to their fossil-fuel counterparts. However, the inside of the tubes contains the reactor coolant, so that inspection and maintenance planning must include consideration of radioactivity. Since the tubesheet and plenum areas of the steam generators become high radiation areas, B&W has developed a system that allows leaking steam generator tubes to be plugged from a remote location by an explosive welding technique (Fig. 20).

Data from nuclear plants with five to ten years of operating experience indicate that the radiation levels in the tubesheet areas are such that only an hour or less of work could be performed before a worker would reach the maximum quarterly radiation dose permitted by the Nuclear Regulatory Commission (*see Health Physics, Chapter 20*). Such a radiation problem requires not only the prescribed radiation safety precautions, but also equipment and techniques designed to reduce working time in the area to the practical minimum.

The principal maintenance problem associated with these heat-exchanger-type steam generators is tube leakage, which can be caused by chemical or mechanical action or a combination of the two. There are four methods of detecting a steam generator tube leak during plant operation:

1. The radiation monitor of the turbine-condenser air-ejector vent will indicate the presence of even trace amounts of radioactive reactor coolant in the secondary system.

2. Chemical and radiochemical analysis of condensate.

3. Chemical and radiochemical analysis of the boiler water.

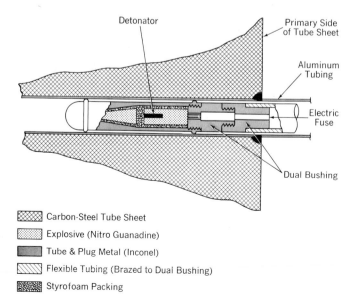

Fig. 20 Equipment for plugging once-through steam generator tubes by explosive technique.

4. The makeup rate to the primary system coupled with the above indications and possibly a decreased condensate makeup.

The order of the above indications matches the increasing seriousness of a progressing leak. When a tube leak is detected, the plant may continue to operate until the technical specification limit for tube leakage is reached. After the plant has been shut down to repair the leak, the following steps are taken to prepare the steam generator for leak location:

1. After cooling, the primary side of the steam generator is drained.

2. A radiation survey of the areas around the upper and lower primary heads of the steam generator is taken to determine the health physics requirements for the work area.

3. Tools and equipment required for manway removal and leak detection are transported to the work area.

4. The manways are removed, providing access to the plenum and tubesheet areas, and seals are placed in the primary piping.

5. A radiation survey is made inside the steam generator heads to determine access, decontamination, shielding, and time limitation requirements.

The steam side of the steam generator is then filled with water. A dye may be put into the water to aid in detecting leaky tube seats. Gross leakers are immediately identified by water flowing from the lower tubesheet. The leaking tubes are marked with marking plugs. Smaller leaks are found by pressurizing the secondary side and again marking the leakers. After all the leaking tubes are identified, the axial locations of the leaks are determined by passing a balloon, alternately inflated and deflated, through the tube, or by using an ultrasonic or eddy current probe. This is necessary to determine the region of the steam generator where leaks are forming so that subsequent operating practices may be corrected if required.

An alternate means for detecting leaks is pressurizing the steam side with a gas, e.g., nitrogen, and scanning the tubesheets with an acoustic probe.

When the leaking tubes are identified, they are plugged by tube plugs, which are either driven, expanded or welded into the tubes. The welding method is the most reliable, but is also very time-consuming.

Another technique used to reduce this time is the explosive tube-plug method. The plug and the tube are welded together by detonating an explosive charge inside the plug, as illustrated in Fig. 20. The explosion, which is detonated remotely, causes the walls of the plug to expand toward the tube wall at such a velocity that, upon impact, a metallurgical bond is created between the tube and the plug. With this technique, the inspection port provides the required access without the necessity of removing the manway or entering the plenum chamber. After plugging of all the leaking tubes, the steam side of the steam generator is hydrotested to verify the integrity of the repairs.

Chemical cleaning. While high-purity feedwater is used in the once-through steam generator, chemical

cleaning of the steam side may be required during the life of the steam generator because of the high feedwater flow rate. The type of dissolved and undissolved solid constituents in the feedwater will depend on the characteristics of the equipment preceding the boiler in the particular plant involved. When the performance of the steam generator indicates that corrective action is necessary, the first step is hot soaking and flushing. This procedure involves filling the steam generator with feedwater to within a few feet of the upper tubesheet and blanketing the remaining space with nitrogen. The water is maintained at about 200F and periodically analyzed for dissolved solids until an equilibrium condition is reached. The unit is then drained while maintaining the nitrogen blanket.

The insoluble material that cannot be removed by the soak and flush techniques consists of metal oxides, about 90% Fe_3O_4. If continued reduced performance indicates that insoluble material is responsible, chemical cleaning is accomplished by the soaking method (*see Soaking*), using dilute organic acids, ammonia, hydrazine, and an inhibitor. As the cleaning operation progresses, the concentrations of oxides, suspended material, and the cleaning chemicals are analyzed to ascertain that the insoluble material is being removed and that the cleaning solution is not being excessively depleted. The process is continued until chemical analysis establishes that an equilibrium condition has been reached. The unit is then drained and flushed with demineralized water with a nitrogen blanket maintained in the voided space. Flushing is repeated until all traces of the cleaning solution have been removed.

Instrumentation and control equipment

The maintenance of instrumentation and control equipment in nuclear plants is similar to maintenance in fossil-fuel plants that incorporate the latest advances in instrument versatility and reliability. Generally, modularization is the one advance that has done the most to simplify nuclear control equipment maintenance. Instead of providing the manpower to accomplish in-situ testing and repair of pressure, flow and temperature transmitters during a maintenance outage, shop-maintained units are exchanged for original units, quick tests to verify operability are performed, and the units removed are sent to the shop. The hours necessary to clean, replace parts, and make fine adjustments are performed in the shop, instead of extending the downtime of the plant. Modularization is used extensively in electronic components such as the push-in-pull-out circuitry of plant computers. The electronics of safety systems requires almost constant periodic surveillance. Multiple-parallel power and control circuits are provided so that one system can be isolated or deactivated for testing and maintenance, while the reactor remains in operation with the other system in service.

Tables of measurement

Length and area

1 statute mile (mi)	= 1760 yards = 5280 feet = 1.609 kilometers
1 yard (yd)	= 3 feet = 0.914 meter
1 foot (ft)	= 12 inches = 304.8 millimeters
1 inch (in.)	= 25.40 millimeters
100 ft per min	= 0.508 meter per sec
1 square mile	= 640 acres = 259 hectares
1 acre	= 4840 sq yards = 0.4047 hectare
1 square yard	= 9 sq feet = 0.836 sq meter
1 square foot	= 144 sq inches = 0.0929 sq meter
1 square inch	= 645.2 sq millimeters
1 kilometer (km)	= 1000 meters = 0.621 statute mile
1 meter (m)	= 1000 millimeters (mm) = 1.094 yards = 3.281 feet = 39.37 inches
1 micron	= 0.001 millimeter = 0.000039 inch
1 meter per sec	= 196.9 ft per min
1 sq kilometer (sq km)	= 100 hectares = 0.3861 sq mile
1 hectare (ha)	= 10,000 sq meters = 2.471 acres
1 sq meter (sq m)	= 10^6 sq millimeters = 1.196 sq yards = 10.76 sq feet

1 nautical mile = 6080 feet = 1.853 kilometers
1 nautical mile per hour = 1 knot

Weight

1 U.S. long ton	= 2240 pounds = 1016 kilograms
1 U.S. short ton	= 2000 pounds = 907 kilograms
1 pound (lb)	= 16 ounces = 7000 grains = 0.454 kilogram
1 ounce (oz)	= 0.0625 pound = 28.35 grams
1 grain	= 64.8 milligrams = 0.0023 ounce
1 pound per foot	= 1.488 kg per meter
1 metric ton (tonne)	= 1 megagram = 1000 kilograms = 0.984 long ton = 1.102 U.S. short tons = 2205 pounds
1 kilogram (kg)	= 1000 grams = 2.205 pounds
1 gram (g)	= 1000 milligrams (mg) = 0.03527 ounce = 15.43 grains
1 kg per meter	= 0.672 pound per ft

Volume

1 cubic yard	= 27 cubic feet
	= 0.765 cubic meter
1 cubic foot	= 1728 cubic inches
	= 28.32 liters
1 cubic inch	= 16,390 cu millimeters
1 imperial gallon	= 277.4 cubic inches
	= 4.55 liters
1 U.S. gallon	= 0.833 imperial gallon
	= 3.785 liters
	= 231 cubic inches
1 U.S. barrel (petroleum)	= 42 U.S. gallons
	= 35 imperial gallons
1 cubic meter (cu m)	= 1000 liters
	= 1.308 cubic yards
	= 35.31 cubic feet
1 liter	= 10^6 cu millimeters
	= 0.2200 imperial gallon
	= 0.2642 U.S. gallon
	= 61.0 cubic inches
1 board foot	= 12 in. x 12 in. x 1 in. thick
	= 144 cubic inches
1 cu ft per min	= 1.699 cu m per hour
1 cu m per hour	= 0.589 cu ft per min

Density

1 cu ft per lb	= 0.0624 cu m per kg
1 lb per cu ft	= 16.02 kg per cu m
1 grain per cu ft	= 2.288 grams per cu m
1 grain per U.S. gallon	= 17.11 grams per cu m
	= 17.11 milligrams/liter
1 cu m per kilogram	= 16.02 cu ft per lb
1 kilogram per cu m	= 0.0624 lb per cu ft
1 gram per cu m	= 0.437 grain per cu ft
	= 0.0584 grain per U.S. gal
1 gram per liter	= 58.4 grain per U.S. gal

Water at 62 F (16.7 C)

1 cubic foot	= 62.3 lb
1 lb	= 0.01604 cu ft
1 U.S. gal	= 8.33 lb

Water at 39.2 F (4 C), maximum density

1 cubic foot	= 62.4 pounds
1 cubic meter	= 1000 kilograms
1 pound	= 0.01602 cubic foot
1 liter	= 1.0 kilogram

1 kg per cu m = 1 gram per liter = 1 part per thousand
1 g per cu m = 1 mg per liter = 1 part per million (ppm)

Pressure

1 atmosphere (standard)	= 101,325 pascals
	= 760 mm (29.92 in.) mercury with density 13.595 grams per cc
	= 14.696 pounds per square inch
	= 1.033 kg per sq cm
	= 1013 millibars
1 atmosphere (metric)	= 98,066.5 pascals
	= 1 kg force (kgf) per sq cm
	= 10,000 kg per sq m
	= 10 m head of water
	= 14.22 lb per sq in.
1 bar (megadyne per sq cm)	= 100,000 pascals
	= 1000 millibars
	= 750.1 mm head of mercury
	= 1.02 kg per sq cm
	= 14.50 lb per sq in.
1 lb per square foot	= 47.88 pascals
	= 0.1924 in. of water
	= 4.88 kilograms per sq m
1 lb per square inch	= 6894 pascals
	= 2.036 in. head of mercury
	= 2.309 ft head of water
	= 0.0703 kilogram per sq cm
	= 0.0690 bar
1 ton per square inch	= 13,789 kilopascals
	= 1.406 kilograms per sq mm
1 inch head of water	= 248.976 pascals
	= 5.20 pounds per sq ft
1 foot head of water	= 2987.7 pascals
	= 0.433 pound per sq in.
1 m head of water	= 9806 pascals
	= 0.1 kg per sq cm
1 in. head of mercury	= 3386 pascals
	= 0.491 pound per sq in.
1 m head of mercury	= 133.3 kilopascals
	= 1.360 kg per sq cm
	= 1333 millibars
1 kilogram per sq m	= 9.806 pascals
	= 1 mm head of water
	= 0.2048 lb per sq ft
1 kilogram per sq cm	= 98.066 kilopascals
	= 735.5 mm of mercury
	= 0.981 bar
	= 14.22 lb per sq in.
1 kg per sq mm	= 9.8066 megapascals
	= 0.711 ton per sq in.

In these conversions, inches and feet of water are measured at 62 F (16.7 C), millimeters and meters of water at 39.2 F (4 C), and inches, millimeters, and meters of mercury at 32 F (0 C).

Heat, work, and power

The British thermal unit (Btu) or the kilogram-Calorie (Cal) were originally defined as the heat required to raise the temperature of 1 pound or 1 kilogram of water by 1 F or 1 C, respectively. Recently the International Calorie has been defined as 1/860 International kilowatt-hour. The Btu is derived from the International Calorie from the relation 1 Cal per kg = 1.8 Btu per lb. The differences are less than 0.05 of 1% and are therefore, for the purposes of these tables, negligible.

The modern metric system (System International) is being adopted in almost all countries of the world, including the U.S.A. The unit for energy is the joule and for power, the watt.

1 British thermal unit (Btu)	= 778.17 foot-pounds (778)
	= 107.6 kilogram-meters
	= 0.2520 Calorie
1 Btu per lb	= 0.556 Calorie per kg
1 Btu per cu ft	= 8.90 Cal per cu meter
1 Btu per sq ft	= 2.712 Cal per sq meter
1 Btu per sq ft, F	= 4.88 Cal per sq m, C
1 Btu/hr, sq ft, F/ft	= 1.488 Cal/hr, sq m, C/m
1 Btu/hr, sq ft, F/in.	= 0.1240 Cal/hr, sq m, C/m
1 therm	= 100,000 Btu
1 Calorie (Cal)	= 3088 foot-pounds
	= 427 kilogram-meters
	= 3.968 Btu
1 Cal per kilogram	= 1.8 Btu per pound
1 Cal per cu meter	= 0.1124 Btu per cubic foot
1 Cal per sq meter	= 0.3687 Btu per square foot
1 Cal/sq meter, C	= 0.2048 Btu/sq ft, F
1 Cal/hr, sq m, C/m	= 0.672 Btu/hr, sq ft, F/ft
	= 8.06 Btu/hr, sq ft, F/in.

1 electrical unit	= 1 kilowatt-hour
1 foot-pound (ft lb)	= 0.1383 kilogram-meter
1 kilogram-meter (kg m)	= 7.23 foot-pounds
1 kilowatt (kw)	= 738 foot-pounds per sec
	= 102 kilogram-meters per sec
	= 1.341 horsepower
	= 1.360 metric horsepower
1 horsepower (hp)	= 33,000 foot-pounds per min
	= 550 foot-pounds per sec
	= 76.04 kilogram-meters per sec
	= 0.746 kilowatt
	= 1.014 metric horsepower
1 metric horsepower	= 32,550 foot-pounds per min
	= 542 foot-pounds per sec
	= 75 kilogram-meters per sec
	= 0.735 kilowatt
	= 0.986 horsepower
1 kilowatt-hour (kwhr)	= 3412.14 Btu (3412)
	= 860 Calories
	= 3.6×10^6 joules
	= 3.600×10^{16} dyne-cm
1 horsepower-hour	= 2545.1 Btu (2545)
1 metric horsepower-hour	= 632 Calories
1 lb per horsepower-hour	= 0.447 kg per metric hp-hr
1 kg per metric hp-hour	= 2.235 lb per horsepower-hr
1 boiler horsepower	= 10 sq ft of boiler heating surface
	= 34.5 lb per hour evaporation from and at 212 F
100% boiler rating	= 3348 Btu (i.e., 3.45 lb evaporation from and at 212 F) per sq ft heating surface per hour

Glossary/symbols and abbreviations

Symbols
(*See also Tables 1 and 2, Chapter 35, for Control symbols*)

A—area, usually cross sectional, sq ft; mass number (number of nucleons in nucleus); total work function

A_g—gas flow area, sq ft

A_s—steam flow area, sq ft

a—inside radius; major axis of ellipsoid

B—barometric pressure, in. of mercury; buckling; buildup factor

Btu_{pc}—Btu/lb on pure coal basis

b—minor axis of ellipsoid; outside radius; width of duct

C—a coefficient; conversion factor

C_q—coefficient of discharge

C_v—flow coefficient

c—specific heat, Btu/lb, F—hotter fluid; velocity of light

c_a—specific heat, Btu/lb, F—air

c_g—specific heat, Btu/lb, F—flue gas

c_p—specific heat, Btu/lb, F—at constant pressure

c_v—specific heat, Btu/lb, F—at constant volume

c'—specific heat, Btu/lb, F—colder fluid

D—diameter, ft; distance from radioactive source to source side of weld

D_e—equivalent diameter, ft

DF—dose distribution factor (nuclear radiation)

D_i—inside diameter, ft

D_o—outside diameter, ft

d—depth; deuteron; diameter, usually in.; differential operator; inside diameter, in.

d_e—equivalent diameter, in.; equivalent thermocouple depth

d_i—inside diameter, in.

d_o—outside diameter, usually in.

E—energy; modulus of elasticity

E_f—energy produced per fission, MeV

E_p—reactor-power-level error signal

e—exergy = maximum energy available for useful work, Btu/lb

F—a function; force, lb; Gibbs function (free energy)

F_a—arrangement factor, depending on geometry

F_c—correction factor

FC_{pc}—fixed carbon, %, on pure-coal basis

F_d—depth factor

F_I—inertial force

F_{LF}—laminar flow factor

F_{pp}—physical properties factor

F_s—surface effectiveness factor

F_T—temperature factor

F_μ—viscous force

F_{12}—angle factor

f—friction factor; thermal utilization factor; true reaction

f_{LB}—modified friction factor

G—geometrical factor; mass velocity, lb/sq ft, hr, or lb/sq ft, sec $= w/A = \rho V$

G_a—air mass velocity, lb/sq ft, hr

G_g—mass velocity of gas, lb/sq ft, hr

G_s—steam mass velocity, lb/sq ft, hr

G_w—water mass velocity, lb/sq ft, hr

g—fixed end reaction; gravitational acceleration, 32.17 ft/sec^2

g_c—conversion constant, 32.17 ft lb mass/lb force, sec^2

H—head of fluid flowing, ft; heating value Btu/lb; static head, ft lb force/lb mass

H_d—net head in downcomer

H_r—net head in riser

H_{sp}—static head, in. of water

H_{tp}—total head, in. of water

H_w—velocity pressure, or fan pressure differential, in. of water

h—enthalpy of fluid, Btu/lb; height; vessel thickness

h_{ac}—acceleration loss

h_b—bend loss

h_{en}—entrance loss

h_{ex}—exit loss

h_f—enthalpy of saturated liquid, Btu/lb; fluid friction

h_{fg}—enthalpy of evaporation, Btu/lb

h_g—enthalpy of saturated vapor or flue gas, Btu/lb

h_k—change-in-section loss

h_s—steam separator loss

h_v—velocity head (pitot tube differential), in. of water

$h_{\Sigma d}$—sum of downcomer losses, ft of std water

$h_{\Sigma r}$—sum of riser losses, ft of std water

h'—enthalpy of colder fluid, Btu/lb

h_1'—enthalpy of feedwater entering, Btu/lb

h_2'—enthalpy of primary steam leaving superheater, Btu/lb

h_1''—enthalpy of steam entering reheater, Btu/lb

h_2''—enthalpy of steam leaving reheater, Btu/lb

Δh_s—change in enthalpy corresponding to change in pressure at constant entropy

I—intensity; moment of inertia of member

J—mechanical equivalent of heat, 778.17 ft lb/Btu

K—a factor or coefficient

K_{eq}—equilibrium constant

K_f—constant

K_{Re}—Reynolds number factor

K_t—stress concentration

k—a constant; exponent for constant entropy; multiplication factor (nuclear chain reaction); thermal conductivity, Btu/sq ft, hr, F/in., or Btu/sq ft, hr, F/ft

k_{eff}—effective multiplication factor (nuclear chain reaction)

k_T—isothermal compressibility

k_∞—multiplication factor for a hypothetical infinite system

Δk—nuclear chain reaction $= k - 1$

$\Delta k_{\mathrm{eff}} - k_{\mathrm{eff}} - 1$

L—length, usually ft; stack height, ft; thermal diffusion length

L_f—fast nonleakage factor

L_t—thermal nonleakage factor

ℓ or l—thickness, in.

ℓ_e or l_e—equivalent thickness, in.

$l_\parallel$—tube spacing on centers parallel to gas flow, in.

$l_\perp$—tube spacing on centers transverse to gas flow, in.

M—atomic weight, grams/gram-atom; molecular weight of a gas; % moisture in steam sample

Ⓜ—motor

Mc_p—mean molal specific heat, Btu/mole, F

MD—mass defect, amu

M_o—moment

Mw_d—megawatt demand

m—an exponent; mass

m_e—mass of nuclide, including electrons, amu

m_h—mass of hydrogen atom, amu

m_n—mass of neutron, amu

N—a number; number of atoms per cc; number of cycles (to failure)

N_b—number of velocity heads lost in bends

N_c—contraction loss factor

N_d—reactor power level demand

N_e—enlargement loss factor

N_i—reactor power level signal

N_o—Avogadro's number, 0.602252 x 10^{24} atoms/gram-atom

$N(t)$—number of atoms per cu cm at time, t

Nu—Nusselt number $= U_c D/k$, dimensionless

N_v—number of velocity heads lost

N_{vh}—number of velocity heads

$N(0)$—number of atoms per cu cm at time zero

n—neutron; neutron density, neutrons/cu cm; number of cycles; number of moles

nv—neutron flux, neutrons/sq cm, sec

P—absolute pressure, lb/sq ft; concentrated load

P_o—redundant force

P_R—p_1/p_2

Pr—Prandtl number, $c_p \mu/k$, dimensionless

P_1—incident particle in a nuclear reaction

P_2—resultant particle in a nuclear reaction

p—pressure, lb/sq in. or lb/sq ft; proton; resonance escape probability

p_r—partial pressure, atmospheres

p_v—velocity pressure, lb/sq ft

p'—pressure, colder fluid, lb/sq in.

Δp—pressure drop of fluid, lb/sq in. or in. of water

Δp_a—pressure drop, acceleration, lb/sq ft

Δp_e—pressure drop, entrance and exit, in. of water

Symbols (cont'd)

Δp_f — pressure drop (draft loss) in straight channel, in. of water or lb/sq ft

Δp_H — fluid head, lb/sq ft

$\Delta p_{TPF}/\Delta p_o$ — Martinelli-Nelson multiplier

$\Delta(pv)$ — pressure head difference, ft

$\Delta p_b'$ — additional pressure drop due to bends, lb/sq in.

$\Delta p_e'$ — pressure drop, entrance and exit, lb/sq in.

$\Delta p_f'$ — pressure drop, friction, lb/sq in.

Q — heat, Btu/lb or ft lb/lb; volumetric flow rate, cu ft/min

QF — quality factor (nuclear radiation)

Q_H — high heat value of fuel, Btu/lb

Q_L — low heat of combustion of fuel, Btu/lb

Q_{rev} — reversible heat flow, Btu/lb

q — rate of heat flow, Btu/hr

q_a — net heat available, Btu/hr

q_c — rate of heat flow by convection, Btu/hr

q/S — heat flux, Btu/sq ft, hr

R — universal gas constant = 1545 ft lb/mole, T

R_g — specific gas constant = $1545/M$

R — a radius; film resistance, sq ft, hr, F/Btu; overall or combined resistance of heat flow path = $1/U$, sq ft, hr, F/Btu

RA — reduction in area, %

R_{ab} — resistance across outside film

R_{bc} — resistance across tube wall

R_c — radius of core

R_{cd} — resistance across inside film

R_{cg} — resistance of gas film to convection heat flow

R_{cs} — resistance of colder fluid film to convection heat flow

Re — Reynolds number = $\rho VD/\mu = GD/\mu$, dimensionless

R_o — radius of bend center line

R/P — reserves/production ratio

R_R — radius of core plus reflector

R_{rg} — resistance of gas film to radiant heat flow

R_{tw} — resistance of tube wall to conduction heat flow

r — a radius, usually in.

r_1 — longitudinal radius

r_2 — hoop radius

S — entropy, Btu/R; heating surface, sq ft; surface area, sq ft

S_R — refractory surface

S_w — water-cooled surface

s — specific entropy, Btu/lb, R (conventionally written Btu/lb, F)

s_f — specific entropy, saturated liquid, Btu/lb, R

s_{fg} — specific entropy of evaporation, Btu/lb, R

s_g — specific entropy, saturated vapor, Btu/lb, R

T — absolute temperature, R (F + 460); distance from radioactive-source side of weld to film; thickness

T_a — temperature of air, R

T_b — bulk fluid temperature, R

T_f — film temperature, R

T_g — gas temperature, R

T_o — temperature of heat sink, R

TS — tensile strength, psi

$T_{\frac{1}{2}}$ — radioactive half-life

T_{250} — temperature, F, for 250-poise viscosity

$\overline{\Delta T}$ — temperature deviation from a set point (control)

t — a point in time; temperature, F — generally of hotter fluid, or at a point; time, hr

t_a — temperature at inside surface, F

t_b — bulk fluid temperature, F

t_F — fluid temperature (air or gas), F

t_f — film temperature, F

t_i — inside fluid temperature, F

t_{LB} — bulk coolant temperature at initiation of local boiling, F

t_o — outside fluid temperature, F

t_s — wall temperature, F

t_{sat} — saturation temperature, F

t_w — tube temperature (cladding surface), F

t' — temperature, F, of colder fluid

t_f' — air film temperature, F

t_s' — receiving surface temperature, F

t_1' — temperature, F, dry-bulb (ambient)

Δt — temperature difference, F

Δt_f — film temperature difference, F; film temperature drop

Δt_m — logarithmic mean temperature difference, F

Δt_{sat} — excess of wall temperature above saturation, F

Δt_1 — initial temperature difference

Δt_2 — final temperature difference

U — film conductance, Btu/sq ft, hr, F; overall or combined conductance = $1/R$, Btu/sq ft, hr, F

U_c — convection conductance general, Btu/sq ft, hr, F

U_{ca} — crossflow convection conductance for air, Btu/sq ft, hr, F

U_{cc} — convection film conductance in crossflow, Btu/sq ft, hr, F

U_{cg} — convection conductance of gas or hotter fluid, Btu/sq ft, hr, F

U_{ci} — inside film convection conductance, Btu/sq ft, hr, F

U_{cl} — convection conductance in longitudinal flow, Btu/sq ft, hr, F

U_{co} — outside film convection conductance, Btu/sq ft, hr, F

U_{cs} — convection conductance of colder fluid, Btu/sq ft, hr, F

U_{fc} — free-convection conductance, Btu/sq ft, hr, F

U_r — radiant conductance, Btu/sq ft, hr, F

U_{rg} — radiant conductance of gas, Btu/sq ft, hr, F

U_s — steam film conductance, Btu/sq ft, hr, F

U'_{cc} — basic crossflow convection conductance, Btu/sq ft, hr, F

U'_{cl} — basic convection conductance in longitudinal flow, Btu/sq ft, hr, F

U'_r — basic radiation conductance, Btu/sq ft, hr, F

u — internal energy of fluid, Btu/lb or ft lb/lb

u_f — internal energy, saturated liquid, Btu/lb

u_g — internal energy, saturated vapor, Btu/lb

V — fluid velocity, ft/sec, ft/min, or ft/hr

V_b — velocity of blade tip

V_c — volume, cu cm

V_r — velocity of air leaving blade relative to blade

V_L — volume of cavity, cu ft

VM_{pc} — volatile matter, %, on pure-coal basis

v — neutron velocity, cm/sec; specific volume of fluid, cu ft/lb; temperature difference ratio

v_a — specific volume of air, cu ft/lb

v_{av} — average specific volume

v_b — specific volume at 1000R and one atmosphere, cu ft/lb

v_f — specific volume, saturated liquid, cu ft/lb

v_{fg} — specific volume, evaporation, cu ft/lb

v_g — specific volume of gas or saturated vapor, cu ft/lb

v_h — losses in bends

v_M — volume, cu ft/mole of gas

v_R — v_2/v_1

W — dead load; mass rate of flow, lb/hr; total load

W_k — work, Btu/lb or ft lb/lb

W_L — lost work, friction and shock; total weight

W'_{rev} — reversible work

w — lb water formed in burning one lb fuel; load per unit length; mass rate of flow (hotter fluid), lb/hr or lb/sec

w_F — fuel input rate, lb/hr

w' — weight rate of flow, colder fluid (primary steam, or feedwater), lb/hr

w'' — reheat steam flow, lb/hr

X — any nuclide or fission fragment

x — length dimension, ft; material thickness; pH; steam quality, % steam by weight

Y — any fission fragment

y — compressibility factor; stiffness matrix; translation displacement

Z — atomic number = number of protons in nucleus; elevation above datum, usually ft

ΔZ — difference in elevation, ft

α — absorptivity; alpha particle; an angle; coefficient of thermal expansion

β — an angle; beta particle; ratio of throat to pipe diameter (flow measurement)

γ — gamma ray

Δ — a difference

δ — a differential operator; a small quantity; growth or displacement; pressure tap diameter

δQ_F — heat equivalent of fluid friction and shock losses

ϵ — average height of roughness projections, in.; emissivity of surface (between 0 and 1.0); factor accounting for fast neutron fission in uranium-238

η — neutron production factor = neutrons produced by fission per neutron absorbed in fuel; thermal efficiency of heat-to-work conversion

θ — an angle; rotation displacement

λ — radioactive decay constant, i.e., the fraction of the total number of atoms which decays in unit time

μ — absolute viscosity of fluid, lb mass/ft, hr, or lb mass/ft, sec, or lb force, sec/sq ft; linear attenuation coefficient; Poisson's ratio

μc — microcurie

μ_s — absolute viscosity of fluid at surface temperature, lb mass/ft, hr

ν — neutrons produced per fission

ξ — temperature difference ratio

π — 3.1416

ρ — mass density, lb/cu ft or grams/cc; reactivity (nuclear chain reaction) = $\Delta k_{eff}/k_{eff}$; reflectivity

ρ_d — density of downcomer fluid, lb/cu ft

ρ_{ex} — density of mixture leaving riser, lb/cu ft

ρ_f — density of water

ρ_g — density of steam

ρ_{mix} — density of mixture

ρ_r — mean density of riser fluid, lb/cu ft

Σ — macroscopic cross section, cm^{-1}; summation

Σ_a — macroscopic cross section for absorption, cm^{-1}

Σ_f — macroscopic fission cross section, cm^{-1}

σ — microscopic cross section, sq cm or barn; Stefan-Boltzman constant, 1.71 x 10^{-9} Btu/sq ft, hr, T^4; stress

σ_a — allowable value of alternating stress intensity amplitude, lb/sq in.; microscopic absorption cross section, usually barns

σ_c — microscopic capture cross section, usually barns

σ_f — microscopic fission cross section, usually barns

σ_{max} — maximum stress

σ_{min} — minimum stress

σ_r — thermal stress, radial

σ_s — microscopic scattering cross section, usually barns

σ_T — total microscopic cross section, usually barns

σ_t — thermal stress, tangential

Symbols (cont'd)

σ_{ta} — thermal stress at inside surface

σ_{tb} — thermal stress at outside surface

$\sigma_{y.p.}$ — yield strength

σ_z — thermal stress, axial

σ_1 — longitudinal stress

σ_2 — hoop stress

τ — Fermi Age; maximum shear stress; transmissivity

τ_w — shear stress at tube wall, lb/sq ft

ϕ — averaging factor

ϕ_f — fast neutron flux, neutrons/sq cm, sec

ϕ_s — thermal neutron flux, neutrons/sq cm, sec

ω — solid angle intercepted by one body as seen from another, steradians

∂ — partial differential operator

$\ominus$ — an electric generator

$^\circ$ — degrees of angle or arc

$'$ — foot

$''$ — inch

Abbreviations

A — ash

ABMA — American Boiler Manufacturers Association

abs — absolute

a-c — alternating current

ACRS — Advisory Committee on Reactor Safeguards

ADS — automatic dispatch system

ADU — ammonium diuranate

AEC — U.S. Atomic Energy Commission

AF — as fired

AH — air heater

ahp — air horsepower

AISC — American Institute of Steel Construction

AM — amplitude modulation

amb — ambient

amu — atomic mass unit

anal. — analysis

ANL — Argonne National Laboratory

ANSI — American National Standards Institute

API — American Petroleum Institute

approx — approximate; approximately

APSRA — axial-power-shaping rod assembly

ASME — American Society of Mechanical Engineers

ASTM — American Society for Testing and Materials

atm — atmosphere

ATR — Advanced Test Reactor

attemp — attemperator

avg — average

B&W — Babcock & Wilcox

bbl — barrel

BCC — body-centered cubic

BHP — brake horsepower

bitum — bituminous

BNL — Brookhaven National Laboratory

BOF — basic-oxygen furnace

Btu — British thermal unit

BWR — boiling water reactor

C — Celsius degrees

Cal — kilogram-Calorie

cc — cubic centimeter

cfm — cubic feet per minute

CIC — compensated-ion-chamber counter

$\mathcal{C}$ — center line

cm — centimeter

CNSG — Consolidated Nuclear Steam Generator

coef — coefficient

col — column

cond — condenser

conn — connection

cont — continuous

cont'd — continued

Corp — corporation

cs — centistoke

cu — cubic

cyl — cylinder

D — steam flow demand

d-c — direct current

deg — degree

diam — diameter

DNB — departure from nucleate boiling

econ — economizer

EDM — electrical discharge machining

eff — efficiency

e.g. — for example

ell — elbow

emf — electromotive force

ENEA — European Nuclear Energy Agency

ERDA — Energy Research and Development Administration

ERW — electric-resistance-welded (tubes)

esu — electrostatic unit

eV — electron volt

evap — evaporation

F — Fahrenheit degrees

FB — firebrick

FC — fixed carbon

FCC — face-centered cubic

FD — forced draft

F.G.—flue gas
Fig.—figure
FM—frequency modulation
fpm—feet per minute
fps—feet per second
FT—fluid temperature
ft—foot
ft lb—foot-pound

g—gram
Ga—gage
gal—gallon
gen—generated; generator
gpm—gallons per minute
GTA—gas-tungsten-arc (welding)

H—enthalpy per mole
ha—hectare
HP—high pressure
hp—horsepower
hp-hr—horsepower-hour
hr—hour
HT—hemispherical temperature
humid.—humidity
HVT—high-velocity thermocouple

IAEA—International Atomic Energy Agency
ID—induced draft; inside diameter
IDT—initial deformation temperature
i.e.—that is
IFB—insulating firebrick
in.—inch
Inc—incorporated
incl—inclusive
inst—instrumentation

K—Kelvin degrees
kg—kilogram
kg-m—kilogram-meter
km—kilometer
ksi—1000 lb/sq in.
kw—kilowatt
kwhr—kilowatt-hour

lb—pound
lbf—pound force
lbm—pound mass
lg—long
LNG—liquefied natural gas
log—logarithm
LP—low pressure

M—bed moisture
m—meter
mag—magnetic

MARAD—U.S. Maritime Administration
max—maximum
MBtu—million British thermal units
MD—mass defect
med—medium
Mev—million electron volts
mg—milligram
mgt—management
MHD—magnetohydrodynamic
MHVT—multiple-shield high-velocity thermocouple
mi—mile
min—minimum; minute
Mm—mineral matter
mm—millimeter
mol.—molecular
MSG—Manufacturer's Standard Gage
MTD—mean temperature difference
Mw—megawatt
Mwd—megawatt days

nat—natural
NFPA—National Fire Protection Association
no.—number
NPHR—net-plant-heat rate
NRC—Nuclear Regulatory Commission
N.S.—Nuclear Ship
NSFO—Navy special fuel oil
NTA—nitrilotriacetic acid

OD—outside diameter
ORA—orifice rod assembly
OTSG—once-through steam generator
OXID.—oxidizing atmosphere
oz—ounce

PA—primary air
PC—proportional counter; pulverized coal
PCO—plastic chrome ore
PERT—program evaluation and review technique
pH—negative log of hydrogen ion concentration
ppb—parts per billion
ppm—parts per million
press.—pressure; pressurizer
pri—primary
prox—proximate
psf—pounds per square foot
psfa—pounds per square foot absolute
psi—gage (or differential) pressure or stress, pounds per square inch
psia—absolute pressure, pounds per square inch
psig—gage pressure, pounds per square inch
PTC—Performance Test Code
pulv—pulverizer
PWR—pressurized water reactor

Abbreviations (cont'd)

R — Rankine degrees
RB — Radiant boiler
RBC — Radiant boiler for pulverized coal or Cyclone Furnace
RBE — Radiant boiler for natural gas and oil
RBE — Relative Biological Effectiveness
RC — reactor coolant
recirc — recirculation
RED. — reducing atmosphere
reg — regulating
rel — relative
rem — roentgen equivalent man
reqd — required
RH — reheater
rpm — revolutions per minute

SAE — Society of Automotive Engineers
sat. — saturated; saturation
sec — second; secondary
sens — sensible
SH — superheater
shp — shaft horsepower
So. — South
spec — specification
sp gr — specific gravity
sp ht — specific heat
sp vol — specific volume
sq — square
SS — stainless steel
S.S. — Steamship
SSF — Seconds Saybolt Furol
std — standard
subbitum — subbituminous
SUS — Saybolt Universal Seconds

t — time
T.A. — total air
TBP — a solution of tributyl phosphate in kerosine
TC — thermocouple
temp — temperature
theo — theoretical
thk — thick
TIG — tungsten-inert-gas (welding)
TS — tensile strength
TV — television

UIC — uncompensated-ion-chamber counter
ult — ultimate
undeter. — undetermined
UP — Universal-Pressure (boiler)
UPC — Universal-Pressure boiler for pulverized coal or Cyclone Furnace
UPH — Universal-Pressure boiler for natural gas and oil
U.S., U.S.A. — United States of America
U.S. AEC — United States Atomic Energy Commission
U.S. ERDA — United States Energy Research and Development Administration
U.S. NRC — United States Nuclear Regulatory Commission
U.S.S. — United States Ship
U.S.S.R. — Union of Soviet Socialist Republics
UV — ultraviolet

VM — volatile matter
vol — volatile; volume
vs — versus

wt — weight

yd — yard
YP — yield point
yr — year
YS — yield strength

Absorptivity, 4-5
Adiabatic flame temperature, 6-6f
Advisory Committee
  on Reactor Safeguards, 21-18
Air
  combustion, 6-2, 6-7, 6-10ff;
    metering, 6-22
  composition, 6-4
  enthalpy, 6-22
  excess, see Excess air
  flow measurement, 35-10
  heater, 13-1, 13-4ff
    calculations, 14-9f
    classification, 13-4f
    corrosion control, 13-4f;
      marine, 24-13
    early design, 13-4
    marine, 24-11, 24-13
    primary, 13-7
    recuperative, 13-4f
      plate, 13-7
      separately-fired, 13-7
      steam coil, 13-7; marine, 24-12
      tubular, 13-5f; marine, 24-13
    regenerative, 13-4f
      rotating plate, 13-7f
      stationary plate
        (B&W-Rothemule), 13-8
  infiltration (leakage), 6-10, 16-6f
  pollution control, 18-1ff
    costs, 18-1
    in Recovery units, 26-9
    legislation, 18-5f
    stacks, 18-1
  pressure, barometric, 17-3
  specific heat, 14-9
  specific volume, 17-1
    standard atmosphere, 17-2
Alkalinity, boiler water, 34-16f
Alloy steels, see Steel; also specific alloys
Alpha
  counters and emitters, 20-15
  particle, 20-3, 20-5, 20-13
Ash—coal, also see Slag
  analysis, 15-2
  and slag, effect on steam
    temperature, 12-13
  content and nature of, 15-1ff
  contents of specific gravity fractions in
    bituminous coal, 8-5
  corrosion, 15-18ff;
    corrective measures, 15-20f

Ash—coal (cont'd)
  deposition and deposits, 15-11ff;
    evaluation techniques, 15-14ff;
    removal, 36-5, also see Sootblowers
  disposal, 18-1f
  effect of additives, 15-16
  effect on boiler design and operation,
    Chapter 15
  effect of iron, 15-5f
  erosion, 15-8f
  fouling, laboratory evaluation, 15-14ff
  fusion temperatures, 15-2f
  handling, 12-5f, 15-7f
  pulverized coal, 15-7
  removal, 18-1f; from flue gas, 18-3f;
    from furnace, 15-7f, 15-9f, 18-2;
    from heating surfaces, 15-10
  sintered strength, 15-15ff
    effect of additives, 15-16;
      of alkali, 15-16;
      of sintering time, 15-17
  stokers, 15-8
  wall-slagging, 15-14f, also see Viscosity
Ash—fuel oil, 15-21ff, also see Slag
  characteristics, 15-22
  corrosion, 15-23ff
    control, 15-24ff
    excess air effect, 15-25ff
    marine boilers, 24-11
    temperature effect with 304, 316,
      and 321 alloys, 15-23
    vanadium effect, 15-24
  deposition, 15-21f
    effect of additives, 15-25
  melting points of constituents, 15-22
Ash—lignite, analysis, 15-2;
  sintered strength, 15-17
Ash—wood, analysis, 5-22

ASME
  Boiler and Pressure Vessel Code,
    12-7, 23-5, 23-14f, 24-3, 29-3,
    29-8, 29-11, 29-13ff, 30-2,
    30-5, 31-5ff, 32-8ff, 36-13;
    allowable stress values, 29-9ff
  Performance Test Code, 33-21ff
  Steam Tables, 2-1 to 2-7
Atom, 20-1ff
Atomic energy, see Fuel, nuclear;
  also Nuclear
Atomic Energy Commission (AEC),
  19-12, see Nuclear Regulatory
  Commission

Atomizer, fuel oil, see Fuel oil atomizer
Attemperator, 12-13, 12-17ff;
  marine, 24-11
Austenite, 28-10ff
Automation and Instrumentation,
  power plant, 35-24f;
  also see Controls
Auxiliaries, power requirements, 22-5;
  22-11ff
Available energy, 2-16
Avogadro number, 20-2
Axial power shaping rod, 23-7f

Babcock, George Herman, 5
Babcock-205, design, 23-16f;
  standardization, 23-20
Baffles, drum, 1-7; marine, 24-14
Bagasse, analysis, 5-20, 5-22
Bainite, 28-12
Barometric pressure, 17-3
Basic-oxygen furnace, 27-6ff
  process, steel, 28-4f
Bearings, maintenance
  axial flow fans, 17-17f
  ball, 36-17
Bernouilli's equation, 3-2
Beta particle (ray), 20-3ff
Blackbody, definition, 4-5
Black liquor, see Recovery unit—
  kraft process
Blast furnace, 28-2
  gas, 5-20f, 25-2, 27-2f
Blowdown, 12-13
Blowing, steam-line, 34-3
Boiler (also see Nuclear steam generator)
  circulation, general theory, 3-13f;
    in marine boilers, 24-14f
  cleaning, see Cleaning, Cleanliness
  control—see Burner controls,
    Combustion, Control(s) and
    control systems, Feedwater,
    Steam temperature, etc.
  definition, 12-1
  design
    calculations, Chapter 14
    chemical and heat recovery boilers
      in paper industry, 26-1ff
    designer's requirements, 22-1ff
    electric utility boilers, 22-1ff, 23-1ff
    general principles, 12-3ff
      ASME Code, 12-7

Boiler (cont'd)
    combustion data, 12-4f
    convection surface, 12-6f
    departure from
        nucleate boiling, 12-7
    heating surface, 12-1, 12-6f
    important items, 12-4
    pressure parts, 12-7
    safety valve, 12-7
    supports, 12-7f
    thermal stress, 12-7
  industrial boilers, 25-1ff
  industrial by-products boilers, 27-1ff
  marine boilers, 24-1ff
development, history of, 1ff
drum—see Drum
efficiency, see Efficiency
energy equation, 2-8
fabrication, 8, Chapters 31 and 32
furnace—see Furnace;
    also Explosion, Implosion
inspection, 36-4ff
operation, 34-1ff
  abnormal, 34-8f
  operator requirements, 34-1
  performance tests, 34-8
  personnel safety, 34-8
  shutdown, 34-9f
  start-up, 34-1ff
scale, effect on tube temperature, 24-9
selection, Section IV
setting, see Setting
shipment, 32-1
supports, 12-7f
types
  bent-tube, 5, 12-1
  electric utility, 22-1ff, 22-6ff
  El Paso, 12-3, 22-8f
  fire-tube, 4
  FM, 25-6f
  header, 24-5, 24-15
  high-pressure, 12-2f
  high-temperature, 12-2f
  industrial, 25-1ff, 27-1ff
  Integral-Furnace, 6, 12-1f, 27-1
    marine, 24-2, 24-4
  marine and naval, Chapter 24;
    see Marine boiler
  nuclear—see Nuclear steam
    generator
  package, 6, 25-5ff
  PFI, 25-1, 25-8
  PFT, 25-9
  Radiant, 12-2f, 22-6ff
  Recovery, chemical and heat, 26-1ff
  shell, 1f
  Stirling, 5, 12-2, 25-10
  straight-tube, 5, 6, 12-1
  Universal-Pressure, 6ff, 12-3f, 22-8ff
  waste-heat, 27-1ff
    bagasse, 27-3f
    blast-furnace, 27-2f
    carbon monoxide, 27-1f

Boiler (cont'd)
    open-hearth, 27-9
    oxygen converter hood, 27-6f
    three-drum, 27-10
    water-tube, 1-2, 1-4, 12-1
  water, solids in, see Solids
  water treatment, see Water treatment
Boiling, 1-1ff, 4-14
  departure from nucleate, 1-2ff
  film, 1-2ff
  local, 1-2ff; heat transfer, 21-7;
    pressure drop 21-9f
  nucleate, 1-2ff
  point, 1-1
  process, 1-2
  subcooled nucleate, see Boiling, local
  water reactor (BWR), 21-2
Bomb calorimeter, 6-5
Boring mill, 31-6, 31-19
Bourdon gage, 33-1
Breeder reactor, 19-3, 20-8, 20-13, 21-1
Breeding, nuclear, 20-12f; gain, 20-13
Brown stock, pulp, 26-2
Buckstays, 16-4f,
    also see Structural design
Burnable poison, 21-5
Burner
  by-product gases, 7-5
  circular register, 7-3f, 9-11
  clearances (marine), 24-8
  coal—see Coal
  controls, 35-11ff
    automatic sequence, 35-12f
    flame detection, 35-14
    flame-proving, 35-11f
    fuel management, 35-13
    manual, 35-11
    remote manual sequence, 35-12
  effectiveness criteria, 7-3
  excess air, 7-3, 7-6f
  fuel oil, 7-3ff; marine types, 24-7f
  lighters and pilots, 7-6, 9-11f
  load range, 7-3, 7-7, 9-12
  movable, 12-17
  multifuel, 7-3f
  natural gas, 7-5f
  performance standards, coal, 9-11
    gas and oil, 7-3
  pulsation, gas and oil, 7-7
  pulverizer coordination, 9-13ff
  selection, effect on
    steam temperature, 12-17
  testing, 7-7f
  types, 7-3, 9-11, marine, 24-7f
Burnup, nuclear, 21-10
Butt welds, 31-15, 32-9
Bypass system,
    Universal-Pressure boiler 34-6f
By-product fuels
  application, 25-2
  gaseous, 27-1ff
  liquid, 27-3
  solid, 27-3ff

Calorimeter
  bomb, 6-5
  throttling, 33-23f
Capitalized cost method,
    see Equipment evaluation
Carbon in steel, 28-3, 28-10ff
Carbon dioxide, in flue gas, 6-22;
    from fuel analysis, 6-21
  properties, 6-2
Carbon loss, see Heat losses
Carbon monoxide (CO),
  as fuel, 27-1f
  boiler, 27-1f
Carbureted water gas, 5-21
Cargo ship (illus), 24-2
Carnot cycle, 2-12f
  thermal efficiency, 2-13
Cased enclosures and casing,
    see Settings
Cast iron, 28-2f
Catalytic cracking unit, CO boiler, 27-1f
Cavity radiation, 4-18, 14-3ff, 14-8
Celsius temperature scale, 33-4
Cementite, 28-10, 28-12
Centigrade temperature scale, 33-4
Chance-Cone coal cleaning, 8-5f
Chain reaction, see Fuel, nuclear
Char, 5-20
Charpy test, 29-2f
Chelant water treatment, 34-17
Chemical
  addition and sampling system, 21-13
  cleaning, 36-5ff
    acid strength, 36-8
    advantages, 36-5
    circulation method, 36-6, 36-10
    cleaning time, 36-8f
    deposits, 36-7f
    evaluation of results, 36-13
    inhibitors, 36-8
    methods, 36-5f
    neutralization-passivation, 36-9ff
    nuclear steam generator, 36-21
    precautions, 36-12f
    preparation, 36-9
    procedures, 36-5f
    soaking method, 36-6, 36-10f
    solvents, 36-7f
    solvent temperature, 36-8
    start-up, 34-2f
  energy, Chapters 5 and 6
  recovery process, pulp, 26-3ff,
    26-11f, 26-13f
  reprocessing, nuclear fuel, 19-8f;
    flowsheet, 19-10
Chimney, see Stack
Chordal thermocouples, see Thermocouple
Circulation, boiler, 1-2, 3-13f, 24-14f
  design criteria, 3-15f
  forced, 3-14ff
  natural, 3-14ff; principles of, 3-16f
  start-up, 34-4

Cladding
    fuel, 19-3; temperature, 21-7f
    pressure vessel, 31-18
Cleaning
    chemical, see Chemical cleaning
    coal, see Coal
    external, 12-12, 36-5
    internal, 36-4f
    start-up, 12-11, 32-11, 34-2f
Cleanliness
    factors, 14-4
    surface, 32-11, 36-4ff
Climate factor, fossil-fuel units, 22-5
Coal, analysis, 5-7f
    ash—see Ash
    ASTM classification by rank, 5-7f
    bituminous-type ash, 5-5, 15-3
    Bradford breaker, 8-7
    bunker design, 8-13f
    bunker fires, 8-15f
    burning equipment, Chapters 10, 11
        and 12; selection, 9-1
    caking properties, 5-12, 5-16
    calorific value, 5-16
    characteristics, 5-7ff; for firing, 9-1
    classification, 5-7ff
    cleaning, 8-1f
    coking properties, 5-10f
    consumption, U.S., by industries, 5-4f
    cost, 5-18f
    crushers, 8-7ff, 10-4
    Cyclone-Furnace firing—
        see Cyclone Furnace
    dedusting and dustproofing, 8-6
    deterioration and spontaneous
        combustion, 8-11
    drying, 8-6
    feeders, 10-4
    fields, U.S., 5-5
    firing method, selection, 9-1, 22-2f, 25-2
    flow in chutes, 8-13f
    formation, 5-7f
    fouling guidelines, 15-16
    free-swelling index, 5-16
    freezeproofing, 8-7ff
    grindability, 5-16; index, 9-5
    hammer mill, 8-8
    handling, 8-9ff, 8-13ff
    heat value, 5-16f
    impurities, 8-1ff; specific gravity, 8-5
    international classification, 5-10ff
        brown coals, 5-12f; hard coals, 5-12
    lignite-type ash, 5-5, 15-3
    mineral matter, 8-2
    moisture, 5-7ff, 5-16, 8-4, 9-4
    oxidation, 8-11
    preparation, 8-1
    production, U.S., 5-5; world, 5-1f
    properties, effect on design, 22-2
    pulverized, see Pulverized coal
    pulverizer, see Pulverizer
    reserves, U.S., 5-3ff; by rank,
        sulfur content and state, 8-3;
        world, 5-1f

Coal (cont'd)
    ring crusher, 8-8f
    sampling, 5-7
    screens, 8-8
    sizing, 5-14f, 8-7, 10-1ff
    specific gravity, 8-5
    storage, 8-9ff
    sulfur, 8-2ff
    testing standards, 5-8
    transportation, 8-8f
Codes and inspections, 32-8ff
    ASME, see ASME
    marine boilers, 24-3
Coke, as fuel, 5-19f
    breeze, 5-19f
    delayed, 5-21
    fluid, 5-21
    -oven gas, 5-20
    petroleum, 5-21
Cold-drawing, tubes, 31-24f
Combustible losses, see Heat losses
Combustion
    air, see Air
    calculations, 6-7ff
        Btu method, 6-17ff
        losses, see Heat losses
        mole method, 6-11f
        use of mole, 6-3ff
        weight method, 6-10f
    chemical reactions, 6-1, 6-4
    complete, 6-1
    constants, 6-2
    control systems, 35-7ff; Cyclone
        Furnace, 35-9; gas, 35-8;
        oil, 35-8; pulverized-coal, 35-8f;
        stoker, 35-8
    definition, 6-1
    equilibrium, 2-19f
    fundamental laws, 6-1f
    guides, 35-9ff
    heat of, 6-2, 6-5
    "three T's" of, 6-1
Compressed water, properties, 2-6f
Compressor, energy equation, 2-9
Condensate
    -polishing system, 34-13, 34-18
    treatment, 34-12f
Condensation, heat transfer, 4-14
Conductance, 4-1
    boiling-water film, 4-14, 4-16
    calculation, 14-3f
    combined, 4-2, 4-11
    convection, gases, 4-8, 4-10
    effect of scale or oil, 4-16
    film, see Film conductance
Conduction, 4-1ff
    in fluids, 4-4
    steady state, 4-2ff
    unsteady state, 4-4f
Conductivity
    effect of pore size, 4-13f
    gases, 4-4
    method, steam purity, 33-23
    selected materials, 4-2

Conductivity (cont'd)
    steels and alloys, 4-2
    thermal, 4-2
Consolidated nuclear steam
    generator, 24-18f
Continuous slowing down model,
    nuclear, 20-11
Contraction
    pressure loss, 3-9
    static pressure difference, 3-10
Control(s) and control systems, 35-1ff
    basic theory, 35-1ff
    burner, 35-11ff, see Burner
    closed-loop, 35-3
    combustion, 35-7ff
    derivative, 35-4
    Element, Self "Drag," 34-7
    feedback, 35-3ff
    feedforward, 35-2, 35-4f
    feedforward-feedback, 35-4f
    feedwater, 35-5f, 35-18, see Feedwater
    integral, 35-4
    nuclear plants, 35-19ff
    nuclear steam generator, 35-22
    open-loop, 35-2f
    proportional, 35-3f
    reactor, 21-10, 23-8f, 35-23f
    reactor coolant loop, 35-22f
    reset, 35-4
    response, 35-4, 35-16
    -Rod
        assembly, 23-7
        drive, 23-7f
        worth, definition, 21-6
    steam temperature, 12-12ff,
        see Steam temperature
    symbols, 35-3, 35-6
    theory, 35-1ff
    throttle-pressure, 35-17
    turbine-generator, 35-17, 35-22
    Universal-Pressure boiler, 35-14ff
        boiler-following, 35-15
        integrated, 35-15ff
        turbine-following, 35-15
Convection,
    boiler surface, 12-6f
    -conductance, gases, 4-8, 4-10
    crossflow, 4-10f
    free or natural, 4-1, 4-7
    forced, 4-1, 4-7ff
    heat transfer, 4-1, 4-7ff
    laminar flow, 4-8
    turbulent flow, 4-9ff
Conversion, nuclear—see Fuel,
    nuclear, fission
Conversion tables,
    Tables of Measurement, T-1—T-3
Converter reactor, 21-1
Corrosion
    ash, see Ash corrosion
    casing, 16-7
    control
        air heaters, 13-4f
        economizers, 13-3f, 22-4
    high temperature, marine, 24-11

Cost evaluation, 22-11ff
Creep
  factors affecting, 29-f
  in steels, 29-3f
  rate, 29-5, 29-7
  -rupture test, 29-6f; apparatus, 29-4
  stress, 29-5, 29-16f
  test, 29-3ff
Critical heat flux, see Departure from
    nucleate boiling
  mass, 20-7; determination, 20-9f
  size, 20-7
Croloy steels, 29-10f
  creep and creep-rupture curves, 29-7
Crossflow, friction factor, 3-13
Cross section—nuclear, 20-8f
  absorption, 20-9
  capture, 20-9f
  fission, 20-9
  macroscopic, 20-9
  microscopic, 20-9
  resonance, 20-9
  scattering, 20-9
Crude oil, see Petroleum
Cycle(s)
  Carnot, 2-12f
  Rankine, 2-13ff
    for nuclear plant, 2-16f
    regenerative Rankine, 2-14ff
  reheat, 2-14ff
  steam, see Steam cycle
  thermodynamics, 2-1, 2-12ff
Cyclone Furnace
  advantages, 9-1, 10-1f, 18-2
  burner, 10-8
  capacities, 10-4
  coal, crushers, 8-8, 10-4; feeders, 10-4;
      sizing, 10-1, 10-3;
      suitability criteria, 10-1ff
  combustion control, 10-5
  design features, 10-3ff
  fabrication, 31-15
  firing
    application, 22-3
    arrangements, 10-2f
  fly-ash emission and recovery, 10-5f
  fuels suitable for, 10-2f, 10-5f
  installations, 10-6ff
  oil and gas burners, 10-4f
  operation and maintenance, 10-7f
  power requirements, 10-5f
Cyclone steam separators, 1-7f
  marine, 24-14f

Decay
  constants, 20-4
  heat-removal system, 21-13f
  radioactive, 20-3, 20-12
Demand charge, 22-11
Demineralization, water, 34-12
Density differential, steam and water, 3-15

Departure from nucleate boiling (DNB),
    10, 1-2ff, 3-15, 12-7, 21-8, 24-9
Desuperheater, see Attemperator
Deuterium, 20-2
Deuteron, 20-5
Diameter, equivalent, definition, 3-3, 4-7
Dimensionless numbers, 4-7ff
Disengaging surface, 1-7
Doppler
  coefficient, nuclear fuel, 21-10f
  effect, resonance, absorption, 20-9
Dose, radiation, nuclear, 20-14;
    equivalent, 20-14
Doubling time, 20-13
Draft
  balanced, 17-1
  forced, 17-1
  induced, 17-1
  loss, 12-7, 14-4ff, 14-7ff, 14-10,
    17-10f, 25-4
  natural, 17-1
"Drag" Control Element, Self, 34-7
Drawbench, 31-13
Drum
  allowable temperature differential, 34-5
  baffles, 1-7, 3-12; marine, 24-14
  erection, 32-5
  fabrication, 31-9ff
  protection, start-up and shutdown, 34-4ff
  size, 1-5
  structural supports, 32-4
Drumhead fabrication, 31-10f
Dry-ash furnace, see Furnace design,
    dry-ash
Ductility, 29-1f

Earthquake requirements, 22-5
  loading, 30-8
Economizer, 13-1ff
  calculations, 14-8f
  cleaning, 13-3
  continuous tube, 13-3
  corrosion, external, 13-1, 13-3f, 22-4,
    24-12f; internal, 13-4, 24-13
  designs, 13-1f
  extended surface, 13-2f, 24-12
  location, 13-3
  marine, 24-11ff
  start-up protection, 34-4
  steaming, 13-2
  stud-tube, marine, 24-12
Efficiency
  boiler or steam
    generating unit, 6-18, 6-20, 12-4f
  maintaining, 36-2f
  marine boiler, 24-2f
  monitoring, 36-3
Electric furnace process, see Steel
Electricity
  demand, 1
  production costs, 22-1

Electric utilities, early history, 5f
Electromagnetic spectrum, 20-3
Electron, 20-1, 20-5;
    -beam X-ray analyzer, 12; shells, 20-2
Electrostatic precipitator, 18-2f, 26-7
Electrostatic unit, 20-1
Emissivity, 4-5f
Enclosure, see Settings
Energy
  atomic, Section III, also see Nuclear
  available, 2-16
  chemical, Section II
  equation, fluid flow, 3-1ff
  general equation, 2-5;
      applications, 2-8f
  solar, 5-1
  sources, distribution by fuels, 5-1
Engineered safeguards, 23-5
  systems, 21-16, 23-15f; actuation, 35-24
Enthalpy, 1-1, 2-8
  air, 6-22
  flue gas, 6-8f
  steam and water, 2-2ff, 2-6f
Entropy, 2-9
  increases, 2-11f
  water and steam, 2-3f, 2-6f
Equipment evaluation, 22-1, 22-10ff
  PWR plant, 21-16f
Equivalent diameter, definition, 3-3, 4-7
Erection
  auxiliaries, 32-12
  cost estimates, 32-1f
  design review, 32-2
  field welding, 32-9ff
  jobsite preparations, 32-3f
  material handling and storage, 32-4
  nonpressure parts, 32-12
  nuclear steam supply system, 32-6f
  planning and coordination, 32-1
  procedure, fossil-fuel unit, 32-4ff
  quality control, 32-8ff
  schedule, 32-2
  structural supports, 32-4f
  time estimates, 32-1f
Evaluation of equipment,
    see Equipment evaluation
Evaporation, 4-14
  heat of, 1-1
  water purification, 34-12
Evaporator (pulp)
  cascade, 26-7
  cyclone, 26-7
  direct-contact, 26-6f;
      air pollution, 26-9
  -scrubber, venturi, 26-7
Examination, nondestructive, 31-7ff
  liquid-penetrant, 31-8
  magnetic-particle, 31-8
  radiography, 31-7
  ultrasonic, 31-7f
Excess air, 6-1, 6-10
  effect on corrosion, 15-25f
  effect on steam temperature, 12-13ff

Excess air (cont'd)
  from flue gas analysis, 6-19, 6-21
  loss, 6-7, 6-10, 36-2f
  measurement, 6-17
  oil and gas, 7-3, 7-6f
  pulverized coal, 9-12
Explosive technique,
  tube plugging, 36-21
Explosion
  casing design, 16-4
  doors, 16-4
  furnace, prevention, 7-8f, 36-1
Extrusion process, tubes, 31-25

Fabric filter, 18-3
Fahrenheit temperature scale, 33-4
Fans, 17-6ff
  acoustics, 17-15
  arrangement, 17-1
  axial flow, 17-11ff
  centrifugal, 17-7ff
  characteristics, 17-6ff
  drives, 17-8
  effect of varying speed, 17-9
  forced draft, 17-6, 17-9f
  gas recirculating, 17-10
  induced-draft, 17-9f
  maintenance, 17-2, 17-6f
  output control, 17-8
  performance, 17-6
  safety factors, 17-8
  selection, 17-10f
  testing, 17-7
Fast nonleakage factor, nuclear, 20-11
Fatigue, 30-5ff
  damage evaluation, 30-6
  design curve, 30-6
Fecheimer probe, 33-28
Feedwater
  control systems, 35-5ff
    single-element, 35-6
    thermohydraulic, 35-5f
    thermostatic, 35-5f
    three-element, 35-7
    two-element, 35-7
  design considerations, 22-4
  regulator, see control systems
  requirements
    drum boiler, 34-14
    nuclear steam generator, 34-24
    Universal-Pressure
      boiler, 34-19, 35-18
  temperature, effect on
    steam temperature, 12-13
  treatment, 34-13f
    changes, 34-14
    nuclear steam generator, 34-24f
    oxygen control, 24-13
    pH control, 34-14
    Universal-Pressure boiler, 34-18f
Ferrite, 28-10, 28-12

Fertile material, 19-1, 20-8, 21-1
  ownership and regulation, 19-12
Field assembly, see Erection
Filling boiler, 34-3f
Film badge, 20-14
Film conductance, 4-2f, 4-7, 4-14, 4-16
  crossflow, 4-10
  longitudinal flow, 4-8f
  steam or water film, 4-16
Filter, fabric, 18-3
Firing-rate control, 35-18
Fissile material, 20-7, 21-1;
  definition, 19-1
Fission—see Fuel, Nuclear
Fittings
  flow resistance, 3-7ff
  removal, 36-15f
Flame detector, 35-14
  photometer, 33-22f
  proving, burner controls, 35-11f
Flash and fire points, 27-3
Flue gas
  analysis, 6-5, 6-19
  enthalpy, 6-8f
  equivalent molecular weight, 17-2
  excess air determination, 6-19ff
  partial pressure, 14-4
  pollutant components, 18-1;
    removal methods, 18-3f
  sampling, 6-22
  specific heat, 14-7
  specific volume, 17-2
Fluid, 3-1
  entrainment, 3-13
  flow, energy equation, 3-1ff;
    measurement, 33-24ff
  friction, pressure loss, 3-3ff
Fly-ash, see Ash
  emission, 10-5f
  removal, 18-2
Fly-carbon reinjection, 11-3
Foaming, 1-6
Forced circulation, 3-14ff
Fossil fuels, Chapters 5 to 11,
  see Fuel, fossil
Fouling, see Ash
Friction factor
  crossflow gases, 3-13, 14-5
  flow in pipes and ducts, 3-5f
  stack, 17-4
Friction loss, 3-3ff
Fuel, fossil, Chapters 5 to 11
  available at site, 22-1, 25-1
  availability, U.S., 5-3ff; world, 5-1ff
  burning equipment, see Burner;
    also Coal, Oil, Natural gas
  coal, see Coal
  combustion constants, 6-2
  consumption, U.S. by electric
    utilities, 5-4ff
  cost, 5-18f, 22-11
  -flow, air-flow combustion guide, 35-10
  flow measurement, 35-10

Fuel (cont'd)
  gaseous, analysis, 6-4;
    by-product, 27-1ff; from coal, 5-20
  lignites, 5-5ff, 15-2
  liquid by-product, 27-3
  miscellaneous, 5-19ff
  oil, also see Ash-fuel oil; Petroleum
    additives, 15-25f
    analyses, 5-18f
    API gravity, 5-16f
    ash—see Ash, fuel oil
    ASTM specifications, 5-15
    atomizer, 7-3ff
      characteristic curves, 7-9
      mechanical, 7-4f
      return flow, 7-4
      steam or air, 7-4f
    burning equipment, 7-3ff;
      marine types, 24-7f
    characteristics, 5-16ff
    cost, 5-18f
    firing, application, 22-3, 25-2
    grades, 5-16ff
    heat values, 5-16ff
    low-load operation, 7-8
    safety precautions, 7-8ff
    shale, 5-18, 7-2
    slag, 15-22f; control, 15-24ff;
      design factors, 15-22f;
      operating factors, 15-23
    starting cold boilers, 7-8
    temperature-volume correction-factor
      curves, 5-18
    viscosity, 5-16, 5-18
  requirement, 14-2f
  types, effect on design, 22-2f
  use, 5-1
Fuel, nuclear, Chapters 19, 20, 21;
  also see Nuclear; Neutrons; Reactor
  assembly, 19-3ff, 19-9, 21-4, 23-6f
    fabrication, 19-8f, 31-22f
    structural design, 21-10
  burnup, definition, 21-10
  chain reaction, 19-1, 19-5, 20-7, 20-12
    control, 19-5, 20-7
    steady-state equation, 20-7
  cladding, 19-3, 19-6
  cost, 19-10f
  cycle, PWR, 19-7; also see uranium below
  fission
    energy, release, 20-6
    fragments, see Fission products
    heat release, 19-1
    neutrons, 20-6;
      energy distribution, 20-7f
    nuclear, 19-1, 20-5ff
    process, 19-1, 20-3, 20-5ff
    product(s), 20-5ff; gaseous 19-6;
      mass distribution, 20-6;
      poisons, 20-12; storage, 19-9
    reaction, 20-5
  fissionable material, 19-1, 20-5f
  ownership and regulation, 19-12
  handling, 19-3, 21-14, 23-12f, 24-18

Fuel, nuclear (cont'd)
  heat removal, 19-3
  loading, 34-21, illus, facing 19-1
  plutonium, 19-1, 19-3, 19-10f
    availability, 19-11
    credit, 19-11
    fuel fabrication, 13
    handling, 19-11
    isotopes, 19-11
    production, 20-12f
    properties, 19-11
    utilization, 19-11
  protection, 19-3
  spent, shipping, 19-8
  temperature, PWR, 21-6f
  thorium, 19-2, 19-11, 20-13
  transfer cask, 24-18
  uranium, 19-1ff
    availability, 19-2f
    chemical reprocessing, 19-8f;
      flowsheet, 19-10
    conversion to UF$_6$, 19-6f;
      flowsheet, 19-8
    conversion to UO$_2$, 19-8
    -dioxide pellets, 19-6ff, 31-22f
    enrichment, 19-6f, 19-9
    foreign resources, 19-2
    isotopes, 19-1
    milling, 19-6
    plutonium fuel, cycle, 19-6f;
      fabrication, 13
    price, 19-2
    refining, 19-6f; flowsheet, 19-8
    spent-fuel shipping, 19-8
    U.S. resources, 19-2
    utilization, 19-3
  uranyl nitrate, reconversion to UF$_6$, 19-9f
Fuller-Kinyon pump, 9-3
Furnace
  basic-oxygen, 27-6ff
  cyclone—see Cyclone Furnace
  design, 12-5ff
    ash effects, 15-5ff
    dry-ash, 12-5, 15-8
    marine boilers, 24-8
    slag tap, 12-5f, 15-9f
    stoker-firing, 11-3, 11-6
    water-cooled walls, 12-5f
  divided, 12-16f
  exit temperature, 4-16ff
  explosion, see Explosion
  heat treating, 31-16
  implosion, see Implosion
  installations, dry-ash and slag-tap, 15-10
  purging, 7-9, 9-16, 34-4
  Ward, bagasse, 27-3f
Fusion process, nuclear, 20-3

Gamma ray, 20-4f, 20-13
Gas, see also Natural gas
  analysis,
    as combustion guide, 35-10f

Gas (cont'd)
    flue gas, 6-5
    fuel gas, 6-4
  bypass for steam temperature
      control, 12-17
  constant, 3-2, 6-3, 33-5
  expansion properties, 33-5
  flow-distribution control, 35-18f
  laws, 3-2, 6-3, 33-5
  molal specific heat, 6-13
  properties, 6-2; physical, 3-7
  recirculation, 12-15f
  safety precautions, 7-8ff
  starting cold boilers, 7-8
  temperature evaluation, 33-18f
  temperature measurement, 33-16ff;
      multipoint probe, 33-19f
  tempering, 12-15f, 15-7f
  viscosity, 3-7
  waste, Chapter 27
Gaseous
  fuels, from coal, 5-20
  pollutant, control, 18-3f
  state, 3-1
Gauss's theorem, 33-19
Geiger counter, 20-14
General energy equation, 2-5;
    applications, 2-8f
Geographical considerations
    in design, 22-4f
German Nuclear Ship Otto Hahn, 24-18f
Graphitization in steel pipe, 29-13
Gravimetric analysis, steam purity, 33-24
Gravity, API, fuel oil, 5-16
Green liquor, pulp, 26-3
Grindability
  coal, 5-16
  effect on pulverizer capacity, 9-8
  index, 9-5
Guarantees, equipment, 22-5

Half-life, heavy elements, 20-4
    radioactive, 20-4
Handholes, 32-10f
Hardness
  scales, conversion chart, 29-2
  test, 29-2
Header
  fabrication, 31-12f
  protection, start-up
      and shutdown, 34-5f
Health physics, 20-13ff
Heat
  absorption
    determination, 14-3f, 14-10
    rates, 4-17ff, 10-2, 24-8
  -balance losses, see Heat losses
  conductance, see Conductance
  flow, general equations, 4-2
  flux measurements, 33-15
  losses, 4-20, 6-7ff, 36-2f
  mechanical equivalent, 2-8

Heat (cont'd)
  of combustion, 6-5
  of evaporation, 1-1
  rate, 22-11
  release rate, furnace ash effect, 15-6f
  nuclear core, 21-6
  -resistant alloys, 29-13, 29-15
  transfer
    applications, 4-14ff
    calculation, 14-3f; examples, 14-6ff
    condensation, 4-14
    conduction, 4-1ff
    convection, 4-1, 4-7ff; banks, 4-15
    furnaces, 4-16ff
    insulation, 4-13f, 4-18f
    local boiling, 21-7
    modes, 4-1
    porous materials, 4-12
    pressurized water reactor,
        4-19f, 21-6ff; limits, 21-8
    radiation, 4-1, 4-5ff
    test apparatus, 11
    waste gases, 27-6
  treatment, welding, 31-5
  values, high and low, 6-6
Heating surface, see Surface
Hero's engine, 2
History of steam generation and use, 1
Hood, oxygen-converter,
    see Oxygen-converter hood
Hook gage, 33-2
Hooke's law, 29-1
Hot cells, 14
Hot channel factors, 21-7f
Hydrogen, heavy, 20-1f
Hydropower, in U.S., 5-1, 5-6
Hydrostatic test, 32-13, 34-2; pit, 31-19f

Ignition stability, 9-11
Ignition temperatures, 6-6
Ignitors, 7-6, 9-11f
Impact test, 29-2f
Implosion, 16-4f
Inconel, 29-16; Alloy 600,
    chemical composition and
    properties, 29-17
In-core instrumentation, 23-9, 35-21
Industrial boiler, see Boiler, industrial
Ingot, steel, 28-7f
  drawing, 31-13
  types, 28-8
Initial deformation temperature, ash, 15-3
Inspection, 32-8f; also see Examination
  door, pressurized furnace, 16-9
  outage, 36-4
  preoperation, 32-12
  start-up, 34-1
Instrumentation, Chapters 33, 35
  in-core, 35-21
  information display, 35-24f
  installation and service, 35-26

Instrumentation (cont'd)
    non-nuclear, 35-21
    nuclear, 35-20; plants, 35-19ff
    reactor, 21-11f, 35-19ff
    start-up, 34-2
Insulating materials, 16-5f
    thermal conductivity, 16-6
Insulation
    erection, 32-12
    heat transfer, 4-18f
    use limits, 4-19
Integral-Furnace boiler, 6, 12-1f, 27-1
    marine, 24-2, 24-4
    package, 25-6f
    type FM, 25-6f
    type PFI, 25-8
    type PFT, 25-9
Integrated control system, 35-15ff;
    nuclear, 23-9, 35-21ff
Interest, compound, factors, 22-12
Internal deposits, boiler, 34-15
Intertube radiation, 4-12, 14-3ff
Ionization chamber, 20-11
Iron
    allotropic transformations, 28-9f
    alpha, 28-9f
    atomic structure, 28-9f
    carbon in, 28-10
    cast, 28-2f
    delta, 28-9f
    effects on coal ash, 15-5f
    equilibrium diagram, 28-10
    gamma, 28-9f
    manufacture, 28-2
    ore, 28-1f
    pig, 28-2, 28-4
Isotope, 20-2; radioactive, 20-3f
Izod test, 29-2f

Kelvin temperature scale, 33-4
Kraft process, 26-2ff
Kraft recovery unit, see Recovery unit,
    kraft process

Lagging, definition, 16-1
Laminar flow, 3-5f, 4-7ff
    inside tubes, 4-8
Lanes, in tube banks, effect of, 4-14
Laws of thermodynamics, 2-9
Licensing process, nuclear plant, 21-17f
Lighters and pilots
    coal burner, 9-11f
    oil and gas, 7-6
Lignite, ash fusion temperatures, 15-2
Limestone addition, sulfur removal, 18-3
Linear accelerator, 31-8
Liquid-penetrant examination, 31-8
Liquid state, 3-1

Liquids
    physical properties, 3-7
    viscosity, 3-6
Local boiling, 1-2ff; heat transfer, 21-7;
    pressure drop, 21-9f
Logic control, definition (footnote), 35-13
Low-load operation
    control, 35-19
    oil and gas, 7-8
Loss, radiation, 4-20
Losses, see Heat losses
Low water, 34-8f

Machine tools, 31-5ff
Machining
    center, 31-9
    electrical discharge, 31-5f
Magnesium-base pulping and
    recovery process, 26-12ff
    flow diagram, 26-12
    recovery unit, 26-13f
    sulfur dioxide absorption system, 26-14
Magnesium-sulfite liquor as fuel, 26-12f
Magnetic-particle examination, 31-8
Maintenance
    ball bearings, 17-17f, 36-17
    fans, 17-16
    furnace and setting, 36-1
    idle equipment, 36-18
    in-service, 36-1ff
    nuclear equipment, 36-20ff
    outage, 36-3ff
    pressure parts, 36-1f
    preventive, 36-1ff
    stacks, 17-5
Makeup and purification system, 21-13
Manholes, 32-10
Manometer, 33-1f
    high pressure, 33-2
    inclined, 33-1
Manufacturing
    fossil-fuel equipment, 31-9ff
    methods, 31-1; development, 8
    nuclear equipment, 31-17ff
    requirements, 31-1
    tubes, 31-23ff
Marine boiler, 24-1ff
    circulation, 24-14f
    code requirements, 24-3
    design, 24-6ff
    development, 7f, 24-1f
    efficiency, 24-2f
    fuels, 24-3
    furnace design, 24-8f
    requirements, 24-2f
    steam separation, 24-14
    steam temperature, 24-3
    superheater design, 24-9
    tube banks, 24-9
    types, 24-3ff
Martensite, 28-10, 28-12
Mass defect, 20-2

Mass-energy equivalence, 19-1, 20-1,
    20-3, 20-5
Mass number, 20-2
Mass-velocity, velocity-head
    relationship for air, 3-12
Material handling and storage,
    erection, 32-4
Mean radiating length,
    gases in tube banks, 14-5
Mean temperature difference
    boiling, 14-1
    counterflow, crossflow,
        parallel flow, 4-12f, 14-1
Measurement, instruments and methods,
    Chapter 33
    tables, Tables of Measurement, T-1—T-3
Mechanical collector, 18-3
Mechanical equivalent of heat, 2-8
Membrane wall, 12-5f, 16-2ff
    fabrication, 31-13f
Metallurgy, iron and steel, 28-1ff
Mine-mouth central station, 5-1
Moderator—see Nuclear
Moisture
    air, 6-13, 6-17
    extraction, turbine steam, 2-16f
    in coal, see Coal, moisture
Molal quantities,
    conversion to lb units, 6-13
Mole
    concept of, 6-1
    in combustion calculations, 6-3ff,
        6-12, 6-14ff
Molecular weights
    combustion, 6-2
    equivalent, air and flue gas, 17-2
Mollier diagram
    nuclear steam cycle, 2-18
    steam, 2-1
Multipurpose steam power plants, 2-17

National Board Inspection Code,
    32-8, 36-13
National Board of Boiler and Pressure
    Vessel Inspectors, 31-6, 32-9
National Fire Protection Association, 9-10
Natural circulation, 3-14ff;
    principles of, 3-16f
Natural gas
    burning equipment, 7-3ff
    characteristics, 5-18f
    cost, 5-18f
    firing, application, 22-3, 25-2
    preparation, 7-2
    production and reserves, U.S., 5-6;
        world, 5-2
    safety precautions, 7-8ff
    storage, 7-2
    transportation, 7-2
Neutron(s), 20-1, 20-5
    absorbers, 20-7
    absorption, 20-8f
    counter, 20-11, 20-15

Neutron(s) (cont'd)
   delayed, 20-8
   detector, 20-11
   dosimeter, 20-14
   fast, 19-6, 20-8
   flux, 20-11; patterns, PWR, 21-5f
   from fission, 20-6;
      energy distribution, 20-7f
   leakage, 20-8f
   poison, 20-7, 20-12, 21-4f
   production, 20-8f
   production factor, 20-10
   prompt, 20-7
   reactions, 20-7
   source, 20-12
   thermal, 20-8
   velocity, 20-8
Newcomen's engine, 3
Nitrogen oxides in flue gas, 18-5
Nondestructive examination, 31-7ff
Nozzle
   energy equations, 2-8
   fabrication, 31-18f
N.S. Savannah, 24-15ff
   contruction, 24-18
   operation, 24-18
   power plant design, 24-16ff
Nuclear
   binding energy, 20-2f
   buckling theory, 20-10f
   chain reaction—see Fuel, nuclear
   components, 32-9; jobsite
      handling, 32-6f; shipment, 32-6f
   containment system, 21-14, 21-16;
      see Reactor building
   core, see Reactor
   cross section, 20-8ff
   fission, see Fuel, nuclear, fission
   four factor equation, 20-11
   merchant ship reactor, 24-17f
   moderator, 20-8
      temperature coefficient, 21-10
      void coefficient, 21-11
   multiplication factor, 20-9ff
   power costs, 21-16f
   power plants, Chapter 23;
      instrumentation and
      control, 35-19ff; marine, 24-15ff;
      see Nuclear steam supply system
   pressurized water reactor,
      see Pressurized water reactor
   propulsion systems, 24-15ff
   radiation, see Radiation, nuclear
   reactions, 20-5
   reactor, see Reactor
   Regulatory Commission (NRC),
      20-15, 21-17f, 32-8, 34-20ff, 36-21
   resonance, escape probability, 20-10
   shielding, 20-13, 21-14
   steam generator, 21-12
      once-through, 23-9ff, 23-17, 31-20f
      control, 35-22
      fabrication, 31-20ff
      feedwater requirements, 34-25

Nuclear (cont'd)
      maintenance, 36-19f
      parameters, 23-5, 23-11
      stress-relief, 31-22
      temperature, 23-12
      tube support plates, 31-21
   steam supply system, Chapters 21
      and 23, 24-17ff
      control, 35-19, 35-21ff
      early, 8
      electric utility applications,
         Chapter 23
      erection, 32-6f
      instrumentation, 35-19ff
      maintenance, 36-20ff
      marine, 24-17;
         improved designs, 24-18f
      operation, 34-20ff
      parameters, 23-4f
Nucleon, 20-2
Nuclide, 20-2; unstable, 20-3
Nusselt number, 4-8

Oconee Nuclear Station, Units 1, 2
   and 3, Chapter 23
Oil, see also Fuel, fossil, oil and Petroleum
   shale, 5-2, 7-2; analysis, 5-19;
      reserves, 5-3
Once-through boiler, see Nuclear steam
   generator, also Universal-Pressure
   boiler
Open-hearth process, steel, 28-4f
Openings
   rules for reinforcement, 30-7
   stress concentrations, 30-6f
Operation
   fossil-fuel units, 34-1ff
      abnormal, 34-8f
      personnel safety, 34-8
   nuclear units, 34-20ff
Operator
   qualifications, welding, 31-6f, 32-9
   requirements
      fossil-fuel units, 34-1ff
      nuclear units, 34-20
Optical pyrometer, 33-6
Orifice, 33-24f
Orsat analysis, 6-5, 6-19
Outdoor installations, 16-8, 22-5
Overfire air, 11-3, 11-5, 11-6
Oxygen
   control, 24-13, 34-14
   in feedwater, 22-4
   required for combustion, 6-2
Oxygen-converter hood, 27-6ff
   design criteria, 27-7
   steam generator hood, 27-8
   wet-scrubber gas cleanup, 27-7f

Package boiler, 6, 25-5ff
Paper industry, 26-1
   recovery processes and units, 26-3ff

Paper industry (cont'd)
   steam requirements, 26-1
   waste fuels, 26-1
Parr formulas for coal, 5-8
Partial pressure of gases, 14-4
Particle(s)
   alpha, 20-3, 20-5
   beta, 20-3, 20-5
   fundamental, 20-1; mass, 20-2
Particulate matter in flue gases, 18-1ff
   removal methods, 18-3f
Peak rating limits, 22-4
Pearlite, 28-10, 28-12
Penetrameter, 31-7, 32-12
Performance
   calculations, 14-1ff
   computations, 35-23
   tests, fossil-fuel units, 34-8;
      nuclear units, 34-22
Personnel safety, rules, 34-8
Petroleum, also see Fuel, fossil, oil
   coke, 5-21
   preparation, 7-1
   production, U.S., 5-6; world, 5-3
   pumping, 7-1f
   reserves, U.S., 5-6; world, 5-1f
   storage, 7-1
   transportation, 7-1
pH, control, feedwater, 34-14
   values, significance, 34-25
   vs conductivity, ammonia
      solutions, 34-20
Phosphate-hydroxide water
   treatment, 34-15f
Phosphate water treatment,
   coordinated, 34-16
Photoelastic stress pattern, 12, 30-2
Physical properties, see name of substance
Physical properties factor, 4-8ff
Piercing and drawing, large stock, 31-12f
Piercing operation, tubes, 31-24
Piping
   reactor coolant, 21-13, 23-11, 31-22
   steam, 29-11, 29-13ff
Pitch, as fuel, 27-3
Pitot tube, 33-27f
Plate forming, 31-9f, 31-17f
Plutonium, see Fuel, nuclear, plutonium
Poison
   fission product, 20-12
   neutron, 20-7, 20-12, 21-4f
Pollutant gases, control, 18-3f
Potentiometer, 33-8, 33-11
Power
   costs, 22-1; nuclear, 21-16f
   cycle diagram, fossil fuel, 2-15;
      nuclear fuel, 2-17
   for auxiliaries, fossil-fuel plants, 22-5
   plant automation, 35-25f
   reactor, types, 21-2
   testing, nuclear equipment, 34-21ff
Prandtl number, 4-8

Pre-critical testing,
    nuclear equipment, 34-20f
Preheated air
    advantages, 13-4
    fuel saving, 13-5
    with pulverized coal, 9-2, 9-4, 9-8
Present worth, 22-12
Pressure
    difference, contraction and
            enlargement, 3-10
    drop
        bends, 3-10
        calculations, 14-4ff
        coils, 3-10f
        equation, closed channels, 3-4
        fittings, 3-7ff
        gas flow across tube banks,
                3-12, 14-4ff
        local boiling, 21-9f
        PWR system, 21-8ff
        rectangular ducts, 3-11
        reheater and superheater, 12-9
        two-phase flow, 3-12f
        valves, 3-7ff
    gage, opposed bellows, 33-2f;
            slack diaphragm, 33-2
    loss
        contraction, 3-9
        enlargement, 3-9
        fluid friction, 3-3ff
    measurement, 33-1ff
        instrument connections, 33-3
    monitoring, 36-2
    parts, repairs by welding, 36-12ff
    readings, 33-3
    stress, primary, 30-2f
    static, 17-1
    velocity, 17-1
Pressurized
    casing, 16-6f
    furnace, 25-6f, 25-8f
    inspection door, 16-9
Pressurized water reactor (PWR),
        21-2ff, 23-1ff, 23-17, 24-17ff;
        see also Reactor
    auxiliary systems, 21-13f
    components, 21-3
    containment system, 21-14ff,
            see Reactor building
    control, 21-10, 23-8f, 35-22ff
    coolant
        control, 35-22f
        pumps, 21-12, 23-5, 23-11
        system, 23-9ff
        temperature, 23-9
        water, solids, 34-24
    core design, 21-3ff, 23-13ff
    electric utility application, Chapter 23
    fuel
        cost, 19-10f
        handling, 21-14
        loading, 19-1, 23-6
        temperature, 21-6f

Pressurized water reactor (cont'd)
    heat release rate, 21-6
    heat transfer, 4-19f, 21-6ff; limits, 21-8
    instrumentation, 21-11f, 23-8f, 35-19ff
    internals, 21-3, 23-3, 23-6,
            23-14f, 34-20
    licensing process, 21-17f
    marine, 24-17ff
    materials, 21-4
    neutron flux patterns, 21-5f
    operation, 34-19ff
    optimization for cost, 21-17
    physics, 21-4ff
    primary loop, 21-2
    protection system, 21-11, 23-15, 35-24
    refueling, 34-22
    shielding, 21-14
    system, 21-2ff; principal parts, 21-3
    vessel, 21-3, 21-12, 23-2f, 23-6, 31-1
        design, 30-1ff
        fabrication, 31-17ff
        flow model, 11
        head, closure,
                23-2f, 30-2, 31-18f, 34-20
        internals, 21-3, 23-6
        stress analysis, Chapter 30
    water treatment, 34-23f
Pressurizer, nuclear,
        21-12f, 23-5, 23-11f, 31-22
Primary air heating, 13-7
Priming, 1-6
Process steam, 25-3
Producer gas, 5-21, analysis, 5-20
Proton, 20-1, 20-5
Pulp products, pulping process,
        see Paper industry
Pulverized coal
    advantages, 9-1
    -air-mixture, 9-2f
    ash, 15-7
    bin system, 9-2
    burners, 9-10ff
    cement industry, 9-16
    classifier, 9-4
    combustible losses, 9-11
    direct-firing system, 9-2ff
    drying, 9-4, 9-8
    excess air, 9-12
    feeding, 9-4
    fineness, 9-5, 9-8f
    firing, application, 22-3, 25-2
    grindability, 5-16, 9-5, 9-8
    ignition, 9-11
    introduction of, 6
    metals industries, 9-15f
    preparation, 9-2ff; cost of, 9-10
    safety precautions, 9-16
    sampling, 9-9
    suction and pressure systems, 9-3
    transporting, 9-5
    transport system, 9-2f
    velocity in pipes, 9-10

Pulverizer, 9-4ff
    auxiliary equipment, 9-9
    -burner coordination, 9-13ff
    capacity factor, 9-8
    design fundamentals, 9-4f
    equipment selection, 9-8ff
    exit temperature, 9-8
    fabrication, 31-15f
    maintenance, 36-16f
    primary-air fan, 9-9f; power, 9-10
    requirements, 9-5
    types, 9-5ff
        type EL, 9-6
        type MPS, 9-6f
Pump, energy equations, 2-9
    reactor coolant, 21-12, 23-11
Purging, furnace, 7-9, 9-16, 34-4
Pyrometers, 33-6
Pyrometric cones, 33-4

Quadric Resistance Law, 3-3
Quality assurance, 31-6ff
Quality control, 9, 31-6ff
    erection, 32-8ff
    tube manufacture, 31-26

Rad, 20-14
Radiant boiler, 1-1, 12-2f, 22-6ff
Radiation
    cavity, 4-18, 14-3ff, 14-8
    heat transfer, 4-1
    intertube, 14-3ff
    loss, 4-20
    nuclear, 20-3f
        damage, 19-5f
        detector, 20-14
        dose, 20-14
        factor in maintenance, 36-20ff
        monitors, 20-14
    pyrometer, 33-6
    thermal, gases, 4-5f; intertube, 4-12;
            penetration of tube banks, 4-15
Radioactive decay, 20-3, 20-12
Radioactive isotopes, 20-3f
Radioactivity, 20-3f
Radiographic examination, 9, 31-7, 32-11f
Rankine cycle, 2-13ff
    nuclear heat source, 2-16f
Rankine temperature scale, 33-4
Raw-water treatment, 34-10ff
Reactivity, 20-11;
        control limits, PWR, 23-13
Reactor
    breeder, 19-3, 20-8, 20-13, 21-1
    building (containment), 21-16, 23-1f
        cooling system, 21-14
    fast, 20-7f, 21-1
    gas-cooled, 21-2
    nuclear, definition, 21-1
    pressurized water,
            see Pressurized water reactor

Reactor (cont'd)
 thermal, 20-7f, 21-1
 types, 21-1f
 vessel, see Pressurized water reactor
Recirculation, air, 13-4; gas, 12-15f
Recovery unit
 kraft process, 26-3ff
  air pollution control, 26-9
  auxiliaries, 26-8
  black-liquor oscillator burner, 26-4
  black-liquor spray nozzle, 26-5
  combustion air control, 26-4
  convection heating surfaces, 26-6
  direct-contact evaporator, 26-6f;
   air pollution, 26-9
  evaporator, 26-6f
  feedwater temperature, 26-6
  furnace, 26-3ff
  heat balance, 26-8f
  heat inputs, 26-10
  losses, 26-10
  odor distribution, 26-9
  oscillator and spray nozzle, 26-4
  performance, 26-10
  slag screen, 26-5
  smelter unit, 26-7f
  sootblowers, 26-6
  streams entering and leaving, 26-10
  venturi evaporator-scrubber, 26-7
 magnesium sulfite process, 26-13f
 soda process, 26-11
 sulfite process, 26-11f
  ammonium-base, 26-12
  calcium-base, 26-12
  magnesium-base, 26-12ff
  sodium-base, 26-11f
Rectangular ducts, flow, 3-11f
Reflectivity, 4-5
Reflector, nuclear reactor, 21-5
Refractories
 installation, 32-12
 start-up, 34-2
 thermal conductivity, 16-6
Refueling, nuclear, 34-22
Regenerative Rankine Cycle, 2-14ff
Reheat
 advantages, 12-8
 cycle, 2-14ff
 temperature, adjustment and
  control, 12-19
 use of, 12-8
Reheater, 12-8, 12-10ff
 allowable tube stress, 12-10f
 cleaning, external, 12-12;
  internal, 12-11f
 design, 12-9ff
 marine, 24-11
 start-up protection, 34-5
 supports, 12-11f
 tube materials, 12-9ff
Relative proportional gain, control, 35-3f
Relief valves, 21-13, 23-12
Rem, 20-14

Repairs
 corroded surfaces, 36-14
 cracked ligaments, 36-14
 fossil-fuel equipment, 36-13ff
 nuclear equipment, 36-20ff
 removing tubes and fittings, 36-14ff
 rotating machinery, 36-16f
 stud surfaces, 36-16
 welding, 36-13
Research and development, 9ff
Resistance—thermal, combined, 4-2;
  definition, 4-1
Reynolds number, 4-7ff
 friction-factor relationship, 3-5
 gases, 14-6
 stack calculations, 17-3
Ribbed tubes, 1-4f
Roentgen, 20-14
Rolling steel tubing, 31-24
Roughness, effect on friction factor, 3-5f

Safety
 analysis, nuclear, 23-16
 criteria, nuclear, 23-16
 maintenance requirements, 36-1f
 personnel, rules, 34-8
 precautions, oil and gas, 7-8ff;
  pulverized coal, 9-16
 valve, 12-7; first, 3; setting, 34-3;
  testing, 34-3
Samarium, 20-12
Saturated steam, properties, 2-3f
Saturated water, properties, 2-3f
Scale detection, 33-15f
Scale or oil in boiler tubes, 4-16, 24-9
Screen, calculations, 14-6f
Scrubber, wet, flue gas, 18-3
Seal welding, 36-13ff
Seal welds, 32-6f, 32-8f, 32-10f
Secondary loop, 21-2
Sectional header boiler, 24-5, 24-15
Self "Drag" Control Element, 34-7
Setting
 cased enclosures and casing
  appearance, 16-9
  corrosion, 16-7
  erection, 32-12
  expansion, 16-3f
  explosion effect, 16-4f
  fabrication and assembly, 16-8f
  heat loss, 16-5
  implosion effect, 16-4f
  inner, 16-3
  leakage, 16-6f
  marine boilers, 24-13f
  pressurized, 16-6f
  resistance to ash and slag, 16-3;
   to weather, 16-8
  serviceability, 16-9
  support, 16-4
  ventilation, 16-6
  vibration, 16-5

Setting (cont'd)
 constructions, 16-2
 definition, 16-1
 enclosures, 16-1ff
 insulation
  erection, 32-14
  heat transfer, 4-18f
  use limits, 4-19
 tube wall, 16-1ff
Shale oil, 5-18, 7-2
Shear, failure theory, 30-5
Shim safety rod, 23-7; drive, 23-7f
Shutdown
 fossil-fuel units, 34-5f, 34-9f
 nuclear units, 34-22ff
Silica, distribution ratio, 1-8
 in boiler water, 34-16
 in steam, 1-8f
Slag, fused deposits, 15-11ff
 oil-slag formation and deposits, 15-22f
 removal, 10-4f, 15-10
 screen, 12-6f
 -tap furnace, see Furnace, slag-tap
 viscosity, see Viscosity, slag
Slagging, wall, 15-14ff
Sludge contact softener, 34-11
Smelt, kraft process, 26-3
Socket welds, 32-9f
Soda process, see Recovery unit
Sodium
 cycle softening, 34-11
 in fuel oil, 15-21
 tracer method, steam purity, 33-22f
Solids
 in boiler water, 1-5, 25-5, 34-17f
 in feedwater, 34-19
 in steam, 33-21ff
 steam vs boiler water, 34-15
Soluble poison, 21-4f
Sootblowers, 15-10, 15-16, 15-18f,
  15-23, 26-6, 36-5
Specific gravity, gases, 6-3
Specific heat, air, 14-9; flue gas, 14-7
Specific volume,
  air and flue gas, 17-2; gases, 6-3;
  water and steam, 2-3f, 2-6f
Spectrum, electromagnetic, 20-3
Spent fuel cooling system, 21-14f
S.S. American Astronaut, 24-1
S.S. Esso Gettysburg, 24-3
Stack(s), 17-1ff
 gas, see Flue gas
Stanton number, 4-8
Start-up, cold boilers, oil and gas, 7-8
 control, 35-19
 fossil-fuel units, 34-3ff;
  preparations, 34-1ff
 nuclear units, 34-21f
Station computer console, 34-24

Steam
 as a thermodynamic system, 2-1
 combination heating and power, 25-3f

Steam (cont'd)
cycle, 7, 2-14
fossil fuel, 2-15f
marine, efficiency, 24-12
nuclear plant, 2-16f
drum, see Drum
-electric generating stations, early, 5
engine, first, 3
enthalpy, 2-2ff, 2-6f
entropy, 2-3f, 2-6f
flow air-flow combustion guide, 35-10
flow requirements, 22-4; peak, 25-3
generating systems, velocities, 3-6f
generation, calculation, 14-10
generator, fossil-fuel, see Boiler; nuclear,
see Nuclear steam generator
history of generation and use, 1
-line blowing, 34-3
maldistribution, 24-10
mass velocity, 12-9
maximum percent leaving risers, 3-15f
Mollier diagram, facing 2-1
piping, 29-11, 29-13
plant control, 35-1, 35-16ff, 35-19ff
power generation, Chapters 22
and 23, 25-4
process and heating, 25-3
properties, 1-1, 2-1ff
purity, 1-5ff, 34-17;
measurement, 33-21ff
quality, 1-1ff
limit for nucleate boiling, 1-4f
measurement, 33-21ff
sample, 33-21f
saturated, 1-1
scrubbers, 1-7ff
separation, 1-5ff, 24-14
separators, 1-6ff; Cyclone, 1-7f
silica in, 1-8, 34-18
solids, removal, 1-6ff, also see Solids
specific volume, 2-3f, 2-6f
tables, 2-1ff
temperature
adjustment, 12-12ff
control, 12-12ff, 12-19f, 24-11, 25-4;
automatic, 12-19f;
gas recirculation, 12-15f
turbine, see Turbine
use, Chapters 22—27 incl.
viscosity, 3-8
washing, 1-8f
Steaming economizers, 13-2
Steel, 28-1ff
alloying elements, 28-11ff
annealing, 28-15
basic-oxygen process, 28-4f
capped, 28-8
creep, 29-3f; rate, 29-5ff;
rupture, 29-6f; stress, 29-5
critical points, 28-10ff
Croloys, 29-10f; creep and
creep-rupture curves, 29-7
definition, 28-3

Steel (cont'd)
degassing, vacuum, 28-1, 28-5ff
ductility, 29-1f
effect of deoxidizers, 28-8f
electric-furnace process, 28-4ff, 31-23;
advantages, 28-4;
alloy tube steel, 28-7
eutectoid point, 28-11
forging, 28-16
grades, 29-15
grain size, 29-8
hardening, quenching, 28-15
heat-treating, 28-15f, 32-11
high-temperature properties, 29-2
hot-working, 28-16
ingot, 28-7f
killed, 28-8
manufacture, 28-3ff
mechanical properties, 29-1ff
mechanical working, 28-16
microscopic examination, 28-11f
normalizing, 28-15
open-hearth process, 28-4ff
phase changes, 28-10
physical metallurgy, 28-10
pipe, 29-11, 29-13
allowable temperature, 29-13
stress values, 29-14
plate production, 28-16
specifications and stress values, 29-9f
rimmed, 28-8
rolling, 28-16
semikilled, 28-8
spheroidizing, 28-15
structural, 31-15
design, see Structural design
tempering, 28-15f
tensile strength, 29-3, 29-9ff
transformation in, 28-11
tube, 29-10; application, 29-11;
stress values, 29-12;
temperature allowable, 29-11
types, 28-8
work hardening, 28-16
Stefan-Boltzmann law, 4-5, 33-6
Stirling boiler, 5, 12-2, 25-10
Stokers
advantages and disadvantages, 11-1
fuel burning rates, 11-1
industrial boiler application, 25-2
types, 11-1
chain-grate, 11-6
spreader, 11-1ff; by-product
waste fuels, 11-4
traveling grate, 11-2, 11-6
underfeed, 11-4
vibrating-grate, water-cooled, 11-5f
Streamline flow, 4-7ff
inside tubes, 4-8
Stress
allowable, see Steel or other material
analysis, 30-1ff; ASME Code, 30-2;
methods, 30-2; photoelastic, 30-2

Stress (cont'd)
concentrations, local, 30-5f;
openings, 30-6f
discontinuity, 30-4
failure theory, 30-5
hoop, 30-2f
in various vessel types, 30-3
longitudinal, 30-2f
secondary, 30-3f
significance, 30-5
steady-state, 30-5
-strain diagram, 29-1
thermal, 4-5, 30-4; in start-up
and shutdown, 34-5f
transient, 30-5
Structural design
codes and standards, 30-7f
computer codes, 30-8f
fossil-fuel units, 30-7
information sources, 30-7f
reactor core, 21-10, 30-9
Stud surfaces, repairs, 36-16
Stud-tube walls, 16-2, 16-4
Subcooled boiling, see Local boiling
Sulfite process, see Recovery unit
Sulfur, content, U.S. coals, 8-3
forms of in U.S. coals, 8-2, 8-4
in coal, 15-2
in flue gas, 13-1, 13-3ff
in fuel oil, 15-21f
organic, 8-2, 8-4
oxides, control and removal, 18-3f
pyritic, 8-2, 8-4
recovery from flue gas, 18-4f
Superheat, see also Steam temperature
use of, 12-8; advantages, 12-8f
variation with location and
firing rate, 12-8f, 24-10
Superheated steam properties, 2-6f
Superheater, 12-8ff
allowable tube stress, 12-10f
calculations, 14-7f
cleaning, external, 12-12;
internal, 12-11f
control, see Controls, steam temperature
convection, 12-8f, 12-13
convection and radiant in series, 12-9
design, 12-9f
marine, 24-4ff, 24-9ff
mass velocity, 12-9
metal requirements, 29-11
platens, 31-14; fabrication, 31-15
radiant, 12-8f, 12-13
separately fired, 12-14
start-up protection, 34-4f
supports, 12-11f; marine, 24-10
tube materials, 12-10f
tube sizes, 12-9
types, 12-8f; marine, 24-4ff, 24-9f
Supports, boiler, 12-7f
erection, 32-4
fossil-fuel units, 30-1, 30-7f
reheater, 12-11f
superheater, 12-11f; marine, 24-10

Surface
   calculation, 14-2f
   cleanliness, 32-11, 36-4ff
   disengaging, 1-7
   temperature, boiler setting, 16-6; effect
      of surface film resistance, 16-8

Tar, 5-20; as fuel, 27-3
Television furnace observation, 35-14
Temperature
   adiabatic flame, 6-6f
   color scale, tabulation, 33-6
   control, see Controls, steam temperature
   difference, log mean, 4-12, 14-1
   -entropy diagrams, 2-12ff
   exit gas, 12-5, 13-1ff, 13-4f, 24-12f
   furnace exit gas, 4-16ff
   gradient, 4-2; measurement, 33-13ff
   ignition, 6-6
   measurement, 33-3ff
      bimetallic strip, 33-5f
      casing, 33-19ff
      fluid, 33-12
      fusion, 33-4f
      gas, 33-16ff; evaluation, 33-18f
      gradient, 33-13ff
      insulation, 33-19ff
      tube, 33-12ff
   monitoring, 36-2
   recorders, 33-11f
   scales, 33-4
Tempering, gas, 12-15f
Tensile test, 29-1f; high temperature, 29-3
Testing, see Examination, also ASME,
   NRC and specific equipment
Thermal
   conductivity, see Conductivity
   diffusion length, 20-10
   dimensional changes, 30-4
   efficiency, Carnot cycle, 2-13
   neutrons, 20-8
   nonleakage factor, nuclear, 20-10
   probe, 4-17
   reactor, 20-7f, 21-1
   stress, 4-5, 30-4; in start-up
      and shutdown, 34-5f
   utilization factor, nuclear, 20-10
Thermocouple, 33-7ff
   chordal, 33-13ff
   circuit, 33-8
   cold junction, 33-7f
   emf vs temperature, 33-8
   error graph, 33-17
   gradient, 33-13ff; limitations, 33-15f
   high-velocity, 33-16ff
   hot junction, 33-7f, 33-10f
   multiple circuits, 33-8
   multiple-shield high-velocity, 33-16ff
   pad-type, 33-10
   peened, 33-10f
   retractable, 33-19
   sheathed-type, 33-9

Thermodynamic(s), cycles, 2-1, 2-12ff
   definitions, 2-1
   laws of, 2-9
   process, 2-5; irreversible, 2-10f;
      reversible, 2-10f
Thermometer, gas, 33-5
   liquid-in-glass, 33-5
   resistance, 33-6f
   vapor pressure, 33-5
   well, 33-12
Thermopile, 33-8
Thorium, see Fuel, nuclear
Throat-tap nozzle, 33-25ff
Throttle pressure control, 35-17
Throttling calorimeter, 33-23f
Time-elongation curves, 29-6
Top-support steel, 30-1, 30-8
Transducer, 33-2f
Transmissivity, 4-5
Tube
   arrangement factor, 4-11
   banks, 4-15, 12-6ff;
      crossflow pressure drop, 3-12;
      depth factor, 4-11; marine, 24-9
   bending, 31-15
   cold-drawing, 31-24f
   connections, 32-6f
   cutters, 36-14ff
   expansion, 32-6f
   electric-resistance-welded, 31-25f
   extrusion process, 31-25
   failures, 34-9
   -hole drilling, 31-5f
   manufacture, 31-23ff
   plugging, explosive technique, 36-21
   removal, 36-14ff
   reeling and sizing, 31-24f
   rolling, 31-24
   -round, centering and piercing, 31-24
   "safe-ended," 24-10
   seamless, 31-23ff
   sections, replacement, 36-14
   sizes, 12-9, 13-2, 13-6, 24-4ff, 24-9, 25-10
   spacing, 12-6
   steels, 29-10ff
      alloy, 28-7
      application, 29-11
      stress values, 29-12
      temperature allowable, 29-11
   stubs, 32-8
   temperature, 33-12ff
   wall enclosures, 16-1ff
Turbine-generator control, 35-17, 35-22
Turbine, steam, deposits, 1-5;
      energy equation, 2-8
Turbulent flow, 3-5f, 4-8
   inside and outside tubes, 4-9
Two-phase flow, pressure drop, 3-12f

Ugine Sejournet process, 31-25
Ultimate analysis, coal, 5-7
Ultrasonic examination, 31-7f

Underfeed stokers, 11-4f
Universal gas constant, 3-2, 6-3, 33-5
Universal-Pressure boiler,
      6ff, 12-3f, 22-1, 22-8ff
   bypass system, 34-6f
   controls, 35-14ff
   operation, 35-14
   water treatment, 34-18f
Uranium, 19-1ff, also see Fuel, nuclear
U.S.S. Belknap, 24-7

Vacuum degassing, steel, 28-1, 28-5ff
Valves, flow resistance, 3-7ff
Vapor, 3-1
Vanadium in fuel oil, 15-21f
Vegetation, as fuel, 5-1, 5-3;
      wastes, as fuel, 5-22
Velocity Control Element,
      Self "Drag," 34-7
Velocity
   fuel gas design, 15-9
   -head, mass-velocity relationship
      for air, 3-12
   steam generating system, 3-6f
Ventilation, boiler room, 16-6
Venturi tube, 33-24ff
Vessel, nuclear,
      see Pressurized water reactor
Vibration, casing, 16-5
Viscometer, 15-3f
Viscosity
   absolute, 3-5ff
      compared with kinetic, 3-8
      in common gases, 3-7
      in common liquids, 3-6
   coal ash slag, 15-3ff
      dolomite percentage, 15-5
      effect on furnace
         wall slagging, 15-14
      effect of iron, 15-5f
      oxidizing vs reducing
         atmosphere, 15-15
      requirements for Cyclone
         Furnaces, 10-1ff
   fuel oil, 5-15ff
   steam, 3-8
Volatile treatment, boiler water, 34-17

Waste-disposal system, nuclear, 21-14f
Waste fuel, application, 25-3
Waste heat, 27-6, boilers, 27-8ff
   temperature of gases, 27-6
Water
   carry-over in steam, 1-5ff
   conditioning, see Water treatment
   cooled walls, 12-5f
   critical point, 1-1
   enthalpy, 2-2ff, 2-6f
   entropy, 2-3f, 2-6f
   gas, 5-21
   -leg correction, gage glass, 33-3

Water (cont'd)
   requirements, fossil-fuel
      units, 34-10ff; nuclear
      steam generators, 34-24f
   solids, see Solids
   specific volume, 2-3f, 2-6f
   subcooling, 1-2
   treatment
      controls, 34-18
      condensate, 34-12f, 34-19
      demineralization, 34-12
      evaporation, 34-12
      feedwater, 34-13f; changes, 34-34f
      fossil-fuel units, 34-10ff
      natural-circulation boilers, 34-15ff
      PWR system, 34-23f
      raw water, 34-10ff
      Universal-Pressure boiler, 34-18ff
Water-washing economizers, 13-3
Watt, James, 3
Welding, 31-1ff
   arc, 31-1ff
   development of, 8f
   electrodes, 31-2, 31-5
   electrogas, 31-4
   electron beam, 31-4
   electroslag, 31-3, 31-16
   field-, 32-9f
   gas, 31-3f
   gas-shielded metal-arc, 31-3
   gas-shielded tungsten-arc, 31-3
   heat treatment, 31-5, 32-9f
   in repairs, 36-13ff
   manual-shielded-metal-arc, 31-1f
   pressure, 31-4f
   processes, 31-1ff, 32-9f
   qualifications, 31-6f, 32-9f
   seal, 36-9f
   submerged-arc, 31-2f, 31-11, 31-17ff
Welds
   butt, 31-14, 32-9
   nondestructive
      examination, 31-7ff, 32-10
   seal, 32-6ff
   socket, 32-9f
Wet scrubber, flue gas, 18-3
White liquor, pulp, 26-2
Wilcox, Stephen, 2, 4
Wind loading, 22-5, 30-8
Wood, 5-21f
   analyses, 5-22
   as fuel, 5-3
   ash, analysis, 5-22
   ash fusion temperatures, 15-2
   refuse, as fuel, 5-22, 27-4ff
      pile burning, 27-5
      thin-bed burning, 27-5f
Work functions, 2-19

Xenon, 20-12
X-ray, 20-1, 20-4
   analyzer, electron beam, 12

X-ray (cont'd)
   machine, 31-11
   testing, see Radiographic examination

Yield point, 29-1
Yield strength, 29-1

Zeolite water softening, 34-11f
Zero power
   experiment, 13, 21-6
   nuclear, 20-11
   testing, 34-21f
Zircaloy, see Zirconium alloy
Zirconium alloy, 19-6f, 29-15, 31-25
   alloying elements, 29-15
   cladding, 31-22
   corrosion, 29-16
   irradiation effects, 29-16
   mechanical properties, 29-16
   physical properties, 29-15